A Note from the Authors

You are about to embark on an amazing journey of discovery. The study of life spans from the inner workings of cells to the complex interactions of entire ecosystems, through the information stored in DNA to the ways genetic information evolves over time. At the same time that our understanding of biology is growing in leaps and bounds, so too are great insights into how learners acquire new knowledge and skills. We are thrilled to join Scott Freeman on *Biological Science*, a book dedicated to active, research-based learning and to exploring the experimental evidence that informs what we know about biology. The next few pages highlight the features in this book and in MasteringBiology® that will help you succeed.

From left to right: Michael Black, Emily Taylor, Jon Monroe, Lizabeth Allison, Greg Podgorski, Kim Quillin

To the Student: How to Use This Book

New chapter-opening **Roadmaps** visually group and organize information to help you anticipate key ideas as well as recognize meaningful relationships and connections between them.

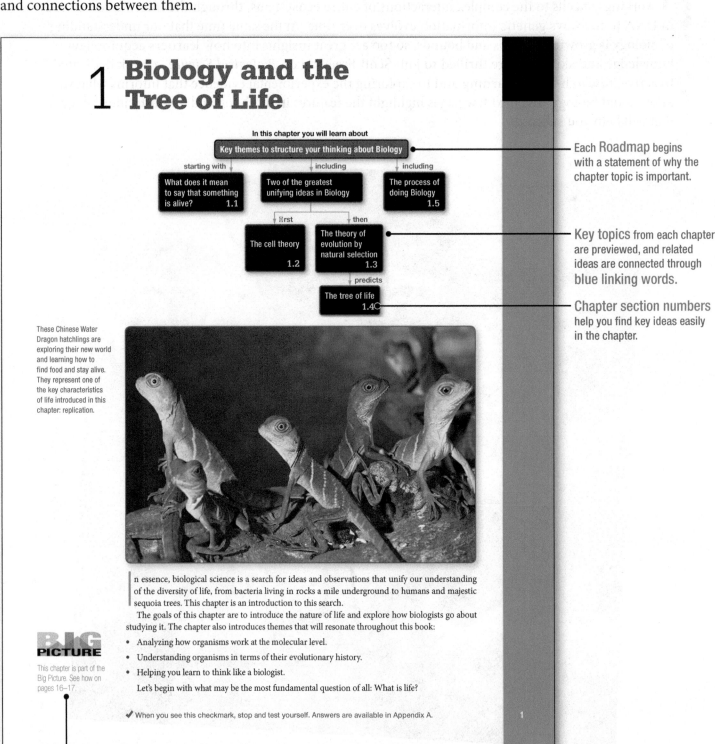

1 Biology and the Tree of Life

In this chapter you will learn about

Key themes to structure your thinking about Biology

starting with — *including* — *including*

What does it mean to say that something is alive? **1.1**

Two of the greatest unifying ideas in Biology

The process of doing Biology **1.5**

first — *then*

The cell theory **1.2**

The theory of evolution by natural selection **1.3**

predicts

The tree of life **1.4**

These Chinese Water Dragon hatchlings are exploring their new world and learning how to find food and stay alive. They represent one of the key characteristics of life introduced in this chapter: replication.

In essence, biological science is a search for ideas and observations that unify our understanding of the diversity of life, from bacteria living in rocks a mile underground to humans and majestic sequoia trees. This chapter is an introduction to this search.

The goals of this chapter are to introduce the nature of life and explore how biologists go about studying it. The chapter also introduces themes that will resonate throughout this book:

- Analyzing how organisms work at the molecular level.
- Understanding organisms in terms of their evolutionary history.
- Helping you learn to think like a biologist.

Let's begin with what may be the most fundamental question of all: What is life?

BIG PICTURE

This chapter is part of the Big Picture. See how on pages 16–17.

✔ When you see this checkmark, stop and test yourself. Answers are available in Appendix A.

1

Each Roadmap begins with a statement of why the chapter topic is important.

Key topics from each chapter are previewed, and related ideas are connected through **blue linking words**.

Chapter section numbers help you find key ideas easily in the chapter.

Big Picture Concept Maps are referenced on the opening page of related chapters, pointing you to summary pages that help you synthesize challenging topics.

Big Picture Concept Maps integrate visuals and words to help you synthesize information about challenging topics in biology that span multiple chapters and units.

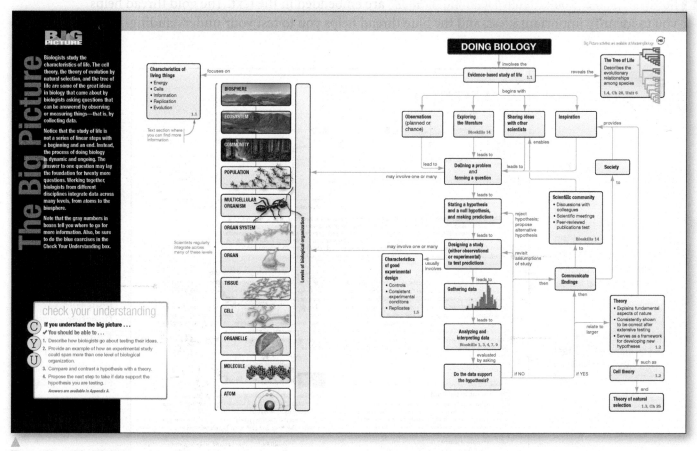

Three New Big Picture topics
have been added to the Fifth Edition:

- NEW! Doing Biology
- NEW! The Chemistry of Life
- Energy for Life
- Genetic Information
- Evolution
- NEW! Plant and Animal Form and Function
- Ecology

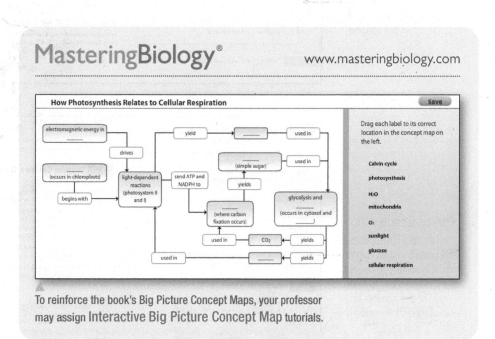

To reinforce the book's Big Picture Concept Maps, your professor may assign Interactive Big Picture Concept Map tutorials.

Practice for success
on tests and exams

Intertwined color-coded "active learning threads" are embedded in the text. The gold thread helps you to identify important ideas, and the blue thread helps you to test your understanding.

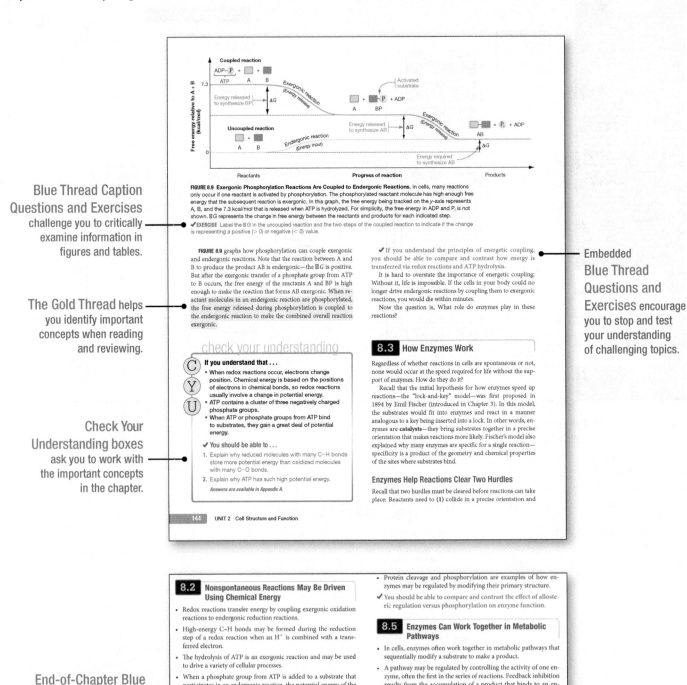

FIGURE 8.9 Exergonic Phosphorylation Reactions Are Coupled to Endergonic Reactions. In cells, many reactions only occur if one reactant is activated by phosphorylation. The phosphorylated reactant molecule has high enough free energy that the subsequent reaction is exergonic. In this graph, the free energy being tracked on the y-axis represents A, B, and the 7.3 kcal/mol that is released when ATP and P_i is hydrolyzed. For simplicity, the free energy in ADP and P_i is not shown. ΔG represents the change in free energy between the reactants and products for each indicated step.

✔ **EXERCISE** Label the ΔG in the uncoupled reaction and the two steps of the coupled reaction to indicate if the change is representing a positive (> 0) or negative (< 0) value.

Blue Thread Caption Questions and Exercises challenge you to critically examine information in figures and tables.

The Gold Thread helps you identify important concepts when reading and reviewing.

Check Your Understanding boxes ask you to work with the important concepts in the chapter.

FIGURE 8.9 graphs how phosphorylation can couple exergonic and endergonic reactions. Note that the reaction between A and B to produce the product AB is endergonic—the ΔG is positive. But after the exergonic transfer of a phosphate group from ATP to B occurs, the free energy of the reactants A and BP is high enough to make the reaction that forms AB exergonic. When reactant molecules in an endergonic reaction are phosphorylated, the free energy released during phosphorylation is coupled to the endergonic reaction to make the combined overall reaction exergonic.

check your understanding

If you understand that . . .
- When redox reactions occur, electrons change position. Chemical energy is based on the positions of electrons in chemical bonds, so redox reactions usually involve a change in potential energy.
- ATP contains a cluster of three negatively charged phosphate groups.
- When ATP or phosphate groups from ATP bind to substrates, they gain a great deal of potential energy.

✔ **You should be able to . . .**
1. Explain why reduced molecules with many C–H bonds store more potential energy than oxidized molecules with many C–O bonds.
2. Explain why ATP has such high potential energy.

Answers are available in Appendix A.

✔ If you understand the principles of energetic coupling, you should be able to compare and contrast how energy is transferred via redox reactions and ATP hydrolysis.

It is hard to overstate the importance of energetic coupling: Without it, life is impossible. If the cells in your body could no longer drive endergonic reactions by coupling them to exergonic reactions, you would die within minutes.

Now the question is, What role do enzymes play in these reactions?

8.3 How Enzymes Work

Regardless of whether reactions in cells are spontaneous or not, none would occur at the speed required for life without the support of enzymes. How do they do it?

Recall that the initial hypothesis for how enzymes speed up reactions—the "lock-and-key" model—was first proposed in 1894 by Emil Fischer (introduced in Chapter 3). In this model, the substrates would fit into enzymes and react in a manner analogous to a key being inserted into a lock. In other words, enzymes are **catalysts**—they bring substrates together in a precise orientation that makes reactions more likely. Fischer's model also explained why many enzymes are specific for a single reaction—specificity is a product of the geometry and chemical properties of the sites where substrates bind.

Enzymes Help Reactions Clear Two Hurdles

Recall that two hurdles must be cleared before reactions can take place: Reactants need to **(1)** collide in a precise orientation and

Embedded Blue Thread Questions and Exercises encourage you to stop and test your understanding of challenging topics.

8.2 Nonspontaneous Reactions May Be Driven Using Chemical Energy

- Redox reactions transfer energy by coupling exergonic oxidation reactions to endergonic reduction reactions.
- High-energy C–H bonds may be formed during the reduction step of a redox reaction when an H^+ is combined with a transferred electron.
- The hydrolysis of ATP is an exergonic reaction and may be used to drive a variety of cellular processes.
- When a phosphate group from ATP is added to a substrate that participates in an endergonic reaction, the potential energy of the substrate is raised enough to make the reaction exergonic and thus spontaneous.

✔ You should be able to explain what energetic coupling means, and why life would not exist without it.

8.3 How Enzymes Work

- Enzymes are protein catalysts. They speed reaction rates but do not affect the change in free energy of the reaction.
- The structure of an enzyme has an active site that brings sub-

End-of-Chapter Blue Thread Exercises, integrated in the chapter summary, help you review the major themes of the chapter and synthesize information.

- Protein cleavage and phosphorylation are examples of how enzymes may be regulated by modifying their primary structure.

✔ You should be able to compare and contrast the effect of allosteric regulation versus phosphorylation on enzyme function.

8.5 Enzymes Can Work Together in Metabolic Pathways

- In cells, enzymes often work together in metabolic pathways that sequentially modify a substrate to make a product.
- A pathway may be regulated by controlling the activity of one enzyme, often the first in the series of reactions. Feedback inhibition results from the accumulation of a product that binds to an enzyme in the pathway and inactivates it.
- Metabolic pathways were vital to the evolution of life, and new pathways continue to evolve in cells.

✔ You should be able to predict how the removal of the intermediate in a two-step metabolic pathway would affect the enzymatic rates of the first and last.

www.masteringbiology.com

1. MasteringBiology Assignments

Identify gaps in your understanding, then fill them

The Fifth Edition provides many opportunities for you to test yourself and offers helpful learning strategies.

Analyze: Can I recognize underlying patterns and structure?

Evaluate: Can I make judgments on the relative value of ideas and information?

Create: Can I put ideas and information together to generate something new?

Apply: Can I use these ideas in the same way or in a new situation?

Understand: Can I explain this concept in my own words?

Remember: Can I recall the key terms and ideas?

◄ **Bloom's Taxonomy** describes six learning levels: Remember, Understand, Apply, Analyze, Evaluate, and Create. Questions in the book span all levels, including self-testing at the higher levels to help you develop higher-order thinking skills that will prepare you for exams.

Steps to Building Understanding
Each chapter ends with three groups of questions that build in difficulty:

✔ **TEST YOUR KNOWLEDGE**

Begin by testing your basic knowledge of new information.

✔ **TEST YOUR UNDERSTANDING**

Once you're confident with the basics, demonstrate your deeper understanding of the material.

✔ **TEST YOUR PROBLEM-SOLVING SKILLS**

Work towards mastery of the content by answering questions that challenge you at the highest level of competency.

BIOSKILL 16 using Bloom's taxonomy

Most students have at one time or another wondered why a particular question on an exam seemed so hard, while others seemed easy. The explanation lies in the type of cognitive skills required to answer the question. Let's take a closer look.

NEW! BioSkill Covering Bloom's Taxonomy helps you to recognize question types using the Bloom's cognitive hierarchy, and it provides specific strategies to help you study for questions at all six levels.

Answer Appendix Includes Bloom's Taxonomy Information Answers to all questions in the text now include the Bloom's level being tested. You can simultaneously practice assessing your understanding of content and recognizing Bloom's levels. Combining this information with the guidance in the BioSkill on Bloom's Taxonomy will help you form a plan to improve your study skills.

▶ ✔ **Test Your Problem-Solving Skills**

13. analyze A scientific theory is not a guess—it is an idea whose validity can be tested with data. Both the cell theory and the theory of evolution have been validated by large bodies of observational and experimental data.
14. apply If all eukaryotes living today have a nucleus, then it is logical to conclude that the nucleus arose in a common ancestor of all eukaryotes, indicated by the arrow you should have added to the figure. See **FIGURE A1.2.** If it had arisen in a common ancestor of Bacteria or Archaea, then species in those groups would have had to lose the trait—an unlikely event.
15. evaluate The data set was so large and diverse that it was no longer reasonable to argue that noncellular life-forms would be discovered. **16.** apply b

---

MasteringBiology®
www.masteringbiology.com

NEW! End-of-chapter questions from the book are now available for your professor to assign as homework in MasteringBiology.

Practice scientific thinking and scientific skills

A unique emphasis on the process of scientific discovery and experimental design teaches you how to think like a scientist as you learn fundamental biology concepts.

RESEARCH

QUESTION: Do horses minimize the cost of locomotion?

HYPOTHESIS: Horses choose gaits that minimize energy use at different speeds.

NULL HYPOTHESIS: Horses do not choose gaits based on cost of locomotion.

EXPERIMENTAL SETUP:

1. Measure oxygen consumption of horses trained to walk, trot, and gallop at a range of speeds on a treadmill. Calculate energy used per distance travelled at different speeds.

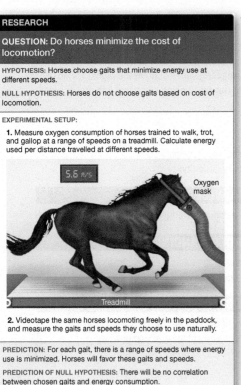

5.6 m/s

Oxygen mask

Treadmill

2. Videotape the same horses locomoting freely in the paddock, and measure the gaits and speeds they choose to use naturally.

PREDICTION: For each gait, there is a range of speeds where energy use is minimized. Horses will favor these gaits and speeds.

PREDICTION OF NULL HYPOTHESIS: There will be no correlation between chosen gaits and energy consumption.

RESULTS:

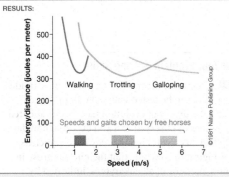

©1981 Nature Publishing Group

Walking Trotting Galloping

Speeds and gaits chosen by free horses

Speed (m/s)

Energy/distance (joules per meter)

CONCLUSION: Horses choose gaits that minimize energy use at different speeds and avoid speeds with high energy consumption.

FIGURE 48.16 Horses Minimize the Cost of Locomotion by Choosing Appropriate Gaits.
SOURCE: Hoyt, D. F., and C. R. Taylor. 1981. Gait and the energetics of locomotion in horses. *Nature* 292: 239–240.

✔ **QUANTITATIVE** Use the graph to estimate the relative energy expense of galloping rather than trotting at 3.5 meters/second (m/s).

All of the Research Boxes cite the original research paper and include a question that asks you to analyze the design of the experiment or study.

Research Boxes explain how research studies are designed and give you additional practice interpreting data. Each Research Box consistently models the scientific method, presenting the research question, hypotheses, experimental setup, predictions, results, and conclusion. 15 Research Boxes are new to the Fifth Edition.

MasteringBiology®
www.masteringbiology.com

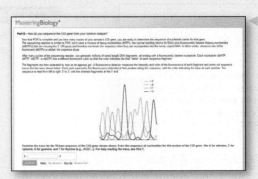

▶ **NEW! Solve It Tutorials** are available for homework assignments in MasteringBiology and give you an opportunity to work like a scientist through a simulated investigation that requires you to analyze and interpret data.

Experimental Inquiry Tutorials based on some of biology's most seminal experiments give you a chance to analyze data and the reasoning that led scientists from the data to their conclusions.

Experimental Inquiry tutorial topics include:

- What Can You Learn About the Process of Science from Investigating a Cricket's Chirp?
- Which Wavelengths of Light Drive Photosynthesis?
- What Is the Inheritance Pattern of Sex-Linked Traits?
- Does DNA Replication Follow the Conservative, Semiconservative, or Dispersive Model?
- How Do Calcium Ions Help to Prevent Polyspermy During Egg Fertilization?
- Did Natural Selection of Ground Finches Occur When the Environment Changed?
- What Effect Does Auxin Have on Coleoptile Growth?
- What Role Do Genes Play in Appetite Regulation?
- Can a Species' Niche Be Influenced by Interspecific Competition?
- What Factors Influence the Loss of Nutrients from a Forest Ecosystem?

Build important skills scientists use to perform, evaluate, and communicate scientific research.

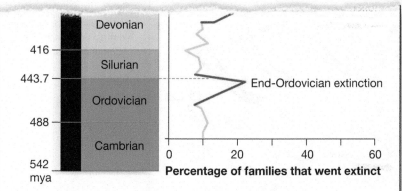

FIGURE 28.14 The Big Five Mass Extinction Events. This graph shows the percentage of lineages called families that went extinct over each interval in the fossil record since the Cambrian explosion. Over 50 percent of families and 90 percent of species went extinct during the end-Permian extinction.

DATA: Benton, M. J., 1995. *Science* 268: 52–58.

✔**QUANTITATIVE** Which extinction event ended the era of the dinosaurs 65 million years ago? About what percentage of families went extinct?

NEW! Graphs and tables now include their data sources, emphasizing the research process that leads to our understanding of biological ideas.

NEW! Quantitative questions are identified throughout the text, helping you practice computational problem solving and data analysis.

Expanded BioSkills Appendix helps you build skills that will be important to your success in biology. At relevant points in the text, you'll find references to the BioSkills appendix that will help you learn and practice foundational skills.

BioSkills Topics include:

- The Metric System and Significant Figures
- Some Common Latin and Greek Roots Used in Biology
- Reading Graphs
- Using Statistical Tests and Interpreting Standard Error Bars
- Combining Probabilities

- Using Logarithms
- Reading a Phylogenetic Tree
- Reading Chemical Structures
- Separating and Visualizing Molecules
- Separating Cell Components by Centrifugation
- Biological Imaging: Microscopy and X-ray Crystallography

- Cell and Tissue Culture Methods
- Model Organisms
- NEW! Primary Literature and Peer Review
- Making Concept Maps
- NEW! Using Bloom's Taxonomy

MasteringBiology®
www.masteringbiology.com

You can access self-paced BioSkills activities in the Study Area, and your instructor can assign additional activities in MasteringBiology.

Visualize biology processes and structures

A carefully crafted visual program helps you gain a better understanding of biology through accurate, appropriately detailed figures.

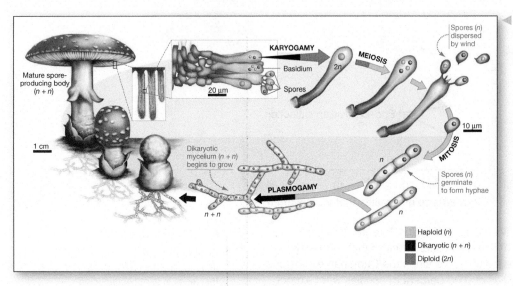

◄ **NEW! Redesigned Life Cycle diagrams** in Unit 6 and 7 help you compare and contrast processes among different organisms.

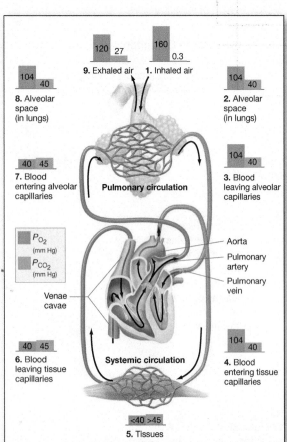

▲ **Informative figures** help you think through complex biological processes in manageable steps.

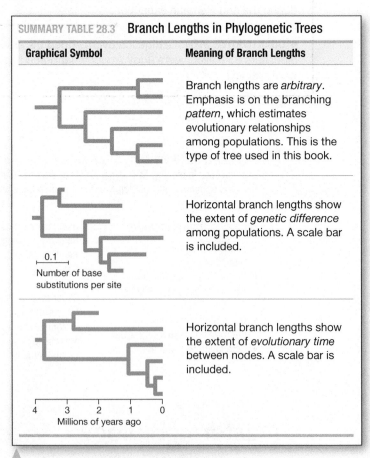

SUMMARY TABLE 28.3	Branch Lengths in Phylogenetic Trees
Graphical Symbol	**Meaning of Branch Lengths**
	Branch lengths are *arbitrary*. Emphasis is on the branching *pattern*, which estimates evolutionary relationships among populations. This is the type of tree used in this book.
0.1 — Number of base substitutions per site	Horizontal branch lengths show the extent of *genetic difference* among populations. A scale bar is included.
4 3 2 1 0 — Millions of years ago	Horizontal branch lengths show the extent of *evolutionary time* between nodes. A scale bar is included.

▲ **Visual Summary Tables** pull together important information in a format that allows for easy comparison and review.

Instructor and Student Resources

For Instructors

Instructor Resource DVD-ROM
978-0-321-86112-2 • 0-321-86112-4
Everything you need for lectures in one place, including video segments that demonstrate how to incorporate active-learning techniques into your own classroom. Enhanced menus make locating and assessing the digital resources for each chapter easy. The Instructor Resource CD/DVD-ROM includes PowerPoint® Lecture Outlines that integrate figures and animations for classroom presentations. All textbook figures, art, and photos are in JPEG format, and all PowerPoint slides and JPEGs have editable labels. Over 300 Instructor Animations accurately depict complex topics and dynamic processes described in the book.

Instructor Guide (Download only)
Available in the instructor resource area of MasteringBiology.®

TestGen® (Download only)
All of the exam questions in the Test Bank have been peer reviewed and student tested, providing questions that set the standard for quality and accuracy. To improve the Test Bank, Metadata from MasteringBiology users has been incorporated directly into the software. Test questions that are ranked according to Bloom's taxonomy and improved TestGen® software makes assembling tests that much easier.

For Students

Study Guide
978-0-321-85832-0 • 0-321-85832-8
The Study Guide presents a breakdown of key biological concepts, difficult topics, and quizzes to help students prepare for exams. Unique to this study guide are four introductory, stand-alone chapters that introduce students to foundational ideas and skills necessary for classroom success: Introduction to Experimentation and Research in the Biological Sciences, Presenting Biological Data, Understanding Patterns in Biology and Improving Study Techniques, and Reading and Writing to Understand Biology. "Looking Forward" and "Looking Back" sections help students make connections across the chapters instead of viewing them as discrete entities.

Practicing Biology: A Student Workbook
978-0-321-88647-7 • 0-321-88647-X
This workbook focuses on key ideas, principles, and concepts that are fundamental to understanding biology. A variety of hands-on activities such as mapping and modeling suit different learning styles and help students discover which topics they need more help on. Students learn biology by doing biology. An instructors guide can be downloaded from the Instructor Area of MasteringBiology.

MasteringBiology®

www.masteringbiology.com

MasteringBiology is an online homework, tutorial, and assessment system that delivers self-paced tutorials that provide individualized coaching, focus on your course objectives, and respond to each student's progress. The Mastering system helps instructors maximize class time with customizable, easy-to-assign, and automatically graded assessments that motivate students to learn outside of class and arrive prepared for lecture. MasteringBiology is also available with a complete Pearson eText edition of *Biological Science*.

Highlights of the Fifth Edition Item Library include:

* NEW! **assignment options** include Solve It activities, end-of-chapter problems, and questions that accompany new BioSkills and new Big Picture Interactive Concept Maps.
* NEW! **"best of" homework pre-built assignments** help professors assign popular, key content quickly, including a blend of tutorials, end-of-chapter problems, and test bank questions.

* ***Get Ready for Biology*** and **Chemistry Review assignment options** help students get up to speed with activities that review chemistry, mathematics, and basic biology.

MasteringBiology® Virtual Labs

978-0-321-88644-6 • 0-321-88644-5
MasteringBiology: Virtual Labs is an online environment that promotes critical-thinking skills using virtual experiments and explorations that might be difficult to perform in a wet-lab environment due to time, cost, or safety concerns. MasteringBiology: Virtual Labs offers unique learning experiences in the areas of microscopy, molecular biology, genetics, ecology, and systematics.

For more information, please visit
www.pearsonhighered.com/virtualbiologylabs

Scott Freeman • Lizabeth Allison • Michael Black • Greg Podgorski
• Kim Quillin • Jon Monroe • Emily Taylor

Biological Science, Volume 1

Custom Edition for El Paso Community College

Taken from:
Biological Science, Fifth Edition
by Scott Freeman, Lizabeth Allison, Michael Black, Greg Podgorski,
Kim Quillin, Jon Monroe, and Emily Taylor

Taken from:

Biological Science, Fifth Edition
by Scott Freeman, Lizabeth Allison, Michael Black, Greg Podgorski, Kim Quillin, Jon Monroe, and Emily Taylor
Copyright © 2014, 2011, 2008 by Pearson Education, Inc.
Published by Pearson
Upper Saddle River, New Jersey 07458

This special edition published in cooperation with Pearson Learning Solutions.

All trademarks, service marks, registered trademarks, and registered service marks are the property of their respective owners and are used herein for identification purposes only.

Pearson Learning Solutions, 501 Boylston Street, Suite 900, Boston, MA 02116
A Pearson Education Company
www.pearsoned.com

Printed in the United States of America

2 3 4 5 6 7 8 9 10 V056 17 16 15 14 13

000200010271783115

AG

ISBN 10: 1-269-39590-4
ISBN 13: 978-1-26939-590-8

Detailed Contents

1 Biology and the Tree of Life 1

1.1 What Does It Mean to Say That Something Is Alive? 2

1.2 The Cell Theory 2
All Organisms Are Made of Cells 2
Where Do Cells Come From? 3

1.3 The Theory of Evolution by Natural Selection 5
What Is Evolution? 5
What Is Natural Selection? 5

1.4 The Tree of Life 6
Using Molecules to Understand the Tree of Life 6
How Should We Name Branches on the Tree of Life? 8

1.5 Doing Biology 9
The Nature of Science 9
Why Do Giraffes Have Long Necks? An Introduction to
    Hypothesis Testing 9
How Do Ants Navigate? An Introduction to Experimental
    Design 11

CHAPTER REVIEW 14

BIG PICTURE DOING BIOLOGY 16

**UNIT 1 THE MOLECULAR ORIGIN AND EVOLUTION
OF LIFE 18**

2 Water and Carbon: The Chemical Basis of Life 18

**2.1 Atoms, Ions, and Molecules: The Building Blocks of
Chemical Evolution** 19
Basic Atomic Structure 19
How Does Covalent Bonding Hold Molecules Together? 21
Ionic Bonding, Ions, and the Electron-Sharing Continuum 22
Some Simple Molecules Formed from C, H, N, and O 23

The Geometry of Simple Molecules 23
Representing Molecules 24

2.2 Properties of Water and the Early Oceans 25
Why Is Water Such an Efficient Solvent? 25
What Properties Are Correlated with Water's Structure? 26
The Role of Water in Acid–Base Reactions 28

**2.3 Chemical Reactions, Energy, and Chemical
Evolution** 30
How Do Chemical Reactions Happen? 30
What Is Energy? 31
What Makes a Chemical Reaction Spontaneous? 31

**2.4 Investigating Chemical Evolution: Approaches and
Model Systems** 32
Early Origin-of-Life Experiments 33
Recent Origin-of-Life Experiments 34

2.5 The Importance of Organic Molecules 36
Linking Carbon Atoms Together 36
Functional Groups 37

CHAPTER REVIEW 38

3 Protein Structure and Function 41

3.1 Amino Acids and Their Polymerization 42
The Structure of Amino Acids 42
The Nature of Side Chains 42
How Do Amino Acids Link to Form Proteins? 44

3.2 What Do Proteins Look Like? 47
Primary Structure 48
Secondary Structure 48
Tertiary Structure 49
Quaternary Structure 50

3.3 Folding and Function 52
Normal Folding Is Crucial to Function 52
Protein Shape Is Flexible 53

**3.4 Proteins Are the Most Versatile Macromolecules
in Cells** 54
Why Are Enzymes Good Catalysts? 54
Was the First Living Entity a Protein Catalyst? 55

CHAPTER REVIEW 55

4 Nucleic Acids and the RNA World 57

4.1 What Is a Nucleic Acid? 58
Could Chemical Evolution Result in the Production
    of Nucleotides? 59
How Do Nucleotides Polymerize to Form Nucleic Acids? 59

4.2 DNA Structure and Function 61
What Is the Nature of DNA's Secondary Structure? 61
DNA Functions as an Information-Containing Molecule 64

Is DNA a Catalytic Molecule? 64

4.3 RNA Structure and Function 65
Structurally, RNA Differs from DNA 65
RNA's Structure Makes It an Extraordinarily Versatile
    Molecule 66
RNA Is an Information-Containing Molecule 67
RNA Can Function as a Catalytic Molecule 67

4.4 In Search of the First Life-Form 68
How Biologists Study the RNA World 68
The RNA World May Have Sparked the Evolution of Life 69

CHAPTER REVIEW 69

5 An Introduction to
Carbohydrates 72

5.1 Sugars as Monomers 73
What Distinguishes One Monosaccharide from Another? 73
Monosaccharides and Chemical Evolution 74

5.2 The Structure of Polysaccharides 75
Starch: A Storage Polysaccharide in Plants 76
Glycogen: A Highly Branched Storage Polysaccharide in
    Animals 76
Cellulose: A Structural Polysaccharide in Plants 76
Chitin: A Structural Polysaccharide in Fungi and Animals 76
Peptidoglycan: A Structural Polysaccharide in Bacteria 76
Polysaccharides and Chemical Evolution 78

5.3 What Do Carbohydrates Do? 78
Carbohydrates Can Provide Structural Support 78
The Role of Carbohydrates in Cell Identity 78
Carbohydrates and Energy Storage 80

CHAPTER REVIEW 81

6 Lipids, Membranes,
and the First Cells 84

6.1 Lipid Structure and Function 85
Bond Saturation Is an Important Aspect of Hydrocarbon
    Structure 85
A Look at Three Types of Lipids Found in Cells 86
The Structures of Membrane Lipids 87
Were Lipids Present during Chemical Evolution? 88

6.2 Phospholipid Bilayers 88
Artificial Membranes as an Experimental System 88
Selective Permeability of Lipid Bilayers 89
How Does Lipid Structure Affect Membrane Permeability? 90
How Does Temperature Affect the Fluidity and Permeability
    of Membranes? 90

**6.3 How Molecules Move across Lipid Bilayers:
Diffusion and Osmosis** 91
Diffusion 91
Osmosis 92
Membranes and Chemical Evolution 93

6.4 Membrane Proteins 94
Development of the Fluid-Mosaic Model 94
Systems for Studying Membrane Proteins 96
Facilitated Diffusion via Channel Proteins 96
Facilitated Diffusion via Carrier Proteins 99
Pumps Perform Active Transport 99

Plasma Membranes and the Intracellular Environment 100
CHAPTER REVIEW 102

BIG PICTURE THE CHEMISTRY OF LIFE 104

UNIT 2 CELL STRUCTURE AND FUNCTION 106

7 Inside the Cell 106

**7.1 Bacterial and Archaeal Cell Structures and Their
Functions** 107
A Revolutionary New View 107
Prokaryotic Cell Structures: A Parts List 107

7.2 Eukaryotic Cell Structures and Their Functions 110
The Benefits of Organelles 110
Eukaryotic Cell Structures: A Parts List 110

7.3 Putting the Parts into a Whole 118
Structure and Function at the Whole-Cell Level 118
The Dynamic Cell 118

7.4 Cell Systems I: Nuclear Transport 119
Structure and Function of the Nuclear Envelope 119
How Do Large Molecules Enter the Nucleus? 120

**7.5 Cell Systems II: The Endomembrane System
Manufactures, Ships, and Recycles Cargo** 121
Studying the Pathway through the Endomembrane
    System 121
Entering the Endomembrane System: The Signal
    Hypothesis 123
Moving from the ER to the Golgi 124
What Happens Inside the Golgi Apparatus? 124
How Do Proteins Reach Their Destinations? 125
Recycling Material in the Lysosome 126

7.6 Cell Systems III: The Dynamic Cytoskeleton 127
Actin Filaments 127
Intermediate Filaments 129
Microtubules 129
Flagella and Cilia: Moving the Entire Cell 131

CHAPTER REVIEW 133

8 Energy and Enzymes:
An Introduction to Metabolic
Pathways 136

8.1 What Happens to Energy in Chemical Reactions? 137
Chemical Reactions Involve Energy Transformations 137
Temperature and Concentration Affect Reaction Rates 139

**8.2 Nonspontaneous Reactions May Be Driven Using
Chemical Energy** 139
Redox Reactions Transfer Energy via Electrons 141
ATP Transfers Energy via Phosphate Groups 143

8.3 How Enzymes Work 144
Enzymes Help Reactions Clear Two Hurdles 144
What Limits the Rate of Catalysis? 147
Do Enzymes Work Alone? 147

8.4 What Factors Affect Enzyme Function? 148
Enzymes Are Optimized for Particular Environments 148
Most Enzymes Are Regulated 149

8.5 Enzymes Can Work Together in Metabolic Pathways 150

Metabolic Pathways Are Regulated 150
Metabolic Pathways Evolve 150

CHAPTER REVIEW 152

9 Cellular Respiration and Fermentation 154

9.1 An Overview of Cellular Respiration 155
What Happens When Glucose Is Oxidized? 155
Cellular Respiration Plays a Central Role in Metabolism 156

9.2 Glycolysis: Processing Glucose to Pyruvate 158
Glycolysis Is a Sequence of 10 Reactions 159
How Is Glycolysis Regulated? 159

9.3 Processing Pyruvate to Acetyl CoA 161

9.4 The Citric Acid Cycle: Oxidizing Acetyl CoA to CO_2 162
How Is the Citric Acid Cycle Regulated? 162
What Happens to the NADH and $FADH_2$? 164

9.5 Electron Transport and Chemiosmosis: Building a Proton Gradient to Produce ATP 166
The Electron Transport Chain 166
The Discovery of ATP Synthase 168
The Chemiosmosis Hypothesis 169
Organisms Use a Diversity of Electron Acceptors 170

9.6 Fermentation 172

CHAPTER REVIEW 173

10 Photosynthesis 176

10.1 Photosynthesis Harnesses Sunlight to Make Carbohydrate 177
Photosynthesis: Two Linked Sets of Reactions 177
Photosynthesis Occurs in Chloroplasts 178

10.2 How Do Pigments Capture Light Energy? 179
Photosynthetic Pigments Absorb Light 179
When Light Is Absorbed, Electrons Enter an Excited State 182

10.3 The Discovery of Photosystems I and II 184
How Does Photosystem II Work? 184

How Does Photosystem I Work? 186
The Z Scheme: Photosystems II and I Work Together 187

10.4 How Is Carbon Dioxide Reduced to Produce Sugars? 190
The Calvin Cycle Fixes Carbon 190
The Discovery of Rubisco 192
Oxygen and Carbon Dioxide Pass through Stomata 192
Mechanisms for Increasing CO_2 Concentration 193
How Is Photosynthesis Regulated? 195
What Happens to the Sugar That Is Produced by Photosynthesis? 195

CHAPTER REVIEW 196

BIG PICTURE ENERGY FOR LIFE 198

11 Cell–Cell Interactions 200

11.1 The Cell Surface 201
The Structure and Function of an Extracellular Layer 201
The Cell Wall in Plants 201
The Extracellular Matrix in Animals 202

11.2 How Do Adjacent Cells Connect and Communicate? 204
Cell–Cell Attachments in Multicellular Eukaryotes 204
Cells Communicate via Cell–Cell Gaps 207

11.3 How Do Distant Cells Communicate? 209
Cell–Cell Signaling in Multicellular Organisms 209
Signal Reception 210
Signal Processing 210
Signal Response 214
Signal Deactivation 214
Crosstalk: Synthesizing Input from Many Signals 215

11.4 Signaling between Unicellular Organisms 215
Responding to Sex Pheromones 215
Responding to Population Density 216

CHAPTER REVIEW 217

12 The Cell Cycle 219

12.1 How Do Cells Replicate? 220
What Is a Chromosome? 220
Cells Alternate between M Phase and Interphase 220
The Discovery of S Phase 220
The Discovery of the Gap Phases 221
The Cell Cycle 222

12.2 What Happens during M Phase? 223
Events in Mitosis 223
How Do Chromosomes Move during Anaphase? 226
Cytokinesis Results in Two Daughter Cells 227

12.3 Control of the Cell Cycle 229
The Discovery of Cell-Cycle Regulatory Molecules 229
Cell-Cycle Checkpoints Can Arrest the Cell Cycle 231

12.4 Cancer: Out-of-Control Cell Division 232
Properties of Cancer Cells 233
Cancer Involves Loss of Cell-Cycle Control 233

CHAPTER REVIEW 235

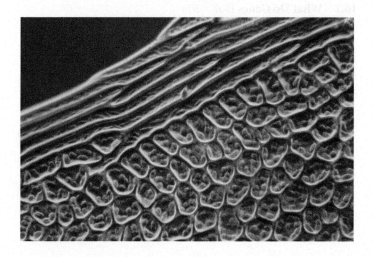

13 Meiosis 237

13.1 How Does Meiosis Occur? 238
Chromosomes Come in Distinct Sizes and Shapes 238
The Concept of Ploidy 238
An Overview of Meiosis 239
The Phases of Meiosis I 242
The Phases of Meiosis II 244
A Closer Look at Synapsis and Crossing Over 246

13.2 Meiosis Promotes Genetic Variation 247
Chromosomes and Heredity 247
The Role of Independent Assortment 247
The Role of Crossing Over 248
How Does Fertilization Affect Genetic Variation? 248

13.3 What Happens When Things Go Wrong in Meiosis? 249
How Do Mistakes Occur? 249
Why Do Mistakes Occur? 250

13.4 Why Does Meiosis Exist? 251
The Paradox of Sex 251
The Purifying Selection Hypothesis 252
The Changing-Environment Hypothesis 253
CHAPTER REVIEW 253

14 Mendel and the Gene 256

14.1 Mendel's Experimental System 257
What Questions Was Mendel Trying to Answer? 257
The Garden Pea Served as the First Model Organism in Genetics 257

14.2 Mendel's Experiments with a Single Trait 259
The Monohybrid Cross 259
Particulate Inheritance 261

14.3 Mendel's Experiments with Two Traits 263
The Dihybrid Cross 263
Using a Testcross to Confirm Predictions 265

14.4 The Chromosome Theory of Inheritance 266
Meiosis Explains Mendel's Principles 266
Testing the Chromosome Theory 267

14.5 Extending Mendel's Rules 269
Linkage: What Happens When Genes Are Located on the Same Chromosome? 270
How Many Alleles Can a Gene Have? 271
Are Alleles Always Dominant or Recessive? 272
Does Each Gene Affect Just One Trait? 272
Is There More to Phenotype than Genotype? 273
QUANTITATIVE METHODS 14.1 Linkage 274
Can Mendel's Principles Explain Traits That Don't Fall into Distinct Categories? 275

14.6 Applying Mendel's Rules to Human Inheritance 277
Identifying Human Alleles as Recessive or Dominant 277
Identifying Human Traits as Autosomal or Sex-Linked 278
CHAPTER REVIEW 279

15 DNA and the Gene: Synthesis and Repair 284

15.1 What Are Genes Made Of? 285
The Hershey–Chase Experiment 285
The Secondary Structure of DNA 286

15.2 Testing Early Hypotheses about DNA Synthesis 287
Three Alternative Hypotheses 287
The Meselson–Stahl Experiment 289

15.3 A Model for DNA Synthesis 289
How Does Replication Get Started? 290
How Is the Helix Opened and Stabilized? 290
How Is the Leading Strand Synthesized? 291
How Is the Lagging Strand Synthesized? 292

15.4 Replicating the Ends of Linear Chromosomes 295
The End Replication Problem 295
Telomerase Solves the End Replication Problem 296
Telomerase Regulation 297

15.5 Repairing Mistakes and DNA Damage 297
Correcting Mistakes in DNA Synthesis 298
Repairing Damaged DNA 299
Xeroderma Pigmentosum: A Case Study 299
CHAPTER REVIEW 301

16 How Genes Work 304

16.1 What Do Genes Do? 305
The One-Gene, One-Enzyme Hypothesis 305
An Experimental Test of the Hypothesis 305

16.2 The Central Dogma of Molecular Biology 307
The Genetic Code Hypothesis 307
RNA as the Intermediary between Genes and Proteins 307
Dissecting the Central Dogma 308

16.3 The Genetic Code 310
How Long Is a Word in the Genetic Code? 310
How Did Researchers Crack the Code? 311

16.4 How Can Mutation Modify Genes and Chromosomes? 313
Point Mutation 313
Chromosome Mutations 314
CHAPTER REVIEW 315

17 Transcription, RNA Processing, and Translation 317

17.1 An Overview of Transcription 318
Initiation: How Does Transcription Begin in Bacteria? 318
Elongation and Termination 320
Transcription in Eukaryotes 320

17.2 RNA Processing in Eukaryotes 321
The Startling Discovery of Split Eukaryotic Genes 321
RNA Splicing 322
Adding Caps and Tails to Transcripts 323

17.3 An Introduction to Translation 324
Ribosomes Are the Site of Protein Synthesis 324
Translation in Bacteria and Eukaryotes 324
How Does an mRNA Triplet Specify an Amino Acid? 325

17.4 The Structure and Function of Transfer RNA 326
What Do tRNAs Look Like? 327
How Are Amino Acids Attached to tRNAs? 327
How Many tRNAs Are There? 327

17.5 The Structure and Function of Ribosomes 328
Initiating Translation 329
Elongation: Extending the Polypeptide 330
Terminating Translation 331
Post-Translational Modifications 331
CHAPTER REVIEW 333

18 Control of Gene Expression in Bacteria 336

18.1 An Overview of Gene Regulation and Information Flow 337
Mechanisms of Regulation 337
Metabolizing Lactose—A Model System 338

18.2 Identifying Regulated Genes 339
Replica Plating to Find Lactose Metabolism Mutants 339
Several Genes Are Involved in Lactose Metabolism 339

18.3 Negative Control of Transcription 341
The Operon Model 342
How Does Glucose Regulate the *lac* Operon? 343
Why Has the *lac* Operon Model Been So Important? 343

18.4 Positive Control of Transcription 344

18.5 Global Gene Regulation 344
CHAPTER REVIEW 346

19 Control of Gene Expression in Eukaryotes 348

19.1 Gene Regulation in Eukaryotes—An Overview 349

19.2 Chromatin Remodeling 349
What Is Chromatin's Basic Structure? 350
Evidence that Chromatin Structure Is Altered in Active Genes 351
How Is Chromatin Altered? 351
Chromatin Modifications Can Be Inherited 352

19.3 Initiating Transcription: Regulatory Sequences and Regulatory Proteins 353

Promoter-Proximal Elements Are Regulatory Sequences Near the Promoter 354
Enhancers Are Regulatory Sequences Far from the Promoter 354
The Role of Transcription Factors in Differential Gene Expression 354
How Do Transcription Factors Recognize Specific DNA Sequences? 355
A Model for Transcription Initiation 356

19.4 Post-Transcriptional Control 356
Alternative Splicing of mRNAs 357
mRNA Stability and RNA Interference 358
How Is Translation Controlled? 359
Post-Translational Control 360

19.5 How Does Gene Expression Compare in Bacteria and Eukaryotes? 360

19.6 Linking Cancer with Defects in Gene Regulation 361
The Genetic Basis of Uncontrolled Cell Growth 361
The *p53* Tumor Suppressor: A Case Study 361
CHAPTER REVIEW 363

BIG PICTURE GENETIC INFORMATION 366

20 Analyzing and Engineering Genes 368

20.1 Case 1–The Effort to Cure Pituitary Dwarfism: Basic Recombinant DNA Technologies 369
Why Did Early Efforts to Treat the Disease Fail? 369
Steps in Engineering a Safe Supply of Growth Hormone 370
Ethical Concerns over Recombinant Growth Hormone 374

20.2 Case 2–Amplification of Fossil DNA: The Polymerase Chain Reaction 374
Requirements of PCR 374
PCR in Action 376

20.3 Case 3–Sanger's Breakthrough: Dideoxy DNA Sequencing 376
The Logic of Dideoxy Sequencing 377
"Next Generation" Sequencing 378

20.4 Case 4–The Huntington's Disease Story: Finding Genes by Mapping 378
How Was the Huntington's Disease Gene Found? 378
What Are the Benefits of Finding a Disease Gene? 382
Ethical Concerns over Genetic Testing 382

20.5 Case 5–Severe Immune Disorders: The Potential of Gene Therapy 383
How Can Genes Be Introduced into Human Cells? 383
Using Gene Therapy to Treat X-Linked Immune Deficiency 383
Ethical Concerns over Gene Therapy 384

20.6 Case 6–The Development of Golden Rice: Biotechnology in Agriculture 385
Rice as a Target Crop 385
Synthesizing β-Carotene in Rice 385
The *Agrobacterium* Transformation System 385
Using the Ti Plasmid to Produce Golden Rice 386
CHAPTER REVIEW 387

21 Genomics and Beyond   389

21.1 Whole-Genome Sequencing   390
How Are Complete Genomes Sequenced?   390
Which Genomes Are Being Sequenced, and Why?   392
Which Sequences Are Genes?   392

21.2 Bacterial and Archaeal Genomes   393
The Natural History of Prokaryotic Genomes   393
Lateral Gene Transfer in Bacteria and Archaea   394
Metagenomics   395

21.3 Eukaryotic Genomes   395
Transposable Elements and Other Repeated Sequences   396
Gene Families   398
Insights from the Human Genome Project   399

21.4 Functional Genomics, Proteomics, and Systems Biology   400
What Is Functional Genomics?   400
What Is Proteomics?   402
What Is Systems Biology?   402

CHAPTER REVIEW   403

UNIT 5   EVOLUTIONARY PROCESSES AND PATTERNS   444

25 Evolution by Natural Selection   444

25.1 The Evolution of Evolutionary Thought   445
Plato and Typological Thinking   445
Aristotle and the Great Chain of Being   445
Lamarck and the Idea of Evolution as Change through Time   445
Darwin and Wallace and Evolution by Natural Selection   446

25.2 The Pattern of Evolution: Have Species Changed, and Are They Related?   446
Evidence for Change through Time   446
Evidence of Descent from a Common Ancestor   449
Evolution's "Internal Consistency"—The Importance of Independent Data Sets   451

25.3 The Process of Evolution: How Does Natural Selection Work?   453
Darwin's Inspiration   453

Darwin's Four Postulates   454
The Biological Definitions of Fitness, Adaptation, and Selection   454

25.4 Evolution in Action: Recent Research on Natural Selection   454
Case Study 1: How Did *Mycobacterium tuberculosis* Become Resistant to Antibiotics?   454
Case Study 2: Why Are Beak Size, Beak Shape, and Body Size Changing in Galápagos Finches?   456

25.5 Common Misconceptions about Natural Selection and Adaptation   459
Selection Acts on Individuals, but Evolutionary Change Occurs in Populations   459
Evolution Is Not Goal Directed   460
Organisms Do Not Act for the Good of the Species   461
There Are Constraints on Natural Selection   461

CHAPTER REVIEW   462

APPENDIX A **Answers**   A:1
APPENDIX B **BioSkills**   B:1
1 The Metric System and Significant Figures   B:1
2 Some Common Latin and Greek Roots Used in Biology   B:3
3 Reading Graphs   B:4
4 Using Statistical Tests and Interpreting Standard Error Bars   B:6
5 Combining Probabilities   B:8
6 Using Logarithms   B:9
7 Reading a Phylogenetic Tree   B:10
8 Reading Chemical Structures   B:12
9 Separating and Visualizing Molecules   B:13
10 Separating Cell Components by Centrifugation   B:17
11 Biological Imaging: Microscopy and X-ray Crystallography   B:18
12 Cell and Tissue Culture Methods   B:21
13 Model Organisms   B:23
14 Primary Literature and Peer Review   B:26
15 Making Concept Maps   B:28
16 Using Bloom's Taxonomy   B:29

APPENDIX C **Periodic Table of Elements**   C:1
Glossary   G:1
Credits   Cr:1
Index   I:1

About the Authors

A Letter from Scott:

I started working on *Biological Science* in 1997 with a simple goal: To help change the way biology is taught. After just shy of 20,000 hours of work on four editions of this text, that goal still gets me out of bed in the morning. But instead of focusing my energies on textbook writing, I've decided to devote myself full-time to research on student learning and developing new courses for undergraduate and graduate students at the University of Washington.

So with this edition I am passing the torch—to an all-star cast of leading scientists and educators who have enthusiastically taught from, and contributed to, previous editions of *Biological Science*. Working with them, I have seen the new team bring their passion, talent, and creativity to the book, with expertise that spans the breadth of the life sciences. Just as important, they work beautifully together because they think alike. They are driven by a shared concern for student learning, a commitment to the craft of writing, and a background in evidence-based teaching.

These pages provide a brief introduction to Liz Allison, Michael Black, Greg Podgorski, Kim Quillin, Jon Monroe, and Emily Taylor. As a group, they've built on the book's existing strengths and infused this edition with fresh energy, perspective, and ideas. I'm full of admiration for what they have accomplished, and excited about the impact this edition will have on biology students from all over the world.—*Scott Freeman*

Scott Freeman received a Ph.D. in Zoology from the University of Washington and was subsequently awarded an Alfred P. Sloan Postdoctoral Fellowship in Molecular Evolution at Princeton University. He has done research in evolutionary biology on topics ranging from nest parasitism to the molecular systematics of the blackbird family and is coauthor, with Jon Herron, of the standard-setting undergraduate text *Evolutionary Analysis*. Scott is the recipient of a Distinguished Teaching Award from the University of Washington and is currently a Senior Lecturer in the UW Department of Biology, where he teaches introductory biology for majors, a writing-intensive course for majors called The Tree of Life, and a graduate seminar in college science teaching. Scott's current research focuses on how active learning affects student learning and academic performance.

Lizabeth A. Allison is professor and chair of the Biology Department at the College of William & Mary. She received her Ph.D. in Zoology from the University of Washington, specializing in molecular and cellular biology. Before coming to William & Mary, she spent eight years as a faculty member at the University of Canterbury in New Zealand. Liz teaches introductory biology for majors and upper-division molecular biology courses. She has mentored graduate students and more than 80 undergraduate research students, many of them coauthoring papers with her on intracellular trafficking of the thyroid hormone receptor in normal and cancer cells. The recipient of numerous awards, including a State Council for Higher Education in Virginia (SCHEV) Outstanding Faculty Award in 2009, Liz received one of the three inaugural Arts & Sciences Faculty Awards for Teaching Excellence in 2011, and a Plumeri Award for Faculty Excellence in 2012. In addition to her work on this text, she is author of *Fundamental Molecular Biology*, now in its second edition.
Lead Author; Chapter 1 and BioSkills
laalli@wm.edu

Michael Black received his Ph.D. in Microbiology & Immunology from Stanford University School of Medicine as a Howard Hughes Predoctoral Fellow. After graduation, he studied cell biology as a Burroughs Wellcome Postdoctoral Fellow at the MRC Laboratory of Molecular Biology in Cambridge, England. His current research focuses on the use of molecules to identify and track the transmission of microbes in the environment. Michael is a professor of Cell & Molecular Biology at California Polytechnic State University in San Luis Obispo, where he teaches introductory and advanced classes for majors in cell biology and microbiology. In addition to his teaching and research activities, Michael serves as the director of the Undergraduate Biotechnology Lab, where he works alongside undergraduate technicians to integrate research projects and inquiry-based activities into undergraduate classes.
Chapters 2–12, 36, and 51
mblack@calpoly.edu

Greg Podgorski received his Ph.D. in Molecular and Cellular Biology from Penn State University and has been a postdoctoral fellow at the Max Plank Institute for Biochemistry and Columbia University. His research interests are in biology education, developmental genetics, and computational biology. Greg's most recent work has been in mathematical modeling of how patterns of different cell types emerge during development and how tumors recruit new blood vessels in cancer. Greg has been teaching at Utah State University for more than 20 years in courses that include introductory biology for majors and for nonmajors, genetics, cell biology, developmental biology, and microbiology, and he has offered courses in nonmajors biology in Beijing and Hong Kong. He's won teaching awards at Utah State University and has been recognized by the National Academies as a Teaching Fellow and a Teaching Mentor.

Chapters 13–24

greg.podgorski@usu.edu

Jon Monroe is professor of Biology at James Madison University in Harrisonburg, Virginia. Jon completed his undergraduate work in Botany at the University of Michigan and his graduate work in Plant Physiology at Cornell University. He began his current position after a postdoc in biochemistry at Michigan State University. He currently teaches Plant Biology, and Cell and Molecular Biology. Jon's interest in plants is broad, ranging from systematics and taxonomy to physiology and biochemistry. His research, mostly with undergraduates, uses Arabidopsis thaliana to study the functions of a family of β-amylase genes in starch metabolism. Jon has been active in promoting undergraduate research through his work with the American Society of Plant Biologists (ASPB) and the Council on Undergraduate Research. He has received ASPB's Excellence in Teaching award and James Madison University Alumni Association's Distinguished Faculty Award.

Chapters 29–32; 37–41

monroejd@jmu.edu

Kim Quillin received her B.A. in Biology at Oberlin College *summa cum laude* and her Ph.D. in Integrative Biology from the University of California, Berkeley (as a National Science Foundation Graduate Fellow). Kim has worked in the trenches with Scott Freeman on every edition of *Biological Science*, starting with the ground-up development of the illustrations in the first edition in 1999 and expanding her role in each edition, always with the focus of helping students to think like biologists. Kim currently teaches introductory biology at Salisbury University, a member of the University System of Maryland, where she is actively involved in the ongoing student-centered reform of the concepts-and-methods course for biology majors. Her current research focuses on the scholarship of teaching and learning with an emphasis on measuring science process skills and the advantages and pitfalls of active multimedia learning.

Chapters 25–28; 33–35; 48; 52–57

kxquillin@salisbury.edu

Emily Taylor earned a B.A. in English at the University of California, Berkeley followed by a Ph.D. in Biological Sciences from Arizona State University, where she conducted research in the field of environmental physiology as a National Science Foundation Graduate Research Fellow. She is currently an associate professor of Biological Sciences at the California Polytechnic State University in San Luis Obispo, California. Her student-centered research program focuses on the endocrine and reproductive physiology of free-ranging reptiles, especially rattlesnakes. She teaches numerous undergraduate and graduate courses, including introductory biology, anatomy and physiology, and herpetology, and received the California Faculty Association's Distinguished Educator Award in 2010 and Cal Poly's Distinguished Teaching Award in 2012. Her revision of Unit 8 is her first foray into textbook writing.

Chapters 42–50

etaylor@calpoly.edu

Preface to Instructors

The first edition of *Biological Science* was visionary in its unique emphasis on the process of scientific discovery and experimental design—teaching how we know what we know. The goal was for students not only to learn the language of biology and understand fundamental concepts but also to begin to apply those concepts in new situations, analyze experimental design, synthesize results, and evaluate hypotheses and data—to learn how to think like biologists. Each edition since has proudly expanded on this vision. The Fifth Edition is no exception.

A team of six dedicated teacher-scholars has joined Scott to build on and refine the original vision, and by so doing, make the book an even better teaching and learning tool. The pace of biological discovery is rapid, and with each novel breakthrough it becomes even more challenging to decide what is essential to include in an introductory biology text. Pulling together an author team with firsthand expertise from molecules to ecosystems has ensured that the content of the Fifth Edition reflects cutting-edge biology that is pitched at the right level for introductory students and is as accurate and as exciting as ever for instructors and students alike.

New findings from education research continue to inform and inspire the team's thinking about *Biological Science*—we know more today than ever before about how students learn. These findings demand that we constantly look for new ways to increase student engagement in the learning process, and to help instructors align course activities and learning goals with testing strategies.

The New Coauthors

The new coauthor team brings a broad set of talents and interests to the project, motivated by a deep commitment to undergraduate teaching, whether at a small liberal arts college or a large university. Kim Quillin has been a partner in this textbook in every edition. For the Fifth Edition, she revised chapters across three units in addition to spearheading the continued effort to enhance the visual-teaching program. Michael Black, Greg Podgorski, Jon Monroe, and Emily Taylor, who served as unit advisors on the Fourth Edition, were already familiar with the book. And most of the authorial team have been avid users of previous editions for many years.

Core Values

Together, the coauthor team has worked to extend the vision and maintain the core values of *Biological Science*—to provide a book for instructors who embrace the challenge of boosting students to higher levels of learning, and to provide a book for students that helps them each step of the way in learning to think like scientists. Dedicated instructors have high expectations of their students—the Fifth Edition provides scaffolding to help students learn at the level called for by the National Academy of Sciences, the Howard Hughes Medical Institute, the American Association of Medical Academies, and the National Science Foundation.

What's New in This Edition

The Fifth Edition contains many new or expanded features, all of them targeted at ways to help students learn to construct their own knowledge and think like biologists.

- **Road Maps** The new Road Maps at the beginning of each chapter pair with the Big Picture concept maps introduced in the Fourth Edition. Together they help students navigate chapter content and see the forest for the trees. Each Road Map starts with a purpose statement that tells students what they can expect to learn from each chapter. It then goes on to visually group and organize information to help students anticipate key ideas as well as recognize meaningful relationships and connections between the ideas.

- **The Big Picture** Introduced in the Fourth Edition, Big Picture concept maps integrate words and visuals to help students synthesize information about challenging topics that span multiple chapters and units. In response to requests from instructors and students, three new Big Pictures focused on additional tough topics have been added: Doing Biology, The Chemistry of Life, and Plant and Animal Form and Function. In addition, the Ecology Big Picture is completely revised to reflect changes to that unit.

- **New Chapters** Two new chapters are added to better serve instructors and students. Unit 2 now contains a new Chapter 8, Energy and Enzymes: An Introduction to Metabolic Pathways. This chapter consolidates these critical topics in a place where students and instructors need it most—right before the chapters on cellular respiration and photosynthesis. In the Fourth Edition, animal movement was discussed in a chapter largely focused on animal sensory systems. In the Fifth Edition, this important topic is treated in depth in a new Chapter 48, Animal Movement, that explores how muscle and skeletal systems work together to produce locomotion.

- **New BioSkills** Instructors recognize that biology students need to develop foundational science skills in addition to content knowledge. While these skills are emphasized throughout the book, *Biological Science*, beginning with the Third

Edition, has provided a robust set of materials and activities to guide students who need extra help. To promote even fuller use of this resource, the BioSkills are now updated, expanded, and reorganized. New in this edition are a discussion of significant figures within the BioSkills on the Metric System, and two new BioSkills on Primary Literature and Peer Review and Using Bloom's Taxonomy. BioSkills are located in Appendix B, and practice activities can be assigned online in MasteringBiology®.

- **Promotion of Quantitative Skills** Reports like *Biology 2010*, *Scientific Foundations for Future Physicians*, and *Vision and Change* all place a premium on quantitative skills. To infuse a quantitative component throughout the text, new and existing quantitative questions are flagged in each chapter to encourage students to work on developing their ability to read or create a graph, perform or interpret a calculation, or use other forms of quantitative reasoning.

- **Bloom's Taxonomy** In the Fifth Edition, all questions in the text are assigned a Bloom's Taxonomy level to help both students and instructors understand whether a question requires higher-order or lower-order cognitive skills. Questions span all six Bloom's levels. (Bloom's levels are identified in Appendix A: Answers.) The coauthors were trained by experts Mary Pat Wenderoth and Clarissa Dirks[1] to ensure we followed a process that would result in high inter-rater reliability— or agreement among raters—in assigning Bloom's levels to questions. The new BioSkill, Using Bloom's Taxonomy, explains the six Bloom's levels to students and offers a practical guide to the kinds of study activities best suited for answering questions at each level.

- **Expanded Emphasis on "Doing Biology"** A constant hallmark of this text is its emphasis on experimental evidence— on teaching how we know what we know. To reflect the progress of science, in the Fifth Edition, the coauthor team replaced many experiments with fresh examples and added new Research Boxes. And as noted earlier, they added a new Big Picture on Doing Biology, focusing on the process of science and the organizational levels of biology. Data sources are now cited for all graphs and data tables to model the importance of citing data sources to students. Updated Research Box questions continue to encourage students to analyze some aspect of experimental design. Also new to this edition is a BioSkill on Primary Literature and Peer Review.

- **Art Program** The art program is further enhanced in this edition by the addition of more illustrated summary tables. These tables make subject areas more accessible to visual learners and reinforce key concepts of the chapter. Many of the life-cycle figures in Unit 6 are significantly overhauled.

[1] Crowe, A., C. Dirks, and M. P. Wenderoth. 2008. Biology in Bloom: Implementing Bloom's Taxonomy to enhance student learning in biology. *CBE–Life Sciences Education* 7: 368–381.

Updated Blue Thread Scaffolding

In the Third and Fourth editions of *Biological Science*, a metacognitive tool was formulated as the now popular feature known as "Blue Thread"—sets of questions designed to help students identify what they do and don't understand. The fundamental idea is that if students really understand a piece of information or a concept, they should be able to do something with it.

In the Fifth Edition, the Blue Thread is revised to reflect changes in chapter content, and to incorporate user feedback. Blue-Thread questions appear in the following locations:

- **In-text "You should be able to's"** offer exercises on topics that professors and students have identified as the most difficult concepts in each chapter.

- **Caption questions and exercises** challenge students to examine the information in a figure or table critically—not just absorb it.

- **Check Your Understanding boxes** present two to three tasks that students should be able to complete in order to demonstrate a mastery of summarized key ideas.

- **Chapter summaries** include "You should be able to" problems or exercises related to each key concept.

- **End-of-chapter** questions are organized in three levels of increasing difficulty so students can build from lower to higher-order cognitive questions.

Integration of Media

The textbook continues to be supported by MasteringBiology®, the most powerful online homework, tutorial, and assessment system available. Tutorials follow the Socratic method, coaching students to the correct answer by offering feedback specific to a student's misconceptions as well as providing hints students can access if they get stuck. Instructors can associate content with publisher-provided learning outcomes or create their own. Content highlights include the following:

- **NEW! Solve It Tutorials** These activities allow students to act like scientists in simulated investigations. Each tutorial presents an interesting, real-world question that students will answer by analyzing and interpreting data.

- **Experimental Inquiry Tutorials** The call to teach students about the process of science has never been louder. To support such teaching, there are 10 interactive tutorials on classic scientific experiments—ranging from Meselson–Stahl on DNA replication to the Grants' work on Galápagos finches and Connell's work on competition. Students who use these tutorials should be better prepared to think critically about experimental design and evaluate the wider implications of the data—preparing them to do the work of real scientists in the future.

- **BioFlix® Animations and Tutorials** BioFlix are movie-quality, 3-D animations that focus on the most difficult core topics and are accompanied by in-depth, online tutorials that provide hints and feedback to guide student learning. Eighteen BioFlix animations and tutorials tackle topics such as meiosis, mitosis, DNA replication, photosynthesis, homeostasis, and the carbon cycle.

- **NEW! End-of-Chapter Questions** Multiple choice end-of-chapter questions are now available to assign in MasteringBiology.

- **Blue-Thread Questions** Over 500 questions based on the Blue-Thread Questions in the textbook are assignable in MasteringBiology.

- **Big Picture Tutorials** Interactive concept map activities based on the Big Picture figures in the textbook are assignable in MasteringBiology, including tutorials to support the three new Big Pictures: Doing Biology, The Chemistry of Life, and Plant and Animal Form and Function.

- **BioSkills Activities** Activities based on the BioSkills content in the textbook are assignable in MasteringBiology, including activities to support the new BioSkills on Primary Literature and Peer Review and Using Bloom's Taxonomy.

- **Reading Quiz Questions** Every chapter includes reading quiz questions you can assign to ensure students read the textbook and understand the basics. These quizzes are perfect as a pre-lecture assignment to get students into the content before class, allowing you to use class time more effectively.

Serving a Community of Teachers

All of us on the coauthor team are deeply committed to students and to supporting the efforts of dedicated teachers. Doing biology is what we love. At various points along our diverse paths, we have been inspired by our own teachers when we were students, and now are inspired by our colleagues as we strive to become even better teacher-scholars. In the tradition of all previous editions of *Biological Science*, we have tried to infuse this textbook with the spirit and practice of evidence-based teaching. We welcome your comments, suggestions, and questions.

Thank you for your work on behalf of your students.

Content Highlights of the Fifth Edition

As discussed in the preface, a major focus of this revision is to enhance the pedagogical utility of *Biological Science*. Another major goal is to ensure that the content reflects the current state of science and is accurate. The expanded author team has scrutinized every chapter to add new, relevant content, update descriptions when appropriate, and adjust the approach to certain topics to enhance student comprehension. In this section, some of the key content improvements to the textbook are highlighted.

Chapter 1 Biology and the Tree of Life   A concept map summarizing the defining characteristics of life is added. The process of doing biology coverage is expanded to include discussion of both experimental and descriptive studies, and more rigorous definitions of the terms hypothesis and theory.

Chapter 2 Water and Carbon: The Chemical Basis of Life   A stronger emphasis on chemical evolution is threaded throughout the chapter to bring chemistry to life for the student reader. Two prominent models for chemical evolution are introduced; the historic Miller prebiotic soup experiment was moved here. Advanced discussion of energy and chemical reactions was moved to a new chapter (see Chapter 8).

Chapter 3 Protein Structure and Function   The chapter is reorganized to emphasize the link between structure and function, from amino acids to folded proteins. Updated content illustrates that protein shapes are flexible and dynamic, and may remain incompletely folded until the protein interacts with other molecules or ions. Details of how enzymes work were moved to Chapter 8.

Chapter 4 Nucleic Acids and the RNA World   New experimental results concerning the synthesis of nucleotides and nucleic acids in a prebiotic environment are discussed. The section on the RNA world is expanded to include the artificial evolution of a novel ribozyme involved in nucleotide synthesis.

Chapter 5 An Introduction to Carbohydrates   The molecular basis for resistance of structural polymers, such as cellulose, to degradation is clarified. A new research box illustrates the role of carbohydrates in cellular recognition and attachment using the egg and sperm of mice as a model system.

Chapter 6 Lipids, Membranes, and the First Cells   New content on lipid and membrane evolution and the proposed characteristics of the first protocell is introduced. The aquaporin and potassium channel figures are updated; how key amino acids serve as selectivity filters is now highlighted.

Chapter 7 Inside the Cell   Several new electron micrographs were selected to more clearly illustrate cell component structure and function. A new figure is added to better depict the pulse–chase assay used to identify the secretory pathway. Coverage of nuclear transport is expanded to differentiate between passive diffusion and active nuclear import. Updated content emphasizes the role of the cytoskeleton in localizing organelles, and how polarity of microtubules and microfilaments influences their growth rate.

Chapter 8 Energy and Enzymes: An Introduction to Pathways   This new chapter pulls together concepts in energy, chemical reactions, and enzymes that previously were covered in three different chapters. Oxidation and reduction reactions are emphasized to prepare students for Chapters 9 and 10. The energetics behind ATP hydrolysis and its role in driving endergonic reactions is discussed, and figures are revised to better illustrate the process. Updated content on enzyme regulation and a new process figure show a model for how metabolic pathways may have evolved.

Chapter 9 Cellular Respiration and Fermentation   Two new summary tables for glycolysis and the citric acid cycle are added that provide the names of the enzymes and the reaction each catalyzes. New content is introduced to propose a connection between the universal nature of the proton motive force and the story of the chemical evolution of life.

Chapter 10 Photosynthesis   More extensive comparison between the chemical reactions in mitochondria and chloroplasts is added. A new figure is introduced to illustrate noncyclic electron flow in the context of the thylakoid membrane. Greater emphasis is placed on the number of ATPs and NADPHs required for each cycle of carbon fixation and reduction.

Chapter 11 Cell–Cell Interactions   Coverage of extracellular matrix structure and function is expanded, including its role in intercellular adhesions and cell signaling. The plant apoplast and symplast are now introduced as key terms in the text and illustrated in a new figure. New content and a new figure on unicellular models for intercellular communication via pheromone sensing (yeast) and quorum sensing (slime mold) are added.

Chapter 12 The Cell Cycle   A new figure helps explain the pulse–chase assay for identifying phases of the cell cycle. Content is added to the text and to a figure that illustrates the similarities between chromosome segregation in eukaryotes and prokaryotes. A revised description of anaphase emphasizes how microtubule fraying at the kinetochore can drive chromosome movement. The explanation of how phosphorylation and dephosphorylation turns on MPF activity is updated to reflect current research.

Chapter 13 Meiosis   To improve the flow of the chapter, the section on advantages of sexual reproduction was moved to before mistakes in meiosis. The discussion of the role and timing of crossing over during meiosis I is updated. A new study that supports the hypothesis that sex evolved in response to the selective pressure of pathogens is introduced.

Chapter 14 Mendel and the Gene   Material on gene linkage is revised to emphasize the importance of genetic mapping. A new matched set of figures on pedigree analysis brings together the various modes of transmission that were previously shown in four individual figures. A new summary table on characteristics of different patterns of inheritance is added.

Chapter 15 DNA and the Gene: Synthesis and Repair   A new research figure is added that focuses on the relationship between telomere length and senescence in cultured somatic cells.

Chapter 16 How Genes Work   Coverage of the evolving concept of the gene and of different types of RNA is expanded. A figure showing the karyotype of a cancer cell is revised to improve clarity.

Chapter 17 Transcription, RNA Processing, and Translation   The sections on transcription in bacteria and eukaryotes are now separated, and content on charging tRNAs was moved to a new section. The discussion of translation is reorganized, first to emphasize the process in bacteria and then to highlight differences in eukaryotes.

Chapter 18 Control of Gene Expression in Bacteria   Coverage of *lac* operon positive regulation is updated to reflect current research. A new section and new process figure on global gene regulation are added, using the *lexA* regulon as an example.

Chapter 19 Control of Gene Expression in Eukaryotes   Extensive updates to the discussion of epigenetics include a new research box and a section on DNA methylation. Coverage of transcription initiation is updated to reflect current science. A new figure illustrates the role of p53 in the cell cycle in normal and cancerous cells.

Chapter 20 Analyzing and Engineering Genes   The material on sequencing the Neanderthal genome is updated, including evidence of limited Neanderthal genetic material in some modern human populations. New information on current generation sequencing technologies and massive parallelism is added. Recent advances in gene therapy are highlighted.

Chapter 21 Genomics and Beyond   Extensive updates throughout reflect recent advances in genomics. Changes include sequence database statistics, genomes that have been sequenced to study evolutionary relationships, and new figures illustrating gene count versus genome size in prokaryotes and eukaryotes and functional classes of human DNA sequences. A new section on systems biology is added. Also included are notes on the discovery of widespread transcription of eukaryotic genomes, deep sequencing, and the spectrum of mutations in human tumors.

Chapter 25 Evolution by Natural Selection   Several new key passages are included, among them the use of the Grand Canyon as a context for understanding relative dating of fossils, Darwin's artificial selection experiments with fancy pigeons, and Malthus's concept of struggle for existence. A new example of people living at high altitude in Tibet clarifies the difference between acclimatization and adaptation. An illustrated summary table of common misconceptions is added.

Acknowledgments

Reviewers

The peer review system is the key to quality and clarity in science publishing. In addition to providing a filter, the investment that respected individuals make in vetting the material—catching errors or inconsistencies and making suggestions to improve the presentation—gives authors, editors, and readers confidence that the text meets rigorous professional standards.

Peer review plays the same role in textbook publishing. The time and care that this book's reviewers have invested is a tribute to their professional integrity, their scholarship, and their concern for the quality of teaching. Virtually every paragraph in this edition has been revised and improved based on insights from the following individuals.

Tamarah Adair, *Baylor University*
Sandra D. Adams, *Montclair State University*
Marc Albrecht, *University of Nebraska at Kearney*
Larry Alice, *Western Kentucky University*
Leo M. Alves, *Manhattan College*
David R. Angelini, *American University*
Dan Ardia, *Franklin & Marshall College*
Paul Arriola, *Elmhurst College*
Davinderjit K. Bagga, *University of Montevallo*
Susan Barrett, *Wheaton College*
Donald Baud, *University of Memphis*
Vernon W. Bauer, *Francis Marion University*
Robert Bauman, *Amarillo College*
Christopher Beck, *Emory University*
Vagner Benedito, *West Virginia University*
Scott Bingham, *Arizona State University*
Stephanie Bingham, *Barry University*
Wendy Birky, *California State University, Northridge*
Jason Blank, *California Polytechnic State University*
Kristopher A. Blee, *California State University, Chico*
Margaret Bloch-Qazi, *Gustavus Adolphus College*
Lanh Bloodworth, *Florida State College at Jacksonville*
Catherine H. Borer, *Berry College*
James Bottesch, *Brevard Community College*
Jacqueline K. Bowman, *Arkansas Tech University*
John Bowman, *University of California, Davis*
Chris Brochu, *University of Iowa*
Matthew Brown, *Dalhousie University*
Mark Browning, *Purdue University*
Carolyn J. W. Bunde, *Idaho State University*
David Byres, *Florida State College at Jacksonville*
Michael Campbell, *Penn State Erie*
Manel Camps, *University of California, Santa Cruz*
Geralyn M. Caplan, *Owensboro Community and Technical College*
Richard Cardullo, *University of California, Riverside*

David Carlini, *American University*
Dale Casamatta, *University of North Florida*
Deborah Chapman, *University of Pittsburgh*
Joe Coelho, *Quincy University*
Allen Collins, *Smithsonian Museum of Natural History*
Robert A. Colvin, *Ohio University*
Kimberly L. Conner, *Florida State College at Jacksonville*
Karen Curto, *University of Pittsburgh*
Clarissa Dirks, *Evergreen State College*
Peter Ducey, *SUNY Cortland*
Erastus Dudley, *Huntingdon College*
Jeffrey P. Duguay, *Delta State University*
Tod Duncan, *University of Colorado, Denver*
Joseph Esdin, *University of California, Los Angeles*
Brent Ewers, *University of Wyoming*
Amy Farris, *Ivy Tech Community College*
Bruce Fisher, *Roane State Community College*
Ryan Fisher, *Salem State University*
David Fitch, *New York University*
Elizabeth Fitch, *Motlow State Community College*
Michael P. Franklin, *California State University, Northridge*
Susannah French, *Utah State University*
Caitlin Gabor, *Texas State University*
Matthew Gilg, *University of North Florida*
Kendra Greenlee, *North Dakota State University*
Patricia A. Grove, *College of Mount Saint Vincent*
Nancy Guild, *University of Colorado, Boulder*
Cynthia Hemenway, *North Carolina State University*
Christopher R. Herlihy, *Middle Tennessee State University*
Kendra Hill, *South Dakota State University*
Sara Hoot, *University of Wisconsin, Milwaukee*
Kelly Howe, *University of New Mexico*
Robin Hulbert, *California Polytechnic State University*
Rick Jellen, *Brigham Young University*
Russell Johnson, *Colby College*
William Jira Katembe, *Delta State University*
Elena K. Keeling, *California Polytechnic State University*
Jill B. Keeney, *Juniata College*
Greg Kelly, *University of Western Ontario*
Scott L. Kight, *Montclair State University*
Charles Knight, *California Polytechnic State University*
Jenny Knight, *University of Colorado, Boulder*
William Kroll, *Loyola University Chicago*
Dominic Lannutti, *El Paso Community College*
Brenda Leady, *University of Toledo*
David Lindberg, *University of California, Berkeley*
Barbara Lom, *Davidson College*
Robert Maxwell, *Georgia State University*
Marshall D. McCue, *St. Mary's University*
Kurt A. McKean, *SUNY Albany*
Michael Meighan, *University of California, Berkeley*
John Merrill, *Michigan State University*

...Community College
...of Illinois at Chicago
...niversity
...man State University
...tar College System, North Harris
...lege
...al Connecticut State University
...ale Community College
...Martin's University
Nathan Okia, *Auburn University at Montgomery*
Robert Osuna, *SUNY Albany*
Daniel Panaccione, *West Virginia University*
Stephanie Pandolfi, *Michigan State University*
Michael Rockwell Parker, *Monell Chemical Senses Center*
Lisa Parks, *North Carolina State University*
Nancy Pelaez, *Purdue University*
Shelley W. Penrod, *Lone Star College System, North Harris*
Andrea Pesce, *James Madison University*
Raymond Pierotti, *University of Kansas*
Melissa Ann Pilgrim, *University of South Carolina Upstate*
Paul Pillitteri, *Southern Utah University*
Debra Pires, *University of California, Los Angeles*
P. David Polly, *Indiana University, Bloomington*
Vanessa Quinn, *Purdue University North Central*
Stacey L. Raimondi, *Elmhurst College*
Stephanie Randell, *McLennan Community College*
Marceau Ratard, *Delgado Community College*
Flona Redway, *Barry University*
Srebrenka Robic, *Agnes Scott College*
Dave Robinson, *Bellarmine University*
George Robinson, *SUNY Albany*
Adam W. Rollins, *Lincoln Memorial University*
Amanda Rosenzweig, *Delgado Community College*
Leonard C. Salvatori, *Indian River State College*
Dee Ann Sato, *Cypress College*
Leena Sawant, *Houston Community College*
Jon Scales, *Midwestern State University*
Oswald Schmitz, *Yale University*
Joan Sharp, *Simon Fraser University*
Julie Schroer, *North Dakota State University*
Timothy E. Shannon, *Francis Marion University*
Lynnette Sievert, *Emporia State University*
Susan Skambis, *Valencia College*
Ann E. Stapleton, *University of North Carolina, Wilmington*
Mary-Pat Stein, *California State University, Northridge*
Christine Strand, *California Polytechnic State University*
Denise Strickland, *Midlands Technical College*
Jackie Swanik, *Wake Technical Community College*
Billie J. Swalla, *University of Washington*
Zuzana Swigonova, *University of Pittsburgh*
Briana Timmerman, *University of South Carolina*
Catherine Ueckert, *Northern Arizona University*
Sara Via, *University of Maryland, College Park*
Thomas J. Volk, *University of Wisconsin–La Crosse*
Jeffrey Walck, *Middle Tennessee State University*
Andrea Weeks, *George Mason University*
Margaret S. White, *Scottsdale Community College*
Steven D. Wilt, *Bellarmine University*
Candace Winstead, *California Polytechnic State University*
James A. Wise, *Hampton University*

Correspondents

One of the most enjoyable interactions we have as textbook authors is correspondence or conversations with researchers and teachers who take the time and trouble to contact us to discuss an issue with the book, or who respond to our queries about a particular data set or study. We are always amazed and heartened by the generosity of these individuals. They care, deeply.

Lawrence Alice, *Western Kentucky University*
David Baum, *University of Wisconsin–Madison*
Meredith Blackwell, *Louisiana State University*
Nancy Burley, *University of California, Irvine*
Thomas Breithaupt, *University of Hull*
Philip Cantino, *Ohio University*
Allen Collins, *Smithsonian Museum of Natural History*
Robert Full, *University of California, Berkeley*
Arundhati Ghosh, *University of Pittsburgh*
Jennifer Gottwald, *University of Wisconsin–Madison*
Jon Harrison, *Arizona State University*
David Hawksworth, *Natural History Museum, London*
Jim Herrick, *James Madison University*
John Hunt, *University of Exeter*
Doug Jensen, *Converse College*
Scott Kight, *Montclair State University*
Scott Kirkton, *Union College*
Mimi Koehl, *University of California, Berkeley*
Rodger Kram, *University of Colorado*
Matthew McHenry, *University of California, Irvine*
Alison Miyamoto, *California State University, Fullerton*
Sean Menke, *Lake Forest College*
Rich Mooi, *California Academy of Sciences*
Michael Oliver, *MalawiCichlids.com*
M. Rockwell Parker, *Monell Chemical Senses Center*
Andrea Pesce, *James Madison University*
Chris Preston, *Monterey Bay Aquarium Research Institute*
Scott Sakaluk, *Illinois State University*
Kyle Seifert, *James Madison University*
Jos Snoeks, *Royal Museum for Central Africa*
Jeffrey Spring, *University of Louisiana*
Christy Strand, *California Polytechnic State University, San Luis Obispo*
Torsten Struck, *University of Osnabrueck, Germany*
Oswald Schmitz, *Yale University*
Ian Tattersall, *American Museum of Natural History*
Robert Turgeon, *Cornell University*
Tom Volk, *University of Wisconsin–La Crosse*
Naomi Wernick, *University of Massachusetts, Lowell*

Supplements Contributors

Instructors depend on an impressive array of support materials—in print and online—to design and deliver their courses. The student experience would be much weaker without the study guide, test bank, activities, animations, quizzes, and tutorials written by the following individuals.

Brian Bagatto, *University of Akron*
Scott Bingham, *Arizona State University*
Jay L. Brewster, *Pepperdine University*

Mirjana Brockett, *Georgia Institute of Technology*
Warren Burggren, *University of North Texas*
Jeff Carmichael, *University of North Dakota*
Tim Christensen, *East Carolina University*
Erica Cline, *University of Washington—Tacoma*
Patricia Colberg, *University of Wyoming*
Elia Crisucci, *University of Pittsburgh*
Elizabeth Cowles, *Eastern Connecticut State University*
Clarissa Dirks, *Evergreen State College*
Lisa Elfring, *University of Arizona, Tucson*
Brent Ewers, *University of Wyoming*
Rebecca Ferrell, *Metropolitan State University of Denver*
Miriam Ferzli, *North Carolina State University*
Cheryl Frederick, *University of Washington*
Cindee Giffen, *University of Wisconsin–Madison*
Kathy M. Gillen, *Kenyon College*
Linda Green, *Georgia Institute of Technology*
Christopher Harendza, *Montgomery County Community College*
Cynthia Hemenway, *North Carolina State University*
Laurel Hester, *University of South Carolina*
Jean Heitz, *University of Wisconsin–Madison*
Tracey Hickox, *University of Illinois, Urbana–Champaign*
Jacob Kerby, *University of South Dakota*
David Kooyman, *Brigham Young University*
Barbara Lom, *Davidson College*
Cindy Malone, *California State University, Northridge*
Jim Manser, retired, *Harvey Mudd College*
Jeanette McGuire, *Michigan State University*
Mark Music, *Indian River State College*
Jennifer Nauen, *University of Delaware*
Chris Pagliarulo, *University of California, Davis*
Stephanie Scher Pandolfi, *Michigan State University*
Lisa Parks, *North Carolina State University*
Debra Pires, *University of California, Los Angeles*
Carol Pollock, *University of British Columbia*
Jessica Poulin, *University at Buffalo, the State University of New York*
Vanessa Quinn, *Purdue University North Central*
Eric Ribbens, *Western Illinois University*
Christina T. Russin, *Northwestern University*
Leonard Salvatori, *Indian River State College*
Joan Sharp, *Simon Fraser University*
Chrissy Spencer, *Georgia Institute of Technology*
Mary-Pat Stein, *California State University, Northridge*
Suzanne Simon-Westendorf, *Ohio University*
Fred Wasserman, *Boston University*
Cindy White, *University of Northern Colorado*
Edward Zalisko, *Blackburn College*

Book Team

Anyone who has been involved in producing a textbook knows that many people work behind the scenes to make it all happen. The coauthor team is indebted to the many talented individuals who have made this book possible.

Development editors Mary Catherine Hager, Moira Lerner-Nelson, and Bill O'Neal provided incisive comments on the revised manuscript. Fernanda Oyarzun and Adam Steinberg used their artistic sense, science skills, and love of teaching to hone the figures for many chapters.

The final version of the text was copyedited b[...] and expertly proofread by Pete Shanks. The final f[...] were rendered by Imagineering Media Services and[...] proofread by Frank Purcell. Maureen Spuhler, Eric Sc[...] and Kristen Piljay researched images for the Fifth Edition[...]

The book's clean, innovative design was developed by Mar[...] Ong and Emily Friel. Text and art were skillfully set in the design by S4Carlisle Publishing Services. The book's production was supervised by Lori Newman and Mike Early.

The extensive supplements program was managed by Brady Golden and Katie Cook. All of the individuals mentioned—and more—were supported with cheerful, dedicated efficiency by Editorial Assistant Leslie Allen for the first half of the project; Eddie Lee has since stepped in to skillfully fill this role.

Creating MasteringBiology® tutorials and activities also requires a team. Media content development was overseen by Tania Mlawer and Sarah Jensen, who benefited from the program expertise of Caroline Power and Caroline Ross. Joseph Mochnick and Daniel Ross worked together as media producers. Lauren Fogel (VP, Director, Media Development), Stacy Treco (VP, Director, Media Product Strategy), and Laura ensured that the complete media program that accompanies the Fifth Edition, including MasteringBiology, will meet the needs of the students and professors who use our offerings.

Pearson's talented sales reps, who listen to professors, advise the editorial staff, and get the book in students' hands, are supported by tireless Executive Marketing Manager Lauren Harp and Director of Marketing Christy Lesko. The marketing materials that support the outreach effort were produced by Lillian Carr and her colleagues in Pearson's Marketing Comunications group. David Theisen, national director for Key Markets, tirelessly visits countless professors each year, enthusiastically discussing their courses and providing us with meaningful editorial guidance.

The vision and resources required to run this entire enterprise are the responsibility of Vice President and Editor-in-Chief Beth Wilbur, who provided inspirational and focused leadership, and President of Pearson Science Paul Corey, who displays unwavering commitment to high-quality science publishing.

Becky Ruden recruited the coauthor team, drawing us to the project with her energy and belief in this book. The editorial team was skillfully directed by Executive Director of Development Deborah Gale. Finally, we are deeply grateful for three key drivers of the Fifth Edition. Project Editor Anna Amato's superb organizational skills and calm demeanor assured that all the wheels and cogs of the process ran smoothly to keep the mammoth project steadily rolling forward. Supervising Development Editor Sonia DiVittorio's deep expertise, creative vision, keen attention to detail, level, and clarity, and inspiring insistence on excellence kept the bar high for everyone on every aspect of the project. Lastly, Senior Acquisitions Editor Michael Gillespie's boundless energy and enthusiasm, positive attitude, and sharp intellect have fueled and united the team and also guided the book through the hurdles to existence. The coauthor team thanks these exceptional people for making the art and science of book writing a productive and exhilarating process.

1 Biology and the Tree of Life

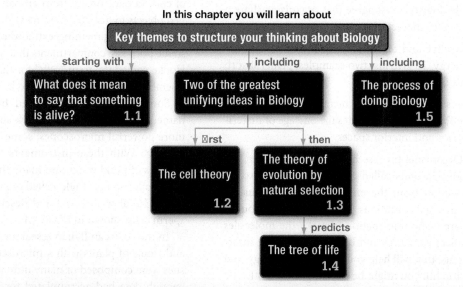

In this chapter you will learn about

Key themes to structure your thinking about Biology

starting with

What does it mean to say that something is alive? 1.1

including

Two of the greatest unifying ideas in Biology

including

The process of doing Biology 1.5

first

The cell theory 1.2

then

The theory of evolution by natural selection 1.3

predicts

The tree of life 1.4

These Chinese water dragon hatchlings are exploring their new world and learning how to find food and stay alive. They represent one of the key characteristics of life introduced in this chapter—replication.

n essence, biological science is a search for ideas and observations that unify our understanding of the diversity of life, from bacteria living in rocks a mile underground to humans and majestic sequoia trees. This chapter is an introduction to this search.

The goals of this chapter are to introduce the nature of life and explore how biologists go about studying it. The chapter also introduces themes that will resonate throughout this book:

- Analyzing how organisms work at the molecular level.

- Understanding organisms in terms of their evolutionary history.

- Helping you learn to think like a biologist.

Let's begin with what may be the most fundamental question of all: What is life?

This chapter is part of the Big Picture. See how on pages 16–17.

✔ When you see this checkmark, stop and test yourself. Answers are available in Appendix A.

1.1 What Does It Mean to Say That Something Is Alive?

An **organism** is a life-form—a living entity made up of one or more cells. Although there is no simple definition of life that is endorsed by all biologists, most agree that organisms share a suite of five fundamental characteristics.

- *Energy*   To stay alive and reproduce, organisms have to acquire and use energy. To give just two examples: plants absorb sunlight; animals ingest food.

- *Cells*   Organisms are made up of membrane-bound units called cells. A cell's membrane regulates the passage of materials between exterior and interior spaces.

- *Information*   Organisms process hereditary, or genetic, information encoded in units called genes. Organisms also respond to information from the environment and adjust to maintain stable internal conditions. Right now, cells throughout your body are using information to make the molecules that keep you alive; your eyes and brain are decoding information on this page that will help you learn some biology, and if your room is too hot you might be sweating to cool off.

- *Replication*   One of the great biologists of the twentieth century, François Jacob, said that the "dream of a bacterium is to become two bacteria." Almost everything an organism does contributes to one goal: replicating itself.

- *Evolution*   Organisms are the product of evolution, and their populations continue to evolve.

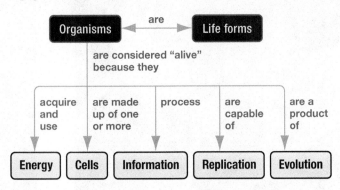

You can think of this text as one long exploration of these five traits. Here's to life!

1.2 The Cell Theory

Two of the greatest unifying ideas in all of science laid the groundwork for modern biology: the cell theory and the theory of evolution by natural selection. Formally, scientists define a **theory** as an explanation for a very general class of phenomena or observations that are supported by a wide body of evidence. The cell theory and theory of evolution address fundamental questions: What are organisms made of? Where do they come from?

When these concepts emerged in the mid-1800s, they revolutionized the way biologists think about the world. They established

two of the five attributes of life: Organisms are cellular, and their populations change over time.

Neither insight came easily, however. The cell theory, for example, emerged after some 200 years of work. In 1665 the Englishman Robert Hooke devised a crude microscope to examine the structure of cork (a bark tissue) from an oak tree. The instrument magnified objects to just 30X (30 times) their normal size, but it allowed Hooke to see something extraordinary. In the cork he observed small, pore-like compartments that were invisible to the naked eye. Hooke coined the term "cells" for these structures because of their resemblance to the cells inhabited by monks in a monastery.

Soon after Hooke published his results, a Dutch scientist named Anton van Leeuwenhoek succeeded in developing much more powerful microscopes, some capable of magnifications up to 300X. With these instruments, van Leeuwenhoek inspected samples of pond water and made the first observations of a dazzling collection of single-celled organisms that he called "animalcules." He also observed and described human blood cells and sperm cells, shown in **FIGURE 1.1**.

In the 1670s an Italian researcher who was studying the leaves and stems of plants with a microscope concluded that plant tissues were composed of many individual cells. By the early 1800s, enough data had accumulated for a German biologist to claim that *all* organisms consist of cells. Did this claim hold up?

All Organisms Are Made of Cells

Advances in microscopy have made it possible to examine the amazing diversity and complexity of cells at higher and higher magnifications. Biologists have developed microscopes that are tens of thousands of times more powerful than van Leeuwenhoek's and have described over a million new species. The basic conclusion made in the 1800s remains intact, however: All organisms are made of cells.

The smallest organisms known today are bacteria that are barely 200 nanometers wide, or 200 *billionths* of a meter. (See **BioSkills 1** in Appendix B to review the metric system and its prefixes.[1]) It would take 5000 of these organisms lined up side by side to span a millimeter. This is the distance between the smallest hash marks on a metric ruler. In contrast, sequoia trees can be over 100 meters tall. This is the equivalent of a 20-story building. Bacteria and sequoias are composed of the same fundamental building block, however—the cell. Bacteria consist of a single cell; sequoias are made up of many cells.

Today a **cell** is defined as a highly organized compartment that is bounded by a thin, flexible structure called a plasma membrane and that contains concentrated chemicals in an aqueous (watery) solution. The chemical reactions that sustain life take place inside cells. Most cells are also capable of reproducing by dividing—in effect, by making a copy of themselves.

The realization that all organisms are made of cells was fundamentally important, but it formed only the first part of the cell

---

[1]BioSkills are located in the second appendix at the back of the book. They focus on general skills that you'll use throughout this course. More than a few students have found them to be a life-saver. Please use them!

(a) van Leeuwenhoek built his own microscopes—which, while small, were powerful. They allowed him to see, for example . . .

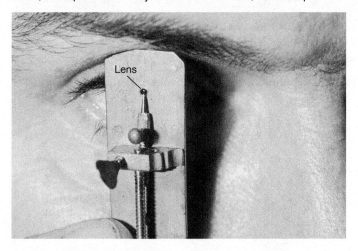

(b) . . . human blood cells (this modern photo was shot through one of van Leeuwenhoek's original microscopes) . . .

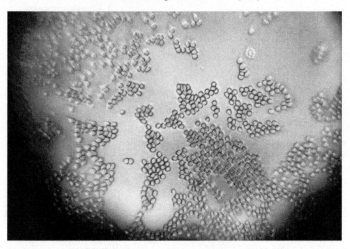

(c) . . . and animal sperm (drawing by van Leeuwenhoek of canine sperm cells on left, human on right).

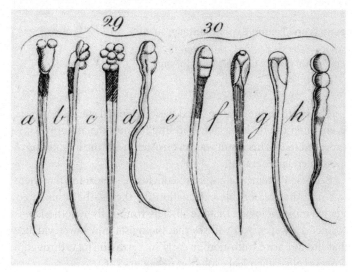

FIGURE 1.1 Van Leeuwenhoek's Microscope Made Cells Visible.

theory. In addition to understanding what organisms are made of, scientists wanted to understand how cells come to be.

Where Do Cells Come From?

Most scientific theories have two components: The first describes a pattern in the natural world; the second identifies a mechanism or process that is responsible for creating that pattern. Hooke and his fellow scientists articulated the pattern component of the cell theory. In 1858, a German scientist named Rudolph Virchow added the process component by stating that all cells arise from preexisting cells.

The complete **cell theory** can be stated as follows: All organisms are made of cells, and all cells come from preexisting cells.

Two Hypotheses The cell theory was a direct challenge to the prevailing explanation of where cells come from, called spontaneous generation. In the mid-1800s, most biologists believed that organisms could arise spontaneously under certain conditions. For example, the bacteria and fungi that spoil foods such as milk and wine were thought to appear in these nutrient-rich media of their own accord—springing to life from nonliving materials. In contrast, the cell theory maintained that cells do not spring to life spontaneously but are produced only when preexisting cells grow and divide. The all-cells-from-cells explanation was a **hypothesis:** a testable statement to explain a phenomenon or a set of observations.

Biologists usually use the word theory to refer to proposed explanations for broad patterns in nature and prefer hypothesis to refer to explanations for more tightly focused questions. A theory serves as a framework for the development of new hypotheses.

An Experiment to Settle the Question Soon after Virchow's all-cells-from-cells hypothesis appeared in print, a French scientist named Louis Pasteur set out to test its predictions experimentally. An experimental **prediction** describes a measurable or observable result that must be correct if a hypothesis is valid.

Pasteur wanted to determine whether microorganisms could arise spontaneously in a nutrient broth or whether they appear only when a broth is exposed to a source of preexisting cells. To address the question, he created two treatment groups: a broth that was not exposed to a source of preexisting cells and a broth that was.

The spontaneous generation hypothesis predicted that cells would appear in both treatment groups. The all-cells-from-cells hypothesis predicted that cells would appear only in the treatment exposed to a source of preexisting cells.

FIGURE 1.2 (on page 4) shows Pasteur's experimental setup. Note that the two treatments are identical in every respect but one. Both used glass flasks filled with the same amount of the same nutrient broth. Both were boiled for the same amount of time to kill any existing organisms such as bacteria or fungi. But because the flask pictured in Figure 1.2a had a straight neck, it was exposed to preexisting cells after sterilization by the heat treatment. These preexisting cells are the bacteria and fungi that cling to dust particles in the air. They could drop into the nutrient broth because the neck of the flask was straight.

In contrast, the flask drawn in Figure 1.2b had a long swan neck. Pasteur knew that water would condense in the crook of the swan neck after the boiling treatment and that this pool of water

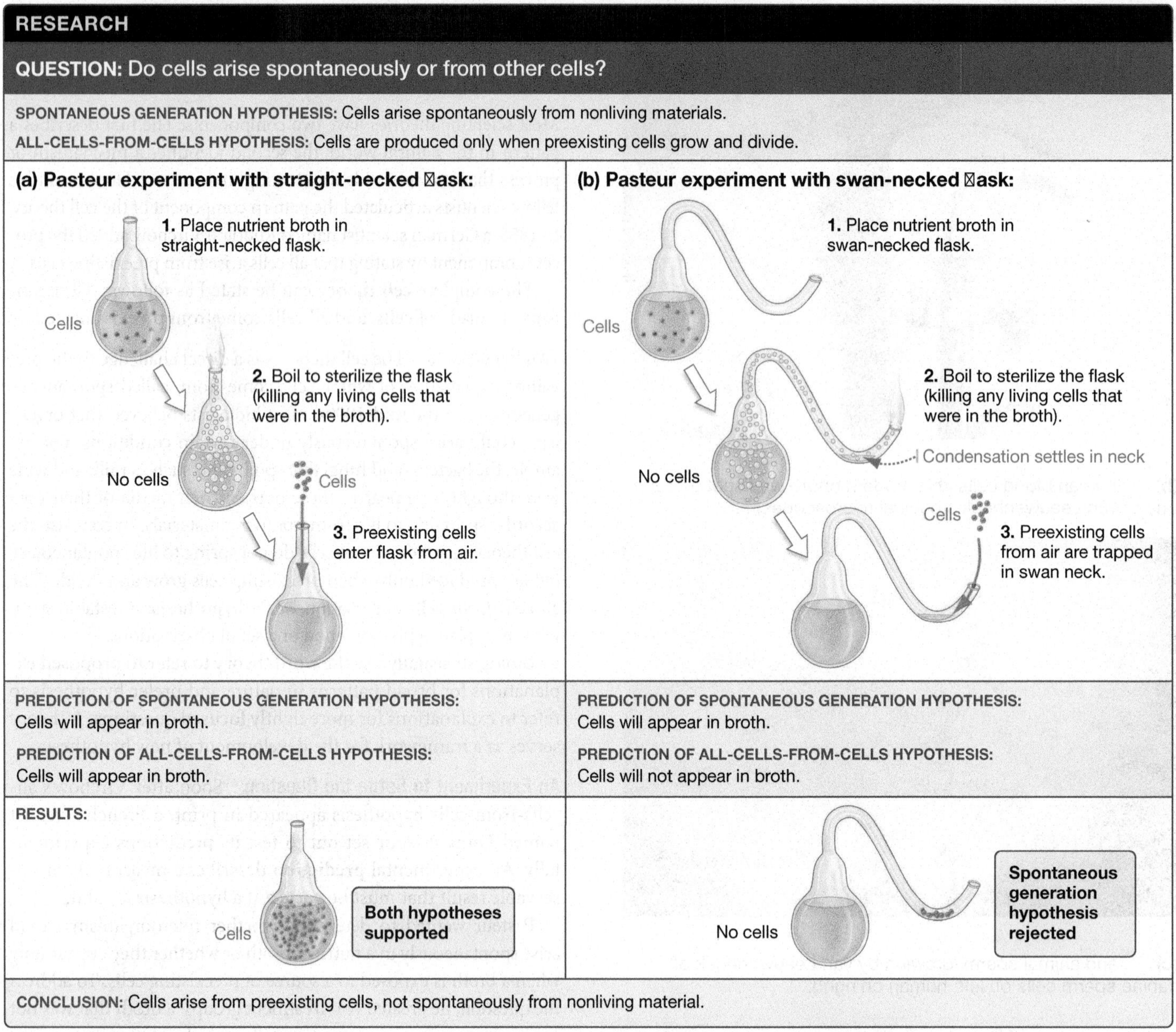

QUESTION: Do cells arise spontaneously or from other cells?

SPONTANEOUS GENERATION HYPOTHESIS: Cells arise spontaneously from nonliving materials.

ALL-CELLS-FROM-CELLS HYPOTHESIS: Cells are produced only when preexisting cells grow and divide.

(a) Pasteur experiment with straight-necked flask:

1. Place nutrient broth in straight-necked flask.

Cells

2. Boil to sterilize the flask (killing any living cells that were in the broth).

No cells

Cells

3. Preexisting cells enter flask from air.

(b) Pasteur experiment with swan-necked flask:

1. Place nutrient broth in swan-necked flask.

Cells

2. Boil to sterilize the flask (killing any living cells that were in the broth).

No cells

Condensation settles in neck

Cells

3. Preexisting cells from air are trapped in swan neck.

PREDICTION OF SPONTANEOUS GENERATION HYPOTHESIS: Cells will appear in broth.

PREDICTION OF ALL-CELLS-FROM-CELLS HYPOTHESIS: Cells will appear in broth.

PREDICTION OF SPONTANEOUS GENERATION HYPOTHESIS: Cells will appear in broth.

PREDICTION OF ALL-CELLS-FROM-CELLS HYPOTHESIS: Cells will not appear in broth.

RESULTS:

Cells

Both hypotheses supported

No cells

Spontaneous generation hypothesis rejected

CONCLUSION: Cells arise from preexisting cells, not spontaneously from nonliving material.

FIGURE 1.2 The Spontaneous Generation and All-Cells-from-Cells Hypotheses Were Tested Experimentally.

✔**QUESTION** What problem would arise in interpreting the results of this experiment if Pasteur had (1) put different types of broth in the two treatments, (2) heated them for different lengths of time, or (3) used a ceramic flask for one treatment and a glass flask for the other?

would trap any bacteria or fungi that entered on dust particles. Thus, the contents of the swan-necked flask were isolated from any source of preexisting cells even though still open to the air.

Pasteur's experimental setup was effective because there was only one difference between the two treatments and because that difference was the factor being tested—in this case, a broth's exposure to preexisting cells.

One Hypothesis Supported And Pasteur's results? As Figure 1.2 shows, the treatment exposed to preexisting cells quickly filled with bacteria and fungi. This observation was important because it showed that the heat sterilization step had not altered the nutrient broth's capacity to support growth.

The broth in the swan-necked flask remained sterile, however. Even when the flask was left standing for months, no organisms appeared in it. This result was inconsistent with the hypothesis of spontaneous generation.

Because Pasteur's data were so conclusive—meaning that there was no other reasonable explanation for them—the results persuaded most biologists that the all-cells-from-cells hypothesis was correct. However, you will see that biologists now have evidence that life did arise from nonlife early in Earth's history, through a process called chemical evolution (Chapters 2–6).

The success of the cell theory's process component had an important implication: If all cells come from preexisting cells, it follows that all individuals in an isolated population of single-celled organisms are related by common ancestry. Similarly, in you and most other multicellular individuals, all the cells present are descended from preexisting cells, tracing back to a fertilized egg. A fertilized egg is a cell created by the fusion of sperm and egg—cells that formed in individuals of the previous generation. In this way, all the cells in a multicellular organism are connected by common ancestry.

The second great founding idea in biology is similar, in spirit, to the cell theory. It also happened to be published the same year as the all-cells-from-cells hypothesis. This was the realization, made independently by the English scientists Charles Darwin and Alfred Russel Wallace, that all species—all distinct, identifiable types of organisms—are connected by common ancestry.

<h2>1.3 The Theory of Evolution by Natural Selection</h2>

In 1858 short papers written separately by Darwin and Wallace were read to a small group of scientists attending a meeting of the Linnean Society of London. A year later, Darwin published a book that expanded on the idea summarized in those brief papers. The book was called *The Origin of Species*. The first edition sold out in a day.

What Is Evolution?

Like the cell theory, the theory of evolution by natural selection has a pattern and a process component. Darwin and Wallace's theory made two important claims concerning patterns that exist in the natural world.

1. Species are related by common ancestry. This contrasted with the prevailing view in science at the time, which was that species represent independent entities created separately by a divine being.

2. In contrast to the accepted view that species remain unchanged through time, Darwin and Wallace proposed that the characteristics of species can be modified from generation to generation. Darwin called this process descent with modification.

Evolution is a change in the characteristics of a population over time. It means that species are not independent and unchanging entities, but are related to one another and can change through time.

What Is Natural Selection?

This pattern component of the theory of evolution was actually not original to Darwin and Wallace. Several scientists had already come to the same conclusions about the relationships between species. The great insight by Darwin and Wallace was in proposing a process, called **natural selection,** that explains *how* evolution occurs.

Two Conditions of Natural Selection Natural selection occurs whenever two conditions are met.

1. Individuals within a population vary in characteristics that are **heritable**—meaning, traits that can be passed on to offspring.

A **population** is defined as a group of individuals of the same species living in the same area at the same time.

2. In a particular environment, certain versions of these heritable traits help individuals survive better or reproduce more than do other versions.

If certain heritable traits lead to increased success in producing offspring, then those traits become more common in the population over time. In this way, the population's characteristics change as a result of natural selection acting on individuals. This is a key insight: Natural selection acts on individuals, but evolutionary change occurs in populations.

Selection on Maize as an Example To clarify how selection works, consider an example of **artificial selection**—changes in populations that occur when *humans* select certain individuals to produce the most offspring. Beginning in 1896, researchers began a long-term selection experiment on maize (corn).

1. In the original population, the percentage of protein in maize kernels was variable among individuals. Kernel protein content is a heritable trait—parents tend to pass the trait on to their offspring.

2. Each year for many years, researchers chose individuals with the highest kernel protein content to be the parents of the next generation. In this environment, individuals with high kernel protein content produced more offspring than individuals with low kernel protein content.

FIGURE 1.3 shows the results. Note that this graph plots generation number on the *x*-axis, starting from the first generation (0 on the graph) and continuing for 100 generations. The average percentage of protein in a kernel among individuals in this population is plotted on the *y*-axis.

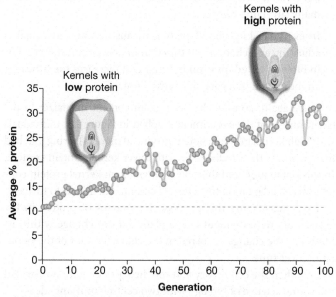

FIGURE 1.3 Response to Selection for High Kernel Protein Content in Maize.

DATA: Moose, S. P., J. W. Dudley, and T. R. Rocheford. 2004. *Trends in Plant Sciences* 9: 358–364; and the Illinois long-term selection experiment for oil and protein in corn (University of Illinois at Urbana–Champaign).

To read this graph, put your finger on the *x*-axis at generation 0. Then read up the *y*-axis, and note that kernels averaged about 11 percent protein at the start of the experiment. Now read the graph to the right. Each dot is a data point, representing the average kernel protein concentration in a particular generation. (A generation in maize is one year.) The lines on this graph simply connect the dots, to make the pattern in the data easier to see. During a few years the average protein content goes down, because of poor growing conditions or chance changes in how the many genes responsible for this trait interact. However, at the end of the graph, after 100 generations of selection, average kernel protein content is about 29 percent. (For more help with reading graphs, see **BioSkills 3** in Appendix B.)

This sort of change in the characteristics of a population, over time, is evolution. Humans have been practicing artificial selection for thousands of years, and biologists have now documented evolution by *natural* selection—where humans don't do the selecting—occurring in thousands of different populations, including humans. Evolution occurs when heritable variation leads to differential success in reproduction.

✔ QUANTITATIVE If you understand the concepts of selection and evolution, you should be able to describe how protein content in maize kernels changed over time, using the same *x*-axis and *y*-axis as in Figure 1.3, when researchers selected individuals with the *lowest* kernel protein content to be the parents of the next generation. (This experiment was actually done, starting with the same population at the same time as selection for high protein content.)

Fitness and Adaptation Darwin also introduced some new terminology to identify what is happening during natural selection.

- In everyday English, fitness means health and well-being. But in biology, **fitness** means the ability of an individual to produce viable offspring. Individuals with high fitness produce many surviving offspring.

- In everyday English, adaptation means that an individual is adjusting and changing to function in new circumstances. But in biology, an **adaptation** is a trait that increases the fitness of an individual in a particular environment.

Once again, consider kernel protein content in maize: In the environment of the experiment graphed in Figure 1.3, individuals with high kernel protein content produced more offspring and had higher fitness than individuals with lower kernel protein content. In this population and this environment, high kernel protein content was an adaptation that allowed certain individuals to thrive.

Note that during this process, the amount of protein in the kernels of any individual maize plant did not change within its lifetime—the change occurred in the characteristics of the population over time.

Together, the cell theory and the theory of evolution provided the young science of biology with two central, unifying ideas:

1. The cell is the fundamental structural unit in all organisms.

2. All species are related by common ancestry and have changed over time in response to natural selection.

If you understand that . . .

- Natural selection occurs when heritable variation in certain traits leads to improved success in reproduction. Because individuals with these traits produce many offspring with the same traits, the traits increase in frequency and evolution occurs.
- Evolution is a change in the characteristics of a population over time.

✔ **You should be able to . . .**

Using the graph you just analyzed in Figure 1.3, describe the average kernel protein content over time in a maize population where *no* selection occurred.

Answers are available in Appendix A.

1.4 The Tree of Life

Section 1.3 focuses on how individual populations change through time in response to natural selection. But over the past several decades, biologists have also documented dozens of cases in which natural selection has caused populations of one species to diverge and form new species. This divergence process is called **speciation.**

Research on speciation has two important implications: All species come from preexisting species, and all species, past and present, trace their ancestry back to a single common ancestor.

The theory of evolution by natural selection predicts that biologists should be able to construct a **tree of life**—a family tree of organisms. If life on Earth arose just once, then such a diagram would describe the genealogical relationships between species with a single, ancestral species at its base.

Has this task been accomplished? If the tree of life exists, what does it look like?

Using Molecules to Understand the Tree of Life

One of the great breakthroughs in research on the tree of life occurred when American biologist Carl Woese (pronounced *woze*) and colleagues began analyzing the chemical components of organisms as a way to understand their evolutionary relationships. Their goal was to understand the **phylogeny** of all organisms—their actual genealogical relationships. Translated literally, phylogeny means "tribe-source."

To understand which organisms are closely versus distantly related, Woese and co-workers needed to study a molecule that is found in all organisms. The molecule they selected is called small subunit ribosomal RNA (rRNA). It is an essential part of the machinery that all cells use to grow and reproduce.

Although rRNA is a large and complex molecule, its underlying structure is simple. The rRNA molecule is made up of sequences of four smaller chemical components called ribonucleotides. These ribonucleotides are symbolized by the letters A, U, C, and G. In rRNA, ribonucleotides are connected to one another linearly, like the boxcars of a freight train.

Analyzing rRNA Why might rRNA be useful for understanding the relationships between organisms? The answer is that the ribonucleotide sequence in rRNA is a trait that can change during the course of evolution. Although rRNA performs the same function in all organisms, the sequence of ribonucleotide building blocks in this molecule is not identical among species.

In land plants, for example, the molecule might start with the sequence A-U-A-U-C-G-A-G (**FIGURE 1.4**). In green algae, which are closely related to land plants, the same section of the molecule might contain A-U-A-U-G-G-A-G. But in brown algae, which are not closely related to green algae or to land plants, the same part of the molecule might consist of A-A-A-U-G-G-A-C.

The research that Woese and co-workers pursued was based on a simple premise: If the theory of evolution is correct, then rRNA sequences should be very similar in closely related organisms but less similar in organisms that are less closely related. Species that are part of the same evolutionary lineage, like the plants, should share certain changes in rRNA that no other species have.

To test this premise, the researchers determined the sequence of ribonucleotides in the rRNA of a wide array of species. Then they considered what the similarities and differences in the sequences implied about relationships between the species. The goal was to produce a diagram that described the phylogeny of the organisms in the study.

A diagram that depicts evolutionary history in this way is called a phylogenetic tree. Just as a family tree shows relationships between individuals, a phylogenetic tree shows relationships between species. On a phylogenetic tree, branches that share a recent common ancestor represent species that are closely related; branches that don't share recent common ancestors represent species that are more distantly related.

The Tree of Life Estimated from Genetic Data To construct a phylogenetic tree, researchers use a computer to find the arrangement of branches that is most consistent with the similarities and differences observed in the data.

Although the initial work was based only on the sequences of ribonucleotides observed in rRNA, biologists now use data sets that include sequences from a wide array of genetic material. **FIGURE 1.5** shows a recent tree produced by comparing these sequences. Because this tree includes such a diverse array of

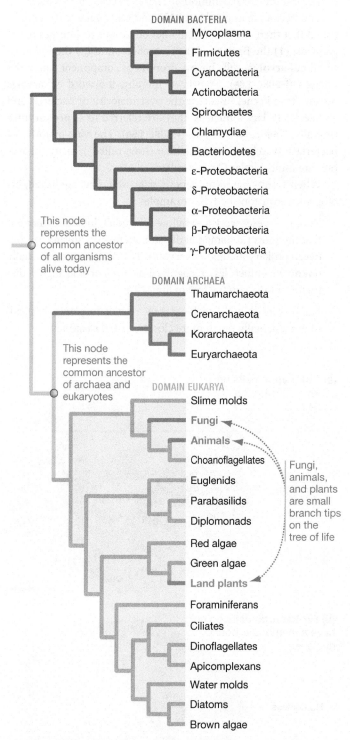

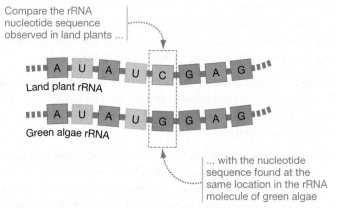

FIGURE 1.4 RNA Molecules Are Made Up of Smaller Molecules. A complete small subunit rRNA molecule contains about 2000 ribonucleotides; just 8 are shown in this comparison.

✔**QUESTION** Suppose that in the same section of rRNA, molds and other fungi have the sequence A-U-A-U-G-G-A-C. Are fungi more closely related to green algae or to land plants? Explain your logic.

FIGURE 1.5 The Tree of Life. A phylogenetic tree estimated from a large amount of genetic sequence data. The three domains of life revealed by the analysis are labeled. Common names are given for lineages in the domains Bacteria and Eukarya. Phyla names are given for members of the domain Archaea, because most of these organisms have no common names.

species, it is often called the universal tree, or the tree of life. (For help in learning how to read a phylogenetic tree, see **BioSkills 7** in Appendix B.) Notice that the tree's main node is the common ancestor of all living organisms. Researchers who study the origin of life propose that the tree's root extends even further back to the "*last universal common ancestor*" of cells, or **LUCA.**

The tree of life implied by rRNA and other genetic data established that there are three fundamental groups or lineages of organisms: **(1)** the Bacteria, **(2)** the Archaea, and **(3)** the Eukarya. In all **eukaryotes,** cells have a prominent component called the nucleus (**FIGURE 1.6a**). Translated literally, the word eukaryotes means "true kernel." Because the vast majority of bacterial and archaeal cells lack a nucleus, they are referred to as **prokaryotes** (literally, "before kernel"; see **FIGURE 1.6b**). The vast majority of bacteria and archaea are unicellular ("one-celled"); many eukaryotes are multicellular ("many-celled").

When results based on genetic data were first published, biologists were astonished. For example:

- Prior to Woese's work and follow-up studies, biologists thought that the most fundamental division among organisms was between prokaryotes and eukaryotes. The Archaea were virtually unknown—much less recognized as a major and highly distinctive branch on the tree of life.

- Fungi were thought to be closely related to plants. Instead, they are actually much more closely related to animals.

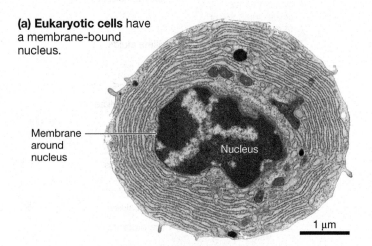

(a) Eukaryotic cells have a membrane-bound nucleus.

Membrane around nucleus

Nucleus

1 μm

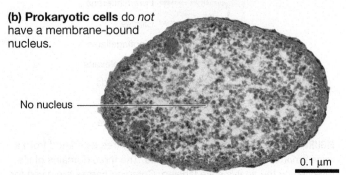

(b) Prokaryotic cells do *not* have a membrane-bound nucleus.

No nucleus

0.1 μm

FIGURE 1.6 Eukaryotes and Prokaryotes.

✔**QUANTITATIVE** How many times larger is the eukaryotic cell in this figure than the prokaryotic cell? (Hint: Study the scale bars.)

- Traditional approaches for classifying organisms—including the system of five kingdoms divided into various classes, orders, and families that you may have learned in high school—are inaccurate in many cases, because they do not reflect the actual evolutionary history of the organisms involved.

The Tree of Life Is a Work in Progress Just as researching your family tree can help you understand who you are and where you came from, so the tree of life helps biologists understand the relationships between organisms and the history of species. The discovery of the Archaea and the accurate placement of lineages such as the fungi qualify as exciting breakthroughs in our understanding of evolutionary history and life's diversity.

Work on the tree of life continues at a furious pace, however, and the location of certain branches on the tree is hotly debated. As databases expand and as techniques for analyzing data improve, the shape of the tree of life presented in Figure 1.5 will undoubtedly change. Our understanding of the tree of life, like our understanding of every other topic in biological science, is dynamic.

How Should We Name Branches on the Tree of Life?

In science, the effort to name and classify organisms is called **taxonomy.** Any named group is called a **taxon** (plural: **taxa**). Currently, biologists are working to create a taxonomy, or naming system, that accurately reflects the phylogeny of organisms.

Based on the tree of life implied by genetic data, Woese proposed a new taxonomic category called the **domain.** The three domains of life are the Bacteria, Archaea, and Eukarya.

Biologists often use the term **phylum** (plural: **phyla**) to refer to major lineages within each domain. Although the designation is somewhat arbitrary, each phylum is considered a major branch on the tree of life. Within the lineage called animals, biologists currently name 30–35 phyla—each of which is distinguished by distinctive aspects of its body structure as well as by distinctive gene sequences. For example, the mollusks (clams, squid, octopuses) constitute a phylum, as do chordates (the vertebrates and their close relatives).

Because the tree of life is so new, though, naming systems are still being worked out. One thing that hasn't changed for centuries, however, is the naming system for individual species.

Scientific (Latin) Names In 1735, a Swedish botanist named Carolus Linnaeus established a system for naming species that is still in use today. Linnaeus created a two-part name unique to each type of organism.

- *Genus* The first part indicates the organism's **genus** (plural: **genera**). A genus is made up of a closely related group of species. For example, Linnaeus put humans in the genus *Homo*. Although humans are the only living species in this genus, at least six extinct organisms, all of which walked upright and made extensive use of tools, were later also assigned to *Homo*.

- *Species* The second term in the two-part name identifies the organism's species. Linnaeus gave humans the species name *sapiens*.

An organism's genus and species designation is called its **scientific name** or Latin name. Scientific names are always italicized. Genus names are always capitalized, but species names are not—as in *Homo sapiens*.

Scientific names are based on Latin or Greek word roots or on words "Latinized" from other languages. Linnaeus gave a scientific name to every species then known, and also Latinized his own name—from Karl von Linné to Carolus Linnaeus.

Linnaeus maintained that different types of organisms should not be given the same genus and species names. Other species may be assigned to the genus *Homo*, and members of other genera may be named *sapiens*, but only humans are named *Homo sapiens*. Each scientific name is unique.

Scientific Names Are Often Descriptive Scientific names and terms are often based on Latin or Greek word roots that are descriptive. For example, *Homo sapiens* is derived from the Latin *homo* for "man" and *sapiens* for "wise" or "knowing." The yeast that bakers use to produce bread and that brewers use to brew beer is called *Saccharomyces cerevisiae*. The Greek root *saccharo* means "sugar," and *myces* refers to a fungus. *Saccharomyces* is aptly named "sugar fungus" because yeast is a fungus and because the domesticated strains of yeast used in commercial baking and brewing are often fed sugar. The species name of this organism, *cerevisiae*, is Latin for "beer." Loosely translated, then, the scientific name of brewer's yeast means "sugar-fungus for beer."

Scientific names and terms often seem daunting at first glance. So, most biologists find it extremely helpful to memorize some of the common Latin and Greek roots. To aid you in this process, new terms in this text are often accompanied by a translation of their Latin or Greek word roots in parentheses. (A glossary of common root words with translations and examples is also provided in **BioSkills 2** in Appendix B.)

check your understanding

If you understand that . . .

- A phylogenetic tree shows the evolutionary relationships between species.
- To infer where species belong on a phylogenetic tree, biologists examine genetic and other characteristics of the species involved. Closely related species should have similar characteristics, while less closely related species should be less similar.

✔ **You should be able to . . .**

Examine the following rRNA ribonucleotide sequences and draw a phylogenetic tree showing the relationships between species A, B, and C that these data imply:

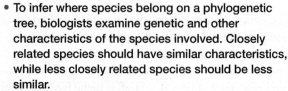

Species A: A A C T A G C G C G A T

Species B: A A C T A G C G C C A T

Species C: T T C T A G C G G T A T

Answers are available in Appendix A.

1.5 Doing Biology

This chapter has introduced some of the great ideas in biology. The development of the cell theory and the theory of evolution by natural selection provided cornerstones when the science was young; the tree of life is a relatively recent insight that has revolutionized our understanding of life's diversity.

These theories are considered great because they explain fundamental aspects of nature, and because they have consistently been shown to be correct. They are considered correct because they have withstood extensive testing.

How do biologists go about testing their ideas? Before answering this question, let's step back a bit and consider the types of questions that researchers can and cannot ask.

The Nature of Science

Biologists ask questions about organisms, just as physicists and chemists ask questions about the physical world or geologists ask questions about Earth's history and the ongoing processes that shape landforms.

No matter what their field, all scientists ask questions that can be answered by observing or measuring things—by collecting data. Conversely, scientists cannot address questions that can't be answered by observing or measuring things.

This distinction is important. It is at the root of continuing controversies about teaching evolution in publicly funded schools. In the United States and in Turkey, in particular, some Christian and Islamic leaders have been particularly successful in pushing their claim that evolution and religious faith are in conflict. Even though the theory of evolution is considered one of the most successful and best-substantiated ideas in the history of science, they object to teaching it.

The vast majority of biologists and many religious leaders reject this claim; they see no conflict between evolution and religious faith. Their view is that science and religion are compatible because they address different types of questions.

- Science is about formulating hypotheses and finding evidence that supports or conflicts with those hypotheses.

- Religious faith addresses questions that cannot be answered by data. The questions addressed by the world's great religions focus on why we exist and how we should live.

Both types of questions are seen as legitimate and important.

So how do biologists go about answering questions? After formulating hypotheses, biologists perform experimental studies, or studies that yield descriptive data, such as observing a behavior, characterizing a structure within a cell by microscopy, or sequencing rRNA. Let's consider two recent examples of this process.

Why Do Giraffes Have Long Necks? An Introduction to Hypothesis Testing

If you were asked why giraffes have long necks, you might say based on your observations that long necks enable giraffes to reach food that is unavailable to other mammals. This hypothesis is expressed in African folktales and has traditionally been accepted by many biologists. The food competition hypothesis is so plausible, in fact, that for decades no one thought to test it.

In the mid-1990s, however, Robert Simmons and Lue Scheepers assembled data suggesting that the food competition hypothesis is only part of the story. Their analysis supports an alternative hypothesis—that long necks allow giraffes to use their heads as effective weapons for battering their opponents, and that longer-necked giraffes would have a competitive advantage in fights.

Before exploring these alternative explanations, it's important to recognize that hypothesis testing is a two-step process:

Step 1 State the hypothesis as precisely as possible and list the predictions it makes.

Step 2 Design an observational or experimental study that is capable of testing those predictions.

If the predictions are accurate, the hypothesis is supported. If the predictions are not met, then researchers do further tests, modify the original hypothesis, or search for alternative explanations. But the process does not end here. Biologists also talk to other researchers. Over coffee, at scientific meetings, or through publications, biologists communicate their results to the scientific community and beyond. (You can see the Big Picture of the process of doing biology on pages 16–17.)

Now that you understand more about hypothesis testing, let's return to the giraffes. How did biologists test the food competition hypothesis? What data support their alternative explanation?

The Food Competition Hypothesis: Predictions and Tests

The food competition hypothesis claims that giraffes compete for food with other species of mammals. When food is scarce, as it is during the dry season, giraffes with longer necks can reach food that is unavailable to other species and to giraffes with shorter necks. As a result, the longest-necked individuals in a giraffe population survive better and produce more young than do shorter-necked individuals, and average neck length of the population increases with each generation.

To use the terms introduced earlier, long necks are adaptations that increase the fitness of individual giraffes during competition for food. This type of natural selection has gone on so long that the population has become extremely long necked.

The food competition hypothesis makes several explicit predictions. For example, the food competition hypothesis predicts that:

• neck length is variable among giraffes;

• neck length in giraffes is heritable; and

• giraffes feed high in trees, especially during the dry season, when food is scarce and the threat of starvation is high.

The first prediction is correct. Studies in zoos and natural populations confirm that neck length is variable among individuals.

The researchers were unable to test the second prediction, however, because they studied giraffes in a natural population and were unable to do breeding experiments. As a result, they simply had to accept this prediction as an assumption. In

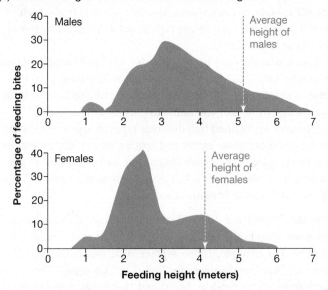

(a) Most feeding is done at about shoulder height.

(b) Typical feeding posture in giraffes

FIGURE 1.7 Giraffes Do Not Usually Extend Their Necks Upward to Feed.

DATA: Young, T. P., L. A. Isbell. 1991. *Ethology* 87: 79–89.

general, though, biologists prefer to test every assumption behind a hypothesis.

What about the prediction regarding feeding high in trees? According to Simmons and Scheepers, this is where the food competition hypothesis breaks down.

Consider, for example, data collected by a different research team on the amount of time that giraffes spend feeding in vegetation of different heights. **FIGURE 1.7a** plots the height of vegetation versus the percentage of bites taken by a giraffe, for males and for females from the same population in Kenya. The dashed line on each graph indicates the average height of a male or female in this population.

Note that the average height of a giraffe in this population is much greater than the height where most feeding takes place. In this population, both male and female giraffes spend most of their feeding time eating vegetation that averages just 60 percent of their full height. Studies on other populations of giraffes, during both the wet and dry seasons, are consistent with these data. Giraffes usually feed with their necks bent (**FIGURE 1.7b**).

These data cast doubt on the food competition hypothesis, because one of its predictions does not appear to hold. Biologists have not abandoned this hypothesis completely, though, because feeding high in trees may be particularly valuable during extreme droughts, when a giraffe's ability to reach leaves far above the ground could mean the difference between life and death. Still, Simmons and Scheepers have offered an alternative explanation for why giraffes have long necks. The new hypothesis is based on the mating system of giraffes.

The Sexual Competition Hypothesis: Predictions and Tests Giraffes have an unusual mating system. Breeding occurs year round rather than seasonally. To determine when females are coming into estrus or "heat" and are thus receptive to mating, the males nuzzle the rumps of females. In response, the females urinate into the males' mouths. The males then tip their heads back and pull their lips to and fro, as if tasting the liquid. Biologists who have witnessed this behavior have proposed that the males taste the females' urine to detect whether estrus has begun.

Once a female giraffe enters estrus, males fight among themselves for the opportunity to mate. Combat is spectacular. The bulls stand next to one another, swing their necks, and strike thunderous blows with their heads. Researchers have seen males knocked unconscious for 20 minutes after being hit and have cataloged numerous instances in which the loser died. Giraffes are not the only animals known to fight in this way—male giraffe weevils also use enormously long necks to fight for mating rights.

These observations inspired a new explanation for why giraffes have long necks. The sexual competition hypothesis is based on the idea that longer-necked giraffes are able to strike harder blows during combat than can shorter-necked giraffes. In engineering terms, longer necks provide a longer "moment arm." A long moment arm increases the force of an impact. (Think about the type of sledgehammer you'd use to bash down a concrete wall—one with a short handle or one with a long handle?)

The idea here is that longer-necked males should win more fights and, as a result, father more offspring than shorter-necked males do. If neck length in giraffes is inherited, then the average neck length in the population should increase over time. Under the sexual competition hypothesis, long necks are adaptations that increase the fitness of males during competition for females.

Although several studies have shown that long-necked males are more successful in fighting and that the winners of fights gain access to estrous females, the question of why giraffes have long necks is not closed. With the data collected to date, most biologists would probably concede that the food competition hypothesis needs further testing and refinement and that the sexual competition hypothesis appears promising. It could also be true that both hypotheses are correct. For our purposes, the important take-home message is that all hypotheses must be tested rigorously.

In many cases in biological science, testing hypotheses rigorously involves experimentation. Experimenting on giraffes is difficult. But in the case study considered next, biologists were able to test an interesting hypothesis experimentally.

How Do Ants Navigate? An Introduction to Experimental Design

Experiments are a powerful scientific tool because they allow researchers to test the effect of a single, well-defined factor on a particular phenomenon. Because experiments testing the effect of neck length on food and sexual competition in giraffes haven't been done yet, let's consider a different question: When ants leave their nest to search for food, how do they find their way back?

The Saharan desert ant lives in colonies and makes a living by scavenging the dead carcasses of insects. Individuals leave the burrow and wander about searching for food at midday, when temperatures at the surface can reach 60°C (140°F) and predators are hiding from the heat.

Foraging trips can take the ants hundreds of meters—an impressive distance when you consider that these animals are only about a centimeter long. But when an ant returns, it doesn't follow the same long, wandering route it took on its way away from the nest. Instead, individuals return in a straight line (**FIGURE 1.8**).

Once individuals are close to the nest, they engage in a characteristic set of back-and-forth U-turns until they find their nest hole. How do they do know how far they are from the nest?

The Pedometer Hypothesis Early work on navigation in desert ants showed that they use the Sun's position as a compass—meaning that they always know the approximate direction of the nest relative to the Sun. But how do they know how far to go?

After experiments had shown that the ants do not use landmarks to navigate, Matthias Wittlinger and co-workers set out to test a novel idea. The biologists proposed that Saharan desert ants know how far they are from the nest by integrating information from leg movements.

According to this pedometer hypothesis, the ants always know how far they are from the nest because they track the number

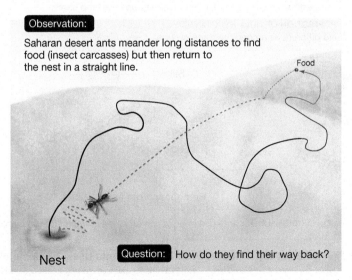

Observation:

Saharan desert ants meander long distances to find food (insect carcasses) but then return to the nest in a straight line.

Food

Nest

Question: How do they find their way back?

FIGURE 1.8 Navigation in Foraging Desert Ants.

of steps they have taken and their stride length. The idea is that they can make a beeline back toward the burrow because they integrate information on the angles they have traveled *and* the distance they have gone—based on step number and stride length.

If the pedometer hypothesis is wrong, however, then stride length and step number should have no effect on the ability of an ant to get back to its nest. This latter possibility is called a **null hypothesis.** A null hypothesis specifies what should be observed when the hypothesis being tested isn't correct.

Testing the Hypothesis To test their idea, Wittlinger's group allowed ants to walk from a nest to a feeder through a channel—a distance of 10 m. Then they caught ants at the feeder and created three test groups, each with 25 individuals (**FIGURES 1.9** and **1.10**):

- *Stumps* By cutting the lower legs of some individuals off, they created ants with shorter-than-normal legs.

- *Normal* Some individuals were left alone, meaning that they had normal leg length.

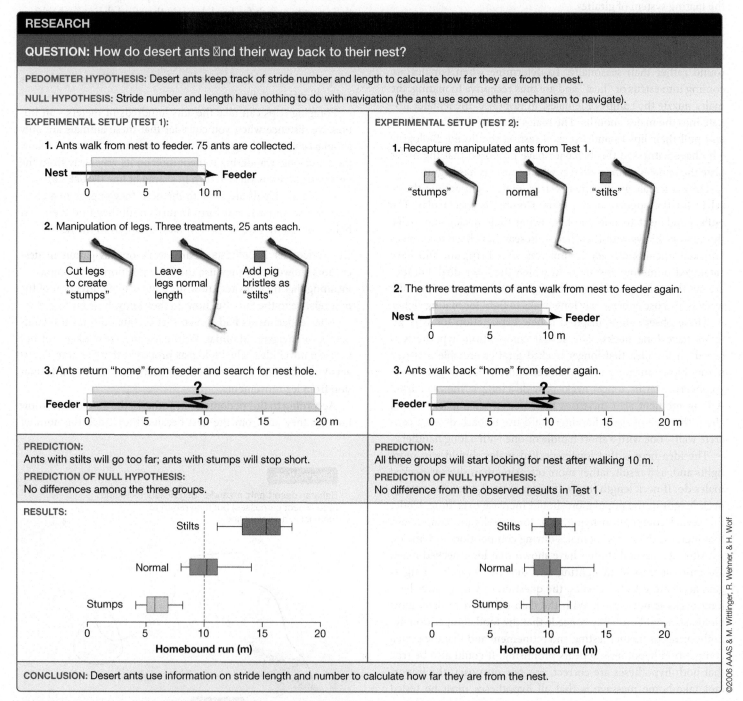

FIGURE 1.9 An Experimental Test: Do Desert Ants Use a "Pedometer"?

SOURCE: Wittlinger, M., R. Wehner, and H. Wolf. 2006. The ant odometer: Stepping on stilts and stumps. *Science* 312: 1965–1967.

✔**QUESTION** What is the advantage of using 25 ants in each group instead of just one?

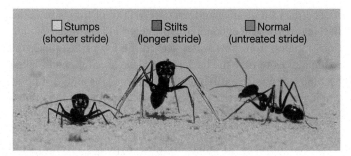

☐ Stumps (shorter stride)   ■ Stilts (longer stride)   ☐ Normal (untreated stride)

FIGURE 1.10 Manipulation of Desert Ant Stride Length.

- *Stilts* By gluing pig bristles onto each leg, the biologists created ants with longer-than-normal legs.

Next they put the ants in a different channel and recorded how far they traveled in a direct line before starting their nest-searching behavior. To see the data they collected, look at the graph on the left side of the "Results" section in Figure 1.9.

- *Stumps* The ants with stumps stopped short, by about 5 m, before starting to search for the nest opening.

- *Normal* The normal ants walked the correct distance—about 10 m.

- *Stilts* The ants with stilts walked about 5 m too far before starting to search for the nest opening.

To check the validity of this result, the researchers put the test ants back in the nest and recaptured them one to several days later, when they had walked to the feeder on their stumps, normal legs, or stilts. Now when the ants were put into the other channel to "walk back," they all traveled the correct distance—10 m—before starting to search for the nest (see the graph on the right side of the "Results" section in Figure 1.9).

The graphs in the "Results" display "box-and-whisker" plots that allow you to easily see where most of the data fall. Each box indicates the range of distances where 50 percent of the ants stopped to search for the nest. The whiskers indicate the lower extreme (stopping short of the nest location) and the upper extreme (going too far) of where the ants stopped to search. The vertical line inside each box indicates the median—meaning that half the ants stopped above this distance and half below. (For more details on how biologists report medians and indicate the variability and uncertainty in data, see **BioSkills 4** in Appendix B.)

Interpreting the Results The pedometer hypothesis predicts that an ant's ability to walk home depends on the number and length of steps taken on its outbound trip. Recall that a prediction specifies what we should observe if a hypothesis is correct. Good scientific hypotheses make testable predictions—predictions that can be supported or rejected by collecting and analyzing data. In this case, the researchers tested the prediction by altering stride length and recording the distance traveled on the return trip. Under the null hypothesis in this experiment, all the ants—altered and unaltered—should have walked 10 m in the first test before they started looking for their nest.

Important Characteristics of Good Experimental Design In relation to designing effective experiments, this study illustrates several important points:

- It is critical to include **control** groups. A control checks for factors, other than the one being tested, that might influence the experiment's outcome. In this case, there were two controls. Including a normal, unmanipulated individual controlled for the possibility that switching the individuals to a new channel altered their behavior. In addition, the researchers had to control for the possibility that the manipulation itself—and not the change in leg length—affected the behavior of the stilts and stumps ants. This is why they did the second test, where the outbound and return runs were done with the same legs.

- The experimental conditions must be as constant or equivalent as possible. The investigators used ants of the same species, from the same nest, at the same time of day, under the same humidity and temperature conditions, at the same feeders, in the same channels. Controlling all the variables except one—leg length in this case—is crucial because it eliminates alternative explanations for the results.

- Repeating the test is essential. It is almost universally true that larger sample sizes in experiments are better. By testing many individuals, the amount of distortion or "noise" in the data caused by unusual individuals or circumstances is reduced.

✔ If you understand these points, you should be able to explain: (1) What you would conclude if in the first test, the normal individual had not walked 10 m on the return trip before

check your understanding

If you understand that . . .

- Hypotheses are proposed explanations that make testable predictions.
- Predictions describe observable outcomes of particular conditions.
- Well-designed experiments alter just one condition—a condition relevant to the hypothesis being tested.

✔ **You should be able to . . .**

Design an experiment to test the hypothesis that desert ants feed during the hottest part of the day because it allows them to avoid being eaten by lizards. Then answer the following questions about your experimental design:

1. How does the presence of a control group in your experiment allow you to test the hypothesis?

2. How are experimental conditions controlled or standardized in a way that precludes alternative explanations of the data?

Answers are available in Appendix A.

looking for the nest; and (2) What you would conclude if the stilts and stumps ants had not navigated normally during the second test.

From the outcomes of these experiments, the researchers concluded that desert ants use stride length and number to measure how far they are from the nest. They interpreted their results as strong support for the pedometer hypothesis.

The giraffe and ant studies demonstrate a vital point: Biologists practice evidence-based decision making. They ask questions about how organisms work, pose hypotheses to answer those questions, and use experimental or observational evidence to decide which hypotheses are correct.

The data on giraffes and ants are a taste of things to come. In this text you will encounter hypotheses and research on questions ranging from how water gets to the top of 100-meter-tall sequoia trees to how the bacterium that causes tuberculosis has become resistant to antibiotics. As you work through this book, you'll get lots of practice thinking about hypotheses and predictions, analyzing the nature of control treatments, and interpreting graphs.

A commitment to tough-minded hypothesis testing and sound experimental design is a hallmark of biological science. Understanding their value is an important first step in becoming a biologist.

CHAPTER 1 REVIEW

For media, go to MasteringBiology

If you understand . . .

1.1 What Does It Mean to Say That Something Is Alive?

- There is no single, well-accepted definition of life. Instead, biologists point to five characteristics that organisms share.

✔ You should be able to explain why the cells in a dead organism are different from the cells in a live organism.

1.2 The Cell Theory

- The cell theory identified the fundamental structural unit common to all life.

✔ You should be able to describe the evidence that supported the pattern and the process components of the cell theory.

1.3 The Theory of Evolution by Natural Selection

- The theory of evolution states that all organisms are related by common ancestry.

- Natural selection is a well-tested explanation for why species change through time and why they are so well adapted to their habitats.

✔ You should be able to explain why the average protein content of seeds in a natural population of a grass species would increase over time, if seeds with higher protein content survive better and grow into individuals that produce many seeds with high protein content when they mature.

1.4 The Tree of Life

- The theory of evolution predicts that all organisms are part of a genealogy of species, and that all species trace their ancestry back to a single common ancestor.

- To construct this phylogeny, biologists have analyzed the sequences in rRNA and in an array of genetic material found in all cells.

- A tree of life, based on similarities and differences in these molecules, has three fundamental lineages, or domains: the Bacteria, the Archaea, and the Eukarya.

✔ You should be able to explain how biologists can determine which of the three domains a newly discovered species belongs to by analyzing its rRNA.

1.5 Doing Biology

- Biology is a hypothesis-driven, experimental science.

✔ You should be able to explain (1) the relationship between a hypothesis and a prediction and (2) why experiments are convincing ways to test predictions.

MasteringBiology

1. MasteringBiology Assignments

Tutorials and Activities An Introduction to Graphing; Experimental Inquiry: What Can You Learn about the Process of Science from Investigating a Cricket's Chirp?; Introduction to Experimental Design; Levels of Life Card Game; Metric System Review; The Scientific Method

Questions Reading Quizzes, Blue-Thread Questions, Test Bank

2. eText Read your book online, search, take notes, highlight text, and more.

3. The Study Area Practice Test, Cumulative Test, BioFlix® 3-D Animations, Videos, Activities, Audio Glossary, Word Study Tools, Art

You should be able to . . .

✔ **TEST YOUR KNOWLEDGE**   *Answers are available in Appendix A*

1. Anton van Leeuwenhoek made an important contribution to the development of the cell theory. How?
   a. He articulated the pattern component of the theory—that all organisms are made of cells.
   b. He articulated the process component of the theory—that all cells come from preexisting cells.
   c. He invented the first microscope and saw the first cell.
   d. He invented more powerful microscopes and was the first to describe the diversity of cells.

2. What does it mean to say that experimental conditions are controlled?
   a. The test groups consist of the same individuals.
   b. The null hypothesis is correct.
   c. There is no difference in outcome between the control and experimental treatment.
   d. All physical conditions except for one are identical for all groups tested.

3. The term *evolution* means that _____ change through time.

4. What does it mean to say that a characteristic of an organism is heritable?
   a. The characteristic evolves.
   b. The characteristic can be passed on to offspring.
   c. The characteristic is advantageous to the organism.
   d. The characteristic does not vary in the population.

5. In biology, to what does the term *fitness* refer?

6. Could *both* the food competition hypothesis and the sexual competition hypothesis explain why giraffes have long necks? Why or why not?
   a. No. In science, only one hypothesis can be correct.
   b. No. Observations have shown that the food competition hypothesis cannot be correct.
   c. Yes. Long necks could be advantageous for more than one reason.
   d. Yes. All giraffes have been shown to feed at the highest possible height and fight for mates.

✔ **TEST YOUR UNDERSTANDING**   *Answers are available in Appendix A*

7. What would researchers have to demonstrate to convince you that they had discovered life on another planet?

8. What did Linnaeus's system of naming organisms ensure?
   a. Two different organisms never end up with the same genus and species name.
   b. Two different organisms have the same genus and species name if they are closely related.
   c. The genus name is different for closely related species.
   d. The species name is the same for each organism in a genus.

9. What does it mean to say that a species is adapted to a particular habitat?

10. Explain how selection occurs during natural selection. What is selected, and why?

11. The following two statements explain the logic behind the use of molecular sequence data to estimate evolutionary relationships:

    "If the theory of evolution is true, then rRNA sequences should be very similar in closely related organisms but less similar in organisms that are less closely related."

    "On a phylogenetic tree, branches that share a recent common ancestor represent species that are closely related; branches that don't share recent common ancestors represent species that are more distantly related."

    Is the logic of these statements sound? Why or why not?

12. Explain why researchers formulate a null hypothesis in addition to a hypothesis when designing an experimental study.

✔ **TEST YOUR PROBLEM-SOLVING SKILLS**   *Answers are available in Appendix A*

13. A scientific theory is a set of propositions that defines and explains some aspect of the world. This definition contrasts sharply with the everyday usage of the word theory, which often carries meanings such as "speculation" or "guess." Explain the difference between the two definitions, using the cell theory and the theory of evolution by natural selection as examples.

14. Turn back to the tree of life shown in Figure 1.5. Note that Bacteria and Archaea are prokaryotes, while Eukarya are eukaryotes. On the simplified tree below, draw an arrow that points to the branch where the structure called the nucleus originated. Explain your reasoning.

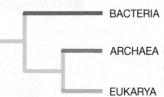

15. The proponents of the cell theory could not "prove" that it was correct in the sense of providing incontrovertible evidence that all organisms are made up of cells. They could state only that all organisms examined to date were made of cells. Why was it reasonable for them to conclude that the theory was valid?

16. Some humans have heritable traits that make them resistant to infection by HIV. In areas of the world where HIV infection rates are high, are human populations evolving? Explain your logic.
    a. No. HIV infection rates would not affect human evolution.
    b. Yes. The heritable traits that confer resistance to HIV should increase over time.
    c. No. The heritable traits that confer resistance to HIV should decrease over time.
    d. Yes. The heritable traits that confer resistance to HIV should decrease over time.

The Big Picture

Biologists study the characteristics of life. The cell theory, the theory of evolution by natural selection, and the tree of life are some of the great ideas in biology that came about by biologists asking questions that can be answered by observing or measuring things—that is, by collecting data.

Notice that the study of life is not a series of linear steps with a beginning and an end. Instead, the process of doing biology is dynamic and ongoing. The answer to one question may lay the foundation for twenty more questions. Working together, biologists from different disciplines integrate data across many levels, from atoms to the biosphere.

Note that the gray numbers in boxes tell you where to go for more information. Also, be sure to do the blue exercises in the Check Your Understanding box.

Characteristics of living things
- Energy
- Cells
- Information
- Replication
- Evolution

1.1

Text section where you can find more information

focuses on

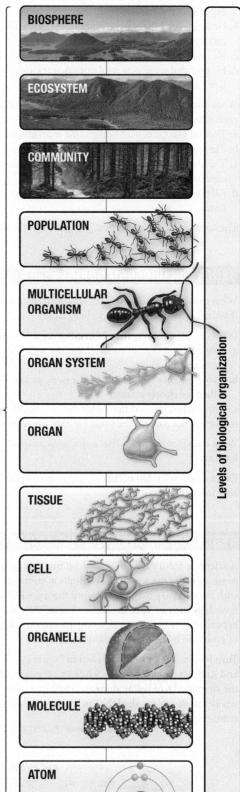

Scientists regularly integrate across many of these levels

Levels of biological organization

check your understanding

(C)(Y)(U)

If you understand the big picture . . .

✔ **You should be able to . . .**

1. Describe how biologists go about testing their ideas.
2. Provide an example of how an experimental study could span more than one level of biological organization.
3. Compare and contrast a hypothesis with a theory.
4. Propose the next step to take if data support the hypothesis you are testing.

Answers are available in Appendix A.

DOING BIOLOGY

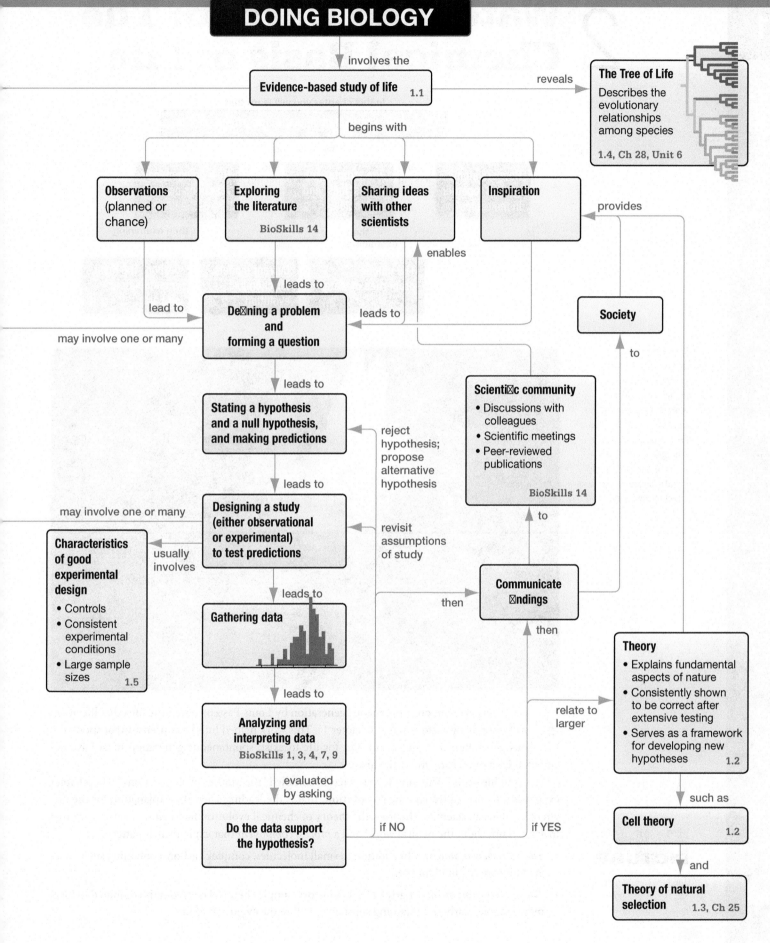

Evidence-based study of life 1.1

involves the

reveals

The Tree of Life
Describes the evolutionary relationships among species

1.4, Ch 28, Unit 6

begins with

Observations
(planned or chance)

Exploring the literature

BioSkills 14

Sharing ideas with other scientists

Inspiration

provides

lead to

may involve one or many

leads to

enables

De☒ning a problem and forming a question

leads to

Society

to

leads to

Stating a hypothesis and a null hypothesis, and making predictions

reject hypothesis; propose alternative hypothesis

Scienti☒c community
• Discussions with colleagues
• Scientific meetings
• Peer-reviewed publications

BioSkills 14

leads to

may involve one or many

Designing a study (either observational or experimental) to test predictions

Characteristics of good experimental design
• Controls
• Consistent experimental conditions
• Large sample sizes   **1.5**

usually involves

revisit assumptions of study

to

leads to

Communicate ☒ndings

then

then

Gathering data

Theory
• Explains fundamental aspects of nature
• Consistently shown to be correct after extensive testing
• Serves as a framework for developing new hypotheses   **1.2**

leads to

relate to larger

Analyzing and interpreting data

BioSkills 1, 3, 4, 7, 9

such as

evaluated by asking

Cell theory   **1.2**

Do the data support the hypothesis?

if NO

if YES

and

Theory of natural selection   **1.3, Ch 25**

2 Water and Carbon: The Chemical Basis of Life

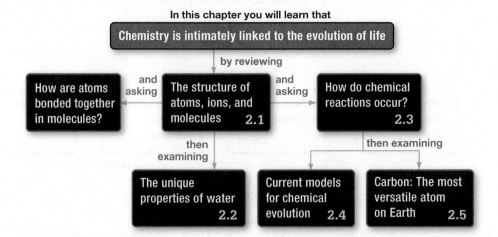

In this chapter you will learn that

Chemistry is intimately linked to the evolution of life

by reviewing

How are atoms bonded together in molecules?

and asking

The structure of atoms, ions, and molecules 2.1

and asking

How do chemical reactions occur? 2.3

then examining

The unique properties of water 2.2

then examining

Current models for chemical evolution 2.4

Carbon: The most versatile atom on Earth 2.5

These deep-sea hydrothermal vents produce hydrogen-rich, highly basic fluids at temperatures that range from 40° to 90°C. It has been proposed that life emerged from similar seafloor chimneys early in Earth's history via chemical evolution.

A classic experiment on spontaneous generation by Louis Pasteur tested the idea that life arises from nonliving materials (see Chapter 1). This work helped build a consensus that spontaneous generation does not occur. But for life to exist, spontaneous generation must have occurred at least once, early in Earth's history.

How did life begin? This simple query has been called "the mother of all questions." This chapter examines a theory, called **chemical evolution,** that is the leading scientific explanation for the origin of life. Like all scientific theories, the theory of chemical evolution has a *pattern component* that makes a claim about the natural world and a *process component* that explains that pattern.

This chapter is part of the Big Picture. See how on pages 104–105.

- *The pattern component* In addition to small molecules, complex carbon-containing substances exist and are required for life.

- *The process component* Early in Earth's history, simple chemical compounds combined to form more complex carbon-containing substances before the evolution of life.

✔ When you see this checkmark, stop and test yourself. Answers are available in Appendix A.

The theory maintains that inputs of energy led to the formation of increasingly complex carbon-containing substances, culminating in a compound that could replicate itself. At this point, there was a switch from chemical evolution to biological evolution.

As the original molecule multiplied, the process of evolution by natural selection took over. Eventually a descendant of the original molecule became metabolically active and acquired a membrane. When this occurred, the five attributes of life (discussed in Chapter 1) were fulfilled. Life had begun.

At first glance, the theory of chemical evolution may seem implausible. But is it? What evidence do biologists have that chemical evolution occurred? What approaches do they take to gathering this evidence?

Let's start with the fundamentals—the atoms and molecules that would have combined to get chemical evolution started.

2.1 Atoms, Ions, and Molecules: The Building Blocks of Chemical Evolution

Just four types of atoms—hydrogen, carbon, nitrogen, and oxygen—make up 96 percent of all matter found in organisms today. Many of the molecules found in your cells contain thousands, or even millions, of these atoms bonded together. But early in Earth's history, these elements existed only in simple substances such as water and carbon dioxide, which contain just three atoms apiece.

Two questions are fundamental to understanding how elements could have evolved into the more complex substances found in living cells:

1. What is the physical structure of the hydrogen, carbon, nitrogen, and oxygen atoms found in living cells?

2. What is the structure of the simple molecules—water, carbon dioxide, and others—that served as the building blocks of chemical evolution?

The focus on structure follows from one of the most central themes in biology: *Structure affects function.* To understand how a molecule affects your body or the role it played in chemical evolution, you have to understand how it is put together.

Basic Atomic Structure

FIGURE 2.1a shows a simple way of depicting the structure of an atom, using hydrogen and carbon as examples. Extremely small particles called electrons orbit an atomic nucleus made up of larger particles called protons and neutrons. **FIGURE 2.1b** provides a sense of scale at the atomic level.

Protons have a positive electric charge (+1), neutrons are electrically neutral, and electrons have a negative electric charge (−1). When the number of protons and the number of electrons in an atom are the same, the charges balance and the atom is electrically neutral.

(a) Diagrams of atoms

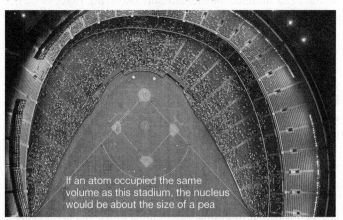

(b) Most of an atom's volume is empty space.

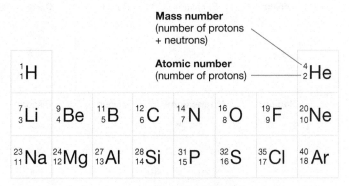

If an atom occupied the same volume as this stadium, the nucleus would be about the size of a pea

FIGURE 2.1 Parts of an Atom. The atomic nucleus, made up of protons and neutrons, is surrounded by orbiting electrons. In reality, electrons do not orbit the nucleus in circles; their actual orbits are complex.

FIGURE 2.2 shows a segment of the periodic table of the elements. Notice that each atom of a given **element** contains a characteristic number of protons, called its **atomic number.** The atomic number is written as a subscript to the left of an element's symbol in Figure 2.2. The sum of the protons and neutrons in an atom is called its **mass number** and is written as a superscript to the left of its symbol.

Mass number
(number of protons + neutrons)

Atomic number
(number of protons)

^1_1H ^4_2He

^7_3Li ^9_4Be $^{11}_5B$ $^{12}_6C$ $^{14}_7N$ $^{16}_8O$ $^{19}_9F$ $^{20}_{10}Ne$

$^{23}_{11}Na$ $^{24}_{12}Mg$ $^{27}_{13}Al$ $^{28}_{14}Si$ $^{31}_{15}P$ $^{32}_{16}S$ $^{35}_{17}Cl$ $^{40}_{18}Ar$

FIGURE 2.2 A Portion of the Periodic Table. Each element has a unique atomic number and is represented by a unique one- or two-letter symbol. The mass numbers given here are the most common for each element. (Appendix C provides a complete periodic table of elements.)

The number of protons in an element does not vary—if the atomic number of an atom changes, then it is no longer the same element. The number of neutrons present in an element can vary, however. Forms of an element with different numbers of neutrons are known as **isotopes** (literally, "equal-places" in regard to position in the periodic table).

Different isotopes have different masses, yet are the same element. For example, all atoms of the element carbon have 6 protons. But naturally occurring isotopes of carbon can have 6, 7, or even 8 neutrons, giving them a mass number of 12, 13, or 14, respectively. The **atomic weight** of an element is an average of all the mass numbers of the naturally occurring isotopes based on their abundance. This is why the atomic weights for elements are often slightly different from the mass numbers—the atomic weight of carbon, for example, is 12.01.

Most isotopes are stable, but not all. For example, ^{14}C, with 6 protons and 8 neutrons, represents an unstable **radioactive isotope.** Its nucleus will eventually decay and release energy (radiation). When ^{14}C decays, one of its neutrons changes into a proton, converting ^{14}C to the stable ^{14}N isotope of nitrogen, with 7 protons and 7 neutrons. Timing of decay is specific to each radioisotope, a fact that has been very useful in estimating the dates of key events in the fossil record (see Chapter 25).

Although the masses of protons, neutrons, and electrons can be measured in grams, the numbers involved are so small that biologists prefer to use a special unit called the **dalton.** The masses of protons and neutrons are virtually identical and are routinely rounded to 1 dalton. A carbon atom that contains 6 protons and 6 neutrons has a mass of 12 daltons, while a carbon atom with 6 protons and 7 neutrons would have a mass of 13 daltons. These isotopes would be written as ^{12}C and ^{13}C,

respectively. The mass of an electron is so small that it is normally ignored.

To understand how the atoms involved in chemical evolution behave, focus on how electrons are arranged around the nucleus:

- Electrons move around atomic nuclei in specific regions called **orbitals.**

- Each orbital can hold up to two electrons.

- Orbitals are grouped into levels called **electron shells.**

- Electron shells are numbered 1, 2, 3, and so on, to indicate their relative distance from the nucleus. Smaller numbers are closer to the nucleus.

- Each electron shell contains a specific number of orbitals. An electron shell comprising a single orbital can hold up to two electrons; a shell with four orbitals can contain up to eight electrons.

- The electrons of an atom fill the innermost shells first, before filling outer shells.

To understand how the structures of atoms differ, take a moment to study **FIGURE 2.3.** This chart highlights the elements that are most abundant in living cells. The gray ball in the center of each box represents an atomic nucleus, and the orange circle or circles represent the electron shells around that nucleus. The small orange balls on the circles indicate the number of electrons that are distributed in the shells of each element. Electrons shown as pairs share the same orbital within a shell.

Now focus on the outermost shell of each atom. This is the element's **valence shell.** The electrons found in this shell are referred to as **valence electrons.** Two observations are important:

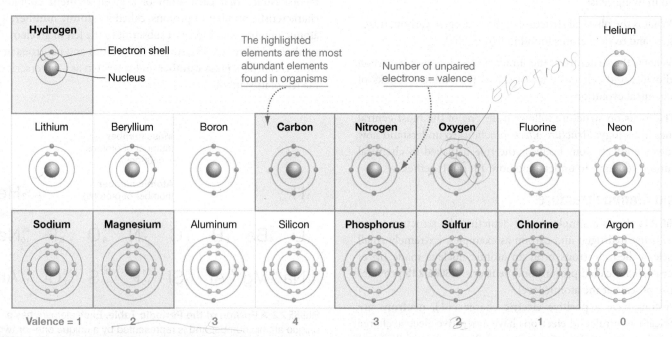

FIGURE 2.3 The Structure of Atoms Found in Organisms.

✔**QUESTION** If the mass number of phosphorus is 31, how many neutrons exist in the most common isotope of phosphorus?

1. In each of the highlighted elements, the outermost electron shell is not full—not all orbitals in the valence shell have two electrons. The highlighted elements have at least one unpaired valence electron—meaning at least one unfilled valence shell orbital.

2. The number of unpaired valence electrons varies among elements. Carbon, for example, has four valence electrons, all unpaired. Oxygen has six valence electrons; four are paired, two are not. The number of unpaired electrons found in an atom is called its **valence.** Carbon's valence is four, oxygen's is two.

These observations are significant because an atom is most stable when its valence shell is filled. One way that shells can be filled is through the formation of strong **chemical bonds**—attractions that bind atoms together. A strong attraction where two atoms share one or more pairs of electrons is called a **covalent bond.**

How Does Covalent Bonding Hold Molecules Together?

To understand how atoms can become more stable by making covalent bonds, consider hydrogen. The hydrogen atom has just one electron, which resides in a shell that can hold two electrons.

Because it has an unpaired valence electron, the hydrogen atom is not very stable. But when two atoms of hydrogen come into contact, the two electrons become shared by the two nuclei (**FIGURE 2.4**). Both atoms now have a completely filled outer shell. Together, the hydrogen atoms are more stable than the two individual hydrogen atoms.

Shared electrons "glue" two hydrogen atoms together. Substances held together by covalent bonds are called **molecules.** In the case of two hydrogen atoms, the bonded atoms form a single molecule of hydrogen, written as H—H or H_2.

It can also be helpful to think about covalent bonding as electrical attraction and repulsion. Opposite charges attract; like charges repel. As two hydrogen atoms move closer together, their positively charged nuclei repel each other and their negatively charged electrons repel each other. But each proton attracts both electrons, and each electron attracts both protons. Covalent bonds form when the attractive forces overcome the repulsive forces. This is the case when hydrogen atoms interact to form the hydrogen molecule (H_2).

Nonpolar and Polar Bonds   In **FIGURE 2.5a**, the covalent bond between hydrogen atoms is represented by a dash and the electrons are drawn as dots halfway between the two nuclei. This depiction shows that the electrons are shared equally between the two hydrogen atoms, resulting in a covalent bond that is symmetrical.

It's important to note, though, that the electrons participating in a covalent bond are not always shared equally between the atoms involved. This happens because some atoms hold the electrons in covalent bonds much more tightly than do other atoms. Chemists call this property **electronegativity.**

What is responsible for an atom's electronegativity? It's a combination of two things—the number of protons in the nucleus and the distance between the nucleus and the valence shell. If

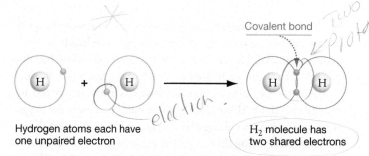

Hydrogen atoms each have one unpaired electron

H_2 molecule has two shared electrons

FIGURE 2.4 Covalent Bonds Result from Electron Sharing. When two hydrogen atoms come into contact, their electrons are attracted to the positive charge in each nucleus. As a result, their orbitals overlap, the electrons are shared by each nucleus, and a covalent bond forms.

you return to Figure 2.3 and move your finger along a row from left to right, you will be moving toward elements that increase in protons and in electronegativity (ignoring the elements in the far right column, which have full outer shells). Each row, however, represents shells of electrons, so if your finger moved down the table, the elements would decrease in electronegativity.

Oxygen, which has eight protons and only two electron shells, is among the most electronegative of all elements. It attracts covalently bonded electrons more strongly than does any other atom commonly found in organisms. Nitrogen's electronegativity is somewhat lower than oxygen's. Carbon and hydrogen, in turn, have relatively low and approximately equal electronegativities. Thus, the electronegativities of the four most abundant elements in organisms are related as follows: O > N > C ⊠ H.

Because carbon and hydrogen have approximately equal electronegativity, the electrons in a C—H bond are shared equally or symmetrically. The result is a **nonpolar covalent bond.** In contrast, asymmetric sharing of electrons results in a **polar covalent bond.** The electrons in a polar covalent bond spend most of their time close to the nucleus of the more electronegative atom. Why is this important?

Polar Bonds Produce Partial Charges on Atoms   To understand the consequences of differences in electronegativity and the formation of polar covalent bonds, consider the water molecule.

Water consists of an oxygen bonded to two hydrogen atoms, and is written H_2O. As **FIGURE 2.5b** illustrates, the electrons

(a) Nonpolar covalent bond in hydrogen molecule

$$H - H$$

Electrons are halfway between the two atoms, shared equally

(b) Polar covalent bonds in water molecule

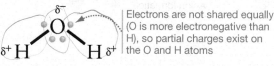

Electrons are not shared equally (O is more electronegative than H), so partial charges exist on the O and H atoms

FIGURE 2.5 Electron Sharing and Bond Polarity. Delta (⊠) symbols in polar covalent bonds refer to partial positive and negative charges that arise owing to unequal electron sharing.

involved in the covalent bonds in water are not shared equally but are held much more tightly by the oxygen nucleus than by the hydrogen nuclei. Hence, water has two polar covalent bonds—one between the oxygen atom and each of the hydrogen atoms.

Here's the key observation: Because electrons are shared unequally in each O–H bond, they spend more time near the oxygen atom, giving it a partial negative charge, and less time near the hydrogen atoms, giving them a partial positive charge. These partial charges are symbolized by the lowercase Greek letter delta, δ.

As Section 2.2 shows, the partial charges on water molecules—due simply to the difference in electronegativity between oxygen and hydrogen—are one of the primary reasons that life exists.

Ionic Bonding, Ions, and the Electron-Sharing Continuum

Ionic bonds are similar in principle to covalent bonds, but instead of being shared between two atoms, the electrons in ionic bonds are completely transferred from one atom to the other. The electron transfer occurs because it gives the resulting atoms a full outermost shell.

Sodium atoms (Na), for example, tend to lose an electron, leaving them with a full second shell. This is a much more stable arrangement, energetically, than having a lone electron in their third shell (**FIGURE 2.6a**). The atom that results has a net electric charge of +1, because it has one more proton than it has electrons.

An atom or molecule that carries a full charge, rather than the partial charges that arise from polar covalent bonds, is called an **ion.** The sodium ion is written Na$^+$ and, like other positively charged ions, is called a **cation** (pronounced *KAT-eye-un*).

Chlorine atoms (Cl), in contrast, tend to gain an electron, filling their outermost shell (**FIGURE 2.6b**). The ion has a net charge of −1, because it has one more electron than protons. This

negatively charged ion, or **anion** (pronounced *AN-eye-un*), is written Cl$^-$ and is called chlor*ide.*

When sodium and chlorine combine to form sodium chloride (NaCl, common table salt), they pack into a crystal structure consisting of sodium cations and chloride anions (**FIGURE 2.6c**). The electrical attraction between the ions is so strong that salt crystals are difficult to break apart.

This discussion of covalent and ionic bonding supports an important general observation: The degree to which electrons are shared in chemical bonds forms a continuum from equal sharing in nonpolar covalent bonds to unequal sharing in polar covalent bonds to the transfer of electrons in ionic bonds.

As the left-hand side of **FIGURE 2.7** shows, covalent bonds between atoms with exactly the same electronegativity—for example, between the atoms of hydrogen in H$_2$—represent one end of the continuum. The electrons in these nonpolar bonds are shared equally.

In the middle of the continuum are bonds where one atom is much more electronegative than the other. In these asymmetric bonds, substantial partial charges exist on each of the atoms. These types of polar covalent bonds occur when a highly electronegative atom such as oxygen or nitrogen is bonded to an atom with a lower affinity for electrons, such as carbon or hydrogen. Ammonia (NH$_3$) and water (H$_2$O) are examples of molecules with polar covalent bonds.

At the right-hand side of the continuum are molecules made up of atoms with extreme differences in their electronegativities. In this case, electrons are transferred rather than shared, the atoms have full charges, and the bonding is ionic. Sodium chloride (NaCl) is a familiar example of a molecule formed by ionic bonds.

Most chemical bonds that occur in biological molecules are on the left-hand side and the middle of the continuum; in the molecules found in organisms, ionic bonding is less common.

(a) A sodium ion being formed

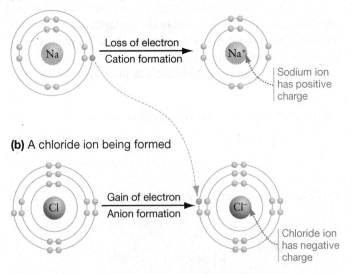

(b) A chloride ion being formed

(c) Table salt (NaCl) is a crystal composed of two ions.

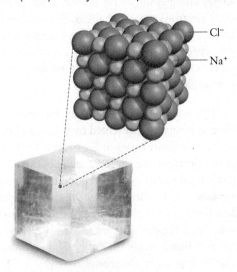

FIGURE 2.6 Ion Formation and Ionic Bonding. The sodium ion (Na$^+$) and the chloride ion (Cl$^-$) are stable because they have full valence shells. In table salt (NaCl), sodium and chloride ions pack into a crystal structure held together by electrical attraction between their positive and negative charges.

Nonpolar covalent bonds (atoms have no charge)	Polar covalent bonds (atoms have partial charge)	Ionic bonds (atoms have full charge)

Hydrogen   Methane   Ammonia   Water   Sodium chloride

FIGURE 2.7 The Electron-Sharing Continuum. The degree of electron sharing in chemical bonds can be thought of as a continuum, from equal sharing in nonpolar covalent bonds to no sharing in ionic bonds.

✔ QUESTION Why do most polar covalent bonds involve nitrogen or oxygen?

Some Simple Molecules Formed from C, H, N, and O

Look back at Figure 2.3 and count the number of unpaired electrons in the valence shells of carbon, nitrogen, oxygen, and hydrogen atoms. Each unpaired electron in a valence shell can make up half of a covalent bond. It should make sense to you that a carbon atom can form a total of four covalent bonds; nitrogen can form three; oxygen can form two; and hydrogen, one.

When each of the four unpaired electrons of a carbon atom covalently bonds with a hydrogen atom, the molecule that results is written CH_4 and is called methane (**FIGURE 2.8a**). Methane is the most common molecule found in natural gas. When a nitrogen atom's three unpaired electrons bond with three hydrogen atoms, the result is NH_3, or ammonia. Similarly, an atom of oxygen can form covalent bonds with two atoms of hydrogen, resulting in a water molecule (H_2O). As Figure 2.4 showed, a hydrogen atom can bond with another hydrogen atom to form hydrogen gas (H_2).

In addition to forming more than one single bond, atoms with more than one unpaired electron in the valence shell can form double bonds or triple bonds. **FIGURE 2.8b** shows how carbon forms double bonds with oxygen atoms to produce carbon dioxide (CO_2). Triple bonds result when three pairs of electrons are shared. **FIGURE 2.8c** shows the structure of molecular nitrogen (N_2), which forms when two nitrogen atoms establish a triple bond.

✔ If you understand how electronegativity affects covalent bonds, you should be able to draw arrows between the atoms in each molecule shown in Figure 2.8 to indicate the relative position of the shared electrons. If they are equally shared, then draw a double-headed arrow.

The Geometry of Simple Molecules

In many cases, the overall shape of a molecule dictates how it behaves. In chemistry and in biology, function is based on structure.

The shapes of the simple molecules you've just learned about are governed by the geometry of their bonds. Nitrogen (N_2) and

(a) Single bonds

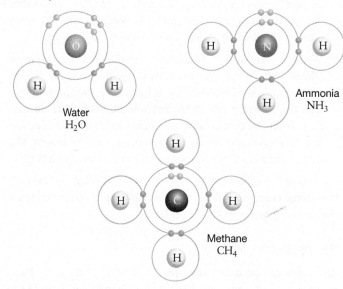

Water
H_2O

Ammonia
NH_3

Methane
CH_4

(b) Double bonds

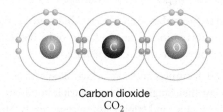

Carbon dioxide
CO_2

(c) Triple bonds

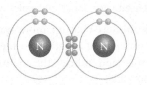

Molecular nitrogen
N_2

FIGURE 2.8 Unpaired Electrons in the Valence Shell Participate in Covalent Bonds. Covalent bonding is based on sharing of electrons in the outermost shell. Covalent bonds can be **(a)** single, **(b)** double, or **(c)** triple.

(a) Methane (CH₄)   **(b)** Water (H₂O)

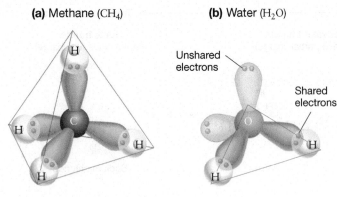

Unshared electrons

Shared electrons

FIGURE 2.9 The Geometry of Methane and Water.

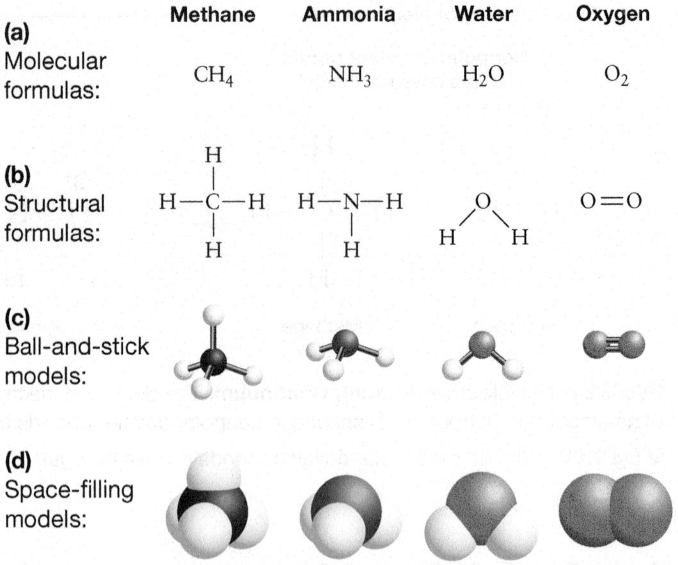

carbon dioxide (CO_2), for example, have linear structures (see Figure 2.8). Molecules with more complex geometries include

- Methane (CH_4)—which is tetrahedral, a structure with four triangular faces like a pyramid (**FIGURE 2.9a**). The tetrahedron forms because the electrons in the four C−H bonds repulse each other equally. The electron pairs are as far apart as they can get.

- Water (H_2O)—which is bent and two-dimensional, or planar (**FIGURE 2.9b**). Why? The electrons in the four orbitals of oxygen's valence shell repulse each other, just as they do in methane. But in water, two of the orbitals are filled with electron pairs from the oxygen atom, and two are filled with electron pairs from covalent bonds between oxygen and hydrogen. The shared electrons form a molecule that is V-shaped and flat.

Section 2.2 explores how water's shape, in combination with the partial charges on the oxygen and hydrogen atoms, makes it the most important molecule on Earth.

Representing Molecules

Molecules can be represented in a variety of increasingly complex ways—only some of which reflect their actual shape. Each method has advantages and disadvantages.

- **Molecular formulas** are compact, but don't contain a great deal of information—they indicate only the numbers and types of atoms in a molecule (**FIGURE 2.10a**).

- **Structural formulas** indicate which atoms in a molecule are bonded together. Single, double, and triple bonds are represented by single, double, and triple dashes, respectively. Structural formulas also indicate geometry in two dimensions (**FIGURE 2.10b**). This method is useful for planar molecules such as water and O_2.

- **Ball-and-stick models** take up more space than structural formulas, but provide information on the three-dimensional shape of molecules and indicate the relative sizes of the atoms involved (**FIGURE 2.10c**).

- **Space-filling models** are more difficult to read than ball-and-stick models but more accurately depict the spatial relationships between atoms. (**FIGURE 2.10d**).

In both ball-and-stick and space-filling models, biologists use certain colors to represent certain atoms. A black ball, for

	Methane	Ammonia	Water	Oxygen
(a) Molecular formulas:	CH_4	NH_3	H_2O	O_2

(b) Structural formulas:

$$H{-}\overset{\displaystyle H}{\underset{\displaystyle H}{C}}{-}H \qquad H{-}\overset{\displaystyle H}{N}{-}H \qquad \overset{\displaystyle O}{H \quad H} \qquad O{=}O$$

(c) Ball-and-stick models:

(d) Space-filling models:

FIGURE 2.10 Molecules Can Be Represented Several Ways. Each method of representing a molecule has particular advantages.

example, always symbolizes carbon. (For more information on interpreting chemical structures, see **BioSkills 8** in Appendix B.)

Some of the small molecules you've just learned about are found in volcanic gases, the atmospheres of nearby planets, and in deep-sea hydrothermal vents, like those shown in the photograph at the start of this chapter. Based on these observations, researchers claim that they were important components of Earth's ancient atmosphere and oceans. If so, then they provided the building blocks for chemical evolution. The question is: How did these simple building blocks combine to form more complex products, early in Earth's history?

Researchers postulate that most of the critical reactions in chemical evolution occurred in an aqueous, or water-based, environment. To understand what happened and why, let's delve into the properties of water and then turn to analyzing the reactions that triggered chemical evolution.

check your understanding

C Y U

If you understand that . . .
- Covalent bonds are based on electron sharing. Electron sharing allows atoms to fill all the orbitals in their valence shell, making them more stable.
- Covalent bonds can be polar or nonpolar, depending on whether the electronegativities of the two atoms involved are the same or different.

✔ **You should be able to . . .**

Draw the structural formula of formaldehyde (CH_2O) and add dots to indicate the relative locations of the electrons being shared in each covalent bond, based on the relative electronegativities of C, H, and O.

Answers are available in Appendix A.

2.2 Properties of Water and the Early Oceans

Life is based on water. It arose in an aqueous environment and remains dependent on water today. In fact, 75 percent of the volume in a typical cell is water; water is the most abundant molecule in organisms (**FIGURE 2.11**). You can survive for weeks without eating, but you aren't likely to live more than 3 or 4 days without drinking.

Water is vital for a simple reason: It is an excellent **solvent**—that is, an agent for dissolving substances and getting them into **solution.** The reactions that were responsible for chemical evolution some 3.5 billion years ago, like those occurring inside your body right now, depend on direct, physical interaction between molecules. Substances are most likely to come into contact with one another and react as **solutes**—meaning, when they are dissolved in a solvent like water. The formation of Earth's first ocean, about 3.8 billion years ago, was a turning point in chemical evolution because it gave the process a place to happen.

Why Is Water Such an Efficient Solvent?

To understand why water is such an effective solvent, recall that

1. Both of the O—H bonds in a water molecule are polar, owing to the difference in the electronegativities of hydrogen and oxygen. As a result, the oxygen atom has a partial negative charge and each hydrogen atom has a partial positive charge.

2. The molecule is bent. Consequently, the partial negative charge on the oxygen atom sticks out, away from the partial positive charges on the hydrogen atoms, giving a water molecule an overall polarity (**FIGURE 2.12a**).

FIGURE 2.12b illustrates how water's structure affects its interactions with other water molecules. When two water molecules approach each other, the partial positive charge on hydrogen attracts the partial negative charge on oxygen. This weak electrical attraction forms a **hydrogen bond** between the molecules.

✔ If you understand how water's structure makes hydrogen bonding possible, you should be able to (1) draw a fictional version of Figure 2.12b that shows water as a linear (not bent)

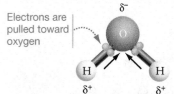
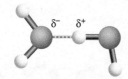

(a) Water is polar.

Electrons are pulled toward oxygen

(b) Hydrogen bonds form between water molecules.

FIGURE 2.12 Water Is Polar and Participates in Hydrogen Bonds. **(a)** Because of oxygen's high electronegativity, the electrons that are shared between hydrogen and oxygen spend more time close to the oxygen nucleus, giving the oxygen atom a partial negative charge and the hydrogen atom a partial positive charge. **(b)** The electrical attraction that occurs between the partial positive and negative charges on water molecules forms a hydrogen bond.

molecule with partial charges on the oxygen and hydrogen atoms; and (2) explain why electrostatic attractions between such water molecules would be much weaker as a result.

In an aqueous solution, hydrogen bonds also form between water molecules and other polar molecules. Similar interactions occur between water and ions. Ions and polar molecules stay in solution because of their interactions with water's partial charges (**FIGURE 2.13**). Substances that interact with water in this way are said to be **hydrophilic** ("water-loving"). Hydrogen bonding makes it possible for almost any charged or polar molecule to dissolve in water.

In contrast, compounds that are uncharged and nonpolar do not interact with water through hydrogen bonding and do not dissolve in water. Substances that do not interact with water are said to be **hydrophobic** ("water-fearing"). Because their interactions with water are minimal or nonexistent, they are forced to interact with each other (**FIGURE 2.14**, see page 26). The water molecules surrounding nonpolar molecules form hydrogen bonds with one another and increase the stability of these **hydrophobic interactions.**

Although individual hydrogen bonds are not as strong as covalent or ionic bonds, many of them occur in a solution. Hydrogen bonding is extremely important in biology owing to the

FIGURE 2.11 Fruits Shrink When They Are Dried Because They Consist Primarily of Water.

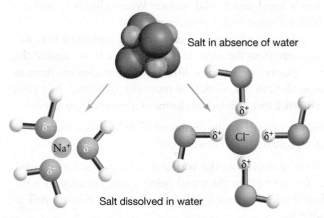

Salt in absence of water

Salt dissolved in water

FIGURE 2.13 Polar Molecules and Ions Dissolve Readily in Water. Water's polarity makes it a superb solvent for polar molecules and ions.

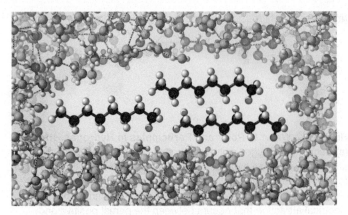

FIGURE 2.14 Nonpolar Molecules Do Not Dissolve in Water.
In aqueous solution, nonpolar molecules and compounds are forced to interact with each other. This occurs because water is much more stable when it interacts with itself rather than with the nonpolar molecules.

✔ **QUESTION** What is the physical basis of the expression, "Oil and water don't mix"?

(a) A meniscus forms where water meets a solid surface, as a result of two forces.

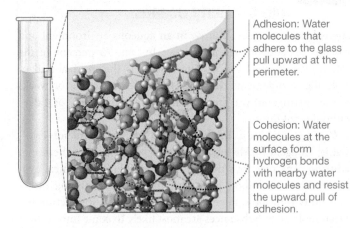

Adhesion: Water molecules that adhere to the glass pull upward at the perimeter.

Cohesion: Water molecules at the surface form hydrogen bonds with nearby water molecules and resist the upward pull of adhesion.

(b) Water has high surface tension.

Because of surface tension, light objects do not fall through the water's surface

FIGURE 2.15 Cohesion, Adhesion, and Surface Tension.
(a) Meniscus formation is based on hydrogen bonding. **(b)** Water resists forces—like the weight of a spider—that increase its surface area. The resistance is great enough that light objects do not break the surface.

sheer number of hydrogen bonds that form between water and hydrophilic molecules.

What Properties Are Correlated with Water's Structure?

Water's small size, highly polar covalent bonds, and bent shape resulting in overall polarity are unique among molecules. Because the structure of molecules routinely correlates with their function, it's not surprising that water has some remarkable properties, in addition to its extraordinary capacity to act as a solvent.

Cohesion, Adhesion, and Surface Tension Attraction between like molecules is called **cohesion.** Water is cohesive—meaning that it stays together—because of the hydrogen bonds that form between individual molecules.

Attraction between unlike molecules, in contrast, is called **adhesion.** Adhesion is usually analyzed in regard to interactions between a liquid and a solid surface. Water adheres to surfaces that have any polar or charged components.

Cohesion and adhesion are important in explaining how water can move from the roots of plants to their leaves against the force of gravity (see Chapter 38). But you can also see them in action in the concave surface, or meniscus, that forms in a glass tube (**FIGURE 2.15a**). A meniscus forms as a result of two forces:

1. Water molecules at the perimeter of the surface adhere to the glass, resulting in an upward pull.

2. Water molecules at the surface hydrogen-bond with water molecules next to them and below them, resulting in a net lateral and downward pull that resists the upward pull of adhesion.

Cohesion is also instrumental in the phenomenon known as **surface tension.** When water molecules are at the surface, there

are no water molecules above them for hydrogen bonding. As a result, they exhibit stronger attractive forces between their nearest neighboring molecules. This enhanced attraction between the surface water molecules results in tension that minimizes the total surface area.

This fact has an important consequence: Water resists any force that increases its surface area. More specifically, any force that depresses a water surface meets with resistance. This resistance makes a water surface act like an elastic membrane (**FIGURE 2.15b**).

In water, the "elastic membrane" is stronger than it is in other liquids. Water's surface tension is extraordinarily high because of the stronger hydrogen bonding that occurs between molecules at the surface. This explains why it is better to cut the water's surface with your fingertips when you dive into a pool, instead of doing a belly flop.

Water Is Denser as a Liquid than as a Solid When factory workers pour molten metal or plastic into a mold and allow it to cool to the solid state, the material shrinks. When molten lava pours out of a volcano and cools to solid rock, it shrinks. But when you fill an ice tray with water and put it in the freezer to make ice, the water expands.

Unlike most substances, water is denser as a liquid than it is as a solid. In other words, there are more molecules of water in a given volume of liquid water than there are in the same volume of solid water, or ice. **FIGURE 2.16** illustrates why this is so.

Note that in ice, each water molecule participates in four hydrogen bonds. These hydrogen bonds cause the water molecules to form a regular and repeating structure, or crystal (Figure 2.16a). The crystal structure of ice is fairly open, meaning that there is a relatively large amount of space between molecules.

Now compare the extent of hydrogen bonding and the density of ice with that of liquid water, illustrated in Figure 2.16b. Note that the extent of hydrogen bonding in liquid water is much less than that found in ice, and that the hydrogen bonds in liquid water are constantly being formed and broken. As a result, molecules in the liquid phase are packed much more closely together than in the solid phase.

Normally, heating a substance causes it to expand because molecules begin moving faster and colliding more often and with greater force. But heating ice causes hydrogen bonds to break and the open crystal structure to collapse. In this way, hydrogen bonding explains why water is denser as a liquid than as a solid.

This property of water has an important result: Ice floats (Figure 2.16c). If it didn't, ice would sink to the bottom of lakes, ponds, and oceans soon after it formed. The ice would stay frozen in the cold depths. Instead, ice serves as a blanket, insulating the liquid below from the cold air above. If water weren't so unusual, it is almost certain that Earth's oceans would have frozen solid before life had a chance to start.

Water Has a High Capacity for Absorbing Energy Hydrogen bonding is also responsible for another of water's remarkable physical properties: Water has a high capacity for absorbing energy.

Specific heat, for example, is the amount of energy required to raise the temperature of 1 gram of a substance by 1°C. Water has a high specific heat because when a source of energy hits it, hydrogen bonds must be broken before heat can be transferred and the water molecules begin moving faster. As **TABLE 2.1** indicates, as molecules increase in overall polarity, and thus in their ability to form hydrogen bonds, it takes an extraordinarily large amount of energy to change their temperature.

TABLE 2.1 Specific Heats of Some Liquids

The specific heats reported in this table were measured at 25°C and are given in units of joules per gram of substance per degree Celsius. (The joule is a unit of energy.)

With extensive hydrogen bonding	Specific Heat
Water (H_2O)	4.18
With some hydrogen bonding	
Ethanol (C_2H_6O)	2.44
Glycerol ($C_3H_8O_3$)	2.38
With little or no hydrogen bonding	
Benzene (C_6H_6)	1.74
Xylene (C_8H_{10})	1.72

DATA: D. R. Lide (editor). 2008. Standard Thermodynamic Properties of Chemical Substances, in *CRC Handbook of Physics and Chemistry.* 89th ed. Boca Raton, FL: CRC Press.

(a) In ice, water molecules form a crystal lattice.

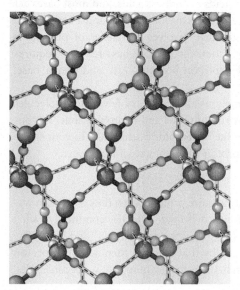

(b) In liquid water, no crystal lattice forms.

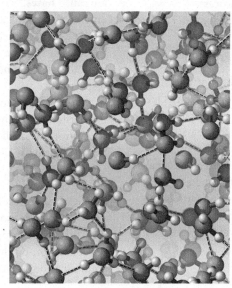

(c) Liquid water is denser than ice. As a result, ice floats.

FIGURE 2.16 Hydrogen Bonding Forms the Crystal Structure of Ice. In ice, each molecule can form four hydrogen bonds at one time. Each oxygen atom can form two; each hydrogen atom can form one.

Property	Cause	Biological Consequences
Solvent for charged or polar compounds		Most chemical reactions important for life take place in aqueous solution.
Denser as a liquid than a solid	As water freezes, each molecule forms a total of four hydrogen bonds, leading to the formation of the low-density crystal structure called ice.	
High specific heat	Water molecules must absorb lots of heat energy to break hydrogen bonds and experience increased movement (and thus temperature).	Oceans absorb and release heat slowly, moderating coastal climates.
High heat of vaporization		Evaporation of water from an organism cools the body.

✔ **EXERCISE** You should be able to fill in the missing cells in this table.

Similarly, it takes a large amount of energy to break the hydrogen bonds in liquid water and change the molecules from the liquid phase to the gas phase. Water's **heat of vaporization**—the energy required to change 1 gram of it from a liquid to gas—is higher than that of most molecules that are liquid at room temperature. As a result, water has to absorb a great deal of energy to evaporate. Water's high heat of vaporization is the reason that sweating or dousing yourself with water is an effective way to cool off on a hot day. Water molecules absorb a great deal of energy from your body before they evaporate, so you lose heat.

Water's ability to absorb energy is critical to the theory of chemical evolution. Molecules that were formed in the ocean were well protected from sources of energy that could break them apart, such as intense sunlight. As a result, they would have persisted and slowly increased in concentration over time, making them more likely to react and continue the process.

TABLE 2.2 summarizes some of the key properties of water.

The Role of Water in Acid–Base Reactions

You've seen that water's high specific heat and heat of vaporization tend to keep its temperature and liquid form stable. One other aspect of water's chemistry is important for understanding chemical evolution and how organisms work: Water is not a completely stable molecule. In reality, water molecules continually undergo a chemical reaction with themselves. When a **chemical reaction** occurs, one substance is combined with others or broken down into another substance. Atoms may also be rearranged; in most cases, chemical bonds are broken and new bonds form. The chemical reaction that takes place between water molecules is called a "dissociation" reaction. It can be written as follows:

$$H_2O \rightleftharpoons H^+ + OH^-$$

The double arrow indicates that the reaction proceeds in both directions.

The substances on the right-hand side of the expression are the **hydrogen ion** (H^+) and the **hydroxide ion** (OH^-). A hydrogen ion is simply a proton. In reality, however, protons do not exist by themselves. In water, for example, protons associate with water molecules to form hydronium ions (H_3O^+). Thus, the dissociation of water is more accurately written as:

$$H_2O + H_2O \rightleftharpoons H_3O^+ + OH^-$$

One of the water molecules on the left-hand side of the expression has given up a proton, while the other water molecule has accepted a proton.

Substances that give up protons during chemical reactions and raise the hydronium ion concentration of water are called **acids;** molecules or ions that acquire protons during chemical reactions and lower the hydronium ion concentration of water are called **bases.** Most acids act only as acids, and most bases act only as bases; but water can act as both an acid and a base.

A chemical reaction that involves a transfer of protons is called an acid–base reaction. Every acid–base reaction requires a proton donor and a proton acceptor—an acid and a base, respectively.

Water is an extremely weak acid—very few water molecules dissociate to form hydronium ions and hydroxide ions. In contrast, strong acids like the hydrochloric acid (HCl) in your stomach readily give up a proton when they react with water.

$$HCl + H_2O \rightleftharpoons H_3O^+ + Cl^-$$

Strong bases readily acquire protons when they react with water. For example, sodium hydroxide (NaOH, commonly called lye) dissociates completely in water to form Na^+ and OH^-. The hydroxide ion produced by that reaction then accepts a proton from a hydronium ion in the water, forming two water molecules.

$$NaOH(aq) \longrightarrow Na^+ + OH^-$$
$$OH^- + H_3O^+ \rightleftharpoons 2 H_2O$$

(The "*aq*" in the first expression indicates that NaOH is in aqueous solution.)

To summarize, adding an acid to a solution increases the concentration of protons; adding a base to a solution lowers the concentration of protons. Water is both a weak acid and a weak base.

Determining the Concentration of Protons
In a solution, the tendency for acid–base reactions to occur is largely a function of the number of protons present. The problem is, there's no simple way to count the actual number of protons present in a sample. Researchers solve this problem using the mole concept.

A **mole** refers to the number 6.022×10^{23}—just as the unit called the dozen refers to the number 12 or the unit million refers to the number 1×10^6. The mole is a useful unit because the mass of one mole of any substance is the same as its molecular weight expressed in grams. **Molecular weight** is the sum of the atomic weights of all the atoms in a molecule.

For example, to get the molecular weight of H_2O, you sum the atomic weights of two atoms of hydrogen and one atom of oxygen. Since the atomic weights of hydrogen and oxygen are very close to their mass numbers (see Figure 2.2), the molecular weight of water would be $1 + 1 + 16$, or a total of 18. Thus, if you weighed a sample of 18 grams of water, it would contain around 6×10^{23} water molecules, or about 1 mole of water molecules.

When substances are dissolved in water, their concentration is expressed in terms of molarity (symbolized by "M"). **Molarity** is the number of moles of the substance present per liter of solution. A 1-molar solution of protons in water, for example, means that 1 mole of protons is contained in 1 liter of solution.

Chemists can measure the concentration of protons in a solution directly using molarity and an instrument called a pH meter. In a sample of pure water at 25°C, the concentration of H^+ is 1.0×10^{-7}M, or 1 ten-millionth molar.

The pH of a Solution Reveals Whether It Is Acidic or Basic
Because the concentration of protons in water is such a small number, exponential notation is cumbersome. So chemists and biologists prefer to express the concentration of protons in a solution, and thus whether it is acidic or basic, with a logarithmic notation called **pH**.[1]

By definition, the pH of a solution is the negative of the base-10 logarithm, or log, of the hydrogen ion concentration:

$$pH = -\log[H^+]$$

(To review logarithms, see **BioSkills 6** in Appendix B. The square brackets are a standard notation for indicating "concentration" of a substance in solution.)

Taking antilogs gives

$$[H^+] = \text{antilog}(-pH) = 10^{-pH}$$

Solutions that contain acids have a proton concentration larger than 1×10^{-7}M and thus a pH < 7. This is because acidic

molecules tend to release protons into solution. In contrast, solutions that contain bases have a proton concentration less than 1×10^{-7}M and thus a pH > 7. This is because basic molecules tend to accept protons from solution.

pH is a convenient way to indicate the concentration of protons in a solution, but take note of what the number represents. For example, if the concentration of H^+ in a sample of water is 1.0×10^{-7}M, then its pH is 7. If the pH changes to 5, then the sample contains 100 times more protons and has become 100 times more acidic. ✔ **QUANTITATIVE** If you understand how pH is related to $[H^+]$, you should be able to calculate the concentration of protons in a solution that has a pH of 8.5.

FIGURE 2.17 shows the pH scale and reports the pH of some selected solutions. Pure water is used as a standard, or point of reference, for pH 7 on the pH scale. The solution inside living cells is about pH 7, which is considered neutral—neither acidic nor basic. The normal function of a cell is dependent on maintaining this neutral internal environment. What is responsible for regulating pH?

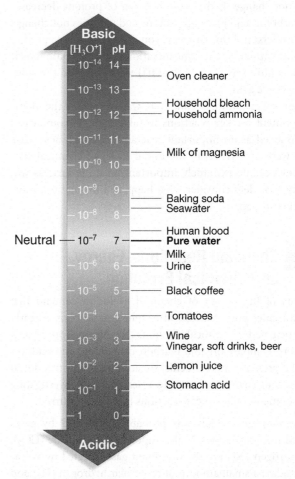

FIGURE 2.17 The pH Scale. Because the pH scale is logarithmic, a change in one unit of pH represents a change in the concentration of hydrogen ions equal to a factor of 10. Coffee has a hundred times more H^+ than pure water has.

✔ **QUESTION** What happens to the concentration of protons in black coffee after you add milk?

---

[1]The term pH is derived from the French *puissance d'hydrogéne*, or "power of hydrogen."

Buffers Protect Against Damaging Changes in pH Life is sensitive to changes in pH. Changes in proton concentration affect the structure and function of polar or charged substances as well as the tendency of acid–base reactions to occur.

Compounds that minimize changes in pH are called **buffers** because they reduce the impact of adding acids or bases on the overall pH of a solution. Buffers are important in maintaining relatively constant conditions, or **homeostasis,** in cells and tissues. In cells, a wide array of naturally occurring molecules act as buffers.

Most buffers are weak acids, meaning that they are somewhat likely to give up a proton in solution, but once the proton concentration rises, the acid is regenerated. To see how buffers work, consider the disassociation of carbonic acid in water to form bicarbonate ions and protons:

$$CH_2O_3 \rightleftharpoons CHO_3^- + H^+$$
$$\text{carbonic acid} \qquad \text{bicarbonate}$$

When carbonic acid and bicarbonate are present in about equal concentrations in a solution, they function as a buffering system. If the concentration of protons increases slightly, the protons react with bicarbonate ions to form carbonic acid and pH does not change. If the concentration of protons decreases slightly, carbonic acid gives up protons and pH does not change. ✔ If you understand this concept, you should be able to predict what would happen to the concentration of bicarbonate ions if a base like sodium hydroxide (NaOH) were added to the solution of carbonic acid.

As chemical evolution began, then, water provided the physical environment for key reactions to take place. In some cases water also acted as an important reactant. Although acid–base reactions were not critical to the initial stages of chemical evolution, they became extremely important once the process was under way. Now let's consider what happened in solution, some 3.5 billion years ago.

2.3 Chemical Reactions, Energy, and Chemical Evolution

Proponents of the theory of chemical evolution contend that simple molecules present in the atmosphere and oceans of early Earth participated in chemical reactions that eventually produced larger, more complex organic (carbon-containing) molecules—such as the proteins, nucleic acids, sugars, and lipids introduced in the next four chapters. Currently, researchers are investigating two environments where these reactions may have occurred:

1. *The atmosphere*, which was probably dominated by gases ejected from volcanoes. Water vapor, carbon dioxide (CO_2), and nitrogen (N_2) are the dominant gases ejected by volcanoes today; a small amount of molecular hydrogen (H_2) and carbon monoxide (CO) may also be present.

2. *Deep-sea hydrothermal vents*, where extremely hot rocks contact deep cracks in the seafloor. In addition to gases such as CO_2 and H_2, certain deep-sea vents are rich in minerals containing reactive metals such as nickel and iron.

When gases like CO_2, N_2, H_2, and CO are put together and allowed to interact on their own, however, very little happens. They do not suddenly link together to create large, complex substances like those found in living cells. Instead, their bonds remain intact. To understand why the bonds of these molecules remain unchanged, you must first learn about how chemical reactions proceed.

How Do Chemical Reactions Happen?

Chemical reactions are written in a format similar to mathematical equations: The initial, or **reactant,** molecules are shown on the left and the resulting reaction **product(s)** shown on the right. For example, the most common reaction in the mix of gases and water vapor that emerges from volcanoes results in the production of carbonic acid, which can be precipitated with water as acid rain:

$$CO_2(g) + H_2O(l) \rightleftharpoons CH_2O_3(aq)$$
$$\text{carbonic acid}$$

The physical state of each reactant and product is indicated as gas (*g*), liquid (*l*), solid (*s*), or in aqueous solution (*aq*).

Note that the expression is balanced; that is, 1 carbon, 3 oxygen, and 2 hydrogen atoms are present on each side of the expression. This illustrates the conservation of mass in closed systems—mass cannot be created or destroyed, but it may be rearranged through chemical reactions.

Note also that the expression contains a double arrow, meaning that the reaction is reversible. When the forward and reverse reactions proceed at the same rate, the quantities of reactants and products remain constant, although not necessarily equal. A dynamic but stable state such as this is termed a **chemical equilibrium.**

Changing the concentration of reactants or products can disturb a chemical equilibrium. For example, adding more CO_2 to the mixture would drive the reaction to the right, creating more CH_2O_3 until the equilibrium proportions of reactants and products are reestablished. Removing CO_2 or adding more CH_2O_3 would drive the reaction to the left.

A chemical equilibrium can also be altered by changes in temperature. For example, the water molecules in the following set of interacting elements, or **system,** would be present as a combination of liquid water and water vapor:

$$H_2O(l) \rightleftharpoons H_2O(g)$$

If liquid water molecules absorb enough energy, like the heat released from a volcano, they transform to the gaseous state. (You may recall that water has a high heat of vaporization and requires a large amount of energy to change its state from liquid to gas.) As a result, this change is termed **endothermic** ("within heating") because heat is absorbed during the process. In contrast, the transformation of water vapor to liquid water releases heat and is **exothermic** ("outside heating"). Raising the temperature of this system drives the equilibrium to the right; cooling the system drives it to the left.

In relation to chemical evolution, though, these reactions and changes of physical state are not particularly interesting. Carbonic acid is not an important intermediate in the formation of more complex molecules. However, interesting things do begin to happen when energy is added to mixtures of volcanic gases.

What Is Energy?

Energy can be defined as the capacity to do work or to supply heat. This capacity exists in one of two ways—as a stored potential or as an active motion.

Stored energy is called **potential energy.** An object gains or loses its ability to store energy because of its position. An electron that resides in an outer electron shell will, if the opportunity arises, fall into a lower electron shell closer to the positive charges on the protons in the nucleus. Because of its position farther from the positive charges in the nucleus, an electron in an outer electron shell has more potential energy than does an electron in an inner shell (**FIGURE 2.18**). When stored in chemical bonds, this form of potential energy is called **chemical energy.**

Kinetic energy is energy of motion. Molecules have kinetic energy because they are constantly in motion.

- The kinetic energy of molecular motion is called **thermal energy.**

- The **temperature** of an object is a measure of how much thermal energy its molecules possess. If an object has a low temperature, its molecules are moving slowly. (We perceive this as "cold.") If an object has a high temperature, its molecules are moving rapidly. (We perceive this as "hot.")

- When two objects with different temperatures come into contact, thermal energy is transferred between them. This transferred energy is called **heat.**

There are many forms of potential energy and kinetic energy, and energy can change from one form into another. However, according to the **first law of thermodynamics,** energy is conserved—it cannot be created or destroyed, but only transferred and transformed. (A more thorough explanation of energy transformation is provided in Chapter 8 in the context of cellular metabolism.)

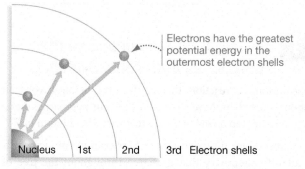

Electrons have the greatest potential energy in the outermost electron shells

Nucleus | 1st | 2nd | 3rd Electron shells

FIGURE 2.18 Potential Energy as a Function of Electron Shells. Electrons in outer shells have more potential energy than do electrons in inner shells, because the negative charges of the electrons in outer shells are farther from the positive charges of the protons in the nucleus. Each shell represents a distinct level of potential energy.

Energy transformation is the heart of chemical evolution. According to the best data available, molecules that were part of the early Earth were exposed to massive inputs of energy. Kinetic energy, in the form of heat, was present in the gradually cooling molten mass that initially formed the planet. The atmosphere and surface of the early Earth were also bombarded with electricity from lightening and radiation from the Sun. Energy stored as potential energy in the chemical bonds of small molecules was also abundant.

Now that you understand that energy transformations are involved in chemical reactions, a big question remains: What determines if a reaction will take place?

What Makes a Chemical Reaction Spontaneous?

When chemists say that a reaction is spontaneous, they have a precise meaning in mind: Chemical reactions are spontaneous if they are able to proceed on their own, without any continuous external influence, such as added energy. Two factors determine if a reaction will proceed spontaneously:

1. Reactions tend to be spontaneous when the product molecules are less ordered than the reactant molecules. For example, nitroglycerin is a single, highly ordered molecule. But when nitroglycerin explodes, it breaks up into gases like carbon dioxide, nitrogen, oxygen, and water vapor. These molecules are much less ordered than the reactant nitroglycerin molecules. The heat that is given off from this explosion also contributes to increasing disorder in the environment. The amount of disorder in a system is called **entropy.** When the products of a chemical reaction are less ordered than the reactant molecules are, entropy increases and the reaction tends to be spontaneous. The **second law of thermodynamics,** in fact, states that entropy always increases in an isolated system.

2. Reactions tend to be spontaneous if the products have lower potential energy than the reactants. If the electrons in the reaction products are held more tightly than those in the reactants, then they have lower potential energy. Recall that highly electronegative atoms such as oxygen or nitrogen hold electrons in covalent bonds much more tightly than do atoms with a lower electronegativity, such as hydrogen or carbon. For example, when hydrogen and oxygen gases react, water is produced spontaneously:

$$2\,H_2(g) + O_2(g) \longrightarrow 2\,H_2O(g)$$

The electrons involved in the O—H bonds of water are held much more tightly by the more electronegative oxygen atom than when they were shared equally in the H—H and O=O bonds of hydrogen and oxygen (see **FIGURE 2.19a** on page 32). As a result, the products have much lower potential energy than the reactants. The difference in chemical energy between reactants and products is given off as heat, so the reaction is exothermic. And although the reaction between hydrogen and oxygen results in less entropy—three molecules of gas produce two molecules of water vapor—the reaction is still spontaneous due to the large drop in potential energy

(a) When hydrogen and oxygen gas react, the product has much lower potential energy than the reactants.

Electrons are held "loosely" in bonds between atoms with equal electronegativities

Electrons are held tightly by highly electronegative atoms

H—H + O=O → H—O—H +

2 Hydrogens (H_2)   1 Oxygen (O_2)   *Potential energy drops* →   2 Waters (H_2O)

(b) The difference in potential energy is released as heat and light, which vaporizes the water produced.

Heat and light

Released energy

FIGURE 2.19 Potential Energy May Change during Chemical Reactions. In the Hindenburg disaster of 1937, the hydrogen gas from this lighter-than-air craft reacted with oxygen in the atmosphere, with devastating results.

✔**EXERCISE** Label which electrons have relatively low potential energy and which electrons have relatively high potential energy.

released as heat. Since heat increases disorder in the environment, the second law of thermodynamics remains intact. The Hindenburg disaster of 1937 illustrates the large and terrifying amount of heat energy that is given off from this relatively simple reaction (**FIGURE 2.19b**).

To summarize: In general, physical and chemical processes proceed in the direction that results in increased entropy and lower potential energy (**FIGURE 2.20**). These two factors—potential energy and entropy—are used to figure out whether a reaction is spontaneous (see Chapter 8 for more detail). Were the reactions that led to chemical evolution spontaneous? Section 2.4 explores how researchers address this question.

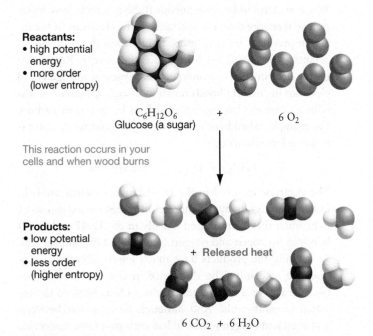

Reactants:
• high potential energy
• more order (lower entropy)

$C_6H_{12}O_6$
Glucose (a sugar)   +   6 O_2

This reaction occurs in your cells and when wood burns

Products:
• low potential energy
• less order (higher entropy)

+ **Released heat**

6 CO_2 + 6 H_2O

FIGURE 2.20 Spontaneous Processes Result in Lower Potential Energy, Increased Disorder, or Both.

check your understanding

C Y U

If you understand that . . .
• Chemical reactions result in the transformation of energy, either through the release of energy stored in chemical bonds or the uptake of energy from external sources.
• Chemical reactions tend to be spontaneous if they lead to lower potential energy and higher entropy (more disorder).

✔ **You should be able to . . .**

1. Determine if the reaction between methane (CH_4) and oxygen (O_2) shown here is spontaneous or not, addressing both potential energy and entropy:

$$CH_4 + 2\,O_2 \longrightarrow CO_2 + 2\,H_2O$$

2. Explain how the positions of the valence electrons in carbon and hydrogen change as methane is converted into carbon dioxide and water.

Answers are available in Appendix A.

2.4 Investigating Chemical Evolution: Approaches and Model Systems

To probe the kinds of reactions that may have set chemical evolution in motion, researchers have used two different approaches—one looking from the "top down" and the other from the "bottom up."

1. In the top-down approach, researchers examine modern cells to identify chemistry that is shared throughout the tree of life. Such ancient reactions are prime candidates for being involved in the chemical evolution that led up to **LUCA**, or last universal common ancestor (introduced in Chapter 1).

2. In the bottom-up approach, the primary focus is on the small molecules and environmental conditions that were present in

early Earth. Here, researchers attempt to identify reactions that could build the molecules found in life using only what was available at the time, without regard to reactions used by modern cells.

These approaches have been used to investigate two different model systems that attempt to explain the process component of the theory of chemical evolution:

1. The **prebiotic soup model** proposes that certain molecules were synthesized from gases in the atmosphere or arrived via meteorites. Afterward they would have condensed with rain and accumulated in oceans. This process would result in an "organic soup" that allowed for continued construction of larger, even more complex molecules.

2. The **surface metabolism model** suggests that dissolved gases came in contact with minerals lining the walls of deep-sea vents and formed more complex, organic molecules.

Since it is impossible to directly examine how and where chemical evolution occurred, the next best thing is to re-create the conditions in the lab and test predictions made by these models. In the following sections, you will learn about how biologists used the top-down and bottom-up approaches to identify reactions that support each of these models for chemical evolution.

Early Origin-of-Life Experiments

Chemical evolution was first taken seriously in 1953 when a graduate student named Stanley Miller performed a breakthrough experiment in the study of the prebiotic soup model.

Miller wanted to answer a simple question: Can complex organic compounds be synthesized from the simple molecules present in Earth's early atmosphere? In other words, is it possible to re-create the first steps in chemical evolution by simulating early-Earth conditions in the laboratory?

Miller's experimental setup (**FIGURE 2.21**) was designed to produce a microcosm of early Earth. The large glass flask represented the atmosphere and contained the gases methane (CH_4), ammonia (NH_3), and hydrogen (H_2), all of which have high potential energy. This large flask was connected to a smaller flask by glass tubing. The small flask held a tiny ocean—200 milliliters (mL) of liquid water.

To connect the mini-atmosphere with the mini-ocean, Miller boiled the water constantly. This added water vapor to the mix of gases in the large flask. As the vapor cooled and condensed, it flowed back into the smaller flask, where it boiled again. In this way, water vapor circulated continuously through the system. This was important: If the molecules in the simulated atmosphere reacted with one another, the "rain" would carry them into the mini-ocean, forming a simulated version of the prebiotic soup.

Had Miller stopped at merely boiling the molecules, little or nothing would have happened. Even at the boiling point of water (100°C), the starting molecules used in the experiment are stable and do not undergo spontaneous chemical reactions.

Something did start to happen in the apparatus, however, when Miller sent electrical discharges across the electrodes he'd inserted into the atmosphere. These miniature lightning bolts

RESEARCH

QUESTION: Can simple molecules and kinetic energy lead to chemical evolution?

HYPOTHESIS: If kinetic energy is added to a mix of simple molecules, reactions will occur that produce more complex molecules, perhaps including some with C–C bonds.

NULL HYPOTHESIS: Chemical evolution will not occur, even with an input of energy.

EXPERIMENTAL SETUP:

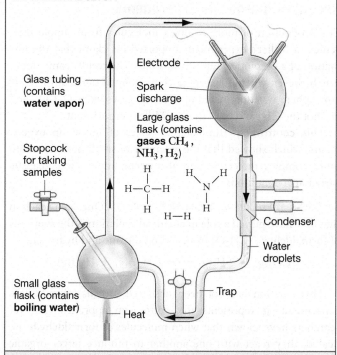

PREDICTION: Complex organic compounds will be found in the liquid water.

PREDICTION OF NULL HYPOTHESIS: Only the starting molecules will be found in the liquid water.

RESULTS

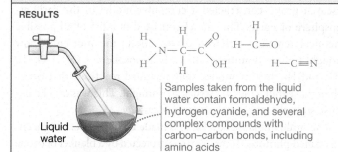

Samples taken from the liquid water contain formaldehyde, hydrogen cyanide, and several complex compounds with carbon–carbon bonds, including amino acids

CONCLUSION: Chemical evolution occurs readily if simple molecules with high free energy are exposed to a source of kinetic energy.

FIGURE 2.21 Miller's Spark-Discharge Experiment. The arrows in the "Experimental setup" diagram indicate the flow of water vapor or liquid. The condenser is a jacket with cold water flowing through it.

SOURCE: Miller, S. L. 1953. A production of amino acids under possible primitive Earth conditions. *Science* 117: 528–529.

✔**QUESTION** Which parts of the apparatus mimic the ocean, atmosphere, rain, and lightning?

added a crucial element to the reaction mix—pulses of intense electrical energy. After a day of continuous boiling and sparking, the solution in the boiling flask began to turn pink. After a week, it was deep red and cloudy.

When Miller analyzed samples from the mini-ocean, he found large quantities of hydrogen cyanide and formaldehyde. Even more exciting, the sparks and heating had led to the synthesis of additional, more complex organic compounds, including amino acids, which are the building blocks of proteins (see Chapter 3).

Recent Origin-of-Life Experiments

The production of more complex molecules from simple molecules in Miller's experiment supported his claim that the formation of a prebiotic soup was possible. The results came under fire, however, when other researchers pointed out that the early atmosphere was dominated by volcanic gases like CO, CO_2, and H_2, not the CH_4 and NH_3 used in Miller's experiment.

This controversy stimulated a series of follow-up experiments, which showed that the assembly of small molecules into more complex molecules can also occur under more realistic early Earth conditions.

Synthesis of Precursors Using Light Energy One such reaction that may have played a role in chemical evolution is the synthesis of formaldehyde (CH_2O) from carbon dioxide and hydrogen:

$$CO_2(g) + 2\,H_2(g) \longrightarrow \underset{\text{formaldehyde}}{CH_2O(g)} + H_2O(g)$$

This reaction has not been observed in cells—like Miller's experiment, it represents the bottom-up approach. But researchers have shown that when molecules of formaldehyde are heated, they react with one another to produce larger organic compounds, including energy-rich molecules like sugars (see Chapter 5). Note, however, that this reaction does not occur spontaneously—a large input of energy is required.

To explore the possibility of early formaldehyde synthesis, a research group constructed a computer model of the early atmosphere of Earth. The model consisted of a list of all possible chemical reactions that can occur among the molecules now thought to have dominated the early atmosphere: CO_2, H_2O, N_2, CO, and H_2. In this model, they included reactions that occur when these molecules are struck by sunlight. This was crucial because sunlight represents a source of energy.

The sunlight that strikes Earth is made up of packets of light energy called **photons.** Today, Earth is protected by a blanket of ozone (O_3) in the upper atmosphere that absorbs most of the higher-energy photons in sunlight. But since Earth's early atmosphere was filled with volcanic gases released as the molten planet cooled, and ozone is not among these gases, it is extremely unlikely that appreciable quantities of ozone existed. Based on this logic, researchers infer that when chemical evolution was occurring, large quantities of high-energy photons bombarded the planet.

To understand why this energy source was so important, recall that the atoms in hydrogen and carbon dioxide molecules have full valence shells through covalent bonding. This arrangement makes these molecules largely unreactive. However, energy

from photons can break up molecules by knocking apart shared electrons. The fragments that result, called **free radicals,** have unpaired electrons in their outermost shells and are extremely reactive (**FIGURE 2.22**). To mimic the conditions on early Earth more accurately, the computer model included several reactions that produce highly reactive free radicals.

The result? The researchers calculated that, under conditions accepted as reasonable approximations of early Earth by most scientists, appreciable quantities of formaldehyde would have been produced. The energy in sunlight was converted to chemical energy in the form of new bonds in formaldehyde.

The complete reaction that results in the formation of formaldehyde is written as

$$CO_2(g) + 2\,H_2(g) + \text{sunlight} \longrightarrow CH_2O(g) + H_2O(g)$$

Notice that the reaction is balanced in terms of the atoms *and* the energy involved. The sunlight on the reactant side balances the higher energy required for the formation of formaldehyde and water. This result makes sense if you take a moment to think about it. Energy is the capacity to do work, and building larger, more complex molecules requires work to be done.

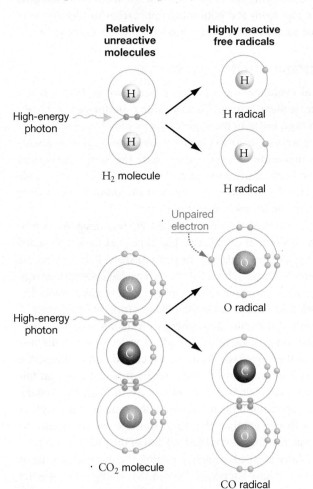

FIGURE 2.22 Free Radicals Are Extremely Reactive. When high-energy photons or pulses of intense electrical energy, such as lightning, strike molecules of hydrogen or carbon dioxide, free radicals can be created. Formation of free radicals is thought to be responsible for some key reactions in chemical evolution.

Using a similar model, other researchers have shown that hydrogen cyanide (HCN)—another important precursor of molecules required for life—could also have been produced in the early atmosphere. According to this research, large quantities of potential precursors for chemical evolution would have formed in the atmosphere and rained out into the early oceans. As a result, organic compounds with relatively high potential energy could have accumulated, and the groundwork would have been in place for the prebiotic soup model of chemical evolution to take off (**FIGURE 2.23a**).

Concentration and Catalysis in Hydrothermal Vents A major stumbling block in the prebiotic soup model is that precursor molecules would have become diluted when they entered the early oceans. Without some means of localized concentration, the formaldehyde and hydrogen cyanide mentioned in the previous section would have been unlikely to meet and react to form larger, more complex molecules. The surface metabolism model offers one possible solution to this dilution effect.

In the surface metabolism model, reactants are recruited to a defined space—a layer of reactive minerals deposited on the

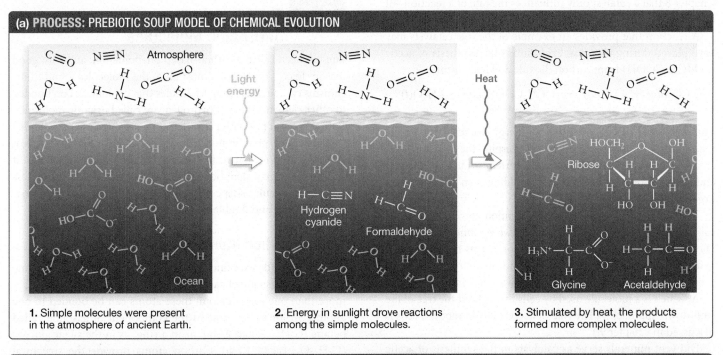

(a) PROCESS: PREBIOTIC SOUP MODEL OF CHEMICAL EVOLUTION

1. Simple molecules were present in the atmosphere of ancient Earth.

2. Energy in sunlight drove reactions among the simple molecules.

3. Stimulated by heat, the products formed more complex molecules.

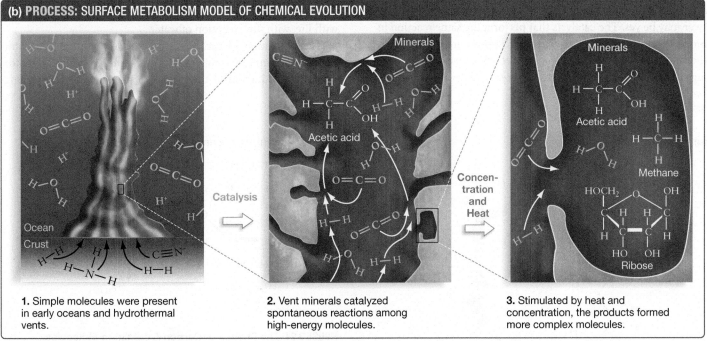

(b) PROCESS: SURFACE METABOLISM MODEL OF CHEMICAL EVOLUTION

1. Simple molecules were present in early oceans and hydrothermal vents.

2. Vent minerals catalyzed spontaneous reactions among high-energy molecules.

3. Stimulated by heat and concentration, the products formed more complex molecules.

FIGURE 2.23 The Start of Chemical Evolution—Two Models. The prebiotic soup and surface metabolism models illustrate how simple molecules containing C, H, O, and N reacted to form organic compounds that served as building blocks for more complex molecules.

walls of deep-sea vent chimneys. Dissolved gases would be attracted by the minerals and concentrated on vent-wall surfaces (**FIGURE 2.23b**).

Here's a key point of this model: Not only would vent-wall minerals bring reactants together, they would also be critical to the rate at which reaction products formed. Even if a potential reaction were spontaneous, it would probably not occur at a level useful for chemical evolution without the support of a **catalyst.** A catalyst provides the appropriate chemical environment for reactants to interact with one another effectively. (You will learn in Chapter 8 that a catalyst only influences the rate of a reaction—it does not provide energy or alter spontaneity.)

A reaction that provides an example of the role catalysts may have played during chemical evolution is the synthesis of acetic acid (CH_3COOH) from carbon dioxide and hydrogen:

$$2\ CO_2(aq) + 4\ H_2(aq) \longrightarrow CH_3COOH(aq) + 2\ H_2O(l)$$
$$\text{acetic acid}$$

The reaction is driven by chemical energy stored in one of the reactants—H_2—and is spontaneous despite the apparent decrease in entropy. It is employed by certain groups of Bacteria and Archaea today as a step toward building even more complex organic molecules.

This reaction has grabbed wide attention among the chemical evolution research community, for two reasons in particular: (**1**) Acetic acid can be formed under conditions that simulate a hydrothermal vent environment (bottom-up approach). (**2**) It is a key intermediate in an ancient pathway that produces acetyl CoA, which is a molecule used by cells throughout the tree of life (top-down approach). (The role of acetyl CoA in modern cells is discussed in Chapter 9.)

Did vent minerals serve as catalysts in the synthesis of acetic acid in early Earth? Evidence from modern cells suggests the answer may be yes. The catalysts that perform the same reaction in modern cells contain minerals similar to those found in hydrothermal vents. These minerals may represent a form of molecular luggage taken from the deep-sea hydrothermal vents as LUCA evolved its independence.

Research is currently under way to establish laboratory systems to more closely mimic surface metabolism conditions in hydrothermal vents. Preliminary results show that in addition to the production of acetic acid, a variety of larger carbon-based molecules can be formed under early Earth conditions. Among these are precursors for the synthesis of nucleotides, the building blocks for the molecules of inheritance used by every living organism on Earth (see Chapter 4).

2.5 The Importance of Organic Molecules

Life has been called a carbon-based phenomenon, and with good reason. Except for water, almost all of the molecules found in organisms contain this atom. Molecules that contain carbon bonded to other elements, such as hydrogen, are called **organic** molecules. (Other types of molecules are referred to as *inorganic* compounds.)

Carbon has great importance in biology because it is the most versatile atom on Earth. Because of its four valence electrons, it will form four covalent bonds. This results in an almost limitless array of molecular shapes, made possible by different combinations of single and double bonds.

Linking Carbon Atoms Together

You have already examined the tetrahedral structure of methane and the linear shape of carbon dioxide. When molecules contain more than one carbon atom, these atoms can be bonded to one another in long chains, as in the component of gasoline called octane (C_8H_{18}; **FIGURE 2.24a**), or in a ring, as in the sugar glucose ($C_6H_{12}O_6$; **FIGURE 2.24b**). Carbon atoms provide the structural framework for virtually all the important compounds associated with life, with the exception of water.

The formation of carbon–carbon bonds was an important event in chemical evolution: It represented a crucial step toward the production of the types of molecules found in living organisms.

(a) Carbons linked in a chain

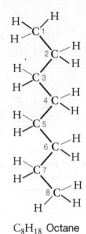 

C_8H_{18} Octane

(b) Carbons linked in a ring

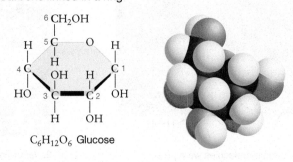

$C_6H_{12}O_6$ Glucose

FIGURE 2.24 The Shapes of Carbon-Containing Molecules. **(a)** Octane is a hydrocarbon chain, and one of the primary ingredients in gasoline. **(b)** Glucose is a sugar that can form a ring-like structure.

Functional Groups

In general, the carbon atoms in an organic molecule furnish a skeleton that gives the molecule its overall shape. But the chemical behavior of the compound—meaning the types of reactions that it participates in—is dictated by groups of H, N, O, P, or S atoms that are bonded to one of the carbon atoms in a specific way.

The critically important H-, N-, O-, P-, and S-containing groups found in organic compounds are called **functional groups.** The composition and properties of six prominent functional groups that are commonly found in organic molecules and recognized by organic chemists are summarized in **TABLE 2.3**. To understand the role that organic compounds play in organisms, it is important to analyze how these functional groups behave.

SUMMARY TABLE 2.3   Six Functional Groups Commonly Attached to Carbon Atoms

Functional Group	Formula*	Family of Molecules	Properties of Functional Group	Example
Amino	H_2N-R	Amines	Acts as a base—tends to attract a proton to form: $H-\,^+NH_3-R$	Glycine (an amino acid)
Carboxyl	$R-C(=O)OH$	Carboxylic acids	Acts as an acid—tends to lose a proton in solution to form: $R-C(=O)O^-$	Acetic acid
Carbonyl	$R-C(=O)H$	Aldehydes	Aldehydes, especially, react with certain compounds to produce larger molecules to form: $R1-C(=O)-H$ + $H-R2$ $\longrightarrow$ $R1-C(OH)(R2)-H$	Acetaldehyde
	$R-C(=O)-R$	Ketones		Acetone
Hydroxyl	$R-OH$	Alcohols	Highly polar, so makes compounds more soluble through hydrogen bonding with water; may also act as a weak acid and drop a proton	Ethanol
Phosphate	$R-O-P(=O)(O^-)-O^-$	Organic phosphates	Molecules with more than one phosphate linked together store large amounts of chemical energy	3–Phosphoglyceric acid
Sulfhydryl	$R-SH$	Thiols	When present in proteins, can form disulfide (S–S) bonds that contribute to protein structure	Cysteine

In the Carbonyl reaction diagram: "R group from aldehyde" points to R1; "R group from another reactant" points to R2.

*In these structural formulas, "R" stands for the rest of the molecule.

✔**EXERCISE** Based on the electronegativities of the atoms involved, predict whether each functional group is polar or nonpolar.

- *Amino and carboxyl functional groups* tend to attract or drop a proton, respectively, when in solution. Amino groups function as bases; carboxyl groups act as acids. During chemical evolution and in organisms today, the most important types of amino- and carboxyl-containing molecules are the amino acids (which Chapter 3 analyzes in detail). Amino acids contain both an amino group and a carboxyl group. (It's common for organic compounds to contain more than one functional group.) Amino acids can be linked together by covalent bonds that form between amino and carboxyl groups. In addition, both of these functional groups participate in hydrogen bonding.

- *Carbonyl groups* are found on aldehyde and ketone molecules such as formaldehyde, acetaldehyde, and acetone. This functional group is the site of reactions that link these molecules into larger, more complex organic compounds.

- *Hydroxyl groups* are important because they act as weak acids. In many cases, the protons involved in acid–base reactions that occur in cells come from hydroxyl groups on organic compounds. Because hydroxyl groups are polar, molecules containing hydroxyl groups will form hydrogen bonds and tend to be soluble in water.

- *Phosphate groups* carry two negative charges. When phosphate groups are transferred from one organic compound to another, the change in charge often dramatically affects the structure of the recipient molecule. In addition, phosphates that are bonded together store chemical energy that can be used in chemical reactions (some of these are discussed in Chapter 3).

- *Sulfhydryl groups* consist of a sulfur atom bonded to a hydrogen atom. They are important because sulfhydryl groups can link to one another via disulfide (S—S) bonds.

To summarize, functional groups make things happen. The number and types of functional groups attached to a framework of carbon atoms imply a great deal about how that molecule is going to behave.

When you encounter an organic compound that is new to you, it's important to do the following three things:

1. Examine the overall size and shape provided by the carbon framework.

2. Identify the types of covalent bonds present based on the electronegativities of the atoms. Use this information to estimate the polarity of the molecule and the amount of potential energy stored in its chemical bonds.

3. Locate any functional groups and note the properties these groups give to the molecule.

Understanding these three features will help you to predict the molecule's role in the chemistry of life.

Once carbon-containing molecules with functional groups had appeared early in Earth's history, what happened next? For chemical evolution to continue, small carbon-based molecules had to form still larger, more complex molecules like those found in living cells. How were the molecules of life—proteins, nucleic acids, carbohydrates, and lipids—formed, and how do they function in organisms today? The rest of this unit explores the next steps in chemical evolution, culminating in the formation of the first living cell.

CHAPTER 2 REVIEW

For media, go to MasteringBiology

If you understand . . .

2.1 Atoms, Ions, and Molecules: The Building Blocks of Chemical Evolution

- When atoms participate in chemical bonds to form molecules, the shared electrons give the atoms full valence shells and thus contribute to the atoms' stability.

- The electrons in a chemical bond may be shared equally or unequally, depending on the relative electronegativities of the two atoms involved.

- Nonpolar covalent bonds result from equal sharing; polar covalent bonds are due to unequal sharing. Ionic bonds form when an electron is completely transferred from one atom to another.

✔ You should be able to compare and contrast the types of bonds found in methane (CH_4), ammonia (NH_3), and sodium chloride (NaCl).

2.2 Properties of Water and the Early Oceans

- The chemical reactions required for life take place in water.

- Water is polar—meaning that it has partial positive and negative charges—because it is bent and has two polar covalent bonds.

- Polar molecules and charged substances, including ions, interact with water and stay in solution via hydrogen bonding and electrostatic attraction.

- Water's ability to participate in hydrogen bonding also gives it an extraordinarily high capacity to absorb heat and cohere to other water molecules.

- Water spontaneously dissociates into hydrogen ions (or protons, H^+) and hydroxide ions (OH^-). The concentration of protons in a solution determines the pH, which can be altered by acids and bases or stabilized by buffers.

✔ You should be able to predict what part of water molecules would interact with amino, carboxyl, and hydroxyl functional groups in solution and the types of bonds that would be involved.

2.3 Chemical Reactions, Energy, and Chemical Evolution

- The first step in chemical evolution was the formation of small organic compounds from molecules such as molecular hydrogen (H_2) and carbon dioxide (CO_2).

- Chemical reactions typically involve bonds being broken, atoms being rearranged, and new bonds being formed. This process involves energy, either from the reactants or external sources (e.g., heat).

- Energy comes in different forms. Although energy cannot be created or destroyed, one form of energy can be transformed into another.

✔ You should be able to explain how the energy in electricity can drive a reaction that is nonspontaneous.

2.4 Investigating Chemical Evolution: Approaches and Model Systems

- Experiments suggest that early in Earth's history, external sources of energy, such as sunlight or lightning, could have driven chemical reactions between simple molecules to form molecules with higher potential energy. In this way, energy in the form of radiation or electricity was transformed into chemical energy.

- The prebiotic soup and surface metabolism models for chemical evolution have been supported by the synthesis of organic molecules in laboratory simulations of the early Earth environment.

✔ You should be able to explain how the surface metabolism model is supported by both the top-down and bottom-up approaches used to investigate reactions involved in chemical evolution.

2.5 The Importance of Organic Molecules

- Carbon is the foundation of organic molecules based on its valence, which allows for the construction of molecules with complex shapes.

- Organic molecules are critical to life because they possess versatility of chemical behavior due to the presence of functional groups.

✔ You should be able to predict how adding hydroxyl groups to the octane molecule in Figure 2.24 would affect the properties of the molecule.

(MB) MasteringBiology

1. MasteringBiology Assignments

Tutorials and Activities Acids, Bases, and pH; Anatomy of Atoms; Atomic Number and Mass Number; BioSkill: Using Logarithms; Carbon Bonding and Functional Groups; Cohesion of Water; Covalent Bonds; Dissociation of Water Molecules; Diversity of Carbon-Based Molecules; Electron Arrangement; Energy Transformations; Functional Groups; Hydrogen Bonding and Water; Hydrogen Bonds; Ionic Bonds; Nonpolar and Polar Molecules; pH Scale; Polarity of Water; Properties of Water; Structure of the Atomic Nucleus

Questions Reading Quizzes, Blue-Thread Questions, Test Bank

2. eText Read your book online, search, take notes, highlight text, and more.

3. The Study Area Practice Test, Cumulative Test, BioFlix® 3-D Animations, Videos, Activities, Audio Glossary, Word Study Tools, Art

You should be able to . . .

✔ TEST YOUR KNOWLEDGE

Answers are available in Appendix A

1. Which of the following occurs when a covalent bond forms?
   a. The potential energy of electrons drops.
   b. Electrons in valence shells are shared between nuclei.
   c. Ions of opposite charge interact.
   d. Polar molecules interact.

2. If a reaction is exothermic, then which of the following statements is true?
   a. The products have lower potential energy than the reactants.
   b. Energy must be added for the reaction to proceed.
   c. The products have lower entropy (are more ordered) than the reactants.
   d. It occurs extremely quickly.

3. Which of the following is most likely to have been the energy source responsible for the formation of acetic acid in deep-sea hydrothermal vents?

   a. heat released from the vents
   b. solar radiation that passed through the ocean water
   c. chemical energy present in the reactants
   d. the increase in entropy in the products

4. What is thermal energy?
   a. a form of potential energy
   b. the temperature increase that occurs when any form of energy is added to a system
   c. mechanical energy
   d. the kinetic energy of molecular motion, measured as heat

5. What factors determine whether a chemical reaction is spontaneous or not?

6. What are the two models that have been proposed to explain the process component of chemical evolution?

7. Which of the following molecules would you predict to have the largest number of polar covalent bonds based on their molecular formulas?
   a. C_2H_6O (ethanol)
   b. C_2H_6 (ethane)
   c. $C_2H_4O_2$ (acetic acid)
   d. C_3H_8O (propanol)

8. Locate fluorine (F) on the partial periodic table provided in Figure 2.2. Predict its relative electronegativity compared to hydrogen, sodium, and oxygen. State the number and type of bond(s) you expect it would form if it reacted with sodium.

9. Oxygen is extremely electronegative, meaning that its nucleus pulls electrons shared in covalent bonds very strongly. Explain the changes in electron position that are illustrated in Figure 2.19 based on oxygen's electronegativity.

10. Draw the electron-sharing continuum and place molecular oxygen (O_2), magnesium chloride ($MgCl_2$), and carbon dioxide (CO_2) on it.

11. Consider the reaction between carbon dioxide and water, which forms carbonic acid:

$$CO_2(g) + H_2O(l) \rightleftharpoons CH_2O_3(aq)$$

In aqueous solution, carbonic acid immediately dissociates to form a proton and bicarbonate ion, as follows:

$$CH_2O_3(aq) \rightleftharpoons H^+(aq) + CHO_3^-(aq)$$

If an underwater volcano bubbled additional CO_2 into the ocean, would this sequence of reactions be driven to the left or the right? How would this affect the pH of the ocean?

12. What is the relationship between the carbon framework in an organic molecule (the "R" in Table 2.3) and its functional groups?

13. When H_2 and CO_2 react, acetic acid can be formed spontaneously while the production of formaldehyde requires an input of energy. Which of the following conclusions may be drawn from this observation?
   a. More heat is released when formaldehyde is produced compared to the production of acetic acid.
   b. Compared to the reactants from which it is formed, formaldehyde has more potential energy than does acetic acid.
   c. Entropy decreases when acetic acid is produced and increases when formaldehyde is produced.
   d. The mineral catalyst involved in acetic acid production provides energy to make the reaction spontaneous.

14. When chemistry texts introduce the concept of electron shells, they emphasize that shells represent distinct potential energy levels. In introducing electron shells, this chapter also emphasizes that they represent distinct distances from the positive charges in the nucleus. Are these two points of view in conflict? Why or why not?

15. Draw a concept map relating water's structure to its properties. (For an introduction to concept mapping, see **BioSkills 15** in Appendix B.) Your concept map should include the following terms or phrases: polar covalent bonds, polarity (on the water molecule), hydrogen bonding, high heat of vaporization, high specific heat, less dense as a solid, effective solvent, unequal sharing of electrons, high energy input required to break bonds, high electronegativity of oxygen.

16. From what you have learned about water, why do coastal regions tend to have climates with lower annual variation in temperature than do inland areas at the same latitude?

3 Protein Structure and Function

In this chapter you will learn that

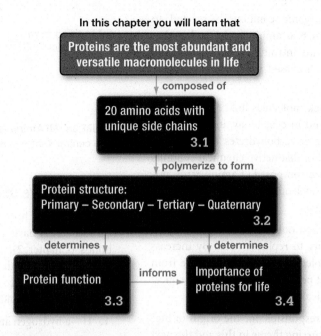

Proteins are the most abundant and versatile macromolecules in life

composed of

20 amino acids with unique side chains
3.1

polymerize to form

Protein structure:
Primary – Secondary – Tertiary – Quaternary
3.2

determines

determines

Protein function
3.3

informs

Importance of proteins for life
3.4

A space-filling model of hemoglobin—a protein that is carrying oxygen in your blood right now.

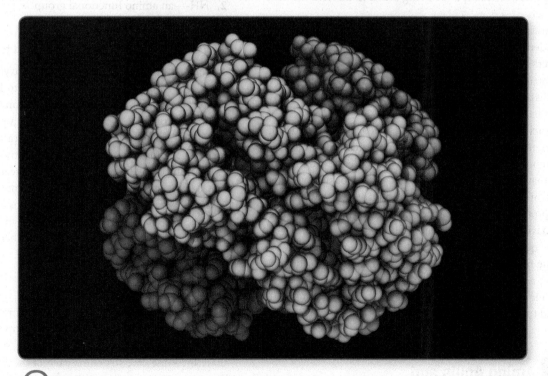

This chapter is part of the Big Picture. See how on pages 104–105.

Chemical reactions in the atmosphere and ocean of ancient Earth are thought to have led to the formation of the first complex carbon-containing compounds. This idea, called chemical evolution, was first proposed by Alexander I. Oparin in 1924. The hypothesis was published again—independently and five years later—by J. B. S. Haldane.

Today, the Oparin–Haldane proposal is considered a formal scientific theory (see Chapter 1). Scientific theories are continuously refined as new information comes to light, and many of Oparin

✔ When you see this checkmark, stop and test yourself. Answers are available in Appendix A.

and Haldane's original ideas have been revised. In its current form, the theory can be broken into four steps.

Step 1 Chemical evolution began with the production of small organic compounds from reactants such as H_2, N_2, NH_3, and CO_2. (Chapter 2 focuses on this step.)

Step 2 These small, simple organic compounds reacted to form mid-sized molecules, such as amino acids, nucleotides, and sugars. (Amino acids are introduced in this chapter. Nucleotides and sugars are discussed in Chapters 4 and 5, respectively.)

Step 3 Mid-sized, building-block molecules linked to form the types of large molecules found in cells today, including proteins, nucleic acids, and complex carbohydrates. Each of these large molecules is composed of distinctive chemical subunits that join together: Proteins are composed of amino acids, nucleic acids are composed of nucleotides, and complex carbohydrates are composed of sugars.

Step 4 Life became possible when one of these large, complex molecules acquired the ability to replicate itself. By increasing in copy number, this molecule would then emerge from the pool of chemicals. At that point, life had begun—chemical evolution gave way to biological evolution.

What type of molecule was responsible for the origin of life? Answering this question is a recurring theme in this and the next three chapters.

To address this question, researchers first designed experiments to identify the types of molecules that could be produced in the waters of prebiotic Earth (Chapter 2). One series of results sparked particular excitement for origin-of-life researchers—the repeated discovery of amino acids among the products of early Earth simulations.

Amino acids have also been found in meteorites and produced in experiments that approximate the environment of interstellar space. Taken together, these observations have led researchers to conclude that amino acids were present and probably abundant during chemical evolution. Since amino acids are the building blocks of proteins, many researchers have therefore asked, Could a protein have been the initial spark of life?

For this question to be valid, proteins would need to possess three of the fundamental attributes of life, namely: information, replication, and evolution. To determine if they do, let's look at the molecules themselves. What are amino acids, and how are they linked to form proteins?

3.1 Amino Acids and Their Polymerization

Modern cells, such as those that make up your body, produce tens of thousands of distinct proteins. Most of these molecules are composed of just 20 different building blocks, called **amino acids.** All 20 of these building blocks have a common structure.

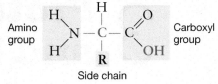

(a) Non-ionized form of amino acid

Amino group

Carboxyl group

Side chain

(b) Ionized form of amino acid

Amino group

Carboxyl group

Side chain

FIGURE 3.1 All Amino Acids Have the Same General Structure. The central ⍺-carbon is shown in red.

The Structure of Amino Acids

To understand how amino acids are put together, recall that carbon atoms have a valence of four—they form four covalent bonds (Chapter 2). All 20 amino acids thus have a common core structure—with a central carbon atom (referred to as the ⍺-carbon) bonded to the four different atoms or groups of atoms diagrammed in **FIGURE 3.1a**:

1. H—a hydrogen atom
2. NH_2—an amino functional group
3. COOH—a carboxyl functional group
4. a distinctive "R-group" (often referred to as a "side chain")

The combination of amino and carboxyl groups not only inspired the name amino acid, but is key to how these molecules behave. In water at pH 7, the concentration of protons causes the amino group to act as a base. It attracts a proton to form NH_3^+ (**FIGURE 3.1b**). The carboxyl group, in contrast, is acidic because its two oxygen atoms are highly electronegative. They pull electrons away from the hydrogen atom, which means that it is relatively easy for this group to lose a proton to form COO^-.

The charges on these functional groups are important for two reasons: **(1)** They help amino acids stay in solution, where they can interact with one another and with other solutes, and **(2)** they affect the amino acid's chemical reactivity.

The Nature of Side Chains

What about the R-group? The R-groups, or side chains, on amino acids vary from a single hydrogen atom to large structures containing carbon atoms linked into rings. While all amino acids share the same core structure, each of the 20 R-groups is unique. The properties of amino acids vary because their R-groups vary.

FIGURE 3.2 highlights the R-groups on the 20 most common amino acids found in cells.[1] As you examine these side chains,

[1]There are actually 22 amino acids found in proteins that occur in organisms, but two are very rare.

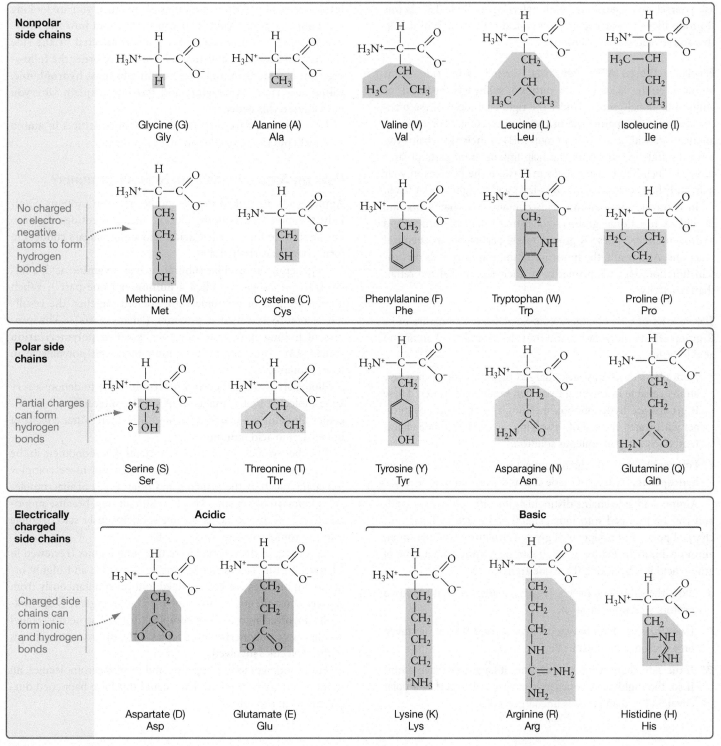

FIGURE 3.2 The 20 Major Amino Acids Found in Organisms. At the pH (about 7.0) found in cells, the 20 major amino acids found in organisms have the structural formulas shown here. The side chains are highlighted, and standard single-letter and three-letter abbreviations for each amino acid are given. For clarity, the carbon atoms in the ring structures of phenylalanine, tyrosine, tryptophan, and histidine are not shown; each bend in a ring is the site of a carbon atom. The hydrogen atoms in these structures are also not shown. A double line inside a ring indicates a double bond.

✔**EXERCISE** Explain why the green R-groups are nonpolar and why the pink R-groups are polar, based on the relative electronegativities of O, N, C, and H (see Chapter 2). Note that sulfur (S) has an electronegativity almost equal to that of carbon and slightly higher than that of hydrogen, making cysteine's side chain mildly hydrophobic.

ask yourself two questions (while referring to Table 2.3): Is this R-group likely to participate in chemical reactions? Will it help this amino acid stay in solution?

Functional Groups Affect Reactivity Several of the side chains found in amino acids contain carboxyl, sulfhydryl, hydroxyl, or amino functional groups. Under the right conditions, these functional groups can participate in chemical reactions. For example, amino acids with a sulfhydryl group (SH) in their side chains can form disulfide (S—S) bonds that help link different parts of large proteins. Such bonds naturally form between the proteins in your hair; curly hair contains many cross-links and straight hair far fewer.

In contrast, some amino acids contain side chains that are devoid of functional groups—consisting solely of carbon and hydrogen atoms. These R-groups rarely participate in chemical reactions. As a result, the influence of these amino acids on protein function depends primarily on their size and shape rather than reactivity.

The Polarity of Side Chains Affects Solubility The nature of its R-group affects the polarity, and thus the solubility, of an amino acid in water.

- Nonpolar side chains lack charged or highly electronegative atoms capable of forming hydrogen bonds with water. These R-groups are **hydrophobic,** meaning that they do not interact with water. Instead of dissolving, hydrophobic side chains tend to coalesce in aqueous solution.

- Polar or charged side chains interact readily with water and are **hydrophilic.** Hydrophilic side chains dissolve in water easily.

Amino acid side chains distinguish the different amino acids and can be grouped into four general types: acidic, basic, uncharged polar, and nonpolar. If given a structural formula for an amino acid, as in Figure 3.2, you can determine which type of amino acid it is by asking three questions:

1. Does the side chain have a negative charge? If so, it has lost a proton, so it must be acidic.

2. Does the side chain have a positive charge? If so, it has taken on a proton, so it must be basic.

3. If the side chain is uncharged, does it have an oxygen atom? If so, the highly electronegative oxygen will result in a polar covalent bond and thus is uncharged polar.

If the answers to all three questions are no, then you are looking at a nonpolar amino acid. ✔ If you understand how the interaction between amino acids and water is affected by the side chains, you should be able to use Figure 3.2 to order the following amino acids from most hydrophilic to most hydrophobic: valine, aspartate, asparagine, and tyrosine. Explain why you have chosen this order.

Now that you have seen the diversity of structures in amino acids, let's put them together to make a protein.

How Do Amino Acids Link to Form Proteins?

Amino acids are linked to one another to form proteins. Similarly, the molecular building blocks called nucleotides attach to one another to form nucleic acids, and simple sugars connect to form complex carbohydrates.

In general, a molecular subunit such as an amino acid, a nucleotide, or a sugar is called a **monomer** ("one-part"). When a large number of monomers are bonded together, the resulting structure is called a **polymer** ("many-parts"). The process of linking monomers together is called **polymerization** (**FIGURE 3.3**). Thus, amino acid monomers can polymerize to form proteins.

Biologists also use the word **macromolecule** to denote a very large molecule that is made up of smaller molecules joined together. Proteins are macromolecules—polymers—that consist of linked amino acid monomers.

The theory of chemical evolution states that monomers in the prebiotic soup polymerized to form larger and more complex molecules, such as the proteins and other types of macromolecules found in organisms. This is a difficult step, because monomers such as amino acids do not spontaneously self-assemble into macromolecules such as proteins.

According to the second law of thermodynamics (reviewed in Chapter 2), this fact is not surprising. Complex and highly organized molecules are not expected to form spontaneously from simpler constituents, because polymerization organizes the molecules involved into a more complex, ordered structure. Stated another way, polymerization decreases the disorder, or entropy, of the molecules involved.

For monomers to link together and form macromolecules, an input of energy is required. How could this have happened during chemical evolution?

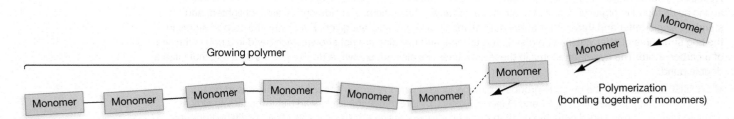

FIGURE 3.3 Monomers Are the Building Blocks of Polymers.

(a) Condensation reaction:
monomer in, water out

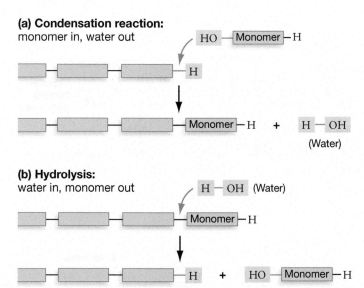

(b) Hydrolysis:
water in, monomer out

FIGURE 3.4 Polymers Can Be Extended or Broken Apart.

Could Polymerization Occur in the Energy-Rich Environment of Early Earth?

Monomers polymerize through **condensation reactions,** also known as **dehydration reactions.** These reactions are aptly named because the newly formed bond results in the loss of a water molecule (**FIGURE 3.4a**). The reverse reaction, called **hydrolysis,** breaks polymers apart by adding a water molecule (**FIGURE 3.4b**). The water molecule reacts with the bond linking the monomers, separating one monomer from the polymer chain.

In a solution such as the prebiotic soup, condensation and hydrolysis represent the forward and reverse reactions of a chemical equilibrium:

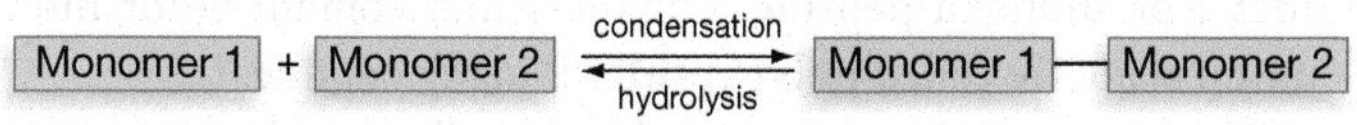

$$\boxed{\text{Monomer 1}} + \boxed{\text{Monomer 2}} \underset{\text{hydrolysis}}{\overset{\text{condensation}}{\rightleftharpoons}} \boxed{\text{Monomer 1}}-\boxed{\text{Monomer 2}}$$

Hydrolysis dominates because it increases entropy and is favorable energetically.

This means that, in the prebiotic soup, polymerization would occur only if there were a very high concentration of amino acids to push the reaction toward condensation. Since the equilibrium favors free monomers over polymers even under concentrated conditions, a polymer is unlikely to have grown much beyond a short chain.

According to recent experiments, though, there are several ways that amino acids could have polymerized early in chemical evolution.

- Researchers evaluating the surface metabolism model of chemical evolution have been able to generate stable polymers by mixing free amino acids with a source of chemical energy and tiny mineral particles. Apparently, growing macromolecules are protected from hydrolysis if they cling, or adsorb, to a mineral surface. One such experiment produced polymers that were 55 amino acids long.

- In conditions that simulate the hot, metal-rich environments of undersea volcanoes, researchers have observed not only amino acid formation but also their polymerization.

- Amino acids have also joined into polymers in experiments in cooler water if a carbon- and sulfur-containing gas—one that is commonly ejected from undersea volcanoes—is present.

The current consensus is that several mechanisms could have led to polymerization reactions between amino acids, early in chemical evolution. What kind of bond is responsible for linking these monomers?

The Peptide Bond As **FIGURE 3.5** shows, amino acids polymerize when a bond forms between the carboxyl group of one amino acid and the amino group of another. The C–N covalent bond that results from this condensation reaction is called a **peptide bond.** When a water molecule is removed in the condensation reaction, the carboxyl group is converted to a carbonyl functional group (C=O) in the resulting polymer, and the amino group is reduced to an N–H.

Peptide bonds are unusually stable compared to linkages in other types of macromolecules. This is because a pair of valence electrons on the nitrogen is partially shared in the C–N bond (see Figure 3.5). The degree of electron sharing is great enough that peptide bonds actually have some of the characteristics of a double bond. For example, the peptide bond is planar, limiting the movement of the atoms participating in the peptide bond.

When amino acids are linked by peptide bonds into a chain, the amino acids are referred to as residues to distinguish them from free monomers.

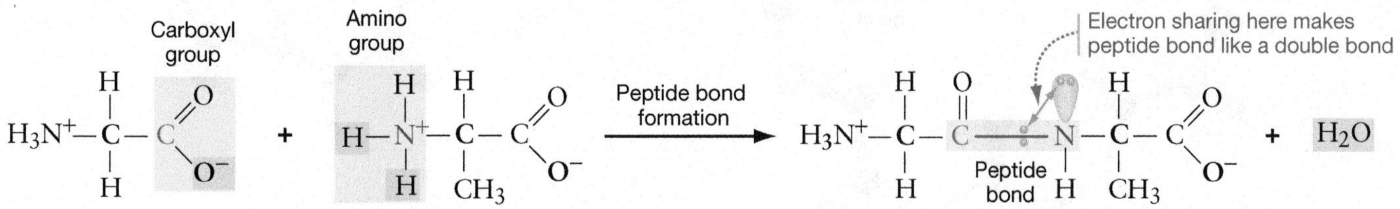

FIGURE 3.5 Peptide Bonds Form When the Carboxyl Group of One Amino Acid Reacts with the Amino Group of a Second Amino Acid.

(a) Peptide chain

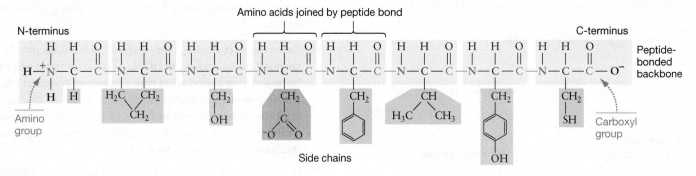

(b) Numbering system

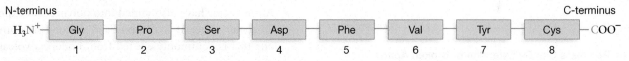

FIGURE 3.6 **Amino Acids Polymerize to Form Chains.**

FIGURE 3.6a shows how the chain of peptide bonds in a short polymer gives the molecule a structural framework, or a "backbone." There are three key points to note about the peptide-bonded backbone:

1. **R-group orientation** The side chains present in each residue extend out from the backbone, making it possible for them to interact with each other and with water.

2. **Directionality** There is an amino group (NH_3^+) on one end of the backbone and a carboxyl group (COO^-) on the other. The end of the sequence that has the free amino group is called the N-terminus, or amino-terminus, and the end with the free carboxyl group is called the C-terminus, or carboxy-terminus. By convention, biologists always write amino acid sequences

from the N-terminus to the C-terminus (**FIGURE 3.6b**), because the N-terminus is the start of the chain when proteins are synthesized in cells.

3. **Flexibility** Although the peptide bond itself cannot rotate because of its double-bond nature, the single bonds on either side of the peptide bond can rotate. As a result, the structure as a whole is flexible (**FIGURE 3.7**).

When fewer than 50 amino acids are linked together in this way, the resulting polymer is called an **oligopeptide** ("few peptides") or simply a **peptide.** Polymers that contain 50 or more amino acids are called **polypeptides** ("many peptides").

The term **protein** is often used to describe any chain of amino acid residues, but formally protein refers to the complete, often

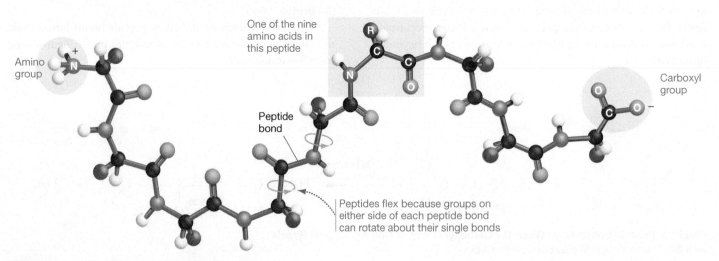

FIGURE 3.7 **Peptide Chains Are Flexible.**

functional form of the molecule. In Section 3.2, you'll see that some proteins consist of a single polypeptide while others are functional only when multiple polypeptides are bonded to one another.

Proteins are the stuff of life. Let's take a look at how they are put together and then see what they do.

check your understanding

If you understand that . . .

- Amino acids are small molecules with a central carbon atom bonded to a carboxyl group, an amino group, a hydrogen atom, and a side chain called an R-group.
- Each amino acid has distinctive chemical properties because each has a unique R-group.
- Proteins are polymers made up of amino acids.
- When the carboxyl group of one amino acid reacts with the amino group of another amino acid, a strong covalent bond called a peptide bond forms. Small chains are called oligopeptides; large chains are called polypeptides, or proteins.

✔ You should be able to . . .

Draw the structural formulas of two glycine residues (glycine's R-group is an H) linked by a peptide bond, and label the amino- and carboxy-terminus.

Answers are available in Appendix A.

3.2 What Do Proteins Look Like?

The unparalleled diversity of proteins—in size, shape, and other aspects of structure—is important because function follows from structure. Proteins can serve diverse functions in cells because they are diverse in size and shape as well as in the chemical properties of their amino acid residues.

FIGURE 3.8 illustrates some of the variety in the sizes and shapes observed in proteins. In the case of the TATA box–binding protein in **FIGURE 3.8a** and the porin protein in **FIGURE 3.8b**, the shape of the molecule has a clear correlation with its function. The TATA box–binding protein has a groove where DNA molecules fit; porin has a hole that forms a pore. The groove in the TATA box–binding protein interacts with specific regions of a DNA molecule, while porin fits in cell membranes and allows certain hydrophilic molecules to pass through. Proteins that provide structural support for cells or tissues, such as the collagen triple helix in **FIGURE 3.8d**, often form long, cable-like fibers.

But many of the proteins found in cells do not have shapes that are noticeably correlated with their functions. For example, the trypsin protein in **FIGURE 3.8c** has an overall globular shape that tells little about its function, which is to bind and cleave peptide bonds of other proteins.

How can biologists make sense of this diversity of protein size and shape? Initially, the amount of variation seems overwhelming. Fortunately, it is not. No matter how large or complex a protein may be, its underlying structure can be broken down into just four basic levels of organization.

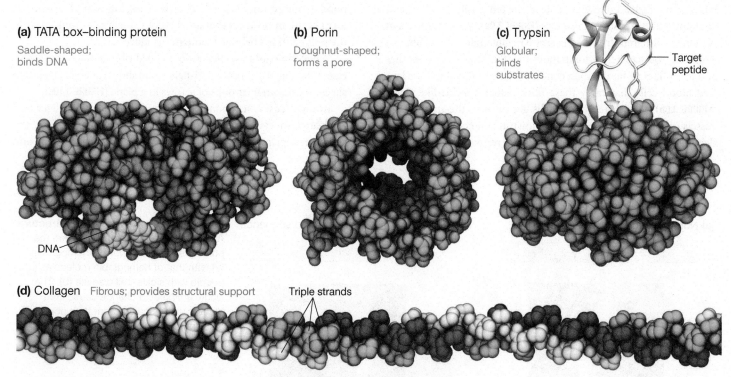

(a) TATA box–binding protein
Saddle-shaped; binds DNA

DNA

(b) Porin
Doughnut-shaped; forms a pore

(c) Trypsin
Globular; binds substrates

Target peptide

(d) Collagen   Fibrous; provides structural support

Triple strands

FIGURE 3.8 In Overall Shape, Proteins Are the Most Diverse Class of Molecules Known.

Primary Structure

Each protein has a unique sequence of amino acids. That simple conclusion was the culmination of 12 years of study by Frederick Sanger and co-workers during the 1940s and 1950s. Sanger's group worked out the first techniques for determining the amino acid sequence of insulin, a hormone that helps regulate sugar concentrations in the blood of humans and other mammals. When other proteins were analyzed, it rapidly became clear that each protein has a definite and distinct amino acid sequence.

Biochemists call the unique sequence of amino acids in a protein the **primary structure** of that protein. The sequence of amino acid residues in Figure 3.6, for example, defines the peptide's primary structure.

With 20 types of amino acids available and length ranging from two amino acid residues to tens of thousands, the number of primary structures that are possible is practically limitless. There may, in fact, be 20^n different combinations of amino acid residues for a polymer with a given length of n. For example, a peptide that is just 10 amino acids long has 20^{10} possible sequences. This is over 10,000 billion.

Why is the order and type of residues in the primary structure of a protein important? Recall that the R-groups present on each amino acid affect its chemical reactivity and solubility. It's therefore reasonable to predict that the R-groups present in a polypeptide will affect that molecule's properties and function.

This prediction is correct. In some cases, even a single change in the sequence of amino acids can cause radical changes in the way the protein as a whole behaves.

As an example, consider hemoglobin, an oxygen-binding protein in human red blood cells. In some individuals, hemoglobin has a valine instead of a glutamate at the 6th position of a strand containing 146 amino acid residues (**FIGURE 3.9a**). Valine's side chain is radically different from the R-group in glutamate. The change in R-group produces hemoglobin molecules that stick to one another and form fibers when oxygen concentrations in the blood are low. Red blood cells that carry these fibers adopt a sickle-like shape (**FIGURE 3.9b**). Sickled red blood cells get stuck in the small blood vessels called capillaries and starve downstream cells of oxygen. A debilitating illness called sickle-cell disease results.

A protein's primary structure is fundamental to its function. Primary structure is also fundamental to the higher levels of protein structure: secondary, tertiary, and quaternary.

Secondary Structure

Even though variation in the amino acid sequence of a protein is virtually limitless, it is only the tip of the iceberg in terms of generating structural diversity.

The next level of organization in proteins—**secondary structure**—is created in part by hydrogen bonding between components of the peptide-bonded backbone. Secondary structures are distinctively shaped sections of proteins that are stabilized largely by hydrogen bonding that occurs between the oxygen on the C=O group of one amino acid residue and the hydrogen on the N—H groups of another (**FIGURE 3.10a**). The oxygen atom in the C=O group has a partial negative charge due to its high electronegativity, while the hydrogen atom in the N—H group has a partial positive charge because it is bonded to nitrogen, which has high electronegativity.

Note a key point: Hydrogen bonding between sections of the same backbone is possible only when a polypeptide bends in a way that puts C=O and N—H groups close together. In most proteins, these polar groups are aligned and form hydrogen bonds with one another when the backbone bends to form one of two possible structures (**FIGURE 3.10b**):

1. an ☒-**helix** (alpha-helix), in which the polypeptide's backbone is coiled; or

2. a ☒-**pleated sheet** (beta-pleated sheet), in which segments of a peptide chain bend 180° and then fold in the same plane.

In both structures, the distance between residues that hydrogen-bond to one another is small. In an ☒-helix, for example, H-bonds form between residues that are just four linear positions apart in the polypeptide's primary sequence (Figure 3.10a).

When biologists use illustrations called ribbon diagrams to represent the shape of a protein, ☒-helices are shown as coils; ☒-pleated sheets are shown by groups of arrows in a plane (**FIGURE 3.10c**).

In most cases, secondary structure consists of ☒-helices and ☒-pleated sheets. Which one forms, if either, depends on the molecule's primary structure—specifically, the geometry and

(a) Normal amino acid sequence

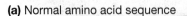

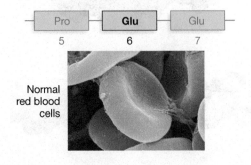

Normal red blood cells

(b) Single change in amino acid sequence

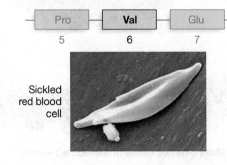

Sickled red blood cell

FIGURE 3.9 Changes in Primary Structure Affect Protein Function. Compare the primary structure of normal hemoglobin **(a)** with that of hemoglobin molecules in people with sickle-cell disease **(b)**. The single amino acid change causes red blood cells to change from their normal disc shape in (a) to a sickled shape in (b) when oxygen concentrations are low.

properties of the amino acids in the sequence. Certain amino acids are more likely to be involved in α-helices than in β-pleated sheets, and vice versa, due to the specific geometry of their side chains. Proline, for example, may be present in β-pleated sheets,

(a) Hydrogen bonds can form between nearby amino and carbonyl groups on the same polypeptide chain.

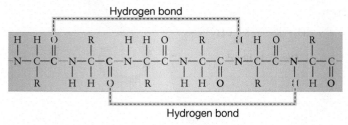

(b) Secondary structures of proteins result.

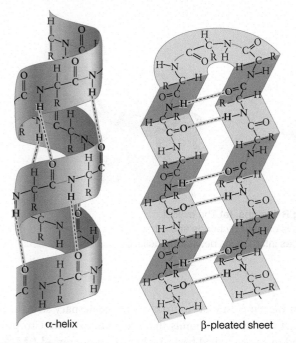

α-helix   β-pleated sheet

(c) Ribbon diagrams of secondary structure

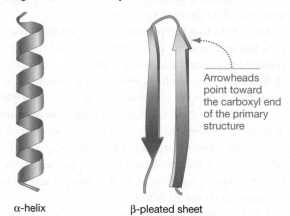

Arrowheads point toward the carboxyl end of the primary structure

α-helix   β-pleated sheet

FIGURE 3.10 Secondary Structures of Proteins. A polypeptide chain can coil or fold in on itself when hydrogen bonds form between N—H and C=O groups on its peptide-bonded backbone.

but it will terminate α-helices due to its unusual side chain. The bond formed between proline's R-group and the nitrogen of the core amino group introduces kinks in the backbone that do not conform to the shape of the helix.

Although each of the hydrogen bonds in an α-helix or a β-pleated sheet is weak relative to a covalent bond, the large number of hydrogen bonds in these structures makes them highly stable. As a result, they increase the stability of the molecule as a whole and help define its shape. In terms of overall shape and stability, though, the tertiary structure of a protein is even more important.

Tertiary Structure

Most of the overall shape, or **tertiary structure,** of a polypeptide results from interactions between R-groups or between R-groups and the backbone. In contrast to the secondary structures, where hydrogen bonds link backbone components together, these side chains can be involved in a wide variety of bonds and interactions. In addition, the amino acid residues that interact with one another are often far apart in the linear sequence. Because each contact between R-groups causes the peptide-bonded backbone to bend and fold, each contributes to the distinctive three-dimensional shape of a polypeptide.

Five types of interactions involving side chains are particularly important:

1. *Hydrogen bonding* Hydrogen bonds form between polar R-groups and opposite partial charges either in the peptide backbone or other R-groups.

2. *Hydrophobic interactions* In an aqueous solution, water molecules interact with the hydrophilic polar side chains of a polypeptide and force the hydrophobic nonpolar side chains to coalesce into globular masses. When these nonpolar R-groups come together, the surrounding water molecules form more hydrogen bonds with each other, increasing the stability of their own interactions.

3. *van der Waals interactions* Once hydrophobic side chains are close to one another, their association is further stabilized by electrical attractions known as **van der Waals interactions.** These weak attractions occur because the constant motion of electrons gives molecules a tiny asymmetry in charge that changes with time. If nonpolar molecules get extremely close to each other, the minute partial charge on one molecule induces an opposite partial charge in the nearby molecule and causes an attraction. Although the interaction is very weak relative to covalent bonds or even hydrogen bonds, a large number of van der Waals attractions can significantly increase the stability of the structure.

4. *Covalent bonding* Covalent bonds can form between the side chains of two cysteines through a reaction between the sulfhydryl groups. These **disulfide ("two-sulfur") bonds** are frequently referred to as bridges, because they create strong links between distinct regions of the same polypeptide or two separate polypeptides.

(a) Interactions that determine the tertiary structure of proteins

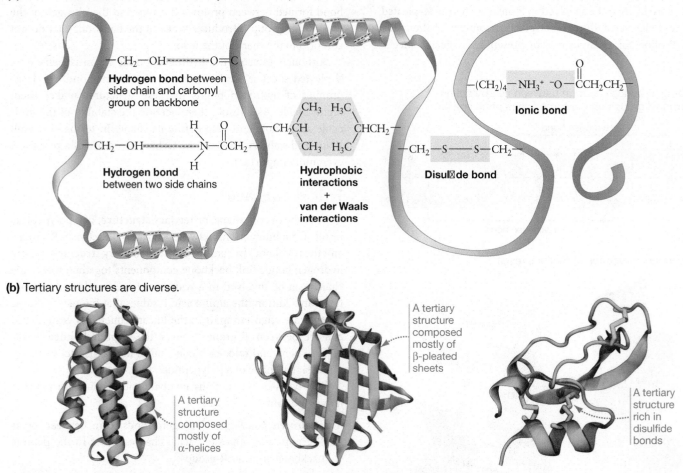

Hydrogen bond between side chain and carbonyl group on backbone

Hydrogen bond between two side chains

Hydrophobic interactions + van der Waals interactions

Ionic bond

Disulfide bond

(b) Tertiary structures are diverse.

A tertiary structure composed mostly of α-helices

A tertiary structure composed mostly of β-pleated sheets

A tertiary structure rich in disulfide bonds

FIGURE 3.11 Tertiary Structure of Proteins Results from Interactions Involving R-Groups. (a) The overall shape of a single polypeptide is called its tertiary structure. This level of structure is created by bonds and other interactions that cause it to fold. **(b)** The tertiary structure of these proteins includes interactions between ⊠-helices and ⊠-pleated sheets.

5. *Ionic bonding*   Ionic bonds form between groups that have full and opposing charges, such as the ionized acidic and basic side chains highlighted on the right in **FIGURE 3.11a**.

In addition, the overall shape of many proteins depends in part on the presence of secondary structures like ⊠-helices and ⊠-pleated sheets. Thus, tertiary structure depends on both primary and secondary structures.

With so many interactions possible between side chains and peptide-bonded backbones, it's not surprising that polypeptides vary in shape from rod-like filaments to ball-like masses. (See **FIGURE 3.11b**, and look again at Figure 3.8.)

Quaternary Structure

The first three levels of protein structure involve individual polypeptides. But some proteins contain multiple polypeptides that interact to form a single structure. The combination of polypeptides, referred to as subunits, gives a protein **quaternary structure.** The individual polypeptides are held together by the same types of bonds and interactions found in the tertiary level of structure.

In the simplest case, a protein with quaternary structure can consist of just two subunits that are identical. The Cro protein found in a virus called bacteriophage λ (pronounced *LAMB-da*) is an example (**FIGURE 3.12a**). Proteins with two polypeptide subunits are called dimers ("two-parts").

More than two polypeptides can be linked into a single protein, however, and the polypeptides involved may be distinct in primary, secondary, and tertiary structure. For example hemoglobin, an oxygen-binding protein, is a tetramer ("four-parts"). It consists of two copies of two different polypeptides (**FIGURE 3.12b**).

In addition, cells contain **macromolecular machines:** groups of multiple proteins that assemble to carry out a particular function. Some proteins are also found in complexes that include other types of macromolecules. The ribosome (introduced in Chapter 7) provides an example; it consists of several nucleic acid molecules and over 50 different proteins.

TABLE 3.1 summarizes the four levels of protein structure, using hemoglobin as an example. The key thing to note is that protein structure is hierarchical. Quaternary structure is based on tertiary structure, which is based in part on secondary

(a) Cro protein, a dimer

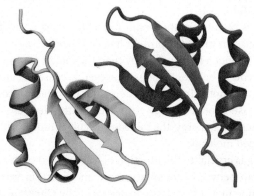

(b) Hemoglobin, a tetramer

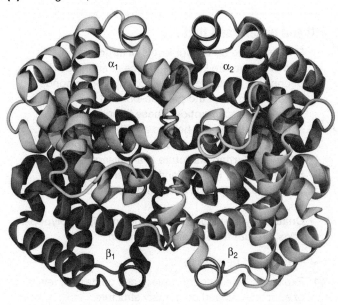

FIGURE 3.12 Quaternary Structures of Proteins Are Created by Multiple Polypeptides. These diagrams represent primary sequences as ribbons. **(a)** The Cro protein is a dimer—it consists of two polypeptide subunits, colored light and dark green. The subunits are identical in this case. **(b)** Hemoglobin is a tetramer—it consists of four polypeptide subunits. The ⍺ subunits (light and dark green) are identical; so are the β subunits (light and dark blue).

structure. All three of the higher-level structures are based on primary structure.

The summary table and preceding discussion convey three important messages:

1. The combination of primary, secondary, tertiary, and quaternary levels of structure is responsible for the fantastic diversity of sizes and shapes observed in proteins.

2. Protein folding is directed by the sequence of amino acids present in the primary structure.

3. Most elements of protein structure are based on folding of polypeptide chains.

Does protein folding occur spontaneously? What happens to the function of a protein if normal folding is disrupted? Let's use these questions as a guide to dig deeper into how proteins fold.

SUMMARY TABLE 3.1 Protein Structure

Level	Description	Stabilized by	Example: Hemoglobin	
Primary	The sequence of amino acids in a polypeptide	Peptide bonds	Gly — Ser — Asp — Cys	
Secondary	Formation of ⍺-helices and β-pleated sheets in a polypeptide	Hydrogen bonding between groups along the peptide-bonded backbone; thus, depends on primary structure		One ⍺-helix
Tertiary	Overall three-dimensional shape of a polypeptide (includes contribution from secondary structures)	Bonds and other interactions between R-groups, or between R-groups and the peptide-bonded backbone; thus, depends on primary structure		One of hemoglobin's subunits
Quaternary	Shape produced by combinations of polypeptides (thus, combinations of tertiary structures)	Bonds and other interactions between R-groups, and between peptide backbones of different polypeptides; thus, depends on primary structure		Hemoglobin consists of four polypeptide subunits

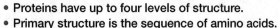

check your understanding

If you understand that . . .

- Proteins have up to four levels of structure.
- Primary structure is the sequence of amino acids.
- Secondary structure results from hydrogen bonds between atoms in the peptide-bonded backbone of the same polypeptide. These bonds produce structures such as ⊠-helices and ⊠-pleated sheets.
- Tertiary structure is the overall shape of a polypeptide. Most tertiary structure is a consequence of bonds or other interactions between R-groups or between R-groups and the peptide-bonded backbone.
- Quaternary structure occurs when multiple polypeptides interact to form a single protein.

✔ **You should be able to . . .**

1. Explain how secondary, tertiary, and quaternary levels of structure depend on primary structure.

2. **QUANTITATIVE** Calculate the number of different primary sequences that could be generated by randomly assembling amino acids into peptides that are five residues long.

Answers are available in Appendix A.

3.3 Folding and Function

If you were able to synthesize one of the polypeptides in hemoglobin from individual amino acids, and you then placed the resulting chain in an aqueous solution, it would

spontaneously fold into the shape of the tertiary structure shown in Table 3.1.

In terms of entropy, this result probably seems counterintuitive. Because an unfolded protein has many more ways to move about, it has much higher entropy than the folded version. Folding *does* tend to be spontaneous, however, because the chemical bonds, hydrophobic interactions, and van der Waals forces that occur release enough energy to overcome the decrease in entropy. In terms of energy, the folded molecule is more stable than the unfolded molecule.

Folding is crucial to the function of a completed protein. This relationship between protein structure and function was hammered home in a set of classic experiments by Christian Anfinsen and colleagues during the 1950s.

Normal Folding Is Crucial to Function

Anfinsen studied a protein called ribonuclease that is found in many organisms. Ribonuclease is an enzyme that cleaves ribonucleic acid polymers. Anfinsen found that ribonuclease could be unfolded, or **denatured,** by treating it with compounds that break hydrogen bonds and disulfide bonds. The denatured ribonuclease was unable to function normally—it could no longer break apart nucleic acids (**FIGURE 3.13**).

When the denaturing agents were removed, however, the molecule refolded and began to function normally again. These experiments confirmed that ribonuclease folds spontaneously and that folding is essential for normal function.

More recent work has shown that in cells, folding is often facilitated by specific proteins called **molecular chaperones.** Many molecular chaperones belong to a family of molecules called the heat-shock proteins. Heat-shock proteins are produced in large quantities after cells experience high temperatures or other

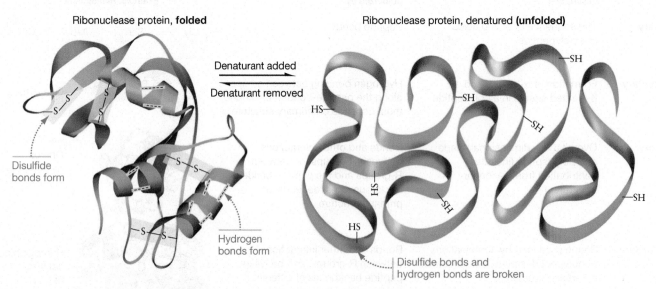

FIGURE 3.13 Protein Structure Determines Function. (left) Ribonuclease is functional when properly folded via hydrogen and disulfide bonds. **(right)** When the disulfide and various noncovalent bonds are broken, ribonuclease is no longer able to function. The double arrow indicates that this process is reversible.

treatments that make other proteins lose their tertiary structure. Heat-shock proteins recognize denatured proteins by binding to hydrophobic patches that would not normally be exposed in properly folded proteins. This interaction blocks inappropriate interactions with other molecules and allows the proteins to refold.

So what is the "normal shape" of a protein? Is only one shape possible for each protein, or could there be several different folded shapes with only one serving as the functional form?

Protein Shape Is Flexible

Although each protein has a characteristic folded shape that is necessary for its function, most proteins are flexible and dynamic, not rigid and static. As it turns out, many polypeptides are unable to fold into their active shape on their own. Over half of the proteins that have been analyzed to date have been found to contain disordered regions lacking any apparent structure. These proteins exist in an assortment of shapes. Only when they interact with particular ions or molecules, or are chemically modified, will they adopt the shape, or conformation, that allows them to perform their function in the cell.

Protein Folding Is Often Regulated   Since the function of a protein is dependent on its shape, controlling when or where it is folded will regulate the protein's activity.

For example, proteins involved in cell signaling are often regulated by controlling their shape. The inactive form of calmodulin—a protein that helps maintain normal blood pressure—has a disordered shape. When the concentration of calcium ions increases in the cell, calmodulin binds these ions, folds into an ordered, active conformation, and sends a signal to increase the diameter of blood vessels. **FIGURE 3.14** illustrates the major shape change that is induced in calmodulin when it binds to calcium.

Misfolding Can Be "Infectious"   In 1982, Stanley Prusiner published what may be the most surprising result to emerge from research on protein folding: Certain proteins can be folded into infectious, disease-causing agents. These proteins are called **prions** (pronounced *PREE-ons*), or proteinaceous infectious particles.

Infectious prions are alternate forms of normal proteins that are present in healthy individuals. The infectious and normal forms do not necessarily differ in amino acid sequence, but their *shapes* are radically different. The infectious form propagates by inducing conformational changes in normal proteins that cause them to adopt the alternate, infectious shape.

FIGURE 3.15 illustrates the differences in shape observed between the normal and infectious forms of the prion responsible for "mad cow disease" in cattle. The molecule in Figure 3.15a is called the prion protein (PrP) and is a normal component of mammalian cells. The improperly folded version of this protein, like the one in Figure 3.15b, represents the infectious form of the prion.

Prions cause a family of diseases known as the spongiform encephalopathies—literally, "sponge-brain-illnesses." Sheep, cows, goats, and humans afflicted with these diseases undergo massive degeneration of the brain. Although some spongiform encephalopathies

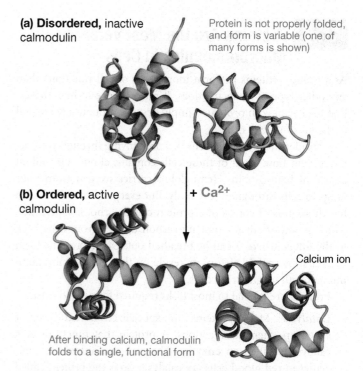

(a) Disordered, inactive calmodulin

Protein is not properly folded, and form is variable (one of many forms is shown)

(b) Ordered, active calmodulin

+ Ca²⁺

Calcium ion

After binding calcium, calmodulin folds to a single, functional form

FIGURE 3.14 Calmodulin Requires Calcium to Fold Properly. Many proteins, like calmodulin, do not complete their folding until after interacting with ions or other molecules. Once calmodulin binds to calcium, it assumes its functional shape.

can be inherited, in many cases the disease is transmitted when individuals eat tissues containing the infectious form of PrP. All the prion illnesses are fatal.

Prions are a particularly dramatic example of how a protein's function depends on its shape as well as how the final shape of a protein depends on folding.

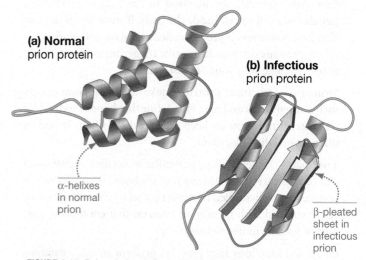

(a) Normal prion protein

(b) Infectious prion protein

α-helixes in normal prion

β-pleated sheet in infectious prion

FIGURE 3.15 Prion Infectivity Is Linked to Structure. Ribbon model of **(a)** a normal, noninfectious prion protein; and **(b)** the infectious form that causes mad cow disease in cattle. Secondary structure is represented by coils (⊠-helices) and arrows (⊠-pleated sheets).

3.4 Proteins Are the Most Versatile Macromolecules in Cells

As a group, proteins perform more types of cell functions than any other type of molecule does. It makes sense to hypothesize that life began with proteins, simply because proteins are so vital to the life of today's cells.

Consider the red blood cells that are moving through your arteries right now. Each of these cells contains about 300 million copies of hemoglobin. Hemoglobin carries oxygen from your lungs to cells throughout the body. But every red blood cell also has thousands of copies of a protein called carbonic anhydrase, which is important for moving carbon dioxide from cells back to the lungs, where it can be breathed out. Other proteins form the cell's internal "skeleton" or reside on the cell's membrane to interact with neighboring cells.

Proteins are crucial to most tasks required for cells to exist:

- *Catalysis* Many proteins are specialized to **catalyze,** or speed up, chemical reactions. A protein that functions as a catalyst is called an **enzyme.** The carbonic anhydrase molecules in red blood cells are catalysts. So is the protein called salivary amylase, found in your mouth. Salivary amylase helps begin the digestion of starch and other complex carbohydrates into simple sugars. Most chemical reactions that make life possible depend on enzymes.

- *Defense* Proteins called antibodies and complement proteins attack and destroy viruses and bacteria that cause disease.

- *Movement* Motor proteins and contractile proteins are responsible for moving the cell itself, or for moving large molecules and other types of cargo inside the cell. As you turn this page, for example, specialized proteins called actin and myosin will slide past one another to flex or extend muscle cells in your fingers and arm.

- *Signaling* Proteins are involved in carrying and receiving signals from cell to cell inside the body. If sugar levels in your blood are low, a small protein called glucagon will bind to receptor proteins on your liver cells, triggering enzymes inside to release sugar into your bloodstream.

- *Structure* Structural proteins make up body components such as fingernails and hair, and define the shape of individual cells. Structural proteins keep red blood cells flexible and in their normal disc-like shape.

- *Transport* Proteins allow particular molecules to enter and exit cells or carry them throughout the body. Hemoglobin is a particularly well-studied transport protein, but virtually every cell is studded with membrane proteins that control the passage of specific molecules and ions.

Of all the functions that proteins perform in cells, catalysis may be the most important. The reason is speed. Life, at its most basic level, consists of chemical reactions. But most don't occur fast enough to support life unless a catalyst is present. Enzymes are the most effective catalysts on Earth. Why is this so?

Why Are Enzymes Good Catalysts?

Part of the reason enzymes are such effective catalysts is that they bring reactant molecules—called **substrates**—together in a precise orientation so the atoms involved in the reaction can interact.

The initial hypothesis for how enzymes work was proposed by Emil Fischer in 1894. According to Fischer's "lock-and-key" model, enzymes are analogous to a lock and the keys are substrates that fit into the lock and then react.

Several important ideas in this model have stood the test of time. For example, Fischer was correct in proposing that enzymes bring substrates together in a precise orientation that makes reactions more likely. His model also accurately explained why most enzymes catalyze one specific reaction effectively. Enzyme specificity is a product of the geometry and types of functional groups in the sites where substrates bind.

As researchers began to test Fischer's model, the location where substrates bind and react became known as the enzyme's **active site.** The active site is where catalysis actually occurs.

When techniques for solving the three-dimensional structure of enzymes became available, the active sites were identified as clefts or cavities within the globular shapes. The digestive enzyme trypsin, which is at work in your body now, is a good example. As **FIGURE 3.16** shows, the active site in trypsin is a small notch that contains three key amino acid residues with functional groups that catalyze the cleavage of peptide bonds in other proteins. No other class of macromolecule can match proteins for their catalytic potential. The variety of reactive functional groups present in amino acids is much better suited for this activity than those found in nucleotides or sugars.

The role of enzymes in catalyzing reactions is discussed in more detail in the next unit (see Chapter 8). There you will see that Fischer's model had to be modified as research on enzyme action progressed.

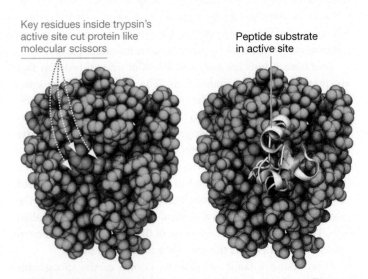

Key residues inside trypsin's active site cut protein like molecular scissors

Peptide substrate in active site

FIGURE 3.16 Substrates Bind to a Specific Location in an Enzyme Called the Active Site. The active site in trypsin, as in many enzymes, is a cleft that contains key amino acid residues that bind substrates and catalyze a reaction.

Was the First Living Entity a Protein Catalyst?

Several observations in the preceding sections could argue that a protein was the first molecule capable of replication. Experimental studies have shown that amino acids were likely abundant during chemical evolution, and that they could have polymerized to form small proteins. In addition, proteins are the most efficient catalysts known.

To date, however, attempts to simulate the origin of life with proteins have not been successful. The only experimental glimpse of a protein's potential to replicate involved an enzyme that could link two oligopeptides together to form a functional duplicate of itself. However, this result required a high concentration of preformed, specific oligopeptides that would not have been present during chemical evolution.

Although it is too early to arrive at definitive conclusions, most origin-of-life researchers are increasingly skeptical that life began with a protein. Their reasoning is that to make a copy of something, a mold or template is required. Proteins cannot furnish this information. Nucleic acids, in contrast, *can*. How they do so is the subject of the next chapter.

If you understand that . . .

- Proteins are the most versatile large molecules in cells, and each function is directly connected to structure.
- Enzymes speed up chemical reactions by binding substrates at their active site, where catalysis takes place.

✔ You should be able to . . .

Predict where amino acid changes would most likely occur in an enzyme that would result in it catalyzing a reaction with a new substrate, and explain how these changes could result in the new activity.

Answers are available in Appendix A.

CHAPTER 3 REVIEW

For media, go to MasteringBiology

If you understand . . .

3.1 Amino Acids and Their Polymerization

- Amino acids have a central carbon bonded to an amino group, a hydrogen atom, a carboxyl group, and an R-group.

- The structure of the R-group affects the chemical reactivity and solubility of the amino acid.

- In proteins, amino acids are joined by a peptide bond between the carboxyl group of one amino acid and the amino group of another amino acid.

✔ You should be able to explain how you could use the structural formula of an amino acid to determine if it is acidic, basic, uncharged polar, or nonpolar.

3.2 What Do Proteins Look Like?

- A protein's primary structure, or sequence of amino acids, is responsible for most of its chemical properties.

- Interactions that take place between C=O and N–H groups in the same peptide-bonded backbone create secondary structures, which are stabilized primarily by hydrogen bonding.

- Tertiary structure results from interactions between R-groups—or R-groups and the peptide-bonded backbone—that stabilize a folded protein into a characteristic overall shape.

- In many cases, a complete protein consists of several different polypeptides, bonded together. The combination of polypeptides represents the protein's quaternary structure.

✔ You should be able to predict where nonpolar amino acid residues would be found in a globular protein, such as the trypsin molecule shown in Figure 3.8c.

3.3 Folding and Function

- Protein folding is a spontaneous process.

- A protein's normal folded shape is essential to its function.

- Many proteins must first bind to other molecules or ions before they can adopt their active conformation.

- Improperly folded proteins can be detrimental to life, and certain proteins even cause deadly infectious diseases.

✔ You should be able to identify one way in which the process of folding in calmodulin and infectious prions is similar.

3.4 Proteins Are the Most Versatile Macromolecules in Cells

- In organisms, proteins function in catalysis, defense, movement, signaling, structural support, and transport of materials.

- Proteins can have diverse functions in cells because they have such diverse structures and chemical properties.

- Catalysis takes place at the enzyme's active site, which has unique chemical properties and a distinctive size and shape.

✔ You should be able to provide the characteristics of proteins that make them especially useful for the following cellular activities: catalysis, defense, and signaling.

1. **MasteringBiology Assignments**

   Tutorials and Activities Activation Energy and Enzymes; Amino Acid Functional Groups; Condensation and Hydrolysis Reactions; Enzyme and Substrate Concentrations; Enzyme Inhibition; Factors That Affect Reaction Rate; How Enzymes Function; How Enzymes Work; Levels of Structure in Proteins; Making and Breaking Polymers; Protein Functions, Protein Structure; Regulating Enzyme Action

   Questions Reading Quizzes, Blue-Thread Questions, Test Bank

2. **eText** Read your book online, search, take notes, highlight text, and more.

3. **The Study Area** Practice Test, Cumulative Test, BioFlix® 3-D Animations, Videos, Activities, Audio Glossary, Word Study Tools, Art

You should be able to . . .

✓ TEST YOUR KNOWLEDGE
Answers are available in Appendix A

1. What two functional groups are present on every amino acid?
   a. a carbonyl (C=O) group and a carboxyl group
   b. an N–H group and a carbonyl group
   c. an amino group and a hydroxyl group
   d. an amino group and a carboxyl group

2. Twenty different amino acids are found in the proteins of cells. What distinguishes these molecules?

3. By convention, biologists write the sequence of amino acids in a polypeptide in which direction?
   a. carboxy- to amino-terminus
   b. amino- to carboxy-terminus
   c. polar residues to nonpolar residues
   d. charged residues to uncharged residues

4. In a polypeptide, what bonds are responsible for the secondary structure called an ⊠-helix?

   a. peptide bonds
   b. hydrogen bonds that form between the core C=O and N–H groups on different residues
   c. hydrogen bonds and other interactions between side chains
   d. disulfide bonds that form between cysteine residues

5. Where is the information stored that directs different polypeptides to fold into different shapes?

6. What is an active site?
   a. the position in an enzyme where substrates bind
   b. the place where a molecule or ion binds to a protein to induce a shape change
   c. the portion of a motor protein that is involved in moving cargo in a cell
   d. the site on an antibody where it binds to bacterial cells or viruses

✓ TEST YOUR UNDERSTANDING
Answers are available in Appendix A

7. Explain how water participates in the development of the interactions that glue nonpolar amino acids together in the interior of globular proteins.

8. If amino acids were mixed together in a solution, resembling the prebiotic soup, would they spontaneously polymerize into polypeptides? Why or why not?

9. Provide an example of how a specific shape of a protein is correlated with its function.

10. A major theme in this chapter is that the structure of molecules correlates with their function. Use this theme to explain why proteins can perform so many different functions in organisms and why enzymes are such effective catalysts.

11. Why are proteins not considered to be a good candidate for the first living molecule?
    a. Their catalytic capability is insufficient.
    b. Their amino acid monomers were likely not present during chemical evolution.
    c. They cannot serve as a template for replication.
    d. They could not have polymerized on their own from amino acids during chemical evolution.

12. If proteins folded only into rigid, inflexible structures, how might this affect the cell's ability to regulate protein function?

✓ TEST YOUR PROBLEM-SOLVING SKILLS
Answers are available in Appendix A

13. Based on what you know of the peptide bonds that link together amino acid residues, why would proline's side chain reduce the flexibility of the backbone?

14. Make a concept map (see **BioSkills 15** in Appendix B) that relates the four levels of protein structure and shows how they can contribute to the formation of an active site. Your map should include the following boxed terms: Primary structure, Secondary structure, Tertiary structure, Quaternary structure, Active site, Amino acid sequence, R-groups, Helices and sheets, 3-D shape.

15. Proteins that interact with DNA often interact with the phosphates that are part of this molecule. Which of the following types of

amino acids would you predict to be present in the DNA binding sites of these proteins?
    a. acidic amino acids
    b. basic amino acids
    c. uncharged polar amino acids
    d. nonpolar amino acids

16. Some prion-associated diseases are inherited, such as fatal familial insomnia. What is likely to be different between the infectious forms of these inherited prions compared to those that arise via transmission from one animal to another?

4 Nucleic Acids and the RNA World

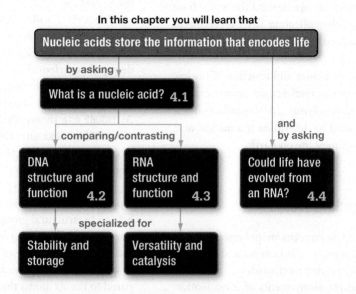

In this chapter you will learn that

Nucleic acids store the information that encodes life

by asking ↓

What is a nucleic acid? 4.1

comparing/contrasting

DNA structure and function 4.2

RNA structure and function 4.3

and by asking

Could life have evolved from an RNA? 4.4

specialized for

Stability and storage

Versatility and catalysis

This is part of the sheet-metal-and-wire model that James Watson and Francis Crick used to figure out the secondary structure of DNA. The large "T" stands for the nitrogen-containing base thymine.

This chapter is part of the Big Picture. See how on pages 104–105.

ife began when chemical evolution led to the production of a molecule that could promote its own replication. The nature of this first "living molecule," however, has been the subject of many investigations and heated debates. Even though proteins are the workhorse molecules of today's cells, relatively few researchers favor the hypothesis that life began as a protein molecule. Instead, the vast majority of biologists contend that life began as a polymer called a nucleic acid—specifically, a molecule of ribonucleic acid (RNA). This proposal is called the **RNA world hypothesis.**

The RNA world hypothesis contends that chemical evolution led to the existence of an RNA molecule that could replicate itself. Once this molecule existed, chance errors in the copying process

✔ When you see this checkmark, stop and test yourself. Answers are available in Appendix A.

created variations that would undergo natural selection—the evolutionary process by which individuals with certain attributes are selectively reproduced (see Chapter 1). At this point, chemical evolution was over and biological evolution was off and running.

To test this hypothesis, several groups around the world have been working to synthesize a self-replicating RNA molecule in the laboratory. If they ever succeed, they will have created a life-form in a test tube.

This chapter focuses on the structure and function of nucleic acids. Let's begin with an analysis of nucleic acid monomers and how they are linked together into polymers. Afterwards, you will learn about the experiments used to determine if a nucleic acid could have triggered the evolution of life on Earth.

4.1 What Is a Nucleic Acid?

Nucleic acids are polymers, just as proteins are polymers. But instead of being made up of monomers called amino acids, **nucleic acids** are made up of monomers called **nucleotides.**

FIGURE 4.1a diagrams the three components of a nucleotide: **(1)** a phosphate group, **(2)** a five-carbon sugar, and **(3)** a nitrogenous (nitrogen-containing) base. The phosphate is bonded to the sugar molecule, which in turn is bonded to the nitrogenous base.

The sugar component of a nucleotide is an organic compound bearing reactive hydroxyl (−OH) functional groups. Notice that the prime symbols (′) in Figure 4.1 indicate that the carbon being referred to is part of the sugar—not of the attached nitrogenous base. The phosphate group in a nucleotide is attached to the 5′ carbon.

Although a wide variety of nucleotides are found in living cells, origin-of-life researchers concentrate on two types: **ribonucleotides,** the monomers of **ribonucleic acid** (**RNA**), and **deoxyribonucleotides,** the monomers of **deoxyribonucleic acid** (**DNA**). In ribonucleotides, the sugar is ribose; in deoxyribonucleotides, it is deoxyribose (*deoxy* means "lacking oxygen"). As **FIGURE 4.1b** shows, these two sugars differ by a single oxygen atom. Ribose has an −OH group bonded to the 2′ carbon. Deoxyribose has an H instead at the same location. In both of these sugars, an −OH group is bonded to the 3′ carbon.

In addition to the type of sugar, nucleotides also differ in the type of nitrogenous base. These bases, diagrammed in **FIGURE 4.1c**, belong to structural groups called **purines** and **pyrimidines.** The purines are adenine (A) and guanine (G); the pyrimidines are cytosine (C), uracil (U), and thymine (T). Note that the two rings in adenine and guanine are linked together by nine atoms, compared to the six atoms that make a single ring in each pyrimidine. This makes remembering which bases are purines easy, since both adenine and guanine include "nine" in their names.

As Figure 4.1c shows, ribonucleotides and deoxyribonucleotides also differ in one of their pyrimidine bases. Ribonucleotides

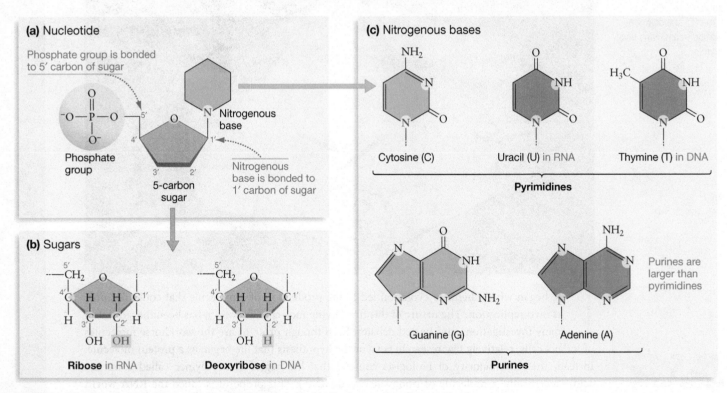

FIGURE 4.1 The General Structure of a Nucleotide. Note that in the bases, the nitrogen that bonds to the sugar is colored blue.

use uracil (U) while deoxyribonucleotides use the closely related base thymine (T).

✔ You should be able to diagram a ribonucleotide and a deoxyribonucleotide. Use a ball for the phosphate group, a pentagon to represent the sugar subunit, and a hexagon to represent the nitrogenous base. Label the 2′, 3′, and 5′ carbons on the sugar molecule, and add the atoms or groups that are bonded to each.

To summarize: After the different sugars and bases are taken into account, eight different nucleotides are used to build nucleic acids—four ribonucleotides (A, G, C, and U) and four deoxyribonucleotides (A, G, C, and T). If nucleic acids played any role in the chemical evolution of life, then at least some of these nucleotides must have been present in the prebiotic oceans. Is there any evidence to suggest that this was possible?

Could Chemical Evolution Result in the Production of Nucleotides?

Based on data from Stanley Miller and researchers who followed (Chapter 2), most biologists contend that amino acids could have been synthesized early in Earth's history. The reactions behind the prebiotic synthesis of nucleotides, however, have been more difficult to identify.

Miller-like laboratory simulations have shown that nitrogenous bases and many different types of sugars can be synthesized readily under conditions that mimic the prebiotic soup. In these experiments, almost all the sugars that have five or six carbons—called pentoses and hexoses, respectively—are produced in approximately equal amounts. If nucleic acids were to form in the prebiotic soup, however, ribose would have had to predominate.

How ribose came to be the dominant sugar during chemical evolution (i.e., what selective process was at work) is still a mystery. Origin-of-life researchers refer to this issue as the "ribose problem." Recent work focusing on the conditions that exist in deep-sea hydrothermal vent systems (see Chapter 2) may point to a possible solution.

Here's the line of reasoning researchers are currently pursuing: Ribose molecules may have been selectively enriched from the mix of sugars in certain early Earth deep-sea vent systems. In one experiment, researchers simulated the conditions that exist in these vents. Then they tested whether minerals that are predicted to have existed in the vent chimneys are able to bind sugars. What they found was striking—the minerals preferentially bound to ribose over other pentoses and hexoses. Did this occur in the ancient vents? If so, the implications are exciting: A high concentration of ribose would be present in the same deep-sea vent environment where chemical evolution is thought to have taken place.

Despite the observed synthesis of nitrogenous bases and the recent discovery of ribose enrichment, the production of nucleotides remains a serious challenge for the theory of chemical evolution. At this time, experiments that attempt to simulate early

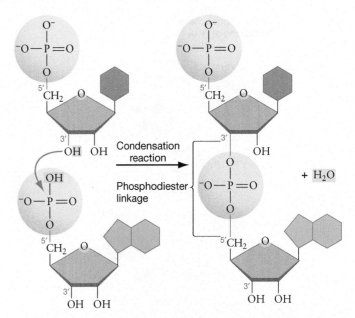

FIGURE 4.2 Nucleotides Polymerize via Phosphodiester Linkages. Ribonucleotides can polymerize via condensation reactions. The resulting phosphodiester linkage connects the 3′ carbon of one ribonucleotide and the 5′ carbon of another ribonucleotide.

Earth environments have yet to synthesize complete nucleotides. But research on this issue continues.

In the meantime, let's consider the next question: Once nucleotides formed, how would they polymerize to form RNA and DNA? This question has an answer.

How Do Nucleotides Polymerize to Form Nucleic Acids?

Nucleic acids form when nucleotides polymerize. As **FIGURE 4.2** shows, the polymerization reaction involves the formation of a bond between a hydroxyl on the sugar component of one nucleotide and the phosphate group of another nucleotide. The result of this condensation reaction is called a **phosphodiester linkage,** or a phosphodiester bond.

A phosphodiester linkage joins the 5′ carbon on the sugar of one nucleotide to the 3′ carbon on the sugar of another. When the nucleotides involved contain the sugar ribose, the polymer that is produced is RNA. If the nucleotides contain the sugar deoxyribose instead, then the resulting polymer is DNA.

DNA and RNA Strands Are Directional **FIGURE 4.3** (see page 60) shows how the chain of phosphodiester linkages in a nucleic acid acts as a backbone, analogous to the peptide-bonded backbone found in proteins.

Like the peptide-bonded backbone of a polypeptide, the sugar-phosphate backbone of a nucleic acid is directional. In a strand of RNA or DNA, one end has an unlinked 5′ phosphate while the other end has an unlinked 3′ hydroxyl—meaning the groups are not linked to another nucleotide. By convention, the

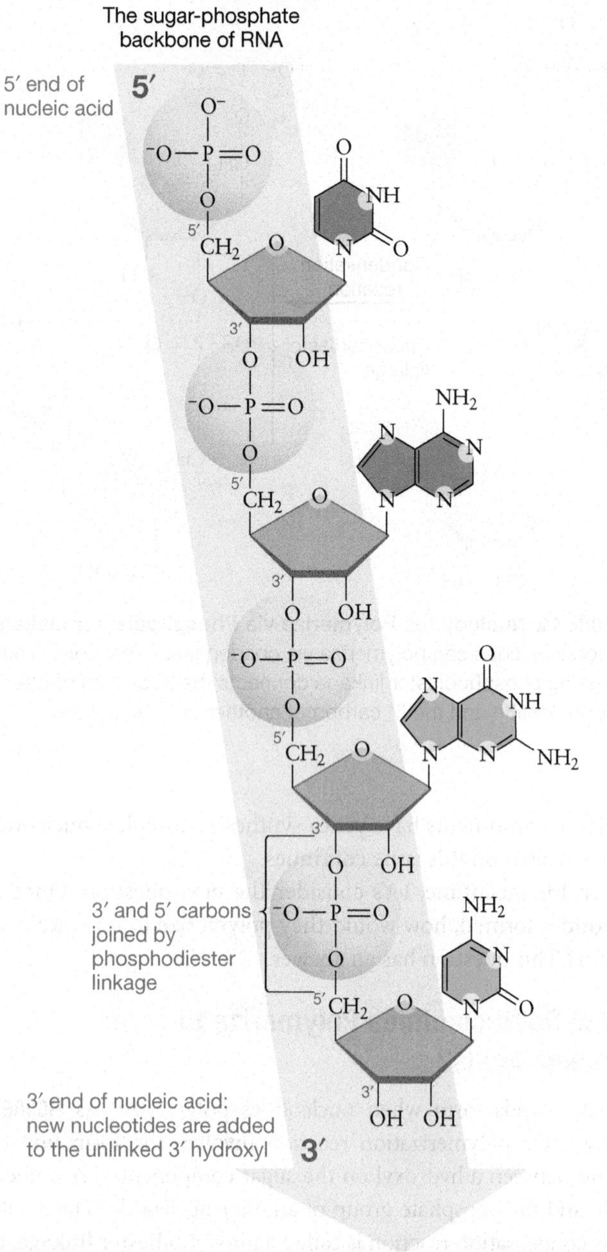

The sugar-phosphate
backbone of RNA

5' end of
nucleic acid

5'

5'

CH$_2$

3'

OH

5'

CH$_2$

3'

OH

5'

CH$_2$

3'

OH

3' and 5' carbons
joined by
phosphodiester
linkage

5'

CH$_2$

3' end of nucleic acid:
new nucleotides are added
to the unlinked 3' hydroxyl

3'

OH   OH

FIGURE 4.3 RNA Has a Sugar-Phosphate Backbone.

✔**EXERCISE** Identify the four bases in this RNA strand, using
Figure 4.1c as a key. Then write down the base sequence, starting
at the 5' end.

sequence of bases found in an RNA or DNA strand is always
written in the 5'→3' direction. (This system is logical because
in cells, RNA and DNA are always synthesized in this direction.
Bases are added only at the 3' end of the growing molecule.)

The order of the different nitrogenous bases in a nucleic acid
forms the primary structure of the molecule. When biologists
write the primary structure of a stretch of DNA or RNA, they
simply list the sequence of nucleotides in the 5'→3' direction,
using their single-letter abbreviations. For example, a six-base-
long DNA sequence might be ATTAGC. It would take roughly

6 billion of these letters to write the primary structure of the
DNA in most of your cells.

Polymerization Requires an Energy Source   In cells, the polymerization reactions that join nucleotides into nucleic acids are
catalyzed by enzymes. Like other polymerization reactions, the
process is not spontaneous. An input of energy is needed to tip
the energy balance in favor of the process.

Polymerization can take place in cells because the potential
energy of the nucleotide monomers is first raised by reactions
that add two phosphate groups to the ribonucleotides or deoxyribonucleotides, creating nucleoside triphosphates.[1] In the case of
nucleic acid polymerization, researchers refer to these nucleotides
as "activated." **FIGURE 4.4a** shows an example of an activated nucleotide; this molecule is called **adenosine triphosphate,** or **ATP.**

Why do added phosphate groups raise the energy content of a
molecule? Recall that phosphates are negatively charged and that
like charges repel (Chapter 2). Linking two or more phosphates
with covalent bonds generates strong repulsive forces. These
bonds therefore carry a large amount of potential energy, which
can be harvested to power other chemical reactions (**FIGURE 4.4b**).
You will see in later chapters that the potential energy stored in
ATP is used to drive other cellular activities, independent of nucleotide polymerization.

This is a key point, and one that you will encounter again and
again in this text: The addition of one or more phosphate groups
raises the potential energy of substrate molecules enough to make
an otherwise nonspontaneous reaction possible. (Chapter 8 explains how this happens in more detail.)

**Could Nucleic Acids Have Formed in the Absence of Cellular
Enzymes?**   Accumulating data suggest that the answer is yes.

Activation of nucleotides has been observed when prebiotic
conditions are simulated experimentally. In a suite of follow-up
experiments, researchers have produced RNA molecules by incubating activated nucleotides with tiny mineral particles—in
one case, molecules up to 50 nucleotides long were observed.
These results support the hypothesis that polymerization of activated nucleotides in the prebiotic world may have been catalyzed
by minerals. This model would be in line with the surface metabolism model for chemical evolution (introduced in Chapter 2).

More recent work has shown that under certain conditions, up
to 100 nucleotides can be linked together, even without first being
activated. To accomplish this, heat was introduced as a source of
energy and small nonpolar molecules, called lipids, were added to
help the monomers interact. This experiment is particularly interesting with respect to the setting for chemical evolution, because
both of these factors—heat and lipids—are thought to have been
present in prebiotic hydrothermal vents. (The chemical origins
and properties of lipids are covered in Chapter 6.)

---

[1]A molecule consisting of a sugar and one of the bases in Figure 4.1c is called a
nucleoside (a nucleotide is a sugar, a base, and one or more phosphate groups).
Thus, a sugar attached to a base and three phosphate groups is called a nucleoside
triphosphate.

(a) ATP is an example of an activated nucleotide.

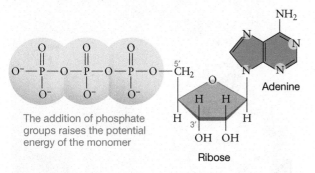

The addition of phosphate groups raises the potential energy of the monomer

Adenine

Ribose

(b) Energy is released when phosphates are removed by hydrolysis.

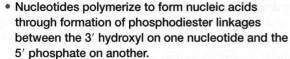

ATP   Water   AMP   Inorganic pyrophosphate   10.9 kcal/mol ATP

Energy used to link nucleotide to RNA

FIGURE 4.4 Activated Monomers Drive Polymerization Reactions. Polymerization reactions are generally nonspontaneous, but those reactions involving nucleoside triphosphates, such as ATP, are spontaneous. The potential energy stored in activated nucleotides is released when the pyrophosphate (PP_i) is removed before the polymerizing condensation reaction shown in Figure 4.2.

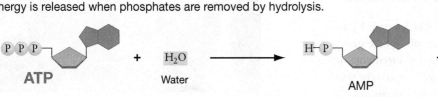

Based on these results, there is a strong consensus that if ribonucleotides and deoxyribonucleotides were able to form during chemical evolution, they would be able to polymerize into DNA and RNA. Now, what do these nucleic acids look like, and what can they do?

check your understanding

If you understand that . . .

- Nucleotides are monomers that consist of a sugar, a phosphate group, and a nitrogen-containing base.
- Nucleotides polymerize to form nucleic acids through formation of phosphodiester linkages between the 3′ hydroxyl on one nucleotide and the 5′ phosphate on another.
- During polymerization, nucleotides are added only to the 3′ end of a nucleic acid strand.

✔ You should be able to . . .

Draw a simplified diagram of the phosphodiester linkage between two nucleotides, indicate the 5′→3′ polarity, and mark where the next nucleotide would be added to the growing chain.

Answers are available in Appendix A.

4.2 DNA Structure and Function

The primary structure of nucleic acids is somewhat similar to the primary structure of proteins. Proteins have a peptide-bonded backbone with a series of R-groups that extend from it. DNA and RNA molecules have a sugar-phosphate backbone, created by phosphodiester linkages, and a sequence of any of four nitrogenous bases that extend from it.

Like proteins, DNA and RNA also have secondary structure. While the ⊠-helices and ⊠-pleated sheets of proteins are formed by hydrogen bonding between groups in the backbone, the secondary structure of nucleic acids is formed by hydrogen bonding between the nitrogenous bases.

Let's analyze the secondary structure and function of DNA first, and then dig into the secondary structure and function of RNA.

What Is the Nature of DNA's Secondary Structure?

The solution to DNA's secondary structure, announced in 1953, ranks among the great scientific breakthroughs of the twentieth century. James Watson and Francis Crick presented a model for the secondary structure of DNA in a one-page paper published in the scientific journal *Nature*.

Early Data Provided Clues Watson and Crick's finding was a hypothesis based on a series of results from other laboratories. They were trying to propose a secondary structure that could explain several important observations about the DNA found in cells:

- Chemists had worked out the structure of nucleotides and knew that DNA polymerized through the formation of phosphodiester linkages. Thus, Watson and Crick knew that the molecule had a sugar-phosphate backbone.

- By analyzing the nitrogenous bases in DNA samples from different organisms, Erwin Chargaff had established two empirical rules: **(1)** The number of purines in a given DNA molecule is equal to the number of pyrimidines, and **(2)** the number of T's and A's in DNA are equal, and the number of C's and G's in DNA are equal.

- By bombarding DNA with X-rays and analyzing how it scattered the radiation, Rosalind Franklin and Maurice Wilkins had calculated the distances between groups of atoms in the molecule (see **BioSkills 11** in Appendix B for an introduction to this technique, called **X-ray crystallography**). The scattering patterns showed that three distances were repeated many times: 0.34 nanometer (nm), 2.0 nm, and 3.4 nm. Because the measurements repeated, the researchers inferred that DNA molecules had a regular and repeating structure. The pattern of X-ray scattering suggested that the molecule was helical, or spiral, in nature.

Based on this work, understanding DNA's structure boiled down to understanding the nature of the helix involved. What type of helix would have a sugar-phosphate backbone and explain both Chargaff's rules and the Franklin–Wilkins measurements?

DNA Strands Are Antiparallel Watson and Crick began by analyzing the size and geometry of deoxyribose, phosphate groups, and nitrogenous bases. The bond angles and measurements suggested that the distance of 2.0 nm probably represented the width of the helix and that 0.34 nm was likely to be the distance between bases stacked in a spiral.

How could they make sense of Chargaff's rules and the 3.4-nm distance, which appeared to be exactly 10 times the distance between a single pair of bases?

To solve this problem, Watson and Crick constructed a series of physical models like the one pictured in **FIGURE 4.5**. The models allowed them to tinker with different types of helical configurations. After many false starts, something clicked:

- They arranged two strands of DNA side by side and running in opposite directions—meaning that one strand ran in the $5' \rightarrow 3'$ direction while the other strand was oriented $3' \rightarrow 5'$. Strands with this orientation are said to be **antiparallel.**

- If the antiparallel strands are twisted together to form a **double helix,** the coiled sugar-phosphate backbones end up on the outside of the spiral and the nitrogenous bases on the inside.

FIGURE 4.5 Building a Physical Model of DNA Structure. Watson (left) and Crick (right) represented the arrangement of the four deoxyribonucleotides in a double helix, using metal plates and wires with precise lengths and geometries.

- For the bases from each backbone to fit in the interior of the 2.0-nm-wide structure, they have to form purine-pyrimidine pairs (see **FIGURE 4.6a**). This is a key point: The pairing allows hydrogen bonds to form between certain purines and pyrimidines. Adenine forms hydrogen bonds with thymine, and guanine forms hydrogen bonds with cytosine (**FIGURE 4.6b**).

- The A-T and G-C bases were said to be complementary. Two hydrogen bonds form when A and T pair, and three hydrogen bonds form when G and C pair. As a result, the G-C interaction is slightly stronger than the A-T bond. In contrast, A-C and G-T pairs allowed no or only one hydrogen bond.

(a) Only purine-pyrimidine pairs fit inside the double helix.

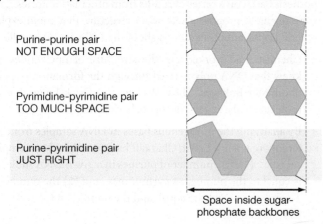

Purine-purine pair
NOT ENOUGH SPACE

Pyrimidine-pyrimidine pair
TOO MUCH SPACE

Purine-pyrimidine pair
JUST RIGHT

Space inside sugar-phosphate backbones

FIGURE 4.6 Complementary Base Pairing Is Based on Hydrogen Bonding.

(b) Hydrogen bonds form between G-C pairs and A-T pairs.

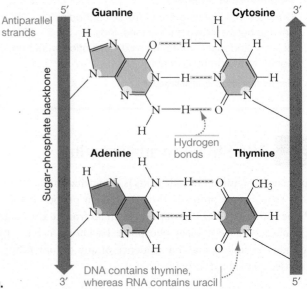

Antiparallel strands

Sugar-phosphate backbone

5′ Guanine
Cytosine 3′

Hydrogen bonds

Adenine
Thymine

DNA contains thymine, whereas RNA contains uracil

3′   5′

Watson and Crick had discovered **complementary base pairing.** In fact, the term **Watson–Crick pairing** is now used interchangeably with the phrase complementary base pairing. The physical restraints posed by these interactions resulted in a full helical twist every 10 bases, or 3.4 nm.

The Double Helix **FIGURE 4.7a** shows how antiparallel strands of DNA form when complementary bases line up and form hydrogen bonds. As you study the figure, notice that DNA is put together like a ladder whose ends have been twisted in opposite directions. The sugar-phosphate backbones form the supports of the ladder; the base pairs represent the rungs of the ladder. The twisting allows the nitrogenous bases to line up in a way that makes hydrogen bonding between them possible.

The nitrogenous bases in the middle of the molecule are hydrophobic. This is a key point, because twisting into a double helix minimizes contact between the bases and surrounding water molecules. In addition to hydrogen bonding, van der Waals interactions between the tightly stacked bases in the interior further contribute to the stability of the helix. You see the same forces—hydrogen bonding, hydrophobicity, and van der Waals interactions—play similar roles in protein folding (Chapter 3). But DNA as a whole is hydrophilic and water soluble because the backbones, which face the exterior of the molecule, contain negatively charged phosphate groups that interact with water.

FIGURE 4.7b highlights additional features of DNA's secondary structure. It's important to note that the outside of the helical DNA molecule forms two types of grooves. The larger of the two is known as the major groove, and the smaller one is known as the minor groove. From this figure, you can identify how DNA's secondary structure explains the measurements observed by Franklin and Wilkins.

Since the model of the double helix was published, experimental tests have shown that the hypothesis is correct in almost every detail. To summarize:

- DNA's secondary structure consists of two antiparallel strands twisted into a double helix.

- The molecule is stabilized by hydrophobic interactions in its interior and by hydrogen bonding between the complementary base pairs A-T and G-C.

✔ You should be able to explain why complementary base pairing would not be possible if two DNA strands were aligned in a parallel fashion—instead of the antiparallel alignment shown in Figure 4.6b.

Now the question is, how does this secondary structure affect the molecule's function?

(a) Cartoons of DNA structure

(b) Space-filling model of DNA double helix

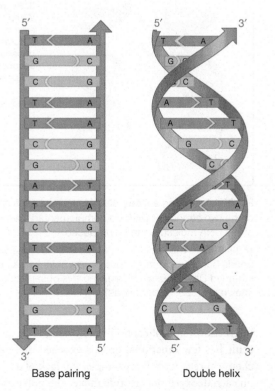

Base pairing   Double helix

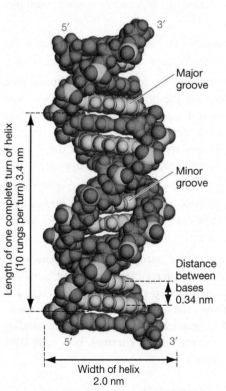

Major groove

Minor groove

Length of one complete turn of helix (10 rungs per turn) 3.4 nm

Distance between bases 0.34 nm

Width of helix 2.0 nm

FIGURE 4.7 The Secondary Structure of DNA Is a Double Helix. (a) The cartoons illustrate complementary base pairing and how strands are twisted into a double helix. **(b)** The space-filling model shows tight packing of the bases inside the double helix. The double-helix structure explains the measurements inferred from X-ray analysis of DNA molecules.

DNA Functions as an Information-Containing Molecule

Watson and Crick's model created a sensation for a simple reason: It revealed how DNA could store and transmit biological information. In literature, information consists of letters on a page. In music, information is composed of the notes on a staff. But inside cells, information consists of a sequence of nucleotides in a nucleic acid. The four nitrogenous bases function like letters of the alphabet. A sequence of bases is like the sequence of letters in a word—it has meaning.

In all organisms that have been examined to date, from tiny bacteria to gigantic redwood trees, DNA carries the information required for the organism's growth and reproduction. Exploring how hereditary information is encoded and translated into action is the heart of several later chapters (Chapters 16 through 19).

Here, however, our focus is on how life began. The theory of chemical evolution holds that life began once a molecule emerged that could make a copy of itself. Does the information contained within DNA allow it to be replicated?

Watson and Crick ended their paper on the double helix with one of the classic understatements in the scientific literature: "It has not escaped our notice that the specific pairing we have postulated immediately suggests a possible copying mechanism." Here's the key insight: DNA's primary structure serves as a mold or template for the synthesis of a complementary strand. DNA contains the information required for a copy of itself to be made. **FIGURE 4.8** shows how a copy of DNA can be made by complementary base pairing.

Step 1 Heating or enzyme-catalyzed reactions can cause the double helix to separate.

Step 2 Free deoxyribonucleotides form hydrogen bonds with complementary bases on the original strand of DNA—also called a **template strand.** As they do, their sugar-phosphate groups form phosphodiester linkages to create a new strand—also called a **complementary strand.** Note that the $5' \rightarrow 3'$ directionality of the complementary strand is opposite that of the template strand.

Step 3 Complementary base pairing allows each strand of a DNA double helix to be copied exactly, producing two identical daughter molecules.

DNA copying is the basis for a second of the five characteristics of life (introduced in Chapter 1): replication. But can DNA catalyze the reactions needed to *self*-replicate? In today's cells and in laboratory experiments, the answer is no. Instead, the molecule is copied through a complicated series of energy-demanding reactions, catalyzed by a large suite of enzymes. Why can't DNA catalyze these reactions itself?

Is DNA a Catalytic Molecule?

The DNA double helix is highly structured. It is regular, symmetric, and held together by hydrogen bonding, hydrophobic

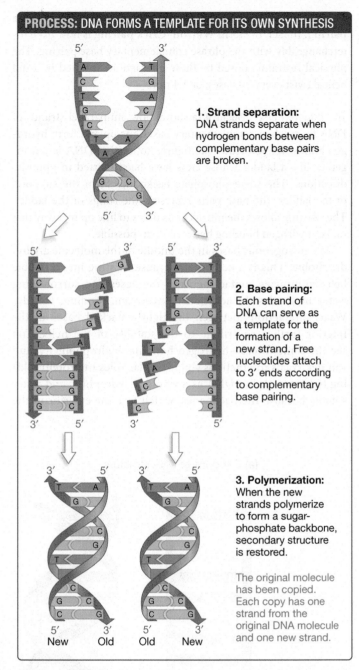

PROCESS: DNA FORMS A TEMPLATE FOR ITS OWN SYNTHESIS

1. Strand separation: DNA strands separate when hydrogen bonds between complementary base pairs are broken.

2. Base pairing: Each strand of DNA can serve as a template for the formation of a new strand. Free nucleotides attach to 3′ ends according to complementary base pairing.

3. Polymerization: When the new strands polymerize to form a sugar-phosphate backbone, secondary structure is restored.

The original molecule has been copied. Each copy has one strand from the original DNA molecule and one new strand.

New   Old   Old   New

FIGURE 4.8 Making a Copy of DNA. If new bases are added to each of the two strands of DNA via complementary base pairing, a copy of the DNA molecule can be produced.

✔ **QUESTION** When double-stranded DNA is heated to 95°C, the bonds between complementary base pairs break and single-stranded DNA results. Considering this observation, is the reaction shown in step 1 spontaneous?

interactions, and phosphodiester linkages. In addition, the molecule has few functional groups exposed that can participate in chemical reactions. For example, the lack of a 2′ hydroxyl group on each deoxyribonucleotide makes the polymer much less reactive than RNA, and thus much more resistant to degradation.

Intact stretches of DNA have been recovered from fossils that are tens of thousands of years old. The molecules have the same sequence of bases as the organisms had when they were alive, despite death and exposure to a wide array of pH, temperature, and chemical conditions. DNA's stability is the key to its effectiveness as a reliable information-bearing molecule. DNA's structure is consistent with its function in cells.

The orderliness and stability that make DNA such a dependable information repository also make it extraordinarily inept at catalysis, however. Recall that enzyme function is based on a specific binding event between a substrate and a protein catalyst (Chapter 3). Thanks to variation in reactivity among R-groups in amino acids, and the enormous diversity of shapes found in proteins, a wide array of catalytic activities can be generated. In comparison, DNA's primary and secondary structures are simple. It is not surprising, then, that DNA has never been observed to catalyze any reaction in any organism. Although researchers have been able to construct single-stranded DNA molecules that can catalyze some reactions in the laboratory, the number and diversity of reactions involved is a minute fraction of the activity catalyzed by enzymes.

In short, DNA furnishes an extraordinarily stable template for copying itself and for storing information encoded in a sequence of bases. But owing to its inability to act as an effective catalyst, there is virtually no support for the hypothesis that the first life-form consisted of DNA. Instead, most biologists who are working on the origin of life support the hypothesis that life began with RNA. How does the structure of RNA differ from DNA?

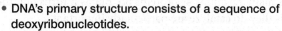

check your understanding

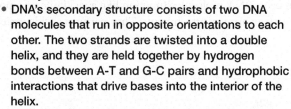

If you understand that . . .

- DNA's primary structure consists of a sequence of deoxyribonucleotides.
- DNA's secondary structure consists of two DNA molecules that run in opposite orientations to each other. The two strands are twisted into a double helix, and they are held together by hydrogen bonds between A-T and G-C pairs and hydrophobic interactions that drive bases into the interior of the helix.
- The sequence of deoxyribonucleotides in DNA contains information. Owing to complementary base pairing, each DNA strand also contains the information required to form its complementary strand.

✔ You should be able to . . .

Make a sketch of a double-stranded DNA molecule in the form of a ladder with the sequence of A-G-C-T. Label the 5′ and 3′ ends, the sugar-phosphate backbones, the hydrogen bonds between complementary bases, and the location of hydrophobic interactions.

Answers are available in Appendix A.

The first living molecule would have needed to perform two key functions: carry information and catalyze reactions that promoted its own replication. At first glance, these two functions appear to conflict. Information storage requires regularity and stability; catalysis requires variation in chemical composition and flexibility in shape. How is it possible for a molecule to do both? The answer lies in structure.

Structurally, RNA Differs from DNA

Recall that proteins can have up to four levels of structure. Single-chain proteins possess a primary sequence of amino acids, secondary folds that are stabilized by hydrogen bonding between atoms in the peptide-bonded backbone, and tertiary folds that are stabilized by interactions involving R-groups. Quaternary structure is found in proteins consisting of multiple polypeptides.

DNA has only primary and secondary structure. But RNA, like single-chained proteins, can have up to three levels of structure.

Primary Structure Like DNA, RNA has a primary structure consisting of a sugar-phosphate backbone formed by phosphodiester linkages and, extending from that backbone, a sequence of four types of nitrogenous bases. But it's important to recall two significant differences between these nucleic acids:

1. The sugar in the sugar-phosphate backbone of RNA is ribose, not deoxyribose as in DNA.

2. The pyrimidine base thymine does not exist in RNA. Instead, RNA contains the closely related pyrimidine base uracil.

The first point is critical. Look back at Figure 4.1b and compare the functional groups attached to ribose and deoxyribose. Notice the hydroxyl (−OH) group on the 2′ carbon of ribose. This additional hydroxyl is much more reactive than the hydrogen atom on the 2′ carbon of deoxyribose. When RNA molecules fold in certain ways, the hydroxyl group can attack the phosphate linkage between nucleotides, which would generate a break in the sugar-phosphate backbone. While this −OH group makes RNA much less stable than DNA, it can also support catalytic activity by the molecule.

Secondary Structure Like DNA molecules, most RNA molecules have secondary structure that results from complementary base pairing between purine and pyrimidine bases. In RNA, adenine forms hydrogen bonds only with uracil, and guanine again forms hydrogen bonds with cytosine. (Other, non-Watson–Crick base pairs occur, although less frequently.) Three hydrogen bonds form between guanine and cytosine, but only two form between adenine and uracil.

This hydrogen bonding should seem familiar, since DNA bonds together in a similar manner—so how do the secondary structures of RNA and DNA differ? In the vast majority of cases, the purine and pyrimidine bases in RNA undergo hydrogen

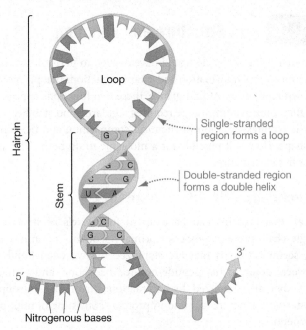

FIGURE 4.9 Complementary Base Pairing and Secondary Structure in RNA: Stem-and-Loop Structures. This RNA molecule has secondary structure. The double-stranded "stem" and single-stranded "loop" form a hairpin. The bonded bases in the stem are antiparallel, meaning that they are oriented in opposite directions.

bonding with complementary bases on the *same strand*, rather than forming hydrogen bonds with complementary bases on a different strand, as in DNA.

FIGURE 4.9 shows how within-strand base pairing works. The key is that when bases on one part of an RNA strand fold over and align with ribonucleotides on another part of the same strand, the two sugar-phosphate strands are antiparallel. In this orientation, hydrogen bonding between complementary bases results in a stable double helix.

If the section where the fold occurs includes unpaired bases, then the stem-and-loop configuration shown in Figure 4.9 results. This type of secondary structure is called a **hairpin.** Several other types of RNA secondary structures are possible, each involving a different length and arrangement of base-paired segments.

Like the ⊠-helices and ⊠-pleated sheets observed in many proteins, RNA secondary structures can form spontaneously. They are directed by hydrophobic interactions and stabilized by hydrogen bonding between the bases. Even though hairpins and other types of secondary structure reduce the entropy of RNA molecules, the energy released in these interactions makes the overall process favorable.

Tertiary Structure   RNA molecules can also have tertiary structure, which arises when secondary structures fold into more complex shapes. As a result, RNA molecules with different base sequences can have very different overall shapes and chemical properties. RNA molecules are much more diverse in size, shape, and reactivity than DNA molecules are. Structurally and chemically, RNA is intermediate between the complexity of proteins and the simplicity of DNA.

TABLE 4.1 summarizes the similarities and differences in the structures of RNA and DNA.

RNA's Structure Makes It an Extraordinarily Versatile Molecule

In terms of structure, you've seen that RNA is intermediate between DNA and proteins. RNA is intermediate in terms of function as well. RNA molecules cannot archive information nearly as efficiently as DNA molecules do, but they do perform key functions in information processing. Likewise, they cannot catalyze as many reactions as proteins do. But as it turns out, the reactions they do catalyze are particularly important.

In cells, RNA molecules function like a jackknife or a pocket tool with an array of attachments: They perform a wide variety of

SUMMARY TABLE 4.1   DNA and RNA Structure

Level of Structure	DNA		RNA	
Primary	Sequence of deoxyribonucleotides; bases are A, T, G, C	5′ A A T G T G C C G 3′	Sequence of ribonucleotides; bases are A, U, G, C	5′ U U A C A C G G C 3′
Secondary	Two antiparallel strands twist into a double helix, stabilized by hydrogen bonding between complementary bases (A-T, G-C) and hydrophobic interactions		Most common are hairpins, formed when a single strand folds back on itself to form a double-helix "stem" and a single-stranded "loop"	
Tertiary	None*		Folds that form distinctive three-dimensional shapes	Example: tRNA

*In cells, DNA coils around proteins that bind to the double helix. In many cases the DNA-protein complex folds into highly organized, compact structures. But DNA does not form tertiary structure on its own.

tasks reasonably well. Some of the most surprising results in the last decade of biological science, in fact, involve new insights into the diversity of roles that RNAs play in cells. These molecules process information stored in DNA, synthesize proteins, and defend against attack by viruses, among other things.

Next let's focus on the roles that RNA could have played in the origin of life—as an information-containing entity and as a catalyst.

RNA Is an Information-Containing Molecule

Because RNA contains a sequence of bases analogous to the letters in a word, it can function as an information-containing molecule. And because hydrogen bonding occurs specifically between A-U pairs and G-C pairs in RNA, it is possible for RNA to furnish the information required to make a copy of itself.

FIGURE 4.10 illustrates how the information stored in an RNA molecule can be used to direct its own replication.

First, a complementary copy of the RNA is made when free ribonucleotides form hydrogen bonds with complementary bases on the original strand of RNA—the template strand. As they do, their sugar-phosphate groups form phosphodiester linkages to produce a double-stranded RNA molecule (steps 1 and 2).

To make a copy of the original single-stranded RNA, the hydrogen bonds between the double-stranded product must first be broken by heating or by a catalyzed reaction (step 3). The newly made complementary RNA molecule now exists independently of the original template strand. If steps 1–3 were repeated with the new strand serving as a template (steps 4–6), the resulting molecule would be a copy of the original. In this way, the primary sequence of an RNA serves as a mold.

RNA Can Function as a Catalytic Molecule

In terms of diversity in chemical reactivity and overall shape, RNA molecules are no match for proteins. The primary structure of RNA molecules is much more restricted because RNA has only four types of nucleotides versus the 20 types of amino acids found in proteins. Secondary through tertiary structure is more limited as a result, meaning that RNA cannot form the wide array of catalysts observed among proteins.

But because RNA has a degree of structural and chemical complexity, it is capable of catalyzing a number of chemical reactions. Sidney Altman and Thomas Cech shared the 1989 Nobel Prize in chemistry for showing that catalytic RNAs, or **ribozymes,** exist in organisms.

FIGURE 4.11 (on page 68) shows the structure of a ribozyme Cech isolated from a single-celled organism called *Tetrahymena*. This ribozyme catalyzes both the hydrolysis and the condensation of phosphodiester linkages in RNA. Researchers have since discovered a variety of ribozymes that catalyze an array of reactions in cells. For example, ribozymes catalyze the formation of peptide bonds when amino acids polymerize to form polypeptides. Ribozymes are at work in your cells right now.

The three-dimensional nature of ribozymes is vital to their catalytic activity. To catalyze a chemical reaction, substrates must

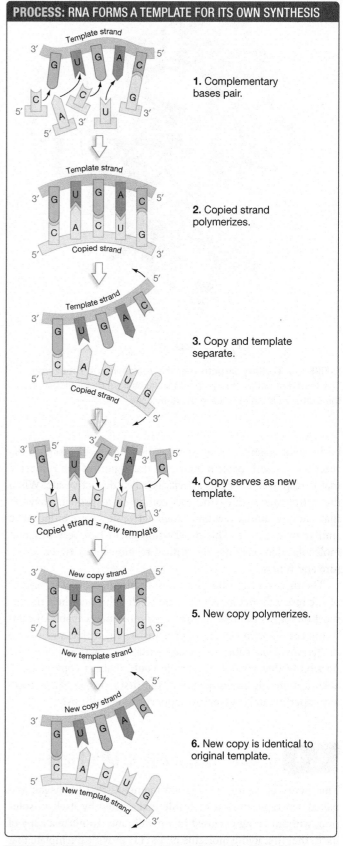

PROCESS: RNA FORMS A TEMPLATE FOR ITS OWN SYNTHESIS

1. Complementary bases pair.

2. Copied strand polymerizes.

3. Copy and template separate.

4. Copy serves as new template.

5. New copy polymerizes.

6. New copy is identical to original template.

FIGURE 4.10 RNA Molecules Contain Information That Allows Them to Be Replicated. For a single-stranded RNA to be copied, it must pass through double-stranded RNA intermediates.

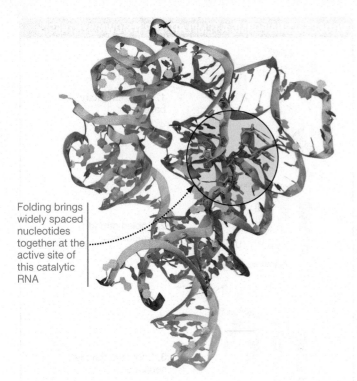

Folding brings widely spaced nucleotides together at the active site of this catalytic RNA

FIGURE 4.11 Tertiary Structure of the *Tetrahymena* Ribozyme. The folded structure brings together bases from distant locations in the primary structure to form the active site.

be brought together in an environment that will promote the reaction. As with protein enzymes, the region of the ribozyme that is responsible for this activity is called the active site. When the *Tetrahymena* ribozyme was compared to protein enzymes that catalyze similar reactions, their active sites were found to be similar in structure. This observation about two very different molecules demonstrates the critical relationship between structure and function

The discovery of ribozymes was a watershed event in origin-of-life research. Before Altman and Cech published their results, most biologists thought that the only molecules capable of catalyzing reactions in cells were proteins. The fact that a ribozyme in *Tetrahymena* catalyzed a condensation reaction raised the possibility that an RNA molecule could make a copy of itself. Such a molecule could qualify as the first living entity. Is there any experimental evidence to support this hypothesis?

4.4 In Search of the First Life-Form

The theory of chemical evolution maintains that life began as a naked self-replicator—a molecule that existed by itself in solution, without being enclosed in a membrane. To make a copy of itself, that first living molecule had to (1) provide a template that could be copied, and (2) catalyze polymerization reactions that would link monomers into a copy of that template. Because RNA is capable of both processes, most origin-of-life researchers propose that the first life-form was made of RNA.

No self-replicating RNA molecules have been discovered in nature, however, so researchers test the hypothesis by trying to simulate the RNA world in the laboratory. The eventual goal is to create an RNA molecule that can catalyze its own replication.

How Biologists Study the RNA World

To understand how researchers go about testing the RNA world hypothesis, consider two recent experiments by researchers in David Bartel's laboratory. In one study, the team attempted to generate an RNA molecule that could catalyze the kind of template-directed polymerization needed for RNA replication—an RNA "replicase." Starting with a ribozyme capable of joining two ribonucleotides together, they generated billions of copies into which random mutations were introduced.

Next they incubated the mutants with free ribonucleotides and began selecting for replicase activity. Molecules that exhibited such activity were isolated and copied. After two weeks and 18 rounds of selection, the team succeeded in isolating a ribozyme that could add 14 nucleotides to an existing RNA strand.

Note that the team's experimental protocol was designed to mimic the process of natural selection introduced in Chapter 1. The population of RNAs from each round had variable characteristics that could be replicated and passed on to the next generation of ribozymes. In addition, the researchers were able to select the most efficient RNAs to be the "parents" of the next generation—and in the process introduce new mutations that potentially could make some of the "offspring" even better ribozymes.

This research created considerable excitement among biologists interested in the origin of life, because adding ribonucleotides to a growing strand is a key attribute of an RNA replicase. However, since the maximum product length generated was less than 10 percent of the ribozyme's own length, an RNA replicase capable of making a full-length copy of itself was far from being discovered. In fact, the difficulty in creating an effective RNA replicase has led many researchers to question the idea of a replicase being the first ribozyme to emerge in the RNA world.

In another study, Bartel's group asked a different question: Would it be possible to select for a ribozyme that could make ribonucleotides? This type of ribozyme is not known to exist in nature but would be a key component in the RNA world.

Recall that the direction of a chemical reaction and how much product it makes is influenced by the amount of reactants present (Chapter 2). Since the chemical evolution of nucleotides is thought to have been inefficient, nucleotides would have been a scarce resource on early Earth. Ribozymes that could catalyze the production of nucleotides would be more likely to be copied due to local accumulation of monomers.

Starting with a large pool of randomly generated RNA sequences, the researchers selected for RNAs that could catalyze the addition of a uracil base to a ribose sugar. By round 11, the group had recovered ribozymes that were 50,000 times better at catalyzing the reaction than those found in the fourth round and over 1 million times more efficient than the uncatalyzed reaction. In effect, molecular evolution had occurred in the reaction tubes.

Thanks to similar efforts at other laboratories around the world, biologists have produced an increasingly impressive set of catalytic activities from RNA molecules. The results from each of these studies help clarify our view of what occurred in the RNA world. If a living ribozyme ever existed, then each round of simulated molecular evolution brings us closer to resurrecting it.

The RNA World May Have Sparked the Evolution of Life

Although ribozymes like these lab-generated molecules may have been present in the RNA world, they have not been observed in nature. Of those that have been discovered in modern cells, most play key roles in the synthesis of proteins. This relationship suggests the order of events in chemical evolution—the RNA world preceded proteins.

The evolution of protein enzymes would have marked the end of the RNA world—providing the means for catalyzing reactions necessary for life to emerge in a cellular form. After this milestone, three of the five fundamental characteristics of life (see Chapter 1) were solidly in place:

1. *Information*   Proteins and ribozymes were processing information stored in nucleic acids for the synthesis of more proteins.

2. *Replication*   Enzymes, and possibly ribozymes, were replicating the nucleic acids that stored the hereditary information.

3. *Evolution*   Random changes in the synthesis of proteins, and selective advantages resulting from some of these changes, allowed for the evolution of new proteins and protein families.

If these events occurred in a hydrothermal vent, the molecular assemblages of nucleic acids and proteins would have been constantly fed with thermal and chemical energy. To gain independence from their undersea hatchery, enzymes would have evolved to store this energy as something more portable—carbohydrates. The structure and function of carbohydrates will be the focus of the next chapter.

CHAPTER 4   REVIEW

For media, go to MasteringBiology

If you understand . . .

4.1   What Is a Nucleic Acid?

- Nucleic acids are polymers of nucleotide monomers, which consist of a sugar, a phosphate group, and a nitrogenous base. Ribonucleotide monomers polymerize to form RNA. Deoxyribonucleotide monomers polymerize to form DNA.

- Ribonucleotides have a hydroxyl (—OH) group on their 2′ carbon; deoxyribonucleotides do not.

- Nucleic acids polymerize when condensation reactions join nucleotides together via phosphodiester linkages.

- Nucleic acids are directional: they have a 5′ end and a 3′ end. During polymerization, new nucleotides are added only to the 3′ end.

✔ You should be able to state what cells do to activate nucleotides for incorporation into a polymer and explain why activation is required.

4.2   DNA Structure and Function

- DNA's primary structure consists of a sequence of linked nitrogenous bases. Its secondary structure consists of two DNA strands running in opposite directions that are twisted into a double helix.

- DNA is an extremely stable molecule that serves as a superb archive for information in the form of base sequences. It lacks a reactive 2′ hydroxyl group, and its secondary structure is stabilized by hydrophobic interactions and hydrogen bonds that form between complementary bases stacked on the inside of the helix.

- DNA is readily copied via complementary base pairing. Complementary base pairing occurs between A-T and G-C pairs in DNA.

- DNA's structural stability and regularity are advantageous for information storage, but they make DNA an ineffective catalyst.

✔ You should be able to explain why DNA molecules with a high percentage of guanine and cytosine are particularly stable.

4.3   RNA Structure and Function

- Like DNA, RNA's primary structure consists of a sequence of linked nitrogenous bases. RNA's secondary structure includes short regions of double helices and looped structures called hairpins.

- RNA molecules are usually single stranded. They have secondary structure because of complementary base pairing between A-U and G-C pairs on the same strand.

- Unlike DNA, the secondary structures of RNA can fold into more complex shapes, stabilized by hydrogen bonding, which give the molecule tertiary structure.

- RNA is versatile. The primary function of proteins is to catalyze chemical reactions, and the primary function of DNA is to carry information. But RNA is an "all-purpose" macromolecule that can do both.

✔ You should be able to explain why many RNA molecules exhibit tertiary structure, while most DNA molecules do not.

4.4 In Search of the First Life-Form

- To test the RNA world hypothesis, researchers are attempting to synthesize new ribozymes in the laboratory. Using artificial selection strategies, they have succeeded in identifying RNAs that catalyze several different reactions.

- Ribozymes that catalyze reactions necessary for the production of nucleotides may have preceded the evolution of RNA replicases.

✔ You should be able to provide two examples of activities in the RNA world you expect would benefit from catalysis and justify your choices.

You should be able to . . .

✔ TEST YOUR KNOWLEDGE   *Answers are available in Appendix A*

1. What are the four nitrogenous bases found in RNA?
   a. uracil, guanine, cytosine, thymine (U, G, C, T)
   b. adenine, guanine, cytosine, thymine (A, G, C, T)
   c. adenine, uracil, guanine, cytosine (A, U, G, C)
   d. alanine, threonine, glycine, cysteine (A, T, G, C)

2. What determines the primary structure of a DNA molecule?
   a. the sugar-phosphate backbone
   b. complementary base pairing and the formation of hairpins
   c. the sequence of deoxyribonucleotides
   d. the sequence of ribonucleotides

3. DNA attains a secondary structure when hydrogen bonds form between the nitrogenous bases called purines and pyrimidines. What are the complementary base pairs that form in DNA?
   a. A-T and G-C
   b. A-U and G-C
   c. A-G and T-C
   d. A-T and G-U

4. Which of the following rules apply to the synthesis of nucleic acids?
   a. Nucleotides are added to the 5′ end of nucleic acids.
   b. The synthesis of nucleic acids cannot occur without the presence of an enzyme to catalyze the reaction.
   c. Strands are synthesized in a parallel direction such that one end of the double-stranded product has the 3′ ends and other has the 5′ ends.
   d. Complementary pairing between bases is required for copying nucleic acids.

5. Nucleic acids are directional, meaning that there are two different ends. What functional groups define the two different ends of a DNA strand?

6. What is responsible for the increased stability of DNA compared to RNA?

✔ TEST YOUR UNDERSTANDING   *Answers are available in Appendix A*

7. Explain how Chargaff's rules relate to the complementary base pairing seen in the secondary structure of DNA. Would you expect these rules to apply to RNA as well? Explain why or why not.

8. **QUANTITATIVE** If nucleotides from the DNA of a human were quantified and 30 percent of them consisted of adenine, what percentage of guanine nucleotides would be present?
   a. 20 percent
   b. 30 percent
   c. 40 percent
   d. 70 percent

9. What would be the sequence of the strand of DNA that is made from the following template: 5′-GATATCGAT-3′ (Your answer must be written 5′→3′.) How would this sequence be different if RNA were made from this DNA template?

10. A major theme in this chapter is that the structure of molecules correlates with their function. Explain how DNA's secondary structure limits its catalytic abilities compared with that of RNA. Why is it expected that RNA molecules can catalyze a modest but significant array of reactions?

11. To replicate a ribozyme, a complete complementary copy must be made. Would you expect the double-stranded intermediate to maintain its catalytic activity? Justify your answer with an explanation.

12. Suppose that Bartel's research group succeeded in producing a molecule that could make a copy of itself. Which of the five fundamental characteristics of life (provided in Chapter 1) would support the claim that this molecule is alive?

13. Make a concept map (see **BioSkills 15** in Appendix B) that relates DNA's primary structure to its secondary structure. Your diagram should include deoxyribonucleotides, hydrophobic interactions, purines, pyrimidines, phosphodiester linkages, DNA primary structure, DNA secondary structure, complementary base pairing, and antiparallel strands.

14. Viruses are particles that infect cells. In some viruses, the genetic material consists of two strands of RNA, bonded together via complementary base pairing. Would these antiparallel strands form a double helix? Explain why or why not.

15. Before Watson and Crick published their model of the DNA double helix, Linus Pauling offered a model based on a triple helix. If the three sugar-phosphate backbones were on the outside of such a molecule, would hydrogen bonding or hydrophobic interactions be more important in keeping such a secondary structure together?

16. How would you expect the structure of ribozymes in organisms that grow in very hot environments, such as hot springs or deep-sea vents, to differ from those in organisms that grow in cooler environments?
    a. These ribozymes would have more hairpin secondary structures.
    b. The hairpins would have more G's and C's in the primary structure.
    c. The hairpins would have more A's and U's in the primary structure.
    d. These ribozymes would exhibit no tertiary structure.

5 An Introduction to Carbohydrates

In this chapter you will learn that

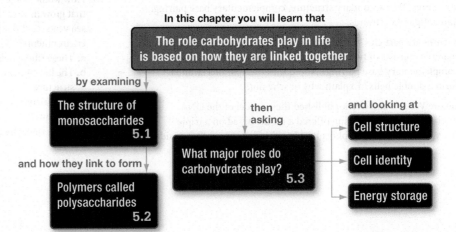

The role carbohydrates play in life is based on how they are linked together

by examining →

The structure of monosaccharides
5.1

then asking →

What major roles do carbohydrates play? **5.3**

and how they link to form →

Polymers called polysaccharides
5.2

and looking at →

Cell structure

Cell identity

Energy storage

A cross section through a buttercup root. Cellulose-rich cell walls are stained green; starch-filled structures are stained purple. Cellulose is a structural carbohydrate; starch is an energy-storage carbohydrate.

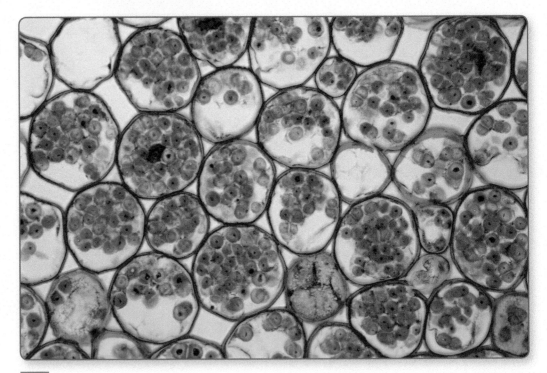

This unit highlights the four types of macromolecules that were key to the evolution of the cell: proteins, nucleic acids, carbohydrates, and lipids. Understanding the structure and function of macromolecules is a basic requirement for exploring how life began and how organisms work. Recall that proteins and nucleic acids could satisfy only three of the five fundamental characteristics of life: information, replication, and evolution (Chapter 4). Carbohydrates, the subject of this chapter, play an important role in a fourth characteristic—energy.

The term **carbohydrate,** or **sugar,** encompasses the monomers called **monosaccharides** (literally, "one-sugar"), small polymers called **oligosaccharides** ("few-sugars"), and the large polymers called **polysaccharides** ("many-sugars"). The name carbohydrate is logical because the molecular formula of many of these molecules is $(CH_2O)_n$, where the n refers to the number of "carbohydrate" groups. The value of n can vary from 3, for the smallest sugar, to well over a thousand for some of the large polymers.

This chapter is part of the Big Picture. See how on pages 104–105.

✔ When you see this checkmark, stop and test yourself. Answers are available in Appendix A.

An aldose
Carbonyl group at end of carbon chain

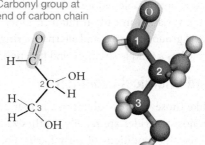

A ketose
Carbonyl group in middle of carbon chain

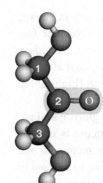

The name can also be misleading, though, because carbohydrates do not consist of carbon atoms bonded to water molecules. Instead, they are molecules with a carbonyl (C=O) and several hydroxyl (−OH) functional groups, along with several to many carbon–hydrogen (C−H) bonds. Consider formaldehyde, which was introduced as one of the molecules present in early Earth (Chapter 2). Even though formaldehyde has the same molecular formula as the one given above (CH_2O), it is not a carbohydrate since it does not contain a hydroxyl group.

Let's begin with monosaccharides, put them together into polysaccharides, and then explore how carbohydrates figured in the origin of life and what they do in cells today. As you study this material, be sure to ask yourself the central question of biological chemistry: How does this molecule's structure relate to its properties and function?

5.1 Sugars as Monomers

Sugars are fundamental to life. They provide chemical energy in cells and furnish some of the molecular building blocks required for the synthesis of larger, more complex compounds. Monosaccharides were important during chemical evolution, early in Earth's history. For example, as you've seen, the sugar called ribose is required for the formation of the nucleotides that make up nucleic acids (Chapter 4).

What Distinguishes One Monosaccharide from Another?

Monosaccharides, or simple sugars, are the monomers of carbohydrates. **FIGURE 5.1** illustrates two of the smallest monosaccharides. Although their molecular formulas are identical ($C_3H_6O_3$), their molecular structures are different. The carbonyl group that serves as one of monosaccharides' distinguishing features can be found either at the end of the molecule, forming an aldehyde sugar (an aldose), or within the carbon chain, forming a ketone sugar (a ketose). The presence of a carbonyl group along with multiple hydroxyl groups provides sugars with an array of reactive and hydrophilic functional groups. Based on this observation, it's not surprising that sugars are able to participate in a large number of chemical reactions.

The number of carbon atoms present also varies in monosaccharides. By convention, the carbons in a monosaccharide are numbered consecutively, starting with the end nearest the carbonyl group. Figure 5.1 features three-carbon sugars, or **trioses**. Ribose, which acts as a building block for nucleotides, has five carbons and is called a **pentose;** the glucose that is coursing through your bloodstream right now is a six-carbon sugar, or a **hexose.**

Besides varying in the location of the carbonyl group and the total number of carbon atoms present, monosaccharides can vary in the spatial arrangement of their atoms. There is, for example, a wide array of pentoses and hexoses. Each is distinguished by the configuration of its hydroxyl functional groups. **FIGURE 5.2**

Glucose

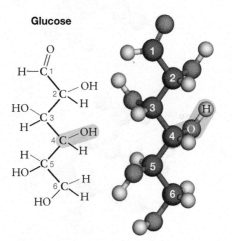

Galactose

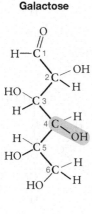

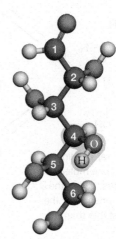

FIGURE 5.2 Sugars May Vary in the Configuration of Their Hydroxyl Groups. The two six-carbon sugars shown here vary only in the spatial orientation of their hydroxyl groups on carbon number 4.

✔**EXERCISE** Mannose is a six-carbon sugar that is identical to glucose, except that the hydroxyl (–OH) group on carbon number 2 is switched in orientation. Circle carbon number 2 in glucose and galactose; then draw the structural formula of mannose.

illustrates glucose and galactose, which are six-carbon sugars. Notice that the two molecules have the same molecular formula ($C_6H_{12}O_6$) but not the same structure. Both are aldose sugars with six carbons, but they differ in the spatial arrangement of the hydroxyl group at the fourth carbon (highlighted in Figure 5.2).

This is a key point: Because the structures of glucose and galactose differ, their functions differ. In cells, glucose is used as a source of carbons for the construction of other molecules and chemical energy that sustains life. But for galactose to be used in these roles, it first has to be converted to glucose via an enzyme-catalyzed reaction. This example underscores a general theme: Even seemingly simple changes in structure—like the location of a single hydroxyl group—can have enormous consequences for function. This is because molecules interact in precise ways, based on their shape.

It's rare for sugars consisting of five or more carbons to exist in the form of the linear chains illustrated in Figure 5.2, however. In aqueous solution they tend to form ring structures. The bond responsible for ring formation occurs only between the carbon containing the carbonyl group and one of the carbons with a hydroxyl group. Glucose serves as the example in **FIGURE 5.3**. When the cyclic structure forms in glucose, the C-1 carbon (the carbon numbered 1 in the linear chain) forms a bond with the oxygen atom of the C-5 hydroxyl and transfers its hydrogen to the C-1 carbonyl, turning it into a hydroxyl group.

Transfer of hydrogen between the C-5 and C-1 functional groups preserves the number of atoms and hydroxyls found in the ring and linear forms. The newly formed C-1 hydroxyl group can be oriented in two distinct ways: above or below the plane of the ring. The different configurations produce the molecules ⊠-glucose and ⊠-glucose.

To summarize, many distinct monosaccharides exist because so many aspects of their structure are variable: aldose or ketose placement of the carbonyl group, variation in carbon number, different arrangements of hydroxyl groups in space, and alternative ring forms. Each monosaccharide has a unique structure and function.

Monosaccharides and Chemical Evolution

Laboratory simulations, like those you read about in Chapter 2, have shown that most monosaccharides are readily synthesized under conditions that mimic the conditions of early Earth. For example, when formaldehyde (CH_2O) molecules are heated in solution, they react with one another to form almost all the pentoses and hexoses.

In addition, researchers have discovered the three-carbon ketose illustrated in Figure 5.1, along with a wide array of compounds closely related to sugars, on a meteorite that struck Murchison, Australia, in 1969. Based on these observations, investigators suspect that sugars are synthesized on dust particles and other debris in interstellar space and could have rained down onto Earth as the planet was forming, as well as being synthesized in the hot water near ancient undersea volcanoes.

More recent evidence suggests that synthesis of sugars could have been catalyzed by minerals found in the walls of deep-sea hydrothermal vents. Most researchers interested in chemical evolution maintain that one or more of the above mechanisms led to the accumulation of monosaccharides in the early oceans.

Modern cells display a wide range of carbohydrates beyond monosaccharides. How do these monomers join together to form polymers? Is the process similar to how amino acids link together to form proteins and nucleotides join to form nucleic acids? Let's explore how the array of functional groups in monosaccharides influences the polymerization of carbohydrates.

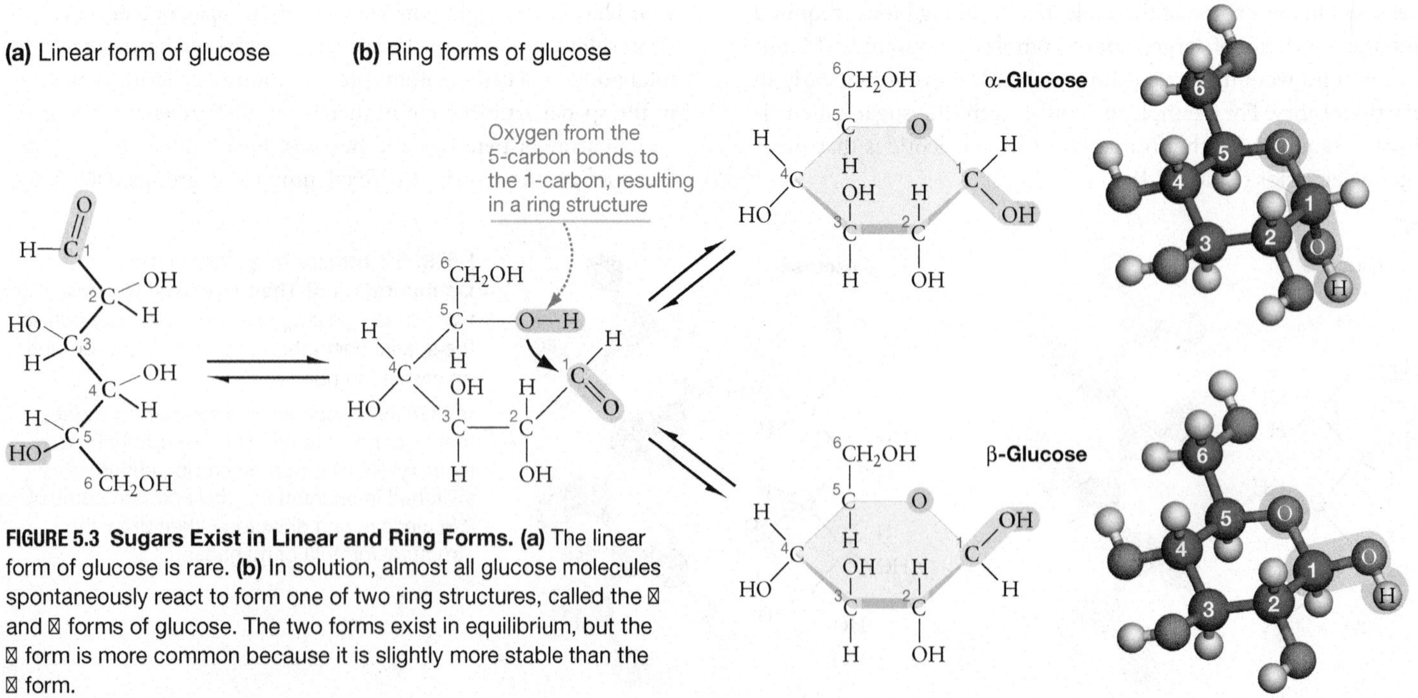

(a) Linear form of glucose

(b) Ring forms of glucose

Oxygen from the 5-carbon bonds to the 1-carbon, resulting in a ring structure

α-Glucose

β-Glucose

FIGURE 5.3 Sugars Exist in Linear and Ring Forms. (a) The linear form of glucose is rare. **(b)** In solution, almost all glucose molecules spontaneously react to form one of two ring structures, called the ⊠ and ⊠ forms of glucose. The two forms exist in equilibrium, but the ⊠ form is more common because it is slightly more stable than the ⊠ form.

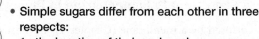

If you understand that . . .

- Simple sugars differ from each other in three respects:
  1. the location of their carbonyl group,
  2. the number of carbon atoms present, and
  3. the spatial arrangement of their atoms—particularly the relative positions of hydroxyl (⊠ OH) groups.

✔ **You should be able to . . .**

Draw the structural formula of a three-carbon monosaccharide ($C_3H_6O_3$) in linear form and then draw three other sugars that illustrate the three differences listed above.

Answers are available in Appendix A.

5.2 The Structure of Polysaccharides

Simple sugars can be covalently linked into chains of varying lengths, also known as complex carbohydrates. These chains range in size from small oligomers, or oligosaccharides, to the large polymers called polysaccharides. When only two sugars are linked together, they are known as **disaccharides.**

Similar to proteins and nucleic acids, the structure and function of larger carbohydrates depends on the types of monomers involved and how they are linked together. For example, maltose, also known as malt sugar, and lactose, an important sugar in milk, are two disaccharides that differ by just one monosaccharide. Maltose consists of two identical glucose molecules (**FIGURE 5.4a**), while lactose is made up of glucose and galactose (**FIGURE 5.4b**).

Monosaccharides polymerize when a condensation reaction occurs between two hydroxyl groups, resulting in a covalent interaction called a **glycosidic linkage.** The inverse reaction, hydrolysis, cleaves these linkages. (To review condensation and hydrolysis reactions, see Chapter 3.)

(a) Formation of α-glycosidic linkage

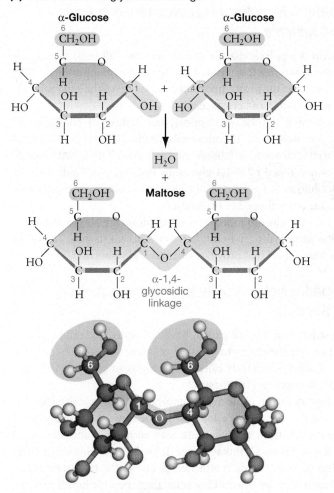

(b) Formation of β-glycosidic linkage

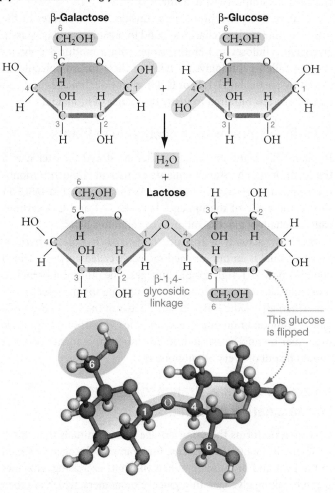

FIGURE 5.4 Monosaccharides Polymerize through Formation of Glycosidic Linkages. A glycosidic linkage occurs when hydroxyl groups on two monosaccharides undergo a condensation reaction. Maltose and lactose are disaccharides.

In that they hold monomers together, glycosidic linkages are analogous to the peptide bonds and phosphodiester linkages in proteins and nucleic acids. There is an important difference, however. Peptide bonds and phosphodiester linkages form between the same locations in their monomers, giving proteins and nucleic acids a standard backbone structure, but this is not the case for polysaccharides. Because glycosidic linkages form between hydroxyl groups, and because every monosaccharide contains at least two hydroxyls, the location and geometry of glycosidic linkages can vary widely among polysaccharides.

Maltose and lactose illustrate two of the most common glycosidic linkages, called the α-1,4-glycosidic linkage and the β-1,4-glycosidic linkage. The numbers refer to the carbons on either side of the linkage, indicating that both linkages are between the C-1 and C-4 carbons. Their geometry, however, is different: α and β refer to the contrasting orientations of the C-1 hydroxyls—on opposite sides of the plane of the glucose rings (i.e., "above" versus "below" the plane).

As Section 5.3 explains, the orientation of this hydroxyl in glycosidic linkages is particularly important in the structure, function, and durability of the molecules. In essence, the difference between polysaccharides used for storage and structural polysaccharides is a simple twist of a link.

To drive this point home, let's consider the structures of the most common polysaccharides found in organisms today: starch, glycogen, cellulose, and chitin, along with a modified polysaccharide called peptidoglycan. Each of these macromolecules is joined by particular α-1,4- or β-1,4-glycosidic linkages and can consist of a few hundred to many thousands of monomers.

Starch: A Storage Polysaccharide in Plants

In plant cells, some monosaccharides are stored for later use in the form of starch. **Starch** consists entirely of α-glucose monomers joined by glycosidic linkages. As the top panel in **TABLE 5.1** shows, the angle of the linkages between C-1 and C-4 carbons causes a chain of glucose subunits to coil into a helix.

Starch is actually a mixture of two such polysaccharides, however. One is an unbranched molecule called amylose, which contains only α-1,4-glycosidic linkages. The other is a branched molecule called amylopectin. The branching in amylopectin occurs when glycosidic linkages form between the C-1 carbon of a glucose monomer on one strand and the C-6 carbon of a glucose monomer on another strand. In amylopectin, branches occur at about one out of every 30 monomers.

Glycogen: A Highly Branched Storage Polysaccharide in Animals

Glycogen performs the same storage role in animals that starch performs in plants. In humans, for example, glycogen is stored in the liver and in muscles. When you start exercising, enzymes begin breaking glycogen into glucose monomers, which are then processed in muscle cells to supply energy. Glycogen is a polymer of α-glucose and is nearly identical to the branched form of starch. However, instead of an α-1,6-glycosidic linkage occurring

in about 1 out of every 30 monomers, a branch occurs in about 1 out of every 10 glucose subunits (see Table 5.1).

Cellulose: A Structural Polysaccharide in Plants

All cells are enclosed by a membrane (Chapter 1). In most organisms living today, the cell is also surrounded by a layer of material called a wall. A **cell wall** is a protective sheet that occurs outside the membrane. In plants, bacteria, fungi, and many other groups, the cell wall is composed primarily of one or more polysaccharides.

In plants, cellulose is the major component of the cell wall. **Cellulose** is a polymer of β-glucose monomers, joined by β-1,4-glycosidic linkages. As Table 5.1 shows, the geometry of the linkage is such that each glucose monomer in the chain is flipped in relation to the adjacent monomer. The flipped orientation is important because **(1)** it generates a linear molecule, rather than the helix seen in starch; and **(2)** it permits multiple hydrogen bonds to form between adjacent, parallel strands of cellulose. As a result, cellulose forms long, parallel strands that are joined by hydrogen bonds. The linked cellulose fibers are strong and give the cell structural support.

Chitin: A Structural Polysaccharide in Fungi and Animals

Chitin is a polysaccharide that stiffens the cell walls of fungi. It is also found in a few types of protists and in many animals. It is, for example, the most important component of the external skeletons of insects and crustaceans.

Chitin is similar to cellulose, but instead of consisting of glucose monomers, the monosaccharide involved is one called N-acetylglucosamine (abbreviated as NAG). These NAG monomers are joined by β-1,4-glycosidic linkages (see Table 5.1). As in cellulose, the geometry of these bonds results in every other residue being flipped in orientation.

Like the glucose monomers in cellulose, the NAG subunits in chitin form hydrogen bonds between adjacent strands. The result is a tough sheet that provides stiffness and protection.

Peptidoglycan: A Structural Polysaccharide in Bacteria

Most bacteria, like all plants, have cell walls. But unlike plants, in bacteria the ability to produce cellulose is extremely rare. Instead, a polysaccharide called **peptidoglycan** gives bacterial cell walls strength and firmness.

Peptidoglycan is the most complex of the polysaccharides discussed thus far. It has a long backbone formed by two types of monosaccharides that alternate with each other and are linked by β-1,4-glycosidic linkages (see Table 5.1). In addition, a short chain of amino acids is attached to one of the two sugar types. When molecules of peptidoglycan align, peptide bonds link the amino acid chains on adjacent strands. These links serve the same purpose as the hydrogen bonds between the parallel strands of cellulose and chitin in the cell walls of other organisms.

Polysaccharides Differ in Structure

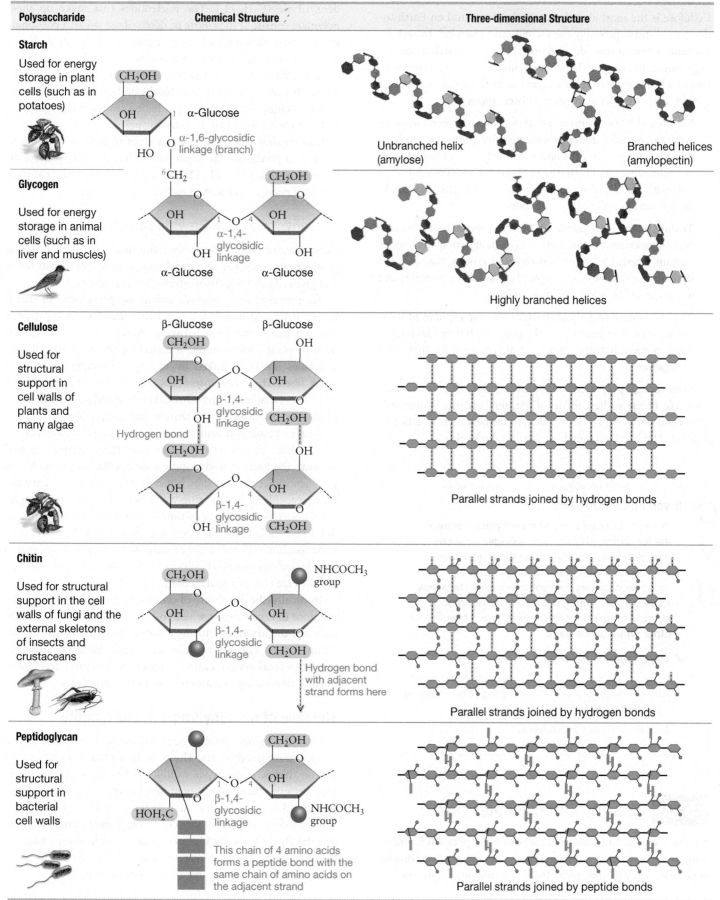

Polysaccharide	Chemical Structure	Three-dimensional Structure

Starch

Used for energy storage in plant cells (such as in potatoes)

CH$_2$OH

α-Glucose

α-1,6-glycosidic linkage (branch)

Unbranched helix (amylose)

Branched helices (amylopectin)

Glycogen

Used for energy storage in animal cells (such as in liver and muscles)

CH$_2$OH

CH$_2$OH

α-1,4-glycosidic linkage

α-Glucose   α-Glucose

Highly branched helices

Cellulose

Used for structural support in cell walls of plants and many algae

β-Glucose   β-Glucose

CH$_2$OH   OH

β-1,4-glycosidic linkage

CH$_2$OH

Hydrogen bond

CH$_2$OH   OH

β-1,4-glycosidic linkage

CH$_2$OH

Parallel strands joined by hydrogen bonds

Chitin

Used for structural support in the cell walls of fungi and the external skeletons of insects and crustaceans

CH$_2$OH

NHCOCH$_3$ group

OH   OH

β-1,4-glycosidic linkage

CH$_2$OH

Hydrogen bond with adjacent strand forms here

Parallel strands joined by hydrogen bonds

Peptidoglycan

Used for structural support in bacterial cell walls

CH$_2$OH

OH   OH

β-1,4-glycosidic linkage

HOH$_2$C

NHCOCH$_3$ group

This chain of 4 amino acids forms a peptide bond with the same chain of amino acids on the adjacent strand

Parallel strands joined by peptide bonds

Polysaccharides and Chemical Evolution

Cellulose is the most abundant organic compound on Earth today, and chitin is probably the second most abundant by weight. Virtually all organisms depend on glycogen or starch as an energy source. But despite their current importance to life, polysaccharides probably played little to no role in the origin of life. This conclusion is supported by several observations:

- *No plausible mechanism exists for the polymerization of monosaccharides under conditions that prevailed early in Earth's history.* In cells and in laboratory experiments, the glycosidic linkages illustrated in Figure 5.4 and Table 5.1 form only with the aid of protein enzymes. No enzyme-like RNAs are known to catalyze these reactions.

- *To date, no polysaccharide has been discovered that can catalyze polymerization reactions.* Even though polysaccharides contain reactive hydroxyl and carbonyl groups, they lack the structural and chemical complexity that makes proteins, and to a lesser extent RNA, effective catalysts.

- *The monomers in polysaccharides are not capable of complementary base pairing.* Like proteins, but unlike nucleic acids, polysaccharides cannot act as templates for their own replication.

Even though polysaccharides probably did not play a significant role in the earliest forms of life, they became enormously important once cellular life evolved. In the next section, let's take a detailed look at how they function in today's cells.

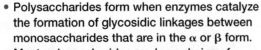

If you understand that . . .

- Polysaccharides form when enzymes catalyze the formation of glycosidic linkages between monosaccharides that are in the α or β form.
- Most polysaccharides are long chains of monosaccharides, but some branch extensively. Among linear forms, it is common for adjacent strands to be connected by hydrogen bonding or other types of linkages.

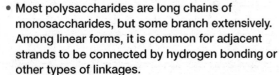

✔ **You should be able to . . .**

Provide four structural differences that could result in different oligosaccharides consisting of two glucose monomers and two galactose monomers.

Answers are available in Appendix A.

5.3 What Do Carbohydrates Do?

One of the basic functions that carbohydrates perform in organisms is to serve as a substrate for synthesizing more-complex molecules. For example, recall that RNA contains the five-carbon sugar ribose ($C_5H_{10}O_5$) and DNA contains the modified sugar deoxyribose ($C_5H_{10}O_4$). The nucleotides that make up these polymers consist of the ribose or deoxyribose sugar, a phosphate group, and a nitrogenous base (Chapter 4). The sugar itself acts as a subunit of each of these monomers.

In addition, sugars frequently furnish the raw "carbon skeletons" that are used as building blocks in the synthesis of important molecules. Your cells are producing amino acids right now, for example, using sugars as a starting point.

Carbohydrates have diverse functions in cells: In addition to serving as precursors to larger molecules, they (1) provide fibrous structural materials, (2) indicate cell identity, and (3) store chemical energy. Let's look at each function in turn.

Carbohydrates Can Provide Structural Support

Cellulose and chitin, along with the modified polysaccharide peptidoglycan, are key structural compounds. They form fibers that give cells and organisms strength and elasticity.

To appreciate why cellulose, chitin, and peptidoglycan are effective structural molecules, recall that they form long strands and that bonds can form between adjacent strands. In the cell walls of plants, for example, a collection of about 80 cellulose molecules are cross-linked by hydrogen bonding to create a tough fiber. These cellulose fibers, in turn, crisscross to form a tough sheet that is able to withstand pulling and pushing forces—what an engineer would call tension and compression.

Besides being stiff and strong, the structural carbohydrates are durable. Almost all organisms have the enzymes required to break the various ⊠-glycosidic linkages that hold starch and glycogen molecules together, but only a few organisms have enzymes capable of hydrolyzing cellulose, chitin, and peptidoglycan. Due to the strong interactions between strands consisting of ⊠-1,4-glycosidic linkages, water is excluded and the fibers tend to be insoluble. The absence of water within these fibers makes their hydrolysis more difficult. As a result, the structural polysaccharides are resistant to degradation and decay.

Ironically, the durability of cellulose supports digestion. The cellulose that you ingest when you eat plant cells—what biologists call dietary fiber—forms a porous mass that absorbs and retains water. This sponge-like mass adds moisture and bulk that helps fecal material move through the intestinal tract more quickly, preventing constipation and other problems.

The Role of Carbohydrates in Cell Identity

Structural polymers tend to be repetitive, with only one or two types of monosaccharides. The same is not true for all complex carbohydrates. Some types exhibit enormous structural diversity, because their component monomers—and the linkages between them—vary a lot. As a result, they are capable of displaying information to other cells through their structure. More specifically, polysaccharides act as an identification badge on the outer surface of the plasma membrane that surrounds a cell. (Chapter 6 describes plasma membranes in detail.)

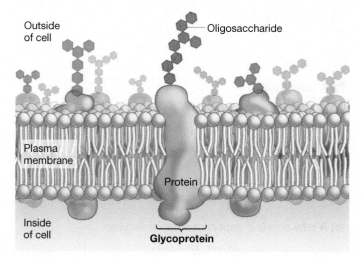

FIGURE 5.5 Carbohydrates Are an Identification Badge for Cells. Glycoproteins contain sugar groups that project outside the cell from the surface of the plasma membrane enclosing the cell. These sugar groups have distinctive structures that identify the type or species of the cell.

FIGURE 5.5 shows how this information about cell identity is displayed. Molecules called glycoproteins project outward from the cell surface into the surrounding environment. A **glycoprotein** is a protein that has one or more carbohydrates covalently bonded to it—usually relatively short oligosaccharides.

Glycoproteins are key molecules in what biologists call cell–cell recognition and cell–cell signaling. Each cell in your body has glycoproteins on its surface that identify it as part of your body. Immune system cells use these glycoproteins to distinguish your body's cells from foreign cells, such as bacteria. In addition, each distinct type of cell in a multicellular organism—for example, the nerve cells and muscle cells in your body—displays a different set of glycoproteins on its surface.

The identification information displayed by glycoproteins helps cells recognize and communicate with each other.

The key point here is to recognize that the variety in the types of monosaccharides and how they can be linked together makes it possible for an enormous number of unique oligosaccharides to exist. As a result, each cell type and each species can display a unique identity.

During the 1980s, Paul Wassarman and colleagues investigated the role of glycoproteins in one of the most important cell–cell recognition events in the life of a plant or animal—the attachment of sperm to eggs during fertilization. This step guarantees specificity—sperm recognize and bind only to eggs of their own species.

In one experiment, the researchers mixed sperm with purified egg-surface glycoproteins and discovered that most of the sperm lost their ability to attach to eggs (**FIGURE 5.6**). Such loss of function is an example of what researchers call competitive inhibition. The glycoproteins had bound to—and thus blocked—the same structure on the sperm that it uses to bind to eggs. This result showed that sperm attach to eggs via egg glycoproteins.

QUESTION: What part of surface glycoproteins do sperm recognize when they attach to eggs?

HYPOTHESIS: Sperm attach to the carbohydrate component.

NULL HYPOTHESIS: Sperm attach to the protein component.

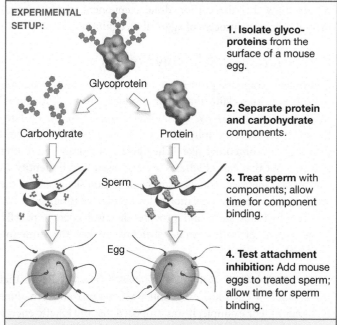

EXPERIMENTAL SETUP:

Glycoprotein

Carbohydrate   Protein

Sperm

Egg

1. **Isolate glycoproteins** from the surface of a mouse egg.

2. **Separate protein and carbohydrate** components.

3. **Treat sperm** with components; allow time for component binding.

4. **Test attachment inhibition:** Add mouse eggs to treated sperm; allow time for sperm binding.

PREDICTION: The carbohydrate component of the glycoprotein will bind to sperm and block their attachment to eggs.

PREDICTION OF NULL HYPOTHESIS: The protein component of the glycoprotein will block sperm attachment to eggs.

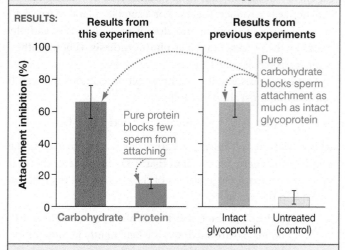

RESULTS:

Results from this experiment

Pure protein blocks few sperm from attaching

Results from previous experiments

Pure carbohydrate blocks sperm attachment as much as intact glycoprotein

Attachment inhibition (%)

Carbohydrate   Protein

Intact glycoprotein   Untreated (control)

CONCLUSION: Sperm recognize and bind to the carbohydrates of egg-surface glycoproteins when they attach to egg cells.

FIGURE 5.6 Carbohydrates Are Required for Cellular Recognition and Attachment.

SOURCES: Florman, H. M., K. B. Bechtol, and P. M. Wassarman. 1984. Enzymatic dissection of the functions of the mouse egg's receptor for sperm. *Developmental Biology* 106: 243–255. Also Florman, H. M., and P. M. Wassarman. 1985. O-linked oligosaccharides of mouse egg ZP3 account for its sperm receptor activity. *Cell* 41: 313–324.

✔**QUANTITATIVE** How would the bars change in the graph if sperm attachment required only the protein portion of egg glycoproteins?

But which part of the egg glycoproteins is essential for recognition and attachment—the protein or the carbohydrate? In follow-up experiments, Wassarman's group used the same type of competitive-binding assay to answer this question. When sperm were mixed with purified carbohydrates alone, most were unable to attach to eggs. In contrast, most sperm treated with purified protein alone were not inhibited and still attached to eggs. Both results show that the carbohydrate component plays a fundamental role in the process of egg-cell recognition.

Carbohydrates and Energy Storage

Candy-bar wrappers promise a quick energy boost, and ads for sports drinks claim that their products provide the "carbs" needed for peak activity. If you were to ask friends or family members what carbohydrates do in your body, they would probably say something like "They give you energy." And after pointing out that carbohydrates are also used in cell identity, as a structural material, and as a source of carbon skeletons for the synthesis of other complex molecules, you'd have to agree.

Carbohydrates store and provide chemical energy in cells. What aspect of carbohydrate structure makes this function possible?

Carbohydrates Store Sunlight as Chemical Energy Recall that the essence of chemical evolution was energy transformations (Chapter 2). For example, it was proposed that the kinetic energy in sunlight may have been converted into chemical energy and stored in bonds of molecules such as formaldehyde (CH_2O).

This same type of transformation from light energy to chemical energy occurs in cells today, but instead of making formaldehyde, cells produce sugars. For example, plants harvest the kinetic energy in sunlight and store it in the bonds of carbohydrates by the process known as **photosynthesis.** (Photosynthesis is the focus of Chapter 10.)

Photosynthesis entails a complex set of reactions that can be summarized most simply as follows:

$$CO_2 + H_2O + sunlight \longrightarrow (CH_2O)_n + O_2$$

where $(CH_2O)_n$ represents a carbohydrate. The key to understanding the energy conversion that is taking place in this reaction is to compare the positions of the electrons in the reactants to those in the products.

1. The electrons in the C=O bonds of carbon dioxide and the C—O bonds of carbohydrates are held tightly because of oxygen's high electronegativity. Thus, they have relatively low potential energy.

2. The electrons involved in the C—H bonds of carbohydrates are shared equally because the electronegativity of carbon and hydrogen is about the same. Thus, these electrons have relatively high potential energy.

3. Electrons are also shared equally in the carbon–carbon C—C bonds of carbohydrates—meaning that they, too, have relatively high potential energy.

(a) Carbon dioxide

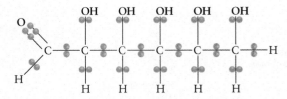

(b) A carbohydrate

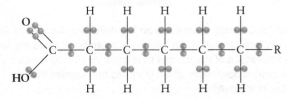

(c) A fatty acid (a component of fat molecules)

FIGURE 5.7 In Organisms, Potential Energy Is Stored in C▢H and C▢C Bonds. **(a)** In carbon dioxide, the electrons involved in covalent bonds are held tightly by oxygen atoms. **(b)** In carbohydrates such as the sugar shown here, many of the covalently bonded electrons are held equally between C and H atoms. **(c)** The fatty acids found in fat molecules have more C–H bonds and fewer C–O bonds than carbohydrates do. ("R" stands for the rest of the molecule.)

✔**EXERCISE** Circle the bonds in this diagram that have high potential energy.

C—C and C—H bonds have much higher potential energy than C—O bonds have. As a result, carbohydrates have much more chemical energy than carbon dioxide has.

FIGURE 5.7 summarizes and extends these points. Start by comparing the structure of carbon dioxide in Figure 5.7a with the carbohydrate in Figure 5.7b. The main difference is the presence of C—C and C—H bonds in the carbohydrate. Now compare the carbohydrate in Figure 5.7b with the fatty acid—a subunit of a fat molecule—in Figure 5.7c. Compared with carbohydrates, fats contain many more C—C and C—H bonds and many fewer C—O bonds.

This point is important. C—C and C—H bonds have high potential energy because the electrons are shared equally by atoms with low electronegativities. C—O bonds, in contrast, have low potential energy because the highly electronegative oxygen atom holds the electrons so tightly. Both carbohydrates and fats are used as fuel in cells, but fats store twice as much energy per gram compared with carbohydrates. (Fats are discussed in more detail in Chapter 6.)

Enzymes Hydrolyze Polysaccharides to Release Glucose Starch and glycogen are efficient energy-storage molecules because they polymerize via ▢-glycosidic linkages instead of the ▢-glycosidic linkages observed in the structural polysaccharides. The

⊠-linkages in storage polysaccharides are readily hydrolyzed to release glucose, while the structural polysaccharides resist enzymatic degradation.

The most important enzyme involved in catalyzing the hydrolysis of ⊠-glycosidic linkages in glycogen molecules is a protein called **phosphorylase.** Many of your cells contain phosphorylase, so they can break down glycogen to provide glucose on demand.

The enzymes involved in breaking the ⊠-glycosidic linkages in starch are called **amylases.** Your salivary glands and pancreas produce amylases that are secreted into your mouth and small intestine, respectively. These amylases are responsible for digesting the starch that you eat.

The glucose subunits that are hydrolyzed from glycogen and starch are processed in reactions that result in the production of chemical energy that can be used in the cell. Glycogen and starch are like a candy bar that has segments, so you can break off chunks whenever you need a boost.

Energy Stored in Glucose is Used to Make ATP When a cell needs energy, reactions lead to the breakdown of the glucose and capture of the released energy through synthesis of the nucleotide adenosine triphosphate (ATP) (introduced in Chapter 4).

More specifically, the energy that is released when sugars are processed is used to synthesize ATP from a precursor called adenosine diphosphate (ADP) plus a free inorganic phosphate (P_i) molecule. The overall reaction can be written as follows:

$$(CH_2O)_n + O_2 + ADP + P_i \longrightarrow CO_2 + H_2O + ATP$$

To put this in words, the chemical energy stored in the C−H and C−C bonds of carbohydrate is transferred to a new bond linking a third phosphate group to ADP to form ATP.

How much energy does it take to form ATP? Consider this example: A cell can use the 10 calories of energy stored in a LifeSavers candy to produce approximately 2×10^{23} molecules of ATP. Although this sounds like a lot of ATP, an average human's energy needs would burn through all of this ATP energy in a little over a minute! The energy in ATP drives reactions like polymerization and cellular processes like moving your muscles.

Carbohydrates are like the water that piles up behind a dam; ATP is like the electricity generated at a dam, which lights up your home. Carbohydrates store chemical energy; ATP makes chemical energy useful to the cell.

Later chapters analyze in detail how cells capture and store energy in sugars and how these sugars are then broken down to provide cells with usable chemical energy in the form of ATP (Chapters 8, 9, and 10). For both of these processes to occur, however, a selectively permeable membrane barrier is required. The following chapter introduces the lipids needed to build these membranes and the role they played in the evolution of the first cell.

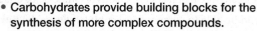

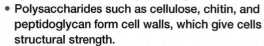
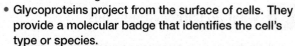

check your understanding

If you understand that . . .

- Carbohydrates provide building blocks for the synthesis of more complex compounds.
- Polysaccharides such as cellulose, chitin, and peptidoglycan form cell walls, which give cells structural strength.
- Glycoproteins project from the surface of cells. They provide a molecular badge that identifies the cell's type or species.
- Starch and glycogen store sugars for later use in reactions that produce ATP. Sugars contain large amounts of chemical energy because they contain carbon atoms that are bonded to hydrogen atoms or other carbon atoms. The C⊠H and C⊠C bonds have high potential energy because the electrons are shared equally by atoms with low electronegativity.

✔ **You should be able to . . .**

1. Identify two aspects of the structures of cellulose, chitin, and peptidoglycan that correlate with their function as structural molecules.

2. Describe how the carbohydrates you ate during breakfast today are functioning in your body right now.

Answers are available in Appendix A.

CHAPTER 5 REVIEW For media, go to MasteringBiology

If you understand . . .

5.1 Sugars as Monomers

- Monosaccharides are organic compounds that have a carbonyl group and several hydroxyl groups. The molecular formula for a sugar is typically $(CH_2O)_n$, but the number of "carbon-hydrate" groups may vary between sugars, as indicated by the *n*.

- Although some monosaccharides may have the same molecular formula, the arrangement of functional groups can lead to differences in the molecular structure of the sugars.

- Individual monosaccharides may form ring structures that differ from one another in the orientation of a hydroxyl group.

✔ You should be able to explain how a relatively small difference in the location of a carbonyl or hydroxyl group can lead to dramatic changes in the properties and function of a monosaccharide.

5.2 The Structure of Polysaccharides

- Monosaccharides can be covalently bonded to one another via glycosidic linkages, which join hydroxyl groups on adjacent molecules.

- In contrast to proteins and nucleic acids, polysaccharides do not always form a single uniform backbone structure. The numerous hydroxyls found in each monosaccharide allow glycosidic linkages to form at different sites and new strands to branch from existing chains.

- The types of monomers involved and the geometries of the glycosidic linkages between monomers distinguish different polysaccharides from one another.

- The most common polysaccharides in organisms today are starch, glycogen, cellulose, and chitin; peptidoglycan is an abundant polysaccharide that has short chains of amino acids attached.

✔ You should be able to compare and contrast glycosidic linkages in polysaccharides with the linkages between monomers in proteins and nucleic acids.

5.3 What Do Carbohydrates Do?

- In carbohydrates, as in proteins and nucleic acids, structure correlates with function.

- Cellulose, chitin, and peptidoglycan are polysaccharides that function in support. They are made up of monosaccharide monomers joined by ☒-1,4-glycosidic linkages. When individual molecules of these polysaccharides align side by side, bonds form between them—resulting in strong, flexible fibers or sheets that resist hydrolysis.

- The oligosaccharides on cell-surface glycoproteins can function as specific signposts or identity tags because their constituent monosaccharides are so diverse in geometry and composition.

- Both starch and glycogen function as energy-storage molecules. They are made up of glucose molecules that are joined by ☒-glycosidic linkages. These linkages are readily hydrolyzed to release glucose for the production of ATP.

✔ You should be able to describe four key differences in the structure of polysaccharides that function in energy storage versus structural support.

MB **MasteringBiology**

1. MasteringBiology Assignments

Tutorials and Activities Carbohydrates; Carbohydrate Structure and Function; Types of Carbohydrates

Questions Reading Quizzes, Blue-Thread Questions, Test Bank

2. eText Read your book online, search, take notes, highlight text, and more.

3. The Study Area Practice Test, Cumulative Test, BioFlix® 3-D Animations, Videos, Activities, Audio Glossary, Word Study Tools, Art

---

You should be able to . . .

✔ TEST YOUR KNOWLEDGE
Answers are available in Appendix A

1. What is the difference between a monosaccharide, an oligosaccharide, and a polysaccharide?
   a. the number of carbon atoms in the molecule
   b. the type of glycosidic linkage between monomers
   c. the spatial arrangement of the various hydroxyl residues in the molecule
   d. the number of monomers in the molecule

2. What are three ways monosaccharides differ from one another?

3. What type of bond is formed between two sugars in a disaccharide?
   a. glycosidic linkage
   b. phosphodiester bond
   c. peptide bond
   d. hydrogen bond

4. What holds cellulose molecules together in bundles large enough to form fibers?
   a. the cell wall
   b. peptide bonds
   c. hydrogen bonds
   d. hydrophobic interactions between different residues in the cellulose helix

5. What are the primary functions of carbohydrates in cells?
   a. energy storage, cell identity, structure, and building blocks for synthesis
   b. catalysis, structure, and energy storage
   c. information storage and catalysis
   d. source of carbon, information storage, and energy storage

6. What is responsible for the difference in potential energy between carbohydrates and carbon dioxide?

7. Which of the differences listed here could be found in the same monosaccharide?

a. different orientation of a hydroxyl in the linear form

b. different number of carbons

c. different orientation of a hydroxyl in the ring form

d. different position of the carbonyl group in the linear form

8. What would most likely occur if the galactose in lactose were replaced with glucose?

a. It would not be digested by human infants or adults.

b. It would be digested by most adult humans.

c. It would be digested by human infants, but not adults.

d. It would be digested by human adults, but not infants.

9. Explain how the structure of carbohydrates supports their function in displaying the identity of a cell.

10. What is the difference between linking glucose molecules with ☒-1,4-glycosidic linkages versus ☒-1,4-glycosidic linkages? What are the consequences?

11. Give three reasons why researchers have concluded that polysaccharides were unlikely to play a large role in the origin of life.

12. Compare and contrast the structures and functions of starch and glycogen. How are these molecules similar? How are they different?

13. A weight-loss program for humans that emphasized minimal consumption of carbohydrates was popular in some countries

in the early 2000s. What was the logic behind this diet? (Note: This diet plan caused controversy and is not endorsed by some physicians and researchers).

14. Galactosemia is a potentially fatal disease that occurs in humans who lack the enzyme that converts galactose to glucose. To treat this disease, physicians exclude the monosaccharide galactose from the diet. Which of the following would you also predict to be excluded from the diet?

a. maltose   b. starch   c. mannose   d. lactose

15. If you hold a salty cracker in your mouth long enough, it will begin to taste sweet. What is responsible for this change in taste?

16. Lysozyme, an enzyme found in human saliva, tears, and other secretions, catalyzes the hydrolysis of the ☒-1,4-glycosidic linkages in peptidoglycan. Predict the effect of this enzyme on bacteria, and explain the role its activity plays in human health.

6 Lipids, Membranes, and the First Cells

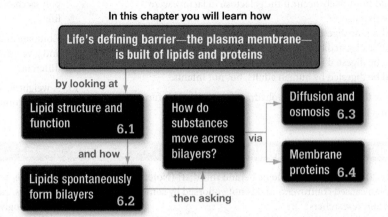

In this chapter you will learn how

Life's defining barrier—the plasma membrane—is built of lipids and proteins

by looking at

Lipid structure and function **6.1**

and how

Lipids spontaneously form bilayers **6.2**

then asking

How do substances move across bilayers?

via

Diffusion and osmosis **6.3**

Membrane proteins **6.4**

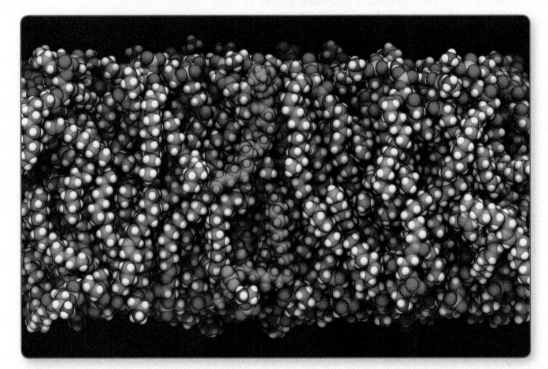

A space-filling model of a phospholipid bilayer. In single-celled organisms, this cluster of molecules forms part of the boundary between life (inside the cell) and nonlife (outside the cell)—the cell membrane.

Currently, most biologists support the hypothesis that biological evolution began with a catalytic RNA molecule that could replicate itself. As the offspring of this molecule multiplied, natural selection would have favored the most efficient versions. A second great milestone in the history of life occurred when descendants of these replicators became enclosed within a membrane.

Why is the presence of a membrane so important? The **plasma membrane,** or **cell membrane,** separates life from nonlife. It is a layer of molecules that surrounds the cell interior and separates it from the environment.

- The plasma membrane serves as a selective barrier: It keeps damaging compounds out of the cell and allows entry of compounds needed by the cell.

- Because the plasma membrane sequesters the appropriate chemicals in an enclosed area, reactants collide more frequently—the chemical reactions necessary for life occur much more efficiently.

This chapter is part of the Big Picture. See how on pages 104–105.

✔ When you see this checkmark, stop and test yourself. Answers are available in Appendix A.

While researchers of chemical evolution are currently debating when membranes arose—whether early or late during the emergence of life—there is little argument about the importance of this event. After life secured a membrane, it continued to evolve into an efficient and dynamic reaction vessel—the cell.

How do membranes form? Which ions and molecules can pass through a membrane and which cannot, and why? These are some of the most fundamental questions in all of biological science. Let's delve into them, beginning with the membrane's foundation—lipids.

6.1 Lipid Structure and Function

Lipid is a catchall term for carbon-containing compounds that are found in organisms and are largely nonpolar and hydrophobic—meaning that they do not dissolve readily in water. (Recall from Chapter 2 that water is a polar solvent.) Lipids do dissolve, however, in liquids consisting of nonpolar organic compounds.

To understand why lipids are insoluble in water, examine the five-carbon compound called isoprene, illustrated in **FIGURE 6.1a**. Note that isoprene consists of carbon atoms bonded to hydrogen atoms. The figure also shows the structural formula of a chain of linked isoprenes, called an isoprenoid.

Molecules that contain only carbon and hydrogen are known as **hydrocarbons.** Hydrocarbons are nonpolar because electrons are shared equally in C–H bonds—owing to the approximately equal electronegativity of carbon and hydrogen. Since these bonds form no partial charges, hydrocarbons are hydrophobic. Thus lipids do not dissolve in water, because they have a significant hydrocarbon component.

Bond Saturation Is an Important Aspect of Hydrocarbon Structure

FIGURE 6.1b gives the structural formula of a **fatty acid,** a simple lipid consisting of a hydrocarbon chain bonded to a carboxyl (–COOH) functional group. Fatty acids and isoprenes are key building blocks of important lipids found in organisms. Just as subtle differences in the orientation of hydroxyls in sugars can lead to dramatic effects in their structure and function, the type of C–C bond used in hydrocarbon chains is a key factor in lipid structure.

When two carbon atoms form a double bond, the attached atoms are found in a plane instead of a three-dimensional tetrahedron. The carbon atoms involved are also locked into place. They cannot rotate freely, as they do in carbon–carbon single bonds. As a result, certain double bonds between carbon atoms produce a "kink" in an otherwise straight hydrocarbon chain (Figure 6.1b, left).

Hydrocarbon chains that consist of only single bonds between the carbons are called **saturated.** If one or more double bonds exist in the hydrocarbon chains, then they are **unsaturated.** The choice of terms is logical. If a hydrocarbon chain does not contain a double bond, it is saturated with the maximum number of hydrogen atoms that can attach to the carbon skeleton. If it is unsaturated, then a C–H bond is removed to form a C=C double bond, resulting in fewer than the maximum number of attached hydrogen atoms.

Foods that contain lipids with many double bonds are said to be polyunsaturated and are advertised as healthier than foods with saturated fats. Recent research suggests that polyunsaturated fats help protect the heart from disease. Exactly how this occurs is under investigation.

(a) Isoprenes can be linked into chains called isoprenoids.

(b) Fatty acids can be saturated or unsaturated.

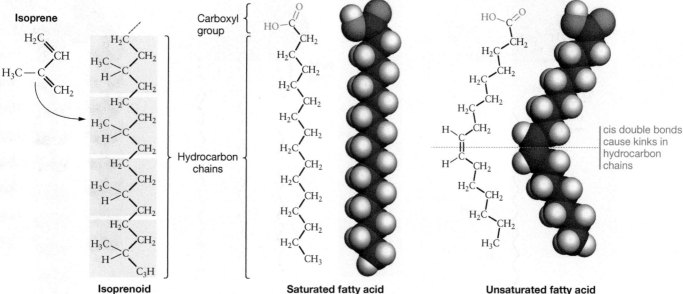

FIGURE 6.1 Hydrocarbon Structure. (a) Isoprene subunits, like the one shown to the left, can be linked to each other, end to end, to form long hydrocarbon chains called isoprenoids. **(b)** Fatty acids typically contain a total of 14–20 carbon atoms, most found in their long hydrocarbon "tails." Unsaturated hydrocarbons contain carbon–carbon double bonds; saturated hydrocarbons do not.

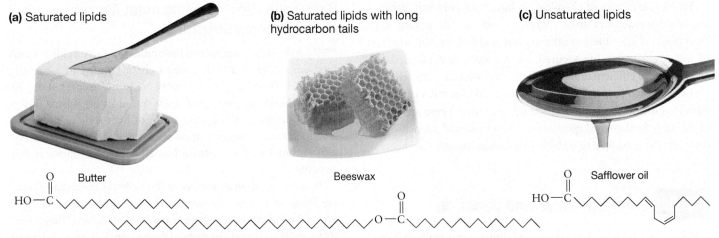

(a) Saturated lipids

Butter

(b) Saturated lipids with long hydrocarbon tails

Beeswax

(c) Unsaturated lipids

Safflower oil

FIGURE 6.2 The Fluidity of Lipids Depends on the Length and Saturation of Their Hydrocarbon Chains. (a) Butter consists primarily of saturated lipids. **(b)** Waxes are lipids with extremely long saturated hydrocarbon chains. **(c)** Oils are dominated by "polyunsaturates"—lipids with hydrocarbon chains that contain multiple C=C double bonds.

Bond saturation also profoundly affects the physical state of lipids. Highly saturated fats, such as butter, are solid at room temperature (**FIGURE 6.2a**). Saturated lipids that have extremely long hydrocarbon tails, like **waxes** do, form particularly stiff solids at room temperature (**FIGURE 6.2b**). Highly unsaturated fats are liquid at room temperature (**FIGURE 6.2c**).

A Look at Three Types of Lipids Found in Cells

Unlike amino acids, nucleotides, and monosaccharides, lipids are characterized by a physical property—their insolubility in water—instead of a shared chemical structure. This insolubility is based on the high proportion of nonpolar C–C and C–H bonds relative to polar functional groups. As a result, the structure of lipids varies widely. For example, consider the most important types of lipids found in cells: fats, steroids, and phospholipids.

Fats   **Fats** are nonpolar molecules composed of three fatty acids that are linked to a three-carbon molecule called **glycerol.** Because of this structure, fats are also called triacylglycerols or triglycerides. When the fatty acids are polyunsaturated, they form liquid triacylglycerols called **oils.** In organisms, the primary role of fats is energy storage.

As **FIGURE 6.3a** shows, fats form when a dehydration reaction occurs between a hydroxyl group of glycerol and the carboxyl

(a) Fats form via dehydration reactions.

Glycerol

H₂O

Dehydration reaction

Fatty acid

(b) Fats consist of glycerol linked by ester linkages to three fatty acids.

Ester linkages

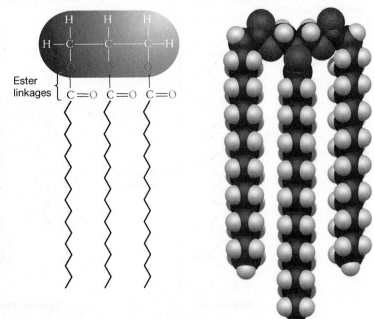

FIGURE 6.3 Fats Are One Type of Lipid Found in Cells. (a) When glycerol and a fatty acid react, a water molecule leaves. The covalent bond that results from this reaction is termed an ester linkage. **(b)** The structural formula and a space-filling model of tristearin, the most common type of fat in beef.

group of a fatty acid. The glycerol and fatty acid molecules become joined by an **ester linkage.** Fats are not polymers, however, and fatty acids are not monomers. As **FIGURE 6.3b** shows, fatty acids are not linked together to form a macromolecule in the way that amino acids, nucleotides, and monosaccharides are.

Steroids   **Steroids** are a family of lipids distinguished by the bulky, four-ring structure shown in orange in **FIGURE 6.4a**. The various steroids differ from one another by the functional groups or side groups attached to different carbons in those hydrophobic rings. The steroid shown in the figure is cholesterol, which has a hydrophilic hydroxyl group attached to the top ring and an isoprenoid "tail" attached at the bottom. Cholesterol is an important component of plasma membranes in many organisms.

Phospholipids   **Phospholipids** consist of a glycerol that is linked to a phosphate group and two hydrocarbon chains of either isoprenoids or fatty acids. The phosphate group is also bonded to a small organic molecule that is charged or polar (**FIGURE 6.4b**).

Phospholipids composed of fatty acids are found in the domains Bacteria and Eukarya; phospholipids with isoprenoid chains are found in the domain Archaea. (The domains of life were introduced in Chapter 1.) In all three domains, phospholipids are crucial components of the plasma membrane.

The lipids found in organisms have a wide array of structures and functions. In addition to storing chemical energy, lipids act as pigments that capture or respond to sunlight, serve as signals between cells, form waterproof coatings on leaves and skin, and act as vitamins used in many cellular processes. The most prominent function of lipids, however, is their role in cell membranes.

The Structures of Membrane Lipids

Not all lipids can form membranes. Membrane-forming lipids have a polar, hydrophilic region—in addition to the nonpolar, hydrophobic region found in all lipids.

To better understand this structure, take another look at the phospholipid illustrated in Figure 6.4b. Notice that the molecule has a "head" region containing highly polar covalent bonds as well as a negatively charged phosphate attached to a polar or charged group. The charges and polar bonds in the head region interact with water molecules when a phospholipid is placed in solution. In contrast, the long hydrocarbon tails of a phospholipid are nonpolar and hydrophobic. Water molecules cannot form hydrogen bonds with the hydrocarbon tail, so they do not interact extensively with this part of the molecule.

Compounds that contain both hydrophilic and hydrophobic elements are **amphipathic** (literally, "dual-sympathy"). Phospholipids are amphipathic. As Figure 6.4a shows, cholesterol is also amphipathic. Because it has a hydroxyl functional group attached to its rings, it has both hydrophilic and hydrophobic regions. ✔ If you understand these concepts, you should be able to look back at Figure 6.1b and explain why fatty acids are also amphipathic.

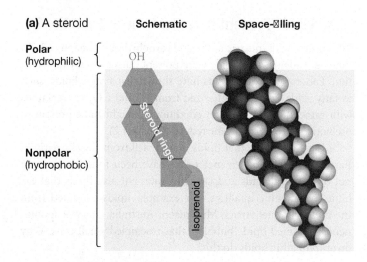

(a) A steroid

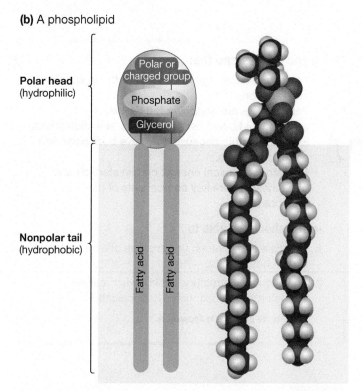

(b) A phospholipid

FIGURE 6.4 Some Lipids Contain Hydrophilic and Hydrophobic Regions. (a) All steroids have the distinctive four-ring structure shown in orange. Cholesterol has a polar hydroxyl group and an isoprenoid chain attached to these rings. **(b)** Most phospholipids consist of two fatty acid or isoprenoid chains that are linked to glycerol, which is linked to a phosphate group, which is linked to a small organic molecule that is polar or charged.

✔**QUESTION** If cholesterol and phospholipids were in solution, which part of the molecules would interact with water molecules?

The amphipathic nature of phospholipids is far and away their most important feature biologically. It is responsible for life's defining barrier—the plasma membrane. If the membrane defines life, then amphipathic lipids must have existed when life first originated during chemical evolution. Was that possible?

Were Lipids Present during Chemical Evolution?

Like amino acids, nucleic acids, and carbohydrates (Chapters 3–5), there is evidence that lipids were present during chemical evolution. Laboratory experiments have shown that simple lipids, such as fatty acids, can be synthesized from H_2 and CO_2 via reactions with mineral catalysts under conditions thought to be present in prebiotic hydrothermal vent systems (Chapter 2).

It is also possible that lipids literally fell from the sky early in Earth's history. Modern meteorites have been found to contain not only amino acids and carbohydrates but also lipids that exhibit amphipathic qualities. For example, lipids extracted from the meteorite that struck Murchison, Australia, in 1969 spontaneously formed lipid "bubbles" that resembled small cells. Why do amphipathic lipids do this?

check your understanding

If you understand that . . .

- Fats, steroids, and phospholipids differ in structure and function.
- Fats and oils are nonpolar; fatty acids, phospholipids, and certain steroids, like cholesterol, are amphipathic because they have both polar and nonpolar regions.
- Fats store chemical energy; certain steroids and phospholipids are key components of plasma membranes.

✔ You should be able to . . .

1. Compare and contrast the structure of a fat, a steroid, and a phospholipid.
2. Based on their structure, explain what makes cholesterol and phospholipids amphipathic.

Answers are available in Appendix A.

6.2 Phospholipid Bilayers

Amphipathic lipids do not dissolve when they are placed in water. Their hydrophilic heads interact with water, but their hydrophobic tails do not. Instead of dissolving in water, then, amphipathic lipids assume one of two types of structures: micelles or lipid bilayers.

- Micelles (**FIGURE 6.5a**) are tiny droplets created when the hydrophilic heads of a set of lipids face the water and form hydrogen bonds, while the hydrophobic tails interact with each other in the interior, away from the water.

- A **lipid bilayer** is created when two sheets of lipid molecules align. As **FIGURE 6.5b** shows, the hydrophilic heads in each layer face the surrounding solution while the hydrophobic tails face one another inside the bilayer. In this way, the hydrophilic heads interact with water while the hydrophobic tails interact with one another.

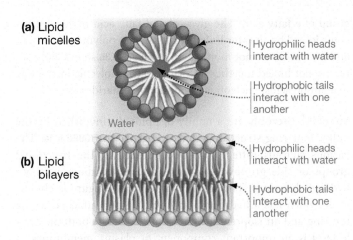

(a) Lipid micelles

Hydrophilic heads interact with water

Hydrophobic tails interact with one another

Water

(b) Lipid bilayers

Hydrophilic heads interact with water

Hydrophobic tails interact with one another

FIGURE 6.5 Lipids Form Micelles and Bilayers in Solution. In **(a)** a micelle or **(b)** a lipid bilayer, the hydrophilic heads of lipids face out, toward water; the hydrophobic tails face in, away from water. Lipid bilayers are the foundation of plasma membranes.

Micelles tend to form from fatty acids or other simple amphipathic hydrocarbon chains. Bilayers tend to form from phospholipids that contain two hydrocarbon tails. For this reason, bilayers are often called phospholipid bilayers.

It's critical to recognize that micelles and phospholipid bilayers form spontaneously—no input of energy is required. This concept can be difficult to grasp because entropy clearly decreases when these structures form. The key is to recognize that micelles and lipid bilayers are much more stable energetically than are independent phospholipids in solution.

Independent lipids are unstable in water because their hydrophobic tails disrupt hydrogen bonds that could otherwise form between water molecules. As a result, the tails of amphipathic molecules are forced together and participate in hydrophobic interactions (introduced in Chapter 2). This point should also remind you of the aqueous behavior of hydrophobic side chains in proteins and bases in nucleic acids.

Artificial Membranes as an Experimental System

When phospholipids are added to an aqueous solution and agitated, lipid bilayers spontaneously form small spherical structures. The hydrophilic heads on both sides of the bilayer remain in contact with the aqueous solution—water is present both inside and outside the vesicle. Artificial membrane-bound vesicles like these are called liposomes (**FIGURE 6.6**).

To explore how membranes work, researchers began creating and experimenting with liposomes and planar bilayers—lipid bilayers constructed across a hole in a glass or plastic wall separating two aqueous solutions (**FIGURE 6.7a**). Some of the first questions they posed concerned the permeability of lipid bilayers. The **permeability** of a structure is its tendency to allow a given substance to pass through it.

Using liposomes and planar bilayers, researchers can study what happens when a known ion or molecule is added to one side of a lipid bilayer (**FIGURE 6.7b**). Does the substance cross the

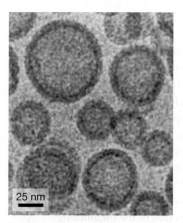
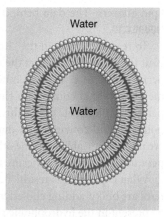

FIGURE 6.6 Liposomes Are Artificial Membrane-Bound Vesicles. Electron micrograph of liposomes in cross section (left) and a cross-sectional diagram of the lipid bilayer in a liposome (right).

(a) Planar bilayers: Artificial membranes

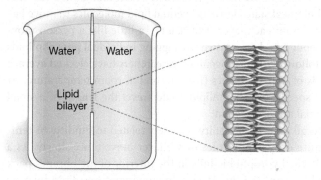

(b) Artificial-membrane experiments

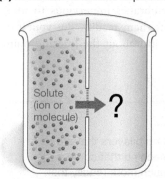

How rapidly can different solutes cross the membrane (if at all) when ...

1. Different types of phospholipids are used to make the membrane?

2. Proteins or other molecules are added to the membrane?

FIGURE 6.7 Use of Planar Bilayers in Experiments. (a) The construction of a planar bilayer across a hole in a wall separating two water-filled compartments. **(b)** A wide variety of experiments are possible with planar bilayers; a few are suggested here.

membrane and show up on the other side? If so, how rapidly does the movement take place? What happens when a different type of phospholipid is used to make the artificial membrane? Does the membrane's permeability change when proteins or other types of molecules become part of it?

Biologists describe such an experimental system as elegant and powerful because it gives them precise control over which factor changes from one experimental treatment to the next.

Control, in turn, is why experiments are such an effective way to explore scientific questions. Recall that good experimental design allows researchers to alter one factor at a time and determine what effect, if any, each has on the process being studied (Chapter 1).

Selective Permeability of Lipid Bilayers

When researchers put molecules or ions on one side of a liposome or planar bilayer and measure the rate at which the molecules arrive on the other side, a clear pattern emerges: Lipid bilayers are highly selective.

Selective permeability means that some substances cross a membrane more easily than other substances do. Small nonpolar molecules move across bilayers quickly. In contrast, large molecules and charged substances cross the membrane slowly, if at all. This difference in membrane permeability is a critical issue because controlling what passes between the exterior and interior environments is a key characteristic of cells.

According to the data in **FIGURE 6.8**, small nonpolar molecules such as oxygen (O_2) move across selectively permeable membranes more than a billion times faster than do chloride ions (Cl^-). In essence, ions cannot cross membranes at all—unless they have "help" in the form of membrane proteins introduced later in the chapter. Very small and uncharged molecules such as water (H_2O) can cross membranes relatively rapidly, even if they are polar. Small polar molecules such as glycerol have intermediate permeability.

The leading hypothesis to explain this pattern is that charged compounds and large polar molecules are more stable dissolved in water than they are in the nonpolar interior of membranes. ✔ If you understand this hypothesis, you should be able to predict where amino acids and nucleotides would be placed in Figure 6.8 and explain your reasoning.

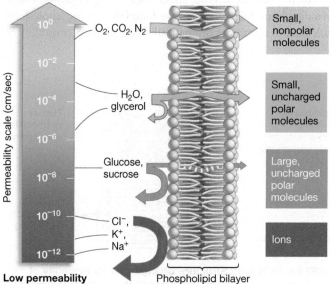

FIGURE 6.8 Lipid Bilayers Show Selective Permeability. Only certain substances cross lipid bilayers readily. Size and polarity or charge affect the rate of diffusion across a membrane.

How Does Lipid Structure Affect Membrane Permeability?

The amphipathic nature of phospholipids allows them to spontaneously form membranes. But not all phospholipid bilayers are the same. The nature of the hydrocarbon tails, in addition to the presence of cholesterol molecules, profoundly influences how a membrane behaves.

Bond Saturation and Hydrocarbon Chain Length Affect Membrane Fluidity and Permeability   The degree of saturation in a phospholipid—along with the length of its hydrocarbon tails—affects key aspects of a lipid's behavior in a membrane.

- When unsaturated hydrocarbon tails are packed into a lipid bilayer, kinks created by double bonds produce spaces among the tails. These spaces reduce the strength of the van der Waals interactions (see Chapter 3) that hold the hydrophobic tails together, weakening the barrier to solutes.

- Packed saturated hydrocarbon tails have fewer spaces and stronger van der Waals interactions. As the length of saturated hydrocarbon tails increases, the forces that hold them together also grow stronger, making the membrane even denser.

These observations have profound impacts on membrane fluidity and permeability—two closely related properties. As **FIGURE 6.9** shows, lipid bilayers are more permeable as well as more fluid when they contain short, kinked, unsaturated hydrocarbon tails. An unsaturated membrane allows more materials to pass because its interior is held together less tightly. Bilayers containing long, straight, saturated hydrocarbon tails are much less permeable and fluid. Experiments on liposomes have shown exactly these patterns.

Cholesterol Reduces Membrane Permeability   Cholesterol molecules are present, to varying extents, in the membranes of every cell in your body. What effect does adding cholesterol have on a membrane? Researchers have found that adding cholesterol molecules to liposomes dramatically reduces the permeability of lipid bilayers. The data behind this conclusion are presented in **FIGURE 6.10**.

To read the graph in the "Results" section of Figure 6.10, put your finger on the *x*-axis at the point marked 20°C, and note that permeability to glycerol is much higher at this temperature in membranes that contain no cholesterol versus 20 percent or 50 percent cholesterol. Using this procedure at other temperature points should convince you that membranes lacking cholesterol are more permeable than the other two membranes at every temperature tested in the experiment.

What explains this result? Because the steroid rings in cholesterol are bulky, adding cholesterol fills gaps that would otherwise be present in the hydrophobic section of the membrane.

How Does Temperature Affect the Fluidity and Permeability of Membranes?

At about 25°C—or "room temperature"—the phospholipids in a plasma membrane have a consistency resembling olive oil. This fluid physical state allows individual lipid molecules to move laterally within each layer (**FIGURE 6.11**), a little like a person moving about in a dense crowd. By tagging individual phospholipids and following their movement, researchers have clocked average speeds of 2 micrometers (µm)/second at room temperature. At these speeds, a phospholipid could travel the length of a small bacterial cell in a second.

Recall that permeability is closely related to fluidity. As temperature drops, molecules in a bilayer move more slowly. As a result, the hydrophobic tails in the interior of membranes pack together more tightly. At very low temperatures, lipid bilayers even begin to solidify. As the graph in Figure 6.10 indicates, low temperatures can make membranes impervious to molecules that would normally cross them readily. Put your finger on the *x*-axis of that graph, just about the freezing point

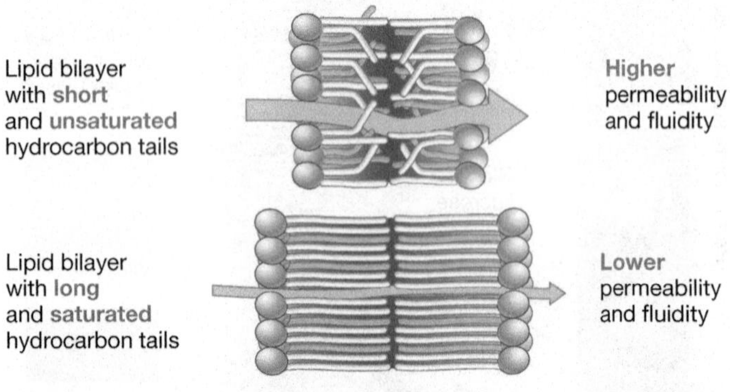

Lipid bilayer with short and unsaturated hydrocarbon tails

Higher permeability and fluidity

Lipid bilayer with long and saturated hydrocarbon tails

Lower permeability and fluidity

FIGURE 6.9 Fatty Acid Structure Changes the Permeability of Membranes. Lipid bilayers consisting of phospholipids containing unsaturated fatty acids should have more gaps and be more permeable than those with saturated fatty acids.

check your understanding

C Y U

If you understand that . . .

- In water, phospholipids form bilayers that are selectively permeable—meaning that some substances cross them much more readily than others do.
- Permeability is a function of the degree of saturation and the length of the hydrocarbon tails in membrane phospholipids, the amount of cholesterol in the membrane, and the temperature.

✔ You should be able to . . .

Fill in a chart with columns labeled Factor, Effect on permeability, and Reason and rows under the Factor column labeled Temperature, Cholesterol, Length of hydrocarbon tails, and Saturation of hydrocarbon tails.

Answers are available in Appendix A.

QUESTION: Does adding cholesterol to a membrane affect its permeability?

HYPOTHESIS: Cholesterol reduces permeability because it fills spaces in phospholipid bilayers.

NULL HYPOTHESIS: Cholesterol has no effect on permeability.

EXPERIMENTAL SETUP:

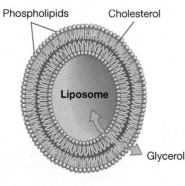

Phospholipids   Cholesterol

Liposome

Glycerol

1. Construct liposomes: Create with no cholesterol, 20% cholesterol, and 50% cholesterol.

2. Measure glycerol movement: Record how quickly glycerol moves across each type of membrane at different temperatures.

PREDICTION: Liposomes with higher cholesterol levels will have reduced permeability.

PREDICTION OF NULL HYPOTHESIS: All liposomes will have the same permeability.

RESULTS:

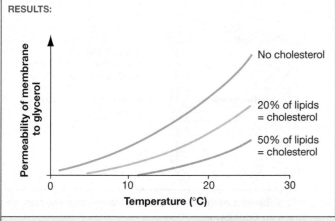

No cholesterol

20% of lipids = cholesterol

50% of lipids = cholesterol

Permeability of membrane to glycerol

Temperature (°C)

CONCLUSION: Adding cholesterol to membranes decreases their permeability to glycerol. The permeability of all membranes analyzed in this experiment increases with increasing temperature.

FIGURE 6.10 The Permeability of a Membrane Depends on Its Composition.

SOURCE: de Gier, J., et al. (1968). Lipid composition and permeability of liposomes. *Biochimica et Biophysica Acta* 150: 666–675.

✔**QUANTITATIVE** Suppose the investigators had instead created liposomes using phospholipids with fully saturated tails and compared them to two other sets of liposomes where either 20 percent or 50 percent of the phospholipids contained polyunsaturated tails. Label the three lines on the graph above with your prediction for the three different liposomes in this new experiment.

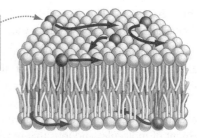

Phospholipids are in constant lateral motion, but rarely flip to the other side of the bilayer

FIGURE 6.11 Phospholipids Move within Membranes. Membranes are dynamic—in part because phospholipid molecules randomly move laterally within each layer in the structure.

of water (0°C), and note that even membranes that lack cholesterol are almost completely impermeable to glycerol. Indeed, trace any of the three lines in Figure 6.10, and as you move to the right (increasing temperature), you also move up (increasing permeability).

These observations on glycerol and lipid movement demonstrate that membranes are dynamic. Phospholipid molecules whiz around each layer, while water and small nonpolar molecules shoot in and out of the membrane. How quickly molecules move within and across membranes is a function of temperature, the structure of hydrocarbon tails, and the number of cholesterol molecules in the bilayer.

6.3 How Molecules Move across Lipid Bilayers: Diffusion and Osmosis

Small uncharged molecules and hydrophobic compounds can cross membranes readily and spontaneously—without an input of energy. The question now is: How is this possible? What process is responsible for movement of molecules across lipid bilayers?

Diffusion

A thought experiment can help explain how substances can cross membranes spontaneously. Suppose you rack up a set of billiard balls in the middle of a pool table and then begin to vibrate the table.

1. Because of the vibration, the billiard balls will move about randomly. They will also bump into one another.

2. After these collisions, some balls will move outward—away from their original position.

3. As movement and collisions continue, the overall or net movement of balls will be outward. This occurs because the random motion of the balls disrupts their original, nonrandom position. As the balls move at random, they are more likely to move away from one another than to stay together.

4. Eventually, the balls will be distributed randomly across the table. The entropy of the billiard balls has increased. Recall that entropy is a measure of the randomness or disorder in

a system (Chapter 2). The second law of thermodynamics states that in an isolated system, entropy always increases.

This hypothetical example illustrates how vibrating billiard balls move at random. More to the point, it also explains how substances located on one side of a lipid bilayer can move to the other side spontaneously. All dissolved molecules and ions, or **solutes,** have thermal energy and are in constant, random motion. Movement of molecules and ions that results from their kinetic energy is known as **diffusion.**

A difference in solute concentrations creates what is called a **concentration gradient.** Solutes move randomly in all directions, but when a concentration gradient exists, there is a net movement from regions of high concentration to regions of low concentration. Diffusion down a concentration gradient, or away from the higher concentration, is a spontaneous process because it results in an increase in entropy.

Once the molecules or ions are randomly distributed throughout a solution, a chemical equilibrium is established. For example, consider two aqueous solutions separated by a lipid bilayer. **FIGURE 6.12** shows how molecules that can pass through the bilayer diffuse to the other side. At equilibrium, these molecules continue to move back and forth across the membrane, but at equal rates—simply because they are equally likely to move in any direction. This means that there is no longer a net movement of molecules across the membrane. ✔ If you understand diffusion, you should be able to predict how a difference in temperature across a membrane would affect the concentration of a solute at equilibrium.

Osmosis

What about water? As the data in Figure 6.8 show, water moves across lipid bilayers relatively quickly. The movement of water is a special case of diffusion that is given its own name: **osmosis.** Osmosis occurs only when solutions are separated by a membrane that permits water to cross, but holds back some or all of the solutes—that is, a selectively permeable membrane.

It's important to note that some of the water molecules in a solution are unavailable to diffuse across the membrane. Recall that solutes form ionic or hydrogen bonds with water molecules (Chapter 2). Water molecules that are bound to a solute that can't cross the membrane are themselves prevented from crossing.

Only unbound water molecules are able to diffuse across the membrane during osmosis. When these unbound water molecules move across a membrane, they flow from the solution with the lower solute concentration into the solution with the higher solute concentration.

To drive this point home, let's suppose the concentration of a particular solute is higher on one side of a selectively permeable membrane than it is on the other side (**FIGURE 6.13**, step 1). Further, suppose that this solute cannot diffuse through the membrane to establish equilibrium. What happens? Water will move from the side with a lower concentration of solute to the side with a higher concentration of solute (Figure 6.13, step 2). Osmosis dilutes the higher concentration and equalizes the concentrations

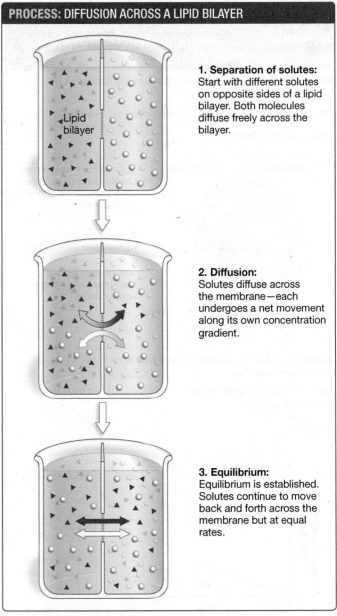

PROCESS: DIFFUSION ACROSS A LIPID BILAYER

1. Separation of solutes: Start with different solutes on opposite sides of a lipid bilayer. Both molecules diffuse freely across the bilayer.

Lipid bilayer

2. Diffusion: Solutes diffuse across the membrane—each undergoes a net movement along its own concentration gradient.

3. Equilibrium: Equilibrium is established. Solutes continue to move back and forth across the membrane but at equal rates.

FIGURE 6.12 Diffusion across a Selectively Permeable Membrane Establishes an Equilibrium.

on both sides. The movement of water is spontaneous. It is driven by the increase in entropy achieved when solute concentrations are equal on both sides of the membrane.

Movement of water by osmosis is important because it can swell or shrink a membrane-bound vesicle. Consider the liposomes illustrated in **FIGURE 6.14**. (Remember that osmosis occurs only when a solute cannot pass through a separating membrane.)

- *Left* If the solution inside the membrane has a lower concentration of solutes than the exterior has, water moves out of the vesicle into the solution outside. The solution inside is said to be **hypotonic** ("lower-tone") relative to the outside of the vesicle. As water leaves, the vesicle shrinks and the membrane shrivels, resulting in lower vesicle firmness.

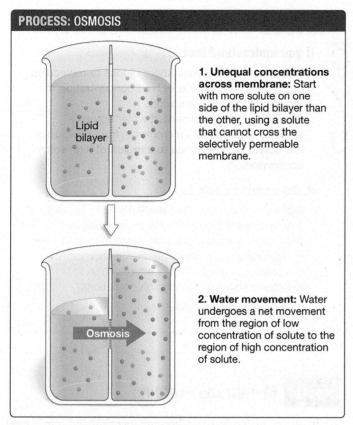

PROCESS: OSMOSIS

1. Unequal concentrations across membrane: Start with more solute on one side of the lipid bilayer than the other, using a solute that cannot cross the selectively permeable membrane.

2. Water movement: Water undergoes a net movement from the region of low concentration of solute to the region of high concentration of solute.

FIGURE 6.13 Osmosis Is the Diffusion of Water.

✓**QUESTION** Suppose you doubled the number of solute molecules on the left side of the membrane (at the start). At equilibrium, would the water level on the left side be higher or lower than what is shown in the second drawing?

- *Middle* If the solution inside the membrane has a higher concentration of solutes than the exterior has, water moves into the vesicle via osmosis. The inside solution is said to be **hypertonic** ("excess-tone") relative to the outside of the vesicle. The incoming water causes the vesicle to swell and increase in firmness, or even burst.

- *Right* If solute concentrations are equal on both sides of the membrane, the liposome maintains its size. When the inside solution does not affect the membrane's shape, that solution is called **isotonic** ("equal-tone").

Note that the terms hypertonic, hypotonic, and isotonic are relative—they can be used only to express the relationship between a given solution and another solution separated by a membrane. Biologists also commonly use these terms to describe the solution that is exterior to the cells or vesicles.

Membranes and Chemical Evolution

What do diffusion and osmosis have to do with the first membranes floating in the prebiotic soup? Both processes tend to *reduce* differences in chemical composition between the inside and outside of membrane-bound compartments.

If liposome-like structures first arose in the oceans of early Earth, their interiors probably didn't offer a radically different environment from the surrounding solution. In all likelihood, the primary importance of the first lipid bilayers was simply to provide a container for replicating RNA, the macromolecule most likely to have been the first "living" molecule (see Chapter 4). But ribonucleotide monomers would need to be available for these

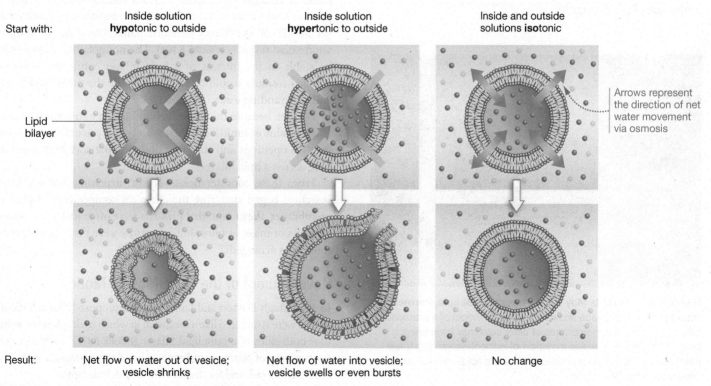

FIGURE 6.14 Osmosis Can Shrink or Burst Membrane-Bound Vesicles.

RNAs to replicate. Can negatively charged ribonucleotides get across lipid bilayers and inside lipid-bounded vesicles?

The answer is yes. Jack Szostak and colleagues first set out to study the permeability of membranes consisting of fatty acids and other simple amphipathic lipids thought to be present in the early oceans. Like phospholipids, fatty acids will spontaneously assemble into lipid bilayers and water-filled vesicles. Their experiments showed that ions, and even ribonucleotides, can diffuse across the fatty acid vesicle membranes—meaning that monomers could have been available for RNA synthesis.

Lending support to this hypothesis, the same minerals found to catalyze the polymerization of RNA from activated nucleotides (see Chapter 4) will also promote the formation of fatty acid vesicles—and in the process, often incorporate themselves and RNA inside. Simple vesicle-like structures that harbor nucleic acids are referred to as **protocells** (**FIGURE 6.15**). Most origin-of-life researchers view protocells as possible intermediates in the evolution of the cell.

Laboratory simulations also showed that free lipids and micelles can become incorporated into fatty acid bilayers, causing protocells to grow. Shearing forces, as from bubbling, shaking, or wave action, cause protocells to divide. Based on these observations, it is reasonable to hypothesize that once replicating RNAs became surrounded by a lipid bilayer, this simple lifeform and its descendants would occupy cell-like structures that grew and divided.

Now let's investigate the next great innovation in the evolution of the cell: the ability to create and maintain a specialized internal environment that is conducive to life. What is necessary to construct an effective plasma membrane—one that imports ions and molecules needed for life while excluding ions and molecules that might damage it?

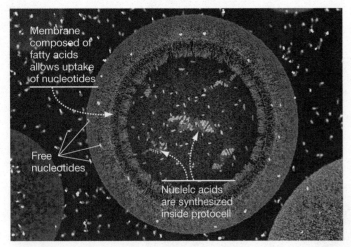

FIGURE 6.15 Protocells May Have Possessed Simple, Permeable Membranes. This image shows a computer model of a protocell. Like this model, the membranes of early cells may have been built of fatty acids. Passive transport of nucleotides across these membranes, as well as replication of nucleic acids inside, has been observed in the laboratory.

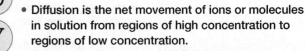

If you understand that . . .

- Diffusion is the net movement of ions or molecules in solution from regions of high concentration to regions of low concentration.
- Osmosis is the movement of water across a selectively permeable membrane, from a region of low solute concentration to a region of high solute concentration.

✔ **You should be able to . . .**

Make a concept map (see **BioSkills 15** in Appendix B) that includes the boxed terms water molecules, solute molecules, osmosis, diffusion, areas of high-to-low concentration, selectively permeable membranes, concentration gradients, hypertonic solutions, hypotonic solutions, and isotonic solutions.

Answers are available in Appendix A.

6.4 Membrane Proteins

What sort of molecule could become incorporated into a lipid bilayer and affect the bilayer's permeability? The title of this section gives the answer away. Proteins that are amphipathic can be inserted into lipid bilayers.

Proteins can be amphipathic because their monomers, amino acids, have side chains that range from highly nonpolar to highly polar or charged (see Figure 3.2). It's conceivable, then, that a protein could have a series of nonpolar amino acid residues in the middle of its primary structure flanked by polar or charged amino acid residues (**FIGURE 6.16a**). The nonpolar residues would be stable in the interior of a lipid bilayer, while the polar or charged residues would be stable alongside the polar lipid heads and surrounding water (**FIGURE 6.16b**).

Further, because the secondary and tertiary structures of proteins are almost limitless in their variety, it is possible for proteins to form openings and thus function as some sort of channel or pore across a lipid bilayer.

From these considerations, it's not surprising that when researchers began analyzing the chemical composition of plasma membranes, they found that proteins were often just as common, in terms of mass, as phospholipids. How were these two types of molecules arranged?

Development of the Fluid-Mosaic Model

In 1935 Hugh Davson and James Danielli proposed that cell membranes were structured like a sandwich in which hydrophilic proteins coat both sides of a pure lipid bilayer (**FIGURE 6.17a**). Early electron micrographs of plasma membranes seemed to be consistent with the sandwich model, and for decades it was widely accepted.

(a) Proteins can be amphipathic.

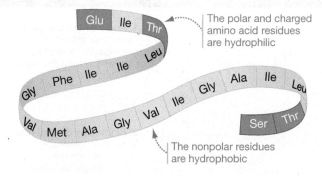

The polar and charged amino acid residues are hydrophilic

The nonpolar residues are hydrophobic

(b) Amphipathic proteins can integrate into lipid bilayers.

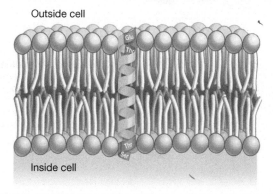

Outside cell

Inside cell

FIGURE 6.16 Amphipathic Proteins Are Anchored in Lipid Bilayers.

(a) Sandwich model

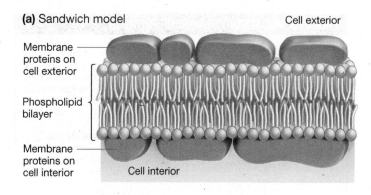

Cell exterior

Membrane proteins on cell exterior

Phospholipid bilayer

Membrane proteins on cell interior

Cell interior

(b) Fluid-mosaic model

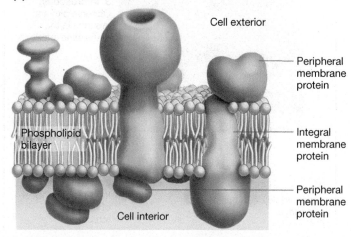

Cell exterior

Peripheral membrane protein

Integral membrane protein

Phospholipid bilayer

Peripheral membrane protein

Cell interior

FIGURE 6.17 Past and Current Models of Membrane Structure Differ in Where Membrane Proteins Reside. (a) The protein-lipid-lipid-protein sandwich model was the first hypothesis for the arrangement of lipids and proteins in cell membranes. **(b)** The fluid-mosaic model was a radical departure from the sandwich hypothesis.

The realization that membrane proteins could be amphipathic, however, led S. Jon Singer and Garth Nicolson to suggest an alternative hypothesis. In 1972, they proposed that at least some proteins span the membrane instead of being found only outside the lipid bilayer. Their hypothesis was called the **fluid-mosaic model** (**FIGURE 6.17b**). Singer and Nicolson suggested that membranes are a mosaic of phospholipids and different types of proteins. The overall structure was proposed to be dynamic and fluid.

The controversy over the nature of the cell membrane was resolved in the early 1970s with the development of an innovative technique for visualizing the surface of plasma membranes. The method is called freeze-fracture electron microscopy because the steps involve freezing and fracturing the membrane before examining it with a **scanning electron microscope (SEM)**, which produces images of an object's surface (see **BioSkills 11** in Appendix B).

As **FIGURE 6.18** (see page 96) shows, the freeze-fracture technique allows researchers to split cell membranes and view the middle of the structure. The scanning electron micrographs that result show pits and mounds studding the inner surfaces of the lipid bilayer. Researchers interpreted these structures as the locations of membrane proteins. As step 4 in the figure shows, the mounds represent proteins that remained attached to one side of the split lipid bilayer and the pits are the holes they left behind.

These observations conflicted with the sandwich model but were consistent with the fluid-mosaic model. Based on these and subsequent observations, the fluid-mosaic model is now widely accepted.

Notice in Figure 6.17b that some proteins span the membrane and have segments facing both the interior and the exterior surfaces. Proteins like these are called **integral membrane proteins,** or **transmembrane proteins.** Proteins that bind to the membrane without passing through it are called **peripheral membrane proteins.**

Certain peripheral proteins are found only on the interior surface of a cellular membrane, while others are found only on the exterior surface. As a result, the interior and exterior surfaces of the plasma membrane are distinct—the peripheral proteins and the ends of transmembrane proteins differ. Peripheral membrane proteins are often attached to transmembrane proteins.

How do these proteins affect the permeability of membranes? The answer to this question starts with an investigation of the structure of proteins involved in the transport of molecules and ions across the plasma membrane.

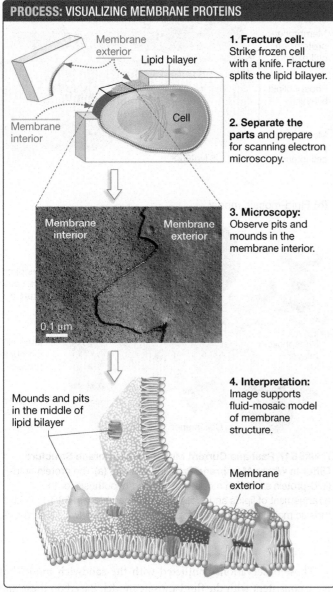

1. **Fracture cell:** Strike frozen cell with a knife. Fracture splits the lipid bilayer.

2. **Separate the parts** and prepare for scanning electron microscopy.

3. **Microscopy:** Observe pits and mounds in the membrane interior.

4. **Interpretation:** Image supports fluid-mosaic model of membrane structure.

FIGURE 6.18 Freeze-Fracture Preparations Allow Biologists to View Membrane Proteins.

✔QUESTION What would be an appropriate control to show that the pits and mounds were not simply irregularities in the lipid bilayer caused by the freeze-fracture process?

Systems for Studying Membrane Proteins

The discovery of transmembrane proteins was consistent with the hypothesis that proteins affect membrane permeability. To test this hypothesis, researchers needed some way to isolate and purify membrane proteins.

FIGURE 6.19 outlines one method that researchers developed to separate proteins from membranes. The key to the technique is the use of detergents. A **detergent** is a small amphipathic molecule. When detergents are added to the solution surrounding a lipid bilayer, the hydrophobic tails of the detergent molecule interact with the hydrophobic tails of the lipids and with the

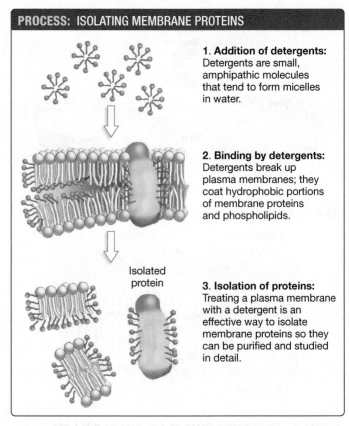

1. **Addition of detergents:** Detergents are small, amphipathic molecules that tend to form micelles in water.

2. **Binding by detergents:** Detergents break up plasma membranes; they coat hydrophobic portions of membrane proteins and phospholipids.

Isolated protein

3. **Isolation of proteins:** Treating a plasma membrane with a detergent is an effective way to isolate membrane proteins so they can be purified and studied in detail.

FIGURE 6.19 Detergents Can Be Used to Isolate Proteins from Membranes.

hydrophobic portions of transmembrane proteins. These interactions displace the membrane phospholipids and end up forming water-soluble detergent–protein complexes that can be isolated.

Since intensive experimentation on membrane proteins began, researchers have identified three broad classes of proteins that affect membrane permeability: channels, carriers, and pumps. Let's consider each class in turn.

Facilitated Diffusion via Channel Proteins

As the data in Figure 6.8 show, ions almost never cross pure phospholipid bilayers on their own. But in cells, ions routinely cross membranes through specialized membrane proteins called **ion channels.**

Ion channels form pores, or openings, in a membrane. Ions move through these pores in a predictable direction: from regions of high concentration to regions of low concentration and from areas of like charge to areas of unlike charge.

In **FIGURE 6.20**, for example, a large concentration gradient favors the movement of sodium ions from the outside of a membrane to the inside. But in addition, the inside of this cell has a net negative charge while the outside has a net positive charge. As a result, the combination of these two factors influences the final concentration of sodium ions inside the cell once equilibrium has been established.

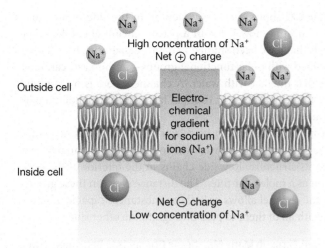

FIGURE 6.20 An Electrochemical Gradient Is a Combined Concentration and Electrical Gradient. Electrochemical gradients are established when ions build up on one side of a membrane.

Ions move in response to a combined concentration and electrical gradient, or what biologists call an **electrochemical gradient.** ✔ If you understand this concept, you should be able to add an arrow to Figure 6.20 indicating the electrochemical gradient for chloride ions.

Is an Ion Channel Involved in Cystic Fibrosis? To understand the types of experiments that biologists do to confirm that a membrane protein is an ion channel, consider work on the cause of cystic fibrosis.

Cystic fibrosis (CF) is the most common genetic disease in humans of Northern European descent. It affects cells that produce mucus, sweat, and digestive juices. Normally these secretions are thin and slippery and act as lubricants. In individuals with CF, however, the secretions become abnormally concentrated and sticky and clog passageways in organs like the lungs.

Experiments published in 1983 suggested that cystic fibrosis is caused by defects in a membrane protein that allow chloride ions (Cl^-) to move across plasma membranes. It was proposed that reduced chloride ion transport would account for the thick mucus.

How is the transport of chloride ions involved in mucus consistency? Water movement across cell membranes is largely determined by the presence of extracellular ions like chloride. If a defective channel prevents chloride ions from leaving cells, water isn't pulled from cells by osmosis to maintain the proper mucus consistency. In effect, the disease results from the mismanagement of osmosis.

Using molecular techniques introduced in Unit 3 (see Chapter 20), biologists were able to (1) find the gene that is defective in people suffering from CF and (2) use the gene to produce copies of the normal protein, which was called CFTR (short for cystic fibrosis transmembrane conductance regulator).

Is CFTR a chloride channel? To answer this question, researchers inserted purified CFTR into planar bilayers and

RESEARCH

QUESTION: Is CFTR a chloride channel?

HYPOTHESIS: CFTR increases the flow of chloride ions across a membrane.

NULL HYPOTHESIS: CFTR has no effect on membrane permeability.

EXPERIMENTAL SETUP:

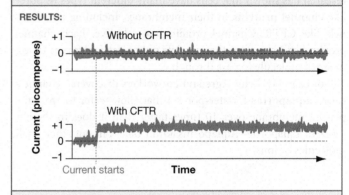

Membrane **without CFTR**   Membrane **with CFTR**

Ion flow?   Ion flow?

1. **Create planar bilayers** with and without CFTR.

2. **Add chloride ions** to one side of the planar bilayer to create an electrochemical gradient.

3. **Record electrical currents** to measure ion flow across the planar bilayers.

PREDICTION: Ion flow will be higher in membrane with CFTR.

PREDICTION OF NULL HYPOTHESIS: Ion flow will be the same in both membranes.

RESULTS:

Without CFTR

With CFTR

Current starts   **Time**

Current (picoamperes)   +1   0   −1

CONCLUSION: CFTR facilitates diffusion of chloride ions along an electrochemical gradient. CFTR is a chloride channel.

FIGURE 6.21 Electric Current Measurements Indicate that Chloride Flows through CFTR.

SOURCE: Bear, C. A., et al. (1992). Purification and functional reconstitution of the cystic fibrosis transmembrane conductance regulator (CFTR). *Cell* 68: 809–818.

✔**QUESTION** The researchers repeated the "with CFTR" treatment 45 times, but recorded a current in only 35 of the replicates. Does this observation negate the conclusion? Explain why or why not.

measured the flow of electric current across the membrane. Because ions carry a charge, ion movement across a membrane produces an electric current.

The graphs in **FIGURE 6.21**, which plot the amount of current flowing across the membrane over time, show the results from this experiment. Notice that when CFTR was absent, no electric current passed through the membrane. But when CFTR was

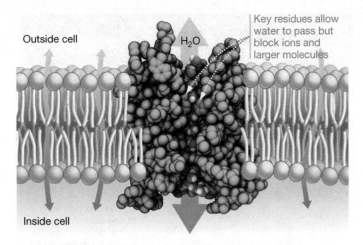

FIGURE 6.22 Membrane Channels Are Highly Selective. A cutaway view looking at the inside of a membrane channel, aquaporin. The key residues identified in the space-filling model selectively filter ions and other small molecules, allowing only water (red and white structures) to pass through.

inserted into the membrane, current began to flow. This was strong evidence that CFTR was indeed a chloride ion channel.

Protein Structure Determines Channel Selectivity Subsequent research has shown that cells have many different types of pore-like **channel proteins** in their membranes, including ion channels like CFTR. Channel proteins are selective. Each channel protein has a structure that permits only a particular type of ion or small molecule to pass through it.

For example, Peter Agre and co-workers discovered channels called **aquaporins** ("water-pores") that allow water to cross the plasma membrane over 10 times faster than it does in the absence of aquaporins. Aquaporins admit water but not other small molecules or ions.

FIGURE 6.22 shows a cutaway view from the side of an aquaporin, indicating how it fits in a plasma membrane. Like other channels that have been studied in detail, aquaporins have a pore that is lined with polar functional groups—in this case, carbonyl groups that interact with water. A channel's pore is hydrophilic relative to the hydrophobic residues facing the phospholipid tails of the membrane.

But how can aquaporin be selective for water and not other polar molecules? The answer was found when researchers examined its structure. Key side chains in the interior of the pore function as a molecular filter. The distance between these groups across the channel allows only those substances capable of interacting with all of them to pass through to the other side.

Movement Through Many Membrane Channels Is Regulated Recent research has shown that many aquaporins and ion channels are **gated channels**—meaning that they open or close in response to a signal, such as the binding of a particular molecule or a change in the electrical voltage across the membrane.

As an example of how voltage-gated channels work, **FIGURE 6.23** shows a potassium channel in closed and open configurations. The electrical charge on the membrane is normally negative on the inside relative to the outside, which causes the channel to adopt a closed shape that prevents potassium ions from passing through. When this charge asymmetry is reversed, the shape changes in a way that opens the channel and allows potassium ions to cross. The key point here is that in almost all cases, the flow of ions and small molecules through membrane channels is carefully controlled.

In all cases, however, the movement of substances through channels is passive—meaning it does not require an input of energy. **Passive transport** is powered by diffusion along an electrochemical gradient. Channel proteins simply enable ions or polar molecules to move across lipid bilayers efficiently, in response to

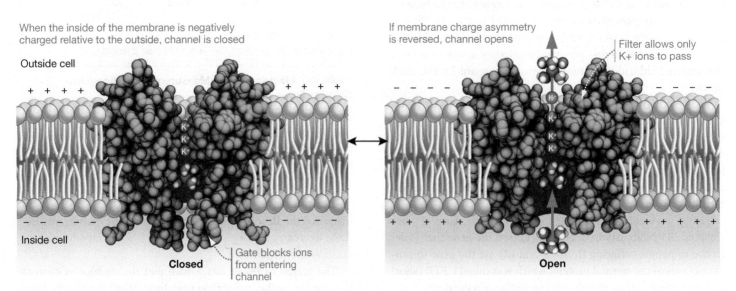

FIGURE 6.23 Some Membrane Channels Are Highly Regulated. A model of a voltage-gated K⁺ channel in the closed and open configurations. The channel filter displaces water molecules that normally surround the K⁺ ions in an aqueous solution.

an existing gradient. They are responsible for **facilitated diffusion:** the passive transport of substances that otherwise would not cross a membrane readily.

Facilitated Diffusion via Carrier Proteins

Facilitated diffusion can also occur through **carrier proteins**—specialized membrane proteins that change shape during the transport process. Perhaps the best-studied carrier protein is one that is involved in transporting glucose into cells.

The Search for a Glucose Carrier Next to ribose, the six-carbon sugar glucose is the most prevalent sugar found in organisms. Virtually all cells alive today use glucose as a building block for important macromolecules and as a source of stored chemical energy (Chapter 5). But as Figure 6.8 shows, lipid bilayers are only moderately permeable to glucose. It is reasonable to expect, then, that plasma membranes have some mechanism for increasing their permeability to this sugar.

This prediction was supported in experiments on pure preparations of plasma membranes from human red blood cells. These plasma membranes turned out to be much more permeable to glucose than are pure lipid bilayers. Why?

After isolating and analyzing many proteins from red blood cell membranes, researchers found one protein that specifically increases membrane permeability to glucose. When they added this purified protein to liposomes, the artificial membrane transported glucose at the same rate as a membrane from a living cell. This experiment convinced biologists that the membrane protein—now called GLUT-1 (short for glucose transporter 1)—was indeed responsible for transporting glucose across plasma membranes.

How Does GLUT-1 Work? Recall that proteins frequently change shape when they bind to other molecules and that such conformational changes are often a critical step in their function (Chapter 3). **FIGURE 6.24** illustrates the current hypothesis for how GLUT-1 works to facilitate the movement of glucose. The idea is that when glucose binds to GLUT-1, it changes the shape of the protein in a way that moves the sugar through the hydrophobic region of the membrane and releases it on the other side.

What powers the movement of molecules through carriers? The answer is diffusion. GLUT-1 facilitates diffusion by allowing glucose to enter the carrier from either side of the membrane. Glucose will pass through the carrier in the direction dictated by its concentration gradient. A large variety of molecules move across plasma membranes via specific carrier proteins.

Pumps Perform Active Transport

Diffusion—whether it is facilitated by proteins or not—is a passive process that will move substances in either direction across a membrane to make the cell interior and exterior more similar. But it is also possible for cells to move molecules or ions in a directed manner, often *against* their electrochemical gradient. Accomplishing this task requires an input of energy, because the cell must counteract the decrease in entropy that occurs when molecules or ions are concentrated. It makes sense, then, that transport against an electrochemical gradient is called **active transport.**

In cells, ATP (adenosine triphosphate) often provides the energy for active transport by transferring a phosphate group (HPO_4^{2-}) to an active transport protein called a **pump.** Recall that ATP contains three phosphate groups (Chapter 4), and that phosphate groups carry two negative charges (Chapter 2). When a phosphate group leaves ATP and binds to a pump, its negative charges interact with charged amino acid residues in the protein. As a result, the protein's potential energy increases and its shape changes.

The Sodium–Potassium Pump A classic example of how structural change leads to active transport is provided in the **sodium–potassium pump,** or more formally, Na⁺/K⁺-ATPase. The Na⁺/K⁺ part of the name refers to the ions that are transported, ATP indicates that adenosine triphosphate is used, and –ase identifies the molecule as an enzyme.

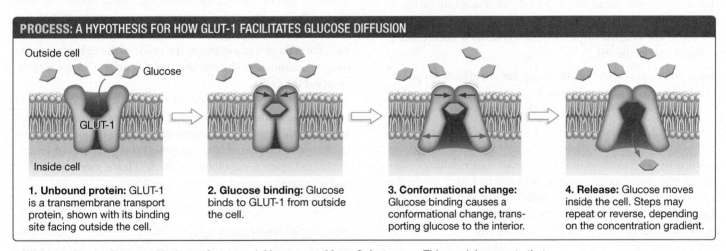

PROCESS: A HYPOTHESIS FOR HOW GLUT-1 FACILITATES GLUCOSE DIFFUSION

Outside cell

Glucose

GLUT-1

Inside cell

1. Unbound protein: GLUT-1 is a transmembrane transport protein, shown with its binding site facing outside the cell.

2. Glucose binding: Glucose binds to GLUT-1 from outside the cell.

3. Conformational change: Glucose binding causes a conformational change, transporting glucose to the interior.

4. Release: Glucose moves inside the cell. Steps may repeat or reverse, depending on the concentration gradient.

FIGURE 6.24 Carrier Proteins Undergo Structural Changes to Move Substances. This model suggests that GLUT-1 binds a glucose molecule, undergoes a conformational change, and releases glucose on the other side of the membrane.

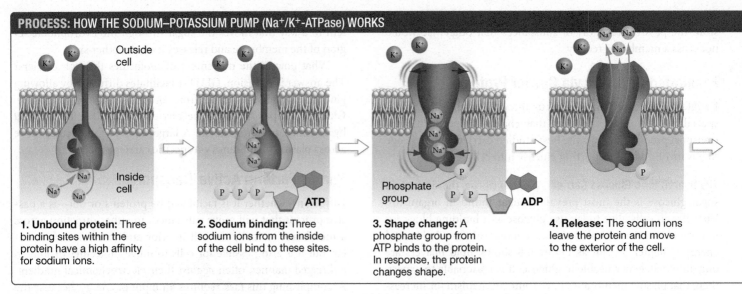

1. **Unbound protein:** Three binding sites within the protein have a high affinity for sodium ions.

2. **Sodium binding:** Three sodium ions from the inside of the cell bind to these sites.

3. **Shape change:** A phosphate group from ATP binds to the protein. In response, the protein changes shape.

4. **Release:** The sodium ions leave the protein and move to the exterior of the cell.

FIGURE 6.25 The Sodium–Potassium Pump Depends on an Input of Chemical Energy Stored in ATP.

As shown in **FIGURE 6.25**, sodium and potassium ions move in a multistep process:

Step 1 When Na⁺/K⁺-ATPase is in the conformation shown here, binding sites with a high affinity for sodium ions are available.

Step 2 Three sodium ions from the inside of the cell bind to these sites and activate the ATPase activity in the pump.

Step 3 A phosphate group from ATP is transferred to the pump. When the phosphate group attaches, the pump changes its shape in a way that opens the ion-binding pocket to the external environment and reduces its affinity for sodium ions.

Step 4 The sodium ions leave the protein and move to the exterior of the cell.

Step 5 In this conformation, the pump has binding sites with a high affinity for potassium ions facing the external environment.

Step 6 Two potassium ions from outside the cell bind to the pump.

Step 7 When the potassium is bound, the phosphate group is cleaved from the protein and its structure changes in response— back to the original shape with the ion-binding pocket facing the interior of the cell.

Step 8 In this conformation, the pump has low affinity for potassium ions. The potassium ions leave the protein and move to the interior of the cell. The cycle then repeats.

Other types of pumps move protons (H⁺), calcium ions (Ca²⁺), or other ions or molecules across membranes in a directed manner, regardless of the gradients. As a result, cells can import and concentrate valuable nutrients and ions inside the cell despite their relatively low external concentration. They can also expel molecules or ions, even when a concentration gradient favors diffusion of these substances into the cell.

Secondary Active Transport Approximately 30 percent of all the ATP generated in your body is used to drive the Na⁺/K⁺-ATPase cycle. Each cycle exports three Na⁺ ions for every two K⁺ ions it

imports. In this way, the sodium–potassium pump converts energy from ATP to an electrochemical gradient across the membrane. The outside of the membrane becomes positively charged relative to the inside. This gradient favors a flow of anions out of the cell and a flow of cations into the cell.

The electrochemical gradients established by the Na⁺/K⁺-ATPase represent a form of stored energy, much like the electrical energy stored in a battery. How do cells use this energy?

Gradients are crucial to the function of the cell, in part because they make it possible for cells to engage in **secondary active transport**—also known as cotransport. When cotransport occurs, a gradient set up by a pump provides the energy required to power the movement of a different molecule against its particular gradient.

Recall that GLUT-1 facilitates the movement of glucose into or out of cells in the direction of its gradient. Can glucose be moved against its gradient? The answer is yes—a cotransport protein in your gut cells uses the Na⁺ gradient created by Na⁺/K⁺-ATPases to import glucose against its chemical gradient. When Na⁺ ions bind to this cotransporter, its shape changes in a way that allows glucose to bind. Once glucose binds, another shape transports both the sodium and glucose to the inside of the cell. After dropping off sodium and glucose, the protein's original shape returns to repeat the cycle.

In this way, glucose present in the food you are digesting is actively transported into your body. The glucose molecules eventually diffuse into your bloodstream and are transported to your brain, where they provide the chemical energy you need to stay awake and learn some biology. (You will learn more about secondary active transport in Units 7 and 8.)

Plasma Membranes and the Intracellular Environment

Taken together, the selective permeability of the lipid bilayer and the specificity of the proteins involved in passive transport and

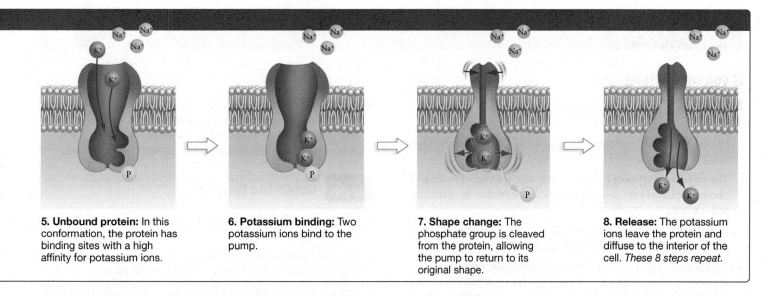

5. Unbound protein: In this conformation, the protein has binding sites with a high affinity for potassium ions.

6. Potassium binding: Two potassium ions bind to the pump.

7. Shape change: The phosphate group is cleaved from the protein, allowing the pump to return to its original shape.

8. Release: The potassium ions leave the protein and diffuse to the interior of the cell. *These 8 steps repeat.*

active transport enable cells to create an internal environment that is much different from the external one (**FIGURE 6.26**).

With the evolution of membrane proteins, the early cells acquired the ability to create an internal environment that was conducive to life—one that contained the substances required for manufacturing ATP and copying ribozymes. Cells with particularly efficient and selective membrane proteins would be favored by natural selection and would come to dominate the population. Cellular life had begun.

Some 3.5 billion years later, cells continue to evolve. What do today's cells look like, and how do they produce and store the chemical energy that makes life possible? Answering these and related questions is the focus of the following unit.

check your understanding

C Y U

If you understand that . . .

• Membrane proteins allow substances that ordinarily do not readily cross lipid bilayers to enter or exit cells.
• Substances may move across a membrane along an electrochemical gradient, via facilitated diffusion through channel or carrier proteins. Or, they may move against a gradient in response to work done by pumps.

✔ You should be able to . . .

Explain what is passive about passive transport, active about active transport, and "co" about cotransport.

Answers are available in Appendix A.

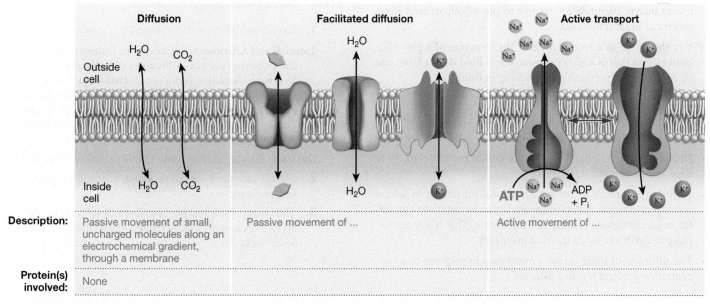

FIGURE 6.26 Summary of the Passive and Active Mechanisms of Membrane Transport.
✔**EXERCISE** Complete the chart.

	Diffusion	Facilitated diffusion	Active transport
Description:	Passive movement of small, uncharged molecules along an electrochemical gradient, through a membrane	Passive movement of ...	Active movement of ...
Protein(s) involved:	None		

If you understand . . .

6.1 Lipid Structure and Function

- Lipids are largely hydrophobic compounds due to their high number of nonpolar C–H bonds.

- The three main types of lipids found in cells are fats, steroids, and phospholipids. These molecules vary considerably in structure and function.

- In hydrocarbon chains, the length and degree of saturation have a profound effect on their physical properties.

- Amphipathic lipids possess a distinct hydrophilic region containing polar or charged groups. Phospholipids have a polar head and a nonpolar tail. The nonpolar tail usually consists of fatty acids or isoprenoids.

✔ You should be able to explain how adding hydrogen (H_2) to vegetable oil, a process called hydrogenation, results in a butter-like solid called margarine.

6.2 Phospholipid Bilayers

- In solution, phospholipids spontaneously assemble into bilayers that can serve as a physical barrier between an internal and external environment.

- Small nonpolar molecules tend to move across lipid bilayers readily; ions cross rarely, if at all.

- The permeability and fluidity of lipid bilayers depend on temperature, on the concentration of steroids, and on the chemical structure of the lipids present, such as the saturation status and length of the hydrocarbon chains. Phospholipids with longer or saturated tails form a dense and highly hydrophobic interior that lowers bilayer permeability, relative to phospholipids containing shorter or unsaturated tails.

✔ You should be able to explain how the structure of a phospholipid bilayer that is highly permeable and fluid differs from one that is highly impermeable and lacking in fluidity.

6.3 How Molecules Move across Lipid Bilayers: Diffusion and Osmosis

- Diffusion is the random movement of ions or molecules owing to their kinetic energy.

- Diffusion can result in the net directional movement of solutes across a membrane, if the membrane separates solutions that differ in concentration, charge, or temperature. This is a spontaneous process driven by an increase in entropy.

- The diffusion of water across a membrane in response to a concentration gradient is called osmosis.

✔ You should be able to imagine a beaker with solutions separated by a planar membrane and then predict what will happen after addition of a solute to one side if the solute (1) crosses the membrane readily or (2) is incapable of crossing the membrane.

6.4 Membrane Proteins

- The permeability of lipid bilayers can be altered significantly by membrane proteins.

- Channel proteins provide pores in the membrane and facilitate the diffusion of specific solutes into and out of the cell.

- Carriers undergo conformational changes that facilitate the diffusion of specific molecules into and out of the cell.

- Pumps use energy to actively move ions or molecules in a single direction, often against the electrical or chemical gradient.

- In combination, the selective permeability of phospholipid bilayers and the specificity of transport proteins make it possible to create an environment inside a cell that is radically different from the exterior.

✔ You should be able to draw and label the membrane of a cell that is placed in a solution containing calcium ions and lactose and show the activity of the following membrane proteins: (1) an H^+ pump that exports protons; (2) a calcium channel; and (3) a lactose carrier. Your drawing should include arrows and labels indicating the direction of solute movement and the direction of the appropriate electrochemical gradients.

(MB) MasteringBiology

1. MasteringBiology Assignments

Tutorials and Activities Active Transport; Diffusion, Diffusion and Osmosis; Facilitated Diffusion Lipids; Membrane Structure; Membrane Transport: Diffusion and Passive Transport; Membrane Transport: The Sodium–Potassium Pump; Membrane Transport Proteins; Osmosis; Membrane Transport: Cotransport; Osmosis and Water Balance in Cells; Selective Permeability of Membranes

Questions Reading Quizzes, Blue-Thread Questions, Test Bank

2. eText Read your book online, search, take notes, highlight text, and more.

3. The Study Area Practice Test, Cumulative Test, BioFlix® 3-D Animations, Videos, Activities, Audio Glossary, Word Study Tools, Art

You should be able to . . .

1. How is the structure of saturated fats different from that of unsaturated fats?
   a. All of the carbons in the hydrocarbon tails of saturated fats are bonded to one another with double bonds.
   b. Saturated fats have three hydrocarbon tails bonded to the glycerol molecule instead of just two.
   c. The hydrocarbon tails in a saturated fat have the maximum number of hydrogens possible.
   d. Saturated fats have no oxygens present.

2. What distinguishes amphipathic lipids from other lipids?
   a. Amphipathic lipids have polar and nonpolar regions.
   b. Amphipathic lipids have saturated and unsaturated regions.
   c. Amphipathic lipids are steroids.
   d. Amphipathic lipids dissolve in water.

3. If a solution surrounding a cell is hypertonic relative to the inside of the cell, how will water move?
   a. It will move into the cell via osmosis.
   b. It will move out of the cell via osmosis.
   c. It will not move, because equilibrium exists.
   d. It will evaporate from the cell surface more rapidly.

4. When does a concentration gradient exist?
   a. when membranes rupture
   b. when solute concentrations are high
   c. when solute concentrations are low
   d. when solute concentrations differ on the two sides of a membrane

5. What two conditions must be present for the effects of osmosis to occur?

6. In terms of structure, how do channel proteins differ from carrier proteins?

7. If a cell were placed in a solution with a high potassium concentration and no sodium, what would happen to the sodium–potassium pump's activity?
   a. It would stop moving ions across the membrane.
   b. It would continue using ATP to pump sodium out of the cell and potassium into the cell.
   c. It would move sodium and potassium ions across the membrane, but no ATP would be used.
   d. It would reverse the direction of sodium and potassium ions to move them against their gradients.

8. Cooking oil lipids consist of long, unsaturated hydrocarbon chains. Would you expect these molecules to form membranes spontaneously? Why or why not? Describe, on a molecular level, how you would expect these lipids to interact with water.

9. Explain why phospholipids form a bilayer in solution, and why the process is spontaneous.

10. Ethanol (C_2H_5OH) is the active ingredient in alcoholic beverages. Would you predict that this molecule crosses lipid bilayers quickly, slowly, or not at all? Explain your reasoning.

11. Integral membrane proteins are anchored in lipid bilayers. Of the following four groups of amino acids—nonpolar, polar, charged/acidic, charged/basic (see Figure 3.2)—which would likely be found in the portion that crosses the lipid bilayer? Explain your reasoning.

12. Examine the experimental chamber in Figure 6.7a. If the lipid bilayer were to contain the CFTR molecule, what would pass through the membrane if you added a 1-molar solution of sodium chloride on the left side and a 1-molar solution of potassium ions on the right? Assume that there is an equal amount of water on each side at the start of the experiment.

13. In an experiment, you create two groups of liposomes—one made from red blood cell membranes and the other from frog egg cell membranes. When placed in water, those made with red blood cell membranes burst more rapidly than those made from frog membranes. What is the best explanation for these results?
    a. The red blood cell liposomes are more hypertonic relative to water than the frog egg liposomes.
    b. The red blood cell liposomes are more hypotonic relative to water than the frog egg liposomes.
    c. The red blood cell liposomes contain aquaporins, which are not abundant in the frog egg liposomes.
    d. The frog egg liposomes contain ion channels, which are not present in the red blood cell liposomes.

14. When phospholipids are arranged in a bilayer, it is theoretically possible for individual molecules in the bilayer to flip-flop. That is, a phospholipid could turn 180° and become part of the membrane's other surface. From what you know about the behavior of polar heads and nonpolar tails, predict whether flip-flops are frequent or rare. Then design an experiment, using a planar bilayer with one side made up of phospholipids that contain a dye molecule on their hydrophilic head, to test your prediction.

15. Unicellular organisms live in a wide range of habitats, from the hot springs in Yellowstone National Park to the freezing temperatures of the Antarctic. Make a prediction about the saturation status of membrane phospholipids in organisms that live in extremely cold environments versus those that live in extremely hot environments. Explain your reasoning.

16. When biomedical researchers design drugs, they sometimes add methyl (CH_3) groups or charged groups to the molecules. If these groups are not directly involved in the activity of the drug, predict the purpose of these modifications and explain why these strategies are necessary.

The Big Picture

The first spark of life ignited when simple chemical reactions began to convert small molecules into larger, more complex molecules with novel 3-D structures and activities. According to the theory of chemical evolution, these reactions eventually led to the formation of the four types of macromolecules characteristic of life—proteins, nucleic acids, carbohydrates, and lipids.

As you look through this concept map, consider how the functions of the four types of macromolecules are determined by their structures, and how these structures stem from the chemical properties of the atoms and bonds used to build them.

Note that each box in the concept map indicates the chapters and sections where you can go for review. Also, be sure to do the blue exercises in the Check Your Understanding box below.

THE CHEMISTRY OF LIFE

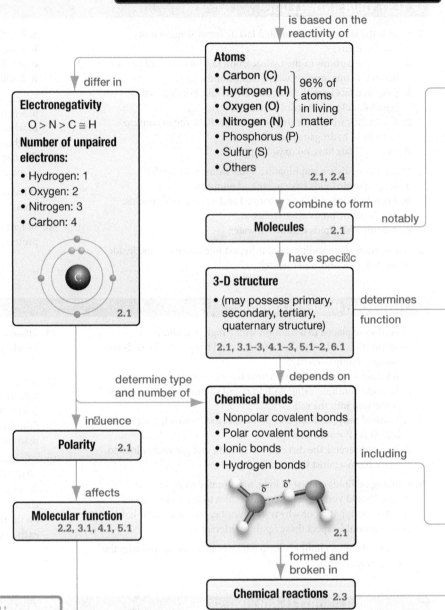

is based on the reactivity of

Atoms
- Carbon (C)
- Hydrogen (H) ⎫ 96% of
- Oxygen (O) ⎬ atoms in living
- Nitrogen (N) ⎭ matter
- Phosphorus (P)
- Sulfur (S)
- Others   2.1, 2.4

differ in

Electronegativity

O > N > C ≅ H

Number of unpaired electrons:
- Hydrogen: 1
- Oxygen: 2
- Nitrogen: 3
- Carbon: 4

2.1

combine to form

Molecules 2.1

notably

have specific

3-D structure
- (may possess primary, secondary, tertiary, quaternary structure)

2.1, 3.1–3, 4.1–3, 5.1–2, 6.1

determines function

determine type and number of

influence

Polarity 2.1

affects

Molecular function
2.2, 3.1, 4.1, 5.1

depends on

Chemical bonds
- Nonpolar covalent bonds
- Polar covalent bonds
- Ionic bonds
- Hydrogen bonds

2.1

including

formed and broken in

Chemical reactions 2.3

check your understanding

If you understand the big picture . . .

✔ **You should be able to . . .**

1. Explain how the relative electronegativities of atoms affect the bonding within and among water molecules.

2. Describe the attributes of RNA that make it a candidate for the origin of life. Why isn't DNA considered a candidate?

3. Circle the atoms in amino acids and nucleotides that engage in creating bonds with other monomers.

4. Draw a protein in the lipid bilayer. What role might it play?

Answers are available in Appendix A.

as demonstrated by

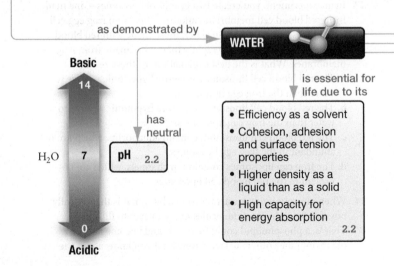

WATER

Basic

14

H_2O 7   **pH** 2.2

has neutral

0

Acidic

is essential for life due to its
- Efficiency as a solvent
- Cohesion, adhesion and surface tension properties
- Higher density as a liquid than as a solid
- High capacity for energy absorption

2.2

Biological macromolecules

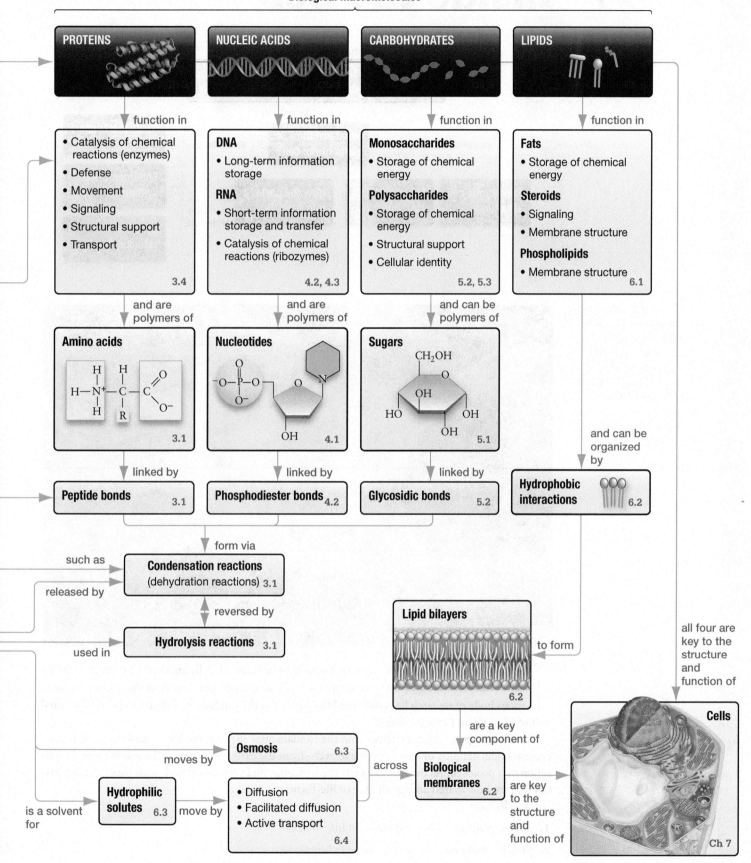

PROTEINS **NUCLEIC ACIDS** **CARBOHYDRATES** **LIPIDS**

function in

PROTEINS
- Catalysis of chemical reactions (enzymes)
- Defense
- Movement
- Signaling
- Structural support
- Transport

3.4

NUCLEIC ACIDS
DNA
- Long-term information storage

RNA
- Short-term information storage and transfer
- Catalysis of chemical reactions (ribozymes)

4.2, 4.3

CARBOHYDRATES
Monosaccharides
- Storage of chemical energy

Polysaccharides
- Storage of chemical energy
- Structural support
- Cellular identity

5.2, 5.3

LIPIDS
Fats
- Storage of chemical energy

Steroids
- Signaling
- Membrane structure

Phospholipids
- Membrane structure

6.1

and are polymers of

Amino acids

3.1

and are polymers of

Nucleotides

4.1

and can be polymers of

Sugars

5.1

and can be organized by

Hydrophobic interactions 6.2

linked by

Peptide bonds 3.1

linked by

Phosphodiester bonds 4.2

linked by

Glycosidic bonds 5.2

form via

Condensation reactions
(dehydration reactions) 3.1

such as

released by

reversed by

Hydrolysis reactions 3.1

used in

Lipid bilayers

6.2

to form

all four are key to the structure and function of

are a key component of

Osmosis 6.3

moves by

across

Biological membranes 6.2

are key to the structure and function of

Cells

is a solvent for

Hydrophilic solutes 6.3

move by

- Diffusion
- Facilitated diffusion
- Active transport

6.4

Ch 7

7 Inside the Cell

In this chapter you will learn that

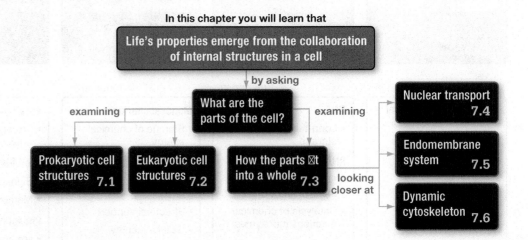

Life's properties emerge from the collaboration of internal structures in a cell

↓ by asking

What are the parts of the cell?

examining — Prokaryotic cell structures **7.1**

examining — Eukaryotic cell structures **7.2**

How the parts ⊠t into a whole **7.3**

looking closer at

Nuclear transport **7.4**

Endomembrane system **7.5**

Dynamic cytoskeleton **7.6**

This cell has been treated with fluorescing molecules that bind to its fibrous cytoskeleton. Microtubules (large protein fibers) are yellow; actin filaments (smaller fibers) are blue. The cell's nucleus has been stained green.

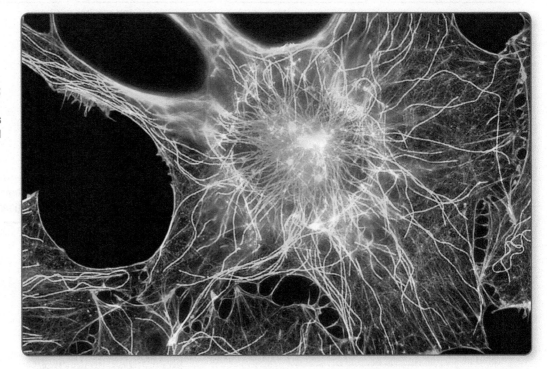

The cell theory states that all organisms consist of cells and all cells are derived from preexisting cells (Chapter 1). Since this theory was initially developed and tested in the 1850s, an enormous body of research has confirmed that the cell is the fundamental structural and functional unit of life. Life on Earth is cellular.

Previous chapters (Unit 1) delved into the fundamental attributes of life by looking at biologists' current understanding of how the cell evolved—from the early chemistry to the assembly and replication of a protocell. As the first cells left the hydrothermal vents, they took with them characteristics that are now shared among all known life-forms.

All cells have

1. nucleic acids that store and transmit information;

2. proteins that perform most of the cell's functions;

✔ When you see this checkmark, stop and test yourself. Answers are available in Appendix A.

3. carbohydrates that provide chemical energy, carbon, support, and identity; and

4. a plasma membrane, which serves as a selectively permeable membrane barrier.

Thanks to the selective permeability of phospholipid bilayers and the activity of membrane transport proteins, the plasma membrane creates an internal environment that differs from conditions outside the cell. Our task now is to explore the structures inside the cell to understand how the properties of life emerged from the combination of these characteristics.

Let's begin by analyzing how the parts inside a cell function individually and then exploring how they work as a unit. This approach is analogous to studying individual organs in the body and then analyzing how they work together to form the nervous system or digestive system. As you study this material, keep asking yourself some key questions: How does the structure of this part or group of parts correlate with its function? What problem does it solve?

7.1 Bacterial and Archaeal Cell Structures and Their Functions

Cells are divided into two fundamental types called eukaryotes and prokaryotes (see Chapter 1). This division is mostly based on cell **morphology** ("form-science")—eukaryotic cells have a membrane-bound compartment called a nucleus, and prokaryotic cells do not.

But according to **phylogeny** ("tribe-source"), or evolutionary history, organisms are divided into three broad domains called (1) Bacteria, (2) Archaea, and (3) Eukarya. Members of the Bacteria and Archaea are prokaryotic; members of the Eukarya—including algae, fungi, plants, and animals—are eukaryotic.

A Revolutionary New View

For almost 200 years, biologists thought that prokaryotic cells were simple in terms of their morphology and that there was little structural diversity among species. This conclusion was valid at the time, given the resolution of the microscopes that were available and the number of species that had been studied.

Things have changed. Recent improvements in microscopy and other research tools have convinced biologists that prokaryotic cells, among which bacteria are the best understood, possess an array of distinctive structures and functions found among millions of species. This conclusion represents one of the most exciting discoveries in cell biology over the past 10 years.

To keep things simple at the start, though, **FIGURE 7.1** offers a low-magnification, stripped-down diagram of a bacterial cell.

Prokaryotic Cell Structures: A Parts List

The labels in Figure 7.1 highlight the components common to all or most bacteria studied to date. Let's explore these elements one by one, and also look at more specialized structures found in particular species, starting from the inside and working out.

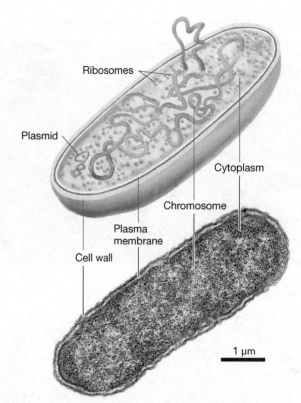

FIGURE 7.1 Overview of a Prokaryotic Cell. Prokaryotic cells are identified by a negative trait—the absence of a membrane-bound nucleus. Although there is wide variation in the size and shape of bacterial and archaeal cells, they all contain a plasma membrane, a chromosome, and protein-synthesizing ribosomes.

The Chromosome Is Organized in a Nucleoid   The most prominent structure inside a bacterial cell is the **chromosome**. Most bacterial species have a single, circular chromosome that consists of a large DNA molecule associated with a small number of proteins. The DNA molecule contains information, and the proteins provide structural support for the DNA.

Recall that the information in DNA is encoded in its sequence of nitrogenous bases. Segments of DNA that contain information for building functional RNAs, some of which may be used to make polypeptides, are called **genes** (Chapter 4). Thus, chromosomes contain DNA, which contains genes.

In the well-studied bacterium *Escherichia coli*, the circular chromosome would be over 1 mm long if it were linear—500 times longer than the cell itself (**FIGURE 7.2a**; see page 108). This situation is typical in prokaryotes. To fit into the cell, the DNA double helix coils on itself with the aid of enzymes to form a compact, "supercoiled" structure. Supercoiled regions of DNA resemble a rubber band that has been held at either end and then twisted until it coils back upon itself.

The location and structural organization of the circular chromosome is called the **nucleoid** (pronounced *NEW-klee-oyd*). The genetic material in the nucleoid is often organized by clustering loops of DNA into distinct domains, but it is not separated from the rest of the cell interior by a membrane. The functional role of this organization of the bacterial chromosome and how it changes over time is currently the subject of intense research.

(a) Compared to the cell, chromosomal DNA is very long.

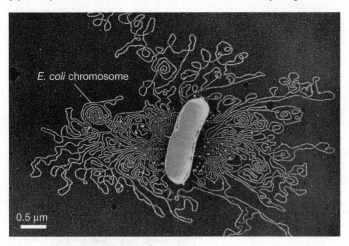

E. coli chromosome

0.5 µm

(b) DNA is packaged by supercoiling.

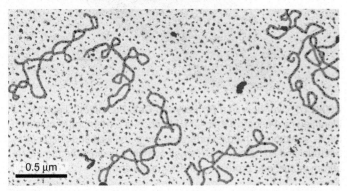

0.5 µm

FIGURE 7.2 Bacterial DNA Is Supercoiled. (a) The chromosomes of bacteria and archaea are often over 1000 times the length of the cell, as shown in this micrograph of *E. coli* that has been treated to release its DNA. To fit inside cells, this DNA must be highly compacted by supercoiling. **(b)** A colorized electron micrograph showing the effect of supercoiling on the DNA of isolated plasmids.

In addition to one or more chromosomes, bacterial cells may contain from one to about a hundred small, usually circular, supercoiled DNA molecules called **plasmids** (**FIGURE 7.2b**). Plasmids contain genes but are physically independent of the cellular chromosome. In many cases the genes carried by plasmids are not required under normal conditions; instead, they help cells adapt to unusual circumstances, such as the sudden presence of a poison in the environment. As a result, plasmids can be considered auxiliary genetic elements.

Ribosomes Manufacture Proteins **Ribosomes** are observed in all prokaryotic cells and are found throughout the cell interior. It is not unusual for a single cell to contain 10,000 ribosomes, each functioning as a protein-manufacturing center.

Ribosomes are complex structures composed of large and small subunits, each of which contains RNA and protein molecules. Biologists often refer to ribosomes, along with other multicomponent complexes that perform specialized tasks, as "macromolecular machines." (Chapter 17 analyzes the structure and function of ribosomes in detail.)

Photosynthetic Species Have Internal Membrane Complexes In addition to the nucleoid and ribosomes found in all bacteria and archaea studied to date, it is common to observe extensive internal membranes in prokaryotes that perform photosynthesis. Photosynthesis is the suite of chemical reactions responsible for converting the energy in sunlight into chemical energy stored in sugars.

The photosynthetic membranes observed in prokaryotes contain the enzymes and pigment molecules required for these reactions to occur and develop as infoldings of the plasma membrane. In some cases, vesicles pinch off as the plasma membrane folds in. In other cases, flattened stacks of photosynthetic membrane remain connected to the plasma membrane, like those shown in **FIGURE 7.3**. The extensive surface area provided by these internal membranes makes it possible for more photosynthetic reactions to occur and thus increases the cell's ability to make food.

Organelles Perform Specialized Functions Recent research indicates that several bacterial species have internal compartments that qualify as **organelles** ("little organs"). An organelle is a membrane-bound compartment inside the cell that contains enzymes or structures specialized for a particular function.

Bacterial organelles perform an array of tasks, including

- storing calcium ions or other key molecules;
- holding crystals of the mineral magnetite, which function like a compass needle to help cells sense a magnetic field and swim in a directed way;
- organizing enzymes responsible for synthesizing complex carbon compounds from carbon dioxide; and
- sequestering enzymes that generate chemical energy from ammonium ions.

The Cytoskeleton Structures the Cell Interior Recent research has also shown that bacteria and archaea contain long, thin fibers that serve a variety of roles inside the cell. All bacterial species,

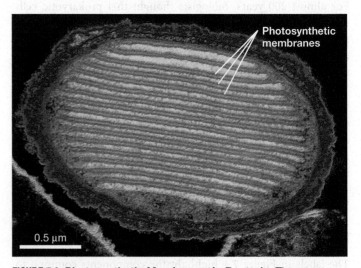

Photosynthetic membranes

0.5 µm

FIGURE 7.3 Photosynthetic Membranes in Bacteria. The green stripes in this photosynthetic bacterium are membranes that contain the pigments and enzymes required for photosynthesis. This photo has been colorized to enhance the membranes.

for example, contain protein fibers that are essential for cell division to take place. Some species also have protein filaments that help maintain cell shape. Protein filaments such as these form the basis of the **cytoskeleton** ("cell skeleton").

The discovery of bacterial cytoskeletal elements is so new that much remains to be learned. Currently, researchers are working to understand how the different cytoskeletal elements enable cells to divide and if they play a role in organizing the cell interior into distinctive regions.

The Plasma Membrane Separates Life from Nonlife

The plasma membrane consists of a phospholipid bilayer and proteins that either span the bilayer or attach to one side. Inside the membrane, all the contents of a cell, excluding the nucleus, are collectively termed the **cytoplasm** ("cell-formed").

Because all archaea and virtually all bacteria are unicellular, the plasma membrane creates an internal environment that is distinct from the outside, nonliving environment. The combined effect of a lipid bilayer and membrane proteins prohibits the entry of many substances that would be dangerous to life while allowing the passage of molecules and ions required for life (see Chapter 6).

The Cell Wall Forms a Protective "Exoskeleton"

Because the cytoplasm contains a high concentration of solutes, in most habitats it is hypertonic relative to the surrounding environment. When this is the case, water enters the cell via osmosis and makes the cell's volume expand. In virtually all bacteria and archaea, this pressure is resisted by a stiff **cell wall.**

Bacterial and archaeal cell walls are a tough, fibrous layer that surrounds the plasma membrane. In prokaryotes, the pressure of the plasma membrane against the cell wall is about the same as the pressure in an automobile tire.

The cell wall protects the organism and gives it shape and rigidity, much like the exoskeleton (external skeleton) of a crab or insect. In addition, many bacteria have another protective layer outside the cell wall that consists of lipids with polysaccharides attached. Lipids that contain carbohydrate groups are termed **glycolipids.**

External Structures Enable Movement and Attachment

Besides having a cell wall to provide protection, as just described, many bacteria also interact with their environment via structures that grow from the plasma membrane. The flagella and fimbriae shown in **FIGURE 7.4** are examples that are commonly found on bacterial surfaces.

Bacterial **flagella** (singular: **flagellum**) are assembled from over 40 different proteins at the cell surface of certain species. The base of this structure is embedded in the plasma membrane, and its rotation spins a long, helical filament that propels cells through water. At top speed, flagellar movement can drive a bacterial cell through water at 60 cell lengths per second. In contrast, the fastest animal in the ocean—the sailfish—can swim at a mere 10 body lengths per second.

Fimbriae (singular: **fimbria**) are needlelike projections that extend from the plasma membrane of some bacteria and promote attachment to other cells or surfaces. These structures are

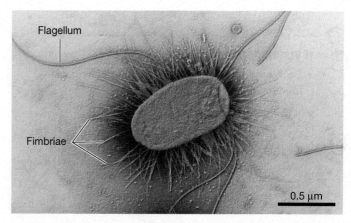

FIGURE 7.4 Extracellular Appendages Found on Bacteria. Some species of bacteria, such as the *E. coli* shown here, assemble large protein structures used for swimming through liquid (flagella) or adhering to surfaces (fimbriae).

more numerous than flagella and are often distributed over the entire surface of the cell. Fimbriae are crucial to the establishment of many infections based on their ability to glue bacteria to the surface of tissues.

The painting in **FIGURE 7.5** shows a cross section of a bacterial cell and provides a close-up view of the internal and external structures introduced in this section. One feature that prokaryotic and eukaryotic cells have in common: They are both packed with dynamic, highly integrated structures.

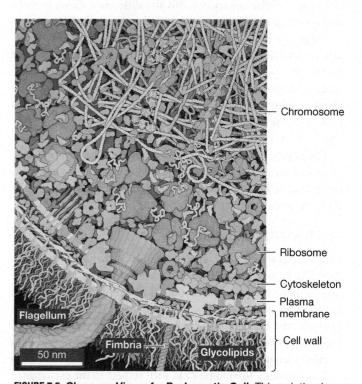

FIGURE 7.5 Close-up View of a Prokaryotic Cell. This painting is David Goodsell's representation of a cross section through part of a bacterial cell. It is based on electron micrographs of bacterial cells and is drawn to scale. Note that the cell is packed with proteins, DNA, ribosomes, and other molecular machinery.

If you understand that . . .

• Each structure in a prokaryotic cell performs a function vital to the cell.

✔ **You should be able to . . .**

Describe the structure and function of (1) the nucleoid, (2) photosynthetic membranes, (3) flagella, and (4) the cell wall.

Answers are available in Appendix A.

7.2 Eukaryotic Cell Structures and Their Functions

The Eukarya includes species that range from microscopic algae to 100-meter-tall redwood trees. Brown algae, red algae, fungi, amoebae, slime molds, green plants, and animals are all eukaryotic. Although multicellularity has evolved several times among eukaryotes (see Chapter 30), many species are unicellular.

The first thing that strikes biologists about eukaryotic cells is how much larger they are on average than bacteria and archaea. Most prokaryotic cells measure 1 to 10 μm in diameter, while most eukaryotic cells range from about 5 to 100 μm in diameter. A micrograph of an average eukaryotic cell, at the same scale as the bacterial cell in Figure 7.3, would fill this page. For many species of unicellular eukaryotes, this size difference allows them to make a living by ingesting bacteria and archaea whole.

Large size has a downside, however. As a cell increases in diameter, its volume increases more than its surface area. In other words, the relationship between them—the surface-area-to-volume ratio—changes. Since the surface is where the cell exchanges substances with its environment, the reduction in this ratio decreases the rate of exchange: Diffusion only allows for rapid movement across very small distances.

Prokaryotic cells tend to be small enough so that ions and small molecules arrive where they are needed via diffusion. The random movement of diffusion alone, however, is insufficient for this type of transport as the cell's diameter increases.

The Benefits of Organelles

How do eukaryotic cells solve the problems that size can engender? The answer lies in their numerous organelles. In effect, the huge volume inside a eukaryotic cell is compartmentalized into many small bins. Because eukaryotic cells are subdivided, the **cytosol**—the fluid portion between the plasma membrane and these organelles—is only a fraction of the total cell volume. This relatively small volume of cytosol reduces the effect of the total cell surface-area-to-volume ratio with respect to the exchange of nutrients and waste products.

Compartmentalization also offers two key advantages:

1. Incompatible chemical reactions can be separated. For example, new fatty acids can be synthesized in one organelle while

SUMMARY TABLE 7.1 How Do the Structures of Prokaryotic and Eukaryotic Cells Differ?

	Bacteria and Archaea	Eukaryotes
Location of DNA	In nucleoid (not membrane bound); plasmids also common	Inside nucleus (membrane bound); plasmids extremely rare
Internal Membranes and Organelles	Extensive internal membranes only in photosynthetic species; limited types and numbers of organelles	Large numbers of organelles; many types of organelles
Cytoskeleton	Limited in extent, relative to eukaryotes	Extensive—usually found throughout volume of cell
Overall Size	Usually small relative to eukaryotes	Most are larger than prokaryotes

excess or damaged fatty acids are degraded and recycled in a different organelle.

2. Chemical reactions become more efficient. First, the substrates required for particular reactions can be localized and maintained at high concentrations within organelles. Second, if substrates are used up in a particular part of the organelle, they can be replaced by substrates that have only a short distance to diffuse. Third, groups of enzymes that work together can be clustered within or on the membranes of organelles instead of floating free in the cytosol. When the product of one reaction is the substrate for a second reaction catalyzed by another enzyme, clustering the enzymes increases the speed and efficiency of both reaction sequences.

If bacteria and archaea can be compared to small, specialized machine shops, then eukaryotic cells resemble sprawling industrial complexes. The organelles and other structures found in eukaryotes are analogous to highly specialized buildings that act as administrative centers, factories, transportation corridors, waste and recycling facilities, warehouses, and power stations.

When typical prokaryotic and eukaryotic cells are compared, four key differences, identified in **TABLE 7.1**, stand out:

1. Eukaryotic chromosomes are found inside a membrane-bound compartment called the **nucleus.**

2. Eukaryotic cells are often much larger than prokaryotes.

3. Eukaryotic cells contain extensive amounts of internal membrane.

4. Eukaryotic cells feature a particularly diverse and dynamic cytoskeleton.

Eukaryotic Cell Structures: A Parts List

FIGURE 7.6 provides a simplified view of a typical animal cell and a plant cell. The artist has removed most of the cytoskeletal elements

(a) Generalized animal cell

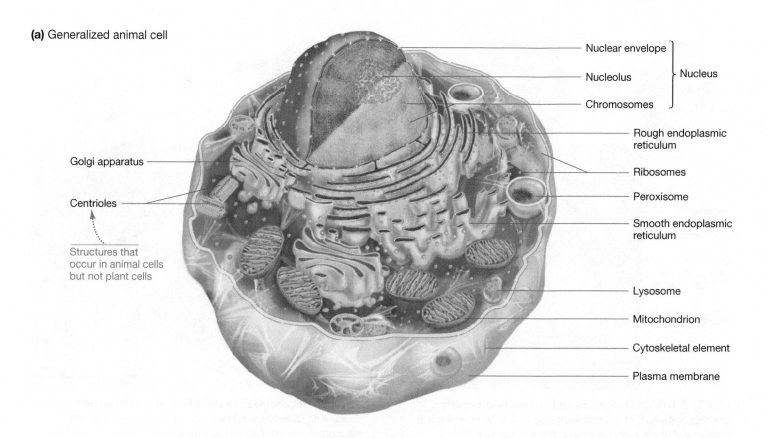

Nuclear envelope ⎤
Nucleolus   ⎬ Nucleus
Chromosomes   ⎦

Rough endoplasmic reticulum

Golgi apparatus

Ribosomes

Peroxisome

Centrioles

Smooth endoplasmic reticulum

Structures that occur in animal cells but not plant cells

Lysosome

Mitochondrion

Cytoskeletal element

Plasma membrane

(b) Generalized plant cell

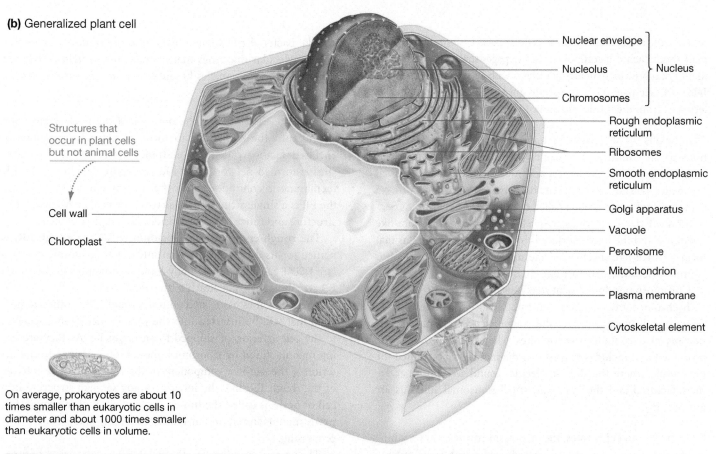

Nuclear envelope ⎤
Nucleolus   ⎬ Nucleus
Chromosomes   ⎦

Rough endoplasmic reticulum

Ribosomes

Structures that occur in plant cells but not animal cells

Smooth endoplasmic reticulum

Golgi apparatus

Cell wall

Vacuole

Chloroplast

Peroxisome

Mitochondrion

Plasma membrane

Cytoskeletal element

On average, prokaryotes are about 10 times smaller than eukaryotic cells in diameter and about 1000 times smaller than eukaryotic cells in volume.

FIGURE 7.6 Overview of Eukaryotic Cells. Generalized images of **(a)** animal and **(b)** plant cells that illustrate the cellular structures in the "typical" eukaryote. The structures have been color-coded for clarity. Compare with the prokaryotic cell, shown at true relative size at bottom left.

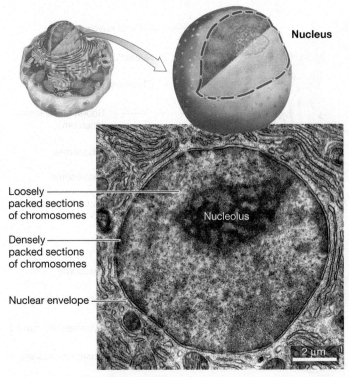

Nucleus

Loosely packed sections of chromosomes

Nucleolus

Densely packed sections of chromosomes

Nuclear envelope

2 μm

FIGURE 7.7 The Nucleus Stores and Transmits Information. The genetic, or hereditary, information is encoded in DNA, which is a component of the chromosomes inside the nucleus.

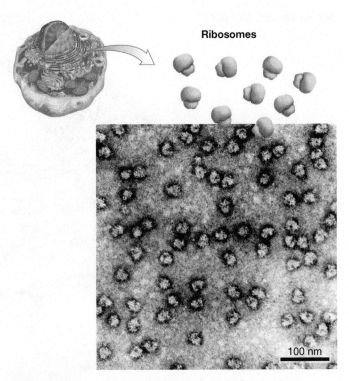

Ribosomes

100 nm

FIGURE 7.8 Ribosomes Are the Site of Protein Synthesis. Eukaryotic ribosomes are larger than bacterial and archaeal ribosomes, but similar in overall structure.

to make the organelles and other cellular parts easier to see. As you read about each cell component in the pages that follow, focus on identifying how its structure correlates with its function. Then use **TABLE 7.2** (see page 117) as a study guide. As with bacterial cells, let's start from the inside and move to the outside.

The Nucleus The nucleus contains the chromosomes and functions as an administrative center for information storage and processing. Among the largest and most highly organized of all organelles (**FIGURE 7.7**), it is enclosed by a unique structure—a complex double membrane called the **nuclear envelope.** As Section 7.4 will detail, the nuclear envelope is studded with pore-like openings, and the inside surface is linked to fibrous proteins that form a lattice-like sheet called the **nuclear lamina.** The nuclear lamina stiffens the structure and maintains its shape.

Chromosomes do not float freely inside the nucleus—instead, each chromosome occupies a distinct area, which may vary in different cell types and over the course of cell replication. The nucleus also contains specific sites where gene products are processed and includes at least one distinctive region called the **nucleolus,** where the RNA molecules found in ribosomes are manufactured and the large and small ribosomal subunits are assembled.

Ribosomes In eukaryotes, the cytoplasm consists of everything inside the plasma membrane excluding the nucleus. Scattered throughout this cytoplasm are millions of ribosomes (**FIGURE 7.8**).

Like bacterial ribosomes, eukaryotic ribosomes are complex macromolecular machines that manufacture proteins. They are not classified as organelles because they are not surrounded by membranes.

Endoplasmic Reticulum The portions of the nuclear envelope extend into the cytoplasm to form an extensive membrane-enclosed factory called the **endoplasmic reticulum** (literally, "inside-formed-network"), or ER. As Figure 7.6 shows, the ER membrane is continuous with the nuclear envelope. Although the ER is a single structure, it has two regions that are distinct in structure and function. Let's consider each region in turn.

The **rough endoplasmic reticulum (RER), or rough ER,** is named for its appearance in transmission electron micrographs (see **FIGURE 7.9**, left). The knobby-looking structures in the rough ER are ribosomes that attach to the membrane.

The ribosomes associated with the rough ER synthesize proteins that will be inserted into the plasma membrane, secreted to the cell exterior, or shipped to an organelle. As they are being manufactured by ribosomes, these proteins move to the interior of the sac-like component of the rough ER. The interior of the rough ER, like the interior of any sac-like structure in a cell or body, is called the **lumen.** In the lumen of the rough ER, newly manufactured proteins undergo folding and other types of processing.

The proteins produced in the rough ER have a variety of functions. Some carry messages to other cells; some act as membrane

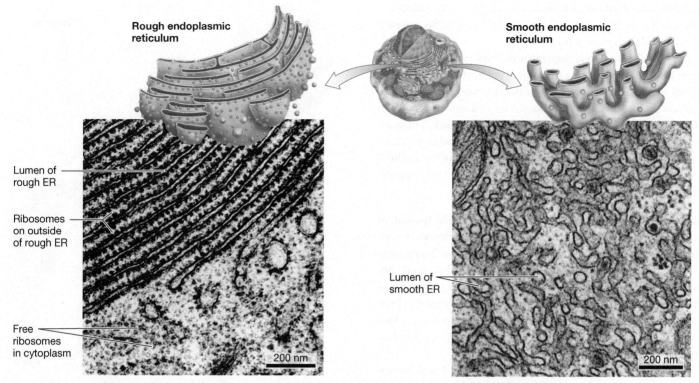

Rough endoplasmic reticulum

Smooth endoplasmic reticulum

Lumen of rough ER

Ribosomes on outside of rough ER

Free ribosomes in cytoplasm

200 nm

Lumen of smooth ER

200 nm

FIGURE 7.9 The Endoplasmic Reticulum Is a Site of Synthesis, Processing, and Storage. The ER is continuous with the nuclear envelope and possesses two distinct regions: on the left, the rough ER is a system of membrane-bound sacs and tubules with ribosomes attached; on the right, the smooth ER is a system of membrane-bound sacs and tubules that lacks ribosomes.

transport proteins or pumps; others are enzymes. The common theme is that many of the rough ER products are packaged into vesicles and transported to various distant destinations—often to the surface of the cell or beyond.

In electron micrographs, parts of the ER that are free of ribosomes appear smooth and even. Appropriately, these parts of the ER are called the **smooth endoplasmic reticulum (SER),** or **smooth ER** (see **FIGURE 7.9**, right).

The smooth ER contains enzymes that catalyze reactions involving lipids. Depending on the type of cell, these enzymes may synthesize lipids needed by the organism or break down lipids and other molecules that are poisonous. For example, the smooth ER is the manufacturing site for phospholipids used in plasma membranes. In addition, the smooth ER functions as a reservoir for calcium ions (Ca^{2+}) that act as a signal triggering a wide array of activities inside the cell.

The structure of the endoplasmic reticulum correlates closely with its function. The rough ER has ribosomes and functions primarily as a protein-manufacturing center; the smooth ER lacks ribosomes and functions primarily as a lipid-processing center.

Golgi Apparatus In many cases, the products of the rough ER pass through the Golgi apparatus before they reach their final destination. The **Golgi apparatus** consists of discrete flattened, membranous sacs called **cisternae** (singular: **cisterna**), which are stacked on top of one another (**FIGURE 7.10**). The organelle also

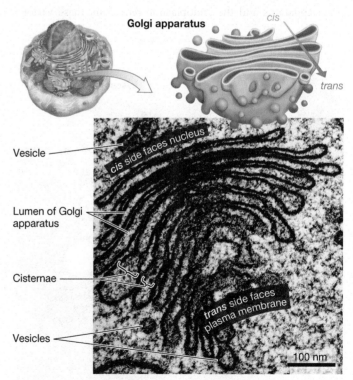

Golgi apparatus

cis

trans

Vesicle

cis side faces nucleus

Lumen of Golgi apparatus

Cisternae

trans side faces plasma membrane

Vesicles

100 nm

FIGURE 7.10 The Golgi Apparatus Is a Site of Protein Processing, Sorting, and Shipping. The Golgi apparatus is a collection of flattened vesicles called cisternae.

has a distinct polarity, or sidedness. The *cis* ("this side") surface is closest to the nucleus, and the *trans* ("across") surface is oriented toward the plasma membrane.

The *cis* side of a Golgi apparatus receives products from the rough ER, and the *trans* side ships them out to other organelles or the cell surface. In between, within the cisternae, the rough ER's products are processed and packaged for delivery. Micrographs often show "bubbles" on either side of the Golgi stack. These are membrane-bound vesicles that carry proteins or other products to and from the organelle. Section 7.5 analyzes the intracellular movement of molecules from the rough ER to the Golgi apparatus and beyond in more detail.

Lysosomes   Animal cells contain organelles called **lysosomes** that function as recycling centers (**FIGURE 7.11**). Lysosomes contain about 40 different enzymes, each specialized for hydrolyzing different types of macromolecules—proteins, nucleic acids, lipids, or carbohydrates. The amino acids, nucleotides, sugars, and other molecules that result from acid hydrolysis leave the lysosome via transport proteins in the organelle's membrane. Once in the cytosol, they can be used as sources of energy or building blocks for new molecules.

These digestive enzymes are collectively called acid hydrolases because under acidic conditions (pH of 5.0), they use water to break monomers from macromolecules. In the cytosol, where the pH is about 7.2, acid hydrolases are less active. Proton pumps in the lysosomal membrane maintain an acidic pH in the lumen of the lysosome by importing hydrogen ions.

Even though lysosomes are physically separated from the Golgi apparatus and the endoplasmic reticulum, these various

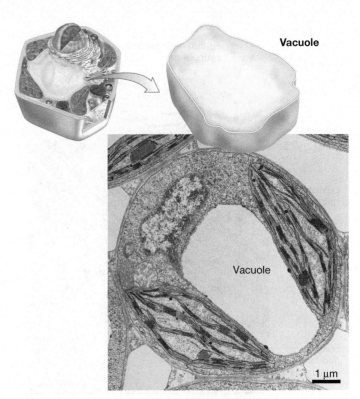

FIGURE 7.12 Vacuoles Are Generally Storage Centers in Plant and Fungal Cells. Vacuoles vary in size and function. Some contain digestive enzymes and serve as recycling centers; most are large storage containers.

✔**QUESTION** Why are toxins like nicotine, cocaine, and caffeine stored in vacuoles instead of the cytosol?

organelles jointly form a key functional grouping referred to as the **endomembrane system.** The endomembrane ("inner-membrane") system is a center for producing, processing, and transporting proteins and lipids in eukaryotic cells. For example, acid hydrolases are synthesized in the ER, processed in the Golgi, and then shipped to the lysosome.

Vacuoles   The cells of plants, fungi, and certain other groups lack lysosomes. Instead, they contain a prominent organelle called a vacuole. Compared with the lysosomes of animal cells, the **vacuoles** of plant and fungal cells are large—sometimes taking up as much as 80 percent of a plant cell's volume (**FIGURE 7.12**).

Although some vacuoles contain enzymes that are specialized for digestion, most of the vacuoles observed in plant and fungal cells act as storage depots. In many cases, ions such as potassium (K^+) and chloride (Cl^-), among other solutes, are stored at such high concentrations they draw water in from the environment. As the vacuole expands in volume, the cytoplasm pushes the plasma membrane against the cell wall, which maintains the plant cell's shape. In other cells, vacuoles have more specialized storage functions:

- Inside seeds, cells may contain a large vacuole filled with proteins. When the embryonic plant inside the seed begins to grow, enzymes begin digesting these proteins to provide amino acids for the growing individual.

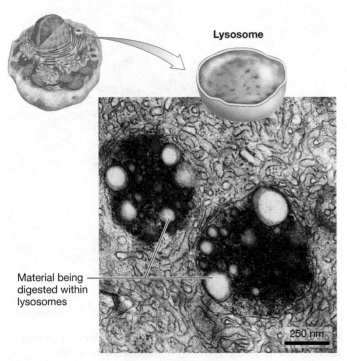

FIGURE 7.11 Lysosomes Are Recycling Centers. Lysosomes are usually oval or globular and have a single membrane.

- In cells that make up flower petals or fruits, vacuoles are filled with colorful pigments.
- Elsewhere, vacuoles may be packed with noxious compounds that protect leaves and stems from being eaten by predators. The type of chemical involved varies by species, ranging from bitter-tasting tannins to toxins such as nicotine, morphine, caffeine, or cocaine.

Peroxisomes   Virtually all eukaryotic cells contain globular organelles called **peroxisomes** (**FIGURE 7.13**). These organelles have a single membrane and originate as buds from the ER.

Although different types of cells from the same individual may have distinct types of peroxisomes, these organelles all share a common function: Peroxisomes are centers for reduction–oxidation (redox) reactions. (Chapter 8 explains in detail how redox reactions transfer electrons between atoms and molecules.) For example, the peroxisomes in your liver cells contain enzymes that remove electrons from, or oxidize, the ethanol in alcoholic beverages.

Different types of peroxisomes contain different suites of redox enzymes. In the leaves of plants, specialized peroxisomes called **glyoxysomes** are packed with enzymes that oxidize fats to form a compound that can be used to store energy for the cell. But plant seeds have a different type of peroxisome—one that is packed with enzymes responsible for releasing energy from stored fatty acids. The young plant uses this energy as it begins to grow.

In animals and plants, the products of these reactions often include hydrogen peroxide (H_2O_2), which is highly reactive.

If hydrogen peroxide escaped from the peroxisome, it would quickly react with and damage DNA, proteins, and cellular membranes. This event is rare, however, because inside the peroxisome, the enzyme catalase quickly "detoxifies" hydrogen peroxide by catalyzing its oxidation to form water and oxygen. The enzymes found inside the peroxisome make a specialized set of oxidation reactions possible and safe for the cell.

Mitochondria   The energy required to build these organelles and do other types of work comes from adenosine triphosphate (ATP), most of which is produced in the cell's **mitochondria** (singular: **mitochondrion**).

As **FIGURE 7.14** shows, each mitochondrion has two membranes. The outer membrane defines the organelle's surface, while the inner membrane is connected to a series of sac-like **cristae**. The solution enclosed within the inner membrane is called the **mitochondrial matrix.** In eukaryotes, most of the enzymes and molecular machines responsible for synthesizing ATP are embedded in the membranes of the cristae or suspended in the matrix (see Chapter 9). Depending on the type of cell, from 50 to more than a million mitochondria may be present.

Each mitochondrion has many copies of a small, circular chromosome that is independent of the nuclear chromosomes. This mitochondrial DNA contains only around 37 genes in most eukaryotes—most of the genes responsible for the function of the organelle reside in the nuclear DNA.

Among the genes present in mitochondrial DNA are those that encode RNAs for mitochondrial ribosomes. These ribosomes are

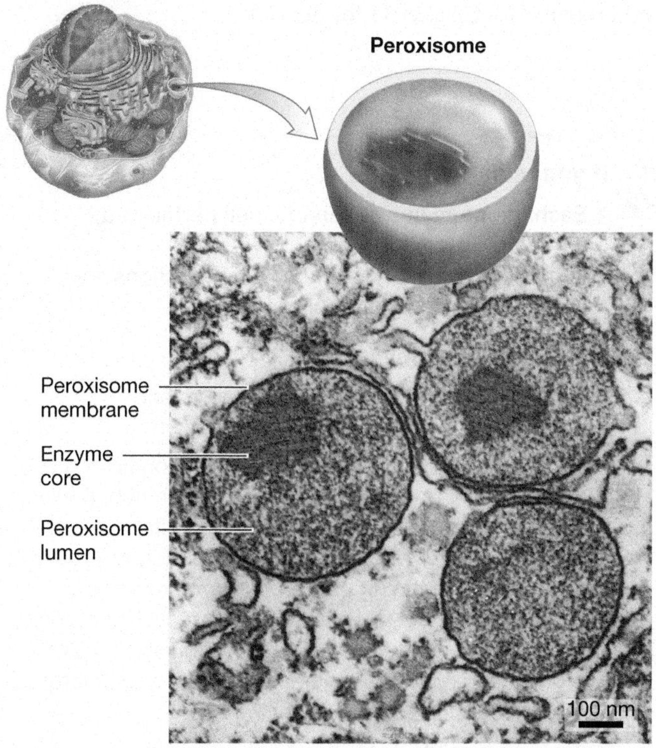

Peroxisome

Peroxisome membrane

Enzyme core

Peroxisome lumen

100 nm

FIGURE 7.13 Peroxisomes Are the Site of Oxidation Reactions. Peroxisomes are globular organelles that are defined by a single membrane.

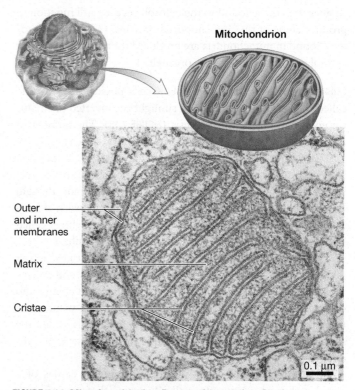

Mitochondrion

Outer and inner membranes

Matrix

Cristae

0.1 μm

FIGURE 7.14 Mitochondria Are Power-Generating Stations. Mitochondria vary in size and shape, but all have a double membrane with sac-like cristae inside.

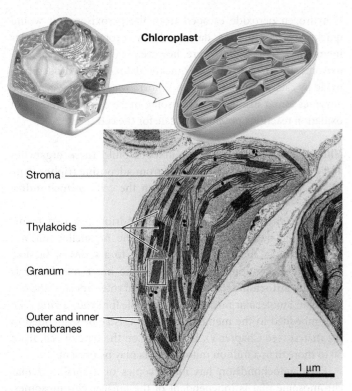

Chloroplast

Stroma

Thylakoids

Granum

Outer and inner membranes

1 μm

FIGURE 7.15 Chloroplasts Are Sugar-Manufacturing Centers in Plants and Algae. Many of the enzymes and other molecules required for photosynthesis are located in membranes inside the chloroplast. These membranes form thylakoids that consist of discs stacked into grana.

smaller than those found in the cytosol, yet they still function to produce some of the mitochondrial proteins. (Most of the proteins found in mitochondria are produced from ribosomes in the cytosol and imported into the organelle.)

Chloroplasts Most algal and plant cells possess an organelle called the **chloroplast,** in which sunlight is converted to chemical energy during photosynthesis (**FIGURE 7.15**). The number of chloroplasts per cell varies from none to several dozen.

The chloroplast has a double membrane around its exterior, analogous to the structure of a mitochondrion. Instead of featuring sac-like cristae that connect to the inner membrane, though, the interior of the chloroplast is dominated by a network of hundreds of membrane-bound, flattened, sac-like structures called **thylakoids,** which are independent of the inner membrane.

Thylakoids have stacks, like pancakes, that are called **grana** (singular: **granum**). Many of the pigments, enzymes, and macromolecular machines responsible for converting light energy into chemical energy are embedded in the thylakoid membranes (see Chapter 10). The region outside the thylakoids, called the **stroma,** contains enzymes that use this chemical energy to produce sugars.

Like mitochondria, each chloroplast contains copies of a circular chromosome and small ribosomes that manufacture some, but not all, of the organelle's proteins. Both mitochondria

and chloroplasts also grow and divide independently of cell division through a process that resembles bacterial fission (see Chapter 12).

These attributes are odd compared with those of the other organelles and have led biologists to propose that mitochondria and chloroplasts were once free-living bacteria. According to the **endosymbiosis theory,** the ancestors of modern eukaryotes ingested these bacteria, but instead of destroying them, established a mutually beneficial relationship with them. (In Chapter 30, you will learn more about the origins of these eukaryotic organelles.)

Cytoskeleton The final major structural feature that is common to all eukaryotic cells is the cytoskeleton, an extensive system of protein fibers. In addition to giving the cell its shape and structural stability, cytoskeletal proteins are involved in moving the cell itself and moving materials within the cell. In essence, the cytoskeleton organizes all the organelles and other cellular structures into a cohesive whole. Section 7.6 will analyze the structure and functions of the cytoskeleton in detail.

The Cell Wall In fungi, algae, and plants, cells possess an outer cell wall in addition to their plasma membrane. The cell wall is located outside the plasma membrane and furnishes a durable, outer layer that provides structural support for the cell. The cells of animals, amoebae, and other groups lack a cell wall—their exterior surface consists of the plasma membrane only.

Although the composition of the cell wall varies among species and even among types of cells in the same individual, the general plan is similar: Rods or fibers composed of a carbohydrate run through a stiff matrix made of other polysaccharides and proteins (see Chapter 11 for details).

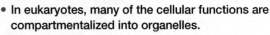
check your understanding

If you understand that . . .
- Each structure in a eukaryotic cell performs a function vital to the cell.
- In eukaryotes, many of the cellular functions are compartmentalized into organelles.

✔ **You should be able to . . .**

1. Explain how the structure of lysosomes and peroxisomes correlates with their function.

2. In Table 7.2, label each component with one of the following roles: administrative/information hub, power station, warehouse, large molecule manufacturing and shipping facility (with subtitles for lipid factory, protein finishing and shipping line, protein synthesis and folding center, waste processing and recycling center), support beams, perimeter fencing with secured gates, protein factory, food-manufacturing facility, and fatty-acid processing and detox center.

Answers are available in Appendix A.

Eukaryotic Cell Components

Icons Not to Scale		Structure		
		Membrane	Components	Function
	Nucleus	Double ("envelope"); openings called nuclear pores	Chromosomes	Information storage and transmission
			Nucleolus	Ribosome subunit assembly
			Nuclear lamina	Structural support
	Ribosomes	None	Complex of RNA and proteins	Protein synthesis
	Endomembrane system			
	Endoplasmic reticulum: rough	Single; contains receptors for entry of selected proteins	Network of branching sacs Ribosomes associated	Protein synthesis and processing
	Endoplasmic reticulum: smooth	Single; contains enzymes for synthesizing phospholipids	Network of branching sacs Enzymes for synthesizing or breaking down lipids	Lipid synthesis and processing
	Golgi apparatus	Single; contains receptors for products of rough ER	Stack of flattened, distinct cisternae	Protein, lipid, and carbohydrate processing
	Lysosomes	Single; contains proton pumps	Acid hydrolases (catalyze hydrolysis reactions)	Digestion and recycling
	Vacuoles	Single; contains transporters for selected molecules	Varies—pigments, oils, carbohydrates, water, or toxins	Varies—coloration, storage of oils, carbohydrates, water, or toxins
	Peroxisomes	Single; contains transporters for selected macromolecules	Enzymes that catalyze oxidation reactions Catalase (processes peroxide)	Oxidation of fatty acids, ethanol, or other compounds
	Mitochondria	Double; inner contains enzymes for ATP production	Enzymes that harvest energy from molecules to make ATP	ATP production
	Chloroplasts	Double; plus membrane-bound sacs in interior	Pigments Enzymes that use light energy to make sugars	Production of sugars via photosynthesis
	Cytoskeleton	None	Actin filaments Intermediate filaments Microtubules	Structural support; movement of materials; in some species, movement of whole cell
	Plasma membrane	Single; contains transport and receptor proteins	Phospholipid bilayer with transport and receptor proteins	Selective permeability—maintains intracellular environment
	Cell wall	None	Carbohydrate fibers running through carbohydrate or protein matrix	Protection, structural support

7.3 Putting the Parts into a Whole

Within a cell, the structure of each component correlates with its function. In the same way, the overall size, shape, and composition of a cell correlate with its function.

Cells might be analogous to machine shops or industrial complexes, but clothing manufacturing centers are very different in layout and composition from airplane production facilities. How does the physical and chemical makeup of a cell correlate with its function?

Structure and Function at the Whole-Cell Level

Inside an individual plant or animal, cells are specialized for certain tasks and have a structure that correlates with those tasks. For example, the muscle cells in your upper leg are extremely long, tube-shaped structures. They are filled with protein fibers that slide past one another as the entire muscle flexes or relaxes. It is this sliding motion that allows your muscles to contract or extend as you run. Muscle cells are also packed with mitochondria, which produce the ATP required for the sliding motion to occur.

In contrast, nearby fat cells are rounded, globular structures that store fatty acids. They consist of little more than a plasma membrane, a nucleus, and a fat droplet. Neither cell bears a close resemblance to the generalized animal cell pictured in Figure 7.6a.

To drive home the correlation between the overall structure and function of a cell, examine the transmission electron micrographs in **FIGURE 7.16**.

- The animal cell in Figure 7.16a, located in the pancreas, manufactures and exports digestive enzymes. It is packed with rough ER and Golgi, which make these functions possible.

- The animal cell in Figure 7.16b, from the testis, synthesizes and exports the steroid hormone testosterone—a lipid-soluble signal. This cell is dominated by smooth ER, where processing of steroids and other lipids takes place.

- The plant cell in Figure 7.16c, from the leaf of a potato, has hundreds of chloroplasts and is specialized for absorbing light and manufacturing sugar.

- The animal cells in Figure 7.16d come from brown fat. The cells have numerous mitochondria that have been altered so they convert energy stored in fat into heat instead of ATP.

In each case, the types of organelles in each cell and their size and number correlate with the cell's specialized function.

The Dynamic Cell

Biologists study the structure and function of organelles and cells with a combination of tools and approaches. For several decades, a technique called **differential centrifugation** was particularly important because it allowed researchers to isolate particular cell components and analyze their chemical composition. Differential centrifugation is based on breaking cells apart to create a complex mixture and separating components in a centrifuge (see **BioSkills 10** in Appendix B). The individual parts of the cell

(a) Animal pancreatic cell: Exports digestive enzymes.

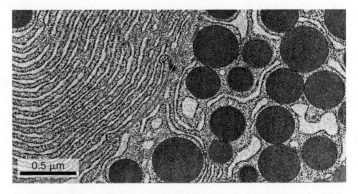

(b) Animal testis cell: Exports lipid-soluble signals.

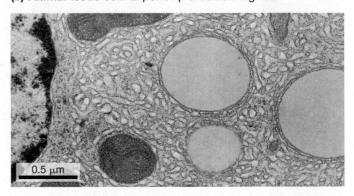

(c) Plant leaf cell: Manufactures ATP and sugar.

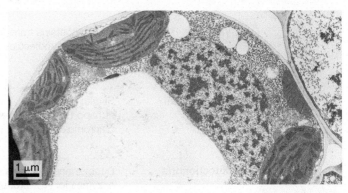

(d) Brown fat cells: Burn fat to generate heat in lieu of ATP.

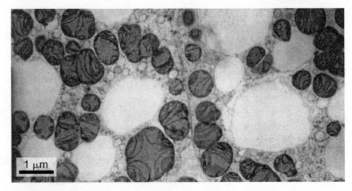

FIGURE 7.16 Cell Structure Correlates with Function.

✔**EXERCISE** In part (a), label the rough ER and the dark, round secretory vesicles. In (b), label the smooth ER. In (c), label the chloroplasts, vacuole, and nucleus. In (d), label the mitochondria.

can then be purified and studied in detail, in isolation from other parts of the cell.

Historically and currently, however, the most important research in cell biology is based on imaging—simply looking at cells. Recent innovations allow biologists to put fluorescing tags or other types of markers on particular cell components and then look at them with increasingly sophisticated light microscopes and electron microscopes. Advances in microscopy provide increasingly high magnification and better resolution.

It's important to recognize, though, that some of these techniques have limitations. Differential centrifugation splits cells into parts that are analyzed independently, and electron microscopy gives a fixed "snapshot" of the cell or organisms being observed. Neither technique allows investigators to explore directly how things move from place to place in the cell or how parts interact. The information gleaned from these techniques can make cells seem static. In reality, cells are dynamic.

The amount of chemical activity and the speed of molecular movement inside cells are nothing short of fantastic. Bacterial ribosomes add up to 20 amino acids per second to a growing polypeptide, and eukaryotic ribosomes typically add 2 per second. Given that there are about 15,000 ribosomes in each bacterium and possibly a million in an average eukaryotic cell, hundreds or even thousands of new protein molecules can be produced each second in every cell. Here are some other remarkable cellular feats:

- In an average second, a typical cell in your body uses an average of 10 million ATP molecules and synthesizes just as many.

- It's not unusual for a cellular enzyme to catalyze 25,000 or more reactions per second; most cells contain hundreds or thousands of different enzymes.

- A minute is more than enough time for each membrane phospholipid in your body to travel the breadth of the organelle or cell where it resides.

- The hundreds of trillions of mitochondria inside you are completely replaced about every 10 days, for as long as you live.

Because humans are such large organisms, it's impossible for us to imagine what life is really like inside a cell. At the scale of a ribosome or an organelle or a cell, gravity is inconsequential. Instead, the dominant forces are the charge- or polarity-based electrostatic attractions between molecules and their energy of motion. At this level, events take nanoseconds, and speeds are measured in micrometers per second. This is the speed of life.

Contemporary methods for studying cells (including some of the imaging techniques featured in **BioSkills 11** in Appendix B) capture this dynamism by tracking how organelles and molecules move and interact over time. The ability to digitize video images of live cells, or take time-lapse photographs of living cells, is allowing researchers to see and study dynamic processes.

The rest of this chapter focuses on this theme of cellular dynamism and movement. Its goal is to put some of the individual pieces of a cell together and ask how they work as systems to accomplish key tasks.

To begin, let's first look at how molecules move into and out of the cell's control center—the nucleus—and then consider how proteins move from ribosomes into the lumen of the rough ER and then to the Golgi apparatus and beyond. The chapter closes by introducing the cytoskeletal elements and their associated motor proteins and how they are used to transport cargo inside the cell or move the cell itself.

7.4 Cell Systems I: Nuclear Transport

The nucleus is the information center of eukaryotic cells—a corporate headquarters, design center, and library all rolled into one. Appropriately enough, its interior is highly organized.

The organelle's overall shape and structure are defined by the mesh-like nuclear lamina. The nuclear lamina provides an attachment point for the chromosomes, each of which occupies a well-defined region in the nucleus.

In addition, specific centers exist where the genetic information in DNA is decoded and processed. At these locations, large suites of enzymes interact to produce RNA messages from specific genes at specific times. Meanwhile, the nucleolus functions as the site of ribosome assembly.

Structure and Function of the Nuclear Envelope

The nuclear envelope separates the nucleus from the rest of the cell. Starting in the 1950s, transmission electron micrographs of cross sections through the nuclear envelope showed that the structure is supported by the fibrous nuclear lamina and bounded by two membranes, each consisting of a lipid bilayer. How does this administrative center communicate with the rest of the cell across the double membrane barrier?

Micrographs like the one in **FIGURE 7.17** (see page 120) show that the nuclear envelope is broken with openings, approximately 60 nanometers (nm) in diameter, called **nuclear pores**. Because these pores extend through both the inner and outer nuclear membranes, they connect the inside of the nucleus with the cytosol. Follow-up research showed that each pore consists of over 50 different proteins. As the diagram on the right side of Figure 7.17 shows, these protein molecules form an elaborate structure called the **nuclear pore complex.**

What substances traverse nuclear pores? Chromosomal DNA clearly does not—it remains in the nucleus as long as the nuclear envelope remains intact. But DNA is used to synthesize RNA inside the nucleus, most of which is exported through nuclear pores to the cytoplasm.

Several types of RNA molecules are produced, each distinguished by size and function. For example, **ribosomal RNAs** are manufactured in the nucleolus, where they bind to proteins to form ribosomes. Molecules called **messenger RNAs (mRNA)** carry the information required to manufacture proteins. Both the newly assembled ribosomes and the mRNAs must be transported from the nucleus to the cytoplasm, where protein synthesis takes place.

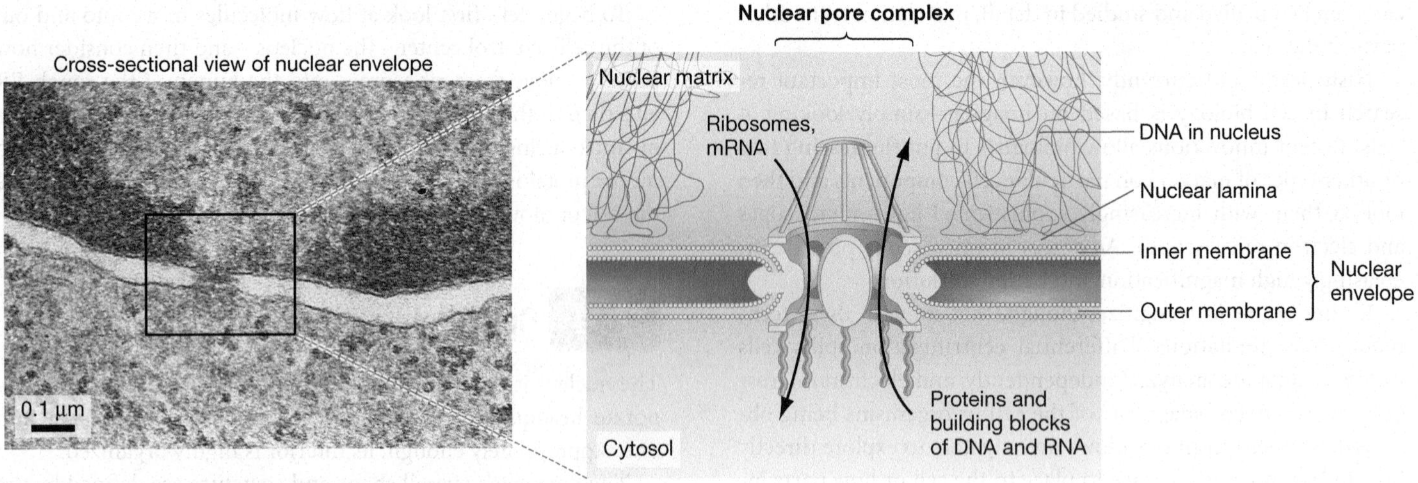

FIGURE 7.17 Structure of the Nuclear Envelope and Nuclear Pore Complex.

Inbound traffic is also impressive. Nucleoside triphosphates that act as building blocks for DNA and RNA enter the nucleus, as do a variety of proteins responsible for copying DNA, synthesizing RNAs, extending the nuclear lamina, or assembling ribosomes.

To summarize, ribosomal subunits and various types of RNAs exit the nucleus; nucleotides and certain proteins enter it. In a typical cell, over 500 molecules pass through each of the 3000–4000 nuclear pores every second. The scale of traffic through the nuclear pores is mind-boggling. How is it regulated and directed?

Experiments in the early 1960s showed that size matters in the passage of molecules through nuclear pores. This conclusion was based on the results from injecting tiny gold particles that varied in diameter and tracking their movement across the pores. In electron micrographs, gold particles show up as defined black dots that can be easily distinguished from cellular structures. Immediately after injection, most of the gold particles were observed in the cytoplasm, and only a few were closely associated with nuclear pores. Ten minutes after injection, only the small particles (< 12.5 nm in diameter) appeared to be distributed throughout both the nucleus and the cytoplasm, and the larger particles were excluded from entering the nucleus.

The fact that the pore opening is almost 5 times larger than this 12.5-nm size limit supports the hypothesis that the nuclear pore complex serves as a gate to control passage through the envelope. If this is the case, then what is required to open these gates so that proteins larger than the size limit, like those responsible for replicating DNA, may pass?

How Do Large Molecules Enter the Nucleus?

It was clear to researchers that size was not the sole factor in selective transport across the nuclear envelope. Certain proteins were concentrated in the nucleus, while others were completely excluded—even if they were similar in size.

A series of experiments on a protein called nucleoplasmin helped researchers understand the nature of nuclear import. Nucleoplasmin is strictly found in the nucleus and plays an important role in the assembly of chromatin. When researchers labeled nucleoplasmin with a radioactive atom and injected it into the cytoplasm of living cells, they found that the radioactive protein was quickly concentrated into the nucleus. Is there a "send-to-nucleus" signal within the nucleoplasmin protein that is responsible for this directed transport?

As shown in **FIGURE 7.18**, the distinctive structure of nucleoplasmin was used to further investigate this process. First, researchers used enzymes called proteases to cleave the core sections of nucleoplasmin from the tails. After separating the tails from the core fragments, they labeled each component with radioactive atoms and injected them into the cytoplasm of different cells.

At various times after the injections, researchers examined the nuclei and cytoplasm of the cells to track down the radioactive label. The results were striking. They found that tail fragments were rapidly transported from the cytoplasm into the nucleus. Core fragments, in contrast, were not allowed to pass through the nuclear envelope and remained in the cytoplasm.

These data led to a key hypothesis: Nuclear proteins are synthesized by ribosomes in the cytosol and contain a "zip code"—a molecular address tag—that marks them for transport through the nuclear pore complex. This zip code allows the nuclear pore complex to open in some way that permits larger proteins and RNA molecules to pass through.

By analyzing different stretches of the tail, the biologists eventually found a 17-amino-acid-long section that had to be present to direct nucleoplasmin to the nucleus. Follow-up work confirmed that other proteins bound for the nucleus, even those expressed by some viruses, have similar amino acid sequences directing their transport. This common sequence came to be called the **nuclear localization signal (NLS).** Proteins that leave the nucleus have a different signal, required for nuclear export.

HYPOTHESIS: Nucleoplasmin contains a discrete "Send to nucleus" signal that resides in either the tail or core region.

NULL HYPOTHESIS: Nucleoplasmin does not require a signal to enter the nucleus, or the entire protein serves as the signal.

EXPERIMENTAL SETUP:

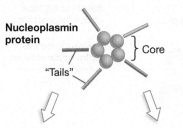

Nucleoplasmin protein

Core

"Tails"

1. Use protease to cleave tails off of nucleoplasmin protein core.

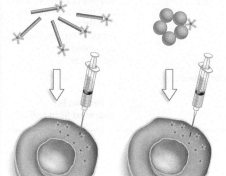

Labeled tails   Labeled cores

2. Attach radioactive labels to protein tails and cores.

3. Inject labeled tails and cores into cytoplasm of different cells.

4. Wait, then locate labeled fragments ....

PREDICTION:

PREDICTION OF NULL HYPOTHESIS:

RESULTS:

Labeled tail fragments **located in nucleus**   Labeled core fragments still **located in cytoplasm**

CONCLUSION:

FIGURE 7.18 Does the Nucleoplasmin Protein Contain a "Send to Nucleus" Signal?

SOURCES: Mills, A. D., R. A. Laskey, P. Black, et al. 1980. *Journal of Molecular Biology* 139: 561–568; Dingwall, C., S. V. Sharnick, and R. A. Laskey. 1982. *Cell* 30: 449–458.

✔**EXERCISE** Without looking at the text, fill in the prediction(s) and conclusion(s) in this experiment.

More recent research has shown that the movement of proteins and other large molecules into and out of the nucleus is an energy-demanding process that involves special transport proteins. These nuclear transport proteins function like trucks that haul cargo into or out of the nucleus through the nuclear pore complex, depending on whether they have an import or export zip code. Currently, biologists are trying to unravel how all this traffic in and out of the nucleus is regulated to avoid backups and head-on collisions.

✔ If you understand the process of nuclear transport, you should be able to compare and contrast the movement of (1) nucleotides and (2) large proteins through the nuclear pore complex. Which would you expect to require the input of energy?

7.5 Cell Systems II: The Endomembrane System Manufactures, Ships, and Recycles Cargo

The nuclear membrane is not the only place in cells where cargo moves in a regulated and energy-demanding fashion. Most of the proteins found in peroxisomes, mitochondria, and chloroplasts are also actively imported from the cytosol. These proteins contain special signal sequences, like the nuclear localization signal, that target them to the appropriate organelles.

If you think about it for a moment, the need to sort proteins and ship them to specific destinations should be clear. Proteins are produced by ribosomes that are either free in the cytosol or on the surface of the ER. Many of these proteins must be transported to a compartment inside the eukaryotic cell. Acid hydrolases must be shipped to lysosomes and catalase to peroxisomes. To get to the right location, each protein has to have an address tag and a transport and delivery system.

To get a better understanding of protein sorting and transport in eukaryotic cells, let's consider perhaps the most intricate of all manufacturing and shipping complexes: the endomembrane system. In this system, proteins that are synthesized in the rough ER move to the Golgi apparatus for processing, and from there they travel to the cell surface or other destinations.

Studying the Pathway through the Endomembrane System

The idea that materials move through the endomembrane system in an orderly way was inspired by a simple observation. According to electron micrographs, cells that secrete digestive enzymes, hormones, or other products have particularly large amounts of rough ER and Golgi. This correlation led to the idea that these organelles may participate in a "secretory pathway" that starts in the rough ER and ends with products leaving the cell (**FIGURE 7.19**, see page 122). How does this hypothesized pathway work?

Tracking Protein Movement via Pulse–Chase Assay George Palade and colleagues did pioneering research on the secretory

FIGURE 7.19 The Secretory Pathway Hypothesis. The secretory pathway hypothesis proposes that proteins intended for secretion from the cell are synthesized and processed in a highly prescribed series of steps. Note that proteins are packaged into vesicles when they move from the RER to the Golgi and from the Golgi to the cell surface.

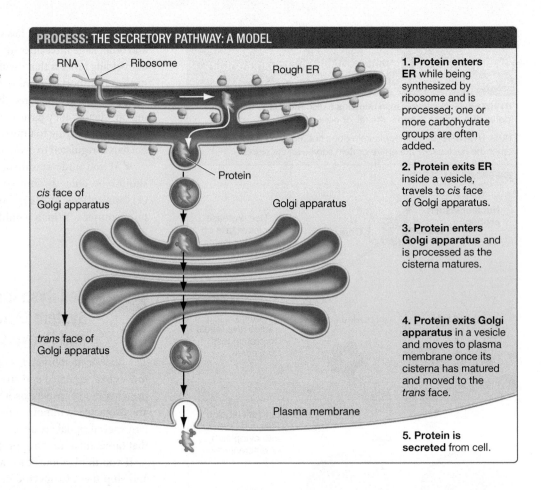

PROCESS: THE SECRETORY PATHWAY: A MODEL

RNA   Ribosome   Rough ER

cis face of Golgi apparatus   Golgi apparatus

Protein

trans face of Golgi apparatus

Plasma membrane

1. Protein enters ER while being synthesized by ribosome and is processed; one or more carbohydrate groups are often added.

2. Protein exits ER inside a vesicle, travels to *cis* face of Golgi apparatus.

3. Protein enters Golgi apparatus and is processed as the cisterna matures.

4. Protein exits Golgi apparatus in a vesicle and moves to plasma membrane once its cisterna has matured and moved to the *trans* face.

5. Protein is secreted from cell.

pathway using a **pulse–chase experiment** to track protein movement. This strategy is based on two steps:

1. *The "Pulse"* Expose experimental cells to a high concentration of a modified amino acid for a short time. For example, if a cell is briefly exposed to a large amount of radioactively labeled amino acid, virtually all the proteins synthesized during that interval will be radiolabeled.

2. *The "Chase"* The pulse ends by washing away the modified amino acid and replacing it with the normal version of the same molecule. The time following the end of the pulse is referred to as the chase. If the chase consists of unlabeled amino acid, then the proteins synthesized during the chase period will *not* be radiolabeled.

The idea is to mark a population of molecules at a particular interval and then follow their fate over time. This approach is analogous to adding a small amount of dye to a stream and then following the movement of the dye molecules.

To understand why the chase is necessary in these experiments, imagine what would happen if you added dye to a stream continuously. Soon the entire stream would be dyed—you could no longer tell where a specific population of dye molecules were moving.

In testing the secretory pathway hypothesis, Palade's team focused on pancreatic cells that were growing in **culture,** or

in vitro.[1] These cells are specialized for secreting digestive enzymes into the small intestine and are packed with rough ER and Golgi.

The basic experimental approach was to pulse the cell culture for 3 minutes with a radiolabeled version of the amino acid leucine, followed by a long chase with nonradioactive leucine (**FIGURE 7.20a**). The pulse produced a population of proteins that were related to one another by the timing of their synthesis. At different points during the chase, the researchers tracked the movement of these proteins by preparing samples of the cells for autoradiography and electron microscopy (see **BioSkills 10** and **11** in Appendix B). The drawings in **FIGURE 7.20b** illustrate what the researchers would have seen in micrographs taken at different times before and after the start of the chase.

Results of the Pulse–Chase Experiment The graph in Figure 7.20b was based on the electron microscopy results, which showed that proteins are trafficked through the secretory pathway in a highly organized and directed manner. Track the movement of proteins through the cell during the chase by covering the graph with a piece of paper and then slowly sliding it off from

[1]The term in vitro is Latin for "in glass." Experiments that are performed outside living organisms are done in vitro. The term in vivo, in contrast, is Latin for "in life." Experiments performed with living organisms are done in vivo.

(a) Setup for a pulse-chase experiment

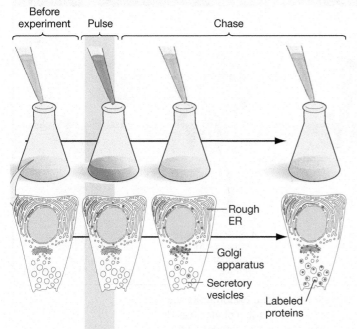

(b) Tracking pulse-labeled proteins during the chase

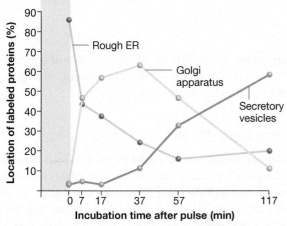

FIGURE 7.20 Tracking Protein Movement in a Pulse–Chase Experiment. Part **(a)** shows how investigators label newly synthesized proteins during the pulse with radioactive amino acids (red). At the start of the chase, this medium is replaced with non-radioactive amino acids (yellow) so only those proteins labeled in the pulse will be tracked. Part **(b)** provides the results of a pulse–chase experiment. The drawings represent micrographs taken that show the radiolabeled proteins (red dots) in the cells. The graph shows the relative abundance of radiolabeled proteins in three different organelles during the chase.

left to right. Notice what is happening to each line at the following three time points:

1. Immediately after the pulse, most of the newly synthesized proteins are inside this cell's rough ER.

2. At 37 minutes into the chase, the situation has changed. Most of the labeled proteins have left the rough ER and entered the

Golgi apparatus, and some of them have accumulated inside structures called secretory vesicles.

3. By the end of the chase, at 117 minutes, most of the labeled proteins have left the Golgi and are either in secretory vesicles or were secreted from the cells.

Over a period of two hours, the labeled population of proteins moved along a defined trail through the rough ER, Golgi apparatus, and secretory vesicles to reach the exterior of the cell. ✔ **QUANTITATIVE** If you understand how the pulse–chase experiment is used to track proteins, use the graph in Figure 7.20b to estimate the time it takes for proteins to pass through the Golgi apparatus.

The results support the hypotheses that a secretory pathway exists and that the rough ER and Golgi apparatus function together as an integrated endomembrane system. Next, let's break this secretory pathway down to examine four of the steps in more detail:

1. How do proteins enter the lumen of the ER?

2. How do the proteins move from the ER to the Golgi apparatus?

3. Once they're inside the Golgi, what happens to them?

4. And finally, how does the Golgi sort out the proteins so each will end up going to the appropriate place?

Entering the Endomembrane System: The Signal Hypothesis

The synthesis of proteins destined to be secreted or embedded in membranes begins in ribosomes free in the cytosol. Günter Blobel and colleagues proposed that at some point these ribosomes become attached to the outside of the ER. But what directs these ribosomes to the ER? The signal hypothesis predicts that proteins bound for the endomembrane system have a molecular zip code analogous to the nuclear localization signal. Blobel proposed that the first few amino acids in the growing polypeptide act as a signal that marks the ribosome for transport to the ER membrane.

This hypothesis received important support when researchers made a puzzling observation: When proteins that are normally synthesized in the rough ER are instead manufactured by isolated ribosomes in vitro—with *no* ER present—they are 20 amino acids longer, on average, than usual.

Blobel seized on these data. He claimed that the extra amino acids are the "send-to-ER" signal, and that the signal is removed inside the organelle. When the same protein is synthesized in vitro, the signal is not removed.

Blobel's group went on to produce convincing data that supported the hypothesis: They identified a sequence of amino acids that will move proteins into the ER lumen, called the **ER signal sequence.**

More recent work has documented the mechanisms responsible for receiving this send-to-ER signal and inserting the

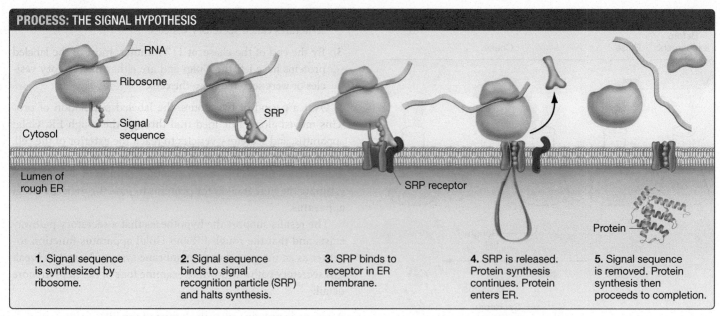

PROCESS: THE SIGNAL HYPOTHESIS

Cytosol — RNA / Ribosome / Signal sequence

SRP

SRP receptor

Lumen of rough ER

Protein

1. Signal sequence is synthesized by ribosome.

2. Signal sequence binds to signal recognition particle (SRP) and halts synthesis.

3. SRP binds to receptor in ER membrane.

4. SRP is released. Protein synthesis continues. Protein enters ER.

5. Signal sequence is removed. Protein synthesis then proceeds to completion.

FIGURE 7.21 The Signal Hypothesis Explains How Proteins Destined for Secretion Enter the Endomembrane System. According to the signal hypothesis, proteins destined for secretion contain a short stretch of amino acids that interact with a signal recognition particle (SRP) in the cytoplasm. This interaction directs the synthesis of the remaining protein into the ER.

protein into the rough ER. **FIGURE 7.21** illustrates the key steps involved.

Step 1 Protein synthesis begins on a free ribosome in the cytosol. The ribosome synthesizes the ER signal sequence.

Step 2 The signal sequence binds to a **signal recognition particle (SRP)**—a complex of RNA and protein. The attached SRP causes protein synthesis to stop.

Step 3 The ribosome ⊠ signal sequence ⊠ SRP complex moves to the ER membrane, where it attaches to the SRP receptor. Think of the SRP as a key that is activated by an ER signal sequence. The SRP receptor in the ER membrane is the lock.

Step 4 Once the lock (the receptor) and key (the SRP) connect, the SRP is released and protein synthesis continues.

Step 5 The growing protein is fed into the ER lumen through a channel, and the signal sequence is removed.

If the protein will eventually be shipped to the inside of an organelle or secreted from the cell, it is completely transferred into the lumen of the rough ER. If it is an integral membrane protein, part of it remains in the cytosol and rough ER membrane while it is being processed.

Once proteins are inside the rough ER or inserted into its membrane, they fold into their three-dimensional shape with the help of chaperone proteins (see Chapter 3). In addition, proteins that enter the ER lumen interact with enzymes that catalyze the addition of carbohydrate side chains (Figure 7.19). Because carbohydrates are polymers of sugar monomers, the addition of one or more carbohydrate groups is called **glycosylation** ("sugar-together"). The resulting molecule is a **glycoprotein**

("sugar-protein"; see Chapter 5). The number and arrangement of these sugars changes as the protein matures, serving as an indicator for shipment to the next destination.

Moving from the ER to the Golgi

How do proteins travel from the ER to the Golgi apparatus? In Palade's pulse–chase experiment, labeled proteins found between the rough ER and the Golgi apparatus were inside membrane-bound structures. Based on these observations, Palade's group suggested that proteins are transported in vesicles that bud off from the ER, move away, fuse with the membrane on the *cis* face of the Golgi apparatus, and dump their cargo inside.

This hypothesis was supported when other researchers used differential centrifugation to isolate and characterize the vesicles that contained labeled proteins. They found that a distinctive type of vesicle carries proteins from the rough ER to the Golgi apparatus. Ensuring that only appropriate cargo is loaded into these vesicles and that the vesicles dock and fuse only with the *cis* face of the Golgi involves a complex series of events and is an area of active research.

What Happens Inside the Golgi Apparatus?

Section 7.2 indicated that the Golgi apparatus consists of a stack of flattened vesicles called cisternae, and that cargo enters one side of the organelle and exits the other. Recent research has shown that the composition of the Golgi apparatus is dynamic. New cisternae constantly form at the *cis* face of the Golgi, while old cisternae break apart at the *trans* face, to be replaced by the cisternae behind it. In this way a new cisterna follows those formed earlier, advancing toward the *trans* face of the Golgi. As it does, it changes in composition and activity through a process called **cisternal maturation.**

By separating individual cisternae and analyzing their contents, researchers have found that cisternae at various stages of maturation contain different suites of enzymes. Many of these enzymes catalyze glycosylation reactions that further modify the oligosaccharides that were attached to the protein in the ER. As the cisternae slowly move from *cis* to *trans*, these enzymes are replaced with those representing more mature cisternae. The result is that proteins are modified in a stepwise manner as they slowly move through the Golgi.

If the rough ER is like a foundry and stamping plant where rough parts are manufactured, then the Golgi can be considered a finishing area where products are polished, painted, and readied for shipping.

How Do Proteins Reach Their Destinations?

The rough ER and Golgi apparatus constitute an impressive assembly line. Certain proteins manufactured by this process remain in these organelles, replacing worn-out resident molecules. But those proteins that are simply passing through as cargo must be sorted and sent to their intended destination as the *trans* cisterna they are in breaks up into vesicles.

How are these finished products put into the right shipping containers, and how are the different containers addressed?

Studies on enzymes that are shipped to lysosomes have provided some answers to both questions. A key finding was that lysosome-bound proteins have a phosphate group attached to a specific sugar subunit on their surface, forming the compound mannose-6-phosphate. If mannose-6-phosphate is removed from these proteins, they are not transported to a lysosome.

This is strong evidence that the phosphorylated sugar serves as a zip code, analogous to the nuclear localization signal and ER signal sequence discussed earlier. Data indicate that mannose-6-phosphate binds to a receptor protein in the membrane of the *trans*-Golgi cisterna. Regions that are enriched with these receptor–cargo complexes will form vesicles that, in turn, have proteins on their cytosolic surfaces that direct their transport and fusion with pre-lysosomal compartments. In this way, the presence of mannose-6-phosphate targets proteins for vesicles that deliver their contents to organelles that eventually become lysosomes.

FIGURE 7.22 presents a simplified model of how cargo is sorted and loaded into specific vesicles that are shipped to different destinations. Each cargo protein has a molecular tag that directs it to particular vesicle budding sites by interacting with receptors in the *trans* cisterna. These receptors, along with other cytosolic proteins that are not shown, direct the transport vesicles to the correct destinations.

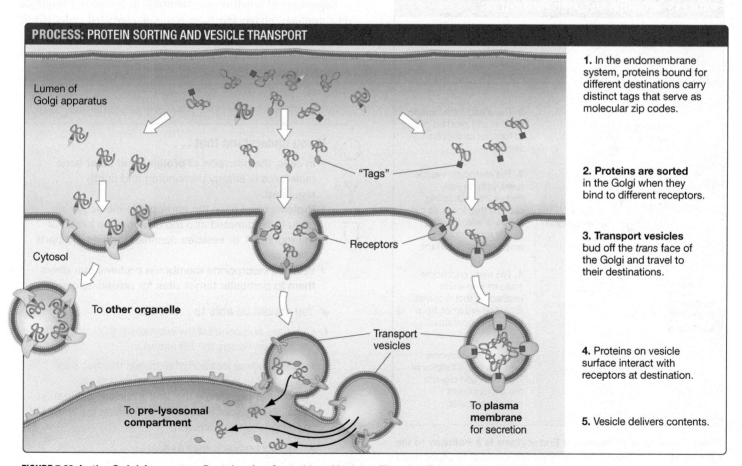

PROCESS: PROTEIN SORTING AND VESICLE TRANSPORT

Lumen of Golgi apparatus

Cytosol

"Tags"

Receptors

To **other organelle**

Transport vesicles

To **pre-lysosomal compartment**

To **plasma membrane** for secretion

1. In the endomembrane system, proteins bound for different destinations carry distinct tags that serve as molecular zip codes.

2. Proteins are sorted in the Golgi when they bind to different receptors.

3. Transport vesicles bud off the *trans* face of the Golgi and travel to their destinations.

4. Proteins on vesicle surface interact with receptors at destination.

5. Vesicle delivers contents.

FIGURE 7.22 In the Golgi Apparatus, Proteins Are Sorted into Vesicles That Are Targeted to a Destination.

In particular, notice that the transport vesicle shown on the right of Figure 7.22 is bound for the plasma membrane, where it will secrete its contents to the outside. This process is called **exocytosis** ("outside-cell-act"). When exocytosis occurs, the vesicle membrane and plasma membrane make contact. As the two membranes fuse, their lipid bilayers rearrange in a way that exposes the interior of the vesicle to the outside of the cell. The vesicle's contents then diffuse into the space outside the cell. This is how cells in your pancreas deliver digestive enzymes to the duct that leads to your small intestine—where food is digested.

Recycling Material in the Lysosome

Now that you have seen how cargo moves out of the cell, let's look at how cargo is brought into the cell. Previously, you learned about how cells import small molecules across lipid bilayers (see Chapter 6), but this is not possible for large molecules like proteins and complex carbohydrates. For these molecules to be recycled and used by the cell, they must first be digested in the lysosome—but how do they get there?

Endocytosis ("inside-cell-act") refers to any pinching off of the plasma membrane that results in the uptake of material from outside the cell. **Receptor-mediated endocytosis** is illustrated in **FIGURE 7.23.** As its name implies, the sequence of events begins when macromolecules outside the cell bind to receptors on the plasma membrane. More than 25 distinct receptors have now been characterized, each specialized for binding to different cargo.

Once receptor binding occurs, the plasma membrane folds in and pinches off to form an endocytic vesicle. These vesicles then drop off their cargo in a transient organelle called the **early endosome** ("inside-body"). The activity of proton pumps in the membrane of this organelle acidifies its lumen, which causes the cargo to be released from their receptors. Many of these emptied cargo receptors are then repackaged into vesicles and returned to the plasma membrane.

As proton pumps continue to lower the early endosome's pH, it undergoes a series of processing steps that cause it to mature into a **late endosome.** The late endosome is the pre-lysosomal compartment introduced earlier (Figure 7.22), where the acid hydrolases from the Golgi apparatus are dropped off. As before, the emptied cargo receptors transported from the Golgi are removed from the late endosome as it matures into a fully active lysosome.

In addition to receptor-mediated endocytosis, the lysosome is involved in recycling material via autophagy and phagocytosis (see **FIGURE 7.24**). During **autophagy** (literally, "same-eating"), damaged organelles are enclosed within an internal membrane and delivered to a lysosome. There the components are digested and recycled. In **phagocytosis** ("eat-cell-act"), the plasma membrane of a cell surrounds a smaller cell or food particle and engulfs it, forming a structure called a phagosome. This structure is delivered to a lysosome, where it is taken in and digested.

Regardless of whether the materials in lysosomes originate via autophagy, phagocytosis, or receptor-mediated endocytosis, the result is similar: Molecules are hydrolyzed. ✔ If you understand the interaction between the endomembrane system

---

PROCESS: RECEPTOR-MEDIATED ENDOCYTOSIS

Recycling of membrane proteins

Endocytic vesicle

H⁺

Early endosome

H⁺   H⁺

Vesicle from Golgi apparatus

Late endosome

Lysosome

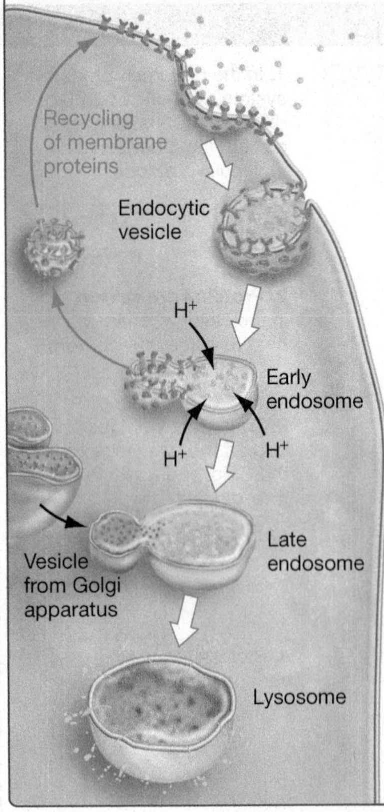

1. Macromolecules outside the cell bind to membrane proteins that act as receptors.

2. The plasma membrane folds in and pinches off to form an endocytic vesicle.

3. The endocytic vesicle fuses with an early endosome, activating protons that lower its pH. Cargo is released and empty receptors are recycled to the surface.

4. The early endosome matures into a late endosome that receives digestive enzymes from the Golgi apparatus.

5. The late endosome matures into a functional lysosome and digests the endocytosed macromolecules.

FIGURE 7.23 Receptor-Mediated Endocytosis Is a Pathway to the Lysosome. Endosomes created by receptor-mediated endocytosis will mature into lysosomes.

---

check your understanding

If you understand that . . .

- In cells, the transport of proteins and other large molecules is energy demanding and tightly regulated.
- Proteins must have the appropriate molecular zip code to be directed into the nucleus, the lumen of the rough ER, or vesicles destined for different parts of the cell.
- Vesicles incorporate membrane proteins that direct them to particular target sites for unloading cargo.

✔ You should be able to . . .

1. Compare and contrast the movement of proteins into the nucleus versus the ER lumen.
2. Predict the final location of a protein that has been engineered to include an ER signal sequence, mannose-6-phosphate tag, and a nuclear localization signal. Justify your answer by addressing the impact of each signal on its transport.

Answers are available in Appendix A.

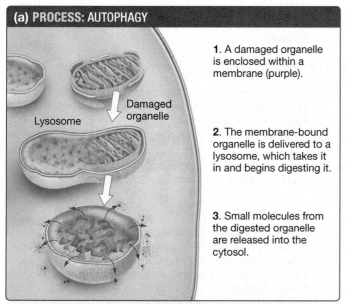

(a) PROCESS: AUTOPHAGY

Lysosome   Damaged organelle

1. A damaged organelle is enclosed within a membrane (purple).

2. The membrane-bound organelle is delivered to a lysosome, which takes it in and begins digesting it.

3. Small molecules from the digested organelle are released into the cytosol.

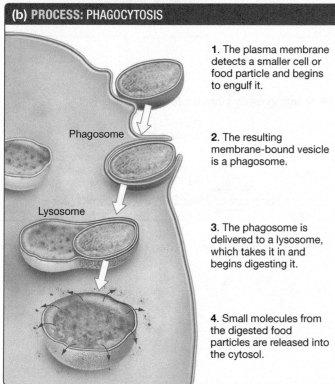

(b) PROCESS: PHAGOCYTOSIS

Phagosome

Lysosome

1. The plasma membrane detects a smaller cell or food particle and begins to engulf it.

2. The resulting membrane-bound vesicle is a phagosome.

3. The phagosome is delivered to a lysosome, which takes it in and begins digesting it.

4. Small molecules from the digested food particles are released into the cytosol.

FIGURE 7.24 Two More Ways to Deliver Materials to Lysosomes. Materials can be transported to lysosomes **(a)** via autophagy or **(b)** after phagocytosis.

and endocytosis, you should be able to predict how the loss of the mannose-6-phosphate receptor would affect receptor-mediated endocytosis.

It is important to note, however, that not all the materials that are surrounded by membrane and taken into a cell end up in lysosomes. In addition to receptor-mediated endocytosis and phagocytosis, small fluid-filled vesicles can be brought into a cell via **bulk-phase endocytosis.** There does not appear to be any cargo selection in bulk-phase endocytosis, and the vesicles are

not transported to lysosomes. These tiny vesicles are used elsewhere in the cell and are likely involved in recycling lipids deposited on the plasma membrane during exocytosis.

Throughout this section, vesicles have been key to the transport of cargo. If these transport steps depended on the random movement of diffusion alone, however, then the vesicles and their cargo might never reach their intended destinations. Are there instead defined tracks that direct the movement of these shipping containers? If so, what are these tracks, and what molecule or molecules function to transport the vesicles along them? Let's delve into these questions in the next section.

7.6 Cell Systems III: The Dynamic Cytoskeleton

The endomembrane system may be the best-studied example of how individual organelles work together in a dynamic, highly integrated way. This integration depends in part on the physical relationship of organelles, which is organized by the cytoskeletal system.

The cytoskeleton is a dense and complex network of fibers that helps maintain cell shape by providing structural support. However, the cytoskeleton is not a static structure like the scaffolding used at construction sites. Its fibrous proteins move and change to alter the cell's shape, shift its contents, and even move the cell itself. Like the rest of the cell, the cytoskeleton is dynamic.

As **TABLE 7.3** (see page 128) shows, there are three distinct cytoskeletal elements in eukaryotic cells: actin filaments, intermediate filaments, and microtubules. Recent research has shown structural and functional relationships between these three eukaryotic filaments and cytoskeletal elements in bacteria.

Each of the three cytoskeletal elements found in eukaryotes has a distinct size, structure, and function. Let's look at each one in turn.

Actin Filaments

Sometimes called **microfilaments** because they are the cytoskeletal element with the smallest diameter, **actin filaments** are fibrous structures made of the globular protein actin (Table 7.3). In animal cells, actin is often the most abundant of all proteins—typically it represents 5–10 percent of the total protein in the cell. Each of your liver cells contains about half a billion of these molecules.

Actin Filament Structure A completed actin filament resembles two long strands that coil around each other. Actin filaments form when individual actin protein subunits assemble, or polymerize, from head to tail through the formation of noncovalent bonds.

Because the actin proteins are not symmetrical, this head-to-tail arrangement of actin subunits results in filaments that have two different ends, or polarity. The two distinct ends of an actin filament are referred to as plus and minus ends. The structural difference between these two ends results in different rates of

Filament	Structure	Subunits	Functions
The three types of filaments that make up the cytoskeleton are distinguished by their size, structure, and type of protein subunit.			
Actin filaments (microfilaments)	Strands in double helix 7 nm – end + end	Actin	• maintain cell shape by resisting tension (pull) • move cells via muscle contraction or cell crawling • divide animal cells in two • move organelles and cytoplasm in plants, fungi, and animals
Intermediate filaments	Fibers wound into thicker cables 10 nm	Keratins, lamins, or others	• maintain cell shape by resisting tension (pull) • anchor nucleus and some other organelles
Microtubules	Hollow tube 25 nm – end + end	α- and β-tubulin dimers	• maintain cell shape by resisting compression (push) • move cells via flagella or cilia • move chromosomes during cell division • assist formation of cell plate during plant cell division • move organelles • provide tracks for intracellular transport

assembling new actin subunits: The plus end grows faster than the minus end.

Each filament is generally unstable and will grow or shrink depending on the concentration of free actin subunits. In addition to controlling the availability of free actin, cells regulate the length and longevity of microfilaments via actin-binding proteins that either stabilize or destabilize their structure.

In animal cells, actin filaments are particularly abundant just under the plasma membrane. They are organized into long, parallel bundles or dense, crisscrossing networks in which individual actin filaments are linked to one another by other proteins. The reinforced bundles and networks of actin filaments help stiffen the cell and define its shape.

Actin Filament Function In addition to providing structural support, actin filaments are involved in movement. In several cases, actin's role in movement depends on the protein myosin. Myosin is a **motor protein:** a protein that converts the potential energy in ATP into the kinetic energy of mechanical work, just as a car's motor converts the chemical energy in gasoline into spinning wheels.

The interaction between actin and myosin is frequently presented in the context of how it produces muscle contraction and movement (Chapter 48). For now, it's enough to recognize that when myosin binds and hydrolyzes ATP to ADP, it undergoes a series of shape changes that extends the "head" region, attaches it to actin, and then contracts to pull itself along the actin filament. The shape change of this protein causes the actin and myosin to slide past each other. After repeated rounds of this contraction cycle, the myosin progressively moves toward the plus end of the actin filament (**FIGURE 7.25a**). This type of movement is analogous to an inchworm contracting its body as it moves along a stick.

(a) Actin and myosin interact to cause movement.

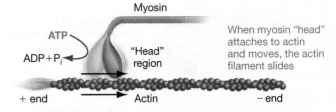

When myosin "head" attaches to actin and moves, the actin filament slides

(b) Examples of movement caused by actin–myosin interactions

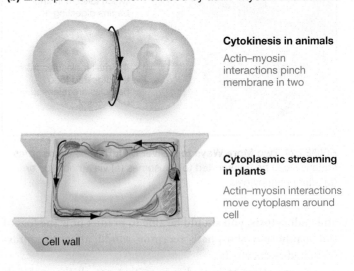

Cytokinesis in animals

Actin–myosin interactions pinch membrane in two

Cytoplasmic streaming in plants

Actin–myosin interactions move cytoplasm around cell

FIGURE 7.25 Many Cellular Movements Are Based on Actin–Myosin Interactions. (a) ATP hydrolysis in the "head" region of myosin causes the protein to attach to actin and change shape. The movement slides the myosin toward the plus end of actin. **(b)** Actin–myosin interactions can divide cells and move organelles and cytoplasm.

As **FIGURE 7.25b** shows, the ATP-powered interaction between actin and myosin is the basis for an array of cell movements:

- **Cytokinesis** ("cell-moving") is the process of cell division. In animals, this occurs by the use of actin filaments that are connected to the plasma membrane and arranged in a ring around the circumference of the cell. Myosin causes the filaments to slide past one another, drawing in the membrane and pinching the cell in two.

- **Cytoplasmic streaming** is the directed flow of cytosol and organelles within plant cells. The movement occurs along actin filaments and is powered by myosin. It is especially common in large cells, where the circulation of cytoplasm facilitates material transport.

In addition, the movement called **cell crawling** occurs when groups of actin filaments grow, creating bulges in the plasma membrane that extend and move the cell. Cell crawling occurs in a wide range of organisms and cell types, including amoebae, slime molds, and certain animal cells.

Intermediate Filaments

Many types of **intermediate filament** exist, each consisting of a different—though similar in size and structure—type of protein (Table 7.3). Humans, for example, have 70 genes that code for intermediate filament proteins. This is in stark contrast to actin filaments and microtubules, which are made from the same protein subunits in all eukaryotic cells.

Moreover, intermediate filaments are not polar; instead, each end of these filaments is identical. They are not involved in directed movement driven by myosin or other motor proteins, but instead serve a purely structural role in eukaryotic cells.

The intermediate filaments that you are most familiar with belong to a family of molecules called the keratins. The cells that make up your skin and line surfaces inside your body contain about 20 types of keratin. These intermediate filaments provide the mechanical strength required for these cells to resist pressure and abrasion. Certain cells in the skin can also produce secreted forms of keratin. Depending on the location of the cell and keratins involved, the secreted filaments form fingernails, toenails, or hair.

Nuclear lamins, which make up the nuclear lamina layer introduced in Section 7.4, also qualify as intermediate filaments. Nuclear lamins form a dense mesh under the nuclear envelope. Recall that in addition to giving the nucleus its shape, they anchor the chromosomes. They are also involved in the breakup and reassembly of the nuclear envelope when cells divide.

Some intermediate filaments project from the nucleus through the cytoplasm to the plasma membrane, where they are linked to intermediate filaments that run parallel to the cell surface. In this way, intermediate filaments form a flexible skeleton that helps shape the cell surface and hold the nucleus in place.

Microtubules

Microtubules are the largest cytoskeletal components in terms of diameter. As Table 7.3 shows, they are assembled from subunits consisting of two polypeptides, called α-tubulin and β-tubulin, that exist as stable protein **dimers** ("two-parts").

Tubulin dimers polymerize from head to tail to form filaments that interact with one another to create relatively large, hollow tubes. Because of this polarity, these microtubules have α-tubulin polypeptides at one end (the minus end) and β-tubulins at the other end (the plus end). Like actin filaments, microtubules are dynamic and grow faster at their plus ends compared with their minus ends.

Microtubules originate from a structure called the **microtubule organizing center (MTOC).** Their plus ends grow outward, radiating throughout the cell. Although plant cells typically have hundreds of sites where microtubules start growing, most animal and fungal cells have just one site that is near the nucleus.

In animals, the microtubule organizing center has a distinctive structure and is called a **centrosome.** As **FIGURE 7.26** shows, animal centrosomes contain two bundles of microtubules called **centrioles.** Although additional microtubules emanate from these structures in animals, they do not grow directly from the centrioles.

(a) In animals, microtubules originate from centrosomes.

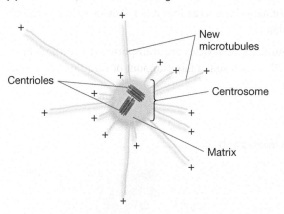

(b) Centrioles consist of microtubules.

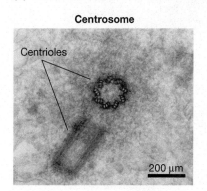

FIGURE 7.26 Centrosomes Are a Type of Microtubule-Organizing Center. (a) Microtubule-organizing centers, such as the centrosomes of animal cells, are the sites where new microtubules are made. Microtubules grow from the matrix surrounding the centrioles, and their positive ends point away from the centrosomes. **(b)** The two centrioles inside a centrosome consist of microtubules as triplets arranged in a circle.

In function, microtubules are similar to actin filaments: They provide stability and are involved in movement. Like steel girders in a skyscraper, the microtubules that radiate from an organizing center stiffen the cell by resisting compression forces. Microtubules also provide a structural framework for organelles. If microtubules are prevented from forming, the network-like configuration of the ER collapses and the Golgi apparatus disappears into vesicles.

Microtubules are best known for their role in separating chromosomes during mitosis and meiosis (see Chapters 12 and 13). But microtubules are involved in many other types of cellular movement as well. Let's first consider their role in moving materials inside cells and then explore how microtubules can help cells to swim.

Microtubules Serve as Tracks for Vesicle Transport Recall from Section 7.5 that vesicles are used to transport materials to a wide array of destinations inside cells. To study how this movement happens, Ronald Vale and colleagues focused on the giant axon, an extremely large nerve cell in squid that runs the length of the animal's body. If the squid is disturbed, the cell signals muscles to contract so it can jet away to safety. The researchers decided to study this particular cell for three reasons.

1. The giant axon is so large that it is relatively easy to see and manipulate.

2. Large numbers of vesicles are transported down the length of the cell. As a result, a large amount of cargo moves a long distance.

(a) Electron micrograph

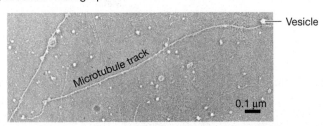

(b) Video image

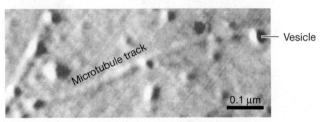

FIGURE 7.27 Transport Vesicles Move along Microtubule Track. The images show extruded cytoplasm from a squid giant axon. **(a)** An electron micrograph that allowed researchers to measure the diameter of the filaments and confirm that they are microtubules. In the upper part of this image, you can see a vesicle on a "track." **(b)** A video microscope image using enhanced contrast that allowed researchers to watch vesicles move in real time.

3. The researchers found that if they gently squeezed the cytoplasm out of the cell, vesicle transport still occurred in the extracellular cytoplasmic material. This allowed them to do experiments on vesicle transport without the plasma membrane being in the way.

In short, the squid giant axon provided a system that could be observed and manipulated efficiently in the lab. To watch vesicle transport in action, the researchers mounted a video camera to a microscope. As **FIGURE 7.27** shows, this technique allowed them to document that vesicle transport occurred along filamentous tracks.

To identify the filament involved, the biologists measured the diameter of the tracks and analyzed their chemical composition. Both types of data indicated that the tracks consist of microtubules. Microtubules also appear to be required for movement of materials elsewhere in the cell. For instance, if experimental cells are treated with a drug that disrupts microtubules, the movement of vesicles from the rough ER to the Golgi apparatus is impaired.

The general message of these experiments is that transport vesicles move through the cell along microtubules. How? Do the tracks themselves move, like a conveyer belt, or are vesicles carried along on some sort of molecular vehicle?

Motor Proteins Pull Vesicles Along the Tracks To study the way vesicles move along microtubules, Vale's group took the squid axon's transport system apart and then determined what components were required to put it back together. A simple experiment convinced the group that this movement is an energy-dependent process: If they depleted the amount of ATP in the cytoplasm, vesicle transport stopped.

To examine this process further, they mixed purified microtubules and vesicles with ATP, but no transport occurred. Something had been left out—but what? To find the missing element or elements, the researchers purified one subcellular part after another and added it to the microtubule ⊠ vesicle ⊠ ATP system.

Through trial and error, and further purification steps, the researchers finally succeeded in isolating a protein that generated vesicle movement. They named the molecule **kinesin**, from the Greek word *kinein* ("to move").

Like myosin, kinesin is a motor protein. Kinesin converts the chemical energy in ATP into mechanical energy in the form of movement. More specifically, when ATP is hydrolyzed by kinesin, the protein moves along microtubules in a directional manner: toward the plus end.

Biologists began to understand how kinesin works when X-ray diffraction studies showed that it has three major regions: a head section with two globular pieces, a tail associated with small polypeptides, and a stalk that connects the head and tail (**FIGURE 7.28a**).

Follow-up studies confirmed that the head region binds to the microtubule while the tail region binds to the transport vesicle. Recent work has shown that kinesin uses these domains to "walk" along the microtubule through a series of conformational changes as it hydrolyzes ATP (**FIGURE 7.28b**). Amazingly, these motors have been found to "walk" up to 375 steps per second.

Cells contain several different versions of the kinesin motor, each specialized for a different role in the cell. If kinesins move

(a) Structure of kinesin

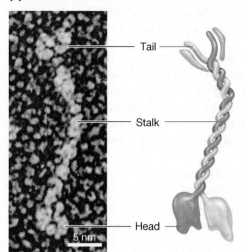

Tail

Stalk

Head

5 nm

(b) Kinesin "walks" along a microtubule track.

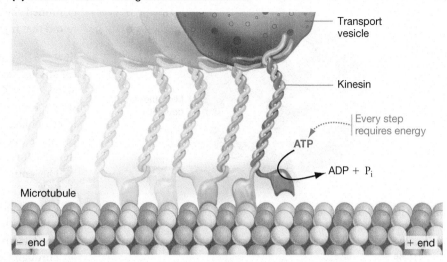

Transport vesicle

Kinesin

Every step requires energy

ATP

ADP + P$_i$

Microtubule

− end

+ end

FIGURE 7.28 Motor Proteins Move Vesicles along Microtubules. (a) Kinesin has three distinct regions. **(b)** The current model depicting how kinesin "walks" along a microtubule track to transport vesicles. The two head segments act like feet that alternately attach, pivot, and release in response to the gain or loss of a phosphate group from ATP.

only toward the plus ends of microtubules, then what is responsible for moving the cargo in the opposite direction? By studying whole-cell locomotion, researchers discovered a motor that could move toward the minus end of microtubules.

Flagella and Cilia: Moving the Entire Cell

Flagella are long, whiplike projections from the cell surface that function in movement. While many bacteria and eukaryotes have flagella, the structure is completely different in the two groups.

• Bacterial flagella are helical rods made of a protein called flagellin; eukaryotic flagella consist of several microtubules constructed from tubulin dimers.

• Bacterial flagella move the cell by rotating the rod like a ship's propeller; eukaryotic flagella move the cell by undulating—they whip back and forth.

• Eukaryotic flagella are surrounded by the plasma membrane and are considered organelles; bacterial flagella are not.

Based on these observations, biologists conclude that the two structures evolved independently, even though their function is similar.

To understand how some cells move, let's focus on eukaryotic flagella. Eukaryotic flagella are closely related to structures called **cilia** (singular: **cilium**), which are short, hairlike projections that are also found in some eukaryotic cells (**FIGURE 7.29**). Flagella are generally much longer than cilia, and the two structures differ in

Cilia

50 μm

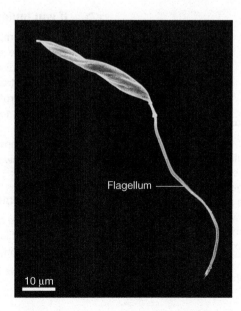

Flagellum

10 μm

FIGURE 7.29 Cilia and Flagella Differ in Length and Number. Cells typically only have 1–4 flagella but may have up to 14,000 cilia. The cells in these scanning electron micrographs have been colorized.

(a) Transmission electron micrograph of axoneme

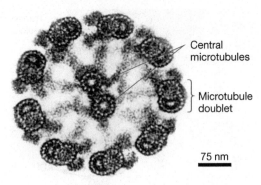

Central
microtubules

Microtubule
doublet

75 nm

(b) Structure of axoneme

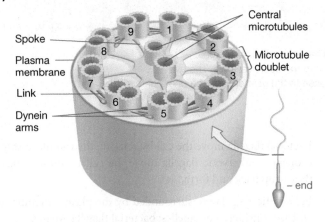

Central
microtubules

Spoke

Plasma
membrane

Microtubule
doublet

Link

Dynein
arms

9 1
8 2
7 3
6 5 4

– end

(c) Mechanism of axoneme bending

Microtubule doublet

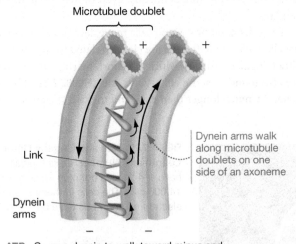

+ +

Link

Dynein
arms

Dynein arms walk
along microtubule
doublets on one
side of an axoneme

– –

+ ATP: Causes dynein to walk toward minus end
and pull toward plus end

FIGURE 7.30 The Structure and Function of Cilia and Flagella.
(a) Transmission electron micrograph of a cross section through an
axoneme. **(b)** The microtubules in cilia and flagella are connected
by links and spokes, and the entire structure is surrounded by
the plasma membrane. **(c)** When dynein arms walk along the
microtubule doublets on one side of a flagellum, force is transmitted
to these links and spokes, causing the entire axoneme to bend.

✔ **QUESTION** If the links and spokes were removed from the
microtubule doublets, what would happen to the axoneme after
adding ATP?

their abundance and pattern of movement. But when researchers
examined the two structures with an electron microscope, they
found that their underlying organization is identical.

How are Cilia and Flagella Constructed? In the 1950s, anatomical studies established that most cilia and flagella have a characteristic "9 ☒ 2" arrangement of microtubules. As **FIGURE 7.30a**
shows, nine microtubule pairs, or doublets, surround two central
microtubules. The doublets consist of one complete and one incomplete microtubule and are arranged around the periphery of
the structure.

The entire 9 ☒ 2 structure is called the **axoneme** ("axle-
thread"). The nine doublets of the axoneme originate from a
structure called the **basal body.** The basal body is identical in
structure with a centriole and plays a central role in the growth
of the axoneme.

Through further study, biologists gained a more detailed view
of the axoneme's structure. Spoke-like proteins connect each doublet to the central pair of microtubules, and molecular links connect the nine doublets to one another (**FIGURE 7.30b**). Each doublet
also has a set of arms that project toward an adjacent doublet.

Axonemes are complex. How do their components interact to
generate motion?

What Provides the Force Required for Movement? In the 1960s
Ian Gibbons began studying the cilia of a common unicellular
eukaryote called *Tetrahymena*. Gibbons found that he could isolate axonemes by using a detergent to remove the plasma membrane that surrounds cilia and then subjecting the resulting
solution to differential centrifugation. These steps gave Gibbons
a cell-free system for studying how the axonemes in cilia and flagella work. He found that the isolated structures would beat only
if he supplied them with ATP, confirming that the beating of cilia
is an energy-demanding process.

check your understanding

C
Y
U

If you understand that . . .

● Each component of the cytoskeleton has a unique
structure and set of functions. Actin filaments,
intermediate filaments, and microtubules all play a
role in structural support. In addition, actin filaments
and microtubules work in conjunction with motor
proteins to move cytoplasmic materials or the entire
cell.

● Most elements of the cytoskeleton are dynamic—
they grow and shrink depending on the needs of the
cell.

✔ **You should be able to . . .**

Compare and contrast the structure and function
of actin filaments, intermediate filaments, and
microtubules.

Answers are available in Appendix A.

In another experiment, Gibbons treated the isolated axonemes with a molecule that disrupts interactions between proteins. The resulting axonemes could not beat even after being supplied with ATP. When Gibbons examined them in the electron microscope, he found that the treatment had removed the arms from the doublets. This result suggested that the arms are required for movement. Follow-up work showed that the arms are made of a large protein that Gibbons named **dynein** (from the Greek word *dyne*, meaning "force").

Like myosin and kinesin, dynein is a motor protein that uses ATP to undergo conformational changes. These shape changes move dynein along microtubules toward the minus end. Note that dynein moves in the opposite direction from the kinesin motor, which moves toward the plus end. In the cytoplasm, dynein motors are known to play various roles similar to the other motors, including the transport of vesicles. In the context of the axoneme, however, the outcome of dynein walking in the axoneme is very different.

So what is special about the axoneme? Remember that each of the nine doublets in the axoneme is connected to the central pair of microtubules by a spoke, and all the doublets are connected to each other by molecular links (Figure 7.30b). As a result, the sliding motion produced by dynein walking is constrained—if one doublet slides, it transmits force to the rest of the axoneme via the links and spokes (**FIGURE 7.30c**). If the dynein arms on just one side of the axoneme are activated, then the localized movement results in bending. The bending of cilia or flagella results in a swimming motion.

Scaled for size, flagella-powered swimming can be rapid. In terms of the number of body or cell lengths traveled per second, a sperm cell from a bull moves faster than a human world-record-holder does when swimming freestyle. At the cellular level, life is fast paced.

Taken together, the data reviewed in this chapter can be summed up in six words: Cells are dynamic, highly integrated structures. To maintain the level of organization that is required for life, chemical reactions must take place at mind-boggling speeds. How cells accomplish this feat is taken up elsewhere (see Chapter 8).

CHAPTER 7 REVIEW

For media, go to MasteringBiology

If you understand . . .

7.1 Bacterial and Archaeal Cell Structures and Their Functions

- There are two basic cellular designs: prokaryotic and eukaryotic. The single defining characteristic that differentiates prokaryotes from eukaryotes is the absence of a nucleus.

- Structures common to most, if not all, prokaryotes are ribosomes, a cell wall, a plasma membrane, an interior cytoskeleton, and a nucleoid.

- Many prokaryotes also possess flagella, fimbriae, and internal membrane structures, some of which are considered organelles.

✔ You should be able to predict what would happen to cells that are exposed to (1) a drug that prevents ribosomes from functioning, (2) an enzyme that degrades the cell wall, or (3) a drug that prevents the assembly of the cytoskeleton.

7.2 Eukaryotic Cell Structures and Their Functions

- Eukaryotic cells are usually much larger and more structurally complex than prokaryotic cells.

- Eukaryotic cells contain numerous specialized organelles, which allow eukaryotic cells to compartmentalize functions and grow to a large size. Organelles common to most, if not all, eukaryotes are as follows:

  1. The nucleus, which contains the cell's chromosomes and serves as its control center.

  2. The endomembrane system, which consists of a diverse group of interrelated organelles, including the endoplasmic reticulum, Golgi apparatus, lysosomes or vacuoles, and endosomes. These organelles work together to synthesize, process, sort, transport, and recycle material.

  3. Peroxisomes, which are organelles where key reactions take place that often result in the generation of toxic by-products. Specialized enzymes are included that safely disarm these by-products soon after they are generated.

  4. Mitochondria and chloroplasts, which have extensive internal membrane systems where the enzymes responsible for ATP generation and photosynthesis reside.

✔ You should be able to predict what would happen to a plant cell that is exposed to (1) a drug that poisons mitochondria, (2) a drug that inhibits catalase in the peroxisome, or (3) a drug that inhibits the formation of centrioles.

7.3 Putting the Parts into a Whole

- Cells have a tightly organized interior, where the presence and quantity of organelles often reflect the function of the cell.

- The activity in a cell illustrates the dynamic nature of life. Organelles and cytosolic proteins continually bustle about with a seemingly nonstop rush hour.

- Much of what is known about cellular activity has come from advances in cell imaging and techniques for isolating cellular components.

✔ You should be able to predict how a liver cell would differ compared with a salivary gland cell in terms of organelles.

7.4 Cell Systems I: Nuclear Transport

- Cells have sophisticated systems for making sure that proteins and other products end up in the right place.

- Traffic across the nuclear envelope occurs through nuclear pores, which contain a multiprotein nuclear pore complex that serves as gatekeeper.

- Small molecules can passively diffuse through the nuclear pore. Larger molecules enter the nucleus only if they contain a specific molecular signal that directs them through the pore via nuclear transport proteins.

✔ You should be able to propose a hypothesis that would address how certain cytoplasmic proteins can be induced to enter the nucleus by either the addition or the removal of phosphates.

7.5 Cell Systems II: The Endomembrane System Manufactures, Ships, and Recycles Cargo

- Molecules synthesized in the ER may be transported as cargo to the Golgi apparatus and then to a number of different sites, depending on the cargo.

- Before products leave the Golgi, they are sorted by their molecular "zip codes" that direct them to specific vesicles. The vesicles interact with receptor proteins at the target location so that the contents are delivered correctly.

- The lysosome is built from enzymes and membranes that are made and processed through the endomembrane system. These organelles are involved in recycling products via autophagy, phagocytosis, and receptor-mediated endocytosis.

✔ You should be able to justify why proteins (see Chapter 3)—and not RNA, DNA, carbohydrates, or lipids—are the molecules responsible for "reading" the array of molecular zip codes in cells.

7.6 Cell Systems III: The Dynamic Cytoskeleton

- The cytoskeleton is an extensive system of fibers that provides (1) structural support and a framework for arranging and organizing organelles and other cell components; (2) paths for moving vesicles inside cells; and (3) machinery for moving the cell as a whole through the beating of flagella or cilia, or through cell crawling.

- Subunits are constantly being added to or removed from cytoskeletal filaments. Actin filaments and microtubules are polarized, meaning different ends of the filaments are designated as plus or minus ends. The plus ends have a higher growth rate than the minus ends.

- Movement often depends on motor proteins, which use chemical energy stored in ATP to change shape and position. Myosin motors move toward the plus ends of actin filaments. Kinesin and dynein motors move along microtubules toward the plus and minus ends, respectively.

- A specific type of dynein is found in the axonemes of eukaryotic cilia and flagella. These motors move microtubules to generate forces that bend the structures and enable cells to swim or generate water currents.

✔ You should be able to predict which of the three motors presented in this section would be responsible for transporting vesicles from the Golgi to the plasma membrane.

(MB) **MasteringBiology**

1. **MasteringBiology Assignments**

   Tutorials and Activities Cilia and Flagella; Endomembrane System; Exocytosis and Endocytosis; Form Fits Function: Cells; Membrane Transport: Bulk Transport; Prokaryotic Cell Structure and Function; Pulse–Chase Experiment; Review: Animal Cell Structure and Function; Tour of a Plant Cell: Structures and Functions; Tour of an Animal Cell: Structures and Functions; Tour of an Animal Cell: The Endomembrane System; Transport into the Nucleus

   Questions Reading Quizzes, Blue-Thread Questions, Test Bank

2. **eText** Read your book online, search, take notes, highlight text, and more.

3. **The Study Area** Practice Test, Cumulative Test, BioFlix® 3-D Animations, Videos, Activities, Audio Glossary, Word Study Tools, Art

You should be able to . . .

1. Which of the following accurately describes a difference between prokaryotic and eukaryotic cells?
   a. Prokaryotic cells have fimbriae that allow the cell to swim whereas eukaryotic cells have flagella.
   b. Eukaryotic cells are generally larger than prokaryotic cells.
   c. Eukaryotic cells have organelles.
   d. Prokaryotic cells have nuclei and eukaryotic cells have nucleoids.

2. What are three attributes of mitochondria and chloroplasts that suggest they were once free-living bacteria?

3. Which of the following is *not* true of secreted proteins?
   a. They are synthesized using ribosomes.
   b. They enter the ER lumen during translation.
   c. They contain a signal that directs them into the lysosome.
   d. They are transported between organelles in membrane-bound vesicles.

4. Which of the following results provided evidence of a nuclear localization signal in the nucleoplasmin protein?
   a. The protein was small and easily slipped through the nuclear pore complex.
   b. After cleavage of the protein, only the tail segments appeared in the nucleus.
   c. Removing the tail allowed the core segment to enter the nucleus.
   d. The SRP bound only to the tail, not the core segment.

5. Molecular zip codes direct molecules to particular destinations in the cell. How are these signals read?
   a. They bind to receptor proteins.
   b. They enter transport vesicles.
   c. They bind to motor proteins.
   d. They are glycosylated by enzymes in the Golgi apparatus.

6. How does the hydrolysis of ATP result in the movement of a motor protein along a cytoskeletal filament?

7. Compare and contrast the structure of a generalized plant cell, animal cell, and prokaryotic cell. Which features are common to all cells? Which are specific to just prokaryotes, or just plants, or just animals?

8. Cells that line your intestines are known to possess a large number of membrane proteins that transport small molecules and ions across the plasma membrane. Which of the following cell structures would you expect to be required for this function of the cells?
   a. the endoplasmic reticulum
   b. peroxisomes
   c. lysosomes
   d. the cell wall

9. Most of the proteins that reside in the nucleus possess a nuclear localization signal (NLS), even if they are small enough to pass

through the pore complex unhindered. Why would a small protein have an NLS, when it naturally diffuses across the pore without one?

10. Make a flowchart that traces the movement of a secreted protein from its site of synthesis to the outside of a eukaryotic cell. Identify all the organelles that the protein passes through. Add notes indicating what happens to the protein at each step.

11. Although all three cytoskeletal fibers constantly replace their subunits, only actin filaments and microtubules demonstrate differences in the rate of growth between the two ends. What is responsible for this difference, and why is this not observed in intermediate filaments?

12. Describe how vesicles move in a directed manner between organelles of the endomembrane system. Explain why this movement requires ATP.

13. Which of the following cell structures would you expect to be most important in the growth of bacteria on the surface of your teeth?
    a. cell wall
    b. fimbriae
    c. flagella
    d. cilia

14. The enzymes found in peroxisomes are synthesized by cytosolic ribosomes. Suggest a hypothesis for how these proteins find their way to the peroxisomes.

15. Propose an experiment that would determine if the NLS in nucleoplasmin is limited to this protein only or if it could direct other structures into the nucleus.

16. George Palade's research group used the pulse–chase assay to dissect the secretory pathway in pancreatic cells. If they had instead performed this assay on muscle cells, which have high energy demands and primarily consist of actin and myosin filaments, where would you expect the labeled proteins to go during the chase?

8 Energy and Enzymes: An Introduction to Metabolic Pathways

In this chapter you will learn how

Enzymes use energy to drive the chemistry of life

looking at energy, asking

What happens to energy in chemical reactions? **8.1**

Can chemical energy drive nonspontaneous reactions? **8.2**

looking at enzymes, asking

How do enzymes help speed chemical reaction rates? **8.3**

What factors affect enzyme function? **8.4**

How do enzymes work together in metabolic pathways? **8.5**

When table sugar is heated in the presence of oxygen, it undergoes the uncontrolled oxidation reaction known as burning. The heat energy in the flame is released as electrons are transferred from sugar to oxygen. Cells use the energy released from this type of reaction to drive the energy-demanding processes required for life.

This chapter is part of the Big Picture. See how on pages 198–199.

Cells are dynamic. Vesicles move cargo from the Golgi apparatus to the plasma membrane and other destinations, enzymes catalyze the synthesis of a complex array of macromolecules, and millions of proteins transport ions and molecules across cellular membranes. These activities change constantly in response to signals from other cells or the environment.

What drives all this action? The answer is twofold—energy and enzymes. Because staying alive takes work, there is no life without energy. Life, at its most basic level, consists of chemical reactions catalyzed by enzymes. By using enzymes to direct which reactions occur and which do not, life possesses the distinguishing feature of creating order from a naturally disordered environment.

✔ When you see this checkmark, stop and test yourself. Answers are available in Appendix A.

This chapter is about how enzymes work to help cells acquire and use energy. It is also your introduction to metabolic pathways—the ordered series of chemical reactions that build up or break down a particular molecule.

Let's begin by reviewing some fundamental concepts about energy and how it is used in cells.

8.1 What Happens to Energy in Chemical Reactions?

When biologists consider energy in chemical reactions, they often use the term **free energy** to describe the amount of energy that is available to do work. Recall that two types of energy exist: kinetic energy or potential energy (Chapter 2). **Kinetic energy** is energy of motion. There are several different forms of kinetic energy—at the molecular level, the energy of motion is called thermal energy. **Potential energy** is energy that is associated with position or configuration. In molecules, this is referred to as chemical energy and is stored in the position of electrons.

Chemical Reactions Involve Energy Transformations

The existence of two types of energy does not mean that energy is locked into either the kinetic or the potential type. Energy is often transformed from one type to the other. To drive this point home, consider a water molecule sitting at the top of a waterfall, as in **FIGURE 8.1**.

Step 1 The molecule has potential energy (E_p) because of its position.

Step 2 As the molecule passes over the waterfall, its potential energy is converted to the kinetic energy (E_k) of motion.

Step 3 When the molecule reaches the rocks below, it undergoes a change in potential energy because it has changed position. The difference in potential energy is transformed into an equal amount of kinetic energy that is manifested in a variety of forms: mechanical energy, which tends to break up the rocks; heat (thermal energy), which raises the temperature of the rocks and the water itself; and sound.

The amount of potential energy in an electron is based on its position relative to other electrons and the protons in the nuclei of nearby atoms (see **FIGURE 8.2a** on page 138). If an electron is close to negative charges on other electrons and far from the positive charges in nuclei, it has high potential energy. In general, the potential energy of a molecule is a function of the way its electrons are configured or positioned.

An electron in an outer electron shell is analogous to the water molecule at the top of a waterfall (**FIGURE 8.2b**). If the electron falls to a lower shell, its potential energy is converted to the kinetic energy of motion. After the electron occupies the lower electron shell, it undergoes a change in potential energy. As panel 3 in Figure 8.1b shows, the change in potential energy is transformed

PROCESS: ENERGY TRANSFORMATION IN A WATERFALL

E_p (higher)

1. Potential energy
A water molecule sitting at the top of a waterfall has a defined amount of potential energy, E_p.

E_k

2. Kinetic energy
As the molecule falls, some of this stored energy is converted to kinetic energy (the energy of motion), E_k.

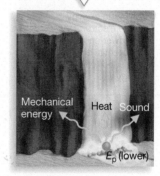

Mechanical energy   Heat   Sound

E_p (lower)

3. Other forms of kinetic energy
When the molecule strikes the rocks below, its energy of motion is converted to thermal, mechanical, and sound energy. The molecule's potential energy is now much lower. The change in potential energy has been transformed into an equal amount of other forms of kinetic energy.

Conclusion: Energy is neither created nor destroyed; it simply changes form.

FIGURE 8.1 Energy Transformations. During an energy transformation, the total amount of energy in the system remains constant.

into an equal amount of kinetic energy—usually thermal energy, but sometimes light.

These examples illustrate the **first law of thermodynamics,** which states that energy is conserved. Energy cannot be created or destroyed, but only transferred and transformed.

The total energy in a molecule is referred to as its **enthalpy** (represented by H). Enthalpy includes the potential energy of the molecule, often referred to as heat content, plus the effect of the molecule on its surroundings in terms of pressure and volume.

(a) The potential energy of an electron is related to its position.

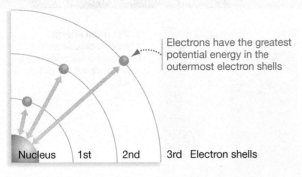

Electrons have the greatest potential energy in the outermost electron shells

Nucleus | 1st | 2nd | 3rd | Electron shells

(b) PROCESS: ENERGY TRANSFORMATION IN AN ATOM

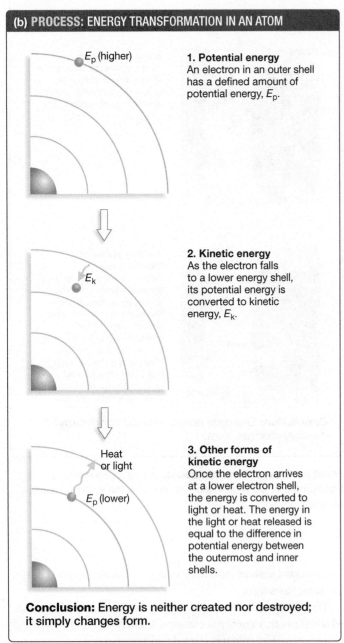

E_p (higher)

1. Potential energy
An electron in an outer shell has a defined amount of potential energy, E_p.

E_k

2. Kinetic energy
As the electron falls to a lower energy shell, its potential energy is converted to kinetic energy, E_k.

Heat or light

E_p (lower)

3. Other forms of kinetic energy
Once the electron arrives at a lower electron shell, the energy is converted to light or heat. The energy in the light or heat released is equal to the difference in potential energy between the outermost and inner shells.

Conclusion: Energy is neither created nor destroyed; it simply changes form.

FIGURE 8.2 Chemical energy transformations Potential energy energy stored in atoms or molecules may be transformed into kinetic energy by changes in electron position.

The contributions of heat, pressure, and volume to the enthalpy of a molecule are best understood by observing the changes in enthalpy in a chemical reaction. For example, let's examine the reaction responsible for the explosive bursts of scalding hot liquid a bombardier beetle can produce when provoked, as seen in **FIGURE 8.3**:

$$2\,H_2O_2(aq) \longrightarrow 2\,H_2O(l) + O_2(g)$$

In this reaction, hydrogen peroxide (H_2O_2) is broken down into water and O_2 gas, which expands to over 500 times the original volume of the H_2O_2. Heat given off from the reaction also increases the temperature of the liquid dramatically. These massive increases in temperature and volume generate the pressure that propels the boiling liquid out of an opening at the tip of the beetle's abdomen.

Changes in enthalpy in chemical reactions can be measured and are represented by ΔH. (The uppercase Greek letter delta, Δ, is often used in chemical and mathematical notation to represent change.) The value of ΔH is primarily based on the difference in heat content, since—apart from the reaction in the bombardier beetle—most biological reactions do not result in substantial changes in pressure and volume. When a reaction releases heat energy (products have less potential energy than the reactants), it is **exothermic** and the ΔH is negative. If heat energy is taken up during the reaction, generating products that have higher potential energy than the reactants, the reaction is **endothermic** and ΔH is positive.

Another factor that changes during a chemical reaction is the amount of disorder or **entropy** (symbolized by ΔS). When the products of a chemical reaction become less ordered than the reactant molecules were, entropy increases and ΔS is positive. The **second law of thermodynamics,** in fact, states that total entropy always increases in an isolated system. Keep in mind that the isolated system in this case is the universe, which includes the surroundings as well as the products of the reaction.

To determine whether a chemical reaction is spontaneous, it's necessary to assess the combined contributions of changes in heat and disorder. Chemists do this with a quantity called the **Gibbs free-energy change,** symbolized by ΔG.

$$\Delta G = \Delta H - T\Delta S$$

Here, T stands for temperature measured on the Kelvin scale (see **BioSkills 1**, in Appendix B). Water freezes at 273.15 K and boils at 373.15 K.

In words, the free-energy change in a reaction is equal to the change in enthalpy minus the change in entropy multiplied by the temperature. The $T\Delta S$ term simply means that entropy becomes more important in determining free-energy change as the temperature of the molecules increases. Thermal energy increases the amount of disorder in the system, so the faster molecules are moving, the more important entropy becomes in determining the overall free-energy change.

Chemical reactions are spontaneous when ΔG is less than zero. Such reactions are said to be **exergonic.** Reactions are

FIGURE 8.3 Reactions May Be Explosive due to Changes in Enthalpy. When provoked, the bombardier beetle mixes reactants with enzymes in a special chamber near the tip of its abdomen. The enzyme-catalyzed reaction releases heat energy and oxygen gas. The result is the projection of boiling hot liquid at a predator.

nonspontaneous when ΔG is greater than zero. Such reactions are termed **endergonic.** When ΔG is equal to zero, reactions are at equilibrium. ✔ If you understand these concepts, you should be able to explain (1) why the same reaction can be nonspontaneous at low temperature but spontaneous at high temperature, and (2) why some exothermic reactions are nonspontaneous.

Free energy changes when the potential energy and/or entropy of substances change. Spontaneous chemical reactions run in the direction that lowers the free energy of the system. Exergonic reactions are spontaneous and release energy; endergonic reactions are nonspontaneous and require an input of energy to proceed.

Temperature and Concentration Affect Reaction Rates

Even if a chemical reaction occurs spontaneously, it may not happen quickly. The reactions that convert iron to rust or sugar molecules to carbon dioxide and water are spontaneous, but at room temperature they occur very slowly, if at all.

For most reactions to proceed, one or more chemical bonds have to break and others have to form. For this to happen, the substances involved must collide in a specific orientation that brings the electrons involved near each other. (See Chapter 2 to review the forces involved in bond formation.)

The number of collisions occurring between the substances in a mixture depends on their temperature and concentration:

- When the concentration of reactants is high, more collisions should occur and reactions should proceed more quickly.

- When their temperature is high, reactants should move faster and collide more frequently.

Higher concentrations and higher temperatures should speed up chemical reactions. To test this hypothesis, students at Parkland College in Champaign, Illinois, performed the experiments shown in **FIGURE 8.4** (see page 140). Pay special attention to the two graphs in the "Results" section:

- *Temperature versus reaction rate* The graph on the left is based on experiments where the concentration of the re-actants was the same, but the temperature varied. Each data point represents one experiment. Notice that the points represent a trend that rises from left to right—meaning, in this case, that the reaction rate speeded up when the temperature of the reaction mixture was higher.

- *Concentration versus reaction rate* The graph on the right is based on experiments where the temperature was constant, but the concentration of reactants varied. Each bar represents the average reaction rate over many replicates of each treatment, or set of concentrations. The thin lines at the top of each bar indicate the standard error of the mean—a measure of variability (see **BioSkills 4** in Appendix B). The take-home message of this graph is that reaction rates are higher when reactant concentrations are higher.

The reactions shown in Figure 8.4 were exergonic, meaning that the products had lower free energy than the reactants, so no input of energy was required. But, what drives nonspontaneous, endergonic reactions? Let's take a closer look.

8.2 Nonspontaneous Reactions May Be Driven Using Chemical Energy

By definition, endergonic reactions require an input of energy to proceed. Recall that radiation from the Sun and electricity from lightning could have driven nonspontaneous reactions during

QUESTION: Do chemical reaction rates increase with increased temperature and concentration?

RATE INCREASE HYPOTHESIS: Chemical reaction rates increase with increased temperature. They also increase with increased concentration of reactants.

NULL HYPOTHESIS: Chemical reaction rates are not affected by increases in temperature or concentration of reactants.

EXPERIMENTAL SETUP:

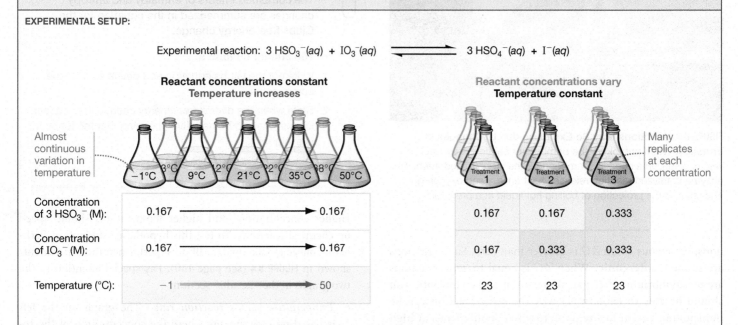

Experimental reaction: $3\ HSO_3^-(aq) + IO_3^-(aq) \rightleftharpoons 3\ HSO_4^-(aq) + I^-(aq)$

Reactant concentrations constant
Temperature increases

Almost continuous variation in temperature

	−1°C	9°C	21°C	35°C	50°C

Concentration of $3\ HSO_3^-$ (M):	0.167 $\longrightarrow$ 0.167
Concentration of IO_3^- (M):	0.167 $\longrightarrow$ 0.167
Temperature (°C):	−1 $\longrightarrow$ 50

Reactant concentrations vary
Temperature constant

Many replicates at each concentration

	Treatment 1	Treatment 2	Treatment 3
	0.167	0.167	0.333
	0.167	0.333	0.333
	23	23	23

PREDICTION: Reaction rate, measured as 1/(time for reaction to go to completion), will increase with increased concentrations of reactants and increased temperature of reaction mix.

PREDICTION OF NULL HYPOTHESIS: There will be no difference in reaction rates among treatments in each setup.

RESULTS:

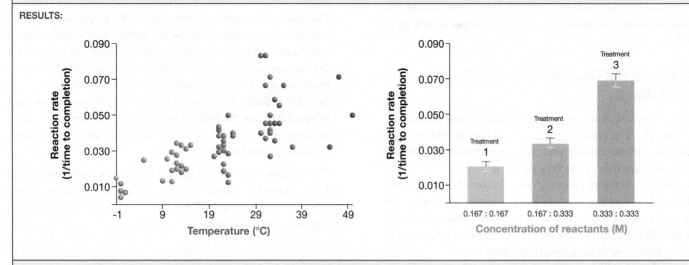

CONCLUSION: Chemical reaction rates increase with increased temperature or concentration.

FIGURE 8.4 Testing the Hypothesis that Reaction Rates Are Sensitive to Changes in Temperature and Concentration.

✔ **QUESTION** Use **BioSkills 4** in Appendix B to explain why no error bars are used for the points shown on the graph on the left side of the "Results" section.

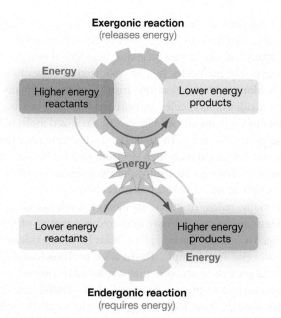

Exergonic reaction
(releases energy)

Energy

Higher energy reactants

Lower energy products

Energy

Lower energy reactants

Higher energy products

Energy

Endergonic reaction
(requires energy)

FIGURE 8.5 Energetic Coupling Allows Endergonic Reactions to Proceed Using the Energy Released from Exergonic Reactions.

chemical evolution (Chapter 2). What source of energy drives these reactions inside cells?

Exergonic reactions release free energy. **FIGURE 8.5** shows how **energetic coupling** between exergonic and endergonic reactions allows chemical energy released from one reaction to drive another. In cells, this process generally occurs in one of two ways, either through the transfer of high-energy electrons or the transfer of a phosphate group.

Redox Reactions Transfer Energy via Electrons

Chemical reactions that involve the loss or gain of one or more electrons are called **reduction–oxidation reactions,** or **redox reactions.** When an atom or molecule loses one or more electrons, it is oxidized. This makes sense if you notice that the term

oxidized sounds as if oxygen has done something to an atom or molecule. Recall that oxygen is highly electronegative and often pulls electrons from other atoms (Chapter 2). On the other hand, when an atom or molecule gains one or more electrons, it is reduced. To keep these terms straight, students often use the mnemonic "OIL RIG"—**Oxidation** *Is* *L*oss of electrons; **Reduction** *Is* *G*ain of electrons.

Oxidation events are always paired with a reduction; if one atom loses an electron, another has to gain it, and vice versa. Since electron position is related to energy levels, redox reactions represent the energetic coupling of two half-reactions, one exergonic and one endergonic. Oxidation is the exergonic half-reaction, and reduction is the endergonic half-reaction. Some of the energy that is lost by the oxidized molecule is used to increase potential energy of the reduced molecule. In cases where more free energy is released by the oxidation step than is necessary for the reduction step, the overall reaction is exergonic.

The gain or loss of an electron can be relative, however. During a redox reaction, an electron can be transferred completely from one atom to another, or an electron can simply shift its position in a covalent bond.

An Example of Redox in Action To see how redox reactions work, consider the spontaneous reaction that occurs when reduced carbons in glucose ($C_6H_{12}O_6$) are oxidized as the sugar is burned in the presence of oxygen (O_2) (**FIGURE 8.6**). The orange dots in the illustration represent the positions of the electrons involved in covalent bonds.

Now compare the position of the electrons in the first reactant, glucose, with their position in the first product, carbon dioxide. Notice that many of the electrons have moved farther from the carbon nucleus in carbon dioxide. This means that carbon has been oxidized: it has "lost" electrons. The change occurred because the carbon and hydrogen atoms in glucose share electrons equally, while the carbon and oxygen atoms in CO_2 don't. In CO_2, the high electronegativity of the oxygen atoms pulled electrons away from the carbon atom.

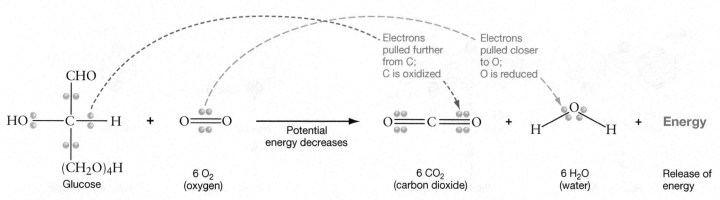

FIGURE 8.6 Redox Reactions Involve the Gain or Loss of One or More Electrons. This diagram shows how the position of electrons changes when glucose reacts with oxygen. The carbons of glucose are oxidized while the oxygen atoms of O_2 are reduced.

Now compare the position of the electrons in the reactant O_2 molecules with their position in the product water molecules. In water, the electrons have moved closer to the oxygen nuclei than they were in the O_2 molecules, meaning that the oxygen atoms have been reduced. Oxygen has "gained" electrons. Thus, when glucose burns, carbon atoms are oxidized while oxygen atoms are reduced.

These shifts in electron position change the amount of chemical energy in the reactants and products. When glucose reacts with oxygen, electrons are held much tighter in the product molecules than in the reactant molecules. This means their potential energy has decreased. The entropy of the products is also much higher than that of the reactants, as indicated by the increase in the number of molecules. As a result, this reaction is exergonic. It releases energy in the form of heat and light.

Another Approach to Understanding Redox During the redox reactions that occur in cells, electrons (e^-) may also be transferred from an atom in one molecule, called the **electron donor,** to an atom in a different molecule, the **electron acceptor.** When this occurs, the electron may be accompanied by a proton (H^+), which would result in the addition of a neutral hydrogen (H) atom to the electron acceptor.

Molecules that obtain hydrogens via redox reactions tend to gain potential energy because the electrons in C−H bonds are equally shared and hence relatively far from the positive charges on the C and H nuclei. This observation should sound familiar,

from what you have learned about carbohydrates (see Chapter 5). Molecules that have a large number of C−H bonds, such as carbohydrates and fats, store a great deal of potential energy.

Conversely, molecules that are oxidized in cells often lose a proton along with an electron. Instead of having many C−H bonds, oxidized molecules in cells tend to have an increased number of C−O bonds (see Figure 8.6). Oxidized molecules tend to lose potential energy. To understand why, remember that oxygen atoms have extremely high electronegativity. Because oxygen atoms hold electrons so tightly, the electrons involved in bonds with oxygen atoms have low potential energy.

In many redox reactions in biology, understanding where oxidation and reduction have occurred is a matter of following hydrogen atoms—reduction often "adds Hs" and oxidation often "removes Hs." For example, **flavin adenine dinucleotide (FAD)** is a cellular electron acceptor that is reduced by two electrons accompanied by two protons to form $FADH_2$ (**FIGURE 8.7a**). $FADH_2$ readily donates these high-energy electrons to other molecules. As a result, it is called an **electron carrier** and is said to have "reducing power."

Another common electron carrier is **nicotinamide adenine dinucleotide (NAD^+),** which is reduced to form **NADH.** Like FAD, two electrons reduce NAD^+. These two carriers differ, however, in the number of hydrogen atoms transferred. NAD^+ acquires only one of the two hydrogens and releases the second into the environment as H^+ (**FIGURE 8.7b**).

(a) Flavin adenine dinucleotide

$$AH_2 + FAD \longrightarrow A + FADH_2$$

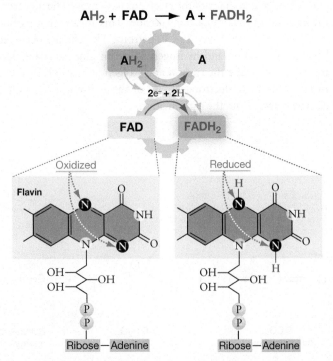

(b) Nicotinamide adenine dinucleotide

$$BH_2 + NAD^+ \longrightarrow B + NADH + H^+$$

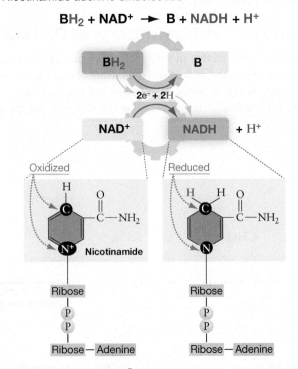

FIGURE 8.7 Redox Reactions May Transfer Protons Along with Electrons. The potential energy of NAD^+ and FAD is increased by redox reactions that transfer high-energy electrons, which may or may not be accompanied by protons. The products $FADH_2$ and NADH are important electron carriers.

The two examples in Figure 8.6 illustrate an important point—all redox reactions involve the transfer of electrons, but they do not always involve the transfer of hydrogens. Redox reactions are central in biology—they transfer energy via electrons. The energy released from certain key redox reactions (see Chapters 9 and 10) is used to drive the endergonic formation of the nucleotide ATP from ADP and P_i. How is the energy stored in ATP used by the cell?

ATP Transfers Energy via Phosphate Groups

Adenosine triphosphate (ATP) (introduced in Chapter 4) makes things happen in cells because it has a great deal of potential energy. As **FIGURE 8.8a** shows, four negative charges are confined to a small area in the three phosphate groups in ATP. In part because these negative charges repel each other, the potential energy of the electrons in the phosphate groups is extraordinarily high.

ATP Hydrolysis Releases Free Energy When ATP reacts with water during a hydrolysis reaction, the bond between ATP's outermost phosphate group and its neighbor is broken, resulting in the formation of ADP and inorganic phosphate, P_i, which has the formula $H_2PO_4^{\boxtimes}$ (**FIGURE 8.8b**). This reaction is highly exergonic. Under standard conditions of temperature and pressure in the laboratory, a total of 7.3 kilocalories of energy per mole of ATP (or 7.3 kcal/mol), is released during the reaction. A **kilocalorie (kcal)** of energy raises 1 kilogram (kg) of water 1°C.

ATP hydrolysis is exergonic because the entropy of the product molecules is higher than that of the reactants, and because there is a large drop in potential energy when ATP breaks down into ADP and P_i. The change in potential energy occurs in part because the electrons from ATP's phosphate groups are now spread across two molecules instead of being clustered on one molecule—meaning that there is now less electrical repulsion.

In addition, the destabilizing effect of the negative charges is reduced in ADP and P_i since these products interact with the partial positive charges on surrounding water molecules more efficiently than the clustered negative charges on ATP did.

How Does ATP Drive Endergonic Reactions? In the time it takes to read this sentence, millions of endergonic reactions have occurred in your cells. This chemical activity is possible, in part, because cells are able to use the energy released from the exergonic hydrolysis of ATP.

If the reaction diagrammed in Figure 8.8b occurred in a test tube, the energy released would be lost as heat. But cells don't lose that 7.3 kcal/mole as heat. Instead, they use it to make things happen. Specifically, the energy that is released when ATP is hydrolyzed may be used to transfer the cleaved phosphate to a target molecule, called a **substrate.**

The addition of a phosphate group to a substrate is called **phosphorylation.** When ATP is used as the phosphate donor, phosphorylation is exergonic because the electrons in ADP and the phosphate added to the substrate have much less potential energy than they did in ATP.

To see how this process works, consider an endergonic reaction between two reactant molecules—compound A and compound B—that results in a product AB needed by your cells. For this reaction to proceed, an input of energy is required.

When a phosphate group from ATP is added to one or both of the reactant molecules, the potential energy of the reactant is increased. This phosphorylated intermediate is referred to as an activated substrate. This is the critical point: Activated substrates have high enough potential energy that the reaction between compound A and, for example, the activated form of compound B is now exergonic. The two compounds then go on to react and form the product molecule AB.

(a) ATP stores a large amount of potential energy.

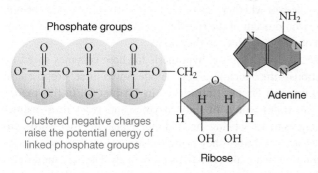

Phosphate groups

Clustered negative charges raise the potential energy of linked phosphate groups

Adenine

Ribose

(b) Energy is released when ATP is hydrolyzed.

ATP + H_2O (Water) → ADP + P_i (Inorganic phosphate) + 7.3 kcal/mol ATP (Energy)

FIGURE 8.8 Adenosine Triphosphate (ATP) Has High Potential Energy. (a) ATP's high potential energy results, in part, from the four negative charges clustered in its three phosphate groups. The negative charges repel each other, raising the potential energy of the electrons. **(b)** When ATP is hydrolyzed to ADP and inorganic phosphate, a large free-energy change occurs.

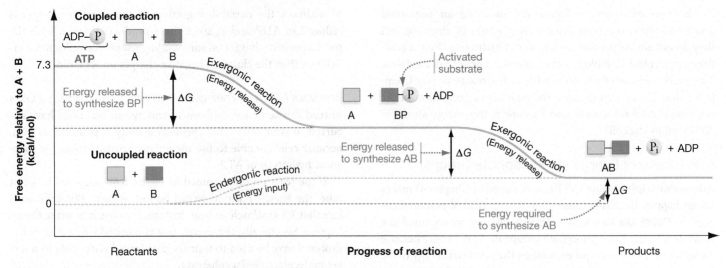

FIGURE 8.9 Exergonic Phosphorylation Reactions Are Coupled to Endergonic Reactions. In cells, many reactions only occur if one reactant is activated by phosphorylation. The phosphorylated reactant molecule has high enough free energy that the subsequent reaction is exergonic. In this graph, the free energy being tracked on the *y*-axis represents A, B, and the 7.3 kcal/mol that is released when ATP is hydrolyzed. For simplicity, the free energy in ADP and P$_i$ is not shown. ΔG represents the change in free energy between the reactants and products for each indicated step.

✔ **EXERCISE** Label the ΔG in the uncoupled reaction and the two steps of the coupled reaction to indicate if the change is representing a positive (> 0) or negative (< 0) value.

FIGURE 8.9 graphs how phosphorylation can couple exergonic and endergonic reactions. Note that the reaction between A and B to produce the product AB is endergonic—the ΔG is positive. But after the exergonic transfer of a phosphate group from ATP to B occurs, the free energy of the reactants A and BP is high enough to make the reaction that forms AB exergonic. When reactant molecules in an endergonic reaction are phosphorylated, the free energy released during phosphorylation is coupled to the endergonic reaction to make the combined overall reaction exergonic.

✔ If you understand the principles of energetic coupling, you should be able to compare and contrast how energy is transferred via redox reactions and ATP hydrolysis.

It is hard to overstate the importance of energetic coupling: Without it, life is impossible. If the cells in your body could no longer drive endergonic reactions by coupling them to exergonic reactions, you would die within minutes.

Now the question is, What role do enzymes play in these reactions?

check your understanding

If you understand that . . .

- When redox reactions occur, electrons change position. Chemical energy is based on the positions of electrons in chemical bonds, so redox reactions usually involve a change in potential energy.
- ATP contains a cluster of three negatively charged phosphate groups.
- When ATP or phosphate groups from ATP bind to substrates, they gain a great deal of potential energy.

✔ You should be able to . . .

1. Explain why reduced molecules with many C–H bonds store more potential energy than oxidized molecules with many C–O bonds.

2. Explain why ATP has such high potential energy.

Answers are available in Appendix A.

8.3 How Enzymes Work

Regardless of whether reactions in cells are spontaneous or not, none would occur at the speed required for life without the support of enzymes. How do they do it?

Recall that the initial hypothesis for how enzymes speed up reactions—the "lock-and-key" model—was first proposed in 1894 by Emil Fischer (introduced in Chapter 3). In this model, the substrates would fit into enzymes and react in a manner analogous to a key being inserted into a lock. In other words, enzymes are **catalysts**—they bring substrates together in a precise orientation that makes reactions more likely. Fischer's model also explained why many enzymes are specific for a single reaction—specificity is a product of the geometry and chemical properties of the sites where substrates bind.

Enzymes Help Reactions Clear Two Hurdles

Recall that two hurdles must be cleared before reactions can take place: Reactants need to (**1**) collide in a precise orientation and

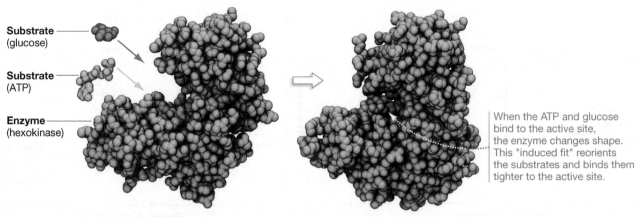

Substrate
(glucose)

Substrate
(ATP)

Enzyme
(hexokinase)

When the ATP and glucose
bind to the active site,
the enzyme changes shape.
This "induced fit" reorients
the substrates and binds them
tighter to the active site.

FIGURE 8.10 Reactant Molecules Bind to Specific Locations in an Enzyme. The reactant molecules, shown in red and yellow, fit into a precise location, called the active site, in the green enzyme. In this enzyme and in many others, the binding event causes the protein to change shape.

(2) have enough kinetic energy to overcome repulsion between electrons that come into contact as a bond forms (Chapter 2). To appreciate how enzymes work, let's consider each hurdle in turn.

Enzymes Bring Substrates Together Part of the reason enzymes are such effective catalysts is that they bring substrate molecules together in a substrate binding site known as the enzyme's **active site** (Chapter 3). In this way, enzymes help substrates collide in a precise orientation so that the electrons involved in the reaction can interact.

Enzymes generally are very large relative to substrates and roughly globular. The active site is in a cleft or cavity within the globular shape. A good example can be seen in the enzyme glucokinase, which catalyzes the phosphorylation of the sugar glucose. (Many enzymes have names that hint at the identity of the substrate and end with *-ase*.) As the left side of **FIGURE 8.10** shows, the active site in glucokinase is a small notch in an otherwise large, crescent-shaped enzyme.

In Fischer's original lock-and-key model, enzymes were conceived of as being rigid—almost literally as rigid as a lock. As research on enzyme action progressed, however, Fischer's model had to be modified. Perhaps the most important realization was that enzymes are not rigid and static, but flexible and dynamic. In fact, many enzymes undergo a significant change in shape, or conformation, when reactant molecules bind to the active site. You can see this conformational change, called an **induced fit,** in the glucokinase molecule on the right side of Figure 8.10. Once glucokinase binds its substrates—ATP and glucose—the enzyme rocks forward over the active site to bring the two substrates together.

In addition, recent research has clarified the nature of Fischer's key. When one or more substrate molecules enter the active site, they are held in place through hydrogen bonding or other weak interactions with amino acids in the active site. Once the substrate is bound, one or more R-groups in the active site come into play. The degree of interaction between the substrate and enzyme increases and reaches a maximum when a temporary,

unstable, intermediate condition called the **transition state** is formed. When Fischer's key is in its lock, it represents the transition state of the substrate.

There is more to achieving this transition state than simply an enzyme binding to its substrates, however. Even if the reaction is spontaneous, a certain amount of kinetic energy is required to strain the chemical bonds in substrates so they can achieve this transition state—called the **activation energy.** How do enzymes help clear the activation energy hurdle?

Enzymes Lower the Activation Energy Reactions happen when reactants have enough kinetic energy to reach the transition state. The kinetic energy of molecules, in turn, is a function of their temperature. (This is why reactions tend to proceed faster at higher temperatures.)

FIGURE 8.11 (see page 146) graphs the changes in free energy that take place during the course of a chemical reaction. As you read along the x-axis from left to right, note that a dramatic rise in free energy occurs when the reactants combine to form the transition state—followed by a dramatic drop in free energy when products form. The free energy of the transition state is high because the bonds that existed in the substrates are destabilized—it is the transition point between breaking old bonds and forming new ones.

The ΔG label on the graph indicates the overall change in free energy in the reaction—that is, the energy of the products minus the energy of the reactants. In this particular case, the products have lower free energy than the reactants, meaning that the reaction is exergonic. But because the activation energy for this reaction, symbolized by E_a, is high, the reaction would proceed slowly—even at high temperature.

This is an important point: The more unstable the transition state, the higher the activation energy and the less likely a reaction is to proceed quickly.

Reaction rates, then, depend on both the kinetic energy of the reactants and the activation energy of the particular reaction—meaning the free energy of the transition state. If the kinetic

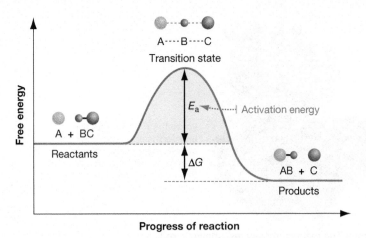

FIGURE 8.11 Changes in Free Energy during a Chemical Reaction. The energy profile shows changes in free energy that occur over the course of a hypothetical reaction between a molecule A and a molecule containing parts B and C. The overall reaction would be written as A + BC → AB + C. E_a is the activation energy of the reaction.

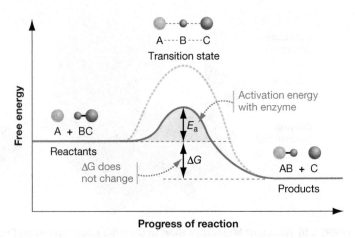

FIGURE 8.12 A Catalyst Changes the Activation Energy of a Reaction. The energy profile for the same reaction diagrammed in Figure 8.11, but now with a catalyst present. Even though the energy barrier to the reaction, E_a, is much lower, ΔG does not change.

✔ **QUESTION** Can a catalyst make a nonspontaneous reaction occur spontaneously? Explain why or why not.

energy of the participating molecules is high, such as at high temperatures, then molecular collisions are more likely to overcome the activation energy barrier. At this point, the transition state is formed and the reaction takes place.

Enzymes don't change the temperature of a solution, though. How do they fit in?

Interactions with amino acid R-groups at the enzyme active site stabilize the transition state and thus lower the activation energy required for the reaction to proceed. At the atomic level, R-groups that line the active site may form short-lived covalent bonds that assist with the transfer of atoms or groups of atoms from one reactant to another. More commonly, the presence of acidic or basic R-groups allows the reactants to lose or gain a proton more readily.

FIGURE 8.12 diagrams how enzymes lower the activation energy for a reaction by lowering the free energy of the transition state. Note that the presence of an enzyme does not affect the overall

energy change, ΔG, or change the energy of the reactants or the products. An enzyme changes only the free energy of the transition state.

Most enzymes are specific in their activity—they catalyze just a single reaction by lowering the activation energy that is required—and many are astonishingly efficient. Most of the important reactions in biology would not occur at all, or else proceed at imperceptible rates, without a catalyst. It's not unusual for enzymes to speed up reactions by a factor of a million; some enzymes make reactions go many *trillions* of times faster than they would without a catalyst.

It's also important to note that an enzyme is not consumed in a chemical reaction, even though it participates in the reaction. The composition of an enzyme is exactly the same after the reaction as it was before.

Enzyme catalysis can be analyzed as a three-step process. **FIGURE 8.13** summarizes this model:

PROCESS: A MODEL OF ENZYME ACTION

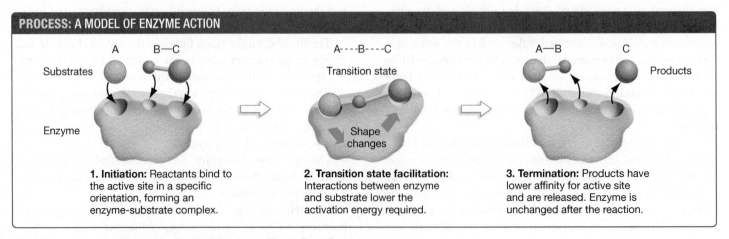

1. Initiation: Reactants bind to the active site in a specific orientation, forming an enzyme-substrate complex.

2. Transition state facilitation: Interactions between enzyme and substrate lower the activation energy required.

3. Termination: Products have lower affinity for active site and are released. Enzyme is unchanged after the reaction.

FIGURE 8.13 Enzyme Action Can Be Analyzed as a Three-Step Process.

1. *Initiation* Instead of reactants occasionally colliding in a random fashion, enzymes orient reactants precisely as they bind at specific locations within the active site.

2. *Transition state facilitation* Inside a catalyst's active site, reactant molecules are more likely to reach their transition state. In some cases the transition state is stabilized by a change in the enzyme's shape. Interactions between the substrate and R-groups in the enzyme's active site lower the activation energy required for the reaction. Thus, the catalyzed reaction proceeds much more rapidly than the uncatalyzed reaction.

3. *Termination* The reaction products have less affinity for the active site than the transition state does. Binding ends, the enzyme returns to its original conformation, and the products are released.

✔ If you understand the basic principles of enzyme catalysis, you should be able to complete the following sentences: (1) Enzymes speed reaction rates by _____ and lowering activation energy. (2) Activation energies drop because enzymes destabilize bonds in the substrates, forming the _____. (3) Enzyme specificity is a function of the active site's shape and the chemical properties of the _____ at the active site. (4) In enzymes, as in many molecules, function follows from _____.

What Limits the Rate of Catalysis?

For several decades after Fischer's model was published, most research on enzymes focused on rates of enzyme action, or what biologists call enzyme kinetics. Researchers observed that, when the amount of product produced per second—indicating the speed of the reaction—is plotted as a function of substrate concentration, a graph like that shown in **FIGURE 8.14** results.

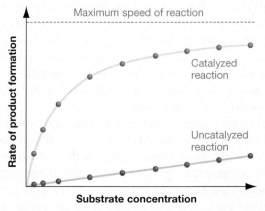

FIGURE 8.14 Enzyme-Catalyzed Reactions Can Be Saturated. At high substrate concentration, enzyme-catalyzed reactions reach a maximum rate. Uncatalyzed reactions slowly increase as substrate concentration increases.

✔**EXERCISE** Label the parts of the *catalyzed reaction curve* that represent where (1) the reaction rate is most sensitive to changes in substrate concentration and (2) most or all of the active sites present are occupied.

In this graph, each data point represents an experiment where reaction rate was measured when substrates were at various concentrations. The two lines represent two series of experiments: one with the reactions catalyzed by an enzyme and the other uncatalyzed. As you read the curve for the catalyzed reaction from left to right, note that it has three basic sections:

1. When substrate concentrations are low, the speed of an enzyme-catalyzed reaction increases in a steep, linear fashion.

2. At intermediate substrate concentrations, the increase in speed begins to slow.

3. At high substrate concentration, the reaction rate plateaus at a maximum speed.

This pattern is in striking contrast to the situation for the uncatalyzed reactions, where the reaction speed is far slower, but tends to show a continuing linear increase with substrate concentration. The "saturation kinetics" of enzyme-catalyzed reactions were taken as strong evidence that the enzyme–substrate complex proposed by Fischer actually exists. The idea was that, at some point, active sites cannot accept substrates any faster, no matter how large the concentration of substrates gets. Stated another way, reaction rates level off because all available enzyme molecules are being used.

Do Enzymes Work Alone?

The answer to this question, in many cases, is no. Atoms or molecules that are not part of an enzyme's primary structure are often required for an enzyme to function normally. These enzyme "helpers" can be divided into three different types:

1. **Cofactors:** Inorganic ions, such as the metal ions Zn^{2+} (zinc), Mg^{2+} (magnesium), and Fe^{2+} (iron), which reversibly interact with enzymes. Cofactors that now participate in key reactions in virtually all living cells are thought to have been involved in catalysis early on in chemical evolution (see Chapter 2).

2. **Coenzymes:** Organic molecules that reversibly interact with enzymes, such as the electron carriers NADH or $FADH_2$.

3. **Prosthetic groups:** Non-amino acid atoms or molecules that are permanently attached to proteins, such as the molecule retinal. Retinal is involved in converting light energy into chemical energy (see Chapter 47).

In many cases, these enzyme helpers are part of the active site and play a key role in stabilizing the transition state. Their presence is therefore essential for the catalytic activity of many enzymes.

To appreciate why this is important, consider that many of the vitamins in your diet are required for the production of coenzymes. Vitamin deficiencies result in coenzyme deficiencies. Lack of coenzymes, in turn, disrupts normal enzyme function and causes disease. For example, thiamine (vitamin B_1) is required for the production of a coenzyme called thiamine pyrophosphate, which is required by three different enzymes. Lack of thiamine in the diet dramatically reduces the activity of these enzymes and causes an array of nervous system and heart disorders collectively known as beriberi.

(a) Enzymes from different organisms may function best at different temperatures.

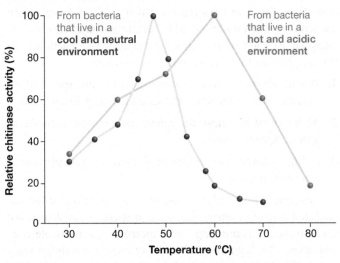

(b) Enzymes from different organisms may function best at different pHs.

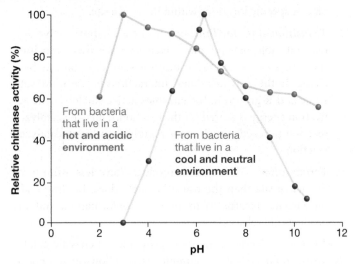

FIGURE 8.15 Enzymes Have an Optimal Temperature and pH. The activity of enzymes is sensitive to changes in temperature **(a)** and pH **(b)**.

DATA: Nawani, N., B. P. Kapadnis, A. D. Das, et al. 2002. *Journal of Applied Microbiology* 93: 865–975. Also Nawani, N., and B. P. Kapadnis. 2001. *Journal of Applied Microbiology* 90: 803–808.

8.4 What Factors Affect Enzyme Function?

Given that an enzyme's structure is critical to its function, it's not surprising that an enzyme's activity is sensitive to conditions that alter protein shape. Recall that protein structure is dependent on the sequence of amino acids and a variety of chemical bonds and interactions that fold the polypeptide into its functional form (Chapter 3).

In particular, the activity of an enzyme often changes drastically as a function of temperature, pH, interactions with other molecules, and modifications of its primary structure. Let's take a look at how enzyme function is affected by, and sometimes even regulated by, each of these factors.

Enzymes Are Optimized for Particular Environments

Temperature affects the folding and movement of an enzyme as well as the kinetic energy of its substrates. The concentration of protons in a solution, as measured by pH, also affects enzyme structure and function. pH affects the charge on carboxyl and amino groups in residue side chains, and also the active site's ability to participate in reactions that involve the transfer of protons or electrons.

Do data support these assertions? **FIGURE 8.15a** shows how the activity of an enzyme, plotted on the y-axis, changes as a function of temperature, plotted on the x-axis. These data were collected for an enzyme called chitinase, which is used by bacteria to digest cell walls of fungi. In this graph, each data point represents the enzyme's relative activity—meaning the rate of the enzyme-catalyzed reaction, scaled relative to the highest rate observed—in

experiments conducted under conditions that differed only in temperature. Results are shown for two types of bacteria.

Note that, in both bacterial species, the enzyme has a distinct optimum or peak—a temperature at which it functions best. One of the bacterial species lives in the cool soil under palm trees, where the temperature is about 25°C, while the other lives in hot springs, where temperatures can be close to 100°C. The temperature optimum for the enzyme reflects these environments.

The two types of bacteria have different versions of the enzyme that differ in primary structure. Natural selection (introduced in Chapter 1) has favored a structure in each species that is best suited for its distinct environment. The two versions are adaptations that allow each species to thrive at different temperatures.

FIGURE 8.15b makes the same point for pH. The effect of pH on enzyme activity was tested on the same chitinases used in Figure 8.15a, but this time using conditions that varied only in pH. The soil-dwelling bacteria described earlier grow in a neutral pH environment, but the species that lives in hot springs is also exposed to acidic conditions.

Note that the organism that thrives in a hot, acidic environment has a version of the enzyme that performs best at high temperatures and low pH; the organism that lives in the cool soil has a version of the enzyme that functions best at cooler temperatures and nearly neutral pH. Each enzyme is sensitive to changes in temperature and pH, but each species' version of the enzyme has a structure that allows it to function best in its particular environment.

To summarize, the rate of an enzyme-catalyzed reaction depends not only on substrate concentration and the enzyme's intrinsic affinity for the substrate but also on temperature and pH (among other factors). Temperature affects the movement of the substrates and enzyme; pH affects the enzyme's shape and reactivity.

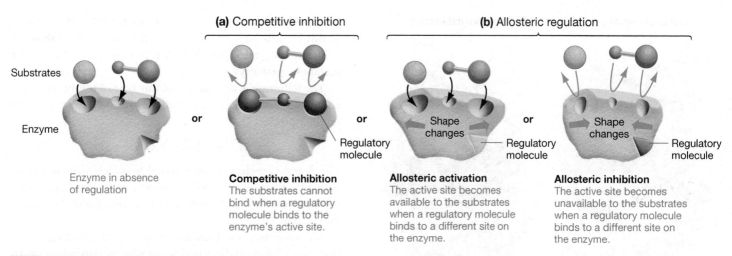

(a) Competitive inhibition   **(b)** Allosteric regulation

Substrates

Enzyme

Enzyme in absence
of regulation

or

Competitive inhibition
The substrates cannot
bind when a regulatory
molecule binds to the
enzyme's active site.

Regulatory
molecule

or

Allosteric activation
The active site becomes
available to the substrates
when a regulatory molecule
binds to a different site on
the enzyme.

Shape
changes

Regulatory
molecule

or

Allosteric inhibition
The active site becomes
unavailable to the substrates
when a regulatory molecule
binds to a different site on
the enzyme.

Shape
changes

Regulatory
molecule

FIGURE 8.16 An Enzyme's Activity Is Precisely Regulated. Enzymes are turned on or off when specific regulatory
molecules bind to them.

Most Enzymes Are Regulated

Controlling when and where enzymes will function is vital to
the work of a cell. While temperature and pH affect the activity of enzymes, they are not often used as a means of regulating
enzyme function. Instead, other molecules, in some cases other
enzymes, regulate most of the cell's enzymatic activity. These regulatory molecules often change the enzyme's structure in some
way, and their activity either activates or inactivates the enzyme.

Regulating Enzymes via Noncovalent Modifications   Many molecules that regulate enzyme activity bind non-covalently to the
enzyme to either activate or inactivate it. Since the interaction
does not alter the enzyme's primary structure, it is often referred
to as a "reversible" modification.

Reversible modifications affect enzyme function in one of two
ways:

1. The regulatory molecule is similar in size and shape to the
   enzyme's natural substrate and inhibits catalysis by binding
   to the enzyme's active site. This event is called **competitive
   inhibition** because the molecule involved competes with the
   substrate for access to the enzyme's active site (**FIGURE 8.16a**).

2. The regulatory molecule binds at a location other than the
   active site and changes the shape of the enzyme. This type
   of regulation is called **allosteric** ("different-structure") **regulation** because the binding event changes the shape of the
   enzyme in a way that makes the active site available or unavailable (**FIGURE 8.16b**). turn on

Both strategies depend on the concentration of the regulatory molecule—the more regulatory molecule present, the more
likely it will be to bind to the enzyme and affect its activity. The
amount of regulatory molecule is often tightly controlled and, as
you'll see in Section 8.5, the regulatory molecules themselves often manage the enzymes that produce them.

Regulating Enzymes via Covalent Modifications   In some cases,
the function of an enzyme is altered by a chemical change in its

primary structure. This change may be reversible or irreversible,
depending on the type of modification.

Irreversible changes often result from the cleavage of peptide
bonds that make up the primary structure of the enzyme. The
enzyme trypsin, for example, is not functional until a small section of the protein is removed by a specific protease.

The most common modification of enzymes is the addition
of one or more phosphate groups, similar to what was described
for activated substrates in Section 8.2. In this case, however, the
enzyme is phosphorylated instead of the substrate molecule. The
transfer of a phosphate from ATP to the enzyme may be catalyzed by the enzyme itself or by a different enzyme.

When phosphorylation adds a negative charge to one or more
amino acid residues in a protein, the electrons in that part of
the protein change configuration. The enzyme's conformation

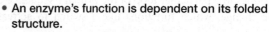
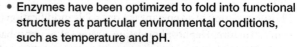
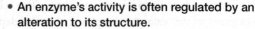

check your understanding

If you understand that . . .
- An enzyme's function is dependent on its folded
  structure.
- Enzymes have been optimized to fold into functional
  structures at particular environmental conditions,
  such as temperature and pH.
- An enzyme's activity is often regulated by an
  alteration to its structure.

✔ **You should be able to . . .**

1. Explain why the relative activity appears to drop off in
   Figure 8.15b, when it has been shown that reaction rates
   tend to increase at higher temperatures (Figure 8.4).

2. Predict how the shape change that occurs when an
   enzyme is phosphorylated would affect its catalytic
   activity.

   Answers are available in Appendix A.

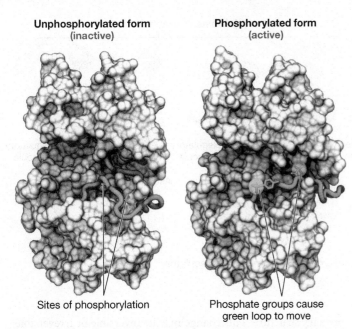

Unphosphorylated form (inactive)	Phosphorylated form (active)
Sites of phosphorylation	Phosphate groups cause green loop to move

FIGURE 8.17 Phosphorylation Changes the Shape and Activity of Proteins. When proteins are phosphorylated, they often change shape in a way that alters their activity. The figure shows the subtle structural change that occurs when mitogen-activated protein kinase (MAPK) is activated by adding two phosphate groups (yellow) to the enzyme.

usually changes as well, which may activate or inactivate its function. Note that although a substrate or an enzyme may be "activated" via phosphorylation, this activation does not represent the same effect. When a substrate is activated, its potential energy has increased, and this energy is used to convert an endergonic reaction to one that is exergonic. When an enzyme is activated, its catalytic function has been turned on—any change in the potential energy of the enzyme is not directly used in driving the reaction.

To see how phosphorylation affects the shape and activity of an enzyme, let's look at an enzyme called mitogen-activated protein kinase (MAPK), which is involved in cell signaling (see Chapter 11). As shown in **FIGURE 8.17**, phosphorylation of amino acid residues in a particular loop of the primary sequence causes a shape change, which functions like a switch to activate the enzyme.

Phosphorylation of an enzyme is a reversible modification to the protein's structure. Dephosphorylation—removal of phosphates—can quickly return the protein to its previous shape. The relative abundance of enzymes that catalyze phosphorylation and dephosphorylation, then, regulates the function of the protein.

8.5 Enzymes Can Work Together in Metabolic Pathways

The eukaryotic cell has been compared to an industrial complex, where distinct organelles are functionally integrated into a cooperative network with a common goal—life (see Chapter 7). Similarly, enzymes often work together in a manner resembling an assembly line in a factory. Each of the molecules of life presented in this book is built by a series of reactions, each catalyzed by a different enzyme. These multistep processes are referred to as **metabolic pathways.**

The following is an example of this type of teamwork, where an initial substrate A is sequentially modified by enzymes 1–3 to produce product D:

$$A \xrightarrow{\text{enzyme 1}} B \xrightarrow{\text{enzyme 2}} C \xrightarrow{\text{enzyme 3}} D$$

The B and C molecules are referred to as intermediates in the pathway—they serve as both a product and a reactant. For example, molecule B is the product of reaction 1 and the reactant for reaction 2.

Although these reactions have been written in a single direction, from left to right, the directionality is dependent on the relative concentrations of the reactants and products. At equilibrium, however, the concentration of the product for each reaction will be higher than the concentration of its respective reactant. Since D is the overall product for this pathway, it will have the highest concentration at equilibrium.

Metabolic Pathways Are Regulated

Since enzymes catalyze the reactions in metabolic pathways, the mechanisms that regulate enzyme function introduced in Section 8.4 also apply to the individual steps in a pathway. For example, to understand how blocking an individual reaction can affect an entire pathway, go back to the three-step model presented earlier and inactivate enzyme 2 by crossing it out. ✔ If you understand the assembly-line behavior of enzymes in a metabolic pathway, you should be able to predict how inactivating enzyme 2 would affect the concentration of molecules A, B, C, and D relative to what they would be if the pathway were fully functional.

When an enzyme in a pathway is inhibited by the product of the reaction sequence, **feedback inhibition** occurs. This is a convenient way for pathways to shut themselves down when their activity is no longer needed. As the concentration of the product molecule becomes abundant, it "feeds back" to stop the reaction sequence (**FIGURE 8.18**). By inhibiting a step early in the pathway, the amount of the initial substrate is not depleted unnecessarily, allowing it to be stored or used for other reactions.

Metabolic Pathways Evolve

While many enzymes are extraordinarily specific, some can catalyze a range of reactions and are able to interact with a family of related substrates. Research suggests that this flexibility allowed new enzymes to evolve and that enzymes specialized for catalyzing key reactions provided cells with a selective advantage. Could the same flexibility also help explain the evolution of the stepwise series of reactions seen in metabolic pathways?

In 1945, Norman Horowitz proposed a simple, stepwise process that could have directed pathway evolution. In Horowitz's model, enzymes first would have evolved to make the building blocks of life from readily available substrates, such as small organic compounds (see Chapter 2).

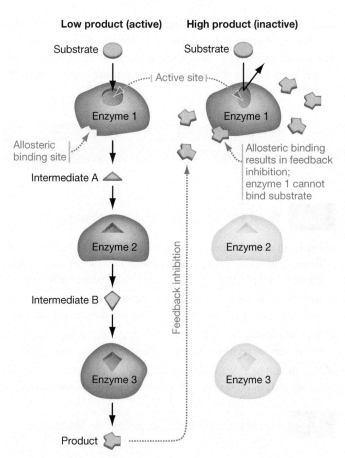

Low product (active)

High product (inactive)

Substrate

Substrate

Active site

Enzyme 1

Enzyme 1

Allosteric
binding site

Allosteric binding
results in feedback
inhibition;
enzyme 1 cannot
bind substrate

Intermediate A

Feedback inhibition

Enzyme 2

Enzyme 2

Intermediate B

Enzyme 3

Enzyme 3

Product

FIGURE 8.18 Feedback Inhibition May Regulate Metabolic Pathways. Feedback inhibition occurs when the product of a metabolic pathway inhibits an enzyme that functions early in the pathway.

If an original substrate were depleted, natural selection would next favor the evolution of a new enzyme to make more of it from other existing molecules. By evolving a new reaction step to produce the original substrate—now serving as an intermediate in a two-step pathway—the original enzyme would have been able to continue its work. **FIGURE 8.19** illustrates this model—referred to as retro-evolution—in which repetition of this backward process produces a multistep metabolic pathway.

Researchers also speculate that as early pathways emerged, early enzymes may have been recruited to new pathways, where they evolved new catalytic activities that performed new tasks. This hypothesis is called patchwork evolution, since the new reaction series would consist of enzymes brought together from different pathways.

Evidence of patchwork evolution has been observed in modern organisms, where new metabolic activities have emerged in response to human-made chemicals. For example, a novel pathway has recently evolved in one species of bacterium to break down the pesticide pentachlorophenol, for use as a source of energy and carbon building blocks. Pentachlorophenol was first introduced into the environment in the 1930s as a timber preservative. The new pathway uses enzymes from two preexisting pathways, which had evolved the ability to work together. The metabolic activity of microbes is now being scrutinized and engineered to clean up a variety of human-made pollutants—giving rise to a new technology called **bioremediation** (see Chapter 29).

Regardless of how they evolved, metabolic pathways are now vital to the function of all cells. Those that break down molecules for sources of energy and carbon building blocks are called **catabolic pathways;** those that use energy and carbon building blocks to synthesize molecules are called **anabolic pathways.**

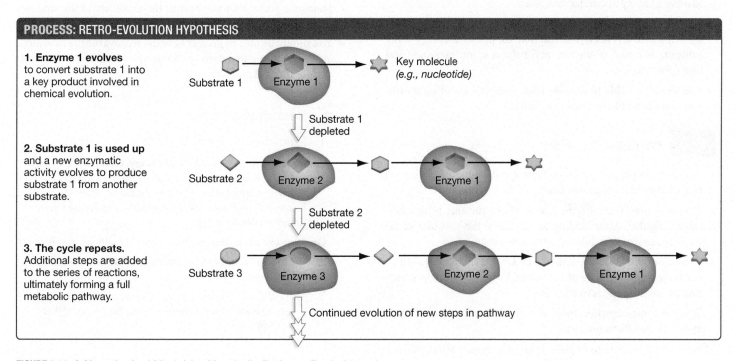

PROCESS: RETRO-EVOLUTION HYPOTHESIS

1. Enzyme 1 evolves to convert substrate 1 into a key product involved in chemical evolution.

Substrate 1   Enzyme 1

Key molecule
(e.g., nucleotide)

Substrate 1 depleted

2. Substrate 1 is used up and a new enzymatic activity evolves to produce substrate 1 from another substrate.

Substrate 2   Enzyme 2   Enzyme 1

Substrate 2 depleted

3. The cycle repeats. Additional steps are added to the series of reactions, ultimately forming a full metabolic pathway.

Substrate 3   Enzyme 3   Enzyme 2   Enzyme 1

Continued evolution of new steps in pathway

FIGURE 8.19 A Hypothetical Model for Metabolic Pathway Evolution.

You are being kept alive by key catabolic and anabolic pathways. The catabolic pathways of cellular respiration (introduced in Chapter 9) harvest high-energy electrons from reduced carbons (from foods such as starch and sugar) and pass them through redox reactions to generate ATP. These reduced carbons are produced by the anabolic pathways of photosynthesis that are driven by light energy (introduced in Chapter 10). The reactions involved in cellular respiration and photosynthesis perform the most important energy transformations to life on Earth.

CHAPTER 8 REVIEW

If you understand . . .

8.1 What Happens to Energy in Chemical Reactions?

- Spontaneous reactions do not require an input of energy to occur.

- The Gibbs free energy change, ΔG, summarizes the combined effects of changes in enthalpy and entropy during a chemical reaction.

- Spontaneous reactions have a negative ΔG and are said to be exergonic; nonspontaneous reactions have a positive ΔG and are said to be endergonic.

✓ You should be able to explain why changes in enthalpy and entropy are used to determine whether a reaction is spontaneous.

8.2 Nonspontaneous Reactions May Be Driven Using Chemical Energy

- Redox reactions transfer energy by coupling exergonic oxidation reactions to endergonic reduction reactions.

- High-energy C–H bonds may be formed during the reduction step of a redox reaction when an H^+ is combined with a transferred electron.

- The hydrolysis of ATP is an exergonic reaction and may be used to drive a variety of cellular processes.

- When a phosphate group from ATP is added to a substrate that participates in an endergonic reaction, the potential energy of the substrate is raised enough to make the reaction exergonic and thus spontaneous.

✓ You should be able to explain what energetic coupling means, and why life would not exist without it.

8.3 How Enzymes Work

- Enzymes are protein catalysts. They speed reaction rates but do not affect the change in free energy of the reaction.

- The structure of an enzyme has an active site that brings substrates together. After binding to substrates, the structure of the enzyme changes to stabilize the transition state.

- Activation energy is the amount of kinetic energy required to reach the transition state of a reaction. Enzymes speed up a reaction by lowering the activation energy.

- Many enzymes function only with the help of cofactors, coenzymes, or prosthetic groups.

✓ You should be able to explain how an enzyme's active site can reduce the activation energy of a reaction.

8.4 What Factors Affect Enzyme Function?

- Enzymes are proteins, and thus their activity can be directly influenced by modifications or environmental factors, such as temperature and pH, that alter their three-dimensional structure.

- Most enzymes are regulated by molecules that either compete with substrates to occupy the active site, or alter enzyme shape.

- Protein cleavage and phosphorylation are examples of how enzymes may be regulated by modifying their primary structure.

✓ You should be able to compare and contrast the effect of allosteric regulation versus phosphorylation on enzyme function.

8.5 Enzymes Can Work Together in Metabolic Pathways

- In cells, enzymes often work together in metabolic pathways that sequentially modify a substrate to make a product.

- A pathway may be regulated by controlling the activity of one enzyme, often the first in the series of reactions. Feedback inhibition results from the accumulation of a product that binds to an enzyme in the pathway and inactivates it.

- Metabolic pathways were vital to the evolution of life, and new pathways continue to evolve in cells.

✓ You should be able to predict how the removal of the intermediate in a two-step metabolic pathway would affect the enzymatic rates of the first and last.

MB MasteringBiology

1. **MasteringBiology Assignments**

   Tutorials and Activities ATP and Energy; Chemical Reactions and ATP; Energy Transformations; Enzyme and Substrate Concentrations; Enzyme Inhibition; Factors That Affect Reaction Rate; How Enzymes Function; Regulating Enzyme Action; Redox Reactions

   Questions Reading Quizzes, Blue-Thread Questions, Test Bank

2. **eText** Read your book online, search, take notes, highlight text, and more.

3. **The Study Area** Practice Test, Cumulative Test, BioFlix® 3-D Animations, Videos, Activities, Audio Glossary, Word Study Tools, Art

You should be able to . . .

1. The first law of thermodynamics states which of the following?
   a. Energy exists in two forms: kinetic and potential.
   b. Reactions will take place only if energy is released.
   c. Energy is conserved: it cannot be created or destroyed.
   d. Disorder always increases in the universe.

2. If a reaction is exergonic, then which of these statements is true?
   a. The products have lower free energy than the reactants.
   b. Energy must be added for the reaction to proceed.
   c. The products have lower entropy (are more ordered) than the reactants.
   d. The reaction occurs extremely quickly.

3. What is a transition state?
   a. the complex formed as covalent bonds are being broken and re-formed during a reaction
   b. the place where an allosteric regulatory molecule binds to an enzyme
   c. an interaction between reactants with high kinetic energy, due to high temperature
   d. the shape adopted by an enzyme that has an inhibitory molecule bound at its active site

4. What often happens to an enzyme after it binds to its substrate? Is this a permanent change?

5. How does pH affect enzyme-catalyzed reactions?
   a. Protons serve as substrates for most reactions.
   b. Energy stored in protons is used to drive endergonic reactions.
   c. Proton concentration increases the kinetic energy of the reactants, allowing them to reach their transition state.
   d. The concentration of protons affects the folded structure of the enzyme.

6. When does feedback inhibition occur?

7. Explain the lock-and-key model of enzyme activity. What was incorrect about this model?

8. If you were to expose glucose to oxygen on your lab bench, why would you not expect to see it burn as shown in Figure 8.6?
   a. The reaction is endergonic and requires an input of energy.
   b. The reaction is not spontaneous unless an enzyme is added to the substrates.
   c. The sugar must first be phosphorylated to increase its potential energy.
   d. Energy is required for the sugar and oxygen to reach their transition state.

9. Explain why substrate phosphorylation using ATP is an exergonic reaction. How does the phosphorylation of reactants result in driving reactions that would normally be endergonic?

10. **QUANTITATIVE** In Figure 8.9, the energetic coupling of ATP hydrolysis and an endergonic reaction are shown. If the hydrolysis of ATP releases 7.3 kcal of free energy, use the graph in this figure to estimate what you would expect the ΔG values to be for the uncoupled reaction and the two steps in the coupled reaction.

11. Compare and contrast competitive inhibition and allosteric regulation.

12. Using what you have learned about changes in free energy, would you predict the ΔG value of catabolic reactions to be positive or negative? What about anabolic reactions? Justify your answers using the terms enthalpy and entropy.

13. Draw a redox reaction that occurs between compounds AH_2 and B^+ to form A, BH, and H^+. On the drawing, connect the reactant and product forms of each compound and state if it is the reduction or oxidation step and how many electrons are transferred. If this represents an exergonic reaction, identify which of the five substances would have the highest-energy electrons.

14. Researchers can analyze the atomic structure of enzymes during catalysis. In one recent study, investigators found that the transition state included the formation of a free radical (see Chapter 2) and that a coenzyme bound to the active site donated an electron to help stabilize the free radical. How would the reaction rate and the stability of the transition state change if the coenzyme were not available?

15. Recently, researchers were able to measure movement that occurred in a single amino acid in an enzyme as reactions were taking place in its active site. The amino acid that moved was located in the active site, and the rate of movement correlated closely with the rate at which the reaction was taking place. Discuss the significance of these findings, using the information in Figures 8.10 and 8.13.

16. You have discovered an enzyme that appears to function only when a particular sugar accumulates. Which of the following scenarios would you predict to be responsible for activating this enzyme?
   a. The sugar cleaves the enzyme so it is now in an active conformation.
   b. The sugar binds to the enzyme and changes the conformation of the active site.
   c. The sugar binds to the active site and competes with the normal substrate.
   d. The sugar phosphorylates the enzyme, triggering a conformational change.

9 Cellular Respiration and Fermentation

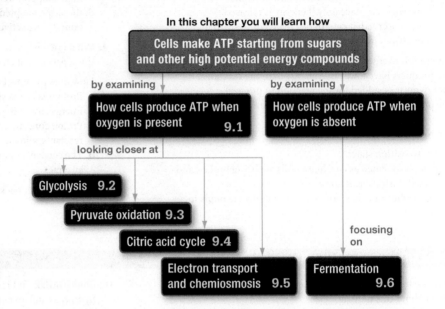

In this chapter you will learn how

Cells make ATP starting from sugars and other high potential energy compounds

by examining

How cells produce ATP when oxygen is present **9.1**

How cells produce ATP when oxygen is absent

looking closer at

Glycolysis **9.2**

Pyruvate oxidation **9.3**

Citric acid cycle **9.4**

Electron transport and chemiosmosis **9.5**

focusing on

Fermentation **9.6**

This hydroelectric dam on the Duero river between Spain and Portugal uses pumps to move water from the lower reservoir to the upper reservoir. During periods of high energy demand, the potential energy stored by this activity is used to generate electricity. A similar process is used by cells to produce ATP during cellular respiration.

This chapter is part of the Big Picture. See how on pages 198–199.

ife requires energy. From the very start, chemical evolution was driven by energy from chemicals, radiation, heat, or other sources (see Chapter 2). Harnessing energy and controlling its flow has been the single most important step in the evolution of life.

What fuels life in cells? The answer is the nucleotide adenosine triphosphate (ATP). ATP has high potential energy and allows cells to overcome life's energy barriers (see Chapter 8).

This chapter investigates how cells make ATP, starting with an introduction to the metabolic pathways that harvest energy from high-energy molecules like **glucose**—the most common source of chemical energy used by organisms. The four central pathways of cellular respiration will be

✔ When you see this checkmark, stop and test yourself. Answers are available in Appendix A.

presented with emphasis on how the oxidation of glucose leads to ATP production. Fermentation will also be introduced as an alternative pathway used to make ATP when key reactions in cellular respiration are either shut down or not available.

As cells process sugar, the energy that is released is used to transfer a phosphate group to adenosine diphosphate (ADP), generating ATP. (You can see the Big Picture of how the production of glucose in photosynthesis is related to its catabolism in cellular respiration on pages 198–199.)

9.1 An Overview of Cellular Respiration

In general, a cell contains only enough ATP to last from 30 seconds to a few minutes. Because it has such high potential energy, ATP is unstable and is not stored. Like many other cellular processes, the production and use of ATP is fast. Most cells are making ATP all the time.

Most of the glucose that is used to make ATP is produced by plants and other photosynthetic species. These organisms use the energy in sunlight to reduce carbon dioxide (CO_2) to glucose and other carbohydrates. While they are alive, photosynthetic species use the glucose that they produce to make ATP for themselves. When photosynthetic species decompose or are eaten, they provide glucose to animals, fungi, and many bacteria and archaea.

All organisms use glucose in the synthesis of complex carbohydrates, fats, and other energy-rich compounds. Storage carbohydrates, such as starch and glycogen, act like savings accounts for chemical energy. ATP, in contrast, is like cash. To withdraw chemical energy from the accounts to get cash, storage carbohydrates are first hydrolyzed into their glucose monomers. The glucose is then used to produce ATP through one of two general processes: cellular respiration or fermentation (**FIGURE 9.1**). The primary difference between these two processes lies in the degree to which glucose is oxidized.

What Happens When Glucose Is Oxidized?

When glucose undergoes the uncontrolled oxidation reaction called burning, some of the potential energy stored in its chemical bonds is converted to kinetic energy in the form of heat:

$$C_6H_{12}O_2 + 6\,O_2 \longrightarrow 6\,CO_2 + 6\,H_2O + \text{Heat}$$
$$\text{glucose} \quad \text{oxygen} \quad \text{carbon dioxide} \quad \text{water}$$

More specifically, a total of about 685 kilocalories (kcal) of heat is released when one mole of glucose is oxidized. To put this in perspective, if you burned this amount of glucose, it would give off enough heat to bring almost 2.5 gallons of room-temperature water to a boil.

Glucose does not burn in cells, however. Instead, the glucose in cells is oxidized through a long series of carefully controlled redox reactions. These reactions are occurring, millions of

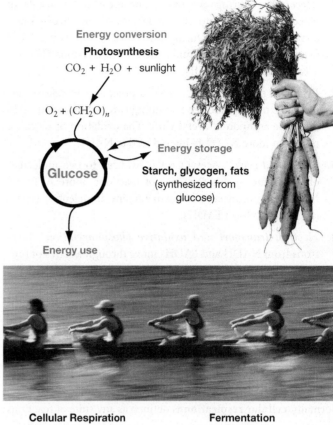

Energy conversion
Photosynthesis
$CO_2 + H_2O + \text{sunlight}$

$O_2 + (CH_2O)_n$

Glucose

Energy storage
Starch, glycogen, fats
(synthesized from glucose)

Energy use

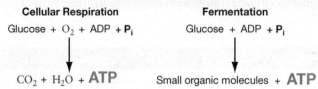

Cellular Respiration	Fermentation
Glucose + O_2 + ADP + P_i	Glucose + ADP + P_i
↓	↓
$CO_2 + H_2O$ + **ATP**	Small organic molecules + **ATP**

FIGURE 9.1 Glucose Is the Hub of Energy Processing in Cells. Glucose is a product of photosynthesis. Both plants and animals store glucose and oxidize it to provide chemical energy in the form of ATP.

times per minute, in your cells right now. Instead of releasing all of this energy as heat, much of it is being used to make the ATP you need to read, think, move, and stay alive. In cells, the change in free energy (Chapter 8) that occurs during the oxidation of glucose is used to synthesize ATP from ADP and P_i.

So how does fermentation differ from cellular respiration? Respiration, like burning, results in the complete oxidation of glucose into CO_2 and water. Fermentation, on the other hand, does not fully oxidize glucose. Instead, small, reduced organic molecules are produced as waste. As a result, cellular respiration releases more energy from glucose than fermentation.

The complete oxidation of glucose via cellular respiration can be thought of as a four-step process used to convert the chemical energy in glucose to chemical energy in ATP. Each of the four steps consists of a series of chemical reactions, and each step has a distinctive starting molecule and a characteristic set of products.

1. *Glycolysis* During **glycolysis,** one 6-carbon molecule of glucose is broken into two molecules of the three-carbon compound pyruvate. During this process, ATP is produced from ADP, and nicotinamide adenine dinucleotide (NAD^+) is reduced to form NADH.

2. *Pyruvate processing* Pyruvate is processed to release one molecule of CO_2, and the remaining two carbons are used to form the compound acetyl CoA. The oxidation of pyruvate results in more NAD^+ being reduced to NADH.

3. *Citric acid cycle* Acetyl CoA is oxidized to two molecules of CO_2. During this sequence of reactions, more ATP and NADH are produced, and flavin adenine dinucleotide (FAD) is reduced to form $FADH_2$.

4. *Electron transport and oxidative phosphorylation* Electrons from NADH and $FADH_2$ move through a series of proteins called an electron transport chain (ETC). The energy released in this chain of redox reactions is used to create a proton gradient across a membrane; the ensuing flow of protons back across the membrane is used to make ATP. Because this mode of ATP production links the phosphorylation of ADP with the oxidation of NADH and $FADH_2$, it is called **oxidative phosphorylation.**

FIGURE 9.2 summarizes the four steps in cellular respiration. Formally, **cellular respiration** is defined as any suite of reactions that uses electrons harvested from high-energy molecules to produce ATP via an electron transport chain.

The enzymes, products, and intermediates involved in cellular respiration and fermentation do not exist in isolation. Instead, they are part of a huge and dynamic inventory of chemicals inside the cell.

This complexity can be boiled down to a simple essence, however. Two of the most fundamental requirements of a cell are energy and carbon. They need a source of high-energy electrons for generating chemical energy in the form of ATP, and a source of carbon-containing molecules that can be used to synthesize DNA, RNA, proteins, fatty acids, and other molecules. Let's take a closer look at the central role cellular respiration plays in metabolic pathways as a whole.

Cellular Respiration Plays a Central Role in Metabolism

Recall that sets of reactions that break down molecules are called catabolic pathways (Chapter 8). These reactions often harvest stored chemical energy to produce ATP. On the other hand, sets of reactions that synthesize larger molecules from smaller components are called anabolic pathways. Anabolic reactions often use energy in the form of ATP.

How does the process of cellular respiration interact with other catabolic and anabolic pathways? Let's first consider how

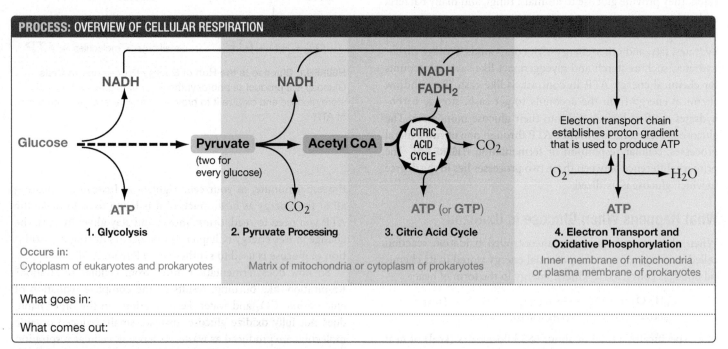

FIGURE 9.2 Cellular Respiration Oxidizes Glucose to Make ATP. Cells produce ATP from glucose via a series of processes: (1) glycolysis, (2) pyruvate processing, (3) the citric acid cycle, and (4) electron transport and oxidative phosphorylation. Each component produces high-energy molecules in the form of nucleotides (ATP or GTP) or electron carriers (NADH or $FADH_2$). Because the four components are connected, glucose oxidation is an integrated metabolic pathway. The first three steps oxidize glucose to produce NADH and $FADH_2$, which then feed the electron transport chain.

✔**EXERCISE** Fill in the chart along the bottom.

eukaryotes extract energy from molecules other than glucose and then examine how intermediates produced in glycolysis and the citric acid cycle are used as building blocks to synthesize cell components.

Catabolic Pathways Break Down a Variety of Molecules

Most organisms ingest, absorb, or synthesize many different carbohydrates. These molecules range from sucrose, maltose, and other simple sugars to large polymers such as glycogen and starch (see Chapter 5).

Recall that both glycogen and starch are polymers of glucose, but differ in the way their long chains of glucose branch. Using enzyme-catalyzed reactions, cells can produce glucose from glycogen, starch, and most simple sugars. Glucose and fructose can then be processed in glycolysis.

Carbohydrates are not the only important source of carbon compounds used in catabolic pathways, however. Fats are highly reduced macromolecules consisting of glycerol bonded to chains of fatty acids (see Chapter 6). In cells, enzymes routinely break down fats to release the glycerol and convert the fatty acids into acetyl CoA molecules. Glycerol can be further processed and enter glycolysis. Acetyl CoA enters the citric acid cycle.

Proteins can also be catabolized, meaning that they can be broken down and used to produce ATP. Once they are hydrolyzed to their constituent amino acids, enzyme-catalyzed reactions remove the amino ($-NH_2$) groups. The amino groups are excreted in urine as waste. The carbon compounds that remain are converted to pyruvate, acetyl CoA, and other intermediates in glycolysis and the citric acid cycle.

The top half of **FIGURE 9.3** summarizes the catabolic pathways of carbohydrates, fats, and proteins and shows how their breakdown products feed an array of steps in glucose oxidation and cellular respiration. When all three types of molecules are available in the cell to generate ATP, carbohydrates are used up first, then fats, and finally proteins.

Catabolic Intermediates Are Used in Anabolic Pathways

Where do cells get the precursor molecules required to synthesize amino acids, RNA, DNA, phospholipids, and other cell components? Not surprisingly, the answer often involves intermediates in carbohydrate metabolism. For example,

- In humans, about half the required amino acids can be synthesized from molecules siphoned from the citric acid cycle.

- Acetyl CoA is the starting point for anabolic pathways that result in the synthesis of fatty acids. Fatty acids can then be used to build phospholipid membranes or fats.

- Intermediates in glycolysis can be oxidized to start the synthesis of the sugars in ribonucleotides and deoxyribonucleotides. Nucleotides, in turn, are building blocks used in RNA and DNA synthesis.

- If ATP is abundant, pyruvate and lactate (from fermentation) can be used in the synthesis of glucose. Excess glucose may be converted to glycogen or starch and stored.

The bottom half of Figure 9.3 summarizes how intermediates in carbohydrate metabolism are drawn off to synthesize macromolecules. The take-home message is that the same molecule can serve many different functions in the cell. As a result, catabolic and anabolic pathways are closely intertwined.

Metabolism comprises thousands of different chemical reactions, yet the amounts and identities of molecules inside cells are relatively constant. By regulating key reactions involved in catabolic and anabolic pathways, the cell is able to maintain its internal environment even under different environmental conditions—a process referred to as **homeostasis.** Cellular respiration and

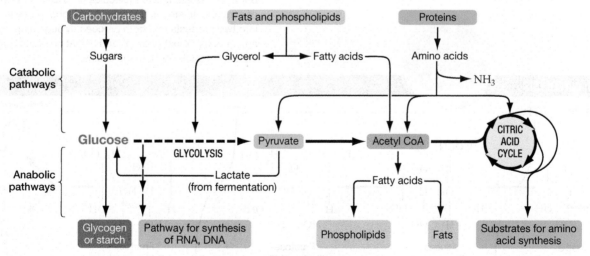

FIGURE 9.3 Cellular Respiration Interacts with Other Catabolic and Anabolic Pathways. A variety of high-energy compounds from carbohydrates, fats, or proteins can be broken down in catabolic reactions and used by cellular respiration for ATP production. Several of the intermediates in carbohydrate metabolism act as precursor molecules in anabolic reactions leading to the synthesis of glycogen or starch, RNA, DNA, fatty acids, and amino acids.

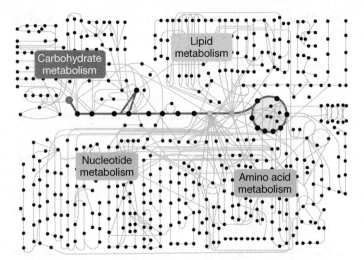

FIGURE 9.4 Pathways of Cellular Respiration Play a Central Role in the Metabolic Activity of Cells. A representation of a few of the thousands of chemical reactions that occur in cells. The dots represent molecules, and the lines represent enzyme-catalyzed reactions. At the center of all this, the first three steps of cellular respiration are emphasized by bold dots and thick lines. For reference, glucose, pyruvate, and acetyl CoA are represented by the distinctive colors used in Figure 9.3.

fermentation pathways may be crucial to the life of a cell, but they also have to be seen as central parts of a whole (**FIGURE 9.4**).

Once you've filled in the chart at the bottom of Figure 9.2, you'll be ready to analyze each of the four steps of cellular respiration in detail. As you delve in, keep asking yourself the same key questions: What goes in and what comes out? What happens to the potential energy that is released? Where does each step occur, and how is it regulated? Then take a look in the mirror. All these processes are occurring right now, in virtually all your cells.

9.2 Glycolysis: Processing Glucose to Pyruvate

Because the enzymes responsible for glycolysis have been observed in nearly every bacterium, archaean, and eukaryote, it is logical to infer that the ancestor of all organisms living today made ATP by glycolysis. It's ironic, then, that the process was discovered by accident.

In the 1890s Hans and Edward Buchner were working out techniques for breaking open baker's yeast cells and extracting the contents for commercial and medicinal use. (Yeast extracts are still added to some foods as a flavor enhancer or nutritional supplement.) In one set of experiments, the Buchners added sucrose to their extracts. At the time, sucrose was commonly used as a preservative—a substance used to preserve food from decay.

Instead of preserving the yeast extracts, though, the sucrose was quickly broken down and fermented, and alcohol appeared as a by-product. This was a key finding: It showed that metabolic pathways like fermentation could be studied in vitro—outside the organism. Until then, researchers thought that metabolism could take place only in intact organisms.

When researchers studied how the sugar was being processed, they found that the reactions could go on much longer than normal if inorganic phosphate were added to the mixture. This result implied that some of the compounds involved were being phosphorylated. Soon after, a molecule called fructose bisphosphate was isolated. (The prefix *bis*– means that the phosphate groups are attached to the fructose molecule at two different locations.) Subsequent work showed that all but the starting

FIGURE 9.5 Glycolysis Pathway. This sequence of 10 reactions oxidizes glucose to pyruvate. Each reaction is catalyzed by a different enzyme to produce two net ATP (4 ATP are produced, but 2 are invested), two molecules of NADH, and two molecules of pyruvate. In step 4, fructose-1,6-bisphosphate is divided into two products that both proceed through steps 6–10. The amounts for "What goes in" and "What goes out" are the combined totals for both molecules.

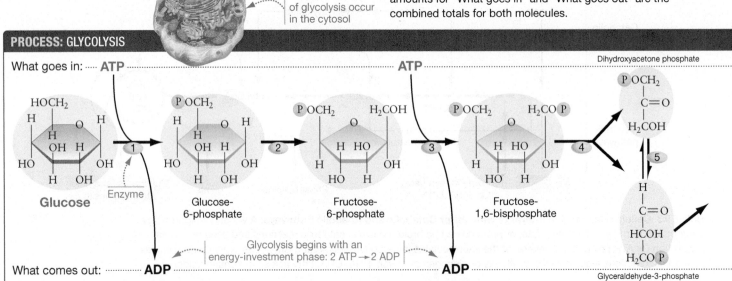

All 10 reactions of glycolysis occur in the cytosol

PROCESS: GLYCOLYSIS

What goes in: ···· **ATP** ·· **ATP** ········

Glucose → Glucose-6-phosphate → Fructose-6-phosphate → Fructose-1,6-bisphosphate → Dihydroxyacetone phosphate / Glyceraldehyde-3-phosphate

Glycolysis begins with an energy-investment phase: 2 ATP → 2 ADP

What comes out: ··········· **ADP** ···················· **ADP** ·····

and ending molecules in glycolysis—glucose and pyruvate—are phosphorylated.

In 1905 researchers found that the processing of sugar by yeast extracts stopped if they boiled the reaction mix. Because it was known that enzymes could be inactivated by heat, their discovery suggested that enzymes were involved in at least some of the processing steps. Years later, investigators realized that each step in glycolysis is catalyzed by a different enzyme. Eventually, each of the reactions and enzymes involved was worked out.

Glycolysis Is a Sequence of 10 Reactions

In both eukaryotes and prokaryotes, all 10 reactions of glycolysis occur in the cytosol (**FIGURE 9.5**). Note three key points about this reaction sequence:

1. Glycolysis starts by *using* ATP, not producing it. In the initial step, glucose is phosphorylated to form glucose-6-phosphate. After the second reaction rearranges the sugar to form fructose-6-phosphate, the third reaction adds a second phosphate group, forming the fructose-1,6-bisphosphate observed by early researchers. Thus, two ATP molecules are used up before any ATP is produced.

2. Once the energy-investment phase of glycolysis is complete, the subsequent reactions represent an energy-payoff phase. The sixth reaction in the sequence results in the reduction of two molecules of $NAD^{\boxtimes}$; the seventh produces two molecules of ATP. This is where the energy "debt"—of two molecules of ATP invested early in glycolysis—is paid off. The final reaction in the sequence produces another two ATPs. For each molecule of glucose processed, the net yield is two molecules of NADH, two of ATP, and two of pyruvate.

3. In reactions 7 and 10 of Figure 9.5, an enzyme catalyzes the transfer of a phosphate group from a phosphorylated substrate to ADP, forming ATP. Enzyme-catalyzed reactions that result in

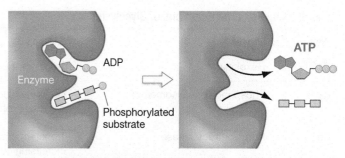

FIGURE 9.6 Substrate-Level Phosphorylation Involves an Enzyme and a Phosphorylated Substrate. Substrate-level phosphorylation occurs when an enzyme catalyzes the transfer of a phosphate group from a phosphorylated substrate to ADP, forming ATP.

ATP production are termed **substrate-level phosphorylation** (**FIGURE 9.6**). The key idea to note here is that the energy to produce the ATP comes from the phosphorylated substrate—not from a proton gradient, as it does when ATP is produced by oxidative phosphorylation.

The discovery and elucidation of the glycolytic pathway ranks as one of the great achievements in the history of biochemistry. For more detail concerning the enzymes that catalyze each step, see **TABLE 9.1** (on page 160). While the catabolism of glucose can occur via other pathways, this set of reactions is among the most ancient and fundamental of all life processes.

How Is Glycolysis Regulated?

An important advance in understanding how glycolysis is regulated occurred when biologists observed that high levels of ATP inhibit a key glycolytic enzyme called phosphofructokinase. **Phosphofructokinase** catalyzes reaction 3 in Figure 9.5—the synthesis of fructose-1,6-bisphosphate from fructose-6-phosphate. This is a crucial step in the sequence.

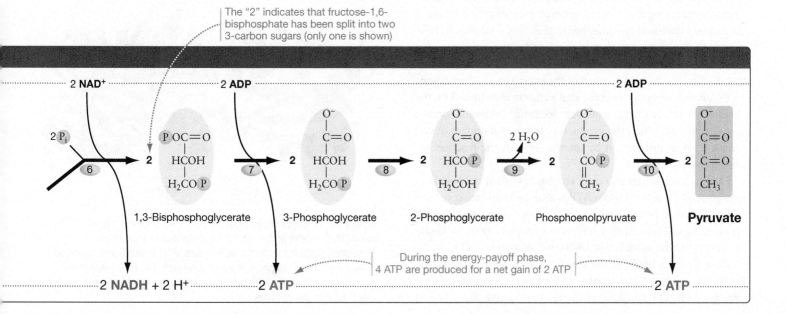

The "2" indicates that fructose-1,6-bisphosphate has been split into two 3-carbon sugars (only one is shown)

1,3-Bisphosphoglycerate   3-Phosphoglycerate   2-Phosphoglycerate   Phosphoenolpyruvate   **Pyruvate**

During the energy-payoff phase, 4 ATP are produced for a net gain of 2 ATP

2 NADH + 2 H⁺   2 ATP   2 ATP

Step	Enzyme	Reaction
1	Hexokinase	Transfers a phosphate from **ATP** to glucose, increasing its potential energy.
2	Phosphoglucose isomerase	Converts glucose-6-phosphate to fructose-6-phosphate; referred to as an isomer of glucose-6-phosphate.
3	Phosphofructokinase	Transfers a phosphate from **ATP** to the opposite end of fructose-6-phosphate, increasing its potential energy.
4	Fructose-bis-phosphate aldolase	Cleaves fructose-1,6-bisphosphate into two different 3-carbon sugars.
5	Triose phosphate isomerase	Converts dihydroxyacetone phosphate (DAP) to glyceraldehyde-3-phosphate (G3P). Although the reaction is fully reversible, the DAP-to-G3P reaction is favored because G3P is immediately used as a substrate for step 6.
6	Glyceraldehyde-3-phosphate dehydrogenase	A two-step reaction that first oxidizes G3P using the **NAD$^{\boxtimes}$** coenzyme to produce **NADH**. Energy from this reaction is used to attach a P_i to the oxidized product to form 1,3-bisphosphoglycerate.
7	Phosphoglycerate kinase	Transfers a phosphate from 1,3-bisphosphoglycerate to **ADP** to make 3-phosphoglycerate and **ATP**.
8	Phosphoglycerate mutase	Rearranges the phosphate in 3-phosphoglycerate to make 2-phosphoglycerate.
9	Enolase	Removes a water molecule from 2-phosphoglycerate to form a C=C double bond and produce phosphoenolpyruvate.
10	Pyruvate kinase	Transfers a phosphate from phosphoenolpyruvate to **ADP** to make pyruvate and **ATP**.

After reactions 1 and 2 occur, an array of enzymes can reverse the process and regenerate glucose for use in other pathways. Before step 3, then, the sequence is not committed to glycolysis. But once fructose-1,6-bisphosphate is synthesized, there is no point in stopping the process. Based on these observations, it makes sense that the pathway is regulated at step 3. How do cells do it?

As shown in Figure 9.5, ATP serves as a substrate for the addition of a phosphate to fructose-6-phosphate. In the vast majority of cases, increasing the concentration of a substrate would *speed* the rate of a chemical reaction, but in this case, it inhibits it. Why would ATP—a substrate that is required for the reaction—also serve as an inhibitor of the reaction? The answer lies in the fact that ATP is also the end product of the overall catabolic pathway.

Recall that when an enzyme in a pathway is inhibited by the product of the reaction sequence, feedback inhibition occurs (see Chapter 8). When the product molecule is abundant, it can inhibit its own production by interfering with the reaction sequence used to create it.

Feedback inhibition increases efficiency. Cells that are able to stop glycolytic reactions when ATP is abundant can conserve their stores of glucose for times when ATP is scarce. As a result, natural selection should favor individuals who have phosphofructokinase molecules that are inhibited by high concentrations of ATP.

How do high levels of the substrate inhibit the enzyme? As **FIGURE 9.7** shows, phosphofructokinase has two distinct binding sites for ATP. ATP can bind at the enzyme's active site, where it

is used to phosphorylate fructose-6-phosphate, or at a regulatory site, where it turns off the enzyme's activity.

The key to feedback inhibition lies in the ability of the two sites to bind to ATP. When concentrations are low, ATP binds

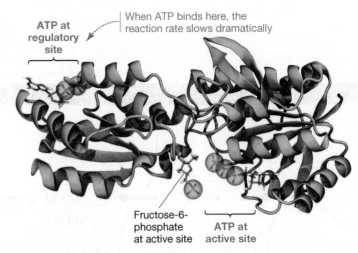

FIGURE 9.7 Phosphofructokinase Has Two Binding Sites for ATP. A model of one of the four identical subunits of phosphofructokinase. In the active site, ATP is used as a substrate to transfer one of its phosphate groups to fructose-6-phosphate. In the regulatory site, ATP binding inhibits the reaction by changing the shape of the enzyme.

only to the active site, which has a greater affinity for ATP than does the regulatory site. As ATP concentrations increase, however, it also binds at the regulatory site on phosphofructokinase. When ATP binds at this second location, the enzyme's conformation changes in a way that dramatically lowers the reaction rate at the active site. In phosphofructokinase, ATP acts as an allosteric regulator (see Chapter 8). ✔ If you understand the principle behind the difference in affinity between the two ATP binding sites, you should be able to predict the consequences if the regulatory site had higher affinity for ATP than the active site did.

To summarize, glycolysis starts with one 6-carbon glucose molecule and ends with two 3-carbon pyruvate molecules. The reactions occur in the cytoplasm, and the energy that is released is used to produce a net total of two ATP and two NADH. Now the question is, what happens to the pyruvate?

9.3 Processing Pyruvate to Acetyl CoA

In eukaryotes, the pyruvate produced by glycolysis is transported from the cytosol to mitochondria. Mitochondria are organelles found in virtually all eukaryotes (see Chapter 7).

As shown in **FIGURE 9.8**, mitochondria have two membranes, called the inner membrane and outer membrane. The interior of the organelle is filled with layers of sac-like structures called **cristae.** Short tubes connect the cristae to the main part of the inner membrane. The region inside the inner membrane but outside the cristae is the **mitochondrial matrix.**

Pyruvate moves across the mitochondrion's outer membrane through small pores, but how it is transported across the inner membrane is still unclear. Current research suggests that either pyruvate is transported directly into the matrix using an unknown transporter, or it is converted first into lactate, transported across the membrane, and then converted back into pyruvate.

Inside the mitochondrion, pyruvate reacts with a compound called **coenzyme A (CoA).** Coenzyme A is sometimes abbreviated as CoA-SH to call attention to its key sulfhydryl functional group. In this and many other reactions, CoA acts as a coenzyme by accepting and then transferring an acetyl group ($-COCH_3$) to a substrate (the A stands for acetylation). Pyruvate reacts with CoA, through a series of steps, to produce **acetyl CoA.**

The reaction sequence occurs inside an enormous and intricate enzyme complex called **pyruvate dehydrogenase.** In eukaryotes, pyruvate dehydrogenase is located in the mitochondrial matrix. In bacteria and archaea, pyruvate dehydrogenase is located in the cytosol.

As pyruvate is being processed, one of the carbons in the pyruvate is oxidized to CO_2 and $NAD^{\boxtimes}$ is reduced to NADH. The remaining two-carbon acetyl unit is transferred to CoA (**FIGURE 9.9**).

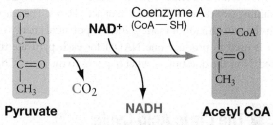

FIGURE 9.9 Pyruvate Is Oxidized to Acetyl CoA. The reaction shown here is catalyzed by pyruvate dehydrogenase.

✔**EXERCISE** Above the reaction arrow, list three molecules whose presence speeds up the reaction. Label them "Positive control." Below the reaction arrow, list three molecules whose presence slows down the reaction. Label them "Negative control by feedback inhibition."

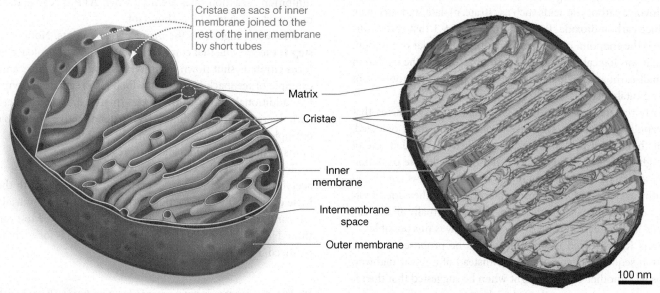

FIGURE 9.8 The Structure of the Mitochondrion. Mitochondria have outer and inner membranes that define the intermembrane space and matrix. Pyruvate processing occurs within the mitochondrial matrix. Recent research using cryo-electron tomography (the colorized micrograph on the right) shows the inner membrane is connected by short tubes to sac-like cristae.

Acetyl CoA is the final product of the pyruvate-processing step in glucose oxidation. Pyruvate, NAD^+, and CoA go in; CO_2, NADH, and acetyl CoA come out.

When supplies of ATP are abundant, however, the process shuts down. Pyruvate processing stops when the pyruvate dehydrogenase complex becomes phosphorylated and changes shape. The rate of phosphorylation increases when other products—specifically acetyl CoA and NADH—are at high concentration.

These regulatory changes are more examples of feedback inhibition. Reaction products feed back to stop or slow down the pathway.

On the contrary, high concentrations of NAD^+, CoA, or adenosine monophosphate (AMP)—which indicates low ATP supplies—*speed up* the reactions catalyzed by the pyruvate dehydrogenase complex.

Pyruvate processing is under both positive and negative control. Large supplies of products inhibit the enzyme complex; large supplies of reactants and low supplies of products stimulate it.

To summarize, pyruvate processing starts with the three-carbon pyruvate molecule and ends with one carbon released as CO_2 and the remaining two carbons in the form of acetyl CoA. The reactions occur in the mitochondrial matrix, and the potential energy that is released is used to produce one NADH for each pyruvate that is processed. Now the question is, what happens to the acetyl CoA?

9.4 The Citric Acid Cycle: Oxidizing Acetyl CoA to CO_2

While researchers were working out the sequence of reactions in glycolysis, biologists in other laboratories were focusing on redox reactions that oxidize small organic acids called **carboxylic acids**. Note that carboxylic acids all have carboxyl functional groups (R-COOH), hence the name.

A key finding emerged from their studies: Redox reactions that involve carboxylic acids such as citrate, malate, and succinate produce carbon dioxide. Recall from Section 9.1 that carbon dioxide is the endpoint of glucose oxidation via cellular respiration. Thus, it was logical for researchers to propose that the oxidation of small carboxylic acids could be an important component of glucose catabolism.

Early researchers identified eight small carboxylic acids that are rapidly oxidized in sequence, from least to most oxidized. What they found next was puzzling. When they added one of the eight carboxylic acids to cells, the rate of glucose oxidation increased, suggesting that the reactions are somehow connected to pathways involved in glucose catabolism. But, the added molecules did not appear to be used up. Instead, virtually all the carboxylic acids added were recovered later. How is this possible?

Hans Krebs solved the mystery when he proposed that the reaction sequence occurs in a cycle instead of a linear pathway. Krebs had another crucial insight when he suggested that the reaction sequence was directly tied to the processing of pyruvate—the endpoint of the glycolytic pathway.

To test these hypotheses, Krebs and a colleague set out to determine if adding pyruvate could link the two ends of the sequence of eight carboxylic acids. If pyruvate is the key link in forming a cycle, it would need to be involved in the conversion of oxaloacetate, the most oxidized of the eight carboxylic acids, to citrate, the most reduced carboxylic acid. When Krebs added pyruvate, the series of redox reactions occurred. The conclusion? The sequence of eight carboxylic acids is indeed arranged in a cycle (**FIGURE 9.10**).

Many biologists now refer to the cycle as the **citric acid cycle** because it starts with citrate, which is the salt of citric acid after the protons are released. The citric acid cycle is also known as the tricarboxylic acid (TCA) cycle, because citrate has three carboxyl groups, and also as the Krebs cycle, after its discoverer.

When radioactive isotopes of carbon became available in the early 1940s, researchers showed that carbon atoms cycle through the reactions just as Krebs had proposed. For more detail concerning the enzymes that catalyze each step, see **TABLE 9.2** (on page 164). In each cycle, the energy released by the oxidation of one molecule of acetyl CoA is used to produce three molecules of NADH, one of $FADH_2$, and one of **guanosine triphosphate (GTP),** or ATP, through substrate-level phosphorylation. Whether GTP or ATP is produced depends on the type of cell being considered.[1] For example, GTP appears to be produced in the liver cells of mammals, while ATP is produced in muscle cells.

In bacteria and archaea, the enzymes responsible for the citric acid cycle are located in the cytosol. In eukaryotes, most of the enzymes responsible for the citric acid cycle are located in the mitochondrial matrix. Because glycolysis produces two molecules of pyruvate, the cycle turns twice for each molecule of glucose processed in cellular respiration.

How Is the Citric Acid Cycle Regulated?

By now, it shouldn't surprise you to learn that the citric acid cycle is carefully regulated. The citric acid cycle can be turned off at multiple points, via several different mechanisms of feedback inhibition. Reaction rates are high when ATP is scarce; reaction rates are low when ATP is abundant.

FIGURE 9.11 highlights the major control points. Notice that in step 1, the enzyme that combines acetyl CoA and oxaloacetate to form citrate is shut down when ATP binds to it. This is another example of feedback inhibition, which also regulates enzymes at two additional points in the cycle. In step 3, NADH interferes with the reaction by binding to the enzyme's active site. This is an example of competitive inhibition (see Chapter 8). In step 4, ATP binds to the enzyme at an allosteric regulatory site.

To summarize, the citric acid cycle starts with the two-carbon acetyl molecule in the form of acetyl CoA and ends with the release of two CO_2. The reactions occur in the mitochondrial matrix, and the potential energy that is released is used to produce three NADH, one $FADH_2$, and one ATP or GTP for each acetyl oxidized. But a major question remains.

[1]Traditionally it was thought that the citric acid cycle produced GTP, which was later converted to ATP in the same cell. Recent work suggests that ATP is produced directly in some cell types, while GTP is produced in other cells. See C. O. Lambeth, Reconsideration of the significance of substrate-level phosphorylation in the citric acid cycle. *Biochemistry and Molecular Biology Education* 34 (2006): 21–29.

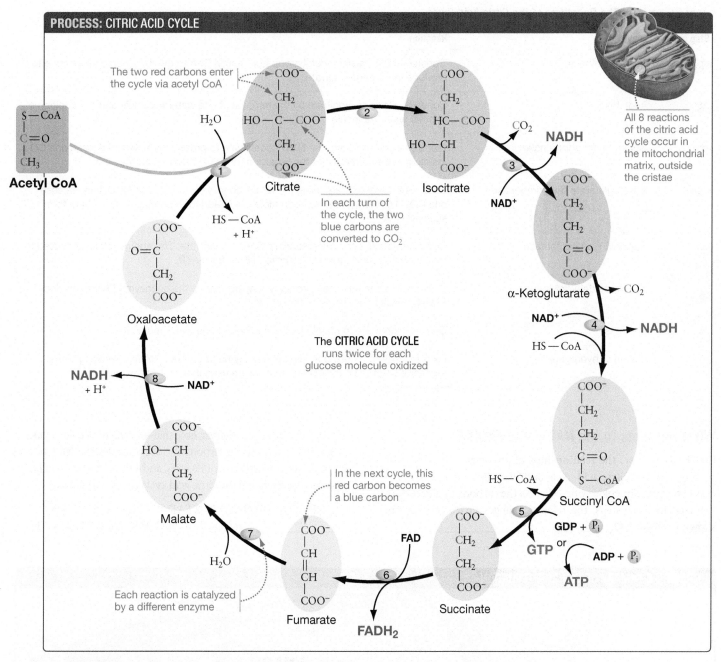

The two red carbons enter the cycle via acetyl CoA

H_2O

$HO-C-COO^-$ ... **Citrate**

In each turn of the cycle, the two blue carbons are converted to CO_2

Acetyl CoA

$HS-CoA$ + H^+

Oxaloacetate

The **CITRIC ACID CYCLE** runs twice for each glucose molecule oxidized

All 8 reactions of the citric acid cycle occur in the mitochondrial matrix, outside the cristae

Isocitrate

CO_2

NADH

NAD^+

α-Ketoglutarate

CO_2

NAD^+

$HS-CoA$

NADH

Succinyl CoA

NADH + H^+ — NAD^+

Malate

H_2O

In the next cycle, this red carbon becomes a blue carbon

$HS-CoA$

GDP + P_i

GTP or

ADP + P_i

ATP

FAD

Succinate

Fumarate

FADH_2

Each reaction is catalyzed by a different enzyme

FIGURE 9.10 The Citric Acid Cycle Completes the Oxidation of Glucose. Acetyl CoA goes into the citric acid cycle, and carbon dioxide, NADH, FADH_2, and GTP or ATP come out. GTP or ATP is produced by substrate-level phosphorylation. If you follow individual carbon atoms around the cycle several times, you'll come to an important conclusion: each of the carbons in the cycle is eventually a "blue carbon" that is released as CO_2.

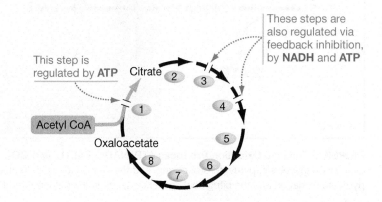

This step is regulated by **ATP**

These steps are also regulated via feedback inhibition, by **NADH** and **ATP**

Citrate

Acetyl CoA

Oxaloacetate

FIGURE 9.11 The Citric Acid Cycle Is Regulated by Feedback Inhibition. The citric acid cycle slows down when ATP and NADH are plentiful. ATP acts as an allosteric regulator, while NADH acts as a competitive inhibitor.

Step	Enzyme	Reaction
1	Citrate synthase	Transfers the 2-carbon acetyl group from acetyl CoA to the 4-carbon oxaloacetate to produce the 6-carbon citrate.
2	Aconitase	Converts citrate to isocitrate by the removal of one water molecule and the addition of another water molecule.
3	Isocitrate dehydrogenase	Oxidizes isocitrate using the **NAD**⊠ coenzyme to produce **NADH** and release one CO_2, resulting in the formation of the 5-carbon molecule ⊠-ketoglutarate.
4	⊠-Ketoglutarate dehydrogenase	Oxidizes ⊠-ketoglutarate using the **NAD**⊠ coenzyme to produce **NADH** and release one CO_2. The remaining 4-carbon molecule is added to coenzyme A (CoA) to form succinyl CoA.
5	Succinyl-CoA synthetase	CoA is removed, converting succinyl CoA to succinate. The energy released is used to transfer P_i to GDP to form **GTP**, or to ADP to form **ATP**.
6	Succinate dehydrogenase	Oxidizes succinate by transferring two hydrogens to the coenzyme **FAD** to produce **FADH₂**, resulting in the formation of fumarate.
7	Fumarase	Converts fumarate to malate by the addition of one water molecule.
8	Malate dehydrogenase	Oxidizes malate by using the **NAD**⊠ coenzyme to produce **NADH**, resulting in the regeneration of the oxaloacetate that will be used in step 1 of the cycle.

What Happens to the NADH and FADH₂?

FIGURE 9.12 reviews the relationships of glycolysis, pyruvate processing, and the citric acid cycle and identifies where each process takes place in eukaryotic cells. As the carbons in glucose are oxidized in these steps, the relative changes in free energy are shown in **FIGURE 9.13**.

As you study these figures, note that for each molecule of glucose that is fully oxidized to 6 carbon dioxide molecules, the cell produces 10 molecules of NADH, 2 of FADH₂, and 4 of ATP. The overall reaction for glycolysis and the citric acid cycle can be written as

$$C_6H_{12}O_2 \boxtimes 10\ NAD^\boxtimes \boxtimes 2\ FAD \boxtimes 4\ ADP \boxtimes 4\ P_i \longrightarrow$$
$$6\ CO_2 \boxtimes 10\ NADH \boxtimes 2\ FADH_2 \boxtimes 4\ ATP$$

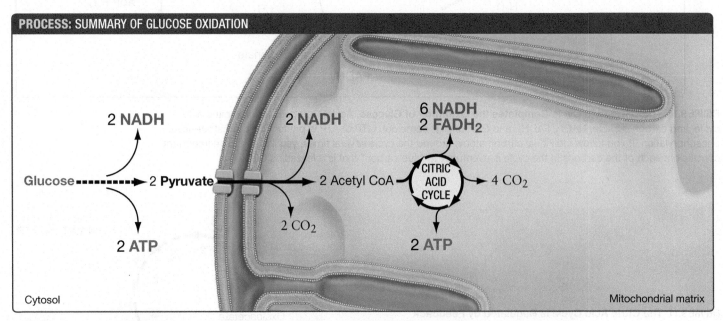

PROCESS: SUMMARY OF GLUCOSE OXIDATION

FIGURE 9.12 Glucose Oxidation Produces ATP, NADH, FADH₂, and CO₂. Glucose is completely oxidized to carbon dioxide via glycolysis, pyruvate processing, and the citric acid cycle. In eukaryotes, glycolysis occurs in the cytosol; pyruvate oxidation and the citric acid cycle take place in the mitochondrial matrix.

Cellular Respiration   10/02/14
      —A series of reaction

     4 steps :
1) Glycolysis.
2) Pyruvate processing
3) Citric acid cycle

after this 3 steps Glucose are broken

Glycolysis Reaction .

Glycolysis consist of
   —energy investment phase
   —energy payoff phase

answer → Cellular Respiration & Glycolysis
1) Glucose
2) Carbon dioxide & Water.
3) Glycolysis, Pyruvate Processing, Critic acid cycle
4) Carbohydrates, fates, Protein
5) Catabolic - break down of molecules
     Anabolic
6) • Substrate - Glucose
   • Product - Pyruvate
   • where - Cytoplasm (cytosol.
7) Energy -
8) Substrate -level Phosphorylation
   -Oxydative phosphorylation

Glucose Oxidation answers.

1)
2) They carring electron
3) ATP, NADH, CO_2
* 4) Sirocoin
5)
6) ~~Prote~~ Mitocondria

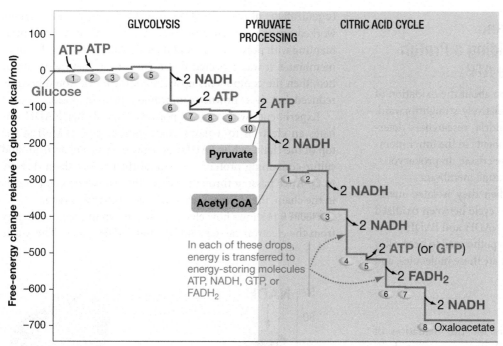

FIGURE 9.13 Free Energy Changes as Glucose Is Oxidized. If you read the vertical axis of this graph carefully, it should convince you that about 685 kcal/mol of free energy is released from the oxidation of glucose. Much of the energy is harnessed in the form of ATP, NADH, and FADH₂. The numbered green ovals identify the reaction steps in glycolysis and the citric acid cycle (see Tables 9.1 and 9.2).

DATA: Li, X., R. K. Dash, R. K. Pradhan, et al. 2010. *Journal of Physical Chemistry B.* 114: 16068–16082.

✔ QUANTITATIVE Based on the data in this graph, which of the three high-energy molecules produced during glucose oxidation would you expect to carry the highest amount of chemical energy? Justify your answer.

The ATP molecules are produced by substrate-level phosphorylation and can be used to drive endergonic reactions. The CO_2 molecules are a gas that is disposed of as waste—you exhale it; plants release it or use it as a reactant in photosynthesis.

What happens to the NADH and FADH₂ produced by glycolysis, pyruvate processing, and the citric acid cycle? Recall that the overall reaction for glucose oxidation is

$$C_6H_{12}O_6 + 6\,O_2 \longrightarrow 6\,CO_2 + 6\,H_2O + Energy$$

These three steps account for the glucose, the CO_2, and—because ATP is produced—some of the chemical energy that results from the overall reaction. But the O_2 and the H_2O are still unaccounted for. As it turns out, so is much of the chemical energy. The reaction that has yet to occur is

$$NADH + FADH_2 + O_2 + ADP + P_i \longrightarrow$$
$$NAD^+ + FAD + 2\,H_2O + ATP$$

In the above reaction, the electrons from NADH and FADH₂ are transferred to oxygen. NADH and FADH₂ are oxidized to NAD^+ and FAD, and oxygen is reduced to form water.

In effect, glycolysis, pyruvate processing, and the citric acid cycle transfer electrons from glucose to NAD^+ and FAD to form NADH and FADH₂. When oxygen accepts electrons from these reduced molecules, water is produced.

At this point, all the components of the overall reaction for glucose oxidation are accounted for, except for the energy. What happens to the energy that is released as electrons are transferred from NADH and FADH₂ to the highly electronegative oxygen atoms?

Specifically, how is the transfer of electrons linked to the production of ATP? In the 1960s—decades after the details of glycolysis and the citric acid cycle had been worked out—a startling answer to these questions emerged.

check your understanding

If you understand that . . .

- During glycolysis, glucose is oxidized to pyruvate, in the cytosol.
- During pyruvate processing, pyruvate is oxidized to acetyl CoA, in the mitochondrial matrix.
- In the citric acid cycle, the acetyl from acetyl CoA is oxidized to carbon dioxide (CO_2), in the mitochondrial matrix.
- Glycolysis, pyruvate processing, and the citric acid cycle are all regulated processes. The cell produces ATP only when ATP is needed.

✔ **You should be able to . . .**

Model the following components of cellular respiration by pretending that a large piece of paper is a cell. Draw a large mitochondrion inside it. Cut out small circles of paper and label them glucose, pyruvate, acetyl CoA, CO_2, ADP → ATP, NAD^+ → NADH, and FAD → FADH₂. Cut out small squares of paper and label them as glycolytic reactions, citric acid cycle reactions, and pyruvate dehydrogenase complex.

1. Put each of the squares in the appropriate location in the cell.
2. Add the circles and draw arrows to connect the appropriate molecules and reactions.
3. Using 12 paper triangles for pairs of electrons, show how electrons from glucose are transferred to NADH or FADH₂ (one pair should go to each NADH or FADH₂ formed) as glucose is oxidized to CO_2.
4. Label points where regulation occurs.

Answers are available in Appendix A.

9.5 Electron Transport and Chemiosmosis: Building a Proton Gradient to Produce ATP

The answer to one fundamental question about the oxidation of NADH and $FADH_2$ turned out to be relatively straightforward. By isolating different parts of mitochondria, researchers determined that NADH is oxidized by components in the inner membrane of the mitochondria, including the cristae. In prokaryotes, the oxidation of NADH occurs in the plasma membrane.

Biologists made a key discovery when they isolated membrane components—they were found to cycle between oxidized and reduced states after the addition of NADH and $FADH_2$. The membrane-associated molecules were hypothesized to be the key to processing NADH and $FADH_2$. What are these molecules, and how do they work?

The Electron Transport Chain

Collectively, the molecules responsible for the oxidation of NADH and $FADH_2$ are designated the **electron transport chain (ETC)**. As electrons are passed from one molecule to another in the chain, the energy released by the redox reactions is used to move protons across the inner membrane of mitochondria.

Several points are fundamental to understanding how the ETC works:

- Most of the molecules are proteins that contain distinctive cofactors and prosthetic groups where the redox events take place (see Chapter 8). They include iron–sulfur complexes, ring-containing structures called flavins, or iron-containing heme groups called cytochromes. Each of these groups is readily reduced or oxidized.

- The inner membrane of the mitochondrion also contains a molecule called **ubiquinone**, which is not a protein. Ubiquinone got its name because it is nearly ubiquitous in organisms and belongs to a family of compounds called quinones. Also called **coenzyme Q** or simply Q, ubiquinone is lipid soluble and moves efficiently throughout the hydrophobic interior of the inner mitochondrial membrane.

- The molecules involved in processing NADH and $FADH_2$ differ in electronegativity, or their tendency to hold electrons. Some of the molecules pick up a proton with each electron, forming hydrogen atoms, while others obtain only electrons.

Because Q and the ETC proteins can cycle between a reduced state and an oxidized state, and because they differ in electronegativity, investigators realized that it should be possible to arrange them into a logical sequence. The idea was that electrons would pass from a molecule with lower electronegativity to one with higher electronegativity, via a redox reaction.

As electrons moved through the chain, they would be held more and more tightly. A small amount of energy would be released in each reaction, and the potential energy in each successive bond would lessen.

Organization of the Electron Transport Chain Researchers worked out the sequence of compounds in the ETC by experimenting with poisons that inhibit particular proteins in the inner membrane. It was expected that if part of the chain were inhibited, then the components upstream of the block would become reduced, but those downstream would remain oxidized.

Experiments with various poisons showed that NADH donates an electron to a flavin-containing protein (FMN) at the top of the chain, while $FADH_2$ donates electrons to an iron- and sulfur-containing protein (Fe·S) that then passes them directly to Q. After passing through each of the remaining components in the chain, the electrons are finally accepted by oxygen.

FIGURE 9.14 shows how electrons step down in potential energy from the electron carriers NADH and $FADH_2$ to O_2. The x-axis

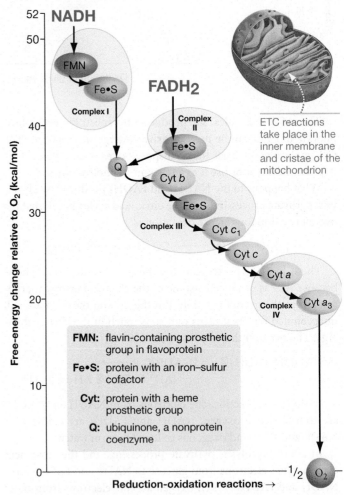

ETC reactions take place in the inner membrane and cristae of the mitochondrion

FMN: flavin-containing prosthetic group in flavoprotein

Fe•S: protein with an iron–sulfur cofactor

Cyt: protein with a heme prosthetic group

Q: ubiquinone, a nonprotein coenzyme

Reduction-oxidation reactions →

FIGURE 9.14 A Series of Reduction–Oxidation Reactions Occur in an Electron Transport Chain. Electrons step down in potential energy from the electron carriers NADH and $FADH_2$ through an electron transport chain to a final electron acceptor. When oxygen is the final electron acceptor, water is formed. The overall free-energy change of 52 kcal/mol (from NADH to oxygen) is broken into small steps.

DATA: Wilson D. F., M. Erecinska, and P. L. Dutton. 1974. *Annual Review of Biophysics and Bioengineering* 3: 203–230. Also Sled, V. D., N. I. Rudnitzky, Y. Hatefi, et al. 1994. *Biochemistry* 33: 10069–10075.

plots the sequence of redox reactions in the ETC; the y-axis plots the free-energy changes that occur.

The components of the electron transport chain are organized into four large complexes of proteins, often referred to as simply complexes I–IV. Q and the protein **cytochrome *c*** act as shuttles that transfer electrons between these complexes. Once the electrons at the bottom of the ETC are accepted by oxygen to form water, the oxidation of glucose is complete. Details on the names of the complexes and their role in the electron transport chain are provided in **TABLE 9.3** (on page 168).

Under controlled conditions in the laboratory, the total potential energy difference from NADH to oxygen is a whopping 53 kilocalories/mole (kcal/mol). Oxidation of the 10 molecules of NADH produced from each glucose accounts for almost 80 percent of the total energy released from the sugar. What does the ETC do with all this energy?

Role of the Electron Transport Chain Throughout the 1950s most biologists working on cellular respiration assumed that electron transport chains include enzymes that catalyze substrate-level phosphorylation. Recall that when substrate-level

phosphorylation occurs, a phosphate group is transferred from a phosphorylated substrate to ADP, forming ATP. Despite intense efforts, however, no one was able to find an enzyme among the components of the ETC that would catalyze the phosphorylation of ADP to produce ATP.

What researchers did find, however, is that the movement of electrons through the ETC actively transports protons from the matrix, across the inner membrane, and into the intermembrane space (see **FIGURE 9.15**). The exact route and mechanism used to pump protons is still being worked out. In some cases, it is not clear how the redox reactions taking place inside each complex result in the movement of protons.

The best-understood interaction between electron transport and proton transport takes place in complex III. Research has shown that when Q accepts electrons from complex I or complex II, it picks up protons from the matrix side of the inner membrane. The reduced form of Q then diffuses through the inner

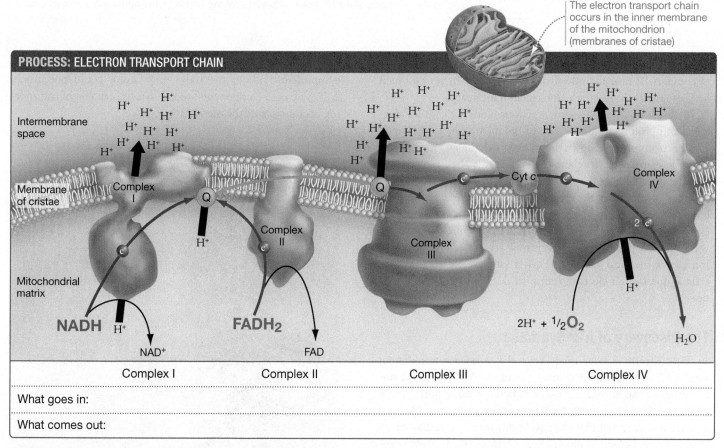

The electron transport chain occurs in the inner membrane of the mitochondrion (membranes of cristae)

PROCESS: ELECTRON TRANSPORT CHAIN

	Complex I	Complex II	Complex III	Complex IV
What goes in:				
What comes out:				

FIGURE 9.15 How Does the Electron Transport Chain Work? The individual components of the electron transport chain diagrammed in Figure 9.14 are found in the inner membrane of mitochondria. Electrons are carried from one complex to another by Q and by cytochrome *c*; Q also shuttles protons across the membrane. The orange arrow indicates Q moving back and forth. Complexes I and IV use the potential energy released by the redox reactions to pump protons from the mitochondrial matrix to the intermembrane space.

✔**EXERCISE** Add an arrow across the membrane and label it "Proton gradient." In the boxes at the bottom, list "What goes in" and "What comes out" for each complex.

ETC Component	Descriptive Name	Reaction
Complex I	NADH dehydrogenase	Oxidizes **NADH** and transfers the two electrons through proteins containing FMN prosthetic groups and Fe·S cofactors to reduce an oxidized form of ubiquinone (Q). Four $H^\boxtimes$ are pumped out of the matrix to the intermembrane space.
Complex II	Succinate dehydrogenase	Oxidizes **FADH$_2$** and transfers the two electrons through proteins containing Fe·S cofactors to reduce an oxidized form of Q. This complex is also used in step 6 of the citric acid cycle.
Q	Ubiquinone	Reduced by complexes I and II and moves throughout the hydrophobic interior of the ETC membrane, where it is oxidized by complex III.
Complex III	Cytochrome c reductase	Oxidizes Q and transfers one electron at a time through proteins containing heme prosthetic groups and Fe·S cofactors to reduce an oxidized form of cytochrome c (cyt c). A total of four $H^\boxtimes$ for each pair of electrons is transported from the matrix to the intermembrane space.
Cyt c	Cytochrome c	Reduced by accepting a single electron from complex III and moves along the surface of ETC membrane, where it is oxidized by complex IV.
Complex IV	Cytochrome c oxidase	Oxidizes cyt c and transfers each electron through proteins containing heme prosthetic groups to reduce oxygen gas (O_2), which picks up two $H^\boxtimes$ from the matrix to produce water. Two additional $H^\boxtimes$ are pumped out of the matrix to the intermembrane space.

membrane, where its electrons are used to reduce a component of complex III near the intermembrane space. The protons held by Q are then released to the intermembrane space.

In this way, through redox reactions alone, Q shuttles electrons and protons from one side of the membrane to the other. The electrons proceed down the transport chain, and the protons contribute to an electrochemical gradient as they are released into the intermembrane space.

Once the nature of the electron transport chain became clear, biologists understood the fate of the electrons and the energy carried by NADH and FADH$_2$. Much of the chemical energy that was originally present in glucose is now accounted for in the proton electrochemical gradient. This is satisfying, except for one crucial question: If electron transport does not make ATP, what does?

The Discovery of ATP Synthase

In 1960 Efraim Racker made several key observations about how ATP is synthesized in mitochondria. When he used mitochondrial membranes to make vesicles, Racker noticed that some vesicles formed with their membrane inside out. Electron microscopy revealed that the inside-out membranes had many large proteins studded along their surfaces. Each protein appeared to have a base in the membrane, from which a lollipop-shaped stalk and a knob project (**FIGURE 9.16**). If the solution was vibrated or treated with a compound called urea, the stalks and knobs fell off.

Racker seized on this technique to isolate the stalks and knobs and do experiments with them. For example, he found that isolated stalks and knobs could hydrolyze ATP, forming ADP and inorganic phosphate. The vesicles that contained just the base component, without the stalks and knobs, could not process ATP. The base components were, however, capable of transporting protons across the membrane.

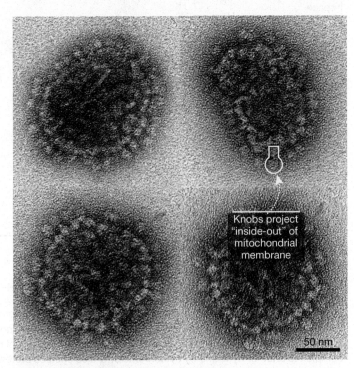

Knobs project "inside-out" of mitochondrial membrane

50 nm

FIGURE 9.16 The Discovery of ATP Synthase. When patches of mitochondrial membrane turn inside out and form vesicles, the lollipop-shaped stalk-and-knob structures of ATP synthase proteins face outward. Normally, the stalk and knob face inward, toward the mitochondrial matrix.

Based on these observations, Racker proposed that the stalk-and-knob component of the protein was an enzyme that both hydrolyzes and synthesizes ATP. To test his idea, Racker added the stalk-and-knob components back to vesicles that had been stripped of them and confirmed that the vesicles regained the ability to synthesize ATP. The entire complex is known as **ATP synthase.** Follow-up work also confirmed his hypothesis that the membrane-bound base component of ATP synthase is a proton channel. Is there a connection between proton transport and ATP synthesis?

The Chemiosmosis Hypothesis

In 1961 Peter Mitchell broke with the prevailing ideas that electron transport produces ATP via substrate phosphorylation. Instead, he proposed something completely new—an indirect connection between electron transport and ATP production. Mitchell's novel hypothesis? The real job of the electron transport chain is to pump protons across the inner membrane of mitochondria from the matrix to the intermembrane space. After a proton gradient is established, an enzyme in the inner membrane, like Racker's ATP synthase, would synthesize ATP from ADP and P_i.

Mitchell introduced the term **chemiosmosis** to describe the use of a proton gradient to drive energy-requiring processes, like the production of ATP. Here, osmosis refers to the force generated from the proton gradient rather than the transport of water. Although proponents of a direct link between electron transport and substrate-level phosphorylation objected vigorously to Mitchell's idea, several key experiments supported it.

FIGURE 9.17 illustrates how the existence of a key element in Mitchell's hypothesis was confirmed: A proton gradient alone can be used to synthesize ATP via ATP synthase. The researchers made vesicles from artificial membranes that contained Racker's ATP synthase isolated from mitochondria. Along with this enzyme, they inserted bacteriorhodopsin, a well-studied membrane protein that acts as a light-activated proton pump.

When light strikes bacteriorhodopsin, it absorbs some of the light energy and changes conformation in a way that pumps protons from the interior of a membrane to the exterior. As a result, the experimental vesicles established a strong electrochemical gradient favoring proton movement to the interior. When the vesicles were illuminated to initiate proton pumping, ATP began to be produced from ADP and P_i inside the vesicles.

Mitchell's prediction was correct: In this situation, ATP production depended solely on the existence of a **proton-motive force,** which is based on a proton electrochemical gradient. It could occur in the *absence* of an electron transport chain. This result, along with many others, has provided strong support for the hypothesis of chemiosmosis. Most of the ATP produced by cellular respiration is made by a flow of protons.

✔ If you understand chemiosmosis, you should be able to explain why ATP production during cellular respiration is characterized as indirect. More specifically, you should be able to explain the relationship between glucose oxidation, the proton gradient, and ATP synthase.

RESEARCH

QUESTION: How are the electron transport chain and ATP production linked?

CHEMIOSMOTIC HYPOTHESIS: The linkage is indirect. The ETC creates a proton-motive force that drives ATP synthesis by the mitochondrial ATP synthase.

ALTERNATIVE HYPOTHESIS: The linkage is direct. The ETC is associated with enzymes that perform substrate-level phosphorylation.

EXPERIMENTAL SETUP:

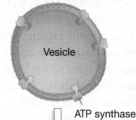

1. **Produce vesicles from artificial membranes;** add ATP synthase, an enzyme found in mitochondria.

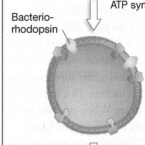

2. **Add bacteriorhodopsin,** a protein that acts as a light-activated proton pump.

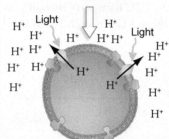

3. **Illuminate vesicle** so that bacteriorhodopsin pumps protons out of vesicle, creating a proton gradient.

PREDICTION OF CHEMIOSMOTIC HYPOTHESIS: ATP will be produced within the vesicle.

PREDICTION OF ALTERNATIVE HYPOTHESIS: No ATP will be produced.

RESULTS:

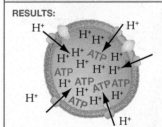

ATP is produced within the vesicle, in the absence of the electron transport chain.

CONCLUSION: The linkage between electron transport and ATP synthesis is indirect; the movement of protons drives the synthesis of ATP.

FIGURE 9.17 Evidence for the Chemiosmotic Hypothesis.

Racker, E., and W. Stoeckenius. 1974. Reconstitution of purple membrane vesicles catalyzing light-driven proton uptake and adenosine triphosphate formation. *Journal of Biological Chemistry.* 249: 662–663.

✔ **QUESTION** If bacteriorhodopsin were not available, what could the researchers have done with the ATP synthase vesicles to test their hypothesis?

Electron transport chains and ATP synthases are used by organisms throughout the tree of life. They are humming away in your cells now. Let's look in more detail at how they function.

The Proton-Motive Force Couples Electron Transport to ATP Synthesis As **FIGURE 9.18** shows, the structure of ATP synthase is now well understood. The ATP synthase "knob" component is called the F_1 unit; the membrane-bound, proton-transporting base component is the F_o unit. The F_1 and F_o units are connected by a shaft, as well as by a stator, which holds the two units in place.

The F_o unit serves as a rotor, whose turning is conveyed to the F_1 unit via the shaft. A flow of protons through the F_o unit causes the rotor and shaft to spin. By attaching long actin filaments to the shaft and examining them with a videomicroscope, researchers have been able to see the rotation, which can reach speeds of 350 revolutions per second. As the shaft spins within the F_1 unit, it is thought to change the conformation of the F_1 subunits in a way that catalyzes the phosphorylation of ADP to ATP.

Chemiosmosis is like the process of generating electricity in a hydroelectric dam (like the one pictured on page 154). The ETC is analogous to a series of gigantic pumps that force water up and behind the dam. The inner mitochondrial membrane functions as the dam, with ATP synthase spinning and generating electricity inside as water passes through—like a turbine. In a mitochondrion, protons are pumped instead of water. When protons move through ATP synthase, the protein spins and generates ATP.

It has been determined that the ETC transports enough protons to produce approximately three ATP for each NADH and

two for each $FADH_2$, depending on the type of ATP synthase used. These yields, however, are not observed in cells, since the proton-motive force is also used to drive other processes, such as the import of phosphates into the mitochondrial matrix.

Unlike the turbines in a hydroelectric dam, however, ATP synthase can reverse its direction and hydrolyze ATP to build a proton gradient. If the proton gradient dissipates, the direction of the spin is reversed and ATP is hydrolyzed to pump protons from the matrix to the intermembrane space. Understanding how these reactions occur is currently the focus of intense research. ATP synthase makes most of the ATP that keeps you alive.

The Proton-Motive Force and Chemical Evolution How was energy first transformed into a usable form during the evolution of life? Since chemiosmosis is responsible for most of the ATP produced by cells throughout the tree of life, it is likely to have arisen early in evolution. But how could a complex electron transport chain evolve to produce the proton-motive force without a proton-motive force to supply the energy?

This apparent conundrum left many of the chemical evolution theorists perplexed until a key discovery was made deep in the ocean along the Mid-Atlantic Ridge—the Lost City hydrothermal vents (see Chapter 2). Researchers propose that the alkaline fluid (low proton concentration) released from these vents in the acidic oceans (high proton concentration) of early Earth may have provided such a gradient.

While there is still considerable debate concerning the role hydrothermal vents may have played in chemical evolution, their discovery has generated much excitement. By harnessing the natural electrochemical gradient deep in the early oceans, the proton-motive force of life may have evolved to mimic the environment of its origin.

Organisms Use a Diversity of Electron Acceptors

FIGURE 9.19 summarizes glucose oxidation and cellular respiration by tracing the fate of the carbon atoms and electrons in glucose. Notice that electrons from glucose are transferred to NADH and $FADH_2$, passed through the electron transport chain, and accepted by oxygen. Proton pumping during electron transport creates the proton-motive force that drives ATP synthesis.

The diagram also indicates the approximate yield of ATP from each component of the process. Recent research shows that about 29 ATP molecules are produced from each molecule of glucose.[2] Of these, 25 ATP molecules are produced by ATP synthase. The fundamental message here? The vast majority of the "payoff" from the oxidation of glucose occurs via oxidative phosphorylation.

Aerobic Versus Anaerobic Respiration During cellular respiration, oxygen is the electron acceptor used by all eukaryotes and

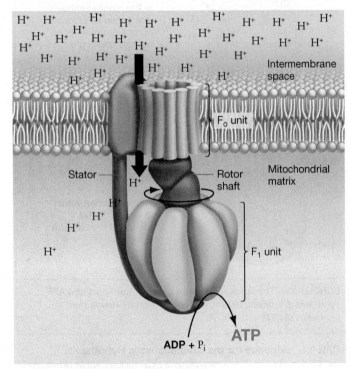

FIGURE 9.18 ATP Synthase Is a Motor. ATP synthase has two major components, designated F_o and F_1, connected by a shaft. The F_o unit spins as protons pass through. The shaft transmits the rotation to the F_1 unit, causing it to make ATP from ADP and P_i.

(Figure labels: H$^+$ · Intermembrane space · F_o unit · Stator · H$^+$ · Rotor shaft · Mitochondrial matrix · F_1 unit · ADP + P_i · ATP)

---

[2]Traditionally, biologists thought that 36 ATP would be synthesized for every molecule of glucose oxidized in eukaryotic cells. More recent work has shown that actual yield is only about 29 ATP [see M. Brand, Approximate yield of ATP from glucose, designed by Donald Nicholson. *Biochemistry and Molecular Biology Education* 31 (2003): 2–4]. Also, it's important to note that yield varies with conditions in the cell.

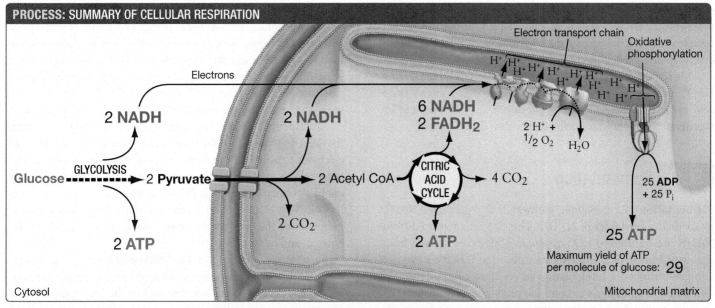

FIGURE 9.19 ATP Yield during Cellular Respiration. The actual yield of ATP per glucose (29 ATP) is lower than the theoretical calculation (38 ATP) because of energy required for the import of NADH from the cytoplasm and the use of the proton-motive force to actively transport P_i into the mitochondrial matrix.

a wide diversity of bacteria and archaea. Species that depend on oxygen as an electron acceptor for the ETC use **aerobic** respiration and are called aerobic organisms. (The Latin root *aero* means "air.")

It is important to recognize, though, that cellular respiration can occur without oxygen. Many thousands of bacterial and archaeal species rely on electron acceptors other than oxygen, and electron donors other than glucose. For example, nitrate (NO_3^-) and sulfate (SO_4^{2-}) are particularly common electron acceptors in species that live in oxygen-poor environments (see Chapter 29). In addition, many bacteria and archaea use H_2, H_2S, CH_4, or other inorganic compounds as electron donors—not glucose.

Cells that depend on electron acceptors other than oxygen are said to use **anaerobic** ("no air") respiration. Even though the starting and ending points of cellular respiration differ, aerobic and anaerobic cells still use electron transport chains to create a proton-motive force that drives the synthesis of ATP. In bacteria and archaea, the ETC and ATP synthase are located in the plasma membrane.

Aerobic Respiration Is Most Efficient Even though an array of compounds can serve as the final electron acceptor in cellular respiration, oxygen is the most efficient. Because oxygen holds electrons so tightly, the potential energy of electrons in a bond between an oxygen atom and a non-oxygenic atom, such as hydrogen, is low. As a result, there is a large difference between the potential energy of electrons in NADH and the potential energy of electrons bonded to an oxygen atom, such as found in water (see Figure 9.14). The large differential in potential energy means that the electron transport chain can generate a large proton-motive force.

Cells that do not use oxygen as an electron acceptor cannot generate such a large potential energy difference. As a result, they make less ATP from each glucose molecule than cells that use aerobic respiration. This finding is important: It means that anaerobic organisms tend to grow much more slowly than aerobic organisms. If cells that use anaerobic respiration compete with cells using aerobic respiration, those that use oxygen as an electron acceptor almost always grow faster and reproduce more.

What happens when oxygen or other electron acceptors get used up? When there is no terminal electron acceptor, the electrons in

check your understanding

If you understand that . . .

- As electrons from NADH and FADH$_2$ move through the electron transport chain, protons are pumped into the intermembrane space of mitochondria.

- The electrochemical gradient across the inner mitochondrial membrane drives protons through ATP synthase, resulting in the production of ATP from ADP.

✔ **You should be able to . . .**

Add paper squares labeled ETC and ATP synthase and a paper circle labeled ½ O$_2$ → H$_2$O to the model you made in Section 9.4. Explain the steps in electron transport and chemiosmosis using paper triangles to represent electron pairs and dimes to represent protons.

Answers are available in Appendix A.

each of the complexes of the electron transport chain have no place to go and the electron transport chain stops. Without an oxidized complex I, NADH remains reduced. The concentration of $NAD^{\boxtimes}$ drops rapidly as cells continue to convert $NAD^{\boxtimes}$ to NADH.

This situation is life threatening. When there is no longer any $NAD^{\boxtimes}$ to drive glycolysis, pyruvate processing, and the citric acid cycle, then no ATP can be produced. If $NAD^{\boxtimes}$ cannot be regenerated somehow, the cell will die. How do cells cope?

9.6 Fermentation

Fermentation is a metabolic pathway that regenerates $NAD^{\boxtimes}$ by oxidizing stockpiles of NADH. The electrons removed from NADH are transferred to pyruvate, or a molecule derived from pyruvate, instead of an electron transport chain (**FIGURE 9.20**).

In respiring cells, fermentation serves as an emergency back-up that allows glycolysis to continue producing ATP even when the ETC is shut down. It allows the cell to survive and even grow in the absence of electron transport chains.

In many cases, the cell cannot use the molecule that is formed when pyruvate (or another electron acceptor) accepts electrons from NADH. This by-product may even be toxic and excreted from the cell as waste even though it has not been fully oxidized.

Many Different Fermentation Pathways Exist When you run up a long flight of stairs, your muscles begin metabolizing glucose so fast that the supply of oxygen is rapidly used up by their mitochondria. When oxygen is absent, the electron transport chains shut down and NADH cannot donate its electrons there. The pyruvate produced by glycolysis then begins to accept electrons from NADH, and fermentation takes place. This process, called **lactic acid fermentation,** regenerates $NAD^{\boxtimes}$ by forming a product molecule called lactate: a deprotonated form of lactic acid (**FIGURE 9.21a**). Your body reacts by making you breathe faster and increasing your heart rate. By getting more oxygen to your muscle cells, the electron transport chain is revived.

FIGURE 9.21b illustrates a different fermentation pathway, **alcohol fermentation,** which occurs in the fungus *Saccharomyces*

cerevisiae—baker's and brewer's yeast. When yeast cells are placed in an environment such as bread dough or a bottle of grape juice and begin growing, they quickly use up all the available oxygen. Instead of depositing the electrons from NADH into pyruvate, yeast first convert pyruvate to the two-carbon compound acet-aldehyde. This reaction gives off carbon dioxide, which causes bread to rise and produces the bubbles in champagne and beer.

Acetaldehyde then accepts electrons from NADH, forming the $NAD^{\boxtimes}$ required to keep glycolysis going. The addition of electrons to acetaldehyde forms ethanol as a waste product. The yeast cells excrete ethanol as waste. In essence, the active ingredi-ent in alcoholic beverages is like yeast urine.

Cells that employ other types of fermentation are used com-mercially in the production of soy sauce, tofu, yogurt, cheese, vinegar, and other products.

Bacteria and archaea that exist exclusively through fermenta-tion are present in phenomenal numbers in the oxygen-free en-vironment of your small intestine and in the first compartment of a cow's stomach, called the rumen. The rumen is a specialized digestive organ that contains over 10^{10} (10 billion) bacterial and archaeal cells per *milliliter* of fluid. The fermentations that occur in these cells produce an array of fatty acids. Cattle don't actu-ally live off grass directly—they eat it to feed their bacteria and archaea and then use the fermentation by-products from these organisms as a source of energy.

Fermentation as an Alternative to Cellular Respiration Even though fermentation is a widespread type of metabolism, it is extremely inefficient compared with aerobic cellular respiration. Fermentation produces just 2 molecules of ATP for each molecule of glucose metabolized, while cellular respiration produces about 29—almost 15 times more energy per glucose molecule than fer-mentation. The reason for the disparity is that oxygen has much higher electronegativity than electron acceptors such as pyruvate and acetaldehyde. As a result, the potential energy drop between the start and end of fermentation is a tiny fraction of the potential energy change that occurs during cellular respiration.

Based on these observations, it is not surprising that organ-isms capable of both processes almost never use fermentation

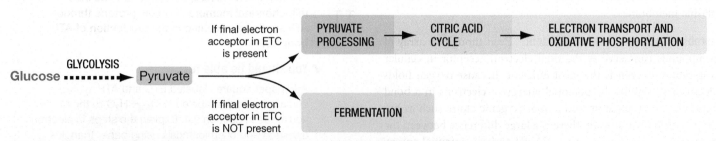

FIGURE 9.20 Cellular Respiration and Fermentation Are Alternative Pathways for Producing Energy. When oxygen or another electron acceptor used by the ETC is present in a cell, the pyruvate produced by glycolysis enters the citric acid cycle and the electron transport system is active. But if no electron acceptor is available to keep the ETC running, the pyruvate undergoes reactions known as fermentation.

(a) Lactic acid fermentation occurs in humans.

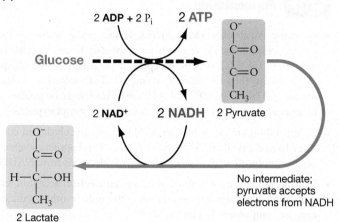

2 Lactate

(b) Alcohol fermentation occurs in yeast.

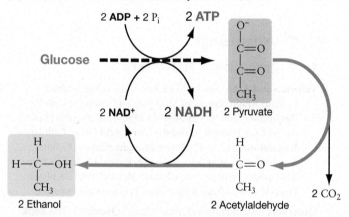

2 Ethanol   2 Acetylaldehyde

FIGURE 9.21 Fermentation Regenerates NAD⁺ So That Glycolysis Can Continue. These are just two examples of the many types of fermentation that occur among bacteria, archaea, and eukaryotes.

when an appropriate electron acceptor is available for cellular respiration. In organisms that usually use oxygen as an electron acceptor, fermentation is an alternative mode of ATP production when oxygen supplies temporarily run out.

Organisms that can switch between fermentation and cellular respiration that uses oxygen as an electron acceptor are called **facultative anaerobes.** The adjective facultative reflects the ability to use cellular respiration when oxygen is present and fermentation when it is absent (anaerobic). Many of your cells can function as facultative anaerobes to a certain extent; however, you cannot survive for long without oxygen. To make this point clear, try holding your breath—it should take only a minute for you to realize how important electron transport is to your cells.

check your understanding

If you understand that . . .

- Fermentation occurs in the absence of an electron acceptor at the end of an ETC. It consists of reactions that oxidize NADH to regenerate the NAD⁺ required for glycolysis.

✔ **You should be able to . . .**

Explain why organisms that have an ETC as well as fermentation pathways seldom ferment pyruvate if an electron acceptor at the end of the ETC is readily available.

Answers are available in Appendix A.

CHAPTER 9 REVIEW

For media, go to MasteringBiology

If you understand . . .

9.1 An Overview of Cellular Respiration

- Cellular respiration is based on redox reactions that transfer electrons from a compound with high free energy, such as glucose, to a molecule with lower free energy, such as oxygen, through an electron transport chain.

- In eukaryotes, cellular respiration consists of four steps: glycolysis, pyruvate processing, the citric acid cycle, and electron transport coupled to oxidative phosphorylation.

- Glycolysis, pyruvate processing, and the citric acid cycle are central to the metabolism of most cells. Other catabolic pathways feed into them, and the intermediates of the central pathways are used in the synthesis of many key molecules.

✔ You should be able to explain why many different molecules—including lipids, amino acids, and CO_2—are radiolabeled when cells are fed glucose with ^{14}C radioactive carbons.

9.2 Glycolysis: Processing Glucose to Pyruvate

- The glycolytic pathway is a 10-step reaction sequence in which glucose is broken down into two molecules of pyruvate. It takes place in the cytosol, where ATP and NADH are produced.

- Glycolysis slows when ATP binds to phosphofructokinase.

✔ QUANTITATIVE You should be able to draw a graph predicting how the rate of ATP production in glycolysis changes as a function of ATP concentration. (Write "ATP concentration" on the x-axis and "ATP production" on the y-axis.)

9.3 Processing Pyruvate to Acetyl CoA

- During pyruvate processing, a series of reactions convert pyruvate to acetyl CoA. NADH is produced and CO_2 is released.

- The pyruvate dehydrogenase complex is inhibited when it is phosphorylated by ATP. It speeds up in the presence of substrates like NAD and ADP.

✔ You should be able to explain why it is not surprising that pyruvate dehydrogenase consists of a large, multi-enzyme complex.

9.4 The Citric Acid Cycle: Oxidizing Acetyl CoA to CO_2

- The citric acid cycle is an eight-step reaction cycle that begins with acetyl CoA. $FADH_2$, NADH, and GTP or ATP are produced; CO_2 is released. By the end of the citric acid cycle, glucose is completely oxidized to CO_2.

- Certain enzymes in the citric acid cycle are inhibited when NADH or ATP binds to them.

✔ You should be able to describe what would happen to NADH levels in a cell in the first few seconds after a drug has poisoned the enzyme that combines acetyl CoA and oxaloacetate to form citrate.

9.5 Electron Transport and Chemiosmosis: Building a Proton Gradient to Produce ATP

- NADH and $FADH_2$ donate electrons to an electron transport chain that resides in the inner membrane of mitochondria and the plasma membrane of many bacteria. The series of redox reactions in these chains gradually steps the electrons down in potential energy until they are transferred to a final electron acceptor (often O_2).

- The energy released from redox reactions in the electron transport chain is used to move protons across the inner mitochondrial membrane, creating an electrochemical gradient. ATP synthase uses the energy stored in this gradient to produce ATP via chemiosmosis—a process called oxidative phosphorylation.

✔ You should be able to predict the effect of a drug that inhibits ATP synthase on the pH in the mitochondrial matrix.

9.6 Fermentation

- In many eukaryotes and bacteria, fermentation occurs when cellular respiration slows down or stops due to an insufficient amount of the final electron acceptor. If the final electron acceptor is absent, then the electron transport chain would no longer oxidize NADH to $NAD^{\boxtimes}$ and ATP could no longer be produced by glycolysis, the citric acid cycle, or oxidative phosphorylation.

- Fermentation pathways regenerate $NAD^{\boxtimes}$, so glycolysis can continue to make ATP and keep the cell alive. This happens when an organic molecule such as pyruvate accepts electrons from NADH.

- Depending on the molecule that acts as an electron acceptor, fermentation pathways produce lactate, ethanol, or other reduced organic compounds as a by-product.

✔ You should be able to explain why you would expect organisms that produce ATP only via fermentation to grow much more slowly than organisms that produce ATP via cellular respiration.

You should be able to . . .

✔ **TEST YOUR KNOWLEDGE**
Answers are available in Appendix A

1. Make a flowchart indicating the relationships among the four steps of cellular respiration. Which steps are responsible for glucose oxidation? Which produce the most ATP?

2. Where does the citric acid cycle occur in eukaryotes?
   a. in the cytosol
   b. in the matrix of mitochondria
   c. in the inner membrane of mitochondria
   d. in the intermembrane space of mitochondria

3. What does the chemiosmotic hypothesis claim?
   a. Substrate-level phosphorylation occurs in the electron transport chain.
   b. Substrate-level phosphorylation occurs in glycolysis and the citric acid cycle.
   c. The electron transport chain is located in the inner membrane of mitochondria.
   d. Electron transport chains generate ATP indirectly, by the creation of a proton-motive force.

4. After glucose is fully oxidized by glycolysis, pyruvate processing, and the citric acid cycle, where is most of the energy stored?

5. What is the function of the reactions in a fermentation pathway?
   a. to generate NADH from NAD^+, so electrons can be donated to the electron transport chain
   b. to synthesize pyruvate from lactate
   c. to generate NAD^+ from NADH, so glycolysis can continue
   d. to synthesize electron acceptors, so that cellular respiration can continue

6. Which of the following would cause cells to switch from cellular respiration to fermentation?
   a. The final electron acceptor in the ETC is not available.
   b. The proton-motive force runs down.
   c. NADH and $FADH_2$ supplies are low.
   d. Pyruvate is not available.

7. Describe the relationship between carbohydrate metabolism, the catabolism of proteins and fats, and anabolic pathways.

8. Compare and contrast substrate-level phosphorylation and oxidative phosphorylation.

9. Why does aerobic respiration produce much more ATP than anaerobic respiration?

10. If you were to expose cells that are undergoing cellular respiration to a radioactive oxygen isotope in the form of O_2, which of the following molecules would you expect to be radiolabeled?
    a. pyruvate
    b. water
    c. NADH
    d. CO_2

11. In step 3 of the citric acid cycle, the enzyme isocitrate dehydrogenase is regulated by NADH. Compare and contrast the regulation of this enzyme with what you have learned about phosphofructokinase in glycolysis.

12. Explain the relationship between electron transport and oxidative phosphorylation. What does ATP synthase look like, and how does it work?

13. Cyanide ($C \equiv N^-$) blocks complex IV of the electron transport chain. Suggest a hypothesis for what happens to the ETC when complex IV stops working. Your hypothesis should explain why cyanide poisoning in humans is fatal.

14. The presence of many sac-like cristae results in a large amount of membrane inside mitochondria. Suppose that some mitochondria had few cristae. How would their output of ATP compare with that of mitochondria with many cristae? Justify your answer.

15. **QUANTITATIVE** Early estimates suggested that the oxidation of glucose via aerobic respiration would produce 38 ATP. Based on what you know of the theoretical yields of ATP from each step, show how this total was determined. Why do biologists now think this amount of ATP/glucose is not achieved in cells?

16. Suppose a drug were added to mitochondria that allowed protons to freely pass through the inner membrane. Which of the following mitochondrial activities would most likely be inhibited?
    a. the citric acid cycle
    b. oxidative phosphorylation
    c. substrate-level phosphorylation
    d. the electron transport chain

10 Photosynthesis

In this chapter you will learn how

Photosynthesis links life to the power of the Sun

by previewing

Conversion of light energy into chemical energy 10.1

by examining

How photosynthetic pigments capture light energy 10.2

then looking closer at

Energy flow and ATP production 10.3 → Photosystem II

Photosystem I

and exploring

CO₂ fixation and reduction to form sugars 10.4 → The Calvin cycle

A close-up of moss cells filled with chloroplasts, where photosynthesis converts the energy in sunlight to chemical energy in the bonds of sugar. The sugar produced by photosynthetic organisms fuels cellular respiration and growth. Photosynthetic organisms, in turn, are consumed by other organisms, including you. Directly or indirectly, most organisms on Earth get their energy from photosynthesis.

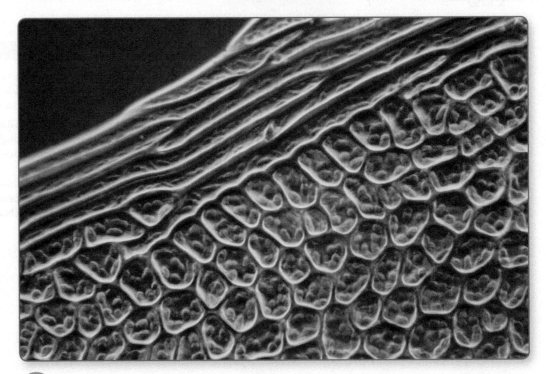

This chapter is part of the Big Picture. See how on pages 198–199.

Some 3 billion years ago, a novel combination of light-absorbing molecules and enzymes gave a bacterial cell the capacity to convert light energy into chemical energy in the C–C and C–H bonds of sugar. The origin of **photosynthesis**—the use of sunlight to manufacture carbohydrate—ranks as one of the great events in the history of life.

The vast majority of organisms alive today rely on photosynthesis, either directly or indirectly, to stay alive. Maples, mosses, and other photosynthetic organisms are termed **autotrophs** (literally, "self-feeders") because they make all their own food from ions and simple molecules. Humans, houseflies, and other non-photosynthetic organisms are called **heterotrophs** ("different-feeders") because they have to obtain the sugars and many of the other macromolecules they need from other organisms.

✔ When you see this checkmark, stop and test yourself. Answers are available in Appendix A.

Because there could be no heterotrophs without autotrophs, photosynthesis is fundamental to almost all life. Glycolysis may qualify as the most ancient set of energy-related chemical reactions from an evolutionary viewpoint, but ecologically—meaning, in terms of how organisms interact with one another—photosynthesis is easily the most important.

How does photosynthesis work? Let's begin with an overview and then delve into a step-by-step analysis of some of the most remarkable chemistry on Earth.

10.1 Photosynthesis Harnesses Sunlight to Make Carbohydrate

Research on photosynthesis began early in the history of biological science. In the 1770s, Joseph Priestley performed a series of experiments showing that the green parts of plants would "restore air" that had been consumed by animals or fire. This work led to the discovery of oxygen (O_2) and the finding that plants produce it in the presence of sunlight, carbon dioxide (CO_2), and water (H_2O).

By the 1840s, enough was known about the process for biologists to propose that photosynthesis allows plants to convert the electromagnetic energy of sunlight into chemical energy in the C–C and C–H bonds of carbohydrates. When glucose is the carbohydrate that is eventually produced, the overall reaction—the sum of many independent reactions—can be simplified and written as

$$6\,CO_2 + 6\,H_2O + \text{light energy} \longrightarrow \underset{\text{glucose}}{C_6H_{12}O_6} + 6\,O_2$$

Now read the reaction again, and note the contrast with cellular respiration. Photosynthesis is an endergonic suite of redox reactions that produce sugars from carbon dioxide and light energy. Cellular respiration is an exergonic suite of redox reactions that produces carbon dioxide and ATP from sugars.

FIGURE 10.1 provides an incomplete electron-sharing diagram for the reaction shown above. ✔ If you understand the fundamental principles of reduction–oxidation (see Chapter 8), you should be able to complete Figure 10.1 (following the instructions in the caption exercise) and then use the data from the figure to explain why the reaction is endergonic.

So how does photosynthesis produce O_2 and glucose? Early investigators assumed that CO_2 and H_2O react directly to produce the CH_2O found in carbohydrates and release O_2 as a by-product. This idea, however, turned out to be incorrect. Instead, CO_2 and H_2O participate in entirely different reactions, and the oxygen atoms in O_2 come from water. How was this discovered?

Photosynthesis: Two Linked Sets of Reactions

Starting in the 1930s, two independent lines of research on photosynthesis converged, leading to a major advance in biologists' understanding of how oxygen gas and carbohydrates are produced.

The first research program, led by Cornelius van Niel, focused on photosynthesis in organisms called purple sulfur bacteria. Van Niel and his group found that these cells are autotrophs that manufacture their own carbohydrates from CO_2, sunlight, and hydrogen sulfide (H_2S).

Van Niel also showed that these cells did not produce oxygen as a by-product of photosynthesis. Instead, elemental sulfur (S) accumulated in their medium. In these organisms, the overall reaction for photosynthesis was

$$CO_2 + 2\,H_2S + \text{light energy} \longrightarrow (CH_2O)_n + H_2O + 2\,S$$

Van Niel's work was crucial for two reasons:

1. It showed that H_2S, the equivalent of H_2O in the plant reactions, and CO_2 do *not* combine directly during photosynthesis.

2. It showed that the oxygen atoms in CO_2 are *not* released as oxygen gas (O_2). The purple sulfur bacteria produced no oxygen, even though carbon dioxide participated in the reaction—just as it did in plants.

Based on these findings, biologists hypothesized that the oxygen atoms released during plant photosynthesis must come from H_2O. The hypothesis was confirmed when heavy isotopes

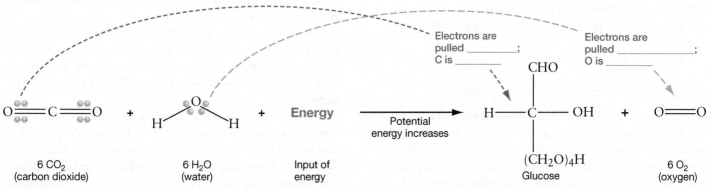

FIGURE 10.1 Electron Transfer during the Reduction of Glucose.

✔**EXERCISE** Fill in the electron positions for each bond in the reaction products, and complete the labels explaining which product is reduced and which is oxidized.

of oxygen—^{18}O in contrast to the normal isotope, ^{16}O—became available to researchers. They observed the ^{18}O in oxygen gas only when algae or plants were exposed to ^{18}O-labeled H_2O, not the ^{18}O-labeled CO_2.

In addition, the reactions responsible for producing oxygen gas occurred only in the presence of sunlight, but did not require the presence of CO_2. These data suggested that there were two distinct sets of reactions: one that uses light to produce O_2 from H_2O and one that converts CO_2 into sugars.

A second major line of research supported the idea of two sets of reactions. Between 1945 and 1955, a team led by Melvin Calvin began introducing radioactively labeled carbon dioxide ($^{14}CO_2$) to algae and identifying the molecules that subsequently became labeled with the radioisotope. These experiments allowed researchers to identify the sequence of reactions involved in reducing CO_2 to sugars.

Because Calvin played an important role in this research, the reactions that reduce carbon dioxide and produce sugar came to be known as the **Calvin cycle.** Later research showed that the Calvin cycle can function only if the light-capturing reactions are occurring.

To summarize: Early research showed that photosynthesis consists of two linked sets of reactions. One set is triggered by light; the other set—the Calvin cycle—requires the products of the light-capturing reactions. The light-capturing reactions produce oxygen from water; the Calvin cycle produces sugar from carbon dioxide.

The two reactions are linked by electrons that are released when water is split to form oxygen gas. During the light-capturing reactions, these electrons are promoted to a high-energy state by light and then transferred through a series of redox reactions to a phosphorylated version of NAD^+, called **NADP$^\boxtimes$** (**nicotinamide adenine dinucleotide phosphate**). This reaction forms **NADPH,** which functions as a reducing agent similar to the NADH produced in cellular respiration. Some of the energy released from these redox reactions is also used to produce ATP (**FIGURE 10.2**).

During the Calvin cycle, the electrons in NADPH and the potential energy in ATP are used to reduce CO_2 to carbohydrate. The resulting sugars are used in cellular respiration to produce ATP for the cell. Plants oxidize sugars in their mitochondria and consume O_2 in the process, just as animals and other eukaryotes do.

Where does all this activity take place?

Photosynthesis Occurs in Chloroplasts

Once experiments had established that photosynthesis takes place only in the green portions of plants, biologists focused on the bright green organelles called **chloroplasts** ("green-formed elements"). One leaf cell typically contains 40 to 50 chloroplasts, and a square millimeter of leaf averages about 500,000 (**FIGURE 10.3**).

When membranes derived from chloroplasts were found to release oxygen after exposure to sunlight, the hypothesis that chloroplasts are the site of photosynthesis became widely accepted.

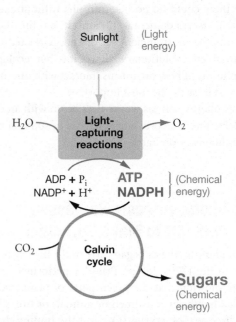

FIGURE 10.2 Photosynthesis Has Two Linked Components. In the light-capturing reactions of photosynthesis, light energy is transformed to chemical energy in the form of ATP and NADPH. During the Calvin cycle, the ATP and NADPH produced in the light-capturing reactions are used to reduce carbon dioxide to carbohydrate.

As Figure 10.3 shows, a chloroplast is enclosed by an outer membrane and an inner membrane (see Chapter 7). The interior is dominated by flattened, sac-like structures called **thylakoids,** which often occur in interconnected stacks called **grana** (singular: **granum**). The space inside a thylakoid is its **lumen.** (Recall that lumen is a general term for the interior of any sac-like structure. Your stomach and intestines have a lumen.) The fluid-filled space between the thylakoids and the inner membrane is the **stroma.**

When researchers analyzed the chemical composition of thylakoid membranes, they found huge quantities of pigments. **Pigments** are molecules that absorb only certain wavelengths of light—other wavelengths are either reflected or transmitted (pass through). Pigments have colors because we see the wavelengths that they do *not* absorb.

The most abundant pigment in the thylakoid membranes turned out to be chlorophyll ("green-leaf"), which reflects or transmits green light. As a result, chlorophyll is responsible for the green color of plants, some algae, and many photosynthetic bacteria.

Before plunging into the details of how photosynthesis occurs, take a moment to consider just how astonishing the process is. Chemists have synthesized an amazing diversity of compounds from relatively simple starting materials, but their achievements pale in comparison to a cell that can synthesize sugar from just carbon dioxide, water, and sunlight. If photosynthesis is not *the* most sophisticated chemistry on Earth, it is certainly a contender.

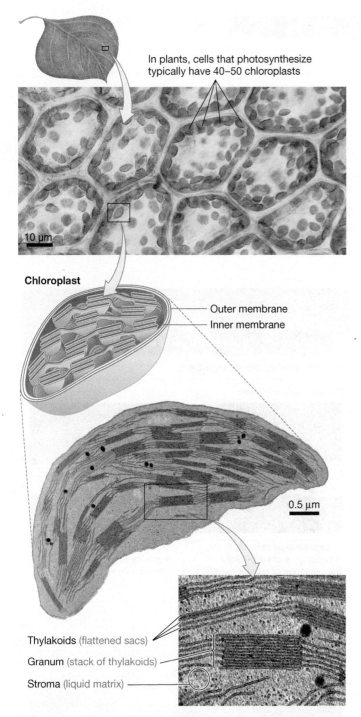

In plants, cells that photosynthesize typically have 40–50 chloroplasts

10 μm

Chloroplast

Outer membrane
Inner membrane

0.5 μm

Thylakoids (flattened sacs)
Granum (stack of thylakoids)
Stroma (liquid matrix)

FIGURE 10.3 Photosynthesis Takes Place in Chloroplasts.

10.2 How Do Pigments Capture Light Energy?

The light-capturing reactions of photosynthesis begin with the simple act of sunlight striking chlorophyll. To understand the consequences of this event, it's helpful to review the nature of light.

Light is a type of electromagnetic radiation, a form of energy. Photosynthesis converts electromagnetic energy in the form of

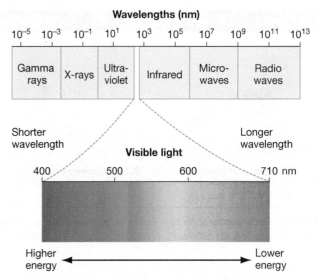

Wavelengths (nm)

| 10^{-5} | 10^{-3} | 10^{-1} | 10^{1} | 10^{3} | 10^{5} | 10^{7} | 10^{9} | 10^{11} | 10^{13} |

| Gamma rays | X-rays | Ultra-violet | Infrared | Micro-waves | Radio waves |

Shorter wavelength

Visible light

Longer wavelength

400   500   600   710 nm

Higher energy ⟷ Lower energy

FIGURE 10.4 The Electromagnetic Spectrum. Electromagnetic energy radiates through space in the form of waves. Humans can see radiation at wavelengths between about 400 nanometers (nm) to 710 nm. The shorter the wavelength of electromagnetic radiation, the higher its energy.

sunlight into chemical energy in the C—C and C—H bonds of sugar.

Physicists describe light's behavior as both wavelike and particle-like. Like water waves or airwaves, electromagnetic radiation is characterized by its **wavelength**—the distance between two successive wave crests (or wave troughs). The wavelength determines the type of electromagnetic radiation.

FIGURE 10.4 illustrates the range of wavelengths of electromagnetic radiation—the **electromagnetic spectrum.** The electromagnetic radiation that humans can see, the **visible light,** ranges in wavelength from about 400 to about 710 nanometers (nm, or 10^{-9} m). Shorter wavelengths of electromagnetic radiation contain more energy than longer wavelengths do. Thus, there is more energy in blue light than in red light.

To emphasize the particle-like nature of light, physicists point out that it exists in discrete packets called **photons.** Each photon of light has a characteristic wavelength and energy level. Pigment molecules absorb the energy of some of these photons. How?

Photosynthetic Pigments Absorb Light

When a photon strikes an object, the photon may be absorbed, transmitted, or reflected. A pigment molecule absorbs photons of particular wavelengths. Sunlight includes white light, which consists of all wavelengths in the visible portion of the electromagnetic spectrum at once.

If a pigment absorbs all the visible wavelengths, the pigment appears black because no visible wavelength of light is reflected back to your eye. If a pigment absorbs many or most of the wavelengths in the blue and green parts of the spectrum but transmits or reflects longer wavelengths, it appears red.

What wavelengths do various plant pigments absorb? In one approach to answering this question, researchers grind up leaves

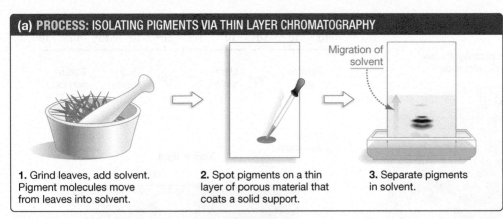

1. Grind leaves, add solvent. Pigment molecules move from leaves into solvent.

2. Spot pigments on a thin layer of porous material that coats a solid support.

3. Separate pigments in solvent.

(b) A finished chromatograph

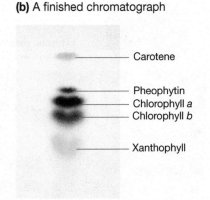

Carotene

Pheophytin
Chlorophyll *a*
Chlorophyll *b*

Xanthophyll

FIGURE 10.5 Chromatography Is a Technique for Separating Molecules. Different species of photosynthetic organisms may contain different types and quantities of pigments. This example shows grass leaves.

in a liquid that acts as a solvent to extract pigment molecules from the leaf mixture. A technique called thin layer chromatography separates the pigments in the extract (**FIGURE 10.5a**).

To begin, spots of raw leaf extract are placed near the bottom of a stiff support that is coated with a thin layer of silica gel, cellulose, or similar porous material. The coated support is then placed in a solvent solution. As the solvent wicks upward through the coating, it carries the pigment molecules in the mixture with it. Because the pigment molecules vary in size, solubility, or both, they are carried at different rates.

FIGURE 10.5b shows a chromatograph from a grass-leaf extract. Notice that this leaf contains an array of pigments. To find out which wavelengths are absorbed by each of these molecules, researchers cut out a single region (color band) of the porous material, extract the pigment, and use an instrument to record the wavelengths absorbed.

Different Pigments Absorb Different Wavelengths of Light Research based on the techniques shown in Figure 10.5 has confirmed that there are two major pigment classes in plant leaves: chlorophylls and carotenoids.

1. **Chlorophylls,** designated chlorophyll *a* and chlorophyll *b*, absorb strongly in the blue and red regions of the visible spectrum. The presence of chlorophylls makes plants look green because they reflect green light, which they do not absorb.

2. **Carotenoids** absorb in the blue and green parts of the visible spectrum. Thus, carotenoids appear yellow, orange, or red. The carotenoids found in plants belong to two classes, called carotenes and xanthophylls.

FIGURE 10.6 Certain Wavelengths of Light Are Used to Drive Photosynthesis.

SOURCE: Engelmann, T. W. 1882. Oxygen excretion from plant cells in a microspectrum. *Botanische Zeitung* 40: 419–426.

✔ **EXERCISE** Draw what you expect the results of this experiment would look like if the pigments that drive photosynthesis in the algae were to absorb most strongly at 500 nm and 560 nm.

RESEARCH

QUESTION: Which of the wavelengths found in white light are responsible for driving photosynthesis?

HYPOTHESIS: No specific hypothesis.

EXPERIMENTAL SETUP:

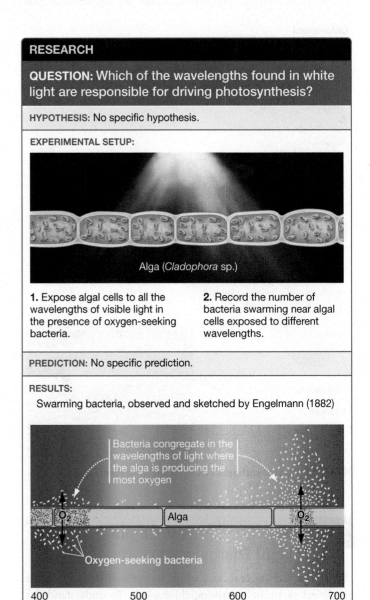

Alga (*Cladophora* sp.)

1. Expose algal cells to all the wavelengths of visible light in the presence of oxygen-seeking bacteria.

2. Record the number of bacteria swarming near algal cells exposed to different wavelengths.

PREDICTION: No specific prediction.

RESULTS:

Swarming bacteria, observed and sketched by Engelmann (1882)

Bacteria congregate in the wavelengths of light where the alga is producing the most oxygen

O₂   Alga   O₂

Oxygen-seeking bacteria

400   500   600   700

CONCLUSION: Pigments that absorb violet-to-blue and red wavelengths are most effective at triggering photosynthesis.

Which of these wavelengths drive photosynthesis?

In 1882, T. W. Engelmann answered this question by laying a filamentous alga across a microscope slide that was illuminated with a spectrum of colors generated by passing light through a prism to separate the wavelengths (**FIGURE 10.6**). The idea was that the algal cells would begin performing photosynthesis in response to the various wavelengths of light and produce oxygen as a by-product. To determine exactly where oxygen was being produced, Engelmann added bacterial cells from a species that is attracted to oxygen.

As the drawing in the "Results" section of Figure 10.6 shows, most of the bacteria congregated in the violet-to-blue and red regions of the slide. Because wavelengths in these parts of the spectrum were associated with high oxygen concentrations, Engelmann concluded that they defined the **action spectrum** for photosynthesis—the wavelengths that drive the light-capturing reactions. Engelmann's data indicate that violet-to-blue and red photons are the most effective at driving photosynthesis. Because the chlorophylls absorb these wavelengths, this early experiment showed that chlorophylls are the main photosynthetic pigments.

Using thin layer chromatography, and more advanced techniques to evaluate photosynthetic activity, biologists have produced data like those shown in **FIGURE 10.7**. This graph shows the action spectrum and the absorption spectra for three different pigments found in chloroplasts. An **absorption spectrum** measures how the wavelength of photons influences the amount of light absorbed by a pigment. In the combined graph, peaks indicate wavelengths where absorbance or photosynthetic activity is high; troughs indicate wavelengths where absorbance or photosynthetic activity is low.

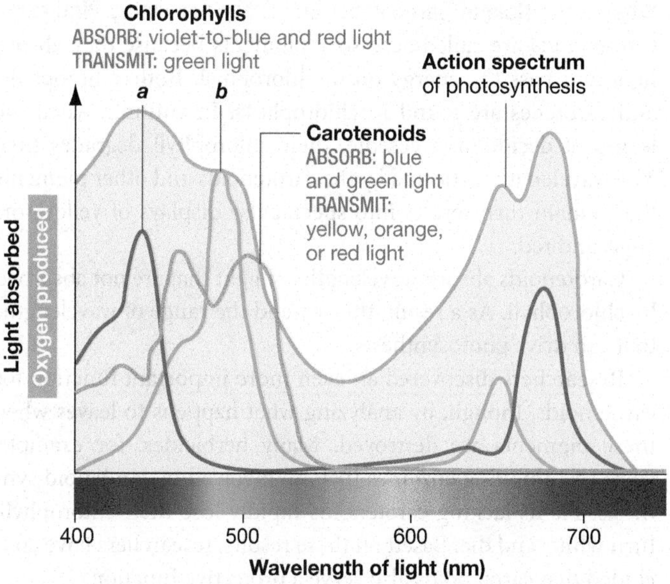

Which Part of a Pigment Absorbs Light?

As **FIGURE 10.8a** shows, chlorophyll *a* and chlorophyll *b* are similar in structure. Both have two fundamental parts: a long isoprenoid "tail" (introduced in Chapter 6) and a "head" consisting of a large ring structure

Chlorophylls
ABSORB: violet-to-blue and red light
TRANSMIT: green light

Action spectrum of photosynthesis

Carotenoids
ABSORB: blue and green light
TRANSMIT: yellow, orange, or red light

Light absorbed / Oxygen produced (vertical axis)

Wavelength of light (nm): 400, 500, 600, 700

FIGURE 10.7 There Is a Strong Correlation between the Absorption Spectra of Pigments and the Action Spectrum for Photosynthesis.

DATA: Singhal, G. S., et al. 1999. *Concepts in Photobiology: Photosynthesis and Photomorphogenesis.* Dordrecht: Kluwer Academic; co-published with Narosa Publishing House (New Delhi), 11–51.

with a magnesium atom in the middle. The tail interacts with proteins embedded in the thylakoid membrane; the head is where light is absorbed.

The structure of β-carotene, shown in **FIGURE 10.8b**, has an isoprenoid chain connecting two rings that are responsible for absorbing light. This pigment is what gives carrots their orange color. A xanthophyll called zeaxanthin, which gives corn kernels their bright yellow color, is nearly identical to β-carotene, except that the ring structures on either end of the molecule contain a hydroxyl (−OH) group.

Researchers had shown that chlorophylls are the main photosynthetic pigments, but carotenoids also absorb light. What do they do? Before analyzing what happens when chlorophyll pigments absorb light, let's first look at the function of the carotenoids.

(a) Chlorophylls *a* and *b*

CH₃ in chlorophyll *a*
CHO in chlorophyll *b*

Head
(ring structure that absorbs light)

Tail
(anchors chlorophyll in thylakoid membrane)

(b) β-Carotene

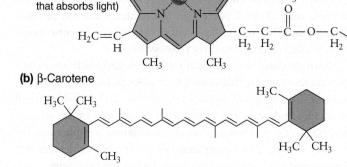

FIGURE 10.8 Photosynthetic Pigments Contain Ring Structures.
(a) Although chlorophylls *a* and *b* are very similar structurally, they have the distinct absorption spectra shown in Figure 10.7.
(b) Carotene is an orange pigment found in carrot roots and other plant tissues.

What Is the Role of Carotenoids and Other Accessory Pigments?

Carotenoids are called accessory pigments because they absorb light and pass the energy on to chlorophyll. Both xanthophylls and carotenes are found in chloroplasts. In autumn, when the leaves of deciduous trees die, their chlorophyll degrades first. The wavelengths reflected by the carotenoids and other pigments that remain turn forests into spectacular displays of yellow, orange, and red.

Carotenoids absorb wavelengths of light that are not absorbed by chlorophyll. As a result, they extend the range of wavelengths that can drive photosynthesis.

Researchers discovered an even more important function for carotenoids, though, by analyzing what happens to leaves when these pigments are destroyed. Many herbicides, for example, work by inhibiting enzymes that are involved in carotenoid synthesis. Plants lacking carotenoids rapidly lose their chlorophyll, turn white, and die. Based on these results, researchers have concluded that carotenoids also serve a protective function.

To understand why carotenoids are protective, recall that photons—especially the high-energy, short-wavelength photons in the ultraviolet part of the electromagnetic spectrum—contain enough energy to knock electrons out of atoms and create free radicals (see Chapter 2). Free radicals, in turn, trigger reactions that can disrupt and degrade molecules.

Carotenoids "quench" free radicals by accepting or stabilizing unpaired electrons. As a result, they protect chlorophyll molecules from harm. When carotenoids are absent, chlorophyll molecules are destroyed and photosynthesis stops. Starvation and death follow.

When Light Is Absorbed, Electrons Enter an Excited State

Just what is absorption? What happens when a photon of a particular wavelength—say, red light with a wavelength of 680 nm—strikes a chlorophyll molecule?

When a photon strikes a chlorophyll molecule, the photon's energy can be transferred to an electron in the chlorophyll molecule's head region. In response, the electron is "excited," or raised to a higher energy state.

The excited electron states that are possible in a particular pigment are discrete—meaning, incremental rather than continuous—and can be represented as lines on an energy scale. These discrete energy levels are a property of the electron configurations in a particular pigment.

FIGURE 10.9 shows the ground state, or unexcited state, as 0 and the higher energy states as 1 and 2. If the difference between the possible energy states is the same as the energy in the photon, the photon can be absorbed and an electron excited to a higher energy state.

In chlorophyll, for example, the energy difference between the ground state and state 1 is equal to the energy in a red photon, while the energy difference between state 0 and state 2 is equal to the energy in a blue photon. Thus, chlorophyll can readily absorb red photons and blue photons.

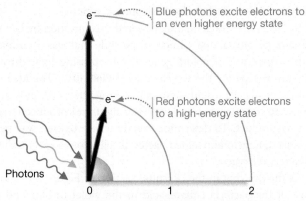

FIGURE 10.9 Electrons Are Promoted to High-Energy States When Photons Strike Chlorophyll. The unexcited, or ground state, is labeled 0, and the discrete energy states are labeled 1 and 2. The wavelength of light that will excite electrons to these energy states is a property of chlorophyll's structure.

✓**QUESTION** Suppose a pigment had a discrete energy state that corresponded to the energy in green light. Where would you draw this energy state on this diagram?

Chlorophyll does not absorb green light well, because there is no discrete step—no difference in possible energy states for its electrons—that corresponds to the amount of energy in a green photon.

Wavelengths in the ultraviolet part of the spectrum have so much energy that they may actually eject electrons from a pigment molecule and create a free radical. In contrast, wavelengths in the infrared regions have so little energy that in most cases they merely increase the movement of atoms in the pigment, generating heat—meaning molecular movement—rather than exciting electrons.

But if a pigment absorbs a photon with the right amount of energy, energy in the form of electromagnetic radiation is transferred to that electron. The electron now has high potential energy. What happens next?

If the excited electron simply falls back to its ground state, the absorbed energy is released as heat or a combination of heat and electromagnetic radiation (light). When the electron energy produces light, it is called **fluorescence.** Because some of the original photon's energy is transformed to heat, the electromagnetic radiation that is given off during fluorescence has lower energy and a longer wavelength than the original photon did.

When photons are absorbed by pigments in chloroplasts though, only about 2 percent of the excited electrons produce fluorescence. The other 98 percent of the energized pigments use their excited electrons to drive photosynthesis.

To understand what happens to these excited electrons, it's important to recognize that chlorophyll molecules work in groups—not individually. In the thylakoid membrane, 200–300 chlorophyll molecules and accessory pigments are organized by an array of proteins to form structures called the **antenna complex** and the **reaction center.** These complexes, along with the molecules that capture and process excited electrons, form a **photosystem.**

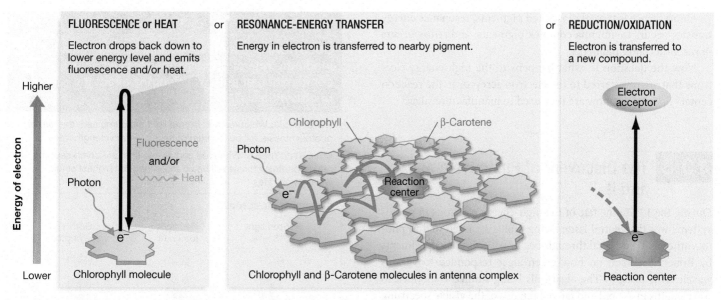

| FLUORESCENCE or HEAT | or | RESONANCE-ENERGY TRANSFER | or | REDUCTION/OXIDATION |

FLUORESCENCE or HEAT
Electron drops back down to lower energy level and emits fluorescence and/or heat.

RESONANCE-ENERGY TRANSFER
Energy in electron is transferred to nearby pigment.

REDUCTION/OXIDATION
Electron is transferred to a new compound.

Higher

Energy of electron

Fluorescence and/or Heat

Photon

e⁻

Lower

Chlorophyll molecule

Chlorophyll

Photon

e⁻

Reaction center

β-Carotene

Chlorophyll and β-Carotene molecules in antenna complex

Electron acceptor

e⁻

Reaction center

FIGURE 10.10 Four Fates for Excited Electrons in Photosynthetic Pigments. When sunlight promotes electrons in pigments to a high-energy state, four things can happen: They can fluoresce, release heat, pass energy to a nearby pigment via resonance, or transfer the electron to an electron acceptor.

The Antenna Complex When a red or blue photon strikes a pigment molecule in the antenna complex, the energy is absorbed and an electron is excited in response. This energy—but not the electron itself—is passed to a nearby chlorophyll molecule, where another electron is excited in response. This phenomenon is known as resonance energy transfer.

Resonance energy transfer is possible only between pigments that are able to absorb different wavelengths of photons—from those absorbing higher-energy photons to those absorbing lower-energy photons. The organization of the antenna complex makes it possible for this resonance energy to be efficiently moved between pigments, as the potential energy drops at each step.

Once the energy is transferred, the original excited electron falls back to its ground state. In this way, energy is transferred inside the antenna complex in a manner that may be likened to the transfer of excitement between fans at a sports event during the "wave." But unlike the stadium wave, most of this resonance energy is directed to a particular location in a photosystem, called the reaction center.

The Reaction Center When a chlorophyll molecule is excited in the **reaction center,** its excited electron is transferred to an electron acceptor. When the acceptor becomes reduced, the energy transformation event that started with the absorption of light becomes permanent: Electromagnetic energy is transformed to chemical energy. The redox reaction that occurs in the reaction center results in the production of chemical energy from sunlight.

Note that in the absence of light, the electron acceptor does not accept electrons. It remains in an oxidized state because the redox reaction that transfers an electron to the electron acceptor is endergonic. But when light excites electrons in chlorophyll to a high-energy state, the reaction becomes exergonic. In this way, the energy in light transforms an endergonic reaction to an exergonic one.

FIGURE 10.10 summarizes the four possible fates of electrons in chlorophyll that are excited by photons. The energy released from these electrons can

1. be emitted in the form of light via fluorescence, or
2. be given off as heat alone, or
3. excite an electron in a nearby pigment and induce resonance, or
4. be transferred to an electron acceptor in a redox reaction.

check your understanding

If you understand that . . .

- Pigments absorb specific wavelengths of light.
- When a chlorophyll molecule in the antenna complex of a chloroplast membrane absorbs red or blue light, one of its electrons is promoted to a high-energy state.
- In the antenna complex, high-energy electrons transmit their energy between chlorophyll molecules toward the reaction center.
- When energy is transferred to a chlorophyll molecule in the reaction center, the excited electron reduces an electron acceptor. In this way, light energy is transformed to chemical energy.

✔ You should be able to . . .

Predict how the pigments of the antenna complex would be organized, with regard to the wavelength of photons absorbed, to allow the directional transport of energy from the outer pigments to the reaction center.

Answers are available in Appendix A.

Fluorescence is typical of isolated pigments, resonance energy transfer occurs in antenna complex pigments, and redox occurs in reaction center pigments.

Now the question is, what happens to the high-energy electrons that are transferred to the electron acceptor in the reaction center? Specifically, how are they used to manufacture sugar?

10.3 The Discovery of Photosystems I and II

During the 1950s, the fate of the high-energy electrons in photosystems was the central issue facing biologists interested in photosynthesis. A key breakthrough began with simple experiments by Robert Emerson on how green algae responded to various wavelengths of light. The algal cells being studied responded to wavelengths in the red and far-red regions of the visible spectrum.

Emerson found that if the algal cells were illuminated with either red or far-red wavelengths of light, the photosynthetic response was moderate. But if cells were exposed to a combination of both wavelengths, the rate of photosynthesis increased more than the sum of the rates produced by each wavelength independently. This phenomenon was called the enhancement effect, and is not limited to algal cells. In follow-up work by other researchers, it was also observed in isolated chloroplasts from plants (**FIGURE 10.11**). Why the enhancement effect occurred was a complete mystery at the time.

A solution to this puzzle was proposed by Robin Hill and Faye Bendall, who hypothesized that this enhancement effect resulted from two distinct types of reaction centers, each absorbing different wavelengths of light. According to the two-photosystem hypothesis, the enhancement effect occurs because photosynthesis is much more efficient when both photosystems operate together.

Subsequent work has shown that the two-photosystem hypothesis is correct for cyanobacteria ("blue-green bacteria") and the chloroplasts of eukaryotes, such as algae and plants. These two photosystems differ in structure and function, but work together in the light-capturing reactions.

To figure out how the two photosystems work, investigators focused on species of photosynthetic bacteria that possess one or the other of the two photosystems, but not both. Once each type of photosystem was understood in isolation, researchers explored how they work in combination. Let's do the same—first let's analyze **photosystem II,** then **photosystem I** (so named because it was discovered first), and then how the two interact.

How Does Photosystem II Work?

To study photosystem II, researchers focused on purple photosynthetic bacteria, including the purple sulfur bacteria that were studied by van Niel (see Section 10.1). These cells have a single photosystem that has many of the same components observed in photosystem II of cyanobacteria and the chloroplasts of algae and plants. (For simplicity, the eukaryotic chloroplast will serve as the model system for the remainder of the chapter.)

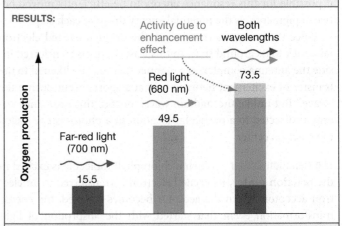

RESEARCH

QUESTION: Red and far-red light each stimulate a moderate rate of photosynthesis. How does a combination of both wavelengths affect the rate of photosynthesis?

HYPOTHESIS: When red and far-red light are combined, the rate of photosynthesis will be the sum of the single wavelength rates.

NULL HYPOTHESIS: When red and far-red light are combined, the rate of photosynthesis will be no more than the highest single wavelength rate.

EXPERIMENTAL SETUP:

Far-red light (713 nm)   Red light (653 nm)   Both wavelengths

O₂?   O₂?   O₂?

1. Expose algal cells to far-red light and then red light. Record oxygen produced as a measure of rate of photosynthesis.   **2.** Expose same cells to a combination of both lights.

PREDICTION: When the two wavelengths are combined, the amount of oxygen produced will be the sum of the single wavelength tests.

PREDICTION OF NULL HYPOTHESIS: When the two wavelengths are combined, the amount of oxygen produced will be no more than the single wavelength test that yielded the highest amount of oxygen.

RESULTS:

Activity due to enhancement effect

Both wavelengths

Red light (680 nm)   73.5

49.5

Far-red light (700 nm)

Oxygen production

15.5

CONCLUSION: Neither hypothesis is correct. The combination of both wavelengths yielded more oxygen than the sum of the single tests. A new hypothesis is required to explain this enhancement effect.

FIGURE 10.11 The "Enhancement Effect" of Two Different Wavelengths in Isolated Chloroplasts.

SOURCE: Govindjee, R., Govindjee, and G. Hoch. 1964. Emerson enhancement effect in chloroplast reactions. *Plant Physiology* 39: 10–14.

✔**QUESTION** Was it important for the researchers to keep the density of chloroplasts fairly constant in each treatment? Explain why or why not.

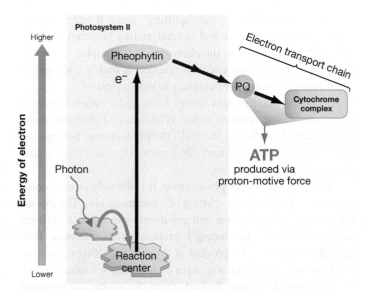

FIGURE 10.12 **Photosystem II Feeds High-Energy Electrons to an Electron Transport Chain.** When an excited electron leaves the chlorophyll in the reaction center of photosystem II, the electron is accepted by pheophytin, transferred to plastoquinone (PQ), and then stepped down in energy along an electron transport chain.

Converting Light Energy into Chemical Energy In photosystem II, the action begins when the antenna complex transmits resonance energy to the reaction center, where the electron acceptor pheophytin comes into play (**FIGURE 10.12**). Structurally,

pheophytin is identical to chlorophyll except that pheophytin lacks a magnesium atom in its head region. Functionally, the two molecules are extremely different.

Instead of acting as a pigment that energizes an electron when it absorbs a photon, pheophytin accepts high-energy electrons from the excited reaction center chlorophylls. The reduction of pheophytin (and the accompanying oxidation of the reaction center chlorophyll pigment) is a key step in the transformation of light energy into chemical energy.

Electrons that reduce pheophytin are passed through additional carriers to an electron transport chain (ETC) in the thylakoid membrane. In both structure and function, this ETC is similar to components in the mitochondrial ETC (see Chapter 9).

- Structurally, the ETC associated with photosystem II and the ETC in the mitochondrion both contain quinones and cytochromes.

- Functionally, the redox reactions that occur in both ETCs result in protons being actively transported from one side of an internal membrane to the other. The resulting proton electrochemical gradient forms a proton-motive force that drives ATP production via ATP synthase. Photosystem II triggers chemiosmosis and ATP synthesis in the chloroplast.

FIGURE 10.13 explains how the electron transport chain associated with photosystem II works in more detail. Start by focusing on the molecule called **plastoquinone (PQ)**—a quinone similar to ubiquinone in the ETC of cellular respiration. Recall that

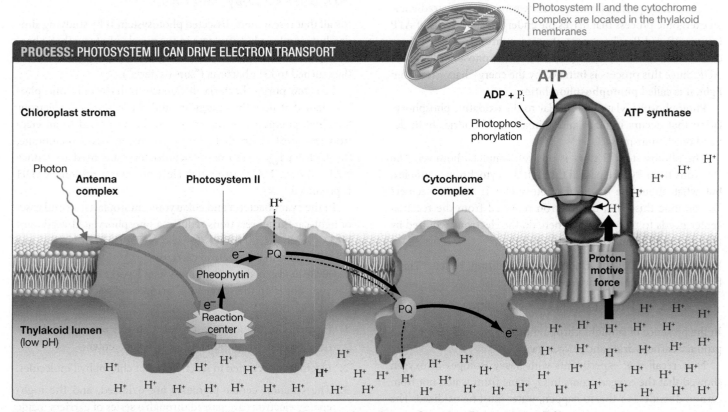

FIGURE 10.13 **Electron Transport between Photosystem II and the Cytochrome Complex.** Plastoquinone (PQ) carries electrons from photosystem II along with protons from the stroma. The cytochrome complex oxidizes plastoquinone, releasing the protons in the thylakoid lumen that drive ATP synthesis.

quinones are small hydrophobic molecules that can transport electrons between molecules (see Chapter 9). Because plastoquinone is lipid soluble and not anchored to the thylakoid membrane, it is free to move from one side of the thylakoid membrane to the other.

When plastoquinone receives electrons from photosystem II, it carries them across the membrane to the lumen side of the thylakoid and delivers them to more electronegative molecules in the cytochrome complex. In this way, plastoquinone shuttles electrons from photosystem II to the cytochrome complex much like ubiquinone shuttled electrons between complexes I or II and complex III in mitochondria. The potential energy released by these reactions allows protons to be picked up from the stroma and dropped off in the lumen side of the thylakoid membrane.

The protons transported by plastoquinone result in a large concentration of protons in the thylakoid lumen. When photosystem II is active, the pH of the thylakoid interior reaches 5 while the pH of the stroma hovers around 8. Because the pH scale is logarithmic, the difference of 3 units means that the concentration of H^+ is 10 ☒ 10 ☒ 10 ☒ 1000 times higher in the lumen than in the stroma. In addition, the stroma becomes negatively charged relative to the thylakoid lumen.

The net effect of electron transport, then, is to set up a large proton electrochemical gradient, resulting in a proton-motive force that drives H^+ out of the thylakoid lumen and into the stroma. Based on what you know of cellular respiration, it should come as no surprise that this proton-motive force drives the production of ATP.

Specifically, proton flow down the electrochemical gradient is an exergonic process that drives the endergonic synthesis of ATP from ADP and P_i. The stream of protons through ATP synthase causes conformational changes that drive the phosphorylation of ADP. Since this process is initiated by the energy harvested from light, it is called **photophosphorylation.**

Photophosphorylation is similar to the oxidative phosphorylation that occurs in plant and animal mitochondria. Both depend on chemiosmosis.

The photosystem II story is not yet complete, however. The electrons from PQ are passed through the cytochrome complex, but what about the oxidized photosystem II reaction center? To continue this ETC, the electron removed from the reaction center needs to be replaced. Where do the electrons required by photosystem II come from?

Photosystem II Obtains Electrons by Oxidizing Water Think back to the overall reaction for photosynthesis:

$$6\,CO_2 + 6\,H_2O + \text{light energy} \longrightarrow C_6H_{12}O_6 + 6\,O_2$$

In the presence of sunlight, carbon dioxide and water are used to produce carbohydrate and oxygen gas.

Now recall that experiments with heavy isotopes of oxygen showed that the oxygen atoms in O_2 come from water, not from carbon dioxide. For this to happen, water must be oxidized. The oxygen-generating reaction can be written as

$$2\,H_2O \longrightarrow 4\,H^+ + 4\,e^- + O_2$$

This reaction is referred to as "splitting" water. It supplies electrons for photosystem II and is catalyzed by enzymes that are physically integrated into the photosystem II complex. Since oxygen is very electronegative, this reaction is highly endergonic. What supplies the energy necessary to oxidize water?

As it turns out, the light energy harvested by photosystem II is responsible for splitting water. When excited electrons leave photosystem II and enter the ETC, the photosystem becomes so electronegative that enzymes can remove electrons from water, leaving protons and oxygen.

Among all life-forms, photosystem II is the only protein complex that can catalyze the splitting of water molecules. The photosystem II of cyanobacteria and eukaryotic chloroplasts perform **oxygenic** ("oxygen-producing") photosynthesis, because they generate oxygen as a by-product of the process. Other organisms that have only a single photosystem do not oxidize water, and thus do not produce O_2 gas. Instead, these organisms use different electron donors, such as H_2S in the purple sulfur bacteria, to perform **anoxygenic** ("no oxygen-producing") photosynthesis.

✔ If you understand photosystem II, you should be able to make an energy flowchart that includes the antenna complex, ATP synthase, pheophytin, light, the proton gradient, an ETC, and a reaction center and then add notes explaining where the enzyme complex that splits water fits in.

What happens next in green algae and land plants? The answer lies in photosystem I. Let's take a closer look.

How Does Photosystem I Work?

Recall that researchers dissected photosystem II by studying similar, but simpler, photosystems in the purple photosynthetic bacteria. To understand the structure and function of photosystem I, they turned to heliobacteria ("sun-bacteria").

Like the purple bacteria, heliobacteria have only one photosystem that uses the energy in sunlight to promote electrons to a high-energy state. But instead of being passed to an electron transport chain that pumps protons across a membrane, the high-energy electrons in heliobacteria are used to reduce NAD^+. When NAD^+ gains two electrons and a proton, NADH is produced.

In the cyanobacteria and eukaryotic chloroplasts, a similar set of light-capturing reactions reduces a phosphorylated version of NAD^+, symbolized $NADP^+$, to yield NADPH. Both NADH and NADPH function as electron carriers.

FIGURE 10.14 explains how photosystem I works in chloroplasts—put your finger on the "2 photons" arrows and trace the steps that follow.

1. Pigments in the antenna complex absorb photons and pass the energy to the photosystem I reaction center.

2. Electrons are excited in reaction center chlorophyll molecules.

3. The reaction center pigments are oxidized, and the high-energy electrons are passed through a series of carriers inside the photosystem, then to a molecule called **ferredoxin,** and then to the enzyme called $NADP^+$ reductase.

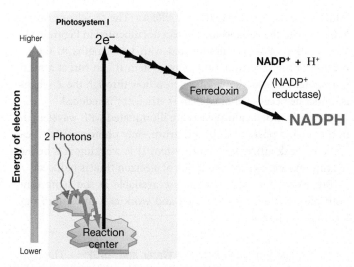

FIGURE 10.14 Photosystem I Produces NADPH. When excited electrons leave the chlorophyll molecule in the reaction center of photosystem I, they pass through a series of iron- and sulfur-containing proteins until they are accepted by ferredoxin. In an enzyme-catalyzed reaction, the reduced form of ferredoxin reacts with NADP$^{\boxtimes}$ to produce NADPH.

4. NADP$^+$ reductase transfers two electrons and a proton to NADP$^+$. This reaction forms NADPH.

Photosystem I and NADP$^+$ reductase are anchored in the thylakoid membrane; ferredoxin is in the stroma, but it is closely associated with the thylakoid membrane.

To summarize: Electrons from photosystem I are used to produce NADPH, which is a reducing agent similar in function to the NADH and FADH$_2$ produced by the citric acid cycle. Electrons from photosystem II, in contrast, are used to produce a proton-motive force that drives the synthesis of ATP.

In combination, then, photosystems II and I produce chemical energy stored in ATP and NADPH. But there are still gaps in the flow of electrons through these two photosystems. Where do the electrons from photosystem II end up? How does the oxidized reaction center of photosystem I obtain electrons so NADPH will continue to be made?

The Z Scheme: Photosystems II and I Work Together

FIGURE 10.15 illustrates the **Z-scheme** model for how photosystems II and I interact. The name was inspired by the changes occurring in electron potential energy as plotted on a vertical axis, which takes on the shape of a Z that has fallen over.

To drive home how energy flows through the light-capturing reactions, trace the route of electrons through Figure 10.15 with your finger. Start on the lower left. The process starts when photons excite electrons in the chlorophyll molecules of photosystem II's antenna complex. When the energy in the excited electrons is transferred to the reaction center, a special pair of chlorophyll molecules, called P680, passes excited electrons to pheophytin. These are the same reaction center pigments described previously, and the name represents the wavelength of photons absorbed (680 nm).

When pheophytin is reduced, it transfers the high-energy electron to an electron transport chain. There the electron is gradually stepped down in potential energy through redox reactions among a series of quinones and cytochromes. Using the energy released by the redox reactions, plastoquinone (PQ) carries protons across the thylakoid membrane, from the stroma to the lumen. ATP synthase uses the resulting proton-motive force to phosphorylate ADP, creating ATP.

When electrons reach the end of the cytochrome complex, they are passed to a small diffusible protein called **plastocyanin**

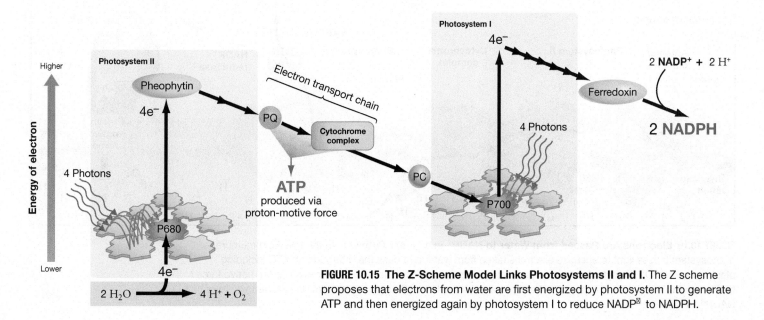

FIGURE 10.15 The Z-Scheme Model Links Photosystems II and I. The Z scheme proposes that electrons from water are first energized by photosystem II to generate ATP and then energized again by photosystem I to reduce NADP$^{\boxtimes}$ to NADPH.

(symbolized as PC in Figure 10.15). The reduced plastocyanin diffuses through the lumen of the thylakoid, and donates the electron to an oxidized reaction center pigment in photosystem I.

Stop tracing for a moment, and consider the following:

- Plastocyanin is critical—it forms a physical link between photosystem II and photosystem I.

- A single plastocyanin molecule can shuttle over 1000 electrons per second between the cytochrome complex and photosystem I.

- The flow of electrons between photosystems, by means of plastocyanin, is important because it replaces electrons that are carried away from the pair of pigments in the photosystem I reaction center. This pair of specialized chlorophyll molecules is called P700 (absorbs 700-nm photons).

Now keep going. The electrons that flow from photosystem II to P700, via plastocyanin, are eventually transferred to the protein ferredoxin, which passes electrons to an enzyme that catalyzes the reduction of $NADP^+$ to NADPH.

Finally, direct your attention back to the lower-left portion of the figure. Note that the electrons that initially left photosystem II are replaced by electrons that are stripped away from water, producing oxygen gas as a by-product.

✔ If you understand the Z-scheme model, you should be able to describe (1) the role of plastocyanin in linking the two photosystems, and (2) the point where the electrons that flow through the system have their highest potential energy.

Understanding the Enhancement Effect The Z-scheme model helps explain the enhancement effect documented in Figure 10.11. When chloroplasts are illuminated with wavelengths in the red portion of the spectrum, only photosystem II can run at a maximum rate. The overall rate of electron flow through the Z scheme is moderate because photosystem I's efficiency is reduced.

Similarly, when chloroplasts are illuminated with wavelengths in the far-red portion of the spectrum, only photosystem I is capable of peak efficiency; photosystem II is working at a below-maximum rate, so the overall rate of electron flow is reduced.

But when both wavelengths are available at the same time, both photosystems are activated and work at a maximum rate, leading to enhanced efficiency.

Noncyclic Electron Flow between Water and NADP$^⊠$ The complete path that electrons follow from photosystem II to photosystem I and how it is oriented in the thylakoid membrane is shown in **FIGURE 10.16**. Note that electrons pass from water to $NADP^+$ through a chain of redox reactions in a linear fashion, referred to as **noncyclic electron flow.**

Compare the movement of electrons and protons in Figure 10.16 with what you have learned about electron transport chains in mitochondria (see Figure 9.15). In both these organelles, the energy released from redox reactions is used to build a proton gradient for ATP production. At the end of the chains, electrons are donated to terminal electron acceptors.

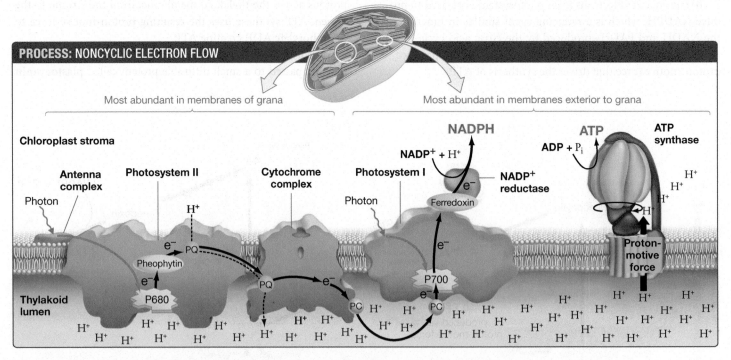

PROCESS: NONCYCLIC ELECTRON FLOW

FIGURE 10.16 Electrons Are Passed from Water to NADP$^⊠$ in a Linear Pathway. In the thylakoid membrane, photosystem II uses light to energize electrons taken from water and pass them through an ETC including plastoquinone (PQ), the cytochrome complex, and plastocyanin (PC). The ETC produces a proton motive force that is used to make ATP. Photosystem I energizes electrons from PC and passes them on to ferredoxin to reduce NADP$^⊠$ to NADPH.

Chloroplasts and mitochondria differ, however, in how electron potential energy changes between the primary electron donor and the terminal electron acceptor. In the mitochondrial ETC, electron potential energy starts high and then steadily drops as the electrons are transferred to the terminal electron acceptor, which has the lowest potential energy. In chloroplasts, the reduced terminal electron acceptor (NADPH) has higher potential energy than the electron donor (H_2O) (see Figure 10.15).

Cyclic Electron Flow Recycles Electrons and Drives Photophosphorylation

Recent evidence indicates that an alternative electron path, called **cyclic electron flow,** also occurs in green algae and plants (**FIGURE 10.17**). In these organisms, ATP is produced via cyclic as well as noncyclic photophosphorylation.

During cyclic electron flow, photosystem I transfers electrons back to the electron transport chain associated with photosystem II, generating ATP through photophosphorylation instead of reducing $NADP^+$. This "extra" ATP is used for the chemical reactions that reduce carbon dioxide (CO_2) and produce sugars. Cyclic electron flow coexists with the noncyclic electron flow and produces additional ATP.

Where Are Photosystems II and I Located?

Although both photosystems reside in the thylakoid membrane, their distribution is far from random. Photosystem II and the cytochrome complex are much more abundant in the interior, stacked membranes of grana, while photosystem I and ATP synthase are much more common in the exterior, unstacked membranes.

This organization seems appropriate for ATP synthase. As shown in Figure 10.16, this enzyme complex is oriented with its bulky head toward the stroma, so avoiding the tightly stacked grana makes sense. In addition, ATP synthase and the $NADP^+$ reductase that is associated with photosystem I require substrates that are found in the stroma, such as ADP, P_i, and $NADP^+$. These substrates would not be as readily available if the enzymes were buried in the membrane folds of the grana.

The benefit of physically separating the two photosystems is the focus of intense research and debate. Unlike ATP synthase, the functions of photosystems I and II are tightly integrated, requiring electrons to be transported between them in noncyclic electron flow. Compared to other electron transport chains, the distance between where plastocyanin is reduced—the cytochrome complex—and where it is oxidized—the photosystem I reaction center—is huge. This separation between the photosystems is currently thought to be involved in regulating the switch between noncyclic and cyclic electron flow.

Oxygenic Photosynthesis and the Evolution of Earth

Although oxygen is a by-product of photosynthesis, the impact of producing this molecule on the environment of early Earth cannot be overstated. Photosynthesis produces the oxygen that is keeping you alive right now. Biologists rank the evolution of Earth's oxygen-rich atmosphere as one of the most important events in the history of life. Why?

According to the geologic record, oxygen levels in the atmosphere and oceans began to rise only about 2 billion years ago, as organisms that performed oxygenic photosynthesis increased in abundance. O_2 was, in fact, almost nonexistent on Earth before enzymes evolved that could catalyze the oxidation of water. Since ozone is formed from O_2 gas, this protective layer would have arisen in our atmosphere only after the evolution of oxygenic photosynthesis. Without the ozone layer, Earth's surface would have been bombarded continually by the searing intensity of ultraviolet radiation—making the evolution of life on land nearly impossible.

As oxygen became more abundant, bacterial cells that evolved the ability to use it as an electron acceptor via cellular respiration began to dominate. O_2 is so electronegative that it creates a huge potential energy drop for the electron transport chains involved in cellular respiration. As a result, organisms that use O_2 as an electron acceptor in cellular respiration can produce much more ATP than can organisms that use other electron acceptors (see Chapter 9). In addition, this accumulation of oxygen was a disaster for anaerobic organisms because O_2 is such a powerful oxidant it is toxic to them.

Determining exactly how photosystem II splits water and generates oxygen may be the greatest challenge currently facing researchers interested in photosynthesis. This issue has important practical applications: If human chemists could replicate the reaction, it might be possible to produce huge volumes of O_2 and hydrogen gas (H_2) from water. The resulting H_2 could provide a clean, inexpensive fuel for vehicles.

Despite the importance of oxygen in the evolution and maintenance of life, in terms of photosynthesis, it is simply waste. The useful products of the light-capturing reactions are ATP and NADPH, which are required to reduce carbon dioxide to sugar. Your life, and the life of most organisms, also depends on this process. How does it happen?

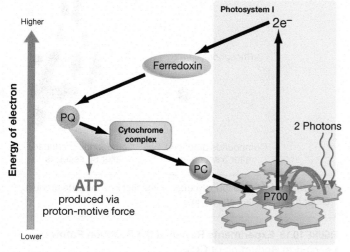

FIGURE 10.17 Cyclic Electron Flow Leads to ATP Production. Cyclic electron flow is an alternative to the Z scheme. Instead of being donated to NADP⊠, electrons are returned to plastoquinone (PQ) and cycle between photosystem I and the ETC, resulting in the production of additional ATP via photophosphorylation.

If you understand that . . .

- Photosystem II contributes high-energy electrons to an electron transport chain that pumps protons, creating a proton-motive force that drives ATP synthase.
- Photosystem I uses high-energy electrons to make NADPH and can produce additional ATP by building a proton-motive force via cyclic electron flow.

✔ **You should be able to . . .**

Compare and contrast the flow of electrons in mitochondria and chloroplasts. What are the primary electron donors and terminal electron acceptors, and how do they differ in terms of energy?

Answers are available in Appendix A.

10.4 How Is Carbon Dioxide Reduced to Produce Sugars?

The reactions analyzed in Section 10.3 are triggered by light. This is logical, because their entire function is focused on transforming electromagnetic energy in the form of sunlight into chemical energy in the phosphate bonds of ATP and the electrons of NADPH. The reactions that produce sugar from carbon dioxide, in contrast, are not triggered directly by light. Instead, they depend on the ATP and NADPH produced by the light-capturing reactions of photosynthesis.

The Calvin Cycle Fixes Carbon

Carbon fixation is the addition of carbon dioxide to an organic compound. The word *fix* is appropriate because the process converts or fixes CO_2 gas to a biologically useful form. Once carbon atoms are fixed, they can be used as sources of energy and as building blocks to construct the molecules found in cells.

Carbon fixation is a redox reaction—the carbon atom in CO_2 is reduced. Research on how this happens in chloroplasts gained momentum just after World War II, when radioactive isotopes of carbon became available for research purposes.

Melvin Calvin's group made great strides early in this effort by tracking the incorporation of $^{14}CO_2$ into molecules during photosynthesis (**FIGURE 10.18**). After injecting $^{14}CO_2$ into a culture of algae that were undergoing photosynthesis, they stopped the reaction after different periods of time by killing the cells in hot alcohol. This treatment immediately denatured the enzymes involved in the reactions, effectively halting any further change in the radiolabeled intermediates.

The molecules labeled with the ^{14}C in this extract were separated by chromatography and detected using X-ray film. If radioactively labeled molecules were present in the chromatograph,

RESEARCH

QUESTION: What intermediates are produced as carbon dioxide is reduced to sugar?

HYPOTHESIS: No specific hypothesis.

EXPERIMENTAL SETUP:

1. Add $^{14}CO_2$ to actively photosynthesizing algae.

2. Wait 5–60 seconds; then homogenize cells by immersing in hot alcohol.

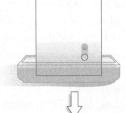

3. Separate molecules via chromatography.

4. Lay X-ray film on chromatograph to locate radioactive label.

PREDICTION: No specific prediction.

RESULTS:

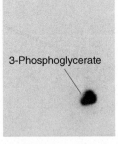
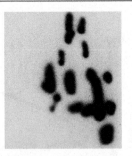

3-Phosphoglycerate

Compounds produced after 5 seconds   Compounds produced after 60 seconds

CONCLUSION: 3-Phosphoglycerate is the first intermediate product. Other intermediates appear later.

FIGURE 10.18 Experiments Revealed the Reaction Pathway Leading to Reduction of CO_2.

SOURCE: Benson, A. A., J. A. Bassham, M. Calvin, et al. 1950. The path of carbon in photosynthesis. V. Paper chromatography and radioautography of the products. *Journal of the American Chemistry Society* 72: 1710–1718.

✔ **QUESTION** Why wasn't this experiment based on a specific hypothesis and set of predictions?

the energy they emitted would expose the film and create a dark spot. The labeled compounds could then be isolated and identified.

By varying the amount of time the algae were exposed to labeled $^{14}CO_2$, Calvin and co-workers pieced together the sequence in which various intermediates formed. For example, when the team analyzed cells almost immediately after adding the $^{14}CO_2$, they found that the ^{14}C was predominantly in a three-carbon compound called 3-phosphoglycerate (3PGA). This result suggested that 3PGA was the initial product of carbon reduction. Stated another way, it appeared that carbon dioxide reacted with some unknown molecule to produce 3PGA.

This was an intriguing result, because 3-phosphoglycerate is also one of the 10 intermediates in glycolysis. The Calvin cycle manufactures carbohydrate; glycolysis breaks it down. Because the two processes are related in this way, it was logical that at least some intermediates in glycolysis and the Calvin cycle are the same.

RuBP Is the Initial Reactant with CO₂ Which compound reacts with CO_2 to produce 3-phosphoglycerate? This was the key, initial step. Calvin's group searched in vain for a two-carbon compound that might serve as the initial carbon dioxide acceptor and yield 3PGA.

Then, while Calvin was running errands one day, it occurred to him that the molecule reacting with carbon dioxide might contain five carbons, not two. Adding CO_2 to a five-carbon molecule would produce a six-carbon compound, which could then split in half to form 2 three-carbon molecules.

Experiments to test this hypothesis confirmed that the five-carbon compound **ribulose bisphosphate (RuBP)** is the initial reactant.

The Calvin Cycle Is a Three-Step Process The complete Calvin cycle, as it came to be called, has three phases (**FIGURE 10.19**):

1. *Fixation phase* The Calvin cycle begins when CO_2 reacts with RuBP. This phase fixes carbon and produces two molecules of 3PGA.

2. *Reduction phase* The 3PGA is phosphorylated by ATP and then reduced by electrons from NADPH. The product is the phosphorylated three-carbon sugar **glyceraldehyde-3-phosphate (G3P)**. Some of the G3P that is synthesized is drawn off to manufacture glucose and fructose.

3. *Regeneration phase* The rest of the G3P keeps the cycle going by serving as the substrate for the third phase in the cycle: reactions that use additional ATP in the regeneration of RuBP.

All three phases take place in the stroma of chloroplasts. One turn of the Calvin cycle fixes one molecule of CO_2. Three turns of the cycle fix three molecules of CO_2, yielding one molecule of G3P and fully regenerated RuBP (Figure 10.19).

The discovery of the Calvin cycle clarified how the ATP and NADPH produced by light-capturing reactions allow cells to reduce CO_2 gas to carbohydrate $(CH_2O)_n$. Because sugars store a great deal of potential energy, producing them takes a great deal of chemical energy. In the Calvin cycle, each mole of CO_2 requires the energy from 3 moles of ATP and 2 moles of

(a) The Calvin cycle has three phases.

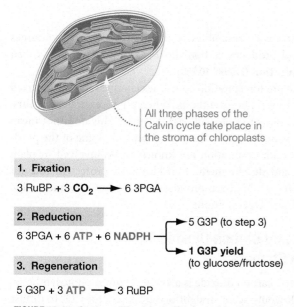

All three phases of the Calvin cycle take place in the stroma of chloroplasts

1. Fixation

3 RuBP + 3 **CO₂** ⟶ 6 3PGA

2. Reduction

6 3PGA + 6 **ATP** + 6 **NADPH** ⟶ 5 G3P (to step 3)
⟶ **1 G3P yield** (to glucose/fructose)

3. Regeneration

5 G3P + 3 **ATP** ⟶ 3 RuBP

(b) The reaction occurs in a cycle.

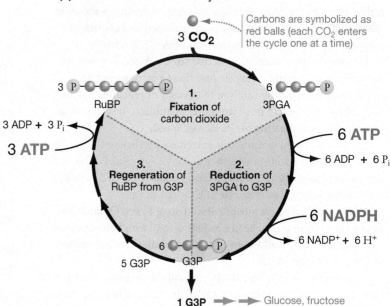

FIGURE 10.19 **Carbon Dioxide Is Reduced in the Calvin Cycle.** The number of reactants and products resulting from three turns of the cycle are shown. Of the six G3Ps that are generated during the reduction phase, one is used in the synthesis of glucose or fructose and the other five are used to regenerate RuBP. The 3 RuBPs that are regenerated participate in fixation reactions for additional turns of the cycle.

NADPH to fix it and reduce it to sugar. ✔ QUANTITATIVE If you understand the Calvin cycle, you should be able to provide the *minimum number* of RuBP, ATP, and NADPH molecules that would be required to run through six complete cycles. Explain why you would not need six RuBP molecules to fix and reduce six CO_2.

The conversion of CO_2 gas into carbohydrate is, without doubt, worthy of this energy investment. Plants use sugars to fuel cellular respiration and build leaves and other structures. Millions of non-photosynthetic organisms—from fungi to mammals—also depend on this reaction to provide the sugars they need for cellular respiration.

Ecologically, the addition of CO_2 to RuBP may be the most important chemical reaction on Earth. The enzyme that catalyzes it is fundamental to life. How does this protein work?

The Discovery of Rubisco

Most reactions involved in reducing CO_2 also occur during glycolysis or other metabolic pathways. The initial CO_2 fixation phase of the Calvin cycle, however, is one of only two reactions that are entirely unique to the Calvin cycle.

To find the enzyme that fixes CO_2 to RuBP, Arthur Weissbach and colleagues ground up spinach leaves, purified a large series of proteins from the resulting cell extracts, and tested each protein to see if it could catalyze this step. Eventually they isolated the catalyst, which happens to be the most abundant enzyme in leaf tissue. The researchers' data suggested that it constituted almost 50 percent of the total protein in spinach leaves.

The CO_2-fixing enzyme, ribulose-1,5-bisphosphate carboxylase/oxygenase (commonly referred to as **rubisco**), is found in all photosynthetic organisms that use the Calvin cycle to fix carbon and is thought to be the most abundant enzyme on Earth. As shown in **FIGURE 10.20a**, the rubisco enzyme is cube-shaped and consists of 16 polypeptides that form eight active sites where CO_2 is fixed.

Despite its large number of active sites, rubisco is a slow enzyme. Each active site catalyzes just three reactions per second; other enzymes typically catalyze thousands of reactions per second. Plants synthesize huge amounts of rubisco, possibly as an adaptation compensating for its lack of speed.

Besides being slow, rubisco is extremely inefficient because it will catalyze the addition of either O_2 or CO_2 to RuBP. This is a key point: Oxygen and carbon dioxide compete at the enzyme's active sites, which slows the rate of CO_2 reduction.

Why would an active site of rubisco accept both O_2 and CO_2? Given rubisco's importance in producing food for photosynthetic species, this trait would appear to be **maladaptive**—it reduces the fitness of individuals.

The reaction of O_2 with RuBP actually does more than just compete with the reaction of CO_2 at the same active site. One of the molecules produced from the addition of oxygen to RuBP is processed in reactions that consume ATP and release CO_2 in order to regenerate 3PGA. Part of this pathway occurs in chloroplasts, and part occurs in peroxisomes and mitochondria. The

(a) Rubisco has 16 subunits and a total of 8 active sites.

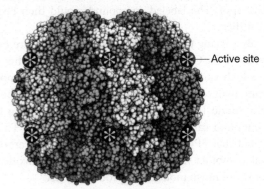

— Active site

(b) Rubisco's active sites can interact with CO_2 or O_2.

Reaction with carbon dioxide during photosynthesis:

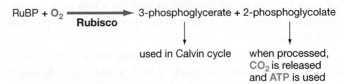

RuBP + CO_2 —Rubisco→ 2 3-phosphoglycerate

used in Calvin cycle

Reaction with oxygen during photorespiration:

RuBP + O_2 —Rubisco→ 3-phosphoglycerate + 2-phosphoglycolate

used in Calvin cycle | when processed, CO_2 is released and ATP is used

FIGURE 10.20 Rubisco Is a Large Enzyme Complex That Can React with CO_2 or O_2. (a) The cube shape of rubisco consists of multiple polypeptides that form eight catalytic active sites. **(b)** In addition to fixing CO_2 in photosynthesis, rubisco catalyzes a competing reaction with O_2 with a very different outcome.

reaction sequence resembles respiration, because it consumes oxygen and produces carbon dioxide. As a result, it is called **photorespiration** (**FIGURE 10.20b**).

Because photorespiration consumes energy and releases fixed CO_2, it "undoes" photosynthesis. When photorespiration occurs, the overall rate of photosynthesis declines. This does not mean that there is no benefit to the plant, however. Some of the products from photorespiration are known to be involved in plant signaling and development. In addition, a protective role for photorespiration has been proposed when plants are under high light and low CO_2 conditions.

Oxygen and Carbon Dioxide Pass through Stomata

Atmospheric carbon dioxide is a key reactant in photosynthesizing cells. It would seem straightforward, then, for CO_2 to diffuse directly into plants along a concentration gradient. But the situation is not this simple, because plants are covered with a waxy coating called a cuticle. This lipid layer prevents water from evaporating out of tissues, but it also prevents the transport of gases like CO_2 and O_2.

How does CO_2 get into photosynthesizing tissues? The surface of a leaf is dotted with openings bordered by two distinctively shaped cells called **guard cells** (**FIGURE 10.21a**). The opening between these paired cells is called a pore, and the entire structure is a **stoma** (plural: **stomata**).

An open stoma allows CO_2 from the atmosphere to diffuse into air-filled spaces inside the leaf and excess O_2 to diffuse out (**FIGURE 10.21b**). Eventually the CO_2 diffuses along a concentration gradient into the chloroplasts of photosynthesizing cells. A strong concentration gradient favoring entry of CO_2 is maintained by the Calvin cycle, which constantly uses up the CO_2 in chloroplasts.

Stomata are normally open during the day, when photosynthesis is occurring, and closed at night. But if the daytime is extremely hot and dry, leaf cells may lose a great deal of water to evaporation through their stomata. When this occurs, they must either close the openings and halt photosynthesis or risk death from dehydration.

(a) Leaf surfaces contain stomata.

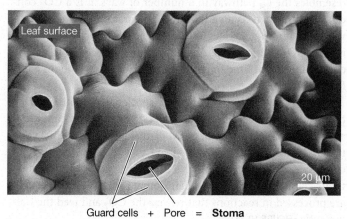

Guard cells   +   Pore   =   **Stoma**

(b) Carbon dioxide diffuses into leaves through stomata.

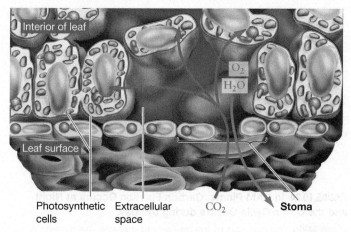

Photosynthetic   Extracellular CO_2 **Stoma**
cells   space

FIGURE 10.21 Leaf Cells Obtain Carbon Dioxide through Stomata.

When conditions are hot and dry, then, stomata must close and CO_2 and O_2 transport stops—meaning that photosynthesis slows and photorespiration increases. How do plants that live in hot, dry environments prevent dehydration while keeping CO_2 supplies high enough to avoid photorespiration?

Mechanisms for Increasing CO_2 Concentration

The oxygenation reaction that triggers photorespiration is favored when oxygen concentrations are high and CO_2 concentrations are low. But even with the stomata open, the atmosphere is 21 percent oxygen and only 0.03 percent carbon dioxide. How can photosynthesizing cells raise CO_2 concentrations to make photosynthesis more efficient? An answer emerged in a surprising experimental result.

The C_4 Pathway After the Calvin cycle had been worked out in algae, researchers in a variety of labs used the same radioactive carbon dioxide tracking approach to investigate how carbon fixation occurs in other species. Hugo Kortschak and colleagues and Y. S. Karpilov and associates exposed leaves of sugarcane and maize (corn) to $^{14}CO_2$ and sunlight; then they isolated and identified the intermediates.

Both research teams expected to find the first of the radioactive carbon atoms in 3-phosphoglycerate—the normal product of carbon fixation by rubisco. Instead, they found that in their species, the radioactive carbon atom ended up in four-carbon compounds such as malate and aspartate.

Instead of creating a three-carbon molecule as in the Calvin cycle, it appeared that these species were able to fix CO_2 to produce four-carbon molecules. This newly identified set of reactions became known as the C_4 **pathway** to distinguish it from Calvin's CO_2 fixation via what is now termed the C_3 **pathway** (**FIGURE 10.22**).

Researchers who followed up on the initial reports found that the C_4 pathway does not replace the Calvin cycle, but serves as an additional fixation step. C_4 plants can actually fix carbon dioxide using both pathways—to a three-carbon compound by an enzyme called **PEP carboxylase** (C_4) and to RuBP by rubisco (C_3). They also showed that the two pathways are found in distinct cell types within the same leaf. PEP carboxylase is common in **mesophyll cells** near the surface of leaves, while rubisco is found in **bundle-sheath cells** that surround the vascular tissue in the

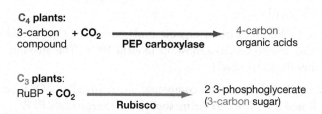

FIGURE 10.22 Initial Carbon Fixation in C_4 Plants Is Different from That in C_3 Plants.

(a) C_4 plant

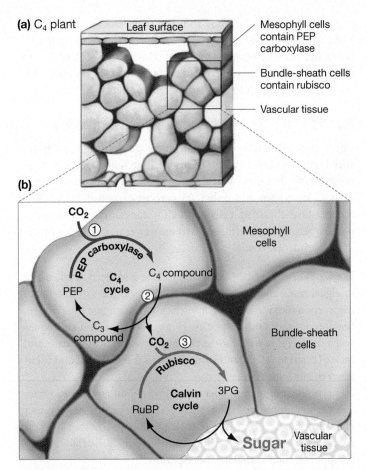

Leaf surface

Mesophyll cells contain PEP carboxylase

Bundle-sheath cells contain rubisco

Vascular tissue

(b)

CO_2

① PEP carboxylase

C_4 cycle

PEP

C_4 compound

②

C_3 compound

CO_2 ③

Rubisco

RuBP

Calvin cycle

3PG

Sugar

Mesophyll cells

Bundle-sheath cells

Vascular tissue

FIGURE 10.23 In C_4 Plants, Carbon Fixation and the Calvin Cycle Occur in Different Cell Types. (a) The carbon-fixing enzyme PEP carboxylase is located in mesophyll cells, while rubisco is in bundle-sheath cells. **(b)** CO_2 is fixed to the three-carbon compound PEP by PEP carboxylase, forming a four-carbon organic acid. A CO_2 molecule from the four-carbon sugar then feeds the Calvin cycle.

interior of the leaf (**FIGURE 10.23a**). Vascular tissue conducts water and nutrients in plants (see Chapter 38).

Based on the observations about C_4 plants, Hal Hatch and Roger Slack proposed a four-step model to explain how CO_2 that is fixed to a four-carbon sugar feeds the Calvin cycle (**FIGURE 10.23b**):

Step 1 PEP carboxylase fixes CO_2 to a three-carbon molecule (phosphoenolpyruvate, or PEP) in mesophyll cells.

Step 2 The four-carbon organic acids that result are transported to bundle-sheath cells via channels called plasmodesmata (see Chapter 11).

Step 3 The four-carbon organic acids release a CO_2 molecule that rubisco uses as a substrate to form 3PGA. This step initiates the Calvin cycle.

Step 4 The three-carbon compound remaining after CO_2 is released is returned to the mesophyll cell to regenerate PEP.

In effect, then, the C_4 pathway acts as a CO_2 concentrator. The reactions that take place in mesophyll cells require energy in the form of ATP, but they increase CO_2 concentrations in cells where rubisco is active. Because it increases the ratio of carbon dioxide to oxygen in photosynthesizing cells, less O_2 binds to rubisco's active sites. As a result, the C_4 pathway improves the efficiency of the Calvin cycle.

The C_4 pathway is an adaptation that keeps CO_2 concentrations in leaves high, but it comes at a cost. For each glucose molecule generated via photosynthesis, C_4 plants expend 30 ATP molecules compared to the 18 ATP molecules required by C_3 plants. This energy expenditure, however, is justified by the increased efficiency of photosynthesis in conditions where stomata are mostly closed to prevent dehydration. The affinity for CO_2 by PEP carboxylase is also much higher than that of rubisco, which means that stomata can be open for shorter periods in C_4 plants.

This strategy is not the only mechanism that plants use to continue growth in hot, dry climates, however. Some environments are so arid that even C_4 plants are unable to avoid dehydration. Nevertheless, certain plants use the C_4 pathway in a unique way that allows them to thrive in these deserts. How do they do it?

CAM Plants Researchers studying a group of flowering plants called the Crassulaceae discovered a second mechanism for limiting the effects of dehydration and photorespiration. This photosynthetic pathway, **crassulacean acid metabolism,** or **CAM,** resembles the C_4 pathway in a number of ways. It is a CO_2 concentrator that acts as an additional, preparatory step to the Calvin cycle. It also generates an organic acid with four carbons in its first CO_2 fixation step. But unlike the C_4 pathway, CAM occurs at a different time than the Calvin cycle does—not in a different place.

CAM occurs in cacti and other species that routinely keep their stomata closed on hot, dry days. At night, when conditions are cooler and more humid, CAM plants open their stomata and take in huge quantities of CO_2. The CO_2 is temporarily fixed to organic acids and stored in the central vacuoles of photosynthetic cells. During the day, when stomata are closed, these acids are processed in reactions that release the CO_2 and feed the Calvin cycle (**FIGURE 10.24**).

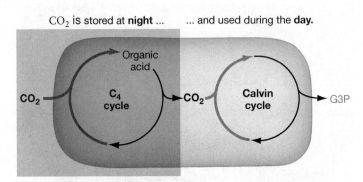

CO_2 is stored at **night** ...   ... and used during the **day.**

CO_2

Organic acid

C_4 cycle

CO_2

Calvin cycle

G3P

FIGURE 10.24 In CAM Plants, Carbon Fixation Occurs at Night and the Calvin Cycle Occurs during the Day.

✔**QUESTION** At what part of the day would there be the highest concentration of four-carbon acids in the vacuoles of CAM plants?

The C_4 and CAM pathways function as CO_2 pumps. They minimize photorespiration when stomata are closed and CO_2 cannot diffuse in directly from the atmosphere. Both are found in species that live in hot, dry environments.

But while C_4 plants stockpile CO_2 by fixing and storing organic acids in cells *where* rubisco is not active, CAM plants store CO_2 *when* rubisco is inactive. In C_4 plants, the reactions catalyzed by PEP carboxylase and rubisco are separated in space; in CAM plants, the reactions are separated in time.

How Is Photosynthesis Regulated?

Like cellular respiration, photosynthesis is regulated. Although the mechanisms responsible for turning photosynthesis on or off are still under investigation, several patterns have emerged:

- The presence of light triggers the production of proteins required for photosynthesis.

- When sugar supplies are high, the production of proteins required for photosynthesis is inhibited, but the production of proteins required to process and store sugars is stimulated.

- Rubisco is activated by regulatory molecules that are produced when light is available, but inhibited in conditions of low CO_2 availability—when photorespiration is favored.

The central message here is that the rate of photosynthesis is finely tuned to use resources efficiently in response to changes in environmental conditions.

What Happens to the Sugar That Is Produced by Photosynthesis?

The products of the Calvin cycle enter one of several reaction pathways. The most important of these reaction sequences produces the monosaccharides glucose and fructose from G3P, a process called **gluconeogenesis.** This glucose is often combined with fructose to form the disaccharide ("two-sugar") **sucrose.**

When photosynthesis is taking place slowly, almost all the glucose that is produced is used to make sucrose. Sucrose is water soluble and readily transported to other parts of the plant. If sucrose is delivered to rapidly growing parts of the plant, it is broken down to fuel cellular respiration and growth.

An alternative pathway occurs when photosynthesis is proceeding rapidly and sucrose is abundant. Under these conditions, the glucose molecules are polymerized to form **starch** in the leaves and in storage cells in the roots. Starch production occurs inside the chloroplast; sucrose synthesis takes place in the cytosol.

In photosynthesizing cells, starch acts as a temporary sugar-storage product. At night, the starch that is stored in leaf cells is broken down and used to manufacture sucrose molecules. The sucrose is then broken down via cellular respiration or transported to other parts of the plant. In this way, chloroplasts provide sugars for cells throughout the plant by day and by night.

If a mouse eats the starch that is stored in the leaves or roots of a plant, however, the chemical energy in the reduced carbons of starch fuels the mouse's growth and reproduction. If an owl eats the mouse, the chemical energy in the mouse's tissues fuels the predator's growth and reproduction. (You can see the Big Picture of how energy is processed via photosynthesis and cellular respiration on pages 198–199.)

In this way, virtually all cell activity can be traced back to the sun's energy that was originally captured by photosynthesis. Photosynthesis is the staff of life.

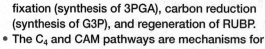

If you understand that . . .

- The Calvin cycle is a three-phase process: CO_2 fixation (synthesis of 3PGA), carbon reduction (synthesis of G3P), and regeneration of RUBP.
- The C_4 and CAM pathways are mechanisms for increasing CO_2 concentrations in photosynthesizing cells. They limit the effect of photorespiration and allow photosynthesis to continue after stomata close.
- In photosynthesizing cells, G3P is used to make sucrose or stored as starch. Sucrose is transported to all plant cells and used to drive cellular respiration.

✔ **You should be able to . . .**

1. Describe how CO_2 is delivered to rubisco (a) via organic acids in mesophyll cells, (b) via organic acids stored in vacuoles, and (c) directly.

2. Predict the relative concentration of starch in leaves at the start of the day versus the end of the day.

Answers are available in Appendix A.

If you understand . . .

10.1 Photosynthesis Harnesses Sunlight to Make Carbohydrate

- The light-capturing reactions occur in internal membranes of the chloroplast that are organized into structures called thylakoids in stacks known as grana.
- The Calvin cycle takes place in a fluid portion of the chloroplast called the stroma.
- The CO_2-reduction reactions of photosynthesis depend on the products of the light-capturing reactions.

✔ You should be able to explain why it is not entirely accurate to adopt the common phrase "light-independent reactions" when referring to the Calvin cycle.

10.2 How Do Pigments Capture Light Energy?

- Pigment molecules capture light energy by exciting electrons after a photon is absorbed. Each pigment absorbs particular photons on the basis of their wavelengths.
- After a pigment molecule absorbs a photon, the energy may be released as fluorescence, resonance energy that excites a neighboring pigment, or the reduction of an electron acceptor.
- Pigments organized into antenna complexes will transfer the absorbed light energy via resonance to the reaction center, where an excited electron is transferred to an electron acceptor. The reduction of this electron acceptor completes the transformation of light energy into chemical energy.

✔ You should be able to explain why extracted chlorophyll molecules produce more fluorescence compared to the same number of chlorophyll molecules that remain in chloroplasts.

10.3 The Discovery of Photosystems I and II

- In photosystem II, high-energy electrons are accepted by pheophytin and passed along an electron transport chain, releasing energy that moves protons across the thylakoid membrane. The resulting proton-motive force drives the synthesis of ATP by ATP synthase. Photosystem II takes electrons from water, releasing oxygen and protons.
- In photosystem I, high-energy electrons are passed to ferredoxin. In an enzyme-catalyzed reaction, the reduced form of ferredoxin passes electrons to $NADP^+$, forming NADPH.
- The Z scheme connects photosystems II and I. Plastocyanin carries electrons from the end of photosystem II's ETC to photosystem I. They are promoted to a high-energy state in photosystem I's reaction center, and subsequently used to reduce $NADP^+$.
- Electrons from photosystem I may occasionally be passed back to photosystem II's ETC instead of being used to reduce $NADP^+$. A cyclic flow of electrons between the two photosystems boosts ATP supplies.

✔ You should be able to explain why measuring the rate of oxygen production in chloroplasts is appropriate for estimating the rate of photosynthesis.

10.4 How Is Carbon Dioxide Reduced to Produce Sugars?

- The Calvin cycle starts when CO_2 is attached to a five-carbon compound called ribulose bisphosphate (RuBP) in a reaction catalyzed by the enzyme rubisco.
- The six-carbon compound that results immediately splits in half to form two molecules of 3-phosphoglycerate (3PGA), which is then phosphorylated by ATP and reduced by NADPH to produce a sugar called glyceraldehyde-3-phosphate (G3P).
- Some G3P is used to synthesize glucose and fructose, which combine to form sucrose; the rest are phosphorylated by more ATP in a series of reactions that regenerate RuBP so the cycle can continue.
- Rubisco catalyzes the addition of oxygen as well as carbon dioxide to RuBP. The reaction with oxygen leads to a loss of fixed CO_2 and ATP and is called photorespiration.
- C_4 plants and CAM plants fix CO_2 to organic acids, before it is transferred to rubisco. As a result, they can increase CO_2 levels in their tissues, reducing the effect of photorespiration and allowing photosynthesis to continue when stomata close.

✔ QUANTITATIVE You should be able to connect the light-capturing reactions and Calvin cycle by estimating the number of photons required to produce one glucose molecule from CO_2. How would photorespiration affect the number of photons required per glucose?

MB MasteringBiology

1. **MasteringBiology Assignments**

Tutorials and Activities Calvin Cycle; Chemiosmosis; Energy Flow in Plants; Experimental Inquiry: Which Wavelengths of Light Drive Photosynthesis?; Light Energy and Pigments; Light Reactions; Overview of Photosynthesis; Photosynthesis: Inputs, Outputs, and Chloroplast Structure; Photosynthesis: The Light Reactions; Photosynthesis in Dry Climates; Sites of Photosynthesis

Questions Reading Quizzes, Blue-Thread Questions, Test Bank

2. **eText** Read your book online, search, take notes, highlight text, and more.

3. **The Study Area** Practice Test, Cumulative Test, BioFlix® 3-D Animations, Videos, Activities, Audio Glossary, Word Study Tools, Art

You should be able to . . .

1. In antenna complexes, how is energy transferred among the pigment molecules?
   a. photophosphorylation
   b. redox reactions
   c. fluorescence
   d. resonance

2. Why is chlorophyll green?
   a. It absorbs all wavelengths in the visible spectrum.
   b. It absorbs wavelengths only in the red portions of the spectrum (680 nm, 700 nm).
   c. It absorbs wavelengths in only the blue and red parts of the visible spectrum.
   d. It absorbs wavelengths only in the blue part of the visible spectrum.

3. What do the light-capturing reactions of photosynthesis produce?
   a. G3P
   b. RuBP
   c. ATP and NADPH
   d. sucrose or starch

4. Why do the absorption spectrum for chlorophyll and the action spectrum for photosynthesis coincide?
   a. Photosystems I and II are activated by different wavelengths of light.
   b. Wavelengths of light that are absorbed by chlorophyll trigger the light-capturing reactions.
   c. Energy from wavelengths absorbed by carotenoids is passed on to chlorophyll.
   d. The rate of photosynthesis depends on the amount of light received.

5. At what point in the light-capturing reactions is the electromagnetic energy of light converted into chemical energy? Where does this occur?

6. In noncyclic electron flow, photosystems I and II function as an integrated unit. What connects the two photosystems?

7. Explain how electrons from water can be used to produce both ATP and NADPH.

8. In addition to their protective function, carotenoids absorb certain wavelengths of light and pass the energy to other pigments via resonance. Based on this function, where would you expect carotenoids to be located in the chloroplast?
   a. the reaction centers of photosystems I and II
   b. the inner membrane of chloroplasts
   c. the antenna complex
   d. the stroma

9. Describe the three phases of the Calvin cycle and how the products of the light-capturing reactions participate in this process.

10. What conditions favor photorespiration? What are its consequences for the plant?

11. Compare and contrast how C_4 plants and CAM plants separate the acquisition of CO_2 from the production of sugar in the Calvin cycle.

12. Why do plants need both chloroplasts and mitochondria? How do their roles differ in the cell?

13. Predict how the following conditions would affect the production of O_2, ATP, and NADPH and state whether noncyclic or cyclic electron flow would occur in each: (1) Only blue photons hit a chloroplast; (2) blue and red photons hit a chloroplast, but no $NADP^+$ is available; (3) blue and red photons hit a chloroplast, but a proton channel has been introduced into the thylakoid membrane, so it is fully permeable to protons.

14. Some biologists claim that photorespiration is an evolutionary "holdover," because rubisco evolved over a billion years ago when O_2 levels were extremely low and CO_2 concentrations relatively high. Do you agree with this hypothesis? Why or why not?

15. An investigator exposes chloroplasts to 700-nm photons and observes low O_2 production, but high ATP production. Which of the following best explains this observation?

   a. The electrons from water are directly transferred to $NADP^+$, which is used to generate ATP.
   b. Photosystem II is not splitting water, and the ATP is being produced by cycling electrons via photosystem I.
   c. The O_2 is being converted to water as a terminal electron acceptor in the production of ATP.
   d. Electron transport has stopped and ATP is being produced by the Calvin cycle.

16. Consider plants that occupy the top, middle, or ground layer of a forest, and algae that live near the surface of the ocean or in deeper water. Would you expect the same photosynthetic pigments to be found in species that live in these different habitats? Why or why not? How would you test your hypothesis?

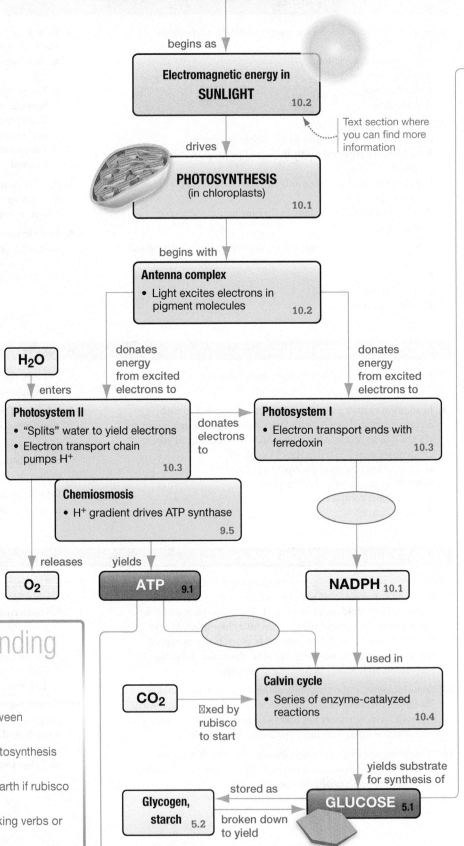

BIG PICTURE

The Big Picture

It takes energy to stay alive. Use this concept map to study how the information on energy and energetics presented in this book fits together.

As you read the map, remember that chemical energy is potential energy. Potential energy is based on the position of matter in space, and chemical energy is all about the position of electrons in covalent bonds. When hydrogen gas reacts explosively with oxygen, all that's happening is that electrons are moving from high-energy positions to lower-energy positions.

In essence, organisms transform energy from the Sun into chemical energy in the C–C and C–H bonds of glucose, and then into chemical energy in the P–P bonds of ATP.

The potential energy in ATP allows cells to do work: pump ions, synthesize molecules, move cargo, and send and receive signals.

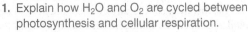

check your understanding

Ⓒ **If you understand the big picture . . .**

Ⓨ ✔ **You should be able to . . .**

Ⓤ
1. Explain how H_2O and O_2 are cycled between photosynthesis and cellular respiration.

2. Explain how CO_2 is cycled between photosynthesis and cellular respiration.

3. Describe what might happen to life on Earth if rubisco were suddenly unable to fix CO_2.

4. Fill in the blue ovals with appropriate linking verbs or phrases.

Answers are available in Appendix A.

ENERGY FOR LIFE

begins as

Electromagnetic energy in SUNLIGHT 10.2

Text section where you can find more information

drives

PHOTOSYNTHESIS (in chloroplasts) 10.1

begins with

Antenna complex
- Light excites electrons in pigment molecules 10.2

donates energy from excited electrons to

donates energy from excited electrons to

H_2O

enters

Photosystem II
- "Splits" water to yield electrons
- Electron transport chain pumps H^+ 10.3

donates electrons to

Photosystem I
- Electron transport ends with ferredoxin 10.3

Chemiosmosis
- H^+ gradient drives ATP synthase 9.5

releases

yields

O_2

ATP 9.1

NADPH 10.1

used in

Calvin cycle
- Series of enzyme-catalyzed reactions 10.4

CO_2

fixed by rubisco to start

yields substrate for synthesis of

Glycogen, starch 5.2

stored as

broken down to yield

GLUCOSE 5.1

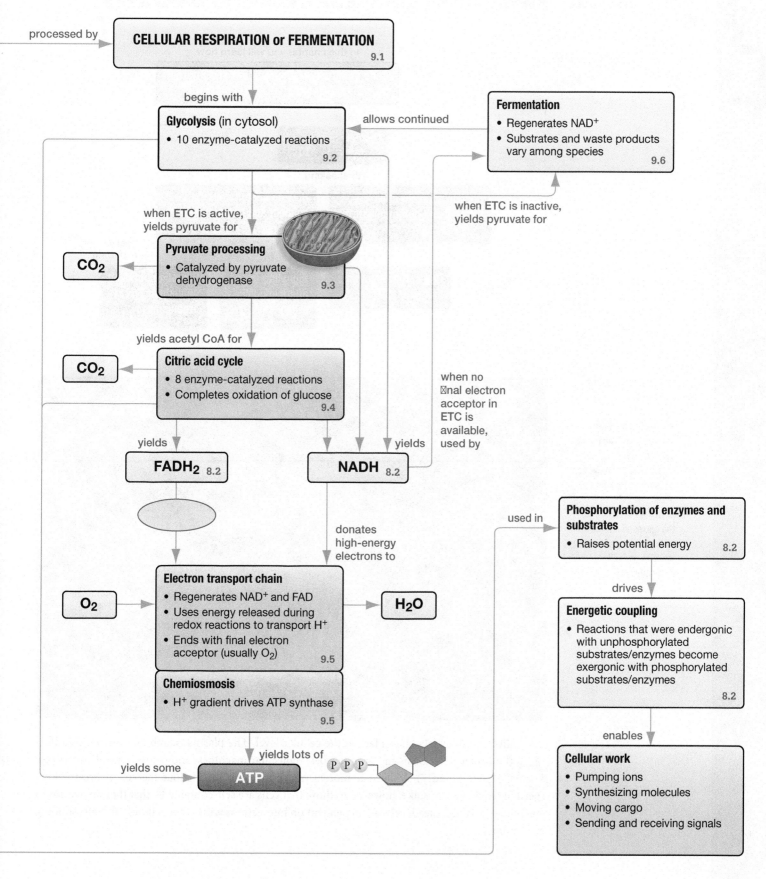

processed by

CELLULAR RESPIRATION or FERMENTATION
9.1

begins with

Glycolysis (in cytosol)
• 10 enzyme-catalyzed reactions
9.2

allows continued

Fermentation
• Regenerates NAD^+
• Substrates and waste products vary among species
9.6

when ETC is active,
yields pyruvate for

when ETC is inactive,
yields pyruvate for

Pyruvate processing
• Catalyzed by pyruvate dehydrogenase
9.3

CO_2

yields acetyl CoA for

CO_2

Citric acid cycle
• 8 enzyme-catalyzed reactions
• Completes oxidation of glucose
9.4

when no ⊠nal electron acceptor in ETC is available, used by

yields

yields

FADH$_2$ 8.2

NADH 8.2

Phosphorylation of enzymes and substrates
• Raises potential energy
8.2

used in

donates high-energy electrons to

drives

O_2

Electron transport chain
• Regenerates NAD^+ and FAD
• Uses energy released during redox reactions to transport H^+
• Ends with final electron acceptor (usually O_2)
9.5

H_2O

Energetic coupling
• Reactions that were endergonic with unphosphorylated substrates/enzymes become exergonic with phosphorylated substrates/enzymes
8.2

Chemiosmosis
• H^+ gradient drives ATP synthase
9.5

enables

Cellular work
• Pumping ions
• Synthesizing molecules
• Moving cargo
• Sending and receiving signals

yields some

yields lots of

P P P

ATP

11 Cell–Cell Interactions

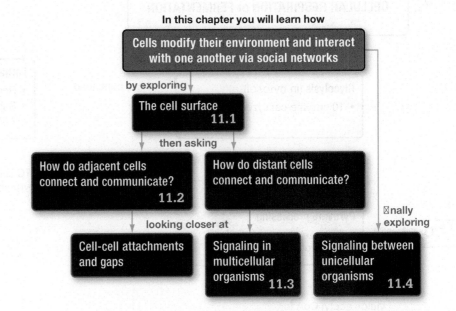

In this chapter you will learn how

Cells modify their environment and interact with one another via social networks

by exploring ↓

The cell surface
11.1

then asking ↓

How do adjacent cells connect and communicate?
11.2

How do distant cells connect and communicate?

finally exploring ↓

looking closer at ↓

Cell-cell attachments and gaps

Signaling in multicellular organisms **11.3**

Signaling between unicellular organisms **11.4**

In this micrograph of cardiac tissue, muscle cells are stained red and their nuclei are stained blue. The green dye highlights a protein called dystrophin, which links the cytoskeleton of muscle cells to proteins that attach to the extracellular matrix. Deficiency in dystrophin leads to muscular dystrophy.

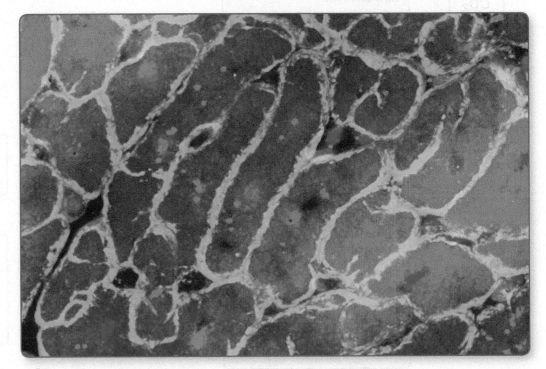

A diversity of events takes place at the cellular level. The plasma membrane surrounds a bustling enterprise consisting of organelles, molecular machines, and cytoskeletal elements (see Chapters 6 and 7). Molecular motors transport cargo throughout the cell at breathtaking speed. It would be a mistake, however, to think that cells are self-contained—that they are worlds in and of themselves. Instead, cells are dependent on interactions with other cells and the surrounding environment.

✔ When you see this checkmark, stop and test yourself. Answers are available in Appendix A.

For most unicellular species, the outside environment is teeming with other organisms. Inside your gut, for example, hundreds of billions of bacterial cells are jostling for space and resources. In addition to interacting with these individuals, every unicellular organism must contend with constant shifts in the physical environment, such as heat, light, ion concentrations, and food supplies. If unicellular organisms are unable to sense these conditions and respond appropriately, they die.

In multicellular species, the environment outside the cell is made up of other cells, both neighboring and distant. The cells that make up a redwood tree, a mushroom, or your body are intensely social. Although biologists often study cells in isolation, an individual tree, fungus, or person is actually an interdependent community of cells. If those cells do not communicate and cooperate, the whole will break into dysfunctional parts and die.

To understand the life of a cell, then, it is critical to analyze how the cell interacts with the world outside its membrane. How do cells obtain information about the world and respond to that information? In particular, how do cells interact with other cells? To answer these questions, let's begin with the cell surface—with the molecules that separate the cell from its environment.

11.1 The Cell Surface

The line between life and nonlife is drawn by the plasma membrane that surrounds every cell. Recall that the structure of this membrane consists of a phospholipid bilayer studded with membrane proteins that are integral, meaning that they are embedded in the bilayer, or peripheral, meaning that they are attached to one surface (see Chapter 6). These proteins participate in the primary function of the plasma membrane: to create an environment inside the cell that is different from conditions outside by regulating the transport of substances.

The plasma membrane does not exist in isolation, however. Cytoskeletal elements attach to the interior face of the bilayer (see Chapter 7), and a complex array of extracellular structures interacts with the membrane's exterior surface. Let's consider the nature of the material outside the cell and then analyze how the cell interacts with it and other cells.

The Structure and Function of an Extracellular Layer

It is actually extremely rare for cells to be bounded simply by a plasma membrane. Most cells secrete products that are assembled into a layer or wall just beyond the membrane. This extracellular material helps define the cell's shape and either attaches it to another cell or acts as a first line of defense against the outside world.

Virtually all types of extracellular structures—from the cell walls of bacteria, algae, fungi, and plants to the extracellular material that surrounds most animal cells—follow the same fundamental design principle. Like reinforced concrete, they are "fiber composites": They consist of a cross-linked network of long

Concrete (the "ground substance") resists compression

Steel rods (the "fibers") resist tension

FIGURE 11.1 Fiber Composites Resist Tension and Compression. Fiber composites, such as reinforced concrete, consist of ground substance that fills spaces between cross-linked rods.

filaments embedded in a stiff surrounding material, or ground substance (**FIGURE 11.1**). The molecules that make up the filaments and the encasing material vary from group to group, but the engineering principle is the same. Why?

- The rods or filaments in a fiber composite are extremely effective at withstanding stretching and straining forces, or tension. The fibers present in extracellular material of most cells are functionally similar to the steel rods in reinforced concrete—they resist being pulled or pushed lengthwise.

- The stiff surrounding substance is effective at withstanding the pressing forces called compression. Concrete performs this function in highways, and a gel-forming mixture of polysaccharides achieves the same end in extracellular material.

Thanks to the combination of tension- and compression-resisting elements, fiber composites are particularly rugged. And in many living cells, the fiber and composite elements are flexible as well as strong.

What molecules make up the rods and ground substance found on the surface of plant and animal cells? How are these extracellular layers synthesized, and what do they do?

The Cell Wall in Plants

Virtually all plant cells are surrounded by a cell wall—a fiber composite that is the basis of major industries. The paper in this book, the threads in your cotton clothing, and the wood in your neighborhood's houses are made up primarily of plant cell walls.

Before analyzing the structure of plant cell walls in detail, it's important to note that these structures are dynamic. If they are damaged by attacking insects, they may release signaling molecules that trigger the reinforcement of walls in nearby cells. Cell walls are also degraded in a controlled way as fruits ripen, making the fruits softer and more digestible for the animals that disperse the seeds inside.

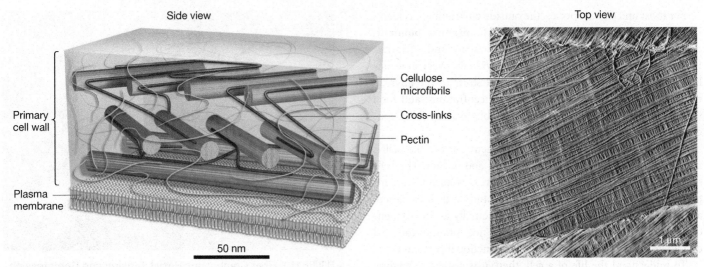

Side view   Top view

Cellulose
microfibrils

Cross-links

Pectin

Primary
cell wall

Plasma
membrane

50 nm

1 μm

FIGURE 11.2 Primary Cell Walls of Plants Are Fiber Composites. In a plant's primary cell wall, cellulose microfibrils are cross-linked by polysaccharide chains. The spaces between the microfibrils are filled with pectin molecules, which form a gelatinous solid.

Primary Cell Walls   When plant cells first form, they secrete an initial fiber composite called a **primary cell wall.**

- The fibrous component of the primary cell wall consists of long strands of cellulose, which are bundled into stout, cable-like structures termed **microfibrils** and then cross-linked by other polysaccharide filaments. The microfibrils are synthesized by a complex of enzymes in the plasma membrane, forming a crisscrossed network (**FIGURE 11.2**).

- The space between microfibrils is filled with gelatinous polysaccharides such as **pectins**—the molecules that are used to thicken jams and jellies. Because the polysaccharides in pectin are hydrophilic, they attract and hold large amounts of water to keep the cell wall moist. The gelatinous components of the cell wall are synthesized in the rough endoplasmic reticulum and Golgi apparatus and secreted to the extracellular space.

The primary cell wall defines the shape of a plant cell. Under normal conditions, the nucleus and cytoplasm fill the entire volume of the cell and push the plasma membrane up against the wall. Because the concentration of solutes is higher inside the cell than outside, water tends to enter the cell via osmosis. The incoming water increases the cell's volume, exerting a force against the wall that is known as **turgor pressure.**

Although plant cells experience turgor pressure throughout their lives, it is particularly important in young cells that are actively growing. Young plant cells secrete proteins named expansins into their cell wall. **Expansins** disrupt hydrogen bonds that cross-link the microfibrils in the wall, allowing them to slide past one another. Turgor pressure then forces the wall to elongate and expand. The result is cell growth (see Chapter 40).

Secondary Cell Walls   As plant cells mature and stop growing, they may secrete an additional layer of material—a **secondary cell wall**—between the plasma membrane and the primary cell wall. The structure of the secondary cell wall varies from cell to cell in the plant and correlates with that cell's function. Cells on the surface of a leaf have secondary cell walls that are impregnated with waxes that form a waterproof coating; the cells that support the plant's stem have secondary cell walls that contain a great deal of cellulose.

In cells that form wood, the secondary cell wall also includes **lignin,** a complex polymer that forms an exceptionally rigid network. Cells that have thick secondary cell walls of cellulose and lignin help plants withstand the forces of gravity and wind.

Although animal cells do not make a cell wall, they do form a fiber composite outside their plasma membrane. What is this substance, and what does it do?

The Extracellular Matrix in Animals

Most animal cells secrete a fiber composite called the **extracellular matrix (ECM).** Like the extracellular materials found in other organisms, structural support is one of the ECM's most important functions.

ECM design follows the same principles observed in the cell walls of bacteria, archaea, algae, fungi, and plants. There is a key difference, however: The animal ECM contains much more protein relative to carbohydrate than does a cell wall.

- The fibrous component of animal ECM is dominated by a cable-like protein termed **collagen** (**FIGURE 11.3a**).

- The matrix that surrounds collagen and other fibrous components contains gel-forming **proteoglycans** that consist of protein cores with many large polysaccharides attached to them. In some tissues, complexes of proteoglycans may also be produced (**FIGURE 11.3b**).

Most ECM components are synthesized in the rough endoplasmic reticulum (ER), processed in the Golgi apparatus, and

(a) Collagen proteins consist of three polypeptide chains that wind around one another to form the fibrous component of the animal ECM.

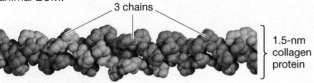

3 chains

1.5-nm collagen protein

(b) Complexes of gelatinous proteoglycans form the ground substance of the animal ECM.

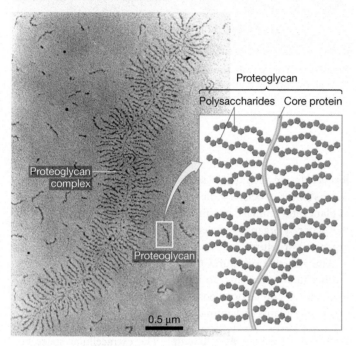

Proteoglycan complex

Proteoglycan

Proteoglycan

Polysaccharides   Core protein

0.5 μm

FIGURE 11.3 The Extracellular Matrix Is a Fiber Composite.
(a) Although several types of fibrous proteins are found in the ECM of animal cells, the most abundant is collagen. Groups of collagen proteins coalesce to form collagen fibrils, and bundles of fibrils link to form collagen fibers. **(b)** The spaces between the collagen fibers are filled with complexes of gelatinous proteoglycans. The proteoglycan subunits consist of a protein core attached to many polysaccharides.

secreted from the cell via exocytosis. After secretion, however, proteins like collagen may then assemble into larger structures, such as the fibrils shown in **FIGURE 11.4**. In addition, the secreted proteoglycans may be attached to long polysaccharides synthesized by cellular enzymes in the extracellular space. These huge complexes, such as the one shown in Figure 11.3b, are responsible for the rubber-like consistency of cartilage.

Even in the same organism, the amount of ECM varies among different types of **tissues,** which consist of similar cells that function as a unit. Bone and cartilage, for example, have relatively few cells surrounded by a large amount of ECM. Skin cells, in contrast, are packed together with a minimal amount of ECM.

The composition of the ECM also varies among tissue types. For example, the ECM surrounding cells in lung tissue contains large amounts of a rubber-like protein called elastin, which allows the ECM to expand and contract during breathing. The structure of a cell's ECM correlates with the function of the tissue.

Although collagen and the other common ECM proteins are much more elastic and bendable than the stiff cell walls of plants, they support cell structure via attachments to the cell surface. As

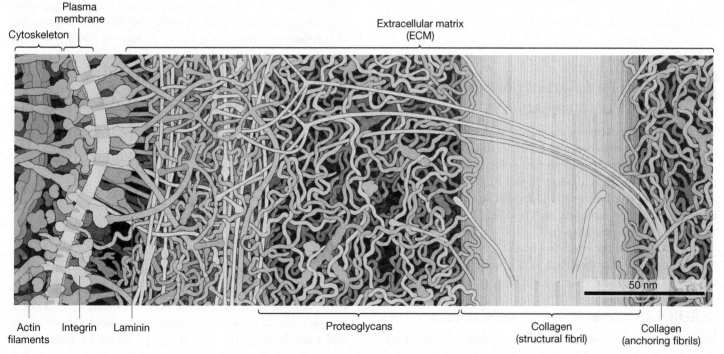

Cytoskeleton

Plasma membrane

Extracellular matrix (ECM)

Actin filaments   Integrin   Laminin

Proteoglycans

Collagen (structural fibril)

Collagen (anchoring fibrils)

50 nm

FIGURE 11.4 Integrins Connect the Extracellular Matrix to the Cytoskeleton.

Figure 11.4 shows, membrane proteins called **integrins** bind to extracellular proteins, including laminins, which in turn bind to other components of the ECM. **Laminins** are ECM crosslinking proteins—not to be confused with lamins, which are intermediate filaments found in the nucleus (see Chapter 7).

The intracellular portions of the integrins also bind to proteins that are connected to the cytoskeleton, effectively forming a bridge between the two support systems. This linkage between the cytoskeleton and ECM is critical. Besides keeping individual cells in place, it helps adjacent cells adhere to each other via their common connection to the ECM.

Cells monitor this cytoskeleton–ECM linkage via signaling pathways that will be introduced in Section 11.3. When integrins bind to the ECM, they transmit signals that inform the cell it is in the right place and properly anchored. If these linkages break down, the signals are not transmitted and cells normally die as a result. For most of the cells in your body, anchorage to the ECM is a matter of life and death.

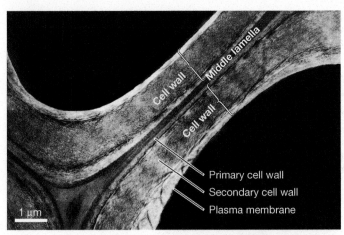

FIGURE 11.5 The Middle Lamella Connects Adjacent Plant Cells. The middle lamella contains gelatinous polysaccharides, called pectins, that help glue together the walls of adjacent cells.

check your understanding

If you understand that . . .

C
Y
U

• Most cells secrete a layer of structural material that supports the cell and helps define its shape. The extracellular material is usually a fiber composite—a combination of cross-linked filaments surrounded by a ground substance.

✔ **You should be able to . . .**

Compare and contrast the molecular composition of a plant cell wall and the ECM of animal cells.

Answers are available in Appendix A.

11.2 How Do Adjacent Cells Connect and Communicate?

Intercellular connections are the basis of **multicellularity.** These physical connections between cells—either direct, or indirect via the ECM—are particularly important in the structure and function of tissues. The muscle tissue in your heart, for example, depends on these attachments to support the structure of the cells as they contract and relax with each beat (see the micrograph on the opening page of this chapter).

Let's look first at the structures that attach cells to each other and then examine how they allow adjacent cells to exchange materials and information.

Cell–Cell Attachments in Multicellular Eukaryotes

Materials and structures that bind cells together are particularly important in the **epithelium** (plural: **epithelia**)—a tissue that forms external and internal surfaces. These epithelial layers function as a barrier between the external and internal environments of plants and animals. In animals, epithelial cells also form layers that separate organs to prevent mixing of solutions from adjacent organs or structures.

The adhesive structures that hold cells together vary among multicellular organisms. To illustrate this diversity, consider the intercellular connections observed in the best-studied groups of organisms: plants and animals.

Indirect Intercellular Attachments The extracellular space between adjacent plant cells comprises three layers (**FIGURE 11.5**). The primary cell walls of adjacent plant cells sandwich a central layer designated the middle lamella, which consists primarily of gelatinous pectins. Because this gel layer is continuous with the primary cell walls of the adjacent cells, it serves to glue them together. The two cell walls are like slices of bread; the middle lamella is like a layer of peanut butter. If enzymes degrade the middle lamella, as they do when flower petals and leaves detach and fall, the surrounding cells separate.

In many animal tissues, integrins connect the cytoskeleton of each cell to the extracellular matrix (see Section 11.1). A middle-lamella-like layer of gelatinous polysaccharides and proteoglycans runs between adjacent animal cells. Along with the cytoskeleton–ECM connections, the polysaccharide glue helps hold cells together in tissues. In addition, in certain animal tissues the polysaccharide glue is reinforced by collagen fibrils that span the ECM to connect adjacent cells.

In animals, where cell walls do not exist, a variety of membrane proteins allow for direct cell–cell attachments in epithelia and other tissues (**FIGURE 11.6**). Let's start by looking at the tight junctions and desmosomes that hold cells together and then examine the role of gap junctions in intercellular communication.

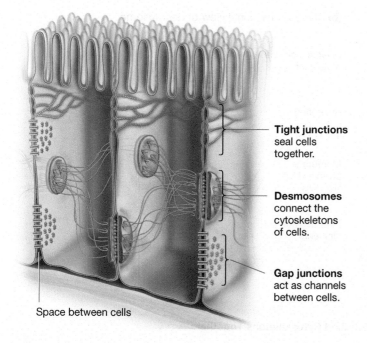

FIGURE 11.6 An Array of Structures Are Involved in Cell–Cell Adhesion and Communication between Animal Cells.

Tight junctions seal cells together.

Desmosomes connect the cytoskeletons of cells.

Gap junctions act as channels between cells.

Space between cells

Tight Junctions Form a Seal between Cells A **tight junction** is a cell–cell attachment composed of specialized proteins in the plasma membranes of adjacent animal cells (**FIGURE 11.7a**). As the drawing in **FIGURE 11.7b** indicates, these proteins line up and bind to one another. The resulting structure resembles quilting, where

the proteins "stitch" the membranes of two cells together to form a watertight seal. In this way, tight junctions prevent solutions from flowing through the space between the two cells.

Because tight junctions form a watertight seal, this type of junction is commonly found in cells that form a barrier, such as the epithelial cells lining your stomach and intestines. There, they restrict the passive movement of substances between the contents of your gut and the rest of your body. Instead, only selected nutrients enter and leave the epithelia via specialized transport proteins and channels in the plasma membrane (Chapter 6).

Although tight junctions are indeed tight, they are variable. The tight junctions between the cells lining your bladder draw the cells closer together than those between the cells lining your small intestine, because they consist of different proteins. As a result, small ions can pass between the cells lining the surface of the small intestine more easily than between those lining the bladder—helping you absorb ions in your food and eliminate them in your waste.

Tight junctions are also dynamic. For example, they loosen to permit more transport between epithelial cells lining the small intestine after a meal and then "retighten" later. In this way, tight junctions can open and close in response to changes in environmental conditions.

Although tight junctions are very good at holding cells close together, they are weak adhesions that can be easily broken. Since epithelial cells often experience pulling and shearing forces, other intercellular adhesions are required to help hold cells together in a tissue. What are these other adhesions, and how do they resist being pulled apart?

(a) Electron micrograph of a tight junction in longitudinal section

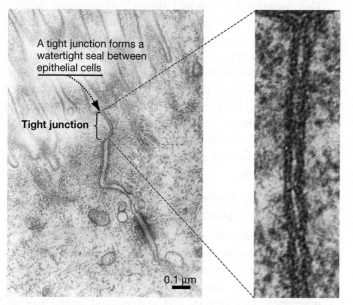

A tight junction forms a watertight seal between epithelial cells

Tight junction

0.1 μm

(b) Three-dimensional view of a tight junction

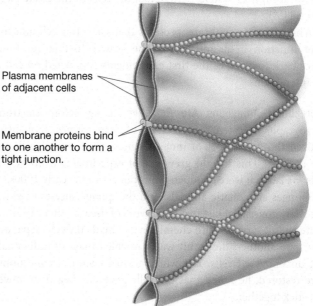

Plasma membranes of adjacent cells

Membrane proteins bind to one another to form a tight junction.

FIGURE 11.7 In Animals, Tight Junctions Form a Seal between Adjacent Cells.

(a) Micrograph of desmosome in longitudinal section

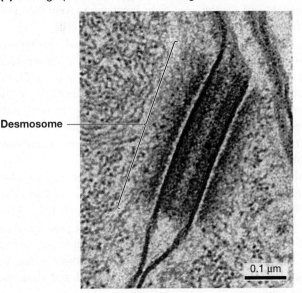

Desmosome

0.1 μm

(b) Three-dimensional view of desmosome

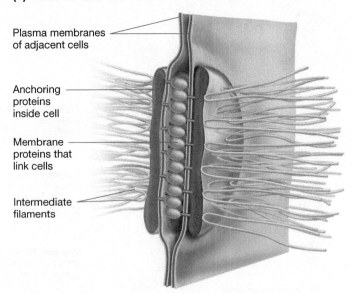

Plasma membranes of adjacent cells

Anchoring proteins inside cell

Membrane proteins that link cells

Intermediate filaments

FIGURE 11.8 Adjacent Animal Cells Are Linked by Desmosomes, Which Bind Cytoskeletons Together.

Desmosomes Form Secure Adhesions **FIGURE 11.8a** illustrates **desmosomes,** cell–cell attachments particularly common in animal epithelial cells and certain muscle cells. The structure and function of a desmosome are analogous to the rivets that hold pieces of sheet metal together.

As **FIGURE 11.8b** indicates, desmosomes are extremely sophisticated cell–cell connections. At their heart are integral membrane attachment proteins that form bridges between anchoring proteins inside adjacent cells. Intermediate filaments help reinforce these connections by attaching to the anchoring proteins in the cytoplasm. In this way, desmosomes help form a continuous structural support system between all the cells in the tissue (see Figure 11.6).

What are the membrane proteins that serve this cell attachment function in desmosomes? The answer to this question traces back to some of the first experiments conducted on cell–cell interactions.

Intercellular Adhesions Are Selective Long before electron micrographs revealed the presence of desmosomes, biologists realized that some sort of molecule must bind animal cells to one another. This insight grew out of experiments from H. V. Wilson's lab that were conducted on sponges in the early 1900s.

Sponges are aquatic animals, and the sponge species used in this study consists of just two basic types of tissues. When Wilson treated adult sponges with chemicals that made the cells separate from one another, the result was a jumbled mass of individual and unconnected cells. But when normal chemical conditions were restored, he noted that the cells gradually began to move and stick together.

As the experiment continued, cells began to aggregate based on their origin—adhering to other cells of the same tissue type.

This phenomenon is now called **selective adhesion.** Eventually the experimental sponge cells re-formed functional adult sponges with two distinct tissues. How could this happen?

The Discovery of Cell–Cell Adhesion Proteins What is the molecular basis of selective adhesion? The initial hypothesis, proposed in the 1970s, was that specialized membrane proteins were involved. The idea was that different types of cells have different types of adhesion proteins in their membranes, and only those with the same or complementary adhesion proteins are able to attach to one another.

This hypothesis was tested through experiments that relied on molecules called antibodies. An **antibody** is a protein produced by an immune response that binds specifically to a unique molecule type, often another protein (see Chapter 51). When an antibody binds to a protein, it can change the target protein's structure or interfere with its ability to interact with other molecules. This property of antibodies was crucial to these experiments.

FIGURE 11.9 shows how researchers tested the hypothesis that cell–cell adhesion takes place via interactions between membrane proteins:

Step 1 Isolate the membrane proteins from a certain cell type. Produce pure preparations of each protein.

Step 2 Inject one of the membrane proteins into a rabbit. The rabbit's immune system cells respond by creating antibodies to the membrane protein, which is recognized as being foreign. Purify those antibodies. Repeat this procedure for the other membrane proteins that were isolated. In this way, obtain a large collection of antibodies—each of which binds specifically to one (and only one) type of membrane protein.

QUESTION: Do animal cells have adhesion proteins on their surfaces?

HYPOTHESIS: Selective adhesion is due to specific membrane proteins.

NULL HYPOTHESIS: Selective adhesion is not due to specific membrane proteins.

EXPERIMENTAL SETUP:

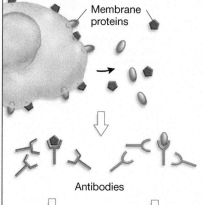

Membrane proteins

Antibodies

Experiment 1:   Experiment 2:

1. Isolate the membrane proteins from a certain cell type that adheres to other cells of the same type. (There are many membrane proteins; only two are shown here.)

2. Produce antibodies that bind to specific membrane proteins. Purify the antibodies.

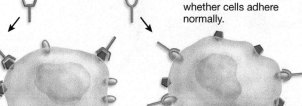

3. Treat cells with an antibody, one type at a time. Wait; then observe whether cells adhere normally.

PREDICTION:

PREDICTION OF NULL HYPOTHESIS:

RESULTS:

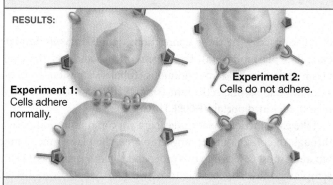

Experiment 2: Cells do not adhere.

Experiment 1: Cells adhere normally.

CONCLUSION: The protein that was blocked in experiment 2 (called a cadherin) is involved in cell–cell adhesion.

FIGURE 11.9 Evidence for Adhesion Proteins on Animal Cells.

SOURCES: Hatta, K., and M. Takeichi. 1986. Expression of N-cadherin adhesion molecules associated with early morphogenetic events in chick development. *Nature* 320: 447–449. Also Takeichi, M. 1988. The cadherins: Cell–cell adhesion molecules controlling animal morphogenesis. *Development* 102: 639–655.

✔**EXERCISE** Fill in the prediction made by each hypothesis.

Step 3 Add one antibody type to a mixture of dissociated cells from a tissue and observe whether the cells reaggregate normally. Repeat this experiment with each of the other antibody types, one type at a time.

If treatment with a particular antibody prevents the cells from attaching to one another, the antibody is probably bound to an adhesion protein. The logic is that if the antibody "shakes hands" with the adhesion protein, the adhesion protein can't shake hands with other adhesion proteins and attach the cells to one another.

This approach allowed biologists to identify several major classes of cell adhesion proteins, including **cadherins**—the attachment molecules in desmosomes. There are various types of cadherins, and cells from different tissues have different forms of cadherin in their plasma membranes. Each cadherin can bind only to cadherins of the same type. In this way, cells of the same tissue type attach specifically to one another.

To summarize: Animal cells attach to one another in a selective manner because different types of cell adhesion proteins can bind and rivet certain cells together. Cadherins provide the physical basis for selective adhesion in many cells and are a critical component of the desmosomes that join mature cells.

✔ If you understand cell–cell attachments, you should be able to predict what would happen if you treated cells in a developing frog embryo with a molecule that blocked a cadherin present in muscle tissue.

In addition to providing structural support to tissues, intercellular connections can direct cell–cell communication. But how can cellular connections pass information between cells?

Cells Communicate via Cell–Cell Gaps

In both plants and animals, direct connections between cells in the same tissue help them to work in a coordinated fashion. One way of accomplishing this is to generate channels in the membranes of adjacent cells, allowing them to communicate via the diffusion of cytosolic ions and small molecules from cell to cell.

How cells respond to this exchange of information varies from signal to signal and from cell to cell, but the result falls into two general categories:

1. Signals may alter which proteins are produced and which are not, by regulating gene expression; or

2. Signals may activate or deactivate particular proteins that already exist in the cell—often those involved in metabolism, membrane transport, secretion, and the cytoskeleton.

Whatever the mechanism, the activity of the cell often changes dramatically after the signal arrives. Let's take a closer look at how these signals are able to travel between adjacent cells connected by gap junctions and plasmodesmata.

Gap Junctions Connect Cells via Protein Channels In most animal tissues, structures called **gap junctions** connect adjacent cells. The key feature of gap junctions is the specialized proteins that assemble in the membranes of adjacent cells, creating

(a) Gap junctions create gaps that connect animal cells.

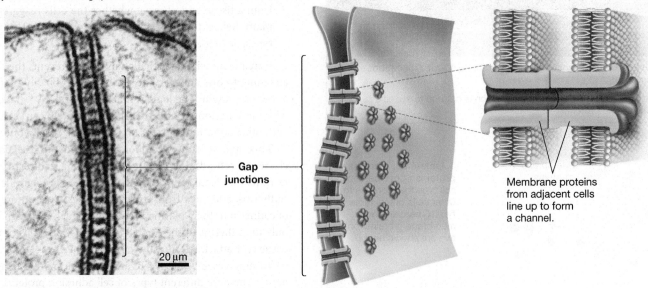

Gap
junctions

20 μm

Membrane proteins
from adjacent cells
line up to form
a channel.

(b) Plasmodesmata create gaps that connect plant cells.

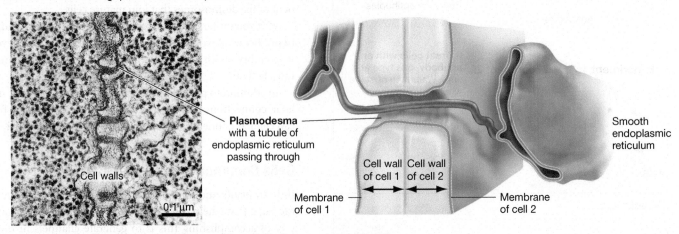

Plasmodesma
with a tubule of
endoplasmic reticulum
passing through

Cell walls

0.1 μm

Cell wall Cell wall
of cell 1 of cell 2

Membrane
of cell 1

Membrane
of cell 2

Smooth
endoplasmic
reticulum

FIGURE 11.10 Adjacent Animal Cells and Adjacent Plant Cells Communicate Directly.

interconnected pores between the cells (**FIGURE 11.10a**). These channels allow water, ions, and small molecules such as amino acids, sugars, and nucleotides to move between adjacent cells.

Gap junctions are communication portals. The flow of small molecules through gap junctions can help adjacent cells coordinate their activities by allowing the rapid passage of regulatory ions or molecules. In the muscle cells of your heart, for example, a flow of ions through gap junctions acts as a signal that coordinates contractions. Without this cell–cell communication, a normal heartbeat would be impossible.

In plants, direct interactions between membrane proteins are impossible due to the presence of cell walls. How do adjacent plant cells communicate?

Plasmodesmata Connect Cells via Membrane Channels In plants, gaps in cell walls create direct connections between the cytoplasm

of adjacent cells. At these connections, named **plasmodesmata** (singular: **plasmodesma**), the plasma membrane and the cytoplasm of the two cells are continuous. Tubular extensions from the smooth endoplasmic reticulum (smooth ER) run through these membrane-lined portals (**FIGURE 11.10b**).

Like gap junctions, plasmodesmata are communication portals through the plasma membrane. In plants, the plasma membrane separates most tissues into two independent compartments: (**1**) the **symplast,** which is a continuous network of cytoplasm connected by plasmodesmata, and (**2**) the **apoplast,** which is the region outside the plasma membrane (**FIGURE 11.11**). The apoplast consists of cell walls, the middle lamella, and air spaces. Small molecules can move through plant tissues in either of these compartments without ever crossing a membrane (see Chapter 38).

Gap junctions and plasmodesmata allow for adjacent cells to transmit information, like a conversation between neighbors.

If you understand that . . .
- In plants and animals, adjacent cells are either directly physically connected or, via the ECM, indirectly connected.
- Adjacent cells may communicate with each other through openings in their plasma membranes.

✔ **You should be able to . . .**

1. Compare and contrast the structure and function of the middle lamella of plants and the tight junctions and desmosomes of animals.

2. Describe the structure and function of plasmodesmata and gap junctions.

Answers are available in Appendix A.

But how do multicellular organisms send messages between different tissues, where in most cases there is no direct contact? For example, suppose that the muscle cells in your arm are exercising so hard they run low on sugar or that leaf cells in a maple tree are attacked by caterpillars. How do these cells signal tissues or organs elsewhere in the organism to release materials that are needed to fend off exhaustion or caterpillars? Distant cell communication is the subject of Section 11.3.

11.3 How Do Distant Cells Communicate?

Cells that are not in physical contact communicate with one another. This is true for unicellular organisms, where hundreds or

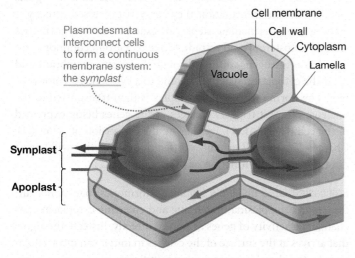

FIGURE 11.11 Most Plant Tissues Are Divided into Two Compartments—Symplast and Apoplast. Small molecules may be transported through plant tissues either within the shared cytoplasm (symplast) or through the extracellular space (apoplast).

thousands of cells may live in close proximity, as well as for multicellular organisms like humans and maple trees, which typically contain trillions of cells and dozens of tissue types.

Cell–cell communication qualifies as one of the most dynamic and important research areas in biology. Let's begin by analyzing how distant cells in humans and other multicellular eukaryotes exchange information, and then in Section 11.4 explore how unicellular organisms communicate.

Cell–Cell Signaling in Multicellular Organisms

Suppose that cells in your brain sense that you are becoming dehydrated. Brain cells can't do much about the water you lose during urination, but kidney cells can. In response to dehydration, certain brain cells release a signaling molecule that travels to the kidneys. The arrival of this molecule activates specialized membrane channels that prevent water from being lost in urine—an important aspect of fighting dehydration.

Thanks to cell–cell signals, the activities of cells in different parts of a multicellular body are coordinated.

Biologists have classified many different types of signaling molecules that keep distant tissues in touch. For example, neurotransmitters activate membrane channel receptors that open to allow a flow of ions into the cytosol of the cell, changing the electrical properties of the membrane. This type of signal is responsible for the transmission of information along neurons, allowing your brain to control the movements of the rest of your body (see Chapters 46 and 48). The best-studied means of distant signaling, however, may be via **hormones**—information-carrying molecules that can act on distant target cells because they are secreted by plant and animal cells into bodily fluids.

Hormones are usually small molecules and are typically present in minute concentrations. Even so, they have a large impact on the activity of target cells and the condition of the body as a whole. Hormones are like a scent or whispered phrase from someone you are attracted to—a tiny signal, but one that makes your cheeks flush and your heart pound.

As **TABLE 11.1** (see page 210) indicates, hormones have a wide array of chemical structures and effects. The important point about a signaling molecule, though, is not whether it is a gas or peptide or steroid, but whether it is lipid soluble or not. The ability of a signaling molecule to pass through lipid bilayers is crucial in determining how a target cell recognizes it. Where does this recognition occur—inside the cell or outside?

- Most lipid-soluble signaling molecules are able to diffuse across the hydrophobic region of the plasma membrane and enter the cytoplasm of their target cells.

- Large or hydrophilic signaling molecules are lipid insoluble and do not cross the plasma membrane. To affect a target cell, they have to be recognized at the cell surface.

How do cells receive and process signals from distant cells? The basic steps are common to all cell–cell signaling systems. Let's consider each step in turn.

TABLE 11.1 Hormones Have Diverse Structures and Functions

Hormone Name	Chemical Structure	Where Is Signal Received?	Function of Signal
Auxin	Small organic compound	At plasma membrane	Signals changes in long axis of plant body
Brassinosteroids	Steroid	At plasma membrane	Stimulate plant cell elongation
Estrogens	Steroid	Inside cell	Stimulate development of female characteristics in animals
Ethylene	C_2H_4 (a gas)	At plasma membrane	Stimulates fruit ripening; regulates aging
FSH	Glycoprotein	At plasma membrane	Stimulates egg maturation, sperm production in animals
Insulin	Protein, 51 amino acids	At plasma membrane	Stimulates glucose uptake in animal bloodstream
Prostaglandins	Modified fatty acid	At plasma membrane	Perform a variety of functions in animal cells
Systemin	Peptide, 111 amino acids	At plasma membrane	Stimulates plant defenses against herbivores
Thyroxine (T4)	Modified amino acid	Inside cell	Regulates metabolism in animals

Signal Reception

Hormones and other types of cell–cell signaling molecules deliver their message by binding to receptor molecules. Even though the molecule that carries the message "We're getting dehydrated—conserve water" is broadcast throughout the body, only certain kidney cells respond because only they have the appropriate receptor. The presence of an appropriate receptor dictates which cells will respond to a particular hormone. Bone and muscle cells don't respond to the "conserve water" message, because they don't have a receptor for it.

Cells in a wide array of tissues may respond to the same signaling molecule, though, if they have the appropriate receptor. If you are startled by a loud noise, cells in your adrenal glands secrete a hormone called adrenaline (also called epinephrine) that carries the message "Get ready to fight or run." In response, your heart rate increases, your breathing rate increases, and cells in your liver release sugars that your muscles can use to power rapid movement. This is the basis of an "adrenaline rush." Heart, lung, and liver cells respond to adrenaline because they each have the receptor that binds to it. Identical receptors in diverse cells and tissues allow long-distance signals to coordinate the activities of cells throughout a multicellular organism.

No matter where signal receptors are located, it's critical to note two important points about these proteins:

1. *Receptors are dynamic.* The number of receptors in a particular cell may decline if hormonal stimulation occurs at high levels over a long period of time. The ability of a receptor molecule to bind tightly to a signaling molecule may also decline in response to intensive stimulation. As a result, the sensitivity of a cell to a particular hormone may change over time.

2. *Receptors can be blocked.* The drugs called beta-blockers, for example, bind to certain receptors for the hormone adrenaline. When adrenaline binds to receptors in heart cells, it stimulates more rapid and forceful contractions. So if a physician wants to reduce a patient's heart cell contraction as a way to lower pressure, she is likely to prescribe a beta-blocker.

Most signal receptors are located in the plasma membrane, where they can bind to signaling molecules that cannot or do not cross the membrane. Other signal receptors exist inside the cell, where they respond to lipid-soluble signaling molecules that readily diffuse through the plasma membrane.

The most important general characteristic of signal receptors, though, is that their conformation—meaning, overall shape—changes when a hormone binds to them. A **signal receptor** is a protein that changes its shape and activity after binding to a signaling molecule.

This is a critical event in cell–cell signaling. The change in receptor structure means that the signal has been received. It's like throwing an "on" switch. What happens next?

Signal Processing

Once a cell receives a signal, something has to happen to initiate the cell's response. This signal processing step happens in one of two ways, depending on whether the signal is received inside the cell or at the membrane surface.

Processing Lipid-Soluble Signals When lipid-soluble signals enter a cell, the information they carry is processed directly—without any intermediate steps. For example, steroid hormones such as testosterone and estradiol (one of a group commonly referred to as estrogens) diffuse through the plasma membrane and enter the cytoplasm, where they bind to a cytosolic receptor protein. The hormone–receptor complex is then transported to the nucleus, where it triggers changes in the genes being expressed in the cell (**FIGURE 11.12**). By altering the expression of genes (see Chapter 17), the cell produces different proteins that will have a direct effect on the function or shape of the cell.

Processing Lipid-Insoluble Signals Hormones that *cannot* diffuse across the plasma membrane and enter the cytoplasm can't change the activity of genes or pumps directly. Instead, the signal that arrives at the surface of the cell has to initiate an intracellular signal—the signal processing step is indirect.

When a signaling molecule binds at the cell surface, it triggers **signal transduction**—the conversion of a signal from one form to another. A long and often complex series of events ensues, collectively called a signal transduction pathway.

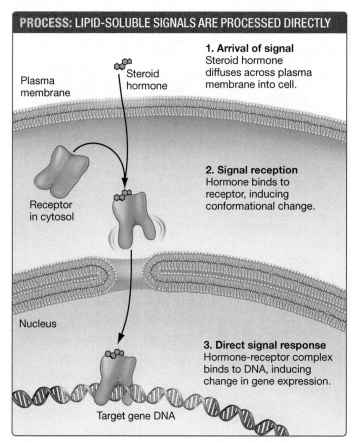

1. Arrival of signal
Steroid hormone diffuses across plasma membrane into cell.

2. Signal reception
Hormone binds to receptor, inducing conformational change.

3. Direct signal response
Hormone-receptor complex binds to DNA, inducing change in gene expression.

Plasma membrane

Steroid hormone

Receptor in cytosol

Nucleus

Target gene DNA

FIGURE 11.12 Some Cell–Cell Signaling Molecules Enter the Cell and Bind to Receptors in the Cytoplasm. Because they are lipids, steroid hormones can diffuse across the plasma membrane and bind to signal receptors inside the cell. The hormone–receptor complex is transported to the nucleus and binds to genes, changing their activity.

✔**QUESTION** Based on what you have learned about nuclear transport (see Chapter 7), what type of signal would you expect to be exposed on the cytosolic receptor after the steroid hormone changes the receptor's conformation?

Signal transduction is a common occurrence in everyday life. For example, the e-mail messages you receive are transmitted from one computer to another over cables or wireless transmissions. These electronic signals can be transmitted efficiently over long distances but would be meaningless to you. Software in your computer has to transduce, or convert, the signals into a form that you can understand and respond to, such as words on the screen.

Signal transduction pathways work the same way (**FIGURE 11.13**). In a cell, signal transduction converts an extracellular signal to an intracellular signal. As in an e-mail transmission, a signal that is easy to transmit is converted to a signal that is easily understood and that triggers a response.

Intracellular Signals May Be Amplified Recall that hormones are present in minuscule concentrations but trigger a large response from cells. Signal amplification is one reason this is possible. When a hormone arrives at the cell surface, the message it transmits may be amplified as it changes form. The amplifier

in your portable music player performs an analogous function: Once it is amplified, a tiny sound signal can get a whole roomful of people dancing.

In cells, signal transduction begins at the plasma membrane; amplification occurs inside. Amplification may occur in a variety of ways. In general, the mechanism of amplification correlates with the mechanism of signal transduction. But the general observation is that the arrival of a single signaling molecule may result in a secondary signal that involves many ions or molecules.

For example, one major type of signal transduction system consists of membrane channel receptors that open to allow a flow of ions into the cytosol of the cell. In muscle cells, this type of amplification occurs when calcium ions flood into the cytosol, activating all the myosin filaments so the entire cell contracts as a whole (see Chapter 48).

Here let's focus on two other major types of signal transduction and amplification systems that are distinguished based on how they are initiated:

1. G-protein-coupled receptors initiate the production of intracellular or "second" messengers that then amplify the signal.

2. Enzyme-linked receptors amplify the signal by triggering the activation of a series of proteins inside the cell, through the addition of phosphate groups.

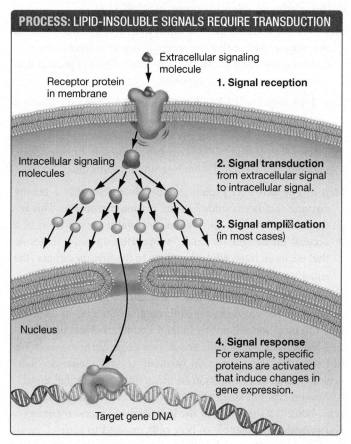

Extracellular signaling molecule

Receptor protein in membrane

1. Signal reception

Intracellular signaling molecules

2. Signal transduction
from extracellular signal to intracellular signal.

3. Signal amplification
(in most cases)

Nucleus

4. Signal response
For example, specific proteins are activated that induce changes in gene expression.

Target gene DNA

FIGURE 11.13 Signal Transduction Converts an Extracellular Signal to an Intracellular Signal. Signal transduction is a multistep process.

Although there are many variations in the signaling pathways that fall within these two categories, the common features are emphasized here. Let's look at these two signal transduction systems in turn.

Signal Transduction via G-Protein-Coupled Receptors Many signal receptors span the plasma membrane and are closely associated with membrane-anchored proteins inside the cell called **G proteins.** When G proteins are activated by a signal receptor, they trigger a key step in signal transduction: the production of a messenger inside the cell. They link the receipt of an extracellular signal to the production of an intracellular signal.

G proteins got their name because the type of guanine nucleotide they are bound to regulates their activity: either guanosine triphosphate (GTP) or guanosine diphosphate (GDP). GTP is a nucleoside triphosphate that is similar in structure to adenosine triphosphate (ATP; introduced in Chapter 4). Recall that nucleoside triphosphates have high potential energy because their three phosphate groups have four negative charges close together.

When GTP binds to a G protein, the addition of the negative charges alters the protein's shape. Changes in shape produce changes in activity. G proteins are turned on or activated when they bind GTP; they are turned off or inactivated when a phosphate group, and thus a negative charge, is removed to form GDP. The G protein will remain in this off position until the GDP is removed and the protein binds to a new GTP.

To understand how G proteins fit into an overall signal transduction pathway, follow the events in **FIGURE 11.14**.

Step 1 A hormone arrives and binds to a receptor in the plasma membrane. Notice that the receptor is a transmembrane protein with the intracellular portion coupled to a G protein that is composed of multiple subunits.

Step 2 In response to hormone binding, the receptor changes shape and activates its G protein. Specifically, the receptor kicks out the GDP from the inactive G protein, allowing it to bind to a new GTP. When GTP is bound, the G protein changes shape radically: the active GTP-binding subunit splits off.

Step 3 The active G protein subunit interacts with a nearby enzyme that is embedded in the plasma membrane. This interaction stimulates the enzyme to catalyze production of a **second messenger**—a small, nonprotein signaling molecule that elicits an intracellular response to the first messenger (the signaling molecule that arrived at the cell surface).

Second messengers are effective because they are small and diffuse rapidly to spread the signal throughout the cell. In addition, they can be produced quickly in large quantities. This characteristic is important. Because the arrival of a single hormone molecule can stimulate the production of many second messenger molecules, the signal transduction event amplifies the original signal.

Several types of small molecules act as second messengers in cells. **TABLE 11.2** lists some of the best-studied second messengers and provides an example of how cells respond to each of them. Note that several second messengers activate **protein kinases**—enzymes that activate or inactivate other proteins by adding a phosphate group to them.

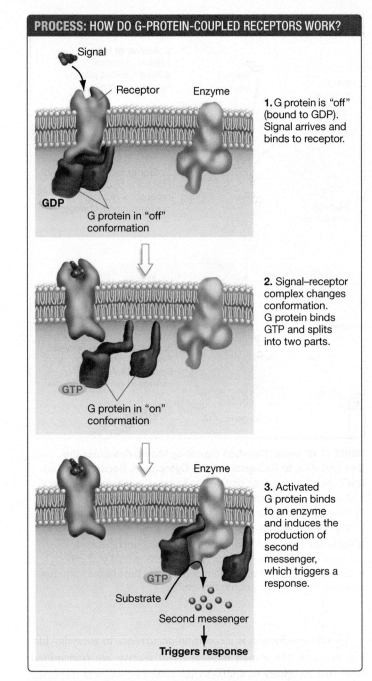

PROCESS: HOW DO G-PROTEIN-COUPLED RECEPTORS WORK?

1. G protein is "off" (bound to GDP). Signal arrives and binds to receptor.

2. Signal–receptor complex changes conformation. G protein binds GTP and splits into two parts.

3. Activated G protein binds to an enzyme and induces the production of second messenger, which triggers a response.

FIGURE 11.14 G-Protein-Coupled Receptors Trigger the Production of a Second Messenger.

It's also important to note two things:

1. Second messengers aren't restricted to a single role or single cell type—the same second messenger can initiate dramatically different events in different cell types; and

2. It is common for more than one second messenger to be involved in triggering a cell's response to the same extracellular signaling molecule.

To make sure that you understand how G proteins and second messengers work, imagine the following movie scene: A spy arrives at a castle gate. The guard receives a note from the spy, but

TABLE 11.2 Examples of Second Messengers

Name	Type of Response
Cyclic guanosine monophosphate (cGMP)	Opens ion channels; activates certain protein kinases
Diacylglycerol (DAG)	Activates certain protein kinases
Inositol trisphosphate (IP$_3$)	Opens calcium channels to transport stored calcium ions
Cyclic adenosine monophosphate (cAMP)	Activates certain protein kinases
Calcium ions (Ca^{2+})	Binds to a receptor called calmodulin; Ca^{2+}/calmodulin complex then activates proteins

he cannot read the coded message. Instead, the guard turns to the queen. She reads the note and summons the commander of the guard, who sends soldiers throughout the castle to warn everyone of approaching danger. ✔ **You should be able to** identify which characters in the scene correspond to the second messenger, G protein, hormone, receptor, and enzyme activated by the G protein.

It's difficult to overstate the importance of signal transduction by G-protein-coupled receptors. Biomedical researchers estimate that half of human drugs target signal receptors that are associated with G proteins.

Signal Transduction via Enzyme-Linked Receptors Enzyme-linked receptors transduce hormonal signals by directly catalyzing a reaction inside the cell. **FIGURE 11.15** focuses on the best-studied group of enzyme-linked receptors: the **receptor tyrosine kinases (RTKs).**

Step 1 A hormone binds to an RTK.

Step 2 The protein forms a dimer. In this conformation, the catalytic activity of the receptor is turned on, allowing it to phosphorylate itself using ATP inside the cell.

Step 3 Proteins inside the cell bind to the phosphorylated RTK to form a bridge between the receptor and a peripheral membrane protein called **Ras,** which is a G protein. The formation of the RTK bridge activates Ras by causing it to exchange its GDP for a GTP.

Step 4 When Ras is activated, it triggers the phosphorylation and activation of another protein.

Step 5 The phosphorylated protein is a protein kinase, which then catalyzes the phosphorylation and activation of other kinases, which phosphorylate yet another population of proteins.

This sequence of events is termed a **phosphorylation cascade,** and it culminates in a response by the cell. The enzymes involved are called **mitogen-activated protein kinases (MAPK).** They are so named because many of the signaling molecules that start

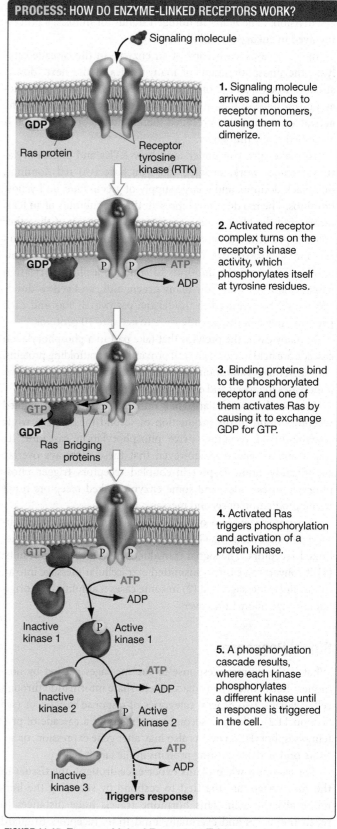

PROCESS: HOW DO ENZYME-LINKED RECEPTORS WORK?

1. Signaling molecule arrives and binds to receptor monomers, causing them to dimerize.

2. Activated receptor complex turns on the receptor's kinase activity, which phosphorylates itself at tyrosine residues.

3. Binding proteins bind to the phosphorylated receptor and one of them activates Ras by causing it to exchange GDP for GTP.

4. Activated Ras triggers phosphorylation and activation of a protein kinase.

5. A phosphorylation cascade results, where each kinase phosphorylates a different kinase until a response is triggered in the cell.

FIGURE 11.15 Enzyme-Linked Receptors Trigger a Phosphorylation Cascade.

these pathways are substances called mitogens, which activate cell division. (The *mito–* in mitogen stands for mitosis, a process involved in eukaryotic cell division.)

In some cases, each copy of an enzyme in the cascade catalyzes the phosphorylation of many copies of the next "downstream" protein, and so on. When this occurs, activated enzymes at a given stage in the cascade exist in greater numbers than the activated enzymes that preceded them, and the original signal is amplified many times over.

To make sure you understand how RTKs and phosphorylation cascades work, imagine that you have two red dominos, one black domino, and a large supply of green, blue, and yellow dominos. The red dominos represent the two subunits of an RTK dimer, and the black domino represents Ras. Each of the other colors represents a different protein kinase in a phosphorylation cascade. ✔ QUANTITATIVE You should be able to (1) explain how you would set up the dominos to simulate a phosphorylation cascade, and (2) state how many green, blue, and yellow dominos would be required to model the pathway if Ras and each protein kinase in the cascade were to activate 10 proteins.

In many cases, the proteins that take part in a phosphorylation cascade are held in close physical proximity by scaffolding proteins. Although this organization limits the amplification of the response, it increases the speed and efficiency of the reaction sequence.

In general, intracellular signals initiated by G-protein-coupled receptors result in the production of second messengers, while enzyme-linked receptors drive phosphorylation cascades. It's important to recognize, however, that these pathways overlap significantly. Some G-protein-coupled receptors trigger phosphorylation cascades, and some enzyme-linked receptors result in the production of second messengers.

To summarize: Many of the key signal transduction events observed in cells occur via G-protein-coupled receptors or enzyme-linked receptors. The signal transduction event has two results: (1) It converts an easily transmitted extracellular message into an intracellular message, and (2) in some cases it amplifies the original message many times over.

Signal Response

What is the ultimate response to the messages carried by hormones? Recall that when adjacent cells share information through cell–cell gaps, two general categories of response may occur (see Section 11.2). Likewise, second messengers or a cascade of protein phosphorylation events also may alter gene expression, or activate or deactivate existing proteins in the target cell.

For example, when plants experience drought, the tissues in the root system are the first to respond by secreting the hormone abscisic acid. This hormone travels huge distances to reach the leaves and eventually bind to its receptors in guard cells that control the stomatal pores that allow for gas exchange (see Chapter 10). When abscisic acid binds to these receptors, a signal transduction pathway ensues that increases the concentration of calcium inside the guard cells. In response, potassium ions (K^+) move out of the guard cells, creating an osmotic

gradient that leads to the movement of water out of the guard cells. The guard cells deflate and close the pore, which prevents water loss from the plant.

At this point, you've analyzed the first three steps of cell–cell communication: signal reception, signal processing, and the response. Now the question is, how is the signal turned off? Consider the flush of testosterone and estrogens that you experienced during puberty, and the morphological changes these hormones induced. Abnormalities would result if these changes continued indefinitely. What limits the response to a cell–cell signal?

Signal Deactivation

Cells have built-in systems for turning off intracellular signals. For example, once activated G proteins turn on downstream enzymes, the GTP is hydrolyzed to GDP and P_i. When this reaction occurs, the G protein's conformation changes and it returns to an inactive state. Activation of its downstream target stops, and production of the second messenger ceases.

The presence of second messengers in the cytosol is also short lived. For example, pumps in the membrane of the smooth ER return calcium ions to storage, and enzymes called phosphodiesterases convert active cAMP and cGMP (see Table 11.2) to inactive AMP and GMP. When second messengers are cleared from the cytosol, the response stops.

To continue the response from G-protein-coupled receptors, the G proteins must be reactivated by the activated signal receptor to start the process again. Otherwise, the signal transduction system quickly shuts down.

Phosphorylation cascades are also sensitive to the presence of the external signal. Enzymes, called **phosphatases**, that remove phosphate groups from cascade proteins are always present in the cell. If hormone stimulation of a receptor tyrosine kinase ends, phosphatases will dephosphorylate enough components of the phosphorylation cascade that the response ceases.

Although an array of specific mechanisms are involved, here is the general observation: Signal transduction systems trigger a rapid response and can be shut down quickly. As a result, they are exquisitely sensitive to small changes in the concentration of hormones or in the number and activity of signal receptors.

It is critical, though, to appreciate what happens when a signal transduction system does not shut down properly. For example, recall that Ras is active when it binds GTP, but is deactivated once it has hydrolyzed GTP to GDP and P_i. If this hydrolysis activity were defective, however, Ras would stay in the GTP-bound "on" position and continue stimulating a phosphorylation cascade even when the external signal is absent.

Why is continuously active Ras a problem? Recall that the phosphorylation cascade that is activated by Ras involves mitogen-activated protein kinases, many of which induce cell replication. If cells express this type of defective Ras, they would receive a never-ending "divide now" signal that may lead to the development of cancer. An estimated 25–30 percent of all human cancers express this type of defective Ras.(To learn more about the family of diseases called cancer, see Chapters 12 and 19.)

Crosstalk: Synthesizing Input from Many Signals

Although the preceding discussion focused on how cells respond to individual signals, it's crucial to realize that every cell has an array of signal receptors on its plasma membrane and in its cytoplasm, and many cells receive an almost constant stream of different signals. Just as you receive information about your environment via text messages, e-mails, phone calls, and snail mail, cells get an array of chemical signals about changes in their environment.

The signal transduction pathways that are triggered by these signals and receptors intersect and connect. In reality, they are not strictly linear like the pathways illustrated in Figures 11.12 through 11.15. Signal transduction pathways form a network. This complexity is important: It allows cells to respond to many different signals in an integrated way.

The diverse signals that a cell receives are integrated by what biologists call **crosstalk**—meaning, the signals from different pathways interact to modify the cell response (**FIGURE 11.16**). This would be like getting advice from multiple people before making a decision. Here are three key things to note:

1. Elements or products from one pathway may inhibit steps in a different pathway—reducing the cell's response, even though the appropriate signal is present.

2. A response from one pathway may stimulate a greater response by a protein in a different pathway, increasing the cell's response to the other signal.

3. The presence of multiple steps in each signaling pathway provides a series of points where crosstalk can regulate the flow of information. These interactions are important, because they allow the cell to respond appropriately to many signals at the same time.

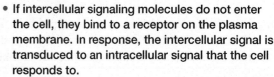

check your understanding

C Y U

If you understand that . . .

- Intercellular signals coordinate the activities of cells throughout the body of a multicellular organism in response to changes in internal or external conditions.
- If intercellular signaling molecules do not enter the cell, they bind to a receptor on the plasma membrane. In response, the intercellular signal is transduced to an intracellular signal that the cell responds to.

✔ **You should be able to . . .**

1. Explain how only certain cells respond to particular signaling molecules that may be sent throughout the body.

2. Explain how some signals are amplified.

Answers are available in Appendix A.

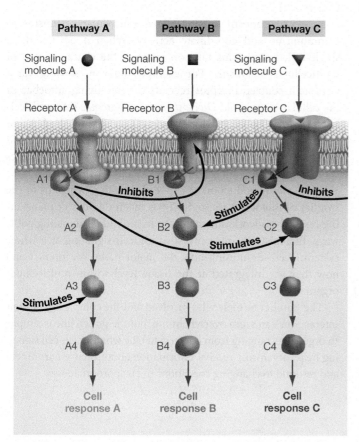

FIGURE 11.16 Signaling Pathways Interact via "Crosstalk."

✔ **EXERCISE** Predict which response would occur in cells exposed to the following signaling molecules: (1) A + B; (2) A + C; (3) C alone.

11.4 Signaling between Unicellular Organisms

Cell–cell signaling has been one of the hottest research areas in biological science over the past two decades. Surprisingly, much of what we know about signal transduction in multicellular organisms has come from the study of unicellular organisms. While single-cell microbes communicate with one another in a manner similar to what is observed in multicellular organisms, the topic of conversation often differs. Rather than asking for help, as when a dehydrated brain asks the kidney to conserve water, the conversations between unicellular microbes are often about sex and environmental change.

Responding to Sex Pheromones

While unicellular eukaryotes generally reproduce by cell division, some also are known to undergo sexual reproduction (see Chapters 12 and 13 to learn more about cellular reproduction). At its most basic level, sex involves the fusion of two cells such that genetic material of the two individuals is combined into one nucleus. What attracts individuals of the opposite sex to each other?

In *Saccharomyces cerevisiae*, or baker's yeast, there are two sexes, or mating types, referred to as "**a**" cells and "**α**" cells. By

(a) Yeast cells alter their growth in response to pheromones of the opposite mating type.

(b) Slime mold amoebae aggregate in response to sensing a quorum.

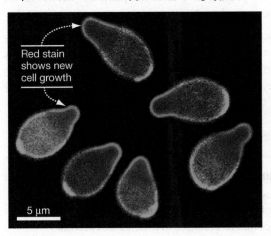

Red stain shows new cell growth

5 μm

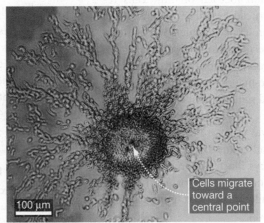

100 μm

Cells migrate toward a central point

FIGURE 11.17 Unicellular Organisms Interact and Respond in a Variety of Ways. (a) Yeast cells respond to pheromone signals from the opposite mating type by growing toward the source of the signal during sexual reproduction. **(b)** Signals secreted by free-living slime mold protists stimulate them to aggregate under high population densities.

studying this eukaryotic model organism, biologists have figured out the cell signaling events that bring yeast of the opposite sex together (to learn more about model organisms, see **BioSkills 13** in Appendix B).

Although the yeast cells are visually indistinguishable, opposite mating types recognize one another via chemical signaling molecules called **pheromones**. The **a** mating type secretes the pheromone **a** factor, and the **α** type secretes the pheromone **α** factor. Receptors on the surface of these cells will bind only to the opposite mating type factor, so when an **a** cell detects the **α** factor, it recognizes that a suitable mate is nearby.

Since yeast cells are not motile, part of the cellular response to the pheromone is to direct new growth toward the signal (**FIGURE 11.17a**). The signaling pathway that is responsible for this morphological change uses both G-protein-coupled receptors and phosphorylation cascades that were presented in Section 11.3. One of the proteins affected by this signaling pathway is actin, which is used to construct new microfilaments at the site where the G proteins have been activated. These new filaments push out new growth toward the highest concentration of the pheromone to allow the cell to find, and eventually fuse with, its mate.

Responding to Population Density

Within a population of unicellular organisms, widespread communication can occur that closely monitors the environment—in particular, the density of the population. Signaling pathways that respond to population density in microbes are collectively referred to as **quorum sensing**. The name was inspired by the observation that cells of the same species may undergo dramatic changes in activity when their numbers reach a threshold, or quorum.

Quorum sensing is based on signaling molecules that are secreted by cells and diffuse through the environment. The response to these molecules varies dramatically between species and ranges from bacterial bioluminescence—or light emission—in the light organs of squid to the secretion of molecules that help glue a community of microbes to a surface in biofilms (see Chapter 29).

In effect, quorum sensing allows unicellular organisms to communicate and coordinate activity. When it occurs, these single-celled organisms take on some of the characteristics of multicellular organisms. For example, quorum sensing via a G-protein-coupled receptor recruits the free-living amoebae of the cellular slime mold *Dictyostelium* to aggregate into multicellular mounds (**FIGURE 11.17b**). Amazingly, the slug-like bodies that are formed from these aggregates can crawl across a surface and eventually organize themselves into a fruiting body that releases spores into the air (see **BioSkills 13** in Appendix B).

This brief introduction to cell–cell signaling brings us to the frontier of biological research. It has taken decades of painstaking research to work out each step in individual signaling pathways. Biologists are now investigating cell signaling at a whole system level—examining how the major pathways interact and how they are integrated at the tissue level within multicellular organisms.

The number of molecules involved and the complexity of their interactions can seem overwhelming, but the punch line is simple: In organisms ranging from bacteria to blue whales, cell–cell signaling helps organisms receive information about their environment and respond to changing conditions in an appropriate way.

If you understand . . .

11.1 The Cell Surface

- The vast majority of cells secrete an extracellular layer.

- In bacteria, archaea, algae, and plants, the extracellular material is stiff and is called a cell wall. In animals, the secreted layer is flexible and is called the extracellular matrix (ECM).

- Extracellular layers are fiber composites. They consist of cross-linked filaments that provide tensile strength and a ground substance that fills space and resists compression.

- In plants, the extracellular filaments are cellulose microfibrils; in animals, the most abundant filaments are made of the protein collagen. In both plants and animals, the ground substance is composed of gel-forming polysaccharides.

✔ You should be able to predict what happens to animal cells when they are treated with an enzyme that (1) cuts integrin molecules, or (2) digests collagen fibrils.

11.2 How Do Adjacent Cells Connect and Communicate?

- In multicellular organisms, molecules in the extracellular layer and plasma membrane mediate interactions between adjacent cells.

- Adjacent cells may be physically bound to one another by glue-like middle lamellae in plants or by tight junctions and desmosomes in animals.

- The cytoplasm of adjacent cells is in direct communication through openings called plasmodesmata in plants and gap junctions in animals.

- Cells may respond to signals by activating certain enzymes, releasing or taking up specific ions or molecules, or changing the activity of target genes. As a result, cells and tissues throughout the body can alter their activity in response to changing conditions, and do so in a coordinated way.

✔ You should be able to predict the consequences of removing the gap junctions between the cells in the cardiac muscle in your heart.

11.3 How Do Distant Cells Communicate?

- Distant cells in multicellular organisms communicate through signaling molecules that bind to receptors found in or on specific target cells.

- Cell–cell signaling molecules that are not lipid soluble bind to receptors in the plasma membrane. The receptor then changes conformation and triggers production of a new type of intracellular signal—a second messenger or phosphorylation cascade.

- Because enzymes inside the cell quickly deactivate the signal and signaling pathways often interact, the cell's response is tightly regulated.

✔ You should be able to explain how the hormone adrenalin can stimulate cells in both the heart and the liver, yet trigger different responses (increasing heart rate versus releasing glucose).

11.4 Signaling between Unicellular Organisms

- Unicellular organisms use chemical signals to sense the pheromones of opposite mating types and population density. Quorum sensing allows closely related cells to coordinate changes in their activity when population density is high.

✔ You should be able to compare and contrast the role of intercellular signaling between unicellular organisms and the cells in a multicellular organism.

(MB) MasteringBiology

1. **MasteringBiology Assignments**

   Tutorials and Activities Build a Signaling Pathway; Cell Junctions; Cell Signaling: Reception; Cell Signaling: Transduction and Response; Cellular Responses; Overview of Cell Signaling; Reception; Signal Transduction Pathways

   Questions Reading Quizzes, Blue-Thread Questions, Test Bank

2. **eText** Read your book online, search, take notes, highlight text, and more.

3. **The Study Area** Practice Test, Cumulative Test, BioFlix® 3-D Animations, Videos, Activities, Audio Glossary, Word Study Tools, Art

You should be able to . . .

1. What is a fiber composite? How do cellular fiber composites resemble reinforced concrete?

2. In animals, where are most components of the extracellular material synthesized?
   a. smooth ER
   b. the rough ER
   c. in the extracellular layer itself
   d. in the plasma membrane

3. Treating dissociated cells with certain antibodies makes the cells unable to reaggregate. Why?
   a. The antibodies bind to cell adhesion proteins.
   b. The antibodies bind to the fiber component of the extracellular matrix.
   c. The antibodies bind to the cell surface and inhibit motility.
   d. The antibodies act as enzymes that break down desmosomes.

4. What does it mean to say that a signal is transduced?
   a. The signaling molecule enters the cell directly and binds to a receptor inside.
   b. The physical form of the signal changes between the outside of the cell and the inside.
   c. The signal is amplified, such that even a single molecule evokes a large response.
   d. The signal triggers a sequence of phosphorylation events inside the cell.

5. What characteristics do tight junctions bestow on tissues that use these adhesions to connect adjacent cells?
   a. They allow communication between adjacent cells.
   b. They provide strong connections to resist pulling forces.
   c. They use the extracellular matrix to indirectly connect adjacent cells.
   d. They form a watertight barrier between the cells.

6. What are the two general categories of cellular responses to an intercellular signal?

7. Which of the following statements represents a fundamental difference between the fibers found in the extracellular layers of plants and those of animals?
   a. Plant fibers resist compression forces; animal fibers resist pulling forces.
   b. Animal fibers consist of proteins; plant fibers consist of polysaccharides instead.
   c. Plant extracellular fibers never move; animal fibers can slide past one another.
   d. Cellulose microfibrils run parallel to one another; collagen filaments crisscross.

8. Explain how it is possible for a phosphorylation cascade to amplify an intercellular signal.

9. Compare and contrast the structure and function of tight junctions, desmosomes, and gap junctions.

10. Animal cells adhere to each other selectively. Summarize experimental evidence that supports this statement. Explain the molecular basis of selective adhesion.

11. Make a flowchart summarizing the reception, processing, response, and deactivation steps for a signaling molecule that binds to an intracellular receptor.

12. What is the significance of the observation that many signal transduction pathways create a network, where they intersect or overlap?

13. What would be the impact on the structure of a plant tissue if the cells lacked the ability to modify the extracellular environment?
    a. Cells would swell and burst if placed in a hypotonic environment.
    b. Cells would not be able to adhere to one another.
    c. No defined tissues, consisting of similar cells with coordinated activities, would be possible.
    d. All of the above.

14. Suppose that a particular cell–cell signaling molecule induces a cellular response without requiring signal transduction (i.e., no second messengers or phosphorylation cascades). Compared to the signal transduction pathways you learned about in this chapter, how would an event like this affect (a) the types of responses that are possible, (b) amplification, and (c) regulation?

15. In most species of fungi, chitin is a major polysaccharide found in cell walls. Review the structure of chitin (see Chapter 5), and then describe what would have to take place for the directional growth that occurs when yeast, a type of fungi, respond to sex pheromones.

16. Suppose you created an antibody that bound to the receptor tyrosine kinase illustrated in Figure 11.15. You expected this antibody to inhibit the cell response, but instead it resulted in activating the response, even when no signal was present. Explain this result.

12 The Cell Cycle

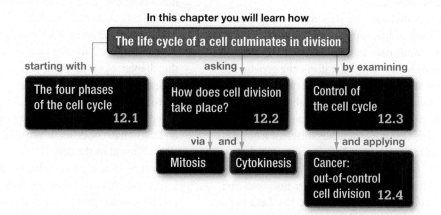

In this chapter you will learn how

The life cycle of a cell culminates in division

starting with

asking

by examining

The four phases of the cell cycle 12.1

How does cell division take place? 12.2

Control of the cell cycle 12.3

via and

Mitosis **Cytokinesis**

and applying

Cancer: out-of-control cell division 12.4

This cell, from a hyacinth plant, is undergoing a type of nuclear division called mitosis. Understanding how mitosis occurs is a major focus of this chapter.

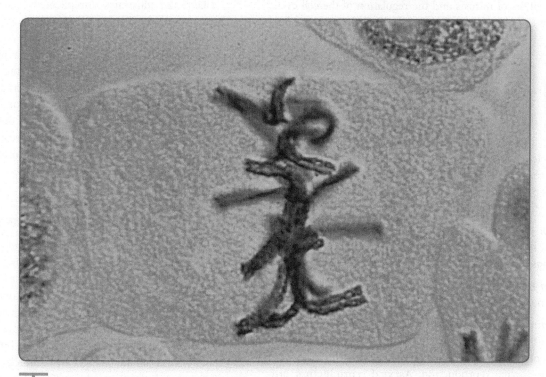

This chapter is part of the Big Picture. See how on pages 366–367.

The cell theory maintains that all organisms are made of cells and all cells arise from preexisting cells (Chapter 1). Although the cell theory was widely accepted among biologists by the 1860s, most believed that new cells arose within preexisting cells by a process that resembled the growth of mineral crystals. But Rudolf Virchow proposed that new cells arise by splitting preexisting cells—that is, by **cell division.**

In the late 1800s, microscopic observations of newly developing organisms, or **embryos,** confirmed Virchow's hypothesis. Multicellular eukaryotes start life as single-celled embryos and grow through a series of cell divisions.

Early studies revealed two fundamentally different ways that nuclei divide before cell division: meiosis and mitosis. In animals, **meiosis** leads to the production of sperm and eggs, which are the male and female reproductive cells termed **gametes. Mitosis** leads to the production of all other cell types, referred to as **somatic** (literally, "body-belonging") **cells.** (You can see the Big Picture of

✔ When you see this checkmark, stop and test yourself. Answers are available in Appendix A.

how these two nuclear divisions are related to each other and the transmission of genetic information on pages 366–367.)

Mitosis and meiosis are usually accompanied by **cytokinesis** ("cell movement")—the division of the cytoplasm into two distinct cells. When cytokinesis is complete, a so-called parent cell has given rise to two daughter cells.

Mitotic and meiotic cell divisions are responsible for one of the five fundamental attributes of life: reproduction (see Chapter 1). But even though mitosis and meiosis share many characteristics, they are fundamentally different. During mitosis, the genetic material is copied and then divided equally between two cells. This is referred to as cellular *replication*, since these daughter cells are genetically identical with the original parent cell. In contrast, meiosis results in daughter cells that are genetically different from each other and that have half the amount of hereditary material as the parent cell.

This chapter focuses on mitotic cell division; meiotic cell division is the subject of the next chapter (Chapter 13). Let's begin with a look at the key events in a cell's life cycle, continue with an in-depth analysis of mitosis and the regulation of the cell cycle, and end by examining how uncontrolled cell division can lead to cancer.

12.1 How Do Cells Replicate?

For life on Earth to exist, cells must replicate. The general requirements for cellular replication are to (1) copy the DNA (deoxyribonucleic acid), (2) separate the copies, and (3) divide the cytoplasm to create two complete cells.

This chapter focuses on eukaryotic cell replication, which is responsible for three key events:

1. *Growth* The trillions of genetically identical cells that make up your body are the product of mitotic divisions that started in a single fertilized egg.

2. *Wound repair* When you suffer a scrape, cellular replication generates the cells that repair your skin.

3. *Reproduction* When yeast cells grow in bread dough or in a vat of beer, they are reproducing by cellular replication. In yeasts and other single-cell eukaryotes, mitotic division is the basis of asexual reproduction. **Asexual reproduction** produces offspring that are genetically identical with the parent.

These events are so basic to life that cell replication has been studied for well over a century. Like much work in biology, the research on how cells divide began by simply observing the process.

What Is a Chromosome?

As studies of cell division in eukaryotes began, biologists found that certain chemical dyes made threadlike structures visible within nuclei. In 1879, Walther Flemming used a dye made from a coal tar to observe these threadlike structures and how they changed in the dividing cells of salamander embryos. The threads first appeared in pairs just before division and then split to produce single, unpaired threads in the daughter cells. Flemming introduced the term mitosis, from the Greek *mitos* ("thread"), to describe this process.

Others studied the roundworm *Ascaris* and noted that the total number of threads in a cell was the same before and after mitosis. All the cells in a roundworm had the same number of threads.

In 1888 Wilhelm Waldeyer coined the term **chromosome** ("colored-body") to refer to these threadlike structures (visible in the chapter-opening photo). A chromosome consists of a single, long DNA double helix that is wrapped around proteins, called **histones,** in a highly organized manner. DNA encodes the cell's hereditary information, or genetic material. A gene is a length of DNA that codes for a particular protein or ribonucleic acid (RNA) found in the cell.

Before mitosis, each chromosome is replicated. As mitosis starts, the chromosomes condense into compact structures that can be moved around the cell efficiently. Then one of the chromosome copies is distributed to each of two daughter cells.

FIGURE 12.1 illustrates unreplicated chromosomes, replicated chromosomes before they have condensed prior to mitosis, and replicated chromosomes that have condensed at the start of mitosis. Each of the DNA copies in a replicated chromosome is called a **chromatid.** Before mitosis, the two chromatids are joined along their entire length by proteins called cohesins. Once mitosis begins, however, many of these connections are removed except for those at a specialized region of the chromosome called the **centromere.** Chromatid copies that remain attached at their centromere are referred to as **sister chromatids.** Even though a replicated chromosome consists of two chromatids, it is still considered a single chromosome.

Cells Alternate between M Phase and Interphase

The division of eukaryotic cells is like a well-choreographed stage performance. The most visually stimulating part of the show occurs when cells are in their dividing phase, called the **M** (*mitotic* or *meiotic*) **phase.** With a light microscope, chromosomes can be stained and observed as discrete units only during M phase, when they condense into compact structures.

The rest of the time, the cell is in **interphase** ("between-phase"). No dramatic changes in the nucleus are visible by light microscopy during interphase. The chromosomes uncoil into the extremely long, thin structures shown in Figure 12.1 and are no longer stained as individual threads. However, this does not mean that the cell is idle. Interphase is an active time: The cell is either growing and preparing to divide or fulfilling its specialized function in a multicellular individual. Cells actually spend most of their time in interphase.

The Discovery of S Phase

Once M phase and interphase were identified by microscopy, researchers could start assigning roles to these distinct phases. They could see that the separation of chromosomes and cytokinesis

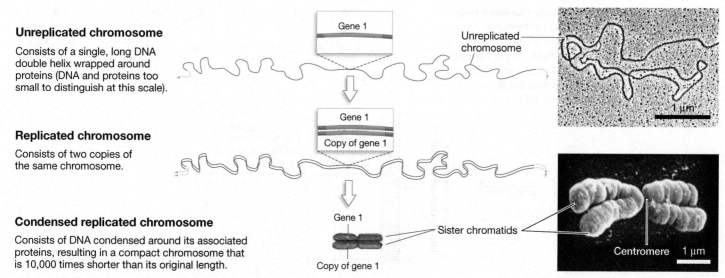

Unreplicated chromosome

Consists of a single, long DNA double helix wrapped around proteins (DNA and proteins too small to distinguish at this scale).

Replicated chromosome

Consists of two copies of the same chromosome.

Condensed replicated chromosome

Consists of DNA condensed around its associated proteins, resulting in a compact chromosome that is 10,000 times shorter than its original length.

Gene 1

Gene 1

Copy of gene 1

Gene 1

Copy of gene 1

Sister chromatids

Unreplicated chromosome

1 μm

Centromere   1 μm

FIGURE 12.1 Changes in Chromosome Morphology. After chromosomes replicate, the two identical copies are attached to each other along their entire length. Early in mitosis, replicated chromosomes condense and sister chromatids remain attached at a region called the centromere.

took place during the M phase, but when are the chromosomes copied?

To answer this question, researchers needed to distinguish cells that were replicating their DNA from those that were not. They were able to do this by adding radioactive phosphorus, in the form of phosphates, to cells. Those cells that were synthesizing DNA would incorporate the radioactive isotope into nucleotides (see Chapter 4 to review where phosphates are in DNA).

The idea was to:

1. label DNA as chromosomes were being copied;

2. wash away any radioactive isotope that hadn't been incorporated and remove RNA, which would also incorporate phosphorus; and then

3. visualize the labeled, newly synthesized DNA by exposing the treated cells to X-ray film. Emissions from radioactive phosphorus create a black dot in the film. This is the technique called autoradiography (see **BioSkills 9** in Appendix B).

In 1951, Alma Howard and Stephen Pelc performed this experiment and looked for cells with black dots—indicating active DNA synthesis—immediately after the exposure to a radioactive isotope ended. They found black dots in some of the interphase cells, but none in M-phase cells. Several years later, these results were verified using radioactive thymidine, which is incorporated into DNA but not RNA. These results were strong evidence that DNA replication occurs during interphase.

Thus, biologists had identified a new stage in the life of a cell. They called it **synthesis** (or **S) phase.** S phase is part of interphase. Replication of the genetic material is separated, in time, from the partitioning of chromosome copies during M phase.

Howard and Pelc coined the term **cell cycle** to describe the orderly sequence of events that leads a eukaryotic cell through the duplication of its chromosomes to the time it divides.

The Discovery of the Gap Phases

In addition to discovering the S phase, Howard and Pelc made another key observation—not all the interphase cells were labeled. This meant that there was at least one "gap" in interphase when DNA was not being copied.

Howard and Pelc, along with researchers in other labs, followed up on these early results by asking where S phase was positioned in interphase. There were three possible scenarios:

1. The S phase is immediately before M phase, with a single gap between the end of M and start of S phase;

2. the S phase is immediately after M phase, with a gap between the end of S and the start of M phase; or

3. two gaps exist, one before and one after the S phase.

To address which of these models, if any, is correct, many experiments were done using cells in culture. Cultured cells are powerful experimental tools because they can be manipulated much more easily than cells in an intact organism (see **BioSkills 12** in Appendix B). In most of these studies, researchers used cultures that were asynchronous, meaning that the cells were randomly distributed in the cycle.

To understand the value of these asynchronous cultures, imagine the cell cycle were a clock. Every complete rotation around the clock would represent one cell division, and each tick would represent a different point in the cycle. At any given time, an asynchronous culture would have at least one cell present at each of the ticks on the clock. As time passes, these cells would move around this cell-cycle clock at the same rate and in the same direction.

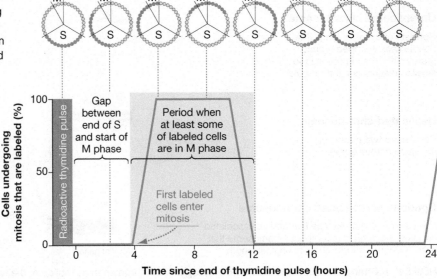

FIGURE 12.2 The Pulse–Chase Assay Reveals a Gap Phase. Cells labeled with radioactive thymidine during the pulse can be tracked during the chase to identify when they enter M phase. In this assay, a gap between the end of S phase and start of M phase was identified based on the delay observed between the pulse and the presence of labeled mitotic cells.

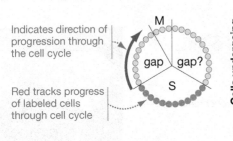

In one experiment, researchers marked the S-phase cells in a human cell culture by exposing it to radioactively labeled thymidine. A short time later, they stopped the labeling by flooding the solution surrounding the cultured cells with nonradioactive thymidine. This pulse–chase approach (introduced in Chapter 7) labeled only those cells that were in S phase during the radioactive pulse. Imagine these marked cells moving like a hand on the clock that could be tracked as they progressed through the cell cycle.

Once the pulse ended, the researchers analyzed samples of the culture at different times during the chase. For each batch of cells, they recorded how many labeled cells were undergoing mitosis, meaning that the cells that were in S phase during the pulse had entered M phase.

One striking result emerged early on: None of the labeled cells started mitosis immediately. Because the cultures were asynchronous, at least some of the cells must have been at the very end of their S phase when exposed to the pulse. If the S phase had been immediately followed by the M phase, some of these labeled cells would have entered M just as the chase began. Instead, it took several hours before any of the labeled cells began mitosis.

The time lag between the end of the pulse and the appearance of the first labeled mitotic nuclei corresponds to a period between the end of S phase and the beginning of M phase. This gap represents the time when chromosome replication is complete, but mitosis has not yet begun. **FIGURE 12.2** shows how cells labeled with radioactive thymidine can be tracked as they progress through the M phase.

After this result, the possibilities for the organization of the cell cycle were narrowed to either one gap between the end of S and start of M phase, or two gaps that flank the S phase. Which of the models best represents the eukaryotic cell cycle? Once researchers determined the lengths of the S and M phases, they found that the combined time, including the gap between these phases, was still short compared with the length of the cell cycle. This discrepancy represents an additional gap phase that is between the end of M and the start of S phase.

The cell cycle was thus finally mapped out. The gap between the end of M and start of S phase is called the **G₁ phase.** The second gap, between the end of S and start of M phase, is called the **G₂ phase.**

The Cell Cycle

FIGURE 12.3 pulls these results together into a comprehensive view of the cell cycle. The cell cycle involves four phases: M phase and an interphase consisting of the G₁, S, and G₂ phases. In the cycle diagrammed here, the G₁ phase is about twice as long as G₂, but the timing of these phases varies depending on the cell type and growth conditions.

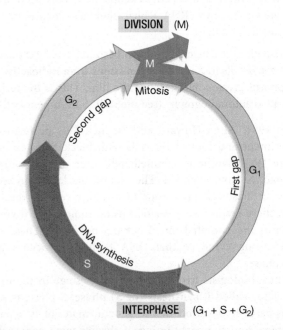

FIGURE 12.3 The Cell Cycle Has Four Phases. A representative cell cycle. The time required for the G₁ and G₂ phases varies dramatically among cells and organisms.

Why do the gap phases exist? Besides needing to copy their chromosomes during interphase, cells also must prepare for division by replicating organelles and increasing in size. Before mitosis can take place, the parent cell must grow large enough to divide into two cells that will be normal in size and function. The two gap phases provide the time required to accomplish these tasks. They allow the cell to complete all the requirements for cell division other than chromosome replication.

Now let's turn to the M phase. Once the genetic material has been copied, how do cells divide it between daughter cells?

12.2 What Happens during M Phase?

The M phase typically consists of two distinct events: the division of the nucleus and the division of the cytoplasm. During cell replication, mitosis divides the replicated chromosomes to form two daughter nuclei with identical chromosomes and genes. Mitosis is usually accompanied by cytokinesis—cytoplasmic division that results in two daughter cells.

FIGURE 12.4 provides an overview of how chromosomes change before, during, and after mitosis and cytokinesis, beginning with a hypothetical plant cell or animal cell in G_1 phase. The first drawing shows a total of four chromosomes in the cell, but chromosome number varies widely among species—chimpanzees and potato plants have a total of 48 chromosomes in each cell; a maize (corn) plant has 20, dogs have 78, and fruit flies have 8.

Eukaryotic chromosomes consist of DNA wrapped around the globular histone proteins. In eukaryotes this DNA–protein material is called **chromatin.** During interphase, the chromatin of each chromosome is in a "relaxed" or uncondensed state, forming long, thin strands (see Figure 12.1, top).

The second drawing in Figure 12.4 shows chromosomes that have been copied before mitosis. Each chromosome now consists of two sister chromatids. Each chromatid contains one long DNA double helix, and sister chromatids represent exact copies of the same genetic information.

At the start of mitosis, then, each chromosome consists of two sister chromatids that are attached to each other at the centromere.

✔ You should be able to explain the relationship between chromosomes and (1) genes, (2) chromatin, and (3) sister chromatids.

Events in Mitosis

As the third drawing in Figure 12.4 indicates, mitosis begins when chromatin condenses to form a much more compact structure. Replicated, condensed chromosomes correspond to the paired threads observed by early biologists.

During mitosis, the two sister chromatids separate to form independent daughter chromosomes. One copy of each chromosome goes to each of the two daughter cells. (See the final drawing in Figure 12.4.) As a result, each cell receives an identical copy of the genetic information that was contained in the parent cell.

Biologists have identified five subphases within M phase based on distinctive events that occur. Interphase is followed by the mitotic subphases of prophase, prometaphase, metaphase, anaphase, and telophase.

Recall that before mitosis begins, chromosomes have already replicated during the S phase of interphase. Now let's look at how cells separate the chromatids in these replicated chromosomes by investigating each subphase of mitosis in turn (**FIGURE 12.5,** on page 224).

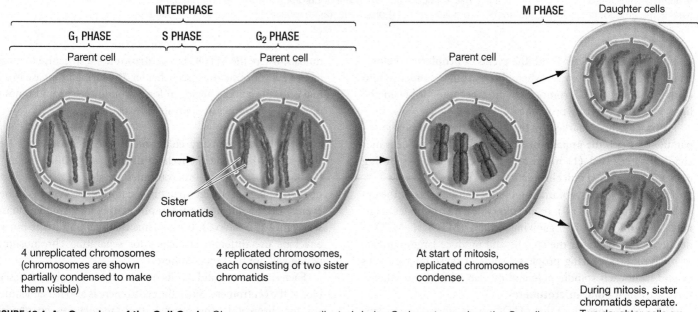

INTERPHASE — G_1 PHASE — S PHASE — G_2 PHASE

Parent cell

Parent cell

Sister chromatids

M PHASE — Daughter cells

Parent cell

4 unreplicated chromosomes (chromosomes are shown partially condensed to make them visible)

4 replicated chromosomes, each consisting of two sister chromatids

At start of mitosis, replicated chromosomes condense.

During mitosis, sister chromatids separate. Two daughter cells are formed by cytokinesis.

FIGURE 12.4 An Overview of the Cell Cycle. Chromosomes are replicated during S phase to produce the G_2 cell. During M phase, the replicated chromosomes are partitioned to the two daughter cells. Each daughter cell contains the same complement of chromosomes as the parent cell.

PROCESS: MITOSIS

Sister chromatids separate; one chromosome copy goes to each daughter nucleus.

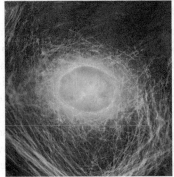

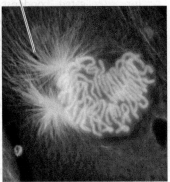

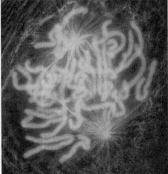

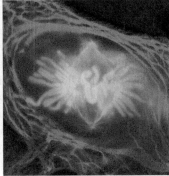

Centrioles
Centrosomes   Chromosomes   Early spindle apparatus   Polar microtubules   Kinetochore microtubules   Astral microtubules

Sister chromatids   Kinetochore

1. Interphase: After chromosome replication, each chromosome is composed of two sister chromatids. Centrosomes have replicated.

2. Prophase: Chromosomes condense, and spindle apparatus begins to form.

3. Prometaphase: Nuclear envelope breaks down. Microtubules contact chromosomes at kinetochores.

4. Metaphase: Chromosomes complete migration to middle of cell.

FIGURE 12.5 Mitosis and Cytokinesis. In the micrographs, under the drawings, chromosomes are stained blue, microtubules are yellow/green, and intermediate filaments are red.

✔**QUANTITATIVE:** If the model cell in this figure has x amount of DNA and four chromosomes in its G_1 phase, then what is the amount of DNA and number of chromosomes in **(1)** prophase; **(2)** anaphase; **(3)** each daughter cell after division is complete?

Prophase   Mitosis begins with the events of **prophase** ("before-phase," Figure 12.5, step 2), when chromosomes condense into compact structures. Chromosomes first become visible in the light microscope during prophase.

Prophase is also marked by the formation of the spindle apparatus. The **spindle apparatus** is a structure that produces mechanical forces that **(1)** move replicated chromosomes during early mitosis and **(2)** pull chromatids apart in late mitosis.

The spindle consists of microtubules—components of the cytoskeleton (see Chapter 7). In all eukaryotes, microtubules originate from microtubule-organizing centers (MTOCs). MTOCs define the two poles of the spindle and produce large numbers of microtubules. During prophase, some of these microtubules extend from each spindle pole and overlap with one another—these are called **polar microtubules.**

Although the nature of this MTOC varies among plants, animals, fungi, and other eukaryotic groups, the spindle apparatus has the same function. Figure 12.5 illustrates an animal cell undergoing

mitosis, where the MTOC is a **centrosome**—a structure that contains a pair of **centrioles** (see Chapter 7). During prophase in animal cells, the spindle begins to form around the chromosomes by moving centrosomes to opposite sides of the nucleus.

Prometaphase   In many eukaryotes, once chromosomes have condensed, the nuclear envelope disintegrates. Once the envelope has been removed, microtubules are able to attach to chromosomes at specialized structures called **kinetochores.** These events occur during **prometaphase** ("before middle-phase"; see Figure 12.5, step 3). (Organisms that maintain their nuclear envelope use different strategies for separating chromosomes, which will not be discussed here.)

Each sister chromatid has its own kinetochore, which is assembled at the centromere. Since the centromere is also the attachment site for chromatids, the result is two kinetochores on opposite sides of each replicated chromosome. The microtubules that are attached to these structures are called **kinetochore microtubules.**

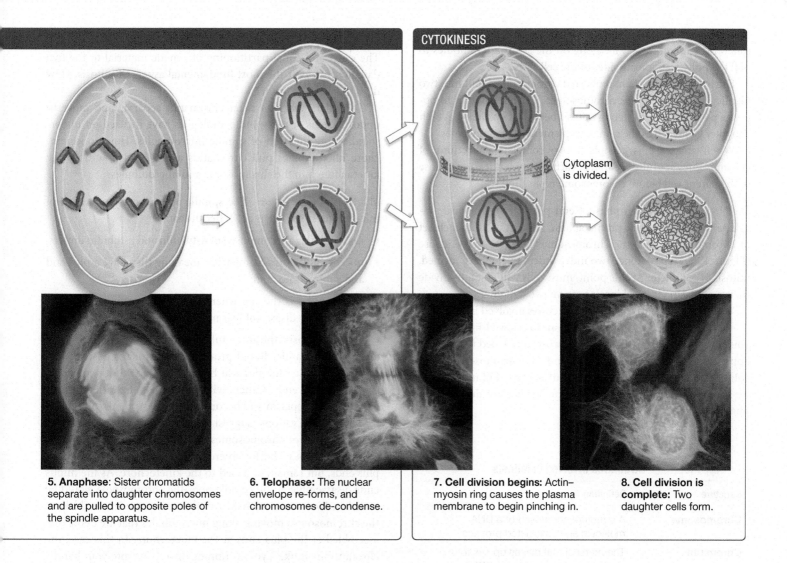

Cytoplasm is divided.

5. Anaphase: Sister chromatids separate into daughter chromosomes and are pulled to opposite poles of the spindle apparatus.

6. Telophase: The nuclear envelope re-forms, and chromosomes de-condense.

7. Cell division begins: Actin–myosin ring causes the plasma membrane to begin pinching in.

8. Cell division is complete: Two daughter cells form.

Early in mitosis, kinesin and dynein motors are recruited to the kinetochore, where they can "walk" the chromosome up and down microtubules. These motors are thought to be very important in the initial attachment of the kinetochore to the plus end of the microtubule. If these ideas are correct, then the process is similar to the way these motors walk along microtubules during vesicle transport (see Chapter 7).

In all eukaryotes, after the kinetochores have attached to microtubules, chromosomes begin to move to the middle of the cell during prometaphase.

Metaphase   Once the kinetochore microtubules have moved all the chromosomes to the middle of the spindle (Figure 12.5, step 4), the mitotic cells enter **metaphase** ("middle-phase"). At this point, the chromosomes are lined up along an imaginary plane between the two spindle poles called the **metaphase plate.**

The formation of the spindle apparatus is now complete. The polar microtubules that extend from each spindle pole overlap in the middle of the cell, thereby forming a pole-to-pole connection. Each chromosome is held by kinetochore microtubules reaching out from opposite poles and exerting the same amount of tension, or pull. The spindle poles are held in place partly because of

astral microtubules that extend from the MTOCs and interact with proteins on the cell membrane.

The alignment of these chromosomes results from the growth and shrinkage of the attached kinetochore microtubules. When chromosomes reach the metaphase plate, the shrinkage of these microtubules at the MTOCs is balanced by slow growth of microtubules at the kinetochores. Since the sister chromatids of each chromosome are connected to opposite poles, a tug of war occurs during metaphase that pulls them in opposite directions.

Anaphase   At the start of **anaphase** ("against-phase"), the cohesins that are holding sister chromatids together at the centromeres split (Figure 12.5, step 5). Because the chromatids are under tension, each replicated chromosome is pulled apart to create two independent daughter chromosomes. By definition, this separation of chromatids instantly doubles the number of chromosomes in the cell.

Two types of movement occur during anaphase. First, the daughter chromosomes move to opposite poles via the attachment of kinetochore proteins to the shrinking kinetochore microtubules. Second, the two poles of the spindle are pushed and pulled farther apart. The motor proteins in overlapping polar microtubules push the poles away from each other. Different motors on the membrane walk along on the astral microtubules to pull the poles to opposite sides of the cell.

During anaphase, then, replicated chromosomes split into two identical sets of daughter chromosomes. Their separation to opposite poles is a critical step in mitosis because it ensures that each daughter cell receives the same complement of chromosomes.

When anaphase is complete, two complete collections of chromosomes are fully separated, each being identical with those of the parent cell before chromosome replication.

Telophase During **telophase** ("end-phase"), the nuclear envelope that dissolved in prometaphase reforms around each set of chromosomes, and the chromosomes begin to de-condense (Figure 12.5, step 6). Once two independent nuclei have formed, mitosis is complete. At this point, most cells will go on to divide their cytoplasm via cytokinesis to form two daughter cells.

TABLE 12.1 summarizes the key structures involved in mitosis.

✔ After you've studied the table and reviewed Figure 12.5, you should be able to make a table with rows titled (1) spindle apparatus, (2) nuclear envelope, and (3) chromosomes, and columns titled with the five phases of mitosis. Fill in the table by summarizing what happens to each structure during each phase of mitosis.

SUMMARY TABLE 12.1 **Structures Involved in Mitosis**

Structure	Definition
Chromosome	A structure composed of a DNA molecule and associated proteins
Chromatin	The material that makes up eukaryotic chromosomes; consists of a DNA molecule complexed with histone proteins (see Chapter 19)
Chromatid	One strand of a replicated chromosome, with its associated proteins
Sister chromatids	The two strands of a replicated chromosome. When chromosomes are replicated, they consist of two sister chromatids. The genetic material in sister chromatids is identical. When sister chromatids separate during mitosis, they become independent chromosomes.
Centromere	The structure that joins sister chromatids
Kinetochores	The structures on sister chromatids where microtubules attach
Microtubule-organizing center	Any structure that organizes microtubules (see Chapter 7)
Centrosome	The microtubule-organizing center in animals and some plants
Centrioles	Cylindrical structures that comprise microtubules, located inside animal centrosomes

How Do Chromosomes Move during Anaphase?

The exact and equal partitioning of genetic material to the two daughter nuclei is the most fundamental aspect of mitosis. How does this process occur?

To understand how sister chromatids separate and move to opposite sides of the spindle, biologists have focused on understanding the function of spindle microtubules. How do kinetochore microtubules pull chromatids apart? And how does the kinetochore join the chromosome and microtubules?

Mitotic Spindle Forces The spindle apparatus is composed of microtubules (see Chapter 7). Recall that:

- microtubules are composed of α-tubulin and β-tubulin dimers,

- microtubules are asymmetric—meaning they have a plus end and a minus end, and

- the plus end is the site where microtubule growth normally occurs while disassembly is more frequent at the minus end.

During mitosis, the microtubules originating from the poles are highly dynamic. Rapid growth and shrinkage ensures that some of the microtubules will be able to attach to kinetochores with their plus ends. Others will be stabilized by different proteins in the cytoplasm and become polar or astral microtubules.

These observations suggest two possible mechanisms for the movement of chromosomes during anaphase. The simplest mechanism would be for microtubules to stop growing at the plus ends, but remain attached to the kinetochore. As the minus ends disassemble at the spindle pole, the chromosome would be reeled in like a hooked fish. An alternative model would have the chromosomes moving along microtubules that are being disassembled at the plus ends at the kinetochore. In this case, the chromosome is like a yo-yo running up a string into your hand.

To test these hypotheses, biologists introduced fluorescently labeled tubulin subunits into prophase or metaphase cells. This treatment made the kinetochore microtubules visible (**FIGURE 12.6**, step 1). Once anaphase began, the researchers marked a region of these microtubules with a bar-shaped beam of laser light. The laser permanently bleached a section of the fluorescently labeled structures, darkening them—although they were still functional (Figure 12.6, step 2).

As anaphase progressed, two things happened: (**1**) The darkened region appeared to remain stationary, and (**2**) the chromosomes moved closer to the darkened regions of the microtubules, eventually overtaking them.

This result suggested that the kinetochore microtubules remain stationary during anaphase, but shorten because tubulin subunits are lost from their plus ends. As microtubule ends shrink back to the spindle poles, the chromosomes are pulled along. But if the microtubule is disassembling at the kinetochore, how does the chromosome remain attached?

Kinetochores Are Linked to Retreating Microtubule Ends The kinetochore is a complex of many proteins that build a base on the centromere region of the chromosome and a "crown" of fibrous proteins projecting outward. **FIGURE 12.7** shows a current

QUESTION: How do kinetochore microtubules shorten to pull daughter chromosomes apart during anaphase?

HYPOTHESIS: Microtubules shorten at the spindle pole.

ALTERNATIVE HYPOTHESIS: Microtubules shorten at the kinetochore.

EXPERIMENTAL SETUP:

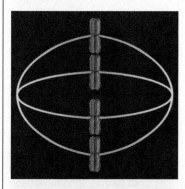

1. Label targets:
Use fluorescent labels to make the metaphase chromosomes fluoresce blue and the microtubules fluoresce yellow.

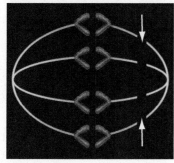

2. Mark microtubules:
At the start of anaphase, darken a section of microtubules to mark them without changing their function.

PREDICTION:

PREDICTION OF ALTERNATIVE HYPOTHESIS: Daughter chromosomes will move toward the pole faster than the darkened section.

RESULTS:

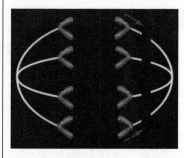

The darkened areas of the microtubules remained stationary as the chromosomes moved through them toward the pole.

CONCLUSION: Kinetochore microtubules shorten at the kinetochore to pull daughter chromosomes apart during anaphase.

FIGURE 12.6 During Anaphase, Microtubules Shorten at the Kinetochore.

SOURCE: Gorbsky, G. J., et al. 1987. Chromosomes move poleward during anaphase along stationary microtubules that coordinately disassemble from their kinetochore ends. *Journal of Cellular Biology* 104: 9–18.

✔**EXERCISE** Complete the prediction for what would occur if chromosome movement were based on microtubules shortening at the spindle pole.

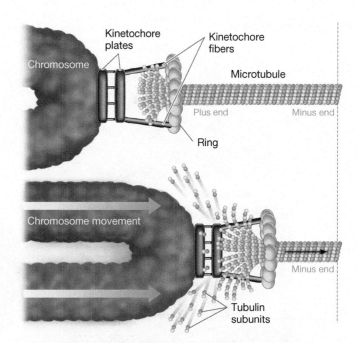

FIGURE 12.7 How Do Microtubules Move Chromosomes during Anaphase? Microtubules are disassembled at the kinetochore during anaphase. In yeast, kinetochore proteins tether the chromosome to a ring that is pushed toward the spindle pole by the fraying plus end of the microtubule.

model for kinetochore structure and function during chromosome movement in anaphase. For simplicity, a yeast kinetochore is shown, which attaches to only one microtubule. (Other eukaryotes can have as many as 30 microtubules attached to each kinetochore.)

Biologists have found that as anaphase gets under way, the plus ends of the kinetochore microtubules begin to fray and disassemble. Fibers that extend from the yeast kinetochore are tethered to this retreating end by attaching to a ring that surrounds the kinetochore microtubule (Figure 12.7, top). As the fraying end widens, its expansion forces the ring, and the attached chromosome, toward the minus end of the microtubule (see Figure 12.7, bottom). The result is that the chromosome is pulled to the spindle pole by the depolymerization of the kinetochore microtubule.

Cytokinesis Results in Two Daughter Cells

At this point, the chromosomes have been replicated in S phase and partitioned to opposite sides of the spindle via mitosis. Now it's time to divide the cell into two daughters that contain identical copies of each chromosome. If these cells are to be viable, however, the parent cell must also ensure that more than just chromosomes make it into each daughter cell.

While the cell is in interphase, the cytoplasmic contents, including the organelles, have increased in number or volume. During cytokinesis (Figure 12.5, steps 7 and 8), the cytoplasm divides to form two daughter cells, each with its own nucleus and complete set of organelles. In most types of cells, cytokinesis directly follows mitosis.

(a) Cytokinesis in plants

Microtubules direct vesicles to center of spindle where they fuse to divide the cell in two

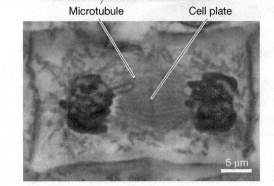

Microtubule   Cell plate

5 μm

(b) Cytokinesis in animals

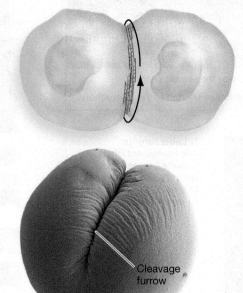

Actin–myosin interactions pinch the membrane in two

Cleavage furrow

100 μm

FIGURE 12.8 The Mechanism of Cytokinesis Varies among Eukaryotes. (a) In plants, the cytoplasm is divided by a cell plate that forms in the middle of the parent cell. **(b)** In animals, the cytoplasm is divided by a cleavage furrow. (The cells in both micrographs have been stained or colorized.)

In plants, polar microtubules left over from the spindle help define and organize the region where the new plasma membranes and cell walls will form. Vesicles from the Golgi apparatus carry components to build a new cell wall to the middle of the dividing cell. These vesicles are moved along the polar microtubules via motor proteins. In the middle of what was the spindle, the vesicles start to fuse together to form a flattened sac-like structure called the **cell plate** (**FIGURE 12.8a**). The cell plate continues to grow as new vesicles fuse with it, eventually contacting the existing plasma membrane. When the cell plate fuses with the existing plasma membrane, it divides the cell into two new daughter cells.

In animals and many other eukaryotes, cytokinesis begins with the formation of a **cleavage furrow** (**FIGURE 12.8b**). The furrow appears because a ring of actin filaments forms just inside the plasma membrane, in the middle of what used to be the spindle. Myosin motor proteins bind to these actin filaments and use adenosine triphosphate (ATP) to contract in a way that causes actin filaments to slide (see Chapter 7).

As myosin moves the ring of actin filaments on the inside of the plasma membrane, the ring shrinks in size and tightens. Because the ring is attached to the plasma membrane, the shrinking ring pulls the membrane with it. As a result, the plasma membrane pinches inward. The actin and myosin filaments continue to slide past each other, tightening the ring further, until the original membrane pinches in two and cell division is complete.

The overall process involved in chromosome separation and cytoplasmic division is a common requirement for all living organisms. The mechanisms involved in accomplishing these events, however, vary depending on the type of cell. What about

bacterial cells? How does chromosomal segregation and cytokinesis compare between prokaryotes and eukaryotes?

Bacterial Cell Replication Many bacteria divide using a process called **binary fission**. Recent research has shown that chromosome segregation and cytokinesis in bacterial division is strikingly similar to what occurs in the eukaryotic M phase (**FIGURE 12.9**). As the bacterial chromosome is being replicated, protein filaments attach to the copies and separate them to opposite sides of the cell.

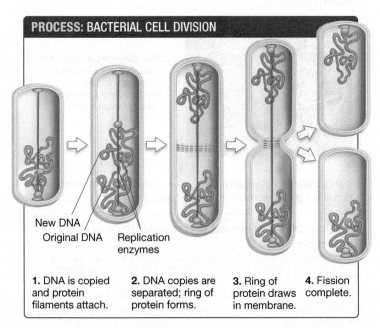

PROCESS: BACTERIAL CELL DIVISION

New DNA
Original DNA   Replication enzymes

1. DNA is copied and protein filaments attach.

2. DNA copies are separated; ring of protein forms.

3. Ring of protein draws in membrane.

4. Fission complete.

FIGURE 12.9 Bacterial Cells Divide but Do Not Undergo Mitosis.

Once the copies of the chromosome have been partitioned to opposite sides of the cell, other filaments, made up of proteins that are similar to eukaryotic tubulin, are responsible for dividing the cytoplasm. These filaments attach to the cell membrane to form a ring between the chromosome copies. A signal from the cell causes the filaments to constrict, drawing in the membrane and eventually cleaving the parent into two genetically identical cells.

Having explored what occurs during cell division, let's focus on how it is controlled in eukaryotes. When does a eukaryotic cell divide, and when does it stop dividing?

check your understanding

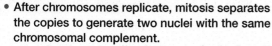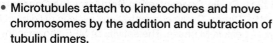

If you understand that . . .

- After chromosomes replicate, mitosis separates the copies to generate two nuclei with the same chromosomal complement.
- Microtubules attach to kinetochores and move chromosomes by the addition and subtraction of tubulin dimers.
- Cytokinesis divides the nuclei and cytoplasmic components into two daughter cells that are genetically identical with each other and the parent cell.

✔ **You should be able to . . .**

1. Draw the mitotic spindle for an animal cell that has two chromosomes in metaphase and label the sister chromatids, kinetochores, centrosomes, and the three types of microtubules.
2. Predict how the inhibition of microtubule motors in a plant cell would affect the activities in M phase.

Answers are available in Appendix A.

12.3 Control of the Cell Cycle

Although the events of mitosis are virtually identical in all eukaryotes, other aspects of the cell cycle vary. In humans, for example, intestinal cells routinely divide more than twice a day to replace tissue that is lost during digestion; mature human nerve and muscle cells do not divide at all.

Most of these differences are due to variation in the length of the G_1 phase. In rapidly dividing cells, G_1 is essentially eliminated. Most nondividing cells, in contrast, are permanently stuck in G_1. Researchers refer to this arrested stage as the G_0 state, or simply "G zero." Cells that are in G_0 have effectively exited the cell cycle and are sometimes referred to as post-mitotic. Nerve cells, muscle cells, and many other cell types enter G_0 once they have matured.

A cell's division rate can also vary in response to changing conditions. For example, human liver cells normally replicate about once per year. But if part of the liver is damaged or lost, the remaining cells divide every one or two days until repair is accomplished. Cells of unicellular organisms such as yeasts, bacteria, or archaeans divide rapidly only if the environment is rich in nutrients; otherwise, they enter a quiescent (inactive) state.

To explain these differences, biologists hypothesized that the cell cycle must be regulated in some way. Cell-cycle control is now the most prominent issue in research on cell division—partly because defects in control can lead to uncontrolled, cancerous growth.

The Discovery of Cell-Cycle Regulatory Molecules

The first solid evidence for cell-cycle control molecules came to light in 1970. Researchers found that certain chemicals, viruses, or an electric shock could fuse the membranes of two mammalian cells that were growing in culture, forming a single cell with two nuclei.

How did cell-fusion experiments relate to cell-cycle regulation? When investigators fused cells that were in different stages of the cell cycle, certain nuclei changed phases. For example, when a cell in M phase was fused with one in interphase, the nucleus of the interphase cell immediately initiated mitosis, even if the chromosomes had not been replicated. The biologists hypothesized that the cytoplasm of M-phase cells contains a regulatory molecule that induces interphase cells to enter M phase.

But cell-fusion experiments were difficult to control and left researchers wondering if it was the nucleus or the cytoplasm that was responsible for the induction. To address this issue, they turned to the South African clawed frog, *Xenopus laevis*.

As an egg of these frogs matures, it changes from a cell called an oocyte, which is arrested in a phase similar to G_2, to a mature egg that is arrested in M phase. The large size of these cells—more than 1 mm in diameter—makes them relatively easy to manipulate. Using instruments with extremely fine needles, researchers could specifically examine the effects of the cytoplasm by pulling a sample from a mature egg or an oocyte and injecting it into another.

When biologists purified cytoplasm from M-phase frog eggs and injected it into the cytoplasm of frog oocytes arrested in G_2, the immature oocytes immediately entered M phase (**FIGURE 12.10**, see page 230). But when cytoplasm from interphase cells was injected into G_2 oocytes, the cells remained in the G_2 phase. The researchers concluded that the cytoplasm of M-phase cells—but not the cytoplasm of interphase cells—contains a factor that drives immature oocytes into M phase to complete their maturation.

The factor that initiates M-phase in oocytes was purified and is now called **M phase–promoting factor,** or **MPF.** Subsequent experiments showed that MPF induces M phase in all eukaryotes. For example, injecting M-phase cytoplasm from mammalian cells into immature frog oocytes results in egg maturation, and human MPF can also trigger M phase in yeast cells.

MPF appears to be a general signal that says "Start M phase." How does it work?

QUESTION: Is M phase controlled by regulatory molecules in the cytoplasm?

HYPOTHESIS: Cytoplasmic regulatory molecules control entry into M phase.

NULL HYPOTHESIS: M-phase regulatory molecules are not in the cytoplasm or do not exist.

EXPERIMENTAL SETUP:

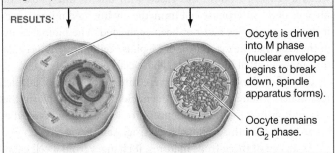

M-phase cytoplasm

Interphase cytoplasm

Microinject cytoplasm from M-phase cell into one frog oocyte and cytoplasm from interphase cell into another frog oocyte.

PREDICTION: Only the oocyte injected with M-phase cytoplasm will begin M phase.

PREDICTION OF NULL HYPOTHESIS: Neither of the frog oocytes will begin M phase.

RESULTS:

Oocyte is driven into M phase (nuclear envelope begins to break down, spindle apparatus forms).

Oocyte remains in G_2 phase.

CONCLUSION: M-phase cytoplasm contains a regulatory molecule that induces M phase in interphase cells.

FIGURE 12.10 Experimental Evidence for Cell-Cycle Control Molecules. When the cytoplasm from M-phase cells is microinjected into cells in interphase, the interphase chromosomes condense and begin M phase.

SOURCE: Masui, Y., and C. L. Markert. 1971. Cytoplasmic control of nuclear behavior during meiotic maturation of frog oocytes. *Journal of Experimental Zoology* 177: 129–145.

✔**QUESTION** This experiment was done using cells that were undergoing meiosis. What could the investigators do to show that the factor used in meiotic division is the same as used for mitotic division?

MPF Contains a Protein Kinase and a Cyclin

MPF is made up of two distinct polypeptide subunits. One subunit is a protein kinase—an enzyme that catalyzes the transfer of a phosphate group from ATP to a target protein. Recall that phosphorylation may activate or inactivate the function of proteins by changing their shape (Chapter 8). As a result, kinases frequently act as regulatory proteins in the cell.

These observations suggested that MPF phosphorylates proteins that trigger the onset of M phase. But research showed that

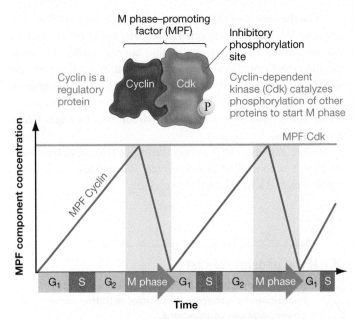

M phase–promoting factor (MPF)

Cyclin is a regulatory protein

Inhibitory phosphorylation site

Cyclin-dependent kinase (Cdk) catalyzes phosphorylation of other proteins to start M phase

MPF component concentration

MPF Cdk

MPF Cyclin

G_1 | S | G_2 | M phase | G_1 | S | G_2 | M phase | G_1 | S

Time

FIGURE 12.11 Cyclin Concentration Regulates the Concentration of the MPF Dimer. Cyclin concentrations cycle in dividing cells, reaching a peak in M phase. The activity of MPF, shown in the blue shaded area, requires both cyclin and Cdk components.

✔**QUESTION** Proteins that degrade cyclin are activated by events that MPF initiates. Why is this important?

the concentration of the protein kinase is more or less constant throughout the cell cycle. How can MPF trigger M phase if the protein kinase subunit is always present?

The answer lies in the second MPF subunit, which belongs to a family of proteins called **cyclins.** Cyclins got their name because their concentrations fluctuate throughout the cell cycle.

As **FIGURE 12.11** shows, the concentration of the cyclin associated with MPF builds during interphase and peaks in M phase. The timing of this increase is important because the protein kinase subunit in MPF is functional only when it is bound to the cyclin subunit. As a result, the protein kinase subunit of MPF is called a **cyclin-dependent kinase,** or **Cdk.**

To summarize, MPF is a dimer consisting of a cyclin and a cyclin-dependent kinase. The cyclin subunit regulates the formation of the MPF dimer; the kinase subunit catalyzes the phosphorylation of other proteins to start M phase.

How Is MPF Turned On?   According to Figure 12.11, the number of cyclins builds up steadily during interphase. Why doesn't this increasing concentration of MPF trigger the onset of M phase?

The answer is that the activity of MPF's Cdk subunit is further regulated by two phosphorylation events. The phosphorylation of one site in Cdk activates the kinase, but when the second site is phosphorylated, it is inactivated. Both these sites are phosphorylated after cyclin binds to the Cdk. This allows the concentration of the dimer to increase without prematurely starting M phase. Late in G_2 phase, however, an enzyme removes the inhibitory phosphate. This dephosphorylation reaction, coupled with the addition of the activating phosphate, changes the Cdk's shape in a way that turns on its kinase activity.

Once MPF is active, it triggers a chain of events. Although the exact mechanisms involved are still under investigation, the result is that chromosomes begin to condense and the spindle apparatus starts to form. In this way, MPF triggers the onset of M phase.

How Is MPF Turned Off? During anaphase, an enzyme complex begins degrading MPF's cyclin subunit. In this way, MPF triggers a chain of events that leads to its own destruction.

MPF deactivation illustrates two key concepts about regulatory systems in cells:

- **Negative feedback** occurs when a process is slowed or shut down by one of its products. Thermostats shut down furnaces when temperatures are high; phosphofructokinase is inhibited by ATP (see Chapter 9); MPF is turned off by an enzyme complex that is activated by events in mitosis.

- Destroying specific proteins is a common way to control cell processes. In this case, the enzyme complex that is activated in anaphase attaches small proteins called ubiquitins to MPF's cyclin subunit. This marks the subunit for destruction by a protein complex called the proteasome.

In response to MPF activity, then, the concentration of cyclin declines rapidly. Slowly, it builds up again during interphase. This sets up an oscillation in cyclin concentration.

✔ If you understand this aspect of cell-cycle regulation, you should be able to explain the relationship between MPF and (1) cyclin, (2) Cdk, and (3) the enzymes that phosphorylate MPF, dephosphorylate MPF, and degrade cyclin.

Cell-Cycle Checkpoints Can Arrest the Cell Cycle

The dramatic changes in cyclin concentrations and Cdk activity drive the ordered events of the cell cycle. These events are occurring in your body right now. Over a 24-hour period, you swallow millions of cheek cells and lose millions of cells from your intestinal lining as waste. To replace them, cells in your cheek and intestinal tissue are making and degrading cyclin and pushing themselves through the cell cycle.

MPF is only one of many protein complexes involved in regulating the cell cycle, however. A different cyclin complex triggers the passage from G_1 phase into S phase, and several regulatory proteins maintain the G_0 state of quiescent cells. An array of regulatory molecules holds cells in particular stages or stimulates passage to the next phase.

To make sense of these observations, Leland Hartwell and Ted Weinert introduced the concept of a **cell-cycle checkpoint.** A cell-cycle checkpoint is a critical point in the cell cycle that is regulated.

Hartwell and Weinert identified checkpoints by analyzing yeast cells with defects in the cell cycle. The defective cells kept dividing under culture conditions when normal cells stopped growing, because the defective cells lacked a specific checkpoint. In multicellular organisms, cells that keep dividing in this way may form a mass of cells called a **tumor.**

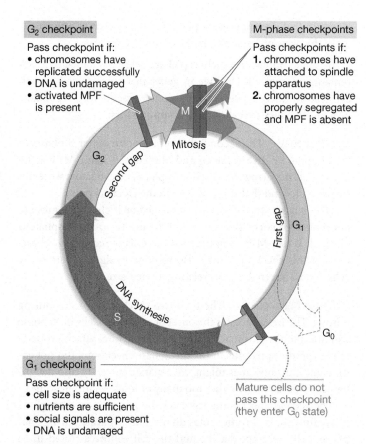

G₂ checkpoint

Pass checkpoint if:
- chromosomes have replicated successfully
- DNA is undamaged
- activated MPF is present

M-phase checkpoints

Pass checkpoints if:
1. chromosomes have attached to spindle apparatus
2. chromosomes have properly segregated and MPF is absent

G₁ checkpoint

Pass checkpoint if:
- cell size is adequate
- nutrients are sufficient
- social signals are present
- DNA is undamaged

Mature cells do not pass this checkpoint (they enter G_0 state)

FIGURE 12.12 The Four Cell-Cycle Checkpoints.

There are distinct checkpoints in three of the four phases of the cell cycle (**FIGURE 12.12**). In effect, interactions among regulatory molecules at each checkpoint allow a cell to "decide" whether to proceed with division or not. If these regulatory molecules are defective, the checkpoint may fail and cells may start dividing in an uncontrolled fashion.

G₁ Checkpoint The first cell-cycle checkpoint occurs late in G_1. For most cells, this checkpoint is the most important in establishing whether the cell will continue through the cycle and divide, or exit the cycle and enter G_0. What determines whether a cell passes the G_1 checkpoint?

- *Size* Because a cell must reach a certain size before its daughter cells will be large enough to function normally, biologists hypothesize that some mechanism exists to arrest the cell cycle if the cell is too small.

- *Availability of nutrients* Unicellular organisms arrest at the G_1 checkpoint if nutrient conditions are poor.

- *Social signals* Cells in multicellular organisms pass (or do not pass) through the G_1 checkpoint in response to signaling molecules from other cells, which are termed social signals.

- *Damage to DNA* If DNA is physically damaged, the protein **p53** activates genes that either stop the cell cycle until the damage can be repaired or cause the cell's programmed, controlled destruction—a phenomenon known as **apoptosis.** In this way, p53 acts as a brake on the cell cycle.

If "brake" molecules such as p53 are defective, damaged DNA remains unrepaired. Damage in genes that regulate cell growth can lead to uncontrolled cell division. Consequently, regulatory proteins like p53 are called **tumor suppressors.**

G₂ Checkpoint The second checkpoint occurs after S phase, at the boundary between the G_2 and M phases. Because MPF is the key signal triggering the onset of M phase, investigators were not surprised to find that it is involved in the G_2 checkpoint.

Data suggest that if DNA is damaged or if chromosomes are not replicated correctly, removal of the inactivating phosphate is blocked. When MPF is not turned on, cells remain in G_2 phase. Cells at this checkpoint may also respond to signals from other cells and to internal signals relating to their size.

M-Phase Checkpoints The final two checkpoints occur during mitosis. The first regulates the onset of anaphase. Cells in M phase will not split the chromatids until all kinetochores attach properly to the spindle apparatus. If the metaphase checkpoint did not exist, some chromosomes might not separate correctly, and daughter cells would receive either too many or too few chromosomes.

The second checkpoint regulates the progression through M phase into G_1. If chromosomes do not fully separate during anaphase, MPF will not decline and the cell will be arrested in M phase. The enzymes that are responsible for cyclin destruction are activated only when all the chromosomes have been properly separated. The presence of MPF activity prevents the cell from undergoing cytokinesis and exiting the M phase.

To summarize, the four cell-cycle checkpoints have the same purpose: They prevent the division of cells that are damaged or that have other problems. The G_1 checkpoint also prevents mature cells that are in the G_0 state from dividing.

Understanding cell-cycle regulation is fundamental. If one of the checkpoints fails, the affected cells may begin dividing in an uncontrolled fashion. For the organism as a whole, the consequences of uncontrolled cell division may be dire: cancer.

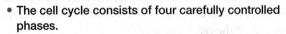

If you understand that . . .

- The cell cycle consists of four carefully controlled phases.

✔ **You should be able to . . .**

1. List the phases of the cell cycle, noting where checkpoints occur.
2. Summarize how levels of Cdk and cyclin change over time and how this is related to MPF activity, noting the particular phases that are involved.

Answers are available in Appendix A.

12.4 Cancer: Out-of-Control Cell Division

Fifty percent of American men and 33 percent of American women will develop cancer during their lifetime. In the United States, one in four of all deaths is from cancer. It is the second leading cause of death, exceeded only by heart disease.

Cancer is a general term for disease caused by cells that divide in an uncontrolled fashion, invade nearby tissues, and spread to other sites in the body. Cancerous cells cause disease because they use nutrients and space needed by normal cells and disrupt the function of normal tissues.

Humans suffer from at least 200 types of cancer. Stated another way, cancer is not a single illness but a complex family of diseases that affect an array of organs, including the breast, colon, brain, lung, and skin (**FIGURE 12.13**). In addition, several types of cancer can affect the same organ. Skin cancers, for example, come in multiple forms.

Although cancers vary in time of onset, growth rate, seriousness, and cause, they have a unifying feature: Cancers arise from cells in which cell-cycle checkpoints have failed.

Cancerous cells have two types of defects related to cell division: (1) defects that make the proteins required for cell growth active when they shouldn't be, and (2) defects that prevent tumor suppressor genes from shutting down the cell cycle.

For example, the protein Ras is a key component in signal transduction systems—including phosphorylation cascades that trigger cell growth (see Chapter 11). Many cancers have defective forms of Ras that do not become inactivated. Instead, the defective Ras constantly sends signals that trigger mitosis and cell division.

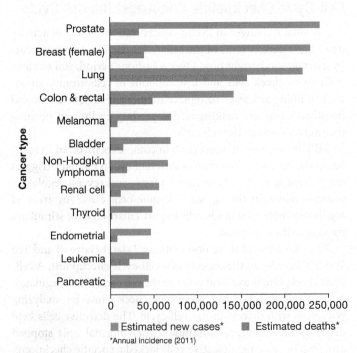

FIGURE 12.13 Cancers Vary in Type and Severity.

DATA: The website of the National Cancer Institute (http://www.cancer.gov), Common Cancer Types, November 2010.

Likewise, a large percentage of cancers have defective forms of the tumor suppressor p53. Instead of being arrested or destroyed, cells with damaged DNA are allowed to continue growing.

Let's review the general characteristics of cancer and then explore how regulatory mechanisms become defective.

Properties of Cancer Cells

When even a single cell in a multicellular organism begins to divide in an uncontrolled fashion, a mass of cells called a tumor may result. If a tumor can be surgically removed without damage to the affected organ, a cure might be achieved. Often, though, surgery doesn't cure cancer. Why?

In addition to uncontrolled replication, cancer cells are invasive—meaning that they are able to spread to adjacent tissues and throughout the body via the bloodstream or the lymphatic vessels (introduced in Chapter 51), which collect excess fluid from tissues and return it to the bloodstream.

Invasiveness is a defining feature of a **malignant tumor**—one that is cancerous. Masses of noninvasive cells are noncancerous and form **benign tumors.** Some benign tumors are largely harmless. Others grow quickly and can cause problems if they are located in the brain or other sensitive parts of the body.

Cells become malignant and cancerous if they gain the ability to detach from the original tumor and invade other tissues. By spreading from the primary tumor site, cancer cells can establish secondary tumors elsewhere in the body (**FIGURE 12.14**). This process is called **metastasis.**

If metastasis has occurred by the time the original tumor is detected, secondary tumors have already formed and surgical removal of the primary tumor will not lead to a cure. This is why early detection is the key to treating cancer most effectively.

Cancer Involves Loss of Cell-Cycle Control

What causes cancer at the molecular level? Recall that when many cells mature, they enter the G_0 phase—meaning their cell cycle is arrested at the G_1 checkpoint. In contrast, cells that do pass through the G_1 checkpoint are irreversibly committed to replicating their DNA and entering G_2.

Based on this observation, biologists hypothesize that many types of cancer involve defects in the G_1 checkpoint. To understand the molecular nature of the disease, then, researchers have focused on understanding the normal mechanisms that operate at that checkpoint. Cancer research and research on the normal cell cycle have become two sides of the same coin.

Social Control In unicellular organisms, passage through the G_1 checkpoint is thought to depend primarily on cell size and the availability of nutrients. If nutrients are plentiful, cells pass through the checkpoint and divide rapidly.

In multicellular organisms, however, cells divide in response to signals from other cells. Biologists refer to this as *social control* over cell division. The general idea is that individual cells should be allowed to divide only when their growth is in the best interests of the organism as a whole.

(a) Benign tumor

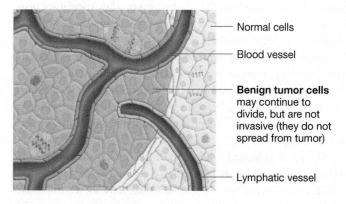

- Normal cells
- Blood vessel
- **Benign tumor cells** may continue to divide, but are not invasive (they do not spread from tumor)
- Lymphatic vessel

(b) Malignant tumor

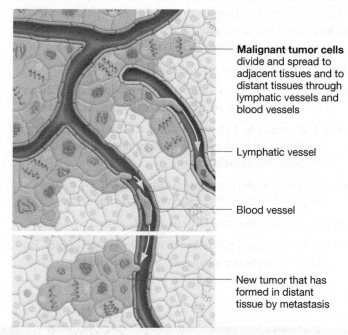

- **Malignant tumor cells** divide and spread to adjacent tissues and to distant tissues through lymphatic vessels and blood vessels
- Lymphatic vessel
- Blood vessel
- New tumor that has formed in distant tissue by metastasis

FIGURE 12.14 Cancers Spread to New Locations in the Body. **(a)** Benign tumors grow in a single location. **(b)** Malignant tumors are metastatic—meaning that their cells can spread to distant parts of the body and initiate new tumors. Malignant tumors cause cancer.

Social control of the cell cycle is based on **growth factors**—polypeptides or small proteins that stimulate cell division. Many growth factors were discovered by researchers who were trying to grow cells in culture. When isolated mammalian cells were placed in a culture flask and provided with adequate nutrients, they arrested in G_1 phase. The cells began to grow again only when biologists added **serum**—the liquid portion of blood that remains after blood cells and cell fragments have been removed. Researchers identified growth factors as the components in the serum that were responsible for allowing cells to pass through the G_1 checkpoint.

Cancer cells are an exception. They can often be cultured successfully without externally supplied growth factors. This observation suggests that the normal social controls on the G_1 checkpoint have broken down in cancer cells.

How Does the G₁ Checkpoint Work? In G₀ cells, the arrival of growth factors stimulates the production of a key regulatory protein called E2F. When E2F is activated, it triggers the expression of genes required for S phase.

When E2F is first produced, however, its activity is blocked by a tumor suppressor protein called Rb. **Rb protein** is one of the key molecules that enforces the G₁ checkpoint. It is called Rb because a nonfunctional version was first discovered in children with retinoblastoma, a cancer in the light-sensing tissue, or retina, of the eye.

When E2F is bound to Rb, it is in the "off" position—it can't activate the genes required for S phase. As long as Rb stays bound to E2F, the cell remains in G₀. But as **FIGURE 12.15** shows, the situation changes dramatically if growth factors continue to arrive. To understand how growth factors affect E2F activity, think back to how cells progress from G₂ to M phase. As in passage from G₂ to M phase, phosphorylation of other proteins catalyzed by an activated cyclin–Cdk dimer permits passage from G₁ to S.

Step 1 Growth factors arrive from other cells.

Step 2 The growth factors stimulate the production of E2F and of G₁ cyclins, which are different from those used in MPF.

Step 3 Rb binds to E2F, inactivating it. The G₁ cyclins begin forming cyclin–Cdk dimers. Initially, the Cdk component is phosphorylated and inactive.

Step 4 When dephosphorylation turns on the G₁ cyclin–Cdk complexes, they catalyze the phosphorylation of Rb.

Step 5 The phosphorylated Rb changes shape and releases E2F.

Step 6 The unbound E2F is free to activate its target genes. Production of S-phase proteins gets S phase under way.

In this way, growth factors function as a social signal that says, "It's OK to override Rb. Go ahead and pass the G₁ checkpoint and divide."

How Do Social Controls and Cell-Cycle Checkpoints Fail? Cells can become cancerous when social controls fail—meaning, when cells begin dividing in the absence of the go-ahead signal from growth factors. One of two things can go wrong: The G₁ cyclin is overproduced, or Rb is defective.

When cyclins are overproduced and stay at high concentrations, the Cdk that binds to cyclin phosphorylates Rb continuously. This activates E2F and sends the cell into S phase.

Cyclin overproduction results from (1) excessive amounts of growth factors or (2) cyclin production in the absence of growth signals. Cyclins are produced continuously when a signaling pathway is defective. Because this pathway includes the Ras protein (highlighted in Chapter 11), it is common to find overactive Ras proteins in cancerous cells.

What happens if Rb is defective? When Rb is missing or does not bind normally to E2F, any E2F that is present pushes the cell through the G₁ checkpoint and into S phase, leading to uncontrolled cell division.

Because cancer is actually a family of diseases with a complex and highly variable molecular basis, there will be no "magic bullet," or single therapy, that cures all forms of the illness. Still, recent progress in understanding the cell cycle and the molecular basis of cancer has been dramatic, and cancer prevention and early detection programs are increasingly effective. The prognosis for many cancer patients is remarkably better now than it was even a few years ago. Thanks to research, almost all of us know someone who is a cancer survivor.

PROCESS: THE G₁ CHECKPOINT IS SUBJECT TO SOCIAL CONTROL

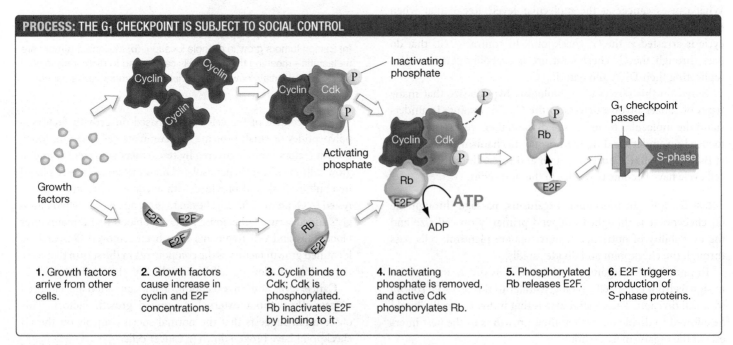

1. Growth factors arrive from other cells.

2. Growth factors cause increase in cyclin and E2F concentrations.

3. Cyclin binds to Cdk; Cdk is phosphorylated. Rb inactivates E2F by binding to it.

4. Inactivating phosphate is removed, and active Cdk phosphorylates Rb.

5. Phosphorylated Rb releases E2F.

6. E2F triggers production of S-phase proteins.

FIGURE 12.15 Growth Factors Move Cells through the G₁ Checkpoint.

If you understand . . .

12.1 How Do Cells Replicate?

- When a cell divides, it must copy its chromosomes, separate the copies, and divide the cytoplasm to generate daughter cells such that each carries the same chromosomal complement as the parent.

- Eukaryotic cells divide by alternating between interphase and M phase.

- Interphase consists of S phase, when chromosomes are replicated, and gap phases called G_1 and G_2, when cells grow and prepare for division.

- Eukaryotic cells divide by cycling through four phases: G_1, S, G_2, and M. Mature cells arrest at G_1 and enter a nonreplicating phase called G_0.

✔ You should be able to explain the roles of each of the four stages of the cell cycle.

12.2 What Happens during M Phase?

- Mitosis and cytokinesis are responsible for the partitioning of chromosomes and division of the parent cell into two daughter cells.

- Mitosis can be described as a sequence of five phases:

  1. *Prophase*   Chromosomes condense. The spindle apparatus begins to form, and polar microtubules overlap each other.
  2. *Prometaphase*   In cells of many organisms, the nuclear envelope disintegrates. Microtubules attach to the kinetochores of chromosomes and begin moving them to the middle of the spindle.
  3. *Metaphase*   All the chromosomes are positioned in the middle of the spindle. The spindle is anchored to the cell membrane by astral microtubules.
  4. *Anaphase*   Sister chromatids are pulled apart by the disassembly of kinetochore microtubules at the kinetochore. The separated chromatids are now daughter chromosomes. The spindle poles are moved farther apart to fully separate the replicated chromosomes.
  5. *Telophase*   Daughter chromosomes are fully separated and are clustered at opposite poles of the spindle. A nuclear envelope forms around each set and the chromosomes de-condense.

- In most cells, mitosis is followed by cytokinesis—division of all cell contents.

✔ You should be able to predict how mitosis would be different in cells where the nuclear envelope remains intact (e.g., yeast).

12.3 Control of the Cell Cycle

- The onset of S and M phases is primarily determined by the activity of protein dimers consisting of cyclin and cyclin-dependent kinases (Cdks).

- Cyclin concentrations oscillate during the cell cycle, regulating the formation of the dimer. The activity of the Cdk is further regulated by addition of a phosphate in its activating site and removal of one from its inhibitory site.

- Progression through the cell cycle is controlled by checkpoints in three phases.

  1. The G_1 checkpoint regulates progress based on nutrient availability, cell size, DNA damage, and social signals.
  2. The G_2 checkpoint delays progress until chromosome replication is complete and any damaged DNA that is present is repaired.
  3. The two M-phase checkpoints will (1) delay anaphase until all chromosomes are correctly attached to the spindle apparatus and (2) delay the onset of cytokinesis and G_1 until all the chromosomes have been properly partitioned.

✔ You should be able to predict what would happen if the kinase that adds the inhibitory phosphates to Cdk were defective.

12.4 Cancer: Out-of-Control Cell Division

- Cancer is characterized by (1) loss of control at the G_1 checkpoint, resulting in cells that divide in an uncontrolled fashion; and (2) metastasis, or the ability of tumor cells to spread throughout the body.

- The G_1 checkpoint depends in part on Rb, which prevents progression to S phase, and G_1 cyclin–Cdk complexes that trigger progression to S phase. Defects in Rb and G_1 cyclin are common in human cancer cells.

✔ You should be able to compare and contrast the effect of removing growth factors from asynchronous cultures of human cells that are normal versus those that are cancerous.

(MB) MasteringBiology

1. MasteringBiology Assignments

Tutorials and Activities Causes of Cancer; Cell Culture Methods; Four Phases of the Cell Cycle; Mitosis (1 of 3): Mitosis and the Cell Cycle; Mitosis (2 of 3): Mechanism of Mitosis; Mitosis (3 of 3): Comparing Cell Division in Animals, Plants, and Bacteria; Mitosis and Cytokinesis Animation; Roles of Cell Division; The Cell Cycle; The Phases of Mitosis

Questions Reading Quizzes, Blue-Thread Questions, Test Bank

2. eText Read your book online, search, take notes, highlight text, and more.

3. The Study Area Practice Test, Cumulative Test, BioFlix® 3-D Animations, Videos, Activities, Audio Glossary, Word Study Tools, Art

You should be able to . . .

1. Which statement about the daughter cells following mitosis and cytokinesis is correct?
   a. They are genetically different from each other and from the parent cell.
   b. They are genetically identical with each other and with the parent cell.
   c. They are genetically identical with each other but different from the parent cell.
   d. Only one of the two daughter cells is genetically identical with the parent cell.

2. Progression through the cell cycle is regulated by oscillations in the concentration of which type of molecule?
   a. p53, Rb, and other tumor suppressors
   b. receptor tyrosine kinases
   c. cyclin-dependent kinases
   d. cyclins

3. After the S phase, what comprises a single chromosome?
   a. two daughter chromosomes
   b. a double-stranded DNA molecule
   c. two single-stranded molecules of DNA
   d. two sister chromatids

4. What major events occur during anaphase of mitosis?
   a. Chromosomes replicate, so each chromosome consists of two identical sister chromatids.
   b. Chromosomes condense and the nuclear envelope disappears.
   c. Sister chromatids separate, and the spindle poles are pushed farther apart.
   d. The chromosomes end up at opposite ends of the cell, and two nuclear envelopes form around them.

5. What evidence suggests that during anaphase, kinetochore microtubules shorten at the kinetochore?

6. Under normal conditions, what happens to the cell cycle if the chromosomes fail to separate properly at anaphase?

7. Identify at least two events in the cell cycle that must be completed successfully for daughter cells to share an identical complement of chromosomes.

8. Make a concept map illustrating normal events at the G_1 checkpoint. Your diagram should include p53, DNA damage, Rb, E2F, social signals, G_1 Cdk, G_1 cyclin, S-phase proteins, phosphorylated (inactivated) cyclin–Cdk, dephosphorylated (activated) cyclin–Cdk, phosphorylated (inactivated) Rb.

9. Explain how microinjection experiments supported the hypothesis that specific molecules in the cytoplasm are involved in the transition from interphase to M phase. What was the control for this experiment?

10. Why are most protein kinases considered regulatory proteins?

11. Why are cyclins called cyclins? Explain their relationship to MPF activity.

12. In multicellular organisms, nondividing cells stay in G_0 phase. For the cell, why is it better to be held in G_1 rather than S, G_2, or M phase?
    a. G_1 cells are larger and more likely to perform the normal functions of the cell.
    b. G_1 cells have not replicated their DNA in preparation for division.
    c. G_1 cells are the only ones that do not have their chromatin in a highly condensed state.
    d. MPF is required to enter S phase, so the cell is committed to entering M phase if the cycle moves beyond G_1.

13. **QUANTITATIVE** A particular cell spends 4 hours in G_1 phase, 2 hours in S phase, 2 hours in G_2 phase, and 30 minutes in M phase. If a pulse–chase assay were performed with radioactive thymidine on an asynchronous culture, what percentage of mitotic cells would be radiolabeled after 9 hours?
    a. 0%
    b. 50%
    c. 75%
    d. 100%

14. When fruit fly embryos first begin to develop, a large cell is generated that contains over 8000 nuclei that are genetically identical with one another. What is most likely responsible for this result?

15. What is most likely responsible for the reduction in death rates over the past several years in cancers of the breast and prostate? How is this related to the development of cancer?

16. Cancer is primarily a disease of older people. Further, a group of individuals may share a genetic predisposition to developing certain types of cancer, yet vary a great deal in time of onset—or not get the disease at all. What conclusion could be drawn based on these observations? How does this relate to the requirements for a cell to become cancerous?

13 Meiosis

In this chapter you will learn how

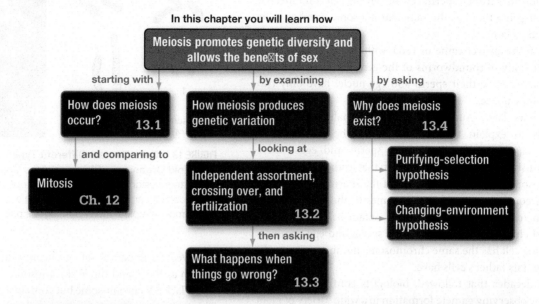

Meiosis promotes genetic diversity and allows the benefits of sex

starting with → How does meiosis occur? **13.1**

and comparing to → Mitosis **Ch. 12**

by examining → How meiosis produces genetic variation

looking at → Independent assortment, crossing over, and fertilization **13.2**

then asking → What happens when things go wrong? **13.3**

by asking → Why does meiosis exist? **13.4**

→ Purifying-selection hypothesis

→ Changing-environment hypothesis

Scanning electron micrograph (with color added) showing human sperm attempting to enter a human egg. This chapter introduces the type of nuclear division called meiosis, which in animals occurs before the formation of sperm and eggs.

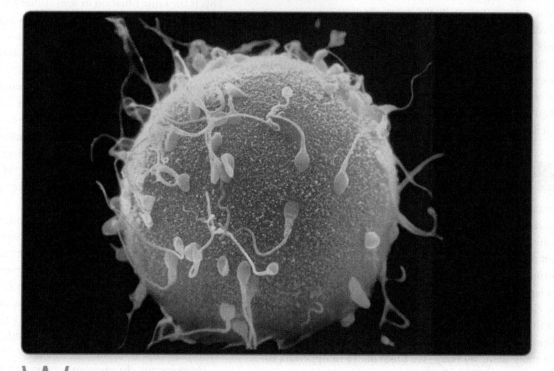

This chapter is part of the Big Picture. See how on pages 366–367.

W hy sex?

Simple questions—such as why sexual reproduction exists—are sometimes the best. This chapter asks what sexual reproduction is and why some organisms employ it. The focus here is on how organisms reproduce, or replicate—one of the five fundamental attributes of life introduced in Chapter 1.

For centuries people have known that during sexual reproduction, a male reproductive cell—a **sperm**—and a female reproductive cell—an **egg**—unite to form a new individual. The process of uniting sperm and egg is called **fertilization.** The first biologists to observe fertilization studied the large, translucent eggs of sea urchins. Owing to the semitransparency of the sea urchin egg cell, researchers were able to see the nuclei of a sperm and an egg fuse.

✔ When you see this checkmark, stop and test yourself. Answers are available in Appendix A.

When these observations were published in 1876, they raised an important question, because biologists had already established that the number of chromosomes is constant from cell to cell within a multicellular organism. The question is, How can the chromosomes from a sperm cell and an egg cell combine, but form an offspring that has the same chromosome number as its mother and its father?

A hint at the answer came in 1883, with the observation that cells in the body of roundworms of the genus *Ascaris* have four chromosomes, while their sperm and egg nuclei have only two chromosomes apiece.

Four years later, August Weismann formally proposed a hypothesis to explain the riddle: During the formation of **gametes**—reproductive cells such as sperm and eggs—there must be a distinctive type of cell division that leads to a reduction in chromosome number. Specifically, if the sperm and egg contribute an equal number of chromosomes to the fertilized egg, Weismann reasoned, they must each contain half of the usual number of chromosomes. Then, when sperm and egg combine, the resulting cell has the same chromosome number as its mother's cells and its father's cells have.

In the decades that followed, biologists confirmed this hypothesis by observing gamete formation in a wide variety of plant and animal species. Eventually this form of cell division came to be called meiosis (literally, "lessening-act").

Meiosis is nuclear division that leads to a halving of chromosome number and ultimately to the production of sperm and egg. (Meiosis is an important part of The Big Picture of Genetic Information on pages 366-367). To a biologist, asking "Why sex?" is equivalent to asking "Why meiosis?" Let's delve in by first looking at how meiosis happens.

13.1 How Does Meiosis Occur?

To understand meiosis, it is critical to grasp some key ideas about chromosomes. For example, when cell biologists began to study the cell divisions that lead to gamete formation, they made an important observation: Each organism has a characteristic number of chromosomes.

Consider the drawings in **FIGURE 13.1**, based on a paper published by Nettie Maria Stevens in 1908. They show the chromosomes of the fruit fly *Drosophila melanogaster*, or *Drosophila* for short. This model organism has been a focus of biological research for more than 100 years (see **BioSkills 13** in Appendix B). Stevens was studying the cell divisions leading up to the formation of egg and sperm. In total, she found eight chromosomes in *Drosophila* cells. Your cells have 46 chromosomes, and some ferns have over 1000.

Chromosomes Come in Distinct Sizes and Shapes

Stevens found that each *Drosophila* cell has eight chromosomes, but just five distinct types, distinguished by their size and shape. Three of these chromosomes always occurred in pairs and are labeled chromosomes 2–4 in Figure 13.1. In males, Stevens

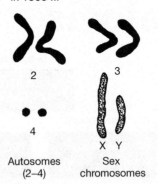 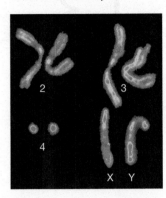

Drosophila chromosomes drawn by Nettie Stevens in 1908 ...

... and photographed through a modern microscope.

Autosomes (2–4) Sex chromosomes

FIGURE 13.1 Cells Contain Different Types of Chromosomes, and in Diploid Organisms, Chromosomes Come in Pairs. Numbers and letters designate the types of *Drosophila* chromosomes. These chromosomes are from the cell of a male, so there is an X and a Y chromosome plus three homologous pairs of autosomes.

observed an unpaired set of chromosomes, which came to be known as the X and the Y chromosomes. Stevens found that females lack a Y chromosome but contain a pair of X chromosomes. This is the same situation in some other insects and in mammals. The X and Y chromosomes are called **sex chromosomes** and are associated with an individual's sex. Non-sex chromosomes, such as chromosomes 2–4 in *Drosophila*, are **autosomes**.

Chromosomes that are the same size and shape are called **homologous** ("same-proportion") **chromosomes**, or **homologs**, and the pair is called a homologous pair. Later work showed that homologous chromosomes are similar in content as well as in size and shape. Homologous chromosomes carry the same genes. A **gene** is a section of DNA that influences some hereditary trait in an individual. For example, each copy of chromosome 2 found in *Drosophila* carries genes that influence eye color, wing size and shape, and bristle size.

The versions of a gene found on homologous chromosomes may differ, however. Biologists use the term **allele** to denote different versions of the same gene. For example, the allele for an eye-color gene on one homolog of chromosome 2 may be associated with red eyes, the normal color in *Drosophila*, whereas the allele of the same eye-color gene on the other homolog may be associated with purple eyes (**FIGURE 13.2**); the particular alleles of the bristle-size gene will influence whether the fly's bristles are long or short, and so on.

Homologous chromosomes carry the same genes, but each homolog may contain different alleles.

The Concept of Ploidy

At this point in her study, Stevens had determined the *Drosophila* **karyotype**—meaning the number and types of chromosomes present. As karyotyping studies became more common, cell biologists realized that, like *Drosophila*, the vast majority of plants and animals have more than one of each type of chromosome.

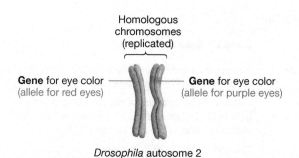

Homologous
chromosomes
(replicated)

Gene for eye color — (allele for red eyes)   **Gene** for eye color (allele for purple eyes)

Drosophila autosome 2

FIGURE 13.2 Homologous Chromosomes May Contain Different Alleles of the Same Gene. The homologs of *Drosophila* chromosome 2 are shown; the location of only one of many genes is indicated.

Insects, humans, oak trees, and other organisms that have two versions of each type of chromosome are called **diploid** ("double-form"). Diploid organisms have two alleles of each gene. One allele is carried on each of the homologous pairs of chromosomes. Although a diploid individual can carry only two different alleles of a gene, there can be many different alleles in a population.

Organisms whose cells contain just one of each type of chromosome—for example, bacteria, archaea, and many algae and fungi—are called **haploid** ("single-form"). Haploid organisms have only one copy of each chromosome and just one allele of each gene.

Biologists use a compact notation to indicate the number of chromosomes and chromosome sets in a particular organism or type of cell:

- By convention, the letter n stands for the number of distinct types of chromosomes in a given cell and is called the **haploid number.** If sex chromosomes are present, they are counted as a single type in the haploid number. In humans, n is 23.

- To indicate the number of complete chromosome sets observed, a number is placed before the n. Thus, a cell can be n, or $2n$, or $3n$, and so on.

The combination of the number of sets and n is termed the cell's **ploidy.** Diploid cells or species are designated $2n$, because two chromosomes of each type are present—one from each parent. A **maternal chromosome** comes from the mother, and a **paternal chromosome** comes from the father.

Humans are diploid; $2n$ is 46. Haploid cells or species are labeled simply n, because they have just one set of chromosomes—no homologs are present. In haploid cells, the number 1 in front of n is implied and is not written out.

To summarize, the haploid number n indicates the number of distinct types of chromosomes present. In contrast, a cell's ploidy (n, $2n$, $3n$, etc.) indicates the number of each type of chromosome present. Stating a cell's ploidy is the same as stating the number of haploid chromosome sets present. ✔ If you understand how these terms relate, you should be able to state the haploid number, ploidy, and total number of chromosomes present in a male *Drosophila*.

Later work revealed that it is common for species in some lineages—particularly certain land plants, such as ferns—to contain more than two of each type of chromosome. Instead of having two homologous chromosomes per cell, **polyploid** ("many-form") species have three or more of each type of chromosome in each cell.

Depending on the number of homologs present, polyploid species are called triploid ($3n$), tetraploid ($4n$), hexaploid ($6n$), octoploid ($8n$), and so on.

Stevens and other early cell biologists did more than just describe the karyotypes observed in their study organisms. Through careful examination, they were able to track how chromosome numbers change during meiosis. These studies confirmed Weismann's hypothesis that a special type of cell division occurs during gamete formation.

An Overview of Meiosis

Cells replicate each of their chromosomes before undergoing meiosis. At the start of meiosis, chromosomes are in the same state they are in before mitosis.

Recall that an unreplicated eukaryotic chromosome consists of a single, long DNA double helix organized around proteins called histones (see Chapter 12). When chromosome replication is complete, each chromosome will consist of two identical **sister chromatids.** Sister chromatids contain identical copies of the DNA double helix present in the unreplicated chromosome and therefore the same genetic information. They remain physically joined along their entire length during much of meiosis (**FIGURE 13.3**).

To understand meiosis, it is critical to understand the relationship between chromosomes and sister chromatids. The trick is to recognize that unreplicated and replicated chromosomes are both considered *single* chromosomes—even though the replicated chromosome contains *two* sister chromatids. This makes sense if you consider that a chromosome carries a particular set of genetic information in its DNA and that the amount of *unique* information is the same whether there is one copy of it present or two.

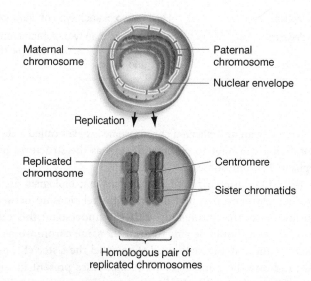

Maternal chromosome — — Paternal chromosome

— Nuclear envelope

Replication

Replicated chromosome — — Centromere

— Sister chromatids

Homologous pair of replicated chromosomes

FIGURE 13.3 Each Chromosome Replicates before Undergoing Meiosis.

Vocabulary for Describing the Chromosomal Makeup of a Cell

Term	Definition	Example or Comment
Chromosome	Structure made up of DNA and proteins; carries the cell's hereditary information (genes)	Eukaryotes have linear chromosomes; most bacteria and archaea have just one, circular, chromosome
• Sex chromosome	Chromosome associated with an individual's sex	X and Y chromosomes of humans (males are XY, females XX); Z and W chromosomes of birds and butterflies (males are ZZ, females ZW)
• Autosome	A non-sex chromosome	Chromosomes 1–22 in humans
Unreplicated chromosome	A chromosome that consists of one double-helical molecule of DNA packaged with proteins	
Replicated chromosome	A chromosome that has been copied; consists of two identical chromatids, each containing one double-helical DNA molecule	— Centromere
Sister chromatids	The two identical chromatid copies in a replicated chromosome	— Sister chromatids
Homologous chromosomes (homologs)	In a diploid organism, chromosomes that are similar in size, shape, and gene content	You have a chromosome 22 from each parent — Homologous chromosomes
Non-sister chromatids	Chromatids belonging to homologous chromosomes	— Non-sister chromatids
Bivalent (or tetrad)	Homologous replicated chromosomes that are joined together during prophase I and metaphase I of meiosis	— Bivalent
Haploid number	The number of different types of chromosomes in a cell; symbolized n	Humans have 23 different types of chromosomes ($n = 23$)
Diploid number	The number of chromosomes present in a diploid cell (see below); symbolized $2n$	In humans all cells except gametes are diploid and contain 46 chromosomes ($2n = 46$)
Ploidy	The number of each type of chromosome present	The number of haploid chromosome sets present
• Haploid	Having one of each type of chromosome (n)	Bacteria and archaea are haploid, as are many algae; plant and animal gametes are haploid
• Diploid	Having two of each type of chromosome ($2n$)	Most familiar plants and animals are diploid
• Polyploid	Having more than two of each type of chromosome; cells may be triploid ($3n$), tetraploid ($4n$), hexaploid ($6n$), and so on	Seedless bananas are triploid; many ferns are tetraploid; bread wheat is hexaploid

Note that an unreplicated chromosome is never called a chromatid; you can refer to chromatids only as the structures in a replicated chromosome.

TABLE 13.1 summarizes the vocabulary that biologists use to describe chromosomes and illustrates the relationship between chromosomes and chromatids. ✔ If you understand this relationship, you should be able to draw the same chromosome in the unreplicated and replicated state, label the sister chromatids, indicate the number of DNA molecules present in each structure, and explain why both structures represent a single chromosome.

Meiosis Comprises Two Cell Divisions Meiosis consists of two cell divisions, called **meiosis I** and **meiosis II**. As **FIGURE 13.4** shows, the two divisions occur consecutively but differ sharply.

During meiosis I, the homologs in each chromosome pair separate from each other. One homolog goes to one daughter cell; the other homolog goes to the other daughter cell. It is a matter of chance which daughter cell receives which homolog.

At the end of meiosis I, each of the two daughter cells has one of each type of chromosome instead of two, and thus half as many chromosomes as the parent cell had. Put another way: During meiosis I, the diploid ($2n$) parent cell produces two haploid (n)

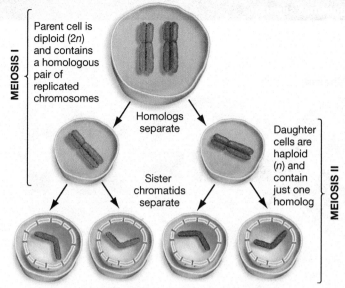

Parent cell is diploid (2n) and contains a homologous pair of replicated chromosomes

MEIOSIS I

Homologs separate

Sister chromatids separate

Daughter cells are haploid (n) and contain just one homolog

MEIOSIS II

Four daughter cells contain one chromosome each (n). In animals, these cells become gametes.

FIGURE 13.4 The Major Events in Meiosis. Before undergoing meiosis, chromosomes are replicated so there are two chromatids per chromosome. Meiosis reduces chromosome number by half. In diploid organisms, the products of meiosis are haploid. Maternal chromosomes are shown in red; paternal chromosomes, blue. Note that in this cell, 2n ☒ 2.

daughter cells. Notice, however, that each chromosome still consists of two sister chromatids—meaning that chromosomes are still replicated at the end of meiosis I.

During meiosis II, sister chromatids from each chromosome separate. One sister chromatid (now called a daughter chromosome) goes to one daughter cell; the other sister chromatid goes to the other daughter cell as a daughter chromosome. Remember that the cell that started meiosis II had one of each type of chromosome, but each chromosome was still replicated (meaning still consisting of two sister chromatids). The cells produced by meiosis II also have one of each type of chromosome, but now the daughter chromosomes are no longer replicated.

To reiterate, sister chromatids separate into daughter chromosomes during meiosis II. This is just what happens during mitosis. Meiosis II is actually equivalent to mitosis occurring in a haploid cell. In meiosis I, on the other hand, sister chromatids stay together. This sets meiosis I apart from both mitosis and meiosis II.

As in mitosis, chromosome movements during meiosis I and II are coordinated by microtubules of the **spindle apparatus** that attach to **kinetochores** located at the **centromere** of each chromosome. Recall that the centromere is a region on the chromosome; kinetochores are structures in that region (see Chapter 12). Chromosome movement is driven by fraying of the ends of microtubules at each kinetochore, just as it is in mitosis (see Figure 12.7).

Meiosis I is a Reduction Division A host of early cell biologists worked out this sequence of events through careful observation of cells with the light microscope. Based on these studies, they came to a key realization: The outcome of meiosis I is a reduction

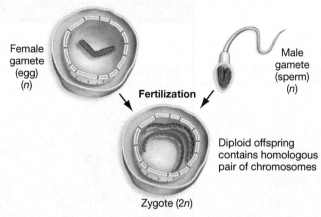

Female gamete (egg) (n)

Male gamete (sperm) (n)

Fertilization

Diploid offspring contains homologous pair of chromosomes

Zygote (2n)

FIGURE 13.5 Fertilization Restores a Full Complement of Chromosomes.

in chromosome number. For this reason, meiosis I is known as a reduction division. Reduction is another important way in which meiosis I differs from meiosis II and mitosis.

In most plants and animals, the original cell entering meiosis is diploid and the four final daughter cells are haploid. In animals, the haploid daughter cells, each containing one of each homologous chromosome, eventually go on to form egg cells or sperm cells via a process called **gametogenesis** ("gamete-origin").

When two haploid gametes fuse during fertilization, a full complement of chromosomes is restored (**FIGURE 13.5**). The cell that results from fertilization is diploid and is called a **zygote**. In this way, each diploid individual receives a haploid chromosome set from its mother and a haploid set from its father.

FIGURE 13.6 puts these events into the context of an animal's **life cycle**—the sequence of events that occurs over the life span of an individual, from fertilization to the production of offspring. As you study the figure, note how ploidy changes as the result of

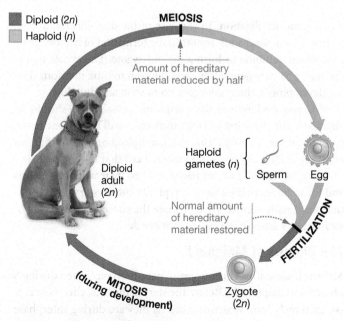

Diploid (2n)
Haploid (n)

MEIOSIS

Amount of hereditary material reduced by half

Haploid gametes (n)

Sperm   Egg

Diploid adult (2n)

Normal amount of hereditary material restored

FERTILIZATION

MITOSIS (during development)

Zygote (2n)

FIGURE 13.6 Ploidy Changes during the Life Cycle of a Dog. Most of the dog life cycle involves diploid cells.

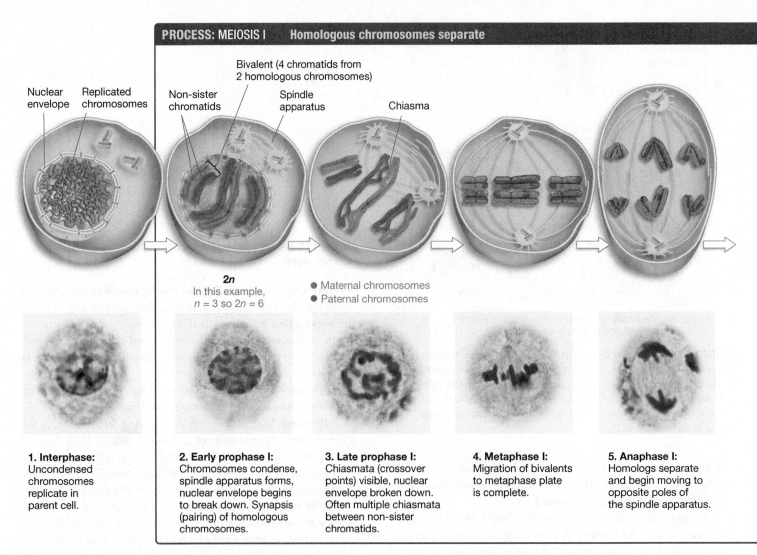

PROCESS: MEIOSIS I   Homologous chromosomes separate

Nuclear envelope
Replicated chromosomes
Non-sister chromatids
Bivalent (4 chromatids from 2 homologous chromosomes)
Spindle apparatus
Chiasma

2n
In this example, n = 3 so 2n = 6

● Maternal chromosomes
● Paternal chromosomes

1. Interphase: Uncondensed chromosomes replicate in parent cell.

2. Early prophase I: Chromosomes condense, spindle apparatus forms, nuclear envelope begins to break down. Synapsis (pairing) of homologous chromosomes.

3. Late prophase I: Chiasmata (crossover points) visible, nuclear envelope broken down. Often multiple chiasmata between non-sister chromatids.

4. Metaphase I: Migration of bivalents to metaphase plate is complete.

5. Anaphase I: Homologs separate and begin moving to opposite poles of the spindle apparatus.

FIGURE 13.7 The Phases of Meiosis. The micrographs of each phase are from a species of salamander.

meiosis and fertilization. In the case of the dog illustrated here, meiosis in a diploid adult results in the formation of haploid gametes, which combine to form a diploid zygote. The zygote marks the start of a new generation, and through mitotic divisions during development, the zygote goes on to form an adult dog.

✔ If you understand the events of meiosis, you should be able to predict how many DNA molecules will be present in the gametes of the fruit fly *Drosophila*, a diploid organism that has eight replicated chromosomes in each cell that enters meiosis.

Once Stevens and others had published their work on meiosis and the accompanying changes in ploidy, the mystery of fertilization was finally solved. To appreciate the consequences of meiosis fully, let's analyze the events in more detail.

The Phases of Meiosis I

Meiosis begins after chromosomes have been replicated during S phase (see Chapter 12). Before the start of meiosis, chromosomes are extremely long structures, just as they are during interphase of the normal cell cycle. The major steps that occur once meiosis begins are shown in **FIGURE 13.7.**

Early Prophase I   During early prophase I, the nuclear envelope begins to break down, chromosomes condense and the spindle apparatus begins to form. Then a crucial event occurs: Homologous chromosome pairs come together. The end result of this process is called **synapsis** and is illustrated in step 2 of Figure 13.7. Synapsis is possible because regions of homologous chromosomes that are similar at the molecular level come together. In most organisms, synapsis requires breaking and then connecting together DNA of the two homologs at one or more spots along their length.

The structure that results from synapsis is called a **bivalent** (*bi* means "two" in Latin) or **tetrad** (*tetra* means "four" in Greek). A bivalent consists of paired homologous chromosomes, with each homolog consisting of two sister chromatids. Chromatids from different homologs are referred to as **non-sister chromatids.** In the figure, the red-colored chromatids are non-sister chromatids with respect to the blue-colored chromatids.

Late Prophase I   During late prophase I, the nuclear envelope breaks down and microtubules of the spindle apparatus attach to

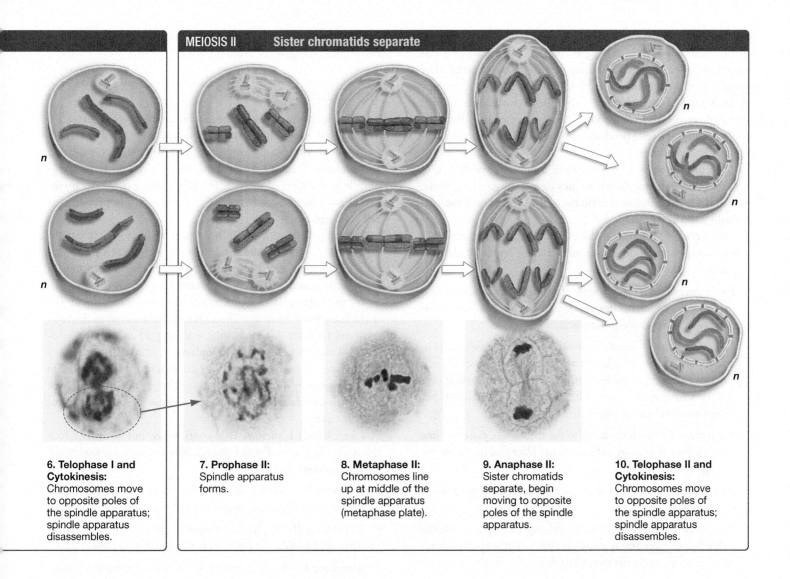

6. Telophase I and Cytokinesis: Chromosomes move to opposite poles of the spindle apparatus; spindle apparatus disassembles.

7. Prophase II: Spindle apparatus forms.

8. Metaphase II: Chromosomes line up at middle of the spindle apparatus (metaphase plate).

9. Anaphase II: Sister chromatids separate, begin moving to opposite poles of the spindle apparatus.

10. Telophase II and Cytokinesis: Chromosomes move to opposite poles of the spindle apparatus; spindle apparatus disassembles.

kinetochores. Non-sister chromatids begin to separate at many points along their length. They stay joined at certain locations, however, each of which forms an X-shaped structure called a **chiasma** (plural: **chiasmata**). (In the Greek alphabet, the letter X is called "chi.") Normally, at least one chiasma forms in every pair of homologous chromosomes; often there are several chiasmata. The chiasmata mark sites where DNA was broken and rejoined between homologs early in prophase I.

As step 3 of Figure 13.7 shows, the chromatids that meet to form a chiasma are non-sister chromatids. At each chiasma there is an exchange of parts of chromosomes between paternal and maternal homologs. These reciprocal exchanges between different homologs create non-sister chromatids that have both paternal and maternal segments. This process of chromosome exchange is called **crossing over.**

In step 4 of Figure 13.7, the result of crossing over is illustrated by chromosomes with a combination of red and blue segments. When crossing over occurs, the chromosomes that result have a mixture of maternal and paternal alleles. Crossing over is a major way that meiosis creates genetic diversity.

Metaphase I   The next major stage in meiosis I is metaphase I. This is when kinetochore microtubules move the pairs of homologous chromosomes (bivalents) to a region called the **metaphase plate** in the middle of the spindle apparatus (step 4). The metaphase plate is not a physical structure but an imaginary plane dividing the spindle apparatus.

Here are two key points about chromosome movement: Each bivalent moves to the metaphase plate independently of the other bivalents, and the alignment on one side or the other of the metaphase plate is random for maternal and paternal homologs from each chromosome. This movement explains the most basic principles of genetics (see Chapter 14).

Anaphase and Telophase I   Sister chromatids of each chromosome remain together. During anaphase I, the homologous chromosomes in each bivalent separate and begin moving to opposite poles of the spindle apparatus (step 5). Meiosis I concludes with telophase I, when the homologs finish moving to opposite sides of the spindle (step 6). When meiosis I is complete, **cytokinesis** (division of cytoplasm) occurs and two haploid daughter cells form.

Meiosis I: A Recap   The end result of meiosis I is that one chromosome of each homologous pair is distributed to a different daughter cell. A reduction division has occurred: The daughter cells of meiosis I are haploid, having only one copy of each type of chromosome. The sister chromatids remain attached in each chromosome, however, meaning that the haploid daughter cells produced by meiosis I still contain replicated chromosomes.

The chromosomes in each cell are a random assortment of maternal and paternal chromosomes as a result of (1) crossing over and (2) the random distribution of maternal and paternal homologs during metaphase.

The preceding discussion shows that although meiosis I is a continuous process, biologists summarize the events by identifying distinct phases:

- *Early Prophase I*   Replicated chromosomes condense and the spindle apparatus forms. Synapsis of homologs forms pairs of homologous chromosomes, or bivalents.

- *Late Prophase I*   Breakdown of the nuclear envelope. Microtubules of the spindle apparatus attach to kinetochores. Chiasmata become visible, marking sites where crossing over occurs. Crossing over results in an exchange of segments between maternal and paternal chromosomes.

- *Metaphase I*   Bivalents move to the metaphase plate and line up. One homolog is on one side of the plate and the other homolog is on the other.

- *Anaphase I*   Homologs separate and begin moving to opposite spindle poles.

- *Telophase I*   Homologs finish moving to opposite spindle poles. Spindle apparatus disassembles. In some species, a nuclear envelope re-forms around each set of chromosomes.

Throughout, chromosome movement takes place as microtubules that are attached to the kinetochore dynamically assemble and disassemble. When meiosis I is complete, the cell divides and two haploid daughter cells are produced.

The Phases of Meiosis II

Recall that chromosome replication occurred before meiosis I. Throughout meiosis I, sister chromatids remained attached. Because no chromosome replication occurs between meiosis I and meiosis II, each chromosome consists of two sister chromatids at the start of meiosis II. And because only one member of each homologous pair of chromosomes is present, the cell is haploid.

During prophase II, a spindle apparatus forms in both daughter cells. Microtubules attach to kinetochores on each side of every chromosome and begin moving the chromosomes toward the middle of each cell (step 7 of Figure 13.7).

In metaphase II, the chromosomes are lined up at the metaphase plate (step 8). The sister chromatids of each chromosome separate during anaphase II (step 9) and move to different daughter cells during telophase II (step 10). Once they are separated, each chromatid is considered an independent daughter chromosome. Meiosis II results in four haploid cells, each with one daughter chromosome of each type in the chromosome set.

Like meiosis I, meiosis II is continuous, but biologists routinely divide it into distinct phases. These stages are essentially those of mitosis. To summarize,

- *Prophase II*   The spindle apparatus forms. If a nuclear envelope formed at the end of meiosis I, it breaks apart.

- *Metaphase II*   Replicated chromosomes, consisting of two sister chromatids, are lined up at the metaphase plate.

- *Anaphase II*   Sister chromatids separate. The daughter chromosomes that result begin moving to opposite poles of the spindle apparatus.

SUMMARY TABLE 13.2   **Key Differences between Mitosis and Meiosis**

Feature	Mitosis	Meiosis
Number of cell divisions	One	Two
Number of chromosomes in daughter cells compared with parent cell	Same	Half
Synapsis of homologs	No	Yes
Number of crossing-over events	None	One or more per pair of homologous chromosomes
Makeup of chromosomes in daughter cells	Identical	Different—various combinations of maternal and paternal chromosomes, paternal and maternal segments mixed within chromosomes
Role in organism life cycle	Asexual reproduction in some eukaryotes; cell division for growth	Halving of chromosome number in cells that will produce gametes

- *Telophase II* Chromosomes finish moving to opposite poles of the spindle apparatus. A nuclear envelope forms around each haploid set of chromosomes.

When meiosis II is complete, each cell divides to form two daughter cells. Because meiosis II occurs in both daughter cells of meiosis I, the process results in a total of four daughter cells from each original, parent cell. To describe meiosis in a nutshell, one diploid cell with replicated chromosomes gives rise to four haploid cells with unreplicated chromosomes.

TABLE 13.2 and **FIGURE 13.8** provide a comparison of mitosis and meiosis. A key difference between the two processes is that homologous chromosomes pair early in meiosis but do not pair at all during mitosis. Because homologs pair through synapsis in prophase of meiosis I, they can migrate to the metaphase plate together and then separate during anaphase of meiosis I, resulting in a reduction division. ✔ If you understand this key distinction between meiosis and mitosis, you should be able to describe the consequences for meiosis if homologs do not pair.

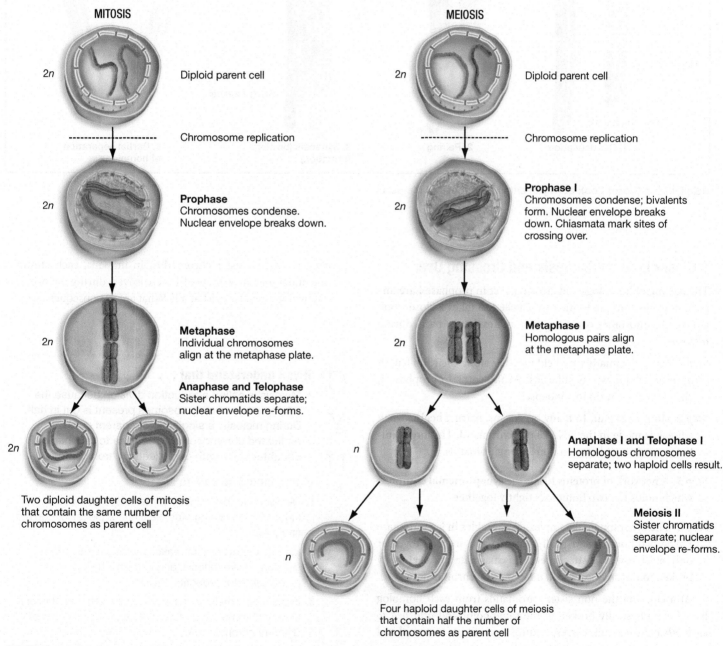

FIGURE 13.8 A Comparison of Mitosis and Meiosis. Mitosis produces two daughter cells with chromosomal complements identical to the parent cell. Meiosis produces four haploid cells with chromosomal complements unlike one another and unlike the diploid parent cell.

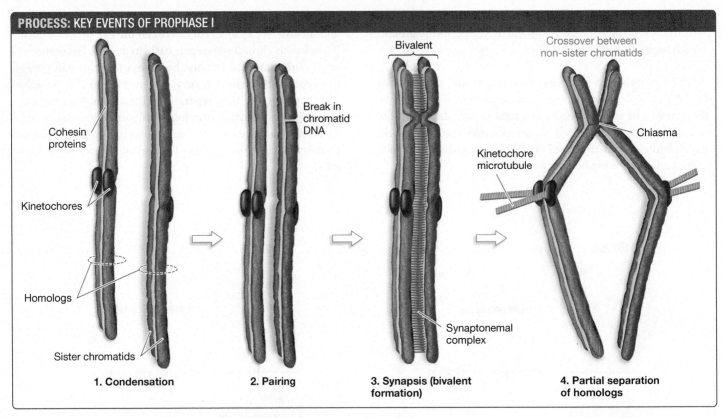

1. Condensation

2. Pairing

3. Synapsis (bivalent formation)

4. Partial separation of homologs

FIGURE 13.9 A Closer Look at Key Events in Prophase of Meiosis I.

A Closer Look at Synapsis and Crossing Over

The pairing of homologs and crossing over in prophase I are important events unique to meiosis. **FIGURE 13.9** takes a closer look at how chromosomes come together and exchange parts during meiosis I.

Step 1 Sister chromatids are held together along their full length by proteins known as cohesins. At the entry to prophase I, chromosomes begin to condense.

Step 2 Homologs pair. In many organisms, pairing begins when a break is made in the DNA of one chromatid. This break initiates a crossover between non-sister chromatids.

Step 3 A network of proteins forms the **synaptonemal complex,** which holds the two homologs tightly together.

Step 4 The synaptonemal complex disassembles in late prophase I. The two homologs partially separate and are held together only at chiasmata. Attachments at chiasmata are eventually broken to restore individual, unconnected chromosomes.

At a chiasma the non-sister chromatids from each homolog have been physically broken at the same point and *attached to each other*. As a result, corresponding segments of maternal and paternal chromosomes are exchanged.

Crossing over can occur at many locations along the length of paired homologs, and it routinely occurs at least once between each pair of non-sister chromatids. In humans, each chromosome undergoes an average of 1½ crossovers during meiosis.

Why does meiosis exist at all? What are its consequences?

check your understanding

If you understand that . . .

- Meiosis is called a reduction division because the total number of chromosomes present is cut in half.
- During meiosis, a single diploid parent cell with replicated chromosomes gives rise to four haploid daughter cells, with unreplicated chromosomes.

✔ **You should be able to . . .**

1. Demonstrate the phases of meiosis I illustrated in Figure 13.7 by using pipe cleaners or pieces of cooked spaghetti.

2. Identify the event that makes meiosis a reduction division, unlike mitosis, and explain why it is responsible for reduction division.

3. Explain how meiosis generates cells with one of every kind of chromosome rather than random mixtures of different chromosomes.

Answers are available in Appendix A.

13.2 Meiosis Promotes Genetic Variation

The cell biologists who worked out the details of meiosis in the late 1800s and early 1900s realized that the process solved the riddle of fertilization. Weismann's hypothesis—that a reduction division precedes gamete formation in animals—was confirmed.

By now, having come to appreciate that meiosis is an intricate, tightly regulated process, you shouldn't be surprised to learn that it involves dozens, if not hundreds, of different proteins. Given this complexity, it is logical to hypothesize that meiosis accomplishes something extremely important: Thanks to the independent shuffling of maternal and paternal chromosomes and crossing over during meiosis I, the chromosomes in one gamete are different from the chromosomes in another gamete and different from the chromosomes in parental cells. Subsequently, fertilization brings haploid sets of chromosomes from a mother and father together to form a diploid offspring. The chromosome complement of this offspring is unlike that of either parent. It is a random combination of genetic material from each parent.

This change in chromosomal complement is crucial. The critical factor here is that changes in chromosome sets occur only during sexual reproduction—*not* during asexual reproduction.

- **Asexual reproduction** is any mechanism of producing offspring that does not involve the production and fusion of gametes. Asexual reproduction in eukaryotes is based on mitosis. The chromosomes in cells produced by mitosis are identical to the chromosomes in the parental cell.

- **Sexual reproduction** is the production of offspring through the production and fusion of gametes. Sexual reproduction results in offspring that have chromosome complements unlike those of their siblings or their parents.

Why is this difference important?

Chromosomes and Heredity

The changes in chromosomes produced by meiosis and fertilization are significant because chromosomes contain the cell's hereditary material. Stated another way, chromosomes contain the instructions for specifying particular traits. These inherited traits range from eye color and height in humans to the number or shape of the bristles on a fruit fly's leg to the color or shape of the seeds found in pea plants.

In the early 1900s, biologists began using the term gene to refer to the inherited instructions for a particular trait. Recall that the term allele refers to a particular version of a gene and that homologous chromosomes may carry different alleles.

Chromosomes are the repositories of genes, and identical copies of chromosomes are distributed to daughter cells during mitosis. Thus, cells that are produced by mitosis are genetically identical to the parent cell, and offspring produced during asexual reproduction are genetically identical to one another as well as to their parent. Offspring produced by asexual reproduction

are **clones**—or exact copies—of their parent. A familiar example of asexual reproduction is growing a new plant from a cutting.

In contrast, the offspring produced by sexual reproduction are genetically different from one another and unlike either their mother or their father.

Let's begin by analyzing two aspects of meiosis that create variation among chromosomes: (**1**) separation and distribution of homologous chromosomes and (**2**) crossing over. We'll then look at how these processes interact with fertilization to produce genetically variable offspring.

The Role of Independent Assortment

Each somatic cell in your body contains 23 homologous pairs of chromosomes and 46 chromosomes in total. Half of these chromosomes came from your mother, and half came from your father. Each chromosome contains genes, and genes influence particular traits. For example, one gene that affects your eye color might be located on one chromosome, while one of the genes that affects your hair color might be located on a different chromosome (**FIGURE 13.10a**).

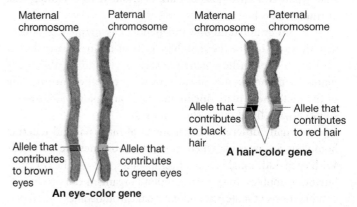

(a) Example: Individual with different alleles of two genes

Maternal chromosome   Paternal chromosome

Allele that contributes to brown eyes   Allele that contributes to green eyes

An eye-color gene

Maternal chromosome   Paternal chromosome

Allele that contributes to black hair   Allele that contributes to red hair

A hair-color gene

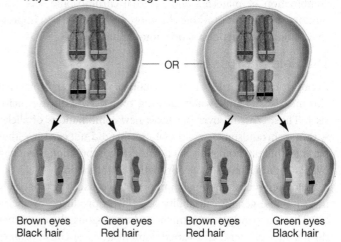

(b) During meiosis I, bivalents can line up two different ways before the homologs separate.

— OR —

Brown eyes Black hair   Green eyes Red hair   Brown eyes Red hair   Green eyes Black hair

FIGURE 13.10 Independent Assortment of Homologous Chromosomes Results in Varied Combinations of Genes.

Suppose that the chromosomes you inherited from your mother contain alleles associated with brown eyes and black hair, but the chromosomes you inherited from your father include alleles associated with green eyes and red hair. (This is a simplification for the purpose of explanation. In reality, several genes with various alleles interact in complex ways to produce human eye color and hair color.)

Will any particular gamete you produce contain the genetic instructions inherited from your mother or the instructions inherited from your father? To answer this question, study the diagram of meiosis in **FIGURE 13.10b**. It shows that when pairs of homologous chromosomes line up during meiosis I and the homologs separate, a variety of combinations of maternal and paternal chromosomes can result. Each daughter cell gets a random assortment of maternal and paternal chromosomes.

This phenomenon is known as the principle of independent assortment. In the example given here, meiosis results in gametes with alleles for brown eyes and black hair, the traits from your mother, and green eyes and red hair, the traits from your father. But two additional combinations also occur: brown eyes and red hair, or green eyes and black hair. The appearance of new combinations of alleles is called **genetic recombination.** Four different combinations of paternal and maternal chromosomes are possible when two chromosomes are distributed to daughter cells during meiosis I.

✔ If you understand how independent assortment produces genetic variation in the daughter cells of meiosis, you should be able to explain how genetic variation would be affected if maternal chromosomes always lined up together on one side of the metaphase plate during meiosis I and paternal chromosomes always lined up on the other side.

How many different combinations of maternal and paternal homologs are possible when more chromosomes are involved? With each additional pair of chromosomes, the number of combinations doubles. In general, a diploid organism can produce 2^n combinations of maternal and paternal chromosomes, where n is the haploid chromosome number. This means that you ($n \boxtimes 23$) can produce 2^{23}, or about 8.4 million, gametes that differ in their combination of maternal and paternal chromosome sets. The random assortment of whole chromosomes generates an impressive amount of genetic variation among gametes.

The Role of Crossing Over

Recall from Section 13.1 that segments of paternal and maternal chromatids exchange when crossing over occurs during meiosis I. Thus, crossing over produces new combinations of alleles within a chromosome—combinations that did not exist in either parent. This phenomenon is known as recombination. Crossing over is an important source of genetic recombination.

Genetic recombination is important because it dramatically increases the genetic variability of gametes produced by meiosis. The independent assortment of homologous chromosomes during meiosis generates varied combinations of chromosomes in gametes; genetic recombination due to crossing over varies the combinations of alleles along each chromosome that is involved

in a crossover. With crossing over, the number of genetically different gametes that you can produce is much more than the 8.4 million—it is virtually limitless.

How Does Fertilization Affect Genetic Variation?

Crossing over and the independent assortment of maternal and paternal chromosomes ensure that each gamete is genetically unique. Even if two gametes produced by the same individual fuse to form a diploid offspring—in which case **self-fertilization,** or "selfing," is taking place—the offspring are very likely to be genetically different from the parent (**FIGURE 13.11**). Selfing is common in many plant species, and it also occurs in animal species in which single individuals—called hermaphrodites—contain both male and female sex organs.

Self-fertilization, however, is rare or nonexistent in many sexually reproducing species. Instead, gametes from different individuals combine to form offspring. This process is called **outcrossing.** Outcrossing increases the genetic diversity of offspring even further because it combines chromosomes from different individuals. These chromosomes are likely to contain different alleles.

How many genetically distinct offspring can be produced when outcrossing occurs? Let's answer this question using humans as an example. Recall that a single human can produce about 8.4 million different gametes by independent assortment alone. When a sperm and egg come together at fertilization, the number of possible genetic combinations that can result is equal to the product of the numbers of different gametes produced by each parent. (To understand this logic, see **BioSkills 5** in Appendix B.) In humans this means that two parents can potentially produce 8.4 million $\boxtimes$ 8.4 million $\boxtimes$ 70.6 $\boxtimes$ 10^{12} genetically distinct offspring, even without crossing over. This number is far greater than the total number of people who have ever lived.

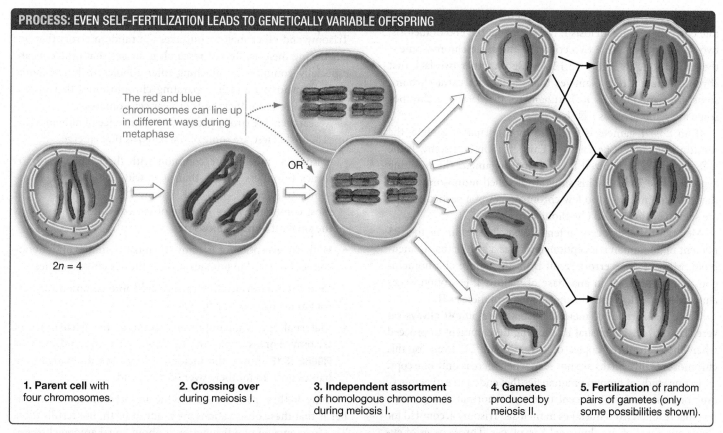

The red and blue chromosomes can line up in different ways during metaphase

OR

$2n = 4$

1. Parent cell with four chromosomes.

2. Crossing over during meiosis I.

3. Independent assortment of homologous chromosomes during meiosis I.

4. Gametes produced by meiosis II.

5. Fertilization of random pairs of gametes (only some possibilities shown).

FIGURE 13.11 Crossing Over, Independent Assortment, and the Random Pairing of Gametes during Fertilization Increase Genetic Variation, Even in Offspring Produced by Self-Fertilization.

✔**EXERCISE** In step 5, only a few of the many types of offspring that could be produced are shown. Sketch two additional types that are different from those shown.

In any complicated process such as meiosis, things can and do go wrong. What happens if there is a mistake, and the chromosomes are not properly distributed?

13.3 What Happens When Things Go Wrong in Meiosis?

Errors in meiosis are surprisingly common. If this were like a spelling mistake, it might be only an annoyance. But in humans, a conservative estimate is that 25 percent of conceptions are spontaneously terminated because of problems in meiosis. What are the consequences for offspring if gametes contain an abnormal set of chromosomes?

In 1866 Langdon Down described a distinctive set of co-occurring conditions observed in some people. The syndrome was characterized by mental retardation, a high risk for heart problems and leukemia, and a degenerative brain disorder similar to Alzheimer's disease. **Down syndrome,** as the disorder came to be called, is observed in about 0.15 percent of live births (1 infant in every 666).

For over 80 years the cause of the syndrome was unknown. Then, in the late 1950s, a study of the chromosome sets of nine Down syndrome children suggested that the condition is associated with the presence of an extra copy of chromosome 21. This situation is called **trisomy** ("three-bodies")—in this case, trisomy-21—because each cell has three copies of the chromosome. The explanation proposed for the trisomy was that a mistake had occurred during meiosis in either the mother or the father.

How Do Mistakes Occur?

For a gamete to get one complete set of chromosomes, two steps in meiosis must be perfectly executed.

1. The chromosomes in each homologous pair must separate from each other during the first meiotic division, so that only one homolog ends up in each daughter cell.

2. Sister chromatids must separate from each other and move to opposite poles of the dividing cell during meiosis II.

If both homologs in meiosis I or both sister chromatids in meiosis II move to the same pole of the parent cell, the products of meiosis will be abnormal. This sort of meiotic error is referred to as **nondisjunction,** because the homologs or sister chromatids fail to separate, or disjoin.

FIGURE 13.12 shows what happens when homologs do not separate correctly during meiosis I. Notice that at the end of meiosis, two daughter cells have two copies of the same chromosome—the smaller one in Figure 13.12—while the other two lack that chromosome entirely. Gametes that contain an extra chromosome are symbolized as $n + 1$; gametes that lack one chromosome are symbolized as $n - 1$.

If an $n + 1$ gamete is fertilized by a normal n gamete, the resulting zygote will be $2n + 1$. This situation is trisomy. If the $n - 1$ gamete is fertilized by a normal n gamete, the resulting zygote will be $2n - 1$. This situation is called **monosomy.** Cells that have too many or too few chromosomes of a particular type are said to be **aneuploid** ("without-form").

Meiotic mistakes occur often. Researchers estimate that 25 percent of all human conceptions produce a zygote that is aneuploid. Most of these errors result from the failure of a homologous pair to separate in anaphase of meiosis I; less often, sister chromatids stay together during anaphase of meiosis II.

The consequences of meiotic mistakes are almost always severe. Trisomy-21 is unusual in allowing development to proceed when there are three copies of chromosome 21. Even for this chromosome, live births are not seen when there is only one copy.

In one study of human pregnancies that ended in early embryonic or fetal death, 38 percent involved abnormal chromosome sets that resulted from mistakes in meiosis. Trisomy accounted for about one-third of the abnormal karyotypes. Three copies of every chromosome ($3n$), a condition called triploidy, was also common. Monosomy and abnormally sized or shaped chromosomes were also seen. Mistakes in meiosis are common and are the leading cause of spontaneous abortion (miscarriage) in humans.

Why Do Mistakes Occur?

Trisomy and other meiotic mistakes are random errors that occur during meiosis. Recent research indicates that problems are especially common in attaching microtubules to kinetochores early in meiosis I and in separating chromosomes that have a single chiasma near their ends or near centromeres.

Researchers see strong patterns in occurrence of human trisomies at birth. Here are some of the patterns that emerge:

- Trisomy is much more common with the smaller chromosomes (numbers 13–22) than it is with the larger chromosomes (numbers 1–12), and trisomy-21 is far and away the most common type of trisomy observed. Chromosome 21 is the smallest human autosome.

- With the exception of trisomy-21, most trisomies and monosomies observed in humans involve the sex chromosomes.

- Errors in meiosis leading to eggs are more common than errors in meiosis leading to sperm.

- Maternal age is an important factor in the occurrence of trisomy. For example, in the case of Down syndrome, as **FIGURE 13.13** shows, the incidence increases dramatically in babies born to mothers over 35 years old.

Why do these patterns occur? One important point to remember is that these observations are made at birth, not fertilization. The frequency of nondisjunction is about equal among chromosomes, but aneuploidy tends to be lethal to embryos if it involves chromosomes that contain a large number of genes. Trisomy-21 is common most likely because it involves a small chromosome with a correspondingly small number of genes.

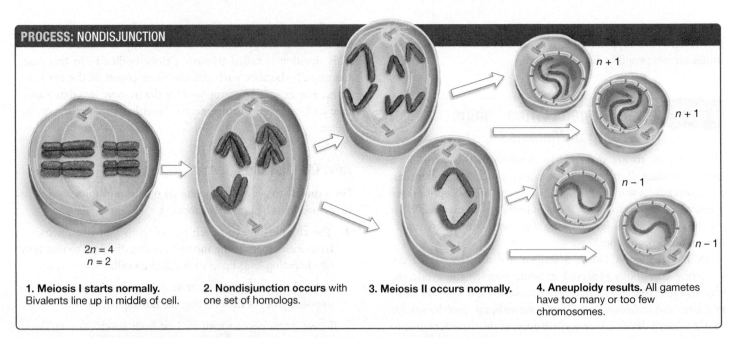

PROCESS: NONDISJUNCTION

$2n = 4$
$n = 2$

1. Meiosis I starts normally. Bivalents line up in middle of cell.

2. Nondisjunction occurs with one set of homologs.

3. Meiosis II occurs normally.

4. Aneuploidy results. All gametes have too many or too few chromosomes.

$n + 1$

$n + 1$

$n - 1$

$n - 1$

FIGURE 13.12 Nondisjunction Leads to Gametes with Abnormal Chromosome Numbers. If homologous chromosomes fail to separate during meiosis I, the gametes that result will have an extra chromosome or will lack a chromosome. Nondisjunction can also occur during meiosis II if sister chromatids fail to separate.

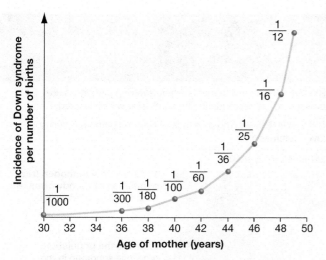

FIGURE 13.13 The Frequency of Down Syndrome Increases as a Function of a Mother's Age.

DATA: National Down Syndrome Society. 2012. www.ndss.org/index.php?option=com_content&view=article&id=61&Itemid=78

There are more questions than answers. Why are there more errors in women than men? Why is there such a strong correlation between maternal age and frequency of trisomy-21?

In part, the answers lie with an unusual feature of human egg development (oogenesis). Diploid precursors to eggs enter meiosis I before birth and arrest in prophase I until ovulation. For some eggs, this is 40 years or more later. Spindle apparatus function and the ability to separate chromosomes properly appear to decline after this long wait. Much remains to be discovered, but one thing is clear: Successful meiosis is critical to the health of offspring.

13.4 Why Does Meiosis Exist?

Why sex and meiosis? Although it seems obvious that sex and meiosis are needed universally for reproduction, that's not the case. Meiosis and sexual reproduction occur in only a small fraction of the lineages on the tree of life. Bacteria and archaea normally undergo only asexual reproduction; most algae, all fungi, and some animals and land plants reproduce asexually as well as sexually. Asexual reproduction is even observed in some vertebrates. Several species of guppy in the genus *Poeciliopsis*, for example, reproduce exclusively by mitosis.

Although sexual reproduction plays a central role in the life of most familiar organisms—including us—until recently, scientists had no clear idea of why it occurs. In fact, on the basis of theory, biologists had good reason to think that sexual reproduction should *not* exist.

The Paradox of Sex

In 1978 John Maynard Smith pointed out that the existence of sexual reproduction presents a paradox. Maynard Smith developed a mathematical model showing that because asexually reproducing individuals do not have to produce male offspring, their progeny on average can produce twice as many offspring as individuals that reproduce sexually. **FIGURE 13.14** diagrams this result by showing the number of females (♀), males (♂), and asexually reproducing organisms (**O**) produced over several generations by asexual versus sexual reproduction.

In this example, each asexually reproducing individual and each sexually reproducing couple produces four offspring over the course of their lifetimes. Note that in the sexual population, it takes two individuals—one male and one female—to produce

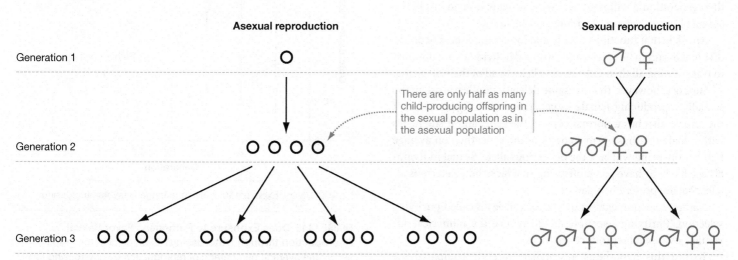

FIGURE 13.14 Asexual Reproduction Produces More Offspring. Each female (♀), male (♂), and asexual (**O**) symbol represents an individual. This hypothetical example assumes that (1) every asexual individual or sexually reproducing couple produces four offspring over the course of a lifetime, (2) sexually reproducing individuals produce half males and half females, and (3) all offspring survive to breed.

✔**QUANTITATIVE** How many asexually produced offspring would be present in generation 4? How many sexually produced offspring?

four offspring. Two out of every four children that each female produces sexually are males who cannot have children of their own. As a result, after one generation (generation 2 in Figure 13.14) the sexual population has just half as many child-producing individuals as the asexual population. Maynard Smith referred to this as the "two-fold cost of males." Asexual reproduction is much more efficient than sexual reproduction because no males are produced.

Based on this analysis, what will happen when asexual and sexual individuals exist in the same population and compete with one another? If all other things are equal, individuals that reproduce asexually should increase in frequency in the population while individuals that reproduce sexually should decline in frequency. In fact, Maynard Smith's model predicts that sexual reproduction is so inefficient that it should be completely eliminated.

To resolve this paradox, biologists began examining the assumption "If all other things are equal." Stated another way, biologists began looking for ways that meiosis and outcrossing could lead to the production of offspring that reproduce more than asexually produced individuals do. After decades of debate and analysis, two solid hypotheses to explain the paradox of sex are beginning to emerge.

The Purifying Selection Hypothesis

The first clue to unraveling the paradox of sex is a simple observation: If a gene is damaged or altered in a way that causes it to function poorly, it will be inherited by *all* of that individual's offspring when asexual reproduction occurs. Suppose the altered gene arose in generation 1 of Figure 13.14. If this gene is important, its alteration might cause the four asexual females present in generation 2 to produce fewer than four offspring apiece—perhaps because the members of generation 2 die young. If so, then generation 3 will not have twice as many individuals in the asexual lineage compared with the sexual lineage.

An allele that functions poorly and lowers the fitness of an individual is said to be deleterious. Asexual individuals are doomed to transmitting all their deleterious alleles to all of their offspring.

Suppose, however, that the same deleterious allele arose in the sexually reproducing female in generation 1 of Figure 13.14. If the female also has a normal copy of the gene, and if she mates with a male that has normal copies of the gene, then on average half her offspring will lack the deleterious allele. Sexual individuals are likely to have some offspring that lack the deleterious alleles that are present in a parent.

Natural selection against deleterious alleles is called purifying selection. Purifying selection should reduce the numerical advantage of asexual reproduction.

To test this hypothesis, researchers recently compared the same genes in two closely related species of *Daphnia,* a tiny crustacean that is a common inhabitant of ponds and lakes (see Chapter 50). One of these species reproduces asexually and the other reproduces sexually. As predicted, the researchers found that individuals in the asexual species contained many more deleterious alleles than individuals in the sexual species. Results like

RESEARCH

QUESTION: Does exposure to evolving pathogens favor outcrossing?

HYPOTHESIS: In environments where evolving pathogens are present, sexual reproduction by outcrosing will be favored.

NULL HYPOTHESIS: The presence of evolving pathogens will not favor outcrossing.

EXPERIMENTAL SETUP:

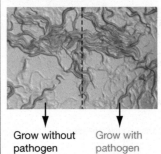

Grow without pathogen   Grow with pathogen

1. Start with a pathogen free population of roundworms with a 20% rate of outcrossing.

2. Divide the population; grow one subgroup in the absence of a pathogen and another subgroup in the presence of an evolving pathogen.

3. Assess the rate of outcrossing over many generations.

PREDICTION: The rate of outcrossing will increase in response to exposure by a pathogen.

PREDICTION OF NULL HYPOTHESIS: The rate of outcrossing will not be influenced by a pathogen.

RESULTS:

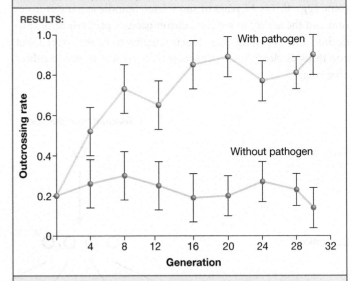

CONCLUSION: Exposure to evolving pathogens favors outcrossing.

FIGURE 13.15 Does Exposure to Pathogens Favor Sexual Reproduction through Outcrossing? Each point in the graph shows the average percentage of reproduction by outcrossing for five populations. The bars indicate the degree of variation in the data (see **BioSkills 4** in Appendix B for a description of error bars).

Morran, L. T., et al. 2011. Running with the red queen: Host-parasite coevolution selects for biparental sex. *Science* 333: 216–218.

✔ **QUESTION** What would you predict if a non-evolving pathogen were used?

these have convinced biologists that purifying selection is an important factor promoting the success of sexual reproduction.

The Changing-Environment Hypothesis

The second hypothesis to explain sexual reproduction also focuses on the benefits of producing genetically diverse offspring. Here's the key idea: Offspring that are genetic clones of their parents are unlikely to thrive if the environment changes.

What type of environmental change might favor genetically diverse offspring? The leading hypothesis points to pressure put on hosts by rapidly changing pathogens and parasites—bacteria, viruses, fungi, and other entities that cause disease. In your own lifetime, for example, several new disease-causing agents have emerged that afflict humans. These include the SARS virus, HIV, and new strains of the tuberculosis bacterium. Hundreds of genes help defend you against these types of invaders. Certain alleles help you fight off particular strains of disease-causing bacteria, eukaryotes, or viruses. In this evolutionary arms race, pathogens and parasites constantly evolve new ways to infect the most common types of host.

What happens if all the offspring produced by an individual are genetically identical? If a new strain of disease-causing agent evolves, then all the asexually produced offspring are likely to be susceptible to that new strain. But if the offspring are genetically varied, then it is likely that at least some offspring will have combinations of alleles that enable them to fight off the new strain of pathogen or parasite and produce offspring of their own.

Recall from Section 13.2 that over multiple generations, outcrossing—mating between two different individuals—increases the amount of genetic diversity relative to self-fertilization. A logical question to ask is: Does exposure to evolving pathogens favor outcrossing in sexually reproducing organisms? To address this question, Levi Morran, Curtis Lively, and colleagues carried out a pivotal study on a tiny (only about 1 mm long) roundworm named *Caenorhabditis elegans*.

C. elegans is an important model organism (see **BioSkills 13** in Appendix B) that was chosen for this study because it leads an unusual sex life. There are no females, only males and hermaphrodites. Because hermaphrodites have both male and female sex

organs, this means that *C. elegans* can reproduce either by self-fertilization or by outcrossing with males. The proportion of roundworms that reproduce by self-fertilization versus outcrossing can vary in different strains or in different environments over time. So, the research team was able to test whether the rate of outcrossing increased in response to intense selection by a pathogen.

The setup of Morran, Lively, and colleagues' experiment is shown in **FIGURE 13.15**. The team began with a population of roundworms that had not been exposed to the pathogen and that reproduced predominantly by self-fertilization. The researchers then split the starting population into different groups. Half the groups were grown in the presence of a pathogen—a deadly bacterium—and the other half were grown without it. Once ingested by a roundworm, the bacterial pathogen could kill a susceptible individual within 24 hours.

At each generation, bacteria were collected from the carcasses of roundworms killed in the previous generation. Companion experiments showed that the pathogen evolved to become even more infectious over the course of the study.

The results are shown at the bottom of Figure 13.15. The rate of outcrossing stayed low over 32 generations in populations that did not encounter the pathogen. In contrast, populations that were exposed to the evolving pathogen showed a rapid increase in the rate of outcrossing.

At the end of the experiment, the roundworms in the pathogen-exposed population were significantly more resistant to the evolved pathogen than their ancestors. In other words, the roundworms in the predominantly outcrossing population had evolved along with the pathogen. In striking contrast, when a parallel experiment was done with a strain of roundworms that could reproduce only by self-fertilization, those populations were unable to evolve resistance to the pathogen. In fact, they became extinct.

These results and many others support the changing-environment hypothesis. Although the paradox of sex remains an active area of research, more biologists are becoming convinced that sexual reproduction is helpful for two reasons: (**1**) Offspring are not doomed to inherit harmful alleles, and (**2**) the production of genetically varied offspring means that at least some may be able to resist rapidly evolving pathogens and parasites.

CHAPTER 13   REVIEW   For media, go to MasteringBiology

If you understand . . .

13.1 How Does Meiosis Occur?

- Meiosis is a nuclear division resulting in cells that have only one of each type of chromosome and half as many chromosomes as the parent cell. In animals it leads to the formation of eggs and sperm.

- In diploid ($2n$) organisms, individuals have two versions of each type of chromosome. The two versions are called homologs. One homolog is inherited from the mother and one from the father. Haploid organisms (n) have just one of each type of chromosome.

- Each chromosome is replicated before meiosis begins. At the start of meiosis I, each chromosome consists of a pair of sister chromatids.

- Homologous pairs of chromosomes synapse early in meiosis I, forming a bivalent—two closely paired homologous chromosomes. Non-sister chromatids undergo crossing over.

- When crossing over is complete, the pair of homologous chromosomes is moved to the metaphase plate.

- At the end of meiosis I, the homologous chromosomes are separated and distributed to two daughter cells. The daughter cells are haploid, because each receives one of each type of chromosome.

- During meiosis II, sister chromatids separate and are distributed to two daughter cells.

- From one diploid cell with replicated chromosomes, meiosis produces four haploid daughter cells with unreplicated chromosomes.

✔ You should be able to diagram a diploid cell with a homologous pair of chromosomes and show when in meiosis this cell produces haploid daughter cells. Be sure to show all chromatids.

13.2 Meiosis Promotes Genetic Variation

- Each cell produced by meiosis receives a different combination of chromosomes. Because genes are located on chromosomes, each cell produced by meiosis receives a different complement of genes. The resulting offspring are genetically distinct from one another and from their parents.

- When meiosis and outcrossing occur, the chromosome complements of offspring differ from one another and from their parents for three reasons:

  1. Gametes receive a random assortment of maternal and paternal chromosomes when homologs separate in meiosis I. This is independent assortment.

  2. Because of crossing over, each chromosome contains a random assortment of paternal and maternal alleles.

  3. Outcrossing results in a combination of chromosome sets from different individuals.

✔ You should be able to draw a diploid cell with four chromosomes entering meiosis and illustrate (a) how different combinations of chromosomes can result from independent assortment; and (b) focusing on a single homologous pair, show how many recombinant chromosomes (chromosomes with mixtures of maternal and paternal segments) are produced when crossing over occurs once along this homologous pair.

13.3 What Happens When Things Go Wrong in Meiosis?

- If mistakes occur during meiosis, the resulting egg and sperm cells may contain the wrong number of chromosomes. It is rare for offspring with an incorrect number of chromosomes to develop normally.

- Mistakes during meiosis lead to gametes and offspring with an abnormal number of chromosomes. Children with Down syndrome, for example, have an extra copy of chromosome 21.

- The leading hypothesis to explain meiotic mistakes is that they are accidental failures of homologous chromosomes or sister chromatids to separate properly during meiosis.

✔ Using pipe cleaners or spaghetti to model a homologous pair of chromosomes, you should be able to demonstrate (a) what happens if one pair of homologous chromosomes fails to separate at anaphase of meiosis I and (b) what happens if sister chromatids of one chromosome fail to separate at anaphase of meiosis II but later separate in a daughter cell.

13.4 Why Does Meiosis Exist?

- Asexual reproduction is much more efficient than sexual reproduction because all individuals produced asexually are capable of bearing progeny. With sexual reproduction, half the offspring (the males) are unable to bear progeny.

- The leading hypotheses to explain the existence of meiosis and sexual reproduction are that:

  1. parents can produce offspring that lack harmful alleles; and
  2. genetically diverse offspring are likely to include some that are better able to resist evolving pathogens and parasites.

✔ You should be able to predict whether, in species that alternate between asexual and sexual reproduction, sexual reproduction occurs during times when environmental conditions are stable or times when conditions change rapidly.

(MB) MasteringBiology

1. MasteringBiology Assignments

Tutorials and Activities Asexual and Sexual Life Cycles; Genetic Variation from Sexual Recombination; Meiosis; Meiosis (1 of 3): Genes, Chromosomes, and Sexual Reproduction; Meiosis (2 of 3): The Mechanism; Meiosis (3 of 3): Determinants of Heredity and Genetic Variation; Meiosis Animation; Mistakes in Meiosis; Origins of Genetic Variation

Questions Reading Quizzes, Blue-Thread Questions, Test Bank

2. eText Read your book online, search, take notes, highlight text, and more.

3. The Study Area Practice Test, Cumulative Test, BioFlix® 3-D Animations, Videos, Activities, Audio Glossary, Word Study Tools, Art

You should be able to . . .

1. In the roundworm *Ascaris*, eggs and sperm have two chromosomes, but all other cells have four. Observations such as this inspired which important hypothesis?
   a. Before gamete formation, a special type of cell division leads to a quartering of chromosome number.
   b. Before gamete formation, a special type of cell division leads to a halving of chromosome number.
   c. After gamete formation, half the chromosomes are destroyed.
   d. After gamete formation, either the maternal or the paternal set of chromosomes disintegrates.

2. What are homologous chromosomes?
   a. chromosomes that are similar in their size, shape, and gene content
   b. similar chromosomes that are found in different individuals of the same species
   c. the two "threads" in a replicated chromosome (they are identical copies)
   d. the products of crossing over, which contain a combination of segments from maternal chromosomes and segments from paternal chromosomes

3. What is a bivalent?
   a. the X that forms when chromatids from homologous chromosomes cross over
   b. a group of four chromatids produced when homologs synapse
   c. the four points where homologous chromosomes touch as they synapse
   d. the group of four genetically identical daughter cells produced by mitosis

4. What is an outcome of genetic recombination?
   a. the synapsing of homologs during prophase of meiosis I
   b. the new combination of maternal and paternal chromosome segments that results when homologs cross over
   c. the new combinations of chromosome segments that result when self-fertilization occurs
   d. the combination of a haploid phase *and* a diploid phase in a life cycle

5. What proportion of chromosomes in a human skin cell are paternal chromosomes?

6. Meiosis II is similar to _____.

7. Explain the relationship between homologous chromosomes and the relationship between sister chromatids.

8. Lay four pens and four pencils on a tabletop, and imagine that they represent replicated chromosomes in a diploid cell where $n = 2$. Explain the phases of meiosis II by moving the pens and pencils around. (If you don't have enough pens and pencils, use strips of paper or fabric.)

9. Meiosis is called a reduction division, but all the reduction occurs during meiosis I—no reduction occurs during meiosis II. Explain why meiosis I is a reduction division but meiosis II is not.

10. Dogs have 78 chromosomes in their diploid cells. If a diploid dog cell enters meiosis, how many chromosomes and chromatids will be present in each daughter cell at the end of meiosis I?

   a. 39 chromosomes and 39 chromatids
   b. 39 chromosomes and 78 chromatids
   c. 78 chromosomes and 78 chromatids
   d. 78 chromosomes and 156 chromatids

11. Triploid ($3n$) watermelons are produced by crossing a tetraploid ($4n$) strain with a diploid ($2n$) plant. Briefly explain why this mating produces a triploid individual. Why can mitosis proceed normally in triploid cells, but meiosis cannot?

12. Some plant breeders are concerned about the susceptibility of asexually cultivated plants, such as seedless bananas, to new strains of disease-causing bacteria, viruses, or fungi. Briefly explain their concern by discussing the differences in the genetic "outcomes" of asexual and sexual reproduction.

13. The gibbon has 44 chromosomes per diploid set, and the siamang has 50 chromosomes per diploid set. In the 1970s a chance mating between a male gibbon and a female siamang produced an offspring. Predict how many chromosomes were observed in the somatic cells of the offspring. Do you predict that this individual would be able to form viable gametes? Why or why not?

14. Meiosis results in a reassortment of maternal and paternal chromosomes. If $n = 3$ for a given organism, there are eight different combinations of paternal and maternal chromosomes. If no crossing over occurs, what is the probability that a gamete will receive *only* paternal chromosomes?
   a. 0; b. 1/16; c. 1/8; d. 1/3

15. Some researchers hypothesize that older women are less responsive to triggers of spontaneous abortion than younger women. How could the data shown in Figure 13.13, which graphs a mother's age

versus the incidence of Down syndrome, be used to support this hypothesis?

16. A species of rotifer, a small freshwater invertebrate, abandoned sexual reproduction millions of years ago. A remarkable feature of the rotifer's life cycle is its ability to withstand extreme drying. When the rotifer's watery environment dries out, so does the rotifer, and it can be blown in the wind to a new environment. Once blown to water, the rotifer rehydrates and resumes an active life. A major pathogen of these rotifers is a species of fungus. Some scientists hypothesize that fungus-infected rotifers rid themselves of the pathogen when they dry.
   a. Design an experimental study to test this hypothesis.
   b. Provide an explanation for how these asexually reproducing rotifers are able to evade pathogens even though they are genetically identical.

14 Mendel and the Gene

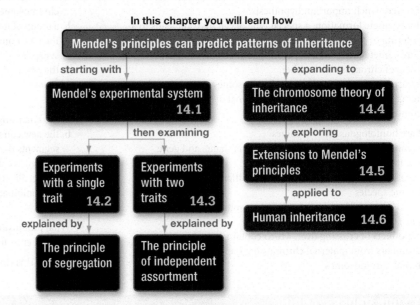

In this chapter you will learn how

Mendel's principles can predict patterns of inheritance

starting with → | expanding to →

Mendel's experimental system 14.1

The chromosome theory of inheritance 14.4

then examining | exploring

Experiments with a single trait 14.2

Experiments with two traits 14.3

Extensions to Mendel's principles 14.5

applied to

Human inheritance 14.6

explained by | explained by

The principle of segregation

The principle of independent assortment

Experiments on garden peas and sweet peas (shown here) helped launch the science of genetics.

This chapter is part of the Big Picture. See how on pages 366–367.

The science of biology is built on a series of great ideas. Two of these—the cell theory and the theory of evolution—were introduced in Chapter 1. The cell theory describes the basic structure of organisms; the theory of evolution by natural selection clarifies why species change through time. Life is cellular; populations evolve. These are two of the five fundamental attributes of life.

This chapter introduces a third great idea in biology: the chromosome theory of inheritance. The chromosome theory explained how genetic information is transmitted from one generation to the next. It shed light on a third fundamental attribute of life: Organisms process information.

✔ When you see this checkmark, stop and test yourself. Answers are available in Appendix A.

An Austrian monk named Gregor Mendel laid the groundwork for the theory in 1865, when he announced that he had worked out the rules of inheritance through a series of experiments on garden peas. Another key insight emerged during the final decades of the nineteenth century, when biologists described the details of meiosis (see Chapter 13).

The chromosome theory of inheritance, formulated in 1902 by Walter Sutton and Theodor Boveri, linked these two insights. This theory contends that meiosis causes the patterns of inheritance that Mendel observed. It also asserts that the hereditary factors called genes are located on chromosomes. (Genes determine inherited traits and are center stage in the Big Picture on pages 366–367.)

The chromosome theory launched the study of **genetics,** the branch of biology that focuses on the inheritance of traits. Let's start at the beginning: What are the rules of inheritance that Mendel discovered?

14.1 Mendel's Experimental System

When biological science began to emerge as an important discipline, questions about **heredity**—meaning inheritance, or the transmission of traits from parents to offspring—were primarily the concern of animal breeders and horticulturists. A **trait** is any characteristic of an individual, ranging from height to the primary structure of a particular membrane protein.

In the city where Gregor Mendel lived, there was particular interest in how selective breeding could result in hardier and more productive varieties of sheep, fruit trees, and vines; and an agricultural society had been formed there to promote research into making selective breeding more efficient. Mendel was an active member of this society, and the monastery he belonged to was also devoted to scientific teaching and research.

What Questions Was Mendel Trying to Answer?

Mendel set out to address the most fundamental of all issues concerning heredity: What are the basic patterns in the transmission of traits from parents to offspring?

At the time, two hypotheses had been formulated to answer this question:

1. *Blending inheritance* claimed that the traits observed in a mother and father blend together to form the traits observed in their offspring. As a result, an offspring's traits are intermediate between the mother's and father's traits.

2. *Inheritance of acquired characters* claimed that traits present in parents are modified, through use, and passed on to their offspring in the modified form.

Each of these hypotheses made predictions. Blending inheritance contended that when black sheep and white sheep mate, their hereditary determinants will blend to form a new hereditary determinant for gray wool. Therefore, their offspring should be gray. Inheritance of acquired characters predicts that if giraffes extend their necks by straining to reach leaves high in the tops of trees, they subsequently produce longer-necked offspring.

These hypotheses were being promoted by the greatest scientists of Mendel's time. Are they correct?

The Garden Pea Served as the First Model Organism in Genetics

After investigating and discarding several candidate species to study, Mendel chose the garden pea, *Pisum sativum*. His reasons were practical: Peas are inexpensive and easy to grow from seed, have a relatively short generation time, and produce reasonably large numbers of seeds. These features made it possible for him to continue experiments over several generations and collect data from large numbers of individuals.

Peas served as a **model organism:** a species that is used for research because it is practical and because conclusions drawn from studying it turn out to apply to many other species as well. **BioSkills 13** in Appendix B introduces some of the important model organisms used in biological science today.

Two additional features of the pea made it possible for Mendel to design his experiments: Individuals were available that differed in easily recognizable traits, such as flower color or seed shape, and he could control which parents were involved in a mating.

How Did Mendel Control Matings? **FIGURE 14.1a** shows the male and female reproductive organs of a garden pea flower. Sperm cells are produced in pollen grains, which are small sacs that

(a) Self-pollination

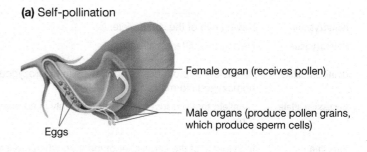

Female organ (receives pollen)

Male organs (produce pollen grains, which produce sperm cells)

Eggs

(b) Cross-pollination

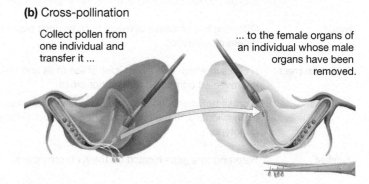

Collect pollen from one individual and transfer it ...

... to the female organs of an individual whose male organs have been removed.

FIGURE 14.1 Peas Can Be Self-Pollinated or Cross-Pollinated.
(a) Under normal conditions, garden peas pollinate themselves.
(b) Mendel developed a method of controlling the matings of his model organism.

mature in the male reproductive structure of the plant. Eggs are produced in the female reproductive structure.

Under normal conditions, garden peas **self-fertilize:** a flower's pollen falls on the female reproductive organ of that same flower. As **FIGURE 14.1b** shows, however, Mendel could prevent self-fertilization by removing the male reproductive organs from a flower before any pollen formed. Later he could transfer pollen from another pea plant to the target flower's female reproductive organ with a brush. This type of mating is referred to as a cross-fertilization, or simply a **cross.** Using this technique, Mendel could control the matings of his model organism.

What Traits Did Mendel Study? Mendel conducted his experiments on varieties of peas that differed in seven traits: seed shape, seed color, pod shape, pod color, flower color, flower and pod position, and stem length. Biologists refer to the observable traits of an individual, such as the shape of a pea seed or the eye color of a person, as its **phenotype** (literally, "show-type"). Phenotype is just one term in the rich vocabulary of genetics. You can review many of these terms in **TABLE 14.1**. In the first pea populations that Mendel studied, two distinct phenotypes existed for each of the seven traits.

Mendel began his work by obtaining individuals from what breeders called pure lines or true-breeding lines. A **pure line** consists of individuals that produce offspring identical to themselves when they are self-pollinated or crossed to another member of the pure-line population. For example, earlier breeders had developed pure lines for wrinkled seeds and round seeds. During two years of trial experiments, Mendel confirmed that individuals that germinated from his wrinkled seeds produced only wrinkled-seeded offspring when they were mated to themselves or to another pure-line individual that germinated from a wrinkled seed, and he confirmed that the same was true for round seeds.

Why is this important? Remember that Mendel wanted to find out how traits are transmitted from parents to offspring. Once he had confirmed that he was working with pure lines, he could compare the results of crosses within a pure line with crosses between individuals from different pure lines.

SUMMARY TABLE 14.1 **Vocabulary Used in Mendelian Genetics**

Term	Definition	Example or Comment
Gene	A hereditary factor that influences a particular trait.	This definition will become more precise in later chapters.
Allele	A particular form of a gene.	The two alleles in a diploid may be the same or different.
Genotype	A listing of the alleles in an individual.	In diploids, the genotype lists two alleles of each gene; in haploids, the genotype lists one allele of each gene.
Phenotype	An individual's observable traits.	Can be observed at levels from molecules to the whole organism; influenced, not dictated, by the genotype.
Homozygous	Having two of the same allele.	Refers to a particular gene.
Heterozygous	Having two different alleles.	Refers to a particular gene.
Dominant allele	An allele that produces its phenotype in heterozygous and homozygous form.	Dominance does not imply high frequency or high fitness.
Recessive allele	An allele that produces its phenotype only in homozygous form.	Phenotype "recedes" or disappears in heterozygous individuals.
Pure line	Individuals of the same phenotype that, when crossed, always produce offspring with the same phenotype.	Pure-line individuals are homozygous for the gene in question.
Hybrid	Offspring from crosses between homozygous parents with different genotypes.	Hybrids are heterozygous.
Reciprocal cross	A cross in which the phenotypes of the male and female are reversed compared with a prior cross.	If reciprocal crosses give identical results, the sex of the parent does not influence transmission of the trait.
Testcross	A cross between a homozygous recessive individual and an individual with the dominant phenotype but an unknown genotype.	Usually used to determine whether a parent with a dominant phenotype is homozygous or heterozygous.
X-linked	Referring to a gene located on the X chromosome.	X-linked genes and traits show different patterns of inheritance in males and females.
Y-linked	Referring to a gene located on the Y chromosome.	In humans, Y-linked genes determine male-specific development.
Autosomal	Referring to a gene located on any non-sex chromosome (an autosome) or a trait determined by an autosomal gene.	Mendel studied only autosomal genes and traits.

Suppose that Mendel arranged matings between a pure-line individual with round seeds and a pure-line individual with wrinkled seeds. He knew that one parent carried a hereditary determinant for round seeds, while the other carried a hereditary determinant for wrinkled seeds. But each offspring from this mating would contain both types of hereditary determinants. They would be **hybrids**—offspring from matings between true-breeding parents that differ in one or more traits.

Would these hybrid offspring have wrinkled seeds, round seeds, or a blended combination of wrinkled and round? What would the seed shape in subsequent generations be when hybrid individuals self-pollinated or were crossed with members of the pure lines?

14.2 Mendel's Experiments with a Single Trait

Mendel's first set of experiments consisted of crossing pure lines that differed in just one trait. This is an important research strategy in biological science: Start with a simple situation. Once you understand what's going on, you can consider more complex questions, such as, What happens in crosses between individuals that differ in two traits?

Mendel began his single-trait crosses by crossing individuals from round-seeded and wrinkled-seeded pure lines. The adults used in an initial experimental cross are the **parental generation**. Their progeny (that is, offspring) are the **F_1 generation**. F_1 stands for "first filial"; the Latin roots *filius* and *filia* mean "son" and "daughter," respectively. Subsequent generations are called the F_2 generation, F_3 generation, and so on.

The Monohybrid Cross

In his first set of crosses, Mendel took pollen from round-seeded plants and placed it on the female reproductive organs of plants from the wrinkled-seeded line. As **FIGURE 14.2a** shows, all the seeds produced by progeny from this cross were round.

This was a remarkable result, for two reasons:

1. The traits did not blend together to form an intermediate phenotype. Instead, the round-seeded form appeared intact. This result was in stark contrast to the predictions of the blending-inheritance hypothesis shown in **FIGURE 14.2b**.

2. The genetic determinant for wrinkled seeds seemed to have disappeared. Where did it go?

Dominant and Recessive Traits   To figure out what was going on, Mendel did something that turned out to be brilliant: He planted the F_1 seeds and allowed the individuals to self-pollinate when they matured.

Remember that he knew that each of these individuals had inherited a genetic determinant for round seeds and a genetic determinant for wrinkled seeds. A mating like this—between parents that each carry two different genetic determinants for the same trait—is called a **monohybrid cross.**

When he collected the seeds that were produced by many plants in the resulting F_2 generation, he observed that 5474 were round and 1850 were wrinkled (see Figure 14.2a). This observation was astonishing. The wrinkled seed shape had reappeared in the F_2 generation after disappearing completely in the F_1 generation. No one had observed the phenomenon before, simply because it had been customary for biologists to stop their breeding experiments with F_1 offspring.

Mendel invented some important terms to describe this result.

- He designated wrinkled shape as a **recessive** trait relative to the round-seed trait. This was an appropriate term because none of the F_1 individuals had wrinkled seeds—meaning the wrinkled-seed phenotype appeared to recede or temporarily become latent or hidden.

- He referred to round seeds as **dominant** to the wrinkled-seed trait. This term was apt because the round-seed phenotype appeared to dominate over the wrinkled-seed determinant when both were present.

It's important to note, though, that in genetics the term dominant has nothing to do with its everyday English usage as powerful

(a) Results of Mendel's single-trait (monohybrid) cross

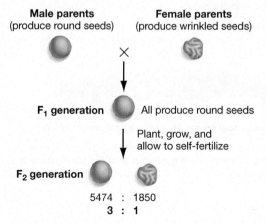

(b) Prediction of blending-inheritance hypothesis

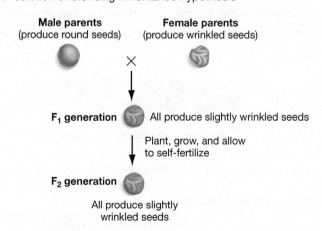

FIGURE 14.2 A Monohybrid Cross. The results of Mendel's crosses involving a single trait **(a)** contrasted strongly with the predictions of the blending-inheritance hypothesis **(b)**.

or superior. Subsequent research has shown that individuals with the dominant phenotype do not necessarily have higher fitness than individuals with the recessive phenotype. Nor are genetic determinants associated with a dominant phenotype necessarily more common than recessive ones. For example, a fatal illness—a type of brain degeneration called Huntington's disease—is caused by a rare, dominant genetic determinant. In genetics, the terms dominant and recessive identify *only* which phenotype is observed in individuals carrying two different genetic determinants for a given trait.

Mendel also noticed that the round and wrinkled seeds of the F_2 generation were present in a ratio of 2.96:1, or essentially 3:1. The 3:1 ratio means that for every four individuals, on average three had the dominant phenotype and one had the recessive phenotype. The results can also be stated in terms of frequencies or proportions: In this case, about ¾ of the F_2 seeds were round and ¼ were wrinkled.

A Reciprocal Cross Mendel wanted to test the hypothesis that it mattered which parent and gamete type had a particular genetic determinant—that gender influenced the inheritance of

seed shape. To do this, he performed a second set of crosses between two pure-breeding lines—this time with pollen taken from an individual from a pure line of wrinkled-seeded peas (**FIGURE 14.3**).

These experiments completed a **reciprocal cross**—a set of matings where the mother's phenotype in the initial cross is the father's phenotype in a subsequent cross, and the father's phenotype in the initial cross is the mother's phenotype in a subsequent cross.

In this case the results of the reciprocal crosses were identical: All the F_1 progeny had round seeds, just as in the initial cross. The reciprocal cross established that it does not matter whether the genetic determinants for seed shape are located in the male or female parent.

Do Mendel's Results Hold for Other Traits? Before he tried to interpret this pattern, it was important for Mendel to establish that the results were not restricted to inheritance of seed shape. So he repeated the experiments with each of the six other traits listed earlier. As **TABLE 14.2** shows, in each case, he obtained similar results:

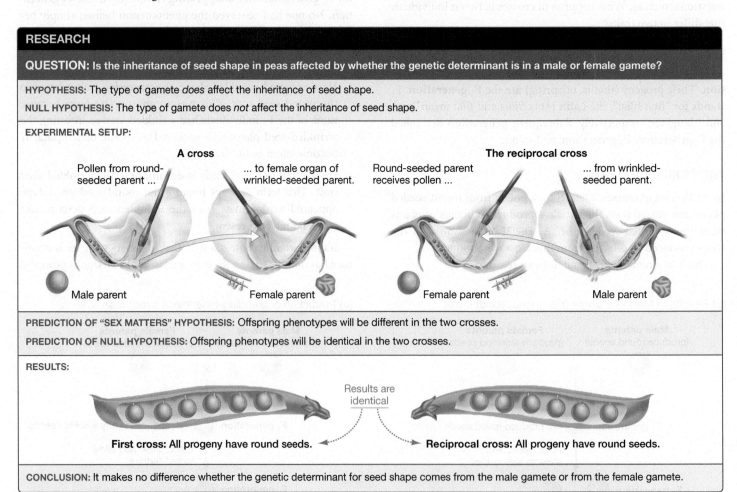

RESEARCH

QUESTION: Is the inheritance of seed shape in peas affected by whether the genetic determinant is in a male or female gamete?

HYPOTHESIS: The type of gamete *does* affect the inheritance of seed shape.

NULL HYPOTHESIS: The type of gamete does *not* affect the inheritance of seed shape.

EXPERIMENTAL SETUP:

A cross

Pollen from round-seeded parent ...

... to female organ of wrinkled-seeded parent.

Male parent   Female parent

The reciprocal cross

Round-seeded parent receives pollen ...

... from wrinkled-seeded parent.

Female parent   Male parent

PREDICTION OF "SEX MATTERS" HYPOTHESIS: Offspring phenotypes will be different in the two crosses.

PREDICTION OF NULL HYPOTHESIS: Offspring phenotypes will be identical in the two crosses.

RESULTS:

Results are identical

First cross: All progeny have round seeds.   **Reciprocal cross:** All progeny have round seeds.

CONCLUSION: It makes no difference whether the genetic determinant for seed shape comes from the male gamete or from the female gamete.

FIGURE 14.3 A Reciprocal Cross.

SOURCE: Mendel, G. 1866. Versuche über Pflanzen-hybriden. *Verhandlungen des naturforschenden Vereines in Brünn.* 4: 3–47. English translation available from ESP: Electronic Scholarly Publishing (www.esp.org).

✔**QUESTION** Some people think that experiments are failures if the hypothesis being tested is not supported. What does it mean to say that an experiment failed? Was this experiment a failure?

TABLE 14.2 F$_2$ Results from Mendel's Monohybrid Reciprocal Cross Experiments*

Trait	Dominant Phenotype	Recessive Phenotype	Ratio
Seed shape	5474 round	1850 wrinkled	2.96 : 1
Seed color	6022 yellow	2001 green	3.01 : 1
Pod shape	882 inflated	299 constricted	2.95 : 1
Pod color	428 green	152 yellow	2.82 : 1
Flower color	705 purple	224 white	3.15 : 1
Flower and pod position	651 axial	207 terminal	____ : __
Stem length	787 tall	____ dwarf	2.96 : 1

*Mendel pooled the results from the reciprocal crosses for each trait because the results were the same whether the dominant trait originated from the male parent or the female parent.
DATA: Mendel, G. 1866. *Verhandlungen des naturforschenden Vereines in Brünn.* 4: 3–47.

✔**EXERCISE** Two entries in the last rows are left blank. Fill in these entries with the correct values calculated from the available data.

- The F$_1$ progeny showed only the dominant trait and did not exhibit an intermediate phenotype.

- Reciprocal crosses produced the same results.

- The ratio of F$_2$ generation individuals with dominant and recessive phenotypes was about 3 to 1.

How could these patterns be explained? Mendel answered this question with a series of propositions about the nature and behavior of the hereditary determinants. These hypotheses are considered some of the most brilliant insights in the history of biological science.

Particulate Inheritance

Mendel's results were clearly inconsistent with either the hypothesis of blending inheritance or the hypothesis of acquired characters. To explain the patterns that he observed, Mendel proposed a competing hypothesis called **particulate inheritance.** He maintained that the hereditary determinants for traits do not blend together or become modified through use. In fact, hereditary determinants maintain their integrity from generation to generation. Instead of blending together, they act as discrete entities or particles.

Mendel's hypothesis was the only way to explain the observation that phenotypes disappeared in one generation and reappeared intact in the next. It also represented a fundamental break with ideas that had prevailed for hundreds of years.

Genes, Alleles, and Genotypes Today, geneticists use the word **gene** to indicate the hereditary determinant for a trait. For example, the hereditary factor that determines whether the seeds of garden peas are round or wrinkled is referred to as the gene for seed shape.

Mendel also proposed that each individual can have two versions of any gene. Today different versions of the same gene are called **alleles.** Different alleles are responsible for the variation in the traits that Mendel studied. In the case of the gene for seed shape, one allele of this gene is responsible for the round form of the seed while another allele is responsible for the wrinkled form.

The alleles found in a particular individual are called the **genotype.** An individual's genotype has a profound effect on the phenotype—the observable physical traits.

The hypothesis that pea plants have two copies of each gene—either two of the same allele or two different alleles—was important because it gave Mendel a framework for explaining dominance and recessiveness. He proposed that some alleles are dominant and others are recessive. Recall that dominance and recessiveness determine which phenotype appears in an individual when two different alleles are present. In garden peas, the allele for round seeds is dominant; the allele for wrinkled seeds is recessive. Therefore, so long as one allele for round seeds is present, seeds are round. When both alleles present are for wrinkled seeds (thus no allele for round seeds is present), seeds are wrinkled.

These hypotheses explain why the wrinkled-seed phenotype disappeared in the F$_1$ generation. But why did wrinkled seeds reappear in the F$_2$, and why was there a 3:1 ratio of round and wrinkled seeds in the F$_2$ generation?

The Principle of Segregation To explain the reappearance of the recessive phenotype and the characteristic 3:1 ratio of phenotypes in F$_2$ individuals, Mendel reasoned that the two members of each gene pair must segregate—that is, separate—into different gamete cells during the formation of eggs and sperm. As a result, each gamete contains one allele of each gene. This idea is called the **principle of segregation.**

To show how this principle works, Mendel used a letter to indicate the gene for a particular trait. For example, he used uppercase *R* to symbolize a dominant allele for seed shape and lowercase *r* to symbolize a recessive allele for seed shape. (Notice that the symbols for genes are always italicized.)

Using this notation, Mendel described the genotype of the individuals in the round-seed pure line as *RR* (having two of the dominant allele). The genotype of the wrinkled-seed pure line is *rr* (two of the recessive allele). Because *RR* and *rr* individuals have two copies of the same allele, they are said to be **homozygous** for the seed-shape gene (*homo* is the Greek root for "same," while *zygo* means "yoked"). Crosses of individuals from the same pure line always produce offspring with the same phenotype because they are homozygous—no other allele is present.

FIGURE 14.4a uses a diagram called a Punnett square to show what happened to these alleles when Mendel crossed the *RR* and *rr* pure lines. R. C. Punnett invented this straightforward technique for predicting the genotypes and phenotypes of different crosses years after Mendel published his work. According to Mendel's hypothesis, *RR* parents produce eggs and sperm that all carry the *R* allele, while *rr* parents produce gametes with the *r* allele only. When two gametes—one from each parent—come together at fertilization, they create offspring with the *Rr* genotype. Such individuals, with two different alleles for the same gene, are said to be **heterozygous** (*hetero* is the Greek root for "different"). Heterozygous individuals, or heterozygotes, show that the *R* allele is dominant because only the round phenotype is expressed even though the wrinkled allele is present.

Why do the two phenotypes appear in a 3:1 ratio in the F_2 generation? Mendel proposed that during gamete formation in the F_1 heterozygotes, the paired *Rr* alleles separate into different gamete cells. As a result, and as shown in the Punnett square of **FIGURE 14.4b**, half the gametes should carry the *R* allele and half should carry the *r* allele. A given sperm has an equal chance of fertilizing either an *R*-bearing egg or an *r*-bearing egg.

Predicting Offspring Genotypes and Phenotypes with a Punnett Square   The box you've just studied in Figure 14.4b is an example of a simple Punnett square. To produce a Punnett square, follow these steps:

1. Write each of the *unique* gamete genotypes produced by one parent in a horizontal row along the top of the diagram.

2. Write each of the *unique* gamete genotypes produced by the other parent in a vertical column down the left side of the diagram.

3. Create a table under the horizontal row of gametes and to the right of the vertical column of gametes.

4. Fill in the table with the entries for the parental gamete genotypes that are written at the top and at the left side. This step represents fertilization and produces the offspring genotypes.

(a) A cross between two **homozygotes**

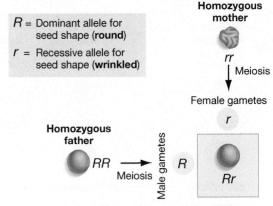

Offspring genotypes: All *Rr* (heterozygous)
Offspring phenotypes: All round seeds

(b) A cross between two **heterozygotes**

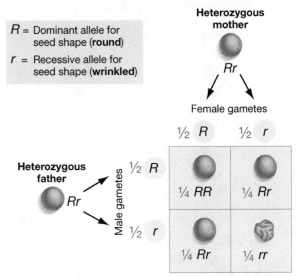

Offspring genotypes: ¼ *RR* : ½ *Rr* : ¼ *rr*
Offspring phenotypes: ¾ round : ¼ wrinkled

FIGURE 14.4 Mendel Analyzed the F_1 and F_2 Offspring of a Cross between Pure Lines. Notice that when you construct a Punnett square, you only need to list each unique type of gamete once at the head of a row or column. For example, even though the *RR* alleles segregate in the male parent of part (a), you have to list just one *R* gamete to represent the male's contribution, not two.

✔ **QUESTION** In constructing a Punnett square, does it matter whether the male or female gametes go on the left or across the top? Why or why not?

5. Tally the proportions or ratios of each offspring genotype and phenotype.

✔ If you understand these concepts, you should be able to state how filling in the top and side of the Punnett square is related to the principle of segregation and predict the phenotype and genotype ratios for a cross between *Rr* and *rr* peas.

Mendel's Model to Explain the Results of a Cross between Pure Lines*

Mendel's Claims	Comments
1. Peas have two copies of each gene and thus may have two different alleles of the gene.	This also turns out to be true for many other organisms.
2. Genes are particles of inheritance that do not blend together.	Genes maintain their integrity from generation to generation.
3. Each gamete contains one copy of each gene (one allele).	This is because of the principle of segregation—the members of each gene pair segregate during the formation of gametes.
4. Males and females contribute equally to the genotype of their offspring.	When gametes fuse, offspring acquire a total of two of each gene—one from each parent.
5. Some alleles are dominant to other alleles.	When a dominant and a recessive allele for the same gene are found in the same individual (a heterozygote), that individual has the dominant phenotype.

*Mendel did not use these modern terms. He expressed these ideas in different words.

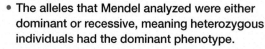

check your understanding

If you understand that . . .

- Mendel discovered that individuals have two alleles of each gene and that these alleles separate (segregate) into gametes. This is the principle of segregation.
- The alleles that Mendel analyzed were either dominant or recessive, meaning heterozygous individuals had the dominant phenotype.

✔ You should be able to . . .

Use the genetic problems at the end of this chapter to practice the following skills:

1. Starting with parents of known genotypes, create and analyze Punnett squares of crosses involving a single trait to predict the genotypes and phenotypes that will occur in their F$_1$ and F$_2$ offspring; then use the Punnett square to determine the expected frequency of each genotype and phenotype. (Do Problem 13 in Test Your Problem-Solving Skills.)

2. Given the outcome of a cross, infer the genotypes and phenotypes of the parents. (Do Problem 15 in Test Your Problem-Solving Skills.)

Answers are available in Appendix A.

As an example of the concluding step in analyzing a cross, the Punnett square in Figure 14.4b predicts that ¼ of the F$_2$ offspring will be *RR*, ½ will be *Rr*, and ¼ will be *rr*. Because the *R* allele is dominant to the *r* allele, ¾ of the offspring should be round-seeded (the sum of the *RR* and the *Rr* offspring) and ¼ should be wrinkled-seeded (the *rr* offspring). These results are what Mendel found in his experiments with peas. In the simplest and most elegant fashion possible, Mendel's interpretation explains the 3 : 1 ratio of round to wrinkled seeds observed in the F$_2$ offspring and the mysterious reappearance of the wrinkled seeds.

The term genetic model refers to a set of hypotheses that explains how a particular trait is inherited. **TABLE 14.3** summarizes Mendel's model for explaining the basic patterns in the transmission of traits from parents to offspring; these hypotheses are sometimes referred to as Mendel's rules. They represent a radical break from the ideas of blending inheritance and the inheritance of acquired characters that had dominated scientific thinking about heredity.

14.3 Mendel's Experiments with Two Traits

Working with one trait at a time allowed Mendel to establish that blending inheritance does not occur. It also allowed him to infer that each pea plant had two copies of each gene and to recognize the principle of segregation.

Mendel's next step extended these results. The important question now was whether the principle of segregation holds true if individuals differ with respect to two traits, instead of just one. Do different genes segregate together, or independently?

The Dihybrid Cross

Mendel crossed a pure-line parent that produced round, yellow seeds with a pure-line parent that produced wrinkled, green seeds. According to his model, the F$_1$ offspring of this cross should be heterozygous for both genes. A mating between two such individuals—both heterozygous for two traits—is called a **dihybrid cross**.

Mendel's earlier experiments had established that the allele for yellow seeds was dominant to the allele for green seeds; these alleles were designated *Y* for yellow and *y* for green. As **FIGURE 14.5** (see page 264) indicates, two distinct possibilities existed for how the alleles of these two different genes—the gene for seed shape and the gene for seed color—would be transmitted to offspring.

- The first possibility was that the allele for seed shape and the allele for seed color originally present in each parent would separate from each other and be transmitted independently. This hypothesis is called independent assortment because the two alleles would be sorted into gametes independently of each other (Figure 14.5a).

- The second possibility was that the allele for seed shape and the allele for seed color originally present in each parent

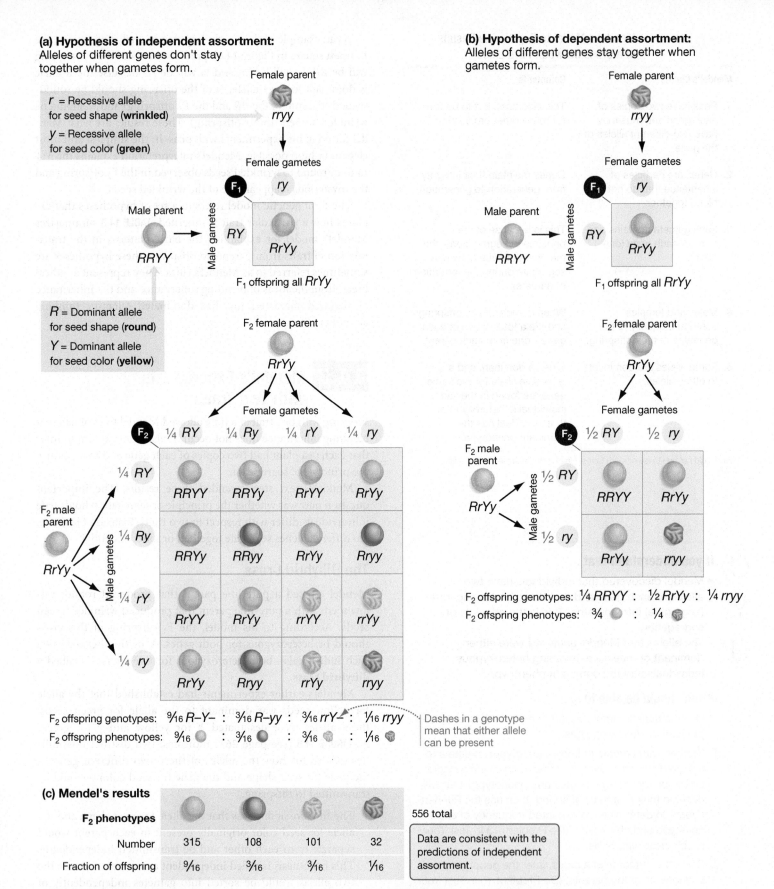

(a) Hypothesis of independent assortment:
Alleles of different genes don't stay together when gametes form.

r = Recessive allele for seed shape (**wrinkled**)

y = Recessive allele for seed color (**green**)

R = Dominant allele for seed shape (**round**)

Y = Dominant allele for seed color (**yellow**)

Female parent
rryy

Female gametes

F_1 *ry*

Male parent
RRYY

Male gametes   *RY*

RrYy

F_1 offspring all *RrYy*

F_2 female parent
RrYy

Female gametes
¼ *RY*   ¼ *Ry*   ¼ *rY*   ¼ *ry*

F_2 male parent
RrYy

Male gametes

¼ *RY* — *RRYY* — *RRYy* — *RrYY* — *RrYy*

¼ *Ry* — *RRYy* — *RRyy* — *RrYy* — *Rryy*

¼ *rY* — *RrYY* — *RrYy* — *rrYY* — *rrYy*

¼ *ry* — *RrYy* — *Rryy* — *rrYy* — *rryy*

F_2 offspring genotypes: ⁹⁄₁₆ *R–Y–* : ³⁄₁₆ *R–yy* : ³⁄₁₆ *rrY–* : ¹⁄₁₆ *rryy*

F_2 offspring phenotypes: ⁹⁄₁₆ : ³⁄₁₆ : ³⁄₁₆ : ¹⁄₁₆

Dashes in a genotype mean that either allele can be present

(b) Hypothesis of dependent assortment:
Alleles of different genes stay together when gametes form.

Female parent
rryy

Female gametes

F_1 *ry*

Male parent
RRYY

Male gametes   *RY*

RrYy

F_1 offspring all *RrYy*

F_2 female parent
RrYy

Female gametes
½ *RY*   ½ *ry*

F_2 male parent
RrYy

Male gametes

½ *RY* — *RRYY* — *RrYy*

½ *ry* — *RrYy* — *rryy*

F_2 offspring genotypes: ¼ *RRYY* : ½ *RrYy* : ¼ *rryy*

F_2 offspring phenotypes: ¾ : ¼

(c) Mendel's results

F_2 phenotypes					556 total
Number	315	108	101	32	
Fraction of offspring	⁹⁄₁₆	³⁄₁₆	³⁄₁₆	¹⁄₁₆	

Data are consistent with the predictions of independent assortment.

FIGURE 14.5 Mendel Analyzed the F_1 and F_2 Offspring of a Cross between Pure Lines for Two Traits. Each of two hypotheses predicted a different pattern for the outcome when alleles of different genes are transmitted to offspring: **(a)** The alleles could be sorted into gametes independently of each other, or **(b)** particular alleles could always be transmitted together. **(c)** Mendel's results supported independent assortment.

would be transmitted to gametes together. This hypothesis can be called dependent assortment because the transmission of one allele would depend on the transmission of another (Figure 14.5b).

As Figure 14.5 shows, the F_1 offspring of Mendel's mating are expected to have the dominant round and yellow phenotypes whether the different genes are transmitted together or independently. When Mendel did the cross and observed the F_1 individuals, this is exactly what he found. All the F_1 offspring had round, yellow seeds.

The two hypotheses make radically different predictions, however, about what will be observed when the F_1 individuals are allowed to self-fertilize and produce an F_2 generation. If the alleles of different genes assort independently to form gametes, then each heterozygous parent should produce four different gamete genotypes, as shown in Figure 14.5a. A 4-row-by-4-column Punnett square results, and it predicts that there should be 9 different offspring genotypes and 4 phenotypes. Further, the yellow-round, green-round, yellow-wrinkled, and green-wrinkled phenotypes should be present in frequencies of $^9/_{16}$, $^3/_{16}$, $^3/_{16}$, and $^1/_{16}$, respectively. This is a ratio of $9:3:3:1$.

On the other hand, if the alleles from each parent stay together, then the prediction is for only three possible offspring genotypes and a $3:1$ ratio of two phenotypes—yellow-round or green-wrinkled—in the F_2, as Figure 14.5b shows.

When Mendel examined the phenotypes of the F_2 offspring, he found that they conformed to the predictions of the hypothesis of independent assortment. Four phenotypes were present in proportions that closely approximated the predicted ratio of $9:3:3:1$ (Figure 14.5c). On the basis of these data, Mendel accepted the hypothesis that alleles of different genes are transmitted independently of one another. This result became known as the **principle of independent assortment**.

✔ If you understand the principle of independent assortment, it should make sense to you that an individual with the genotype *AaBb* produces gametes with the genotypes *AB*, *Ab*, *aB*, and *ab*. You should be able to predict the genotypes of the gametes produced by individuals with the genotypes *AABb*, *PpRr*, and *AaPpRr*.

Using a Testcross to Confirm Predictions

Mendel did experiments with combinations of traits other than seed shape and color and obtained results similar to those in Figure 14.5c. Each paired set of traits produced a $9:3:3:1$ ratio of progeny phenotypes in the F_2 generation. He even did a limited set of crosses examining three traits at a time. Although all these data were consistent with the principle of independent assortment, his most powerful support for the hypothesis came from a different type of experiment.

In designing this study, Mendel's goal was to test the prediction that an *RrYy* plant produces four different types of gametes in equal proportions. To accomplish this, Mendel invented a technique called a testcross. A **testcross** uses a parent that

contributes only recessive alleles to its offspring and helps to determine the unknown genotype of the second parent.

Testcrosses are useful because the genetic contribution of the homozygous recessive parent is known. As a result, a testcross allows experimenters to test the genetic contribution of the other parent. If the other parent has the dominant phenotype but an unknown genotype, the results of the testcross allow researchers to infer whether that parent is homozygous or heterozygous for the dominant allele.

In this case, Mendel performed a cross between a parent that was homozygous for the recessive green and wrinkled phenotypes (*rryy*) and a parent that had an unknown genotype but was known from its yellow- and round-seeded phenotype to possess the dominant *R* and *Y* alleles. Two (of four) possible genotypes for this yellow- and round-seeded parent are *RrYy* and *RRYY*. The types and proportions of offspring that could result from a testcross involving *RrYy* or *RRYY* pea plants can be predicted with the Punnett square shown in **FIGURE 14.6** (see page 266). If the principle of independent assortment is valid, the testcross should produce four types of offspring in equal proportions if the tested parent is *RrYy*, and only one type of offspring if the tested parent is *RRYY*.

What were the actual proportions observed? Mendel did a testcross using the F_1 offspring of a pure line yellow-, round-seeded parent and a green-, wrinkled-seeded parent. These F_1 offspring were expected to have an *RrYy* genotype as shown in Figure 14.5a. When he examined the seeds produced by the testcross, Mendel found that among the 110 progeny, 31 were round

If you understand that . . .
- Mendel found that alleles of different genes are transmitted to gametes independently of one another. This is the principle of independent assortment.
- The genotype of a strain with a dominant phenotype can be revealed in testcrosses between the dominant strain and a homozygous recessive strain.

✔ **You should be able to . . .**

Use the genetics problems at the end of this chapter to practice the following skills:

1. Starting with parents of known genotypes for two different traits, create and analyze Punnett squares to predict the genotypes and phenotypes that will occur in their F_1 and F_2 offspring and then calculate the expected frequency of each genotype and phenotype. (Do Problem 14 in Test Your Problem-Solving Skills.)

2. Given the outcome of a cross, infer the genotypes and phenotypes of the parents. (Do Problem 16 in Test Your Problem-Solving Skills.)

Answers are available in Appendix A.

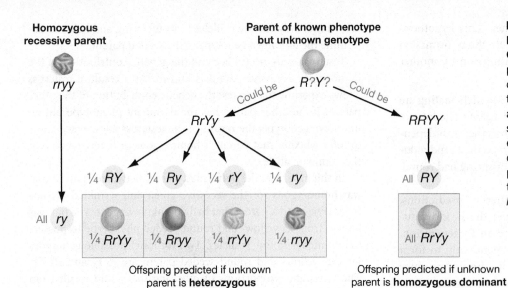

Homozygous
recessive parent

rryy

Parent of known phenotype
but unknown genotype

R?Y?

Could be   Could be

RrYy   *RRYY*

¼ *RY*   ¼ *Ry*   ¼ *rY*   ¼ *ry*   All *RY*

All *ry*

¼ *RrYy*   ¼ *Rryy*   ¼ *rrYy*   ¼ *rryy*   All *RrYy*

Offspring predicted if unknown
parent is **heterozygous**
at both genes

Offspring predicted if unknown
parent is **homozygous dominant**
at both genes

FIGURE 14.6 The Predictions Made by the Principle of Independent Assortment Can Be Evaluated in a Testcross. If the principle of independent assortment is correct, and *RrYy* parents produce four types of gametes in equal proportions, then a mating between *RrYy* and *rryy* parents should produce four types of offspring in equal proportions, as shown on the left. Test crosses can also reveal the genotype of a parent with dominant phenotypes, as seen in the example of different results obtained from *RrYy* and *RRYY* parental genotypes.

and yellow, 26 were round and green, 27 were wrinkled and yellow, and 26 were wrinkled and green. This is almost exactly ¼ of each type, which matched the predicted proportions for offspring of an *RrYy* parent. The testcross had confirmed the principle of independent assortment.

Mendel's work provided a powerful conceptual framework for thinking about transmission genetics—the patterns that occur as alleles pass from one generation to the next. This framework was based on (1) the segregation of discrete, paired genes into separate gametes, and (2) the independent assortment of genes that affect different traits.

The experiments you've just reviewed were brilliant in design, execution, and interpretation. Unfortunately, they were ignored for 34 years.

14.4 The Chromosome Theory of Inheritance

Historians of science debate why Mendel's work was overlooked for so long. It is probably true that his use of ratios and proportions were difficult for biologists of that time to understand and absorb. It may also be true that the theory of blending inheritance was so well entrenched that his results were dismissed as peculiar or unbelievable.

Whatever the reason, Mendel's work was not appreciated until 1900, when three biologists, working with a variety of plants and animals, independently "discovered" Mendel's work and reached the same main conclusions.

The rediscovery of Mendel's work more than three decades after its publication ignited the young field of genetics. Mendel's experiments had established the basic patterns of inheritance, but what process is responsible for these patterns? Two biologists, working independently, came up with the answer. Walter Sutton and Theodor Boveri each realized that meiosis could account for

Mendel's rules. When this hypothesis was published in 1902, research in genetics exploded.

Meiosis Explains Mendel's Principles

What Sutton and Boveri grasped is that meiosis explains the principle of segregation and the principle of independent assortment. The cell at the top of **FIGURE 14.7** illustrates Sutton and Boveri's central insight: Mendel's hereditary determinants, or genes, are located on chromosomes. In this example, the gene for seed shape is shown at a particular position along a certain chromosome. This location is known as a **locus** ("place"; plural, **loci**).

The paternal and maternal chromosomes shown in Figure 14.7 happen to possess different alleles at the seed shape gene locus: One allele specifies round seeds (*R*) and the other specifies wrinkled seeds (*r*).

The subsequent steps in Figure 14.7 show how these alleles segregate into different daughter cells during meiosis I, when homologous chromosomes separate. The physical separation of alleles during anaphase of meiosis I is responsible for Mendel's principle of segregation.

FIGURE 14.8 follows the segregation of two different gene pairs—in this case, for seed shape and seed color—as meiosis proceeds. If the alleles for different genes are located on different chromosomes, they assort independently of one another at meiosis I. This is the physical basis of Mendel's principle of independent assortment. Over many meiotic divisions, four types of gametes will be produced in equal proportions.

Sutton and Boveri formalized these observations in the **chromosome theory of inheritance.** Like other theories in biology, the chromosome theory describes a predictable pattern—a set of observations about the natural world—and a process that explains the pattern. The chromosome theory states that Mendel's rules can be explained by the independent alignment and separation of homologous chromosomes at meiosis I.

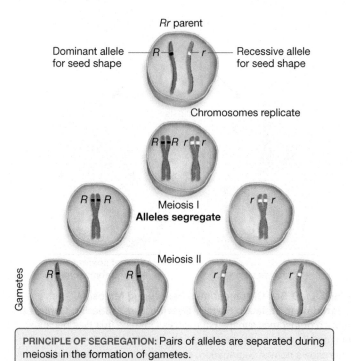

Rr parent

Dominant allele for seed shape — R   r — Recessive allele for seed shape

Chromosomes replicate

Meiosis I
Alleles segregate

Meiosis II

Gametes

PRINCIPLE OF SEGREGATION: Pairs of alleles are separated during meiosis in the formation of gametes.

FIGURE 14.7 Meiosis Explains the Principle of Segregation. The two members of a parent's gene pair segregate into different gametes because homologous chromosomes separate during meiosis I.

When Sutton and Boveri published their ideas, however, the hypothesis that genes are located on chromosomes was untested. What experiments confirmed that chromosomes contain genes?

Testing the Chromosome Theory

During the first decade of the twentieth century, an unassuming insect rose to prominence as a model organism for testing the chromosome theory of inheritance. This organism—the fruit fly *Drosophila melanogaster*—has been at the center of genetic studies ever since (see **BioSkills 13** in Appendix B).

Drosophila melanogaster has all the attributes of a useful model organism for studies in genetics: small size, ease of rearing in the lab, a short generation time (about 10 days), and abundant offspring (up to a few hundred per mating). The elaborate external anatomy of this insect also makes it possible to identify interesting phenotypic variation among individuals (**FIGURE 14.9a;** see page 268).

Drosophila was adopted as a model organism by Thomas Hunt Morgan and his students. But because *Drosophila* is not a domesticated species like the garden pea, common phenotypic variants such as Mendel's round and wrinkled seeds were not available to Morgan. Instead, he had access only to flies with the most common phenotype for each trait, phenotypes referred to as **wild type.** Consequently, an early goal of Morgan's research

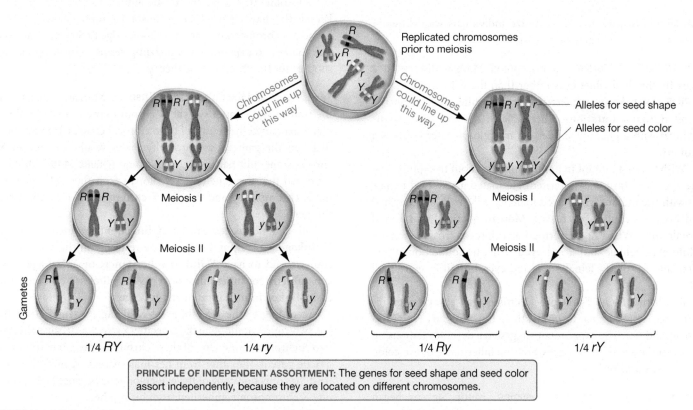

Replicated chromosomes prior to meiosis

Chromosomes could line up this way

Chromosomes could line up this way

Alleles for seed shape

Alleles for seed color

Meiosis I

Meiosis I

Meiosis II

Meiosis II

Gametes

1/4 *RY*   1/4 *ry*   1/4 *Ry*   1/4 *rY*

PRINCIPLE OF INDEPENDENT ASSORTMENT: The genes for seed shape and seed color assort independently, because they are located on different chromosomes.

FIGURE 14.8 Meiosis Is Responsible for the Principle of Independent Assortment. The genes for different traits assort independently because nonhomologous chromosomes assort independently during meiosis.

(a) The fruit fly *Drosophila melanogaster*

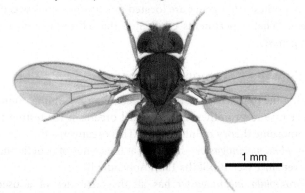

1 mm

(b) Eye color is a variable trait.

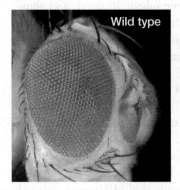

Wild type

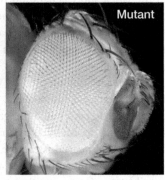

Mutant

FIGURE 14.9 The Fruit Fly *Drosophila melanogaster* Is an Important Model Organism in Genetics.

was simply to find and characterize individuals with different phenotypes to use in genetic studies.

The White-Eyed Mutant At one point, Morgan discovered a male fly that had white eyes rather than the wild-type red eyes (**FIGURE 14.9b**). Morgan inferred that the white-eyed phenotype resulted from a **mutation**—a heritable change in a gene. An individual with a phenotype due to a mutation is referred to as a **mutant.**

With his first mutant in hand, Morgan set out to explore how the eye-color trait was inherited. He mated a red-eyed female fly with the mutant white-eyed male fly. All the F$_1$ progeny had red eyes. By continued crosses, Morgan obtained white-eyed female flies. When he performed a reciprocal cross between a white-eyed female and a red-eyed male, he found something puzzling: All the F$_1$ females had red eyes, but all F$_1$ males had white eyes.

Recall that Mendel's reciprocal crosses had always given results that were similar to each other. But Morgan's reciprocal crosses did not. The experiment suggested a definite relationship between the sex of the progeny and the inheritance of eye color. What was going on?

The Discovery of Sex Chromosomes Nettie Stevens began studying the karyotypes of insects about the time that Morgan began his work with *Drosophila*. First, in the beetle *Tenebrio*

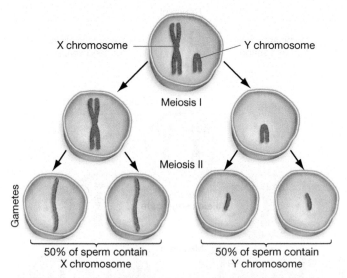

X chromosome

Y chromosome

Meiosis I

Meiosis II

Gametes

50% of sperm contain X chromosome

50% of sperm contain Y chromosome

FIGURE 14.10 Sex Chromosomes Pair during Meiosis I, Then Segregate in Males to Form X-Bearing and Y-Bearing Gametes. Sex chromosomes synapse at meiosis I in male fruit flies because of a small, gene-free region shared by the X and Y chromosomes. This allows normal segregation, so half the sperm cells bear an X chromosome and half have a Y chromosome.

molitor, and later in other insects, including *Drosophila*, she noticed a striking difference in the chromosome complements of males and females.

Recall that Stevens and others discovered that there were sex chromosomes (the X and the Y) and autosomes (see Chapter 13). Female flies have a pair of X chromosomes and male flies have an X and a Y chromosome. Morgan's knowledge of Stevens' findings was the key to explaining his puzzling results and in providing support for the chromosome theory.

Sex Linkage and the Chromosome Theory Morgan realized that the transmission pattern of the X chromosome in males and females explained the results of his reciprocal crosses. He reasoned that half the gametes produced by males would contain an X chromosome and half a Y chromosome (**FIGURE 14.10**). Morgan proposed that the gene for eye color in fruit flies is located on the X chromosome and that the Y chromosome does not carry this gene.

This situation is described as **X-linked inheritance,** or simply **X-linkage.** Correspondingly, a gene residing on the Y chromosome is said to have **Y-linked inheritance,** or **Y-linkage.** The general term for inheritance of genes on either sex chromosome is **sex-linked inheritance,** or **sex-linkage.**

According to the hypothesis of X-linkage, a female fruit fly has two copies of the gene that specifies eye color because she has two X chromosomes. One of these chromosomes came from her female parent, the other from her male parent. A male, in contrast, has only one copy of the eye-color gene because he has only one X chromosome, inherited from his mother.

The Punnett squares in **FIGURE 14.11** show that Morgan's experimental results can be explained if the gene for eye color is located

(a) One half of reciprocal cross

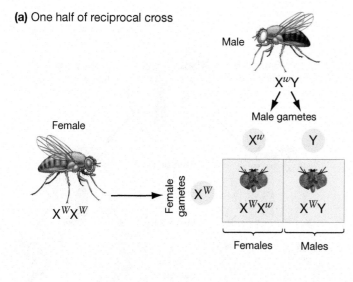

Male

X^wY

→ Male gametes

X^w Y

Female

X^WX^W

→ Female gametes X^W

X^WX^w	X^WY

Females   Males

(b) Other half of reciprocal cross

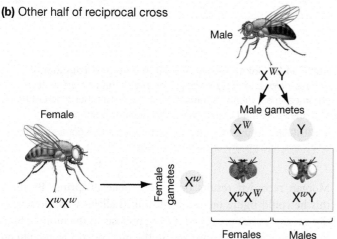

Male

X^WY

→ Male gametes

X^W Y

Female

X^wX^w

→ Female gametes X^w

X^wX^W	X^wY

Females   Males

FIGURE 14.11 Reciprocal Crosses Confirm that Eye Color in Drosophila Is an X-Linked Trait. When Morgan crossed red-eyed females with white-eyed males **(a)** and then crossed white-eyed females with red-eyed males **(b)**, he observed strikingly different results.

on the X chromosome, and if the allele for red color is dominant to the allele for white color. In this figure, the allele for red eyes is denoted X^W while the allele for white eyes is denoted X^w. The Y chromosome present in males is simply designated by Y. Using this notation,[1] the genotypes used in the experiment are written as X^WX^W for red-eyed females; X^wY for white-eyed males; X^wX^w for white-eyed females; and X^WY for red-eyed males.

Notice how the symbol for *Drosophila* alleles represents the mutant phenotype. Instead of showing alleles for the eye color gene with an *R* for wild-type red eyes and an *r* for mutant white eyes, the alleles are shown with a *W* (red eyes) or a *w* (white eyes).

---

[1]Scientific papers on fruit fly genetics use a different notation. The wild-type allele is designated with a superscript ⊠ , and no X is used for X-linked traits. The red-eye allele, for example, is denoted $w^⊠$; the white-eye allele *w*. The notation used here is simplified and conforms to conventions used in human genetics.

By applying the principles of segregation and random fertilization, you should see that the results predicted by the hypothesis of X-linkage match the observed results.

When reciprocal crosses give different results, such as those illustrated in Figure 14.11, it is likely that the gene in question is located on a sex chromosome—it is sex-linked. Recall that non-sex chromosomes are called autosomes (see Chapter 13). Genes on non-sex chromosomes are said to show **autosomal inheritance.**

Morgan's discovery of X-linked inheritance carried an even more fundamental message. In *Drosophila*, the gene for white eye color is clearly correlated with inheritance of the X chromosome. This correlation was important evidence in support of the hypothesis that chromosomes contain genes. The discovery of X-linked inheritance convinced most biologists that the chromosome theory of inheritance was correct.

check your understanding

C Y U

If you understand that . . .

- Meiosis is the process responsible for Mendel's principle of segregation. It occurs because alleles on homologous chromosomes separate at anaphase of meiosis I.

- Meiosis is the process responsible for Mendel's principle of independent assortment. Alleles of different genes go to gametes independently because pairs of homologous chromosomes line up randomly at metaphase of meiosis I.

✔ **You should be able to . . .**

1. Draw the chromosomes involved in a cross between *Pp* and *Pp* peas, and use your diagram to explain the segregation of alleles.

2. Draw the chromosomes involved in a cross between *YyRr* and *YyRr* peas, and use your diagram to explain the independent assortment of alleles.

Answers are available in Appendix A.

14.5 Extending Mendel's Rules

Biologists point out that Mendel analyzed the simplest possible genetic system. The traits that he was studying were not sex-linked. Moreover, they were influenced by just two alleles of each gene, and each allele was completely dominant or recessive.

With this well-chosen model system, Mendel was able to discover the most fundamental rules of inheritance. Mendel probably would have failed, as so many others had done before him, had he been trying to analyze more complex patterns of inheritance.

Once Mendel's work was rediscovered, researchers began to analyze traits and alleles whose inheritance was more complicated.

If experimental crosses produced F_2 progeny that did not conform to the expected 3:1 or 9:3:3:1 ratios, researchers had a strong hint that something interesting was going on. The discovery of sex-linkage is a prominent example. How can other traits that don't appear to follow Mendel's rules contribute to a more complete understanding of heredity?

Linkage: What Happens When Genes Are Located on the Same Chromosome?

Once the chromosome theory had been tested and supported, biologists began to reevaluate Mendel's principle of independent assortment. It seemed unlikely that genes on the same chromosome would assort independently.

Linkage is the tendency of particular alleles of different genes to be inherited together. Linkage is seen when genes are on the same chromosome. Notice that the terms linkage and sex-linkage have different meanings. If genes are linked, it means that they are located on the same chromosome. If a gene is sex-linked, it means that it is located on a sex chromosome but says nothing about its location relative to other genes.

The first examples of linked genes were those on the X chromosome of fruit flies. After Morgan established that the *white-eye* gene was located on *Drosophila*'s X chromosome, he and colleagues established that one of the several genes that affects body color is also located on the X. Red eyes and gray body are the wild-type phenotypes; white eyes and a yellow body occur as rare mutant phenotypes. The alleles for red eyes (X^W) and gray body (X^Y) are dominant to the alleles for white eyes (X^w) and yellow body (X^y). (Be sure not to confuse the notation for the Y chromosome in males, Y, with the gray body allele, X^Y.)

Linked Genes Do Not Assort Independently Because linked genes are located on the same chromosome, it is logical to predict that they should always be transmitted together during gamete formation. Stated another way, linked genes should violate the principle of independent assortment.

Recall from Section 14.4 that genes on different chromosomes show independent assortment because different chromosomes assort independently during meiosis I. How will the X-linked body-color and eye-color genes be inherited? **FIGURE 14.12** shows a cell of a female fruit fly with one X chromosome carrying the white eye and gray body alleles, written X^{wY}, and the homologous X chromosome carrying the red eye and yellow body alleles, written X^{Wy}. This female would be expected to generate just two classes of gametes in equal numbers during meiosis, instead of the four classes that are predicted under the principle of independent assortment. Is this what actually occurs?

The Role of Crossing Over To determine whether linked traits always stay linked, Morgan performed crosses like the one described in the "Experimental Setup" section of **FIGURE 14.13**. In this case, $X^{wY}X^{Wy}$ females mated with $X^{wY}Y$ males.

The "Results" table in Figure 14.13 summarizes the phenotypes and genotypes observed in this experimental cross.

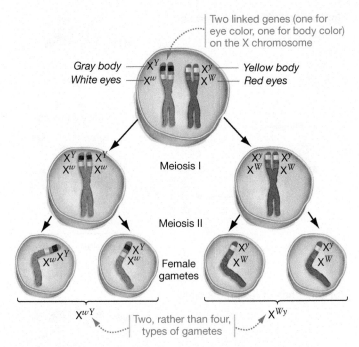

FIGURE 14.12 Linked Genes Are Often Inherited Together. If the eye-color and body-color genes were found on different chromosomes, then this female would generate four different types of gametes instead of just two types as shown here.

✔**EXERCISE** List the four genotypes that would be generated if the white-eye and yellow-body genes were not linked.

Morgan recorded results only from male offspring. By doing this he could figure out which X-linked alleles were present on the chromosomes produced during meiosis in the mother. Since there is a single X chromosome in the male offspring, the phenotype associated with any X-linked allele, dominant or recessive, is expressed:

- Most of these males carried an X chromosome with one of the two combinations of alleles found in the chromosomes of their mothers: X^{wY} or X^{Wy}.

- A small percentage of males had novel combinations of phenotypes and genotypes: X^{wy} and X^{WY}. Morgan referred to these individuals as **recombinant** because the combination of alleles on their X chromosome was different from the combinations of alleles present in their mother.

Morgan concluded that alleles on the same chromosome don't always stay together. To explain the recombinant phenotypes, Morgan proposed that gametes with new combinations of alleles were generated when crossing over occurred during prophase of meiosis I in the females.

Recall that crossing over involves a physical exchange of segments of non-sister chromatids between homologous chromosomes (see Chapter 13). Crossing over typically occurs at least once in every synapsed pair of homologous chromosomes, and usually multiple times. (Male fruit flies are an exception to this rule. For unknown reasons, no crossing over occurs in male fruit flies.)

QUESTION: Will genes undergo independent assortment if they are on the same chromosome?

LINKAGE HYPOTHESIS: Linked genes will violate the principle of independent assortment.

NULL HYPOTHESIS: Linked genes will adhere to the principle of independent assortment.

EXPERIMENTAL SETUP:

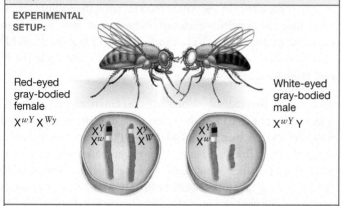

Red-eyed gray-bodied female $X^{wY}X^{Wy}$

White-eyed gray-bodied male $X^{wY}Y$

PREDICTION: Because these two genes are X-linked, male offspring will have only one copy of each gene, from their mother; the two possible male offspring genotypes are $X^{wY}Y$ and $X^{Wy}Y$

PREDICTION OF NULL HYPOTHESIS: Four male genotypes are possible ($X^{wY}Y : X^{Wy}Y : X^{wy}Y : X^{WY}Y$) and will occur with equal frequency.

RESULTS:

Male offspring

	Phenotype	Genotype	Number	
		$X^{wY}Y$	4292	Four male genotypes were observed (rather than two), but not the equal frequencies predicted by independent assortment
		$X^{Wy}Y$	4605	
Recombinant genotypes		$X^{wy}Y$	86	
		$X^{WY}Y$	44	

CONCLUSION: Neither hypothesis is fully supported. Independent assortment does not apply to linked genes—linked genes segregate together except when crossing over and genetic recombination have occurred.

FIGURE 14.13 Linked Genes Are Inherited Together Unless Recombination Occurs.

SOURCE: Morgan, T. H. 1911. An attempt to analyze the constitution of the chromosomes on the basis of sex-limited inheritance in *Drosophila. Journal of Experimental Zoology* 11: 365–414.

✔**QUESTION** Why didn't Morgan observe equal numbers of white-eyed, yellow-bodied males and red-eyed, gray-bodied males?

As **FIGURE 14.14** shows, a crossover between the eye-color and body-color genes in the $X^{wY}X^{Wy}$ females can explain the recombinant gametes. Male progeny produced from fertilization with these gametes are predicted to have either yellow bodies and white eyes or gray bodies and red eyes. This is what Morgan observed.

Notice, however, that the results of Figure 14.14 don't fit either the model of independent assortment or complete linkage. Independent assortment predicts a 1:1:1:1 ratio of all four

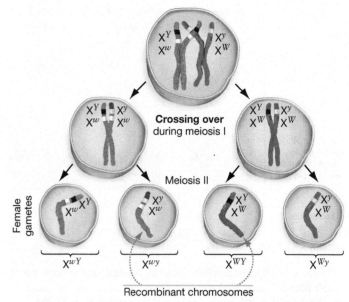

FIGURE 14.14 Genetic Recombination Results from Crossing Over. To explain the results in Figure 14.13, Morgan proposed that crossing over occurred between the body color (*y*) and eye color (*w*) genes in a small percentage of meiotic divisions in the female parent. The recombinant chromosomes that resulted would produce the recombinant phenotypes observed in the male offspring.

combinations of phenotypes, while complete linkage would give only the two phenotypes associated with the nonrecombinant or parental chromosomes. Instead, most flies have parental phenotypes and a smaller number have recombinant phenotypes.

As **Quantitative Methods 14.1** (see page 274) explains, the percentage of recombinant offspring that occur in crosses like the one diagrammed in Figure 14.14 can be used to estimate the relative distance between genes. The reasoning is that the farther genes are apart on the same chromosome, the more likely it is that a crossover will occur someplace between these genes. Data on the frequency of crossing over between many genes on the same chromosome can be used to create a **genetic map**—a diagram showing the relative positions of genes along a particular chromosome.

Knowing a gene's locus relative to others can be very useful. An important example is genes involved in human genetic diseases. Most of these genes have been identified on the basis of mapping their location relative to other known genes.

The take-home message of Morgan's experiments is simple: Linked genes are inherited together unless crossing over occurs between them. When crossing over takes place, genetic recombination occurs. Linkage is an important exception to Mendel's rules.

How Many Alleles Can a Gene Have?

Mendel worked with genes that each had two alleles. In most populations, however, it's not unusual to find dozens of alleles of a single gene. The existence of more than two alleles of the same gene is known as **multiple allelism.** When you consider that

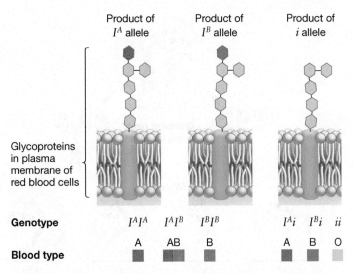

	Product of I^A allele	Product of I^B allele	Product of i allele

Glycoproteins in plasma membrane of red blood cells

Genotype	$I^A I^A$	$I^A I^B$	$I^B I^B$	$I^A i$	$I^B i$	ii
Blood type	A	AB	B	A	B	O

FIGURE 14.15 Phenotypes Produced by Alleles Responsible for ABO Blood Types. Alleles I^A and I^B produce a phenotype called AB when paired with each other in heterozygotes. Both I^A and I^B produce a dominant phenotype when paired with allele i. The different colored hexagons on the products of the I^A and I^B alleles represent related but distinct sugars.

genes are made of DNA sequences that can change over time, the idea of multiple alleles isn't surprising.

The ABO blood group types in humans are coded for by a gene with three common alleles. The gene is known as I, and it has I^A, I^B, and i alleles. As the number of alleles for a gene increases, the number of possible genotypes rises sharply. When more than two distinct phenotypes are present in a population owing to multiple allelism, the trait is **polymorphic** ("many-formed"). ABO blood type is a polymorphic trait.

Each I gene allele controls the production of a different polysaccharide attached to a glycoprotein (see Chapter 5) found in the plasma membrane of red blood cells. The I^A and I^B alleles code for different forms of an enzyme that adds a different sugar to the end of a core polysaccharide. The i allele codes for a nonfunctional form of this enzyme, so no sugar is added to the core polysaccharide. ABO blood group types are important in blood transfusions. Some mismatches of blood type between a donor and recipient are tolerated, but others can cause fatal reactions.

The type of polysaccharide associated with each allele is shown in **FIGURE 14.15** along with all possible genotypes and phenotypes. As you can see, there are six possible genotypes for the three alleles of the I gene. The I^A allele codes for the type A polysaccharide, and the I^B allele codes for the type B polysaccharide. What happens in a person with both alleles?

Are Alleles Always Dominant or Recessive?

The terms dominant and recessive describe which phenotype is observed when two different alleles of a gene occur in a heterozygous individual. In all traits that Mendel studied, only the phenotype associated with one allele—the "dominant" one—appeared in heterozygotes. However, not all combinations of alleles work this way.

Codominance Many alleles show a relationship that is called **codominance.** The type AB blood group shown in Figure 14.15 is an example of codominance. In this case, an AB heterozygote expresses both the A and the B polysaccharides together on the surface of red blood cells. This is the essence of codominance—the simultaneous expression of the phenotype associated with each allele in a heterozygote. An AB individual expresses both the A and the B phenotypes.

The three alleles of the ABO blood group system illustrate another interesting point—alleles of one gene can show more than one form of dominance. Notice in Figure 14.15 that the I^A and I^B alleles are both completely dominant to the i allele while the I^A and I^B alleles are codominant with each other.

Incomplete Dominance Complete dominance and codominance are not the end of the story. Consider the flowers called four-o'clocks, pictured in **FIGURE 14.16a.** Plant breeders have developed a pure line that has red flowers and a pure line that has white flowers. When individuals from these strains are mated, all their offspring are pink (**FIGURE 14.16b**). In Mendel's peas, crosses between dominant and recessive parents produced only offspring with the dominant phenotype. Why the difference?

Biologists answered this question by allowing the pink flowered F_1 plants to self-fertilize and examining the phenotypes of F_2 four-o'clocks. Of the F_2 plants, ¼ have red flowers, ½ have pink flowers, and ¼ have white flowers. This 1:2:1 ratio of phenotypes exactly matches the 1:2:1 ratio of genotypes that is produced when flower color is controlled by one gene with two alleles.

To convince yourself that this explanation is sound, study the genetic model shown in Figure 14.16b. According to the diagram, the pattern of inheritance of flower color genotypes in four-o'clocks and peas is identical, but the four-o'clock alleles show a different form of dominance known as **incomplete dominance.**

When incomplete dominance occurs, heterozygotes have a phenotype that is between the two different homozygous parents. In the case of four-o'clocks, neither red nor white alleles dominate. Instead, the heterozygous F_1 progeny show a phenotype in between the two parental strains.

By this point, it should be clear that the answer to the question of whether alleles are always dominant or recessive is a resounding no. Instead, there are three possible dominance relationships between different alleles: complete, incomplete, and codominance.

Does Each Gene Affect Just One Trait?

Mendel's results led him to hypothesize that one gene influences one trait. The gene for seed color in garden peas, for example, did not appear to affect other aspects of the individual's phenotype. In reality, however, many genes influence more than one trait.

A gene that influences many traits is said to be **pleiotropic** ("more-turning"). For example, mutations in one gene, *FBN1*, cause Marfan syndrome in humans. In this case the mutant

(a) Flower color is variable in four-o'clocks.

(b) Incomplete dominance in flower color

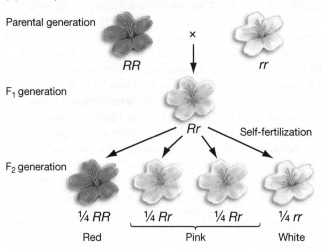

Parental generation

RR   ×   rr

F₁ generation

Rr   Self-fertilization

F₂ generation

¼ RR   ¼ Rr   ¼ Rr   ¼ rr
Red   Pink   White

FIGURE 14.16 When Incomplete Dominance Occurs, Heterozygotes Have Intermediate Phenotypes. The cross in part (b) is explained by hypothesizing that a single gene influences flower color and that alleles R and r exhibit incomplete dominance.

FBN1 allele is dominant to the wild-type allele. What is the phenotype of an individual with a mutant *FBN1* allele?

People with a mutant *FBN1* allele are tall, have disproportionately long limbs and fingers and an abnormally shaped chest, and often have severe heart problems. Therefore, the gene associated with Marfan syndrome influences many traits and is pleiotropic. On the basis of this set of phenotypes, many medical scientists believe Abraham Lincoln had Marfan syndrome.

Is There More to Phenotype than Genotype?

After analyzing the results of Mendel's experiments, it would be tempting to conclude that R alleles dictate that seeds are round and T alleles dictate that individual plants are tall—that there is a strict correspondence between alleles and phenotypes.

It's important to recognize, though, that when Mendel analyzed height in his experiments, he ensured that each plant received a similar amount of sunlight and grew in similar soil. This was critical because even individuals with alleles for tallness will be stunted if they are deprived of nutrients, sunlight, or water—so much so that they look similar to individuals with alleles for dwarfing. Mendel also worked with pure lines that had been inbred for many generations. This breeding method reduces the genetic variation in each line.

For Mendel to analyze the hereditary determinants of height, he had to control the environmental determinants of height. Let's consider how the environment and alleles at other gene loci affect phenotype.

The Environment Affects Phenotypes The phenotypes produced by most genes are strongly affected by the individual's environment. Consequently, an individual's phenotype is often as much a product of the environment as it is a product of the genotype. Environmental influences include temperature, sunlight, nutrient availability, competition, and even a mother's hormone levels during development of an embryo. To capture this point, biologists refer to the combined effect of genes and environment as gene-by-environment interaction.

Gene-by-environment interactions have a profound effect on how physicians treat people with the genetic disease phenylketonuria (PKU). These individuals are homozygous for a recessive allele of an enzyme-coding gene. The enzyme helps convert the amino acid phenylalanine to the amino acid tyrosine. In PKU, this enzyme is absent and, as a result, phenylalanine and a related molecule, phenylpyruvic acid, accumulate. These compounds interfere with the development of the nervous system and produce severe mental retardation.

But are people without the ability to metabolize phenylalanine genetically fated to mental retardation?

In many countries, newborns are routinely tested for the defect. If identified at birth, individuals with PKU can be placed on a low-phenylalanine diet. The change in environment—reduced phenylalanine in the diet—has a dramatic influence on phenotype. Treated individuals develop normally. PKU is a genetic disease, but by controlling the environment, it is neither inevitable nor invariant.

Interactions Between Genes Affect Phenotypes In Mendel's pea plants, there was a one-to-one correspondence between genes and traits. The pea seeds he analyzed were round or wrinkled regardless of the types of alleles present at other loci. Only one gene influenced each trait.

In many cases, however, different genes work together to control a single trait. Consider a classic experiment published in 1905 on comb shape in chickens. William Bateson and R. C. Punnett crossed parents from pure lines with comb shapes called rose and pea and found that the F₁ offspring had a new phenotype, called walnut combs, a new phenotype not seen in either parent. When these individuals bred, their offspring had walnut, rose,

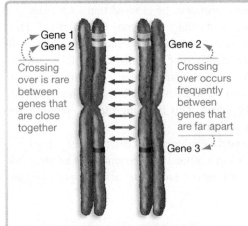

FIGURE 14.17 The Physical Distance between Genes Determines the Frequency of Crossing Over. The arrows show that crossing over is possible at any point between the genes, but the chance of a crossover between a pair of genes increases when the distance between the genes is large.

Gene 1
Gene 2
Crossing over is rare between genes that are close together

Gene 2
Crossing over occurs frequently between genes that are far apart
Gene 3

In experiments like the one diagrammed in Figure 14.13, researchers calculate the recombination frequency as the number of offspring with recombinant phenotypes divided by the total number of offspring. With crosses involving the X-linked traits of white eyes and yellow bodies, 1.4 percent of

offspring have recombinant phenotypes and genotypes.

But in crosses with different pairs of X-linked traits, the fraction of recombinant offspring varies, and this variation provides information on the relative distance separating linked genes. For example, in crosses of fruit flies with X-linked genes for white eyes and another mutant phenotype called singed bristles, recombinant phenotypes are seen 19.6 percent of the time.

To explain these observations, Alfred Sturtevant, an undergraduate student working with Morgan, proposed that the physical distance between genes determines how frequently crossing over occurs between them. His idea was that crossing over occurs at random and can take place at any location along a chromosome. The shorter the distance between a pair of genes, the lower the probability that crossing over will take place between them (**FIGURE 14.17**). Using this reasoning, he set out to create a genetic map.

To define the unit of distance on his genetic map, Sturtevant used the percentage of offspring that have recombinant phenotypes with respect to two genes. One map unit (later called 1 centiMorgan [cM]) is the physical distance that produces 1 percent recombinant offspring.

The eye-color and bristle-shape genes of fruit flies are 19.6 cM apart on the X chromosome, because recombination between these genes results in 19.6 percent recombinant offspring, on average. The genes for yellow body and white eye color, in contrast, are just 1.4 cM apart.

Where is the *yellow-body* gene relative to the *singed-bristles* gene? Twenty-one percent of the offspring were recombinant for these traits, meaning that the *yellow-body* and *singed-bristles* genes are 21.0 cM apart. Sturtevant inferred that the gene for white eyes must be located *between* the genes for yellow body and singed bristles, as shown in **FIGURE 14.18a**.

Mapping genes relative to one another is like fitting pieces into a puzzle: Placing *white* between *yellow* and *singed bristles* is the only way to make the distances between each pair sum correctly. The key observation is that 21.0 cM—the distance between *yellow* and *singed bristles*—is equal to 1.4 cM ⊠ 19.6 cM, or the sum of the distances between *yellow* and *white* and *white* and *singed bristles*.

FIGURE 14.18b provides a partial genetic map of the X chromosome in *Drosophila melanogaster,* along with the data used to establish the map positions. Using this logic and similar data, Sturtevant assembled the first genetic map.

(a) Mapping genetic distance

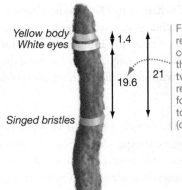

Yellow body
White eyes
1.4
19.6
21
Singed bristles

Frequency of recombinant offspring correlates directly with the distance between two genes; 19.6% recombinant offspring, for example, translates to 19.6 map units (centiMorgans, cM).

(b) Constructing a genetic map

% Frequency of crossing over between some genes on the X chromosome of fruit ⊠ies		
	Miniature Wings	Ruby Eyes
Yellow body	36.1	7.5
White eyes	34.7	6.1
Singed bristles	15.1	13.5
Miniature wings	—	28.6

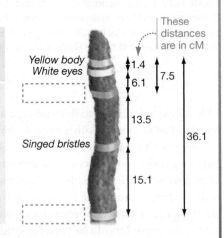

These distances are in cM

Yellow body
White eyes
1.4
6.1
7.5
13.5
Singed bristles
36.1
15.1

FIGURE 14.18 The Locations of Genes Can Be Mapped by Analyzing the Frequency of Recombination. (a) The *yellow body* gene is on the end of the fruit fly X chromosome. To explain the recombination frequencies observed in experimental crosses, the *yellow body, white eyes,* and *singed bristles* genes must be in the locations shown here. **(b)** A partial genetic map of the X chromosome in fruit flies.

✔**EXERCISE** In part (b), label the orange and blue genes. (Which is *ruby* and which is *miniature wings?*)

pea, and a fourth phenotype called single combs in a 9:3:3:1 ratio (**FIGURE 14.19a**).

The genetic model in **FIGURE 14.19b** shows how the interaction between two different genes that control one trait (comb shape) can account for the results. If comb morphology results from interactions between two genes (symbolized *R* and *P*), if a dominant and a recessive allele exist for each gene, and if the four comb phenotypes are associated with the genotypes indicated at the bottom of the figure, then a cross between *RRpp* and *rrPP* parents would give the results that Bateson and Punnett observed.

When gene-by-gene interactions occur, one trait is influenced by the alleles of two or more different genes. If a chicken has an *R* allele, its phenotype depends on the allele present at the *P* gene.

Gene-by-gene interaction is very common and has important implications in human genetics. Imagine that two people have the same genotype at one locus that increases risk for a heart disease. If there is gene-by-gene interaction, then the risk of developing heart disease also depends on the genotype at other loci. Even if they experience identical environments, these two people may have very different overall risks from genetic factors alone.

Can Mendel's Principles Explain Traits That Don't Fall into Distinct Categories?

Mendel worked with **discrete traits**—traits that are clearly different from each other. In garden peas, seed color is either yellow or green—no intermediate phenotypes exist. But many traits in peas and other organisms don't fall into discrete categories. In humans, for example, height, weight, and skin color vary continuously. People are not limited to being either 160 cm tall or 180 cm tall—countless other heights are possible.

For height and many other characteristics, individuals differ by degree. These types of continuously varying traits that don't fall into discrete categories are called **quantitative traits.** Like discrete traits, quantitative traits are greatly influenced by the environment. The effects of nutrition on human height, intelligence, and disease resistance, for example, have been well documented.

Many quantitative traits share a common characteristic: When the frequencies of different trait values observed in a population are plotted on a histogram, or frequency distribution (see **BioSkills 3** in Appendix B), they often form a bell-shaped curve, or normal distribution (**FIGURE 14.20**).

In 1909 Herman Nilsson-Ehle had an important insight: If many genes each contribute a small amount to the value of a quantitative trait, then a normal distribution results for the population as a whole.

(a) Crosses between chickens with different comb phenotypes give odd results.

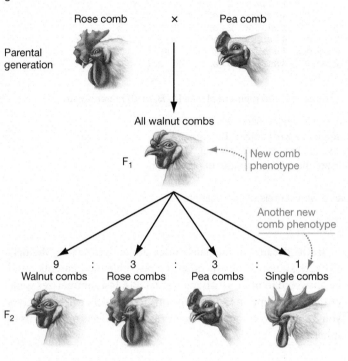

(b) A genetic model based on gene-by-gene interactions can explain the results.

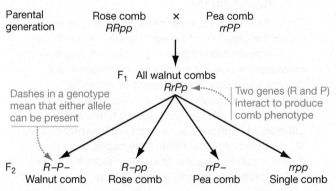

FIGURE 14.19 Genes at Different Loci Can Interact to Influence a Trait. (a) This cross is notable because new phenotypes show up in the F$_1$ and the F$_2$ generation. **(b)** To explain the results, researchers hypothesized that comb shape depends on two genes that interact. The phenotype associated with any one allele of one gene depends on the alleles at a second gene.

✔**EXERCISE** What is different about the 9:3:3:1 ratio in the F$_2$ of this cross compared with the ratio observed in a standard dihybrid cross?

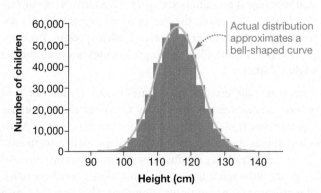

FIGURE 14.20 Quantitative Traits Have a Normal Distribution. A histogram showing the heights of first-grade schoolchildren in Guatemala in 2001.

DATA: Pan American Health Organization/WHO. 2004. *Epidemiological Bulletin* 25: 9-13, Graph 1.

(a) Wheat kernel color is a quantitative trait.

(b) Hypothesis to explain inheritance of kernel color

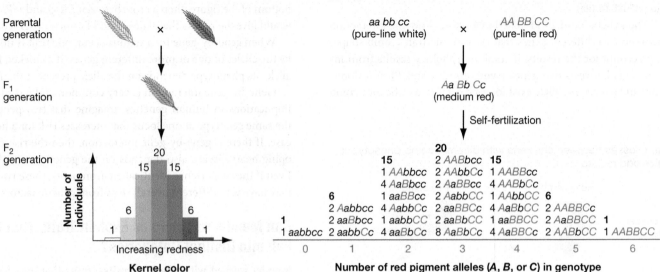

FIGURE 14.21 Quantitative Traits Result from the Action of Many Genes. (a) When wheat plants with white kernels were crossed with wheat plants with red kernels, the F₂ offspring showed a range of kernel colors. The frequency of these phenotypes approximates a normal distribution. **(b)** This model can explain the results of part (a). The bold numbers above each genotype match the numbers shown in part (a) and indicate the relative number of plants with each phenotype.

✔**QUESTION** Why are there fewer very dark or very light wheat kernels compared with kernels of intermediate coloration?

Nilsson-Ehle established this finding using strains of wheat that differed in kernel color. **FIGURE 14.21a** includes a histogram showing the distribution of F₂ phenotypes from a cross he performed between pure lines of white wheat and dark-red wheat. Notice that the frequency of colors in F₂ progeny approximates a bell-shaped curve. To explain these results, Nilsson-Ehle proposed the hypotheses illustrated in **FIGURE 14.21b**:

- The parental strains differ with respect to three genes that control kernel color: *AABBCC* produces dark-red kernels, and *aabbcc* produces white kernels.

- The three genes assort independently.

- The *a*, *b*, and *c* alleles do not contribute to pigment production, but the *A*, *B*, and *C* alleles contribute to pigment production in an equal and additive way. This is a form of incomplete dominance. As a result, the degree of red pigmentation is determined by the number of *A*, *B*, or *C* alleles present. Each uppercase (dominant) allele that is present makes a wheat kernel slightly darker red.

Later work supported Nilsson-Ehle's model. He did not have to propose any new genetic principles to explain the inheritance of a quantitative trait. All that was needed was extension of Mendel's hypotheses about segregation and independent assortment.

Quantitative traits are produced by the independent actions of many genes, although it is now clear that some genes have much greater effects on the trait in question than other genes do. As a result, the transmission of quantitative traits is said to result from polygenic ("many-genes") inheritance. In **polygenic inheritance**, each gene adds a small amount to the value of the phenotype.

In the decades immediately after the rediscovery of Mendel's work, the question of why offspring resemble their parents could be answered in more satisfying ways. **TABLE 14.4** summarizes some of the key exceptions and extensions to Mendel's rules and gives you a chance to compare and contrast their effects on patterns of inheritance.

check your understanding

Ⓒ
Ⓨ
Ⓤ

If you understand that . . .

- Genes near each other on the same chromosome violate the principle of independent assortment. They are not transmitted to gametes independently of each other unless crossing over occurs between them.

- Sex linkage, linkage, incomplete dominance, codominance, multiple allelism, pleiotropy, environmental effects, gene interactions, and polygenic inheritance are aspects of inheritance that Mendel did not study. When they occur, crosses do not result in classical Mendelian monohybrid or dihybrid ratios of offspring phenotypes.

✔ You should be able to . . .

Explain why the following crosses don't produce a 3:1 phenotype ratio in F₂ offspring:

1. Rose-comb ⊠ pea-comb chickens
2. Red-kernel ⊠ white-kernel wheat plants

Answers are available in Appendix A.

Type of Inheritance	Definition	Consequences or Comments
Sex linkage	Genes located on sex chromosomes.	Patterns of inheritance in males and females differ.
Linkage	Two genes found on same chromosome.	Linked genes violate principle of independent assortment.
Incomplete dominance	Heterozygotes have intermediate phenotype.	Polymorphism—heterozygotes have unique phenotype.
Codominance	Heterozygotes have phenotype of both alleles.	Polymorphism is possible—heterozygotes have unique phenotype.
Multiple allelism	In a population, more than two alleles present at a locus.	Polymorphism is possible.
Polymorphism	In a population, more than two phenotypes associated with a single gene are present.	Can result from actions of multiple alleles, incomplete dominance, and codominance.
Pleiotropy	A single gene affects many traits.	This is common.
Gene-by-gene interaction	In discrete traits, the phenotype associated with an allele depends on which alleles are present at another gene.	One allele can be associated with different phenotypes.
Gene-by-environment interaction	Phenotype influenced by environment experienced by individual.	Same genotypes can be associated with different phenotypes.
Polygenic inheritance of quantitative traits	Many genes are involved in specifying traits that exhibit continuous variation.	Unlike alleles that determine discrete traits, each allele adds a small amount to phenotype.

14.6 Applying Mendel's Rules to Human Inheritance

When researchers set out to study how a particular gene is transmitted in wheat or fruit flies or garden peas, they begin by making a series of controlled experimental crosses. For obvious reasons, this strategy is not possible with humans. But suppose you are concerned about an illness that runs in your family and go to a genetic counselor to find out how likely your children are to have the disease. To advise you, the counselor needs to know how the trait is transmitted, including whether the gene involved is autosomal or sex-linked and what type of dominance is associated with the disease allele.

To understand the transmission of human traits, investigators have to analyze human genotypes and phenotypes that already exist. A **mode of transmission** describes a trait as autosomal or sex-linked and gives the type of dominance of the allele. To learn the mode of transmission, scientists construct a **pedigree,** or family tree, of affected and unaffected individuals. By analyzing pedigrees, biomedical researchers have been able to discover how more than 2000 human genetic diseases are inherited.

A pedigree records the genetic relationships between the individuals in a family along with each person's sex and phenotype with respect to the trait in question. If the trait is governed by a single gene, then analyzing the pedigree may reveal whether a given phenotype is due to a dominant or recessive allele and whether the gene responsible is located on a sex chromosome or

on an autosome. Let's look at a series of specific case histories to see how this work is done.

Identifying Human Alleles as Recessive or Dominant

To analyze the inheritance of a discrete trait, biologists begin by assuming that a single autosomal gene is responsible and that the alleles present in the population have a simple dominant–recessive relationship.

This is the simplest possible situation. If the pattern of inheritance fits this model, then the assumptions—of inheritance by a single autosomal gene and simple dominance—are supported. Let's first analyze the pattern of inheritance that is typical of autosomal recessive traits and then examine patterns that emerge in pedigrees for autosomal dominant traits.

Patterns of Inheritance: Autosomal Recessive Traits If a phenotype is due to an autosomal recessive allele, then

- Individuals with the trait must be homozygous.

- If the parents of an affected individual do not have the trait, then the parents are heterozygous for the trait.

Heterozygous individuals who carry a recessive allele for an inherited disease are referred to as **carriers** of the disease. These individuals carry the allele and may transmit it even though they do not exhibit signs of the disease. When two carriers mate,

(a) Autosomal recessive trait (e.g., sickle-cell disease)

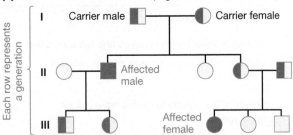

CHARACTERISTICS:
- Males and females are equally likely to be affected
- Affected offspring often have unaffected parents
- Unaffected parents of affected offspring are heterozygous (carriers)
- Affected offspring are homozygous
- If both parents are heterozygous, about ¼ of the offspring will be affected
- Trait often skips generations

(b) Autosomal dominant trait (e.g., Huntington's disease)

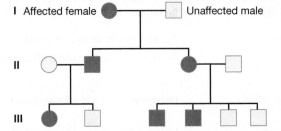

CHARACTERISTICS:
- Males and females are equally likely to be affected
- Affected offspring have at least one affected parent
- Affected offspring are heterozygous if only one parent is affected
- Unaffected offspring are homozygous recessive
- If one parent is heterozygous, about ½ of the offspring will be affected
- Trait does not skip generations

FIGURE 14.22 Pedigrees of Families with Autosomal Recessive and Autosomal Dominant Traits. Pedigrees use standard symbols: squares ☒ males, circles ☒ females; unfilled symbols ☒ unaffected individuals (those without the trait), filled symbols ☒ affected individuals, half-filled symbols ☒ heterozygotes for a recessive trait (carriers); horizontal lines connect parents, vertical lines connect parents to children.

about ¼ of their offspring are expected to express the recessive phenotype.

FIGURE 14.22a is a pedigree from a family in which an autosomal recessive trait, such as sickle-cell disease, occurs. The key feature to notice in this pedigree is that both boys and girls can exhibit the trait even though their parents do not. This is the pattern you would expect when the parents of an individual with the trait are heterozygous. It is also logical to observe that when an affected (homozygous) individual has children, those children do not necessarily have the trait. This pattern is predicted if affected people marry individuals who are homozygous for the dominant allele. This is likely to occur if the recessive allele is rare in the population.

In general, a recessive phenotype should show up in offspring only when both parents have that recessive allele and pass it on to their offspring. By definition, a recessive allele produces a given phenotype only when the individual is homozygous for that allele.

Patterns of Inheritance: Autosomal Dominant Traits When a trait is autosomal dominant, individuals who are homozygous or heterozygous for it must have the dominant phenotype. Even if one parent is heterozygous and the other is homozygous recessive, on average half their children should show the dominant phenotype. And unless a new mutation has occurred in a gamete, any child with the trait must have a parent with this trait. The latter observation is in strong contrast to the pattern seen in autosomal recessive traits.

FIGURE 14.22b shows the inheritance of the degenerative brain disorder called Huntington's disease (see Section 14.2). This pedigree has two features that indicate Huntington's disease is passed to the next generation through an autosomal dominant allele.

First, if a child shows the trait, then one of its parents shows the trait as well. Second, if families have a large number of children, the trait usually shows up in every generation—owing to the high probability of heterozygous parents having affected children.

Identifying Human Traits as Autosomal or Sex-Linked

When it is not possible to arrange reciprocal crosses, can data in a pedigree indicate whether a trait is autosomal or sex-linked? The answer is based on a simple premise. If a trait appears about equally often in males and females, then it is likely to be autosomal. But if males express the trait in question more often than females, then the allele responsible is likely to be recessive and found on the X chromosome.

X-linked Recessive Traits X-linked recessive traits are relatively common. They include the form of red–green color blindness that affects about 10 percent of males and the devastating blood clotting disorder hemophilia. A pedigree for red–green color blindness is shown in **FIGURE 14.23a**.

A key characteristic of X-linked recessive traits is that males express the trait more often than females. This is because males have only one copy of the X chromosome. Therefore, any X-linked allele will be expressed in a male.

Because human females have two X chromosomes, they have two copies of each X-linked gene and a recessive allele will not be expressed in heterozygotes. In the pedigree of Figure 14.23a the fact that only males are affected gives an immediate clue that this is an X-linked recessive trait.

Further, the appearance of an X-linked recessive trait usually skips a generation in the pedigree. Notice how on the right-hand

(a) X-linked recessive trait (e.g., red–green color blindness)

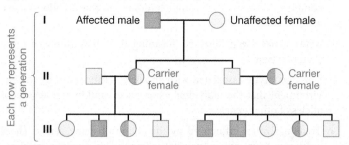

(b) X-linked dominant trait (e.g., hypophosphatemia)

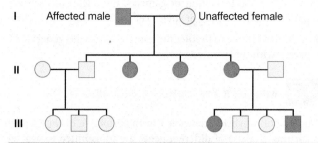

CHARACTERISTICS:
- Males are affected more frequently than females
- Trait is never passed from father to son
- Affected sons are usually born to carrier mothers
- About ½ of the sons of a carrier mother will be affected
- All daughters of affected males and unaffected non-carrier females are carriers
- Trait often skips generations

CHARACTERISTICS:
- Males and females are equally likely to be affected
- All daughters of an affected father are affected, but no sons
- Affected sons always have affected mothers
- About ½ of the offspring of an affected mother will be affected
- Affected daughters can have an affected mother or father
- Trait does not skip generations

FIGURE 14.23 Pedigrees of Families with X-linked Recessive (a) and X-linked Dominant (b) Traits.

✔**QUESTION** What genotype in a mother and a father would be predicted to produce a 1:1 ratio of normal : color-blind offspring? What would the ratio of color-blind male : female be from this mating?

side of the pedigree the trait appears in generations I and III but not in generation II. This pattern occurs because an affected male passes his only X chromosome on to his daughters. But because his daughters almost always receive a wild-type allele from their mother, the daughters don't show the trait. They will pass the defective allele on to about half their sons, however.

Most X-linked traits are recessive. There are only a few rare examples of X-linked dominant traits.

X-linked Dominant Traits One example of an X-linked dominant trait is a bone disorder known as hypophosphatemia, or vitamin D–resistant rickets. What can be predicted about the inheritance of an X-linked dominant trait? As the pedigree in **FIGURE 14.23b** shows, the most telling feature is that an affected male will pass the trait to all his daughters and none of his sons.

This is because daughters receive their father's only X chromosome. In contrast, a heterozygous female will pass the trait to half her daughters and half her sons. This occurs because there is an equal chance that a heterozygous mother will pass on an X chromosome with either the dominant or the recessive trait.

What about Y-linked traits? Although the patterns for Y-linked inheritance can easily be predicted, the reality is that very few genes occur on the Y chromosome. These genes are involved with male-specific sexual development. Except for maleness, there are no known human Y-linked traits.

Within a few decades of the rediscovery of Mendel's work, the burning question in genetics was no longer the nature of inheritance but the nature of the gene. What are genes made of, and how are they copied so that parents pass their alleles on to their offspring? These are the questions turned to in Chapter 15.

CHAPTER 14 REVIEW

For media, go to MasteringBiology

If you understand . . .

14.1 Mendel's Experimental System

- When Mendel began his work, there were two leading hypotheses of inheritance: blending inheritance and the inheritance of acquired characteristics.

- Mendel chose pea plants as a model organism and began his work with pure lines that he crossed to produce hybrids.

- Mendel sought to discover rules of heredity that explained how phenotypes were transmitted from parent to offspring.

✔ You should be able explain why pure lines are homozygous.

14.2 Mendel's Experiments with a Single Trait

- From analysis of the trait expressed in hybrids, Mendel concluded that one trait was dominant and the other recessive.

- From the results of monohybrid crosses, Mendel concluded that inheritance is particulate—genes do not blend together.

- The traits that Mendel studied are specified by paired hereditary determinants (genes) that separate from each other during gamete formation.

- Analysis of monohybrid crosses led to the principle of segregation: Before the formation of gametes, the alleles of each gene separate so that each egg or sperm cell receives only one of them.

✓ You should be able to predict the gamete genotypes generated by a parent with the genotype *Bb*.

14.3 Mendel's Experiments with Two Traits

- Analysis of dihybrid crosses led to the principle of independent assortment: alleles of different genes are transmitted to egg cells and sperm cells independently of each other.

- Testcrosses allow an investigator to determine whether an individual of dominant phenotype is homozygous or heterozygous.

✓ You should be able to predict the gamete genotypes generated by a parent with the genotype *BbRr*.

14.4 The Chromosome Theory of Inheritance

- The chromosome theory states that chromosomes contain genes and that Mendel's rules can be explained by the segregation and independent assortment of homologous chromosomes at meiosis I.

- The chromosome theory was supported by the discovery of sex linkage. Crosses with X-linked traits supported the theory's contention that genes are found on chromosomes.

- X-linked traits give different results in reciprocal crosses.

✓ You should be able to use a Punnett square to show why reciprocal crosses involving an X-linked recessive gene give different results.

14.5 Extending Mendel's Rules

- There are important exceptions and extensions to the basic patterns of inheritance that Mendel discovered.

- All genes follow the principle of segregation, but genes close together on the same chromosome do not follow the principle of independent assortment.

- Crossing over between homologous chromosomes creates new combinations of alleles along each homolog.

- The frequency of crossing over can be used to create genetic maps that show the position and spacing of genes along chromosomes.

- Many genes have more than two alleles; this is multiple allelism. When more than two phenotypes are due to multiple allelism, the trait is polymorphic.

- Not all heterozygotes show a dominant phenotype. In addition to complete dominance, incomplete dominance and codominance are also common.

- Many genes are pleiotropic, meaning that they influence more than one trait.

- The phenotype associated with an allele is influenced by the environment that the individual experiences, and by the actions of alleles of other genes.

- Traits are often influenced by the action of many genes. These polygenic traits show quantitative instead of discrete variation. The frequency of different phenotypes is distributed normally (a plot produces a "bell curve" or normal distribution).

✓ You should be able to explain why crossing over is said to break up linkage between alleles.

14.6 Applying Mendel's Rules to Human Inheritance

- Pedigrees map out the transmission of human traits.

- Applying Mendel's rules to pedigrees can reveal the mode of transmission—whether a trait is dominant or recessive, autosomal or X-linked.

✓ You should be able to draw a pedigree that shows two sons and two daughters produced by a red–green color-blind father and a homozygous mother with normal color vision and explain why all the daughters are expected to be carriers of color blindness and none of the sons are expected to be color-blind.

(MB) MasteringBiology

1. **MasteringBiology Assignments**

   Tutorials and Activities Determining Genotype: Pea Pod Color; What Is the Inheritance Pattern of Sex-Linked Traits? Gregor's Garden; Incomplete Dominance; Inheritance of Fur Color in Mice; Linked Genes and Crossing Over; Linked Genes and Linkage Mapping; Mendel's Experiments; Mendel's Law of Independent Assortment; Mendel's Law of Segregation; Pedigree Analysis: Dominant and Recessive Autosomal Conditions; Pedigree Analysis: Galactosemia, Sex Linkage, Sex-Linked Genes

   Questions Reading Quizzes, Blue-Thread Questions, Test Bank

2. **eText** Read your book online, search, take notes, highlight text, and more.

3. **The Study Area** Practice Test, Cumulative Test, BioFlix® 3-D Animations, Videos, Activities, Audio Glossary, Word Study Tools, Art

You should be able to . . .

✓ TEST YOUR KNOWLEDGE

Answers are available in Appendix A

1. In studies of how traits are inherited, what makes certain species candidates for model organisms?
   a. They are the first organisms to be used in a particular type of experiment, so they are a historical "model" of what researchers expect to find.
   b. They are easy to study because a great deal is already known about them.
   c. They are the best or most fit of their type.
   d. They are easy to maintain, have a short life cycle, produce many offspring, and yield data that are relevant to many other organisms.

2. Why is the allele for wrinkled seed shape in garden peas considered recessive?
   a. It "recedes" in the F_2 generation when homozygous parents are crossed.
   b. The trait associated with the allele is not expressed in heterozygotes.
   c. Individuals with the allele have lower fitness than that of individuals with the dominant allele.
   d. The allele is less common than the dominant allele. (The wrinkled allele is a rare mutant.)

3. The alleles found in haploid organisms cannot be dominant or recessive. Why?
   a. Dominance and recessiveness describe which allele is expressed in phenotype when different alleles occur in the same individual.
   b. Because only one allele is present, alleles in haploid organisms are always dominant.
   c. Alleles in haploid individuals are transmitted like mitochondrial DNA or chloroplast DNA.
   d. Most haploid individuals are bacteria, and bacterial genetics is completely different from eukaryotic genetics.

4. Why can you infer that individuals that are "pure line" are homozygous for the gene in question?
   a. Because they are highly inbred.
   b. Because only two alleles are present at each gene in the populations to which these individuals belong.
   c. Because in a pure line, phenotypes are not affected by environmental conditions or gene interactions.
   d. Because no other phenotype is ever observed in a pure-line population, this implies that only one allele is present.

5. The genes for the traits that Mendel worked with are either located on different chromosomes or so far apart on the same chromosome that crossing over almost always occurs between them. How did this circumstance help Mendel recognize the principle of independent assortment?
   a. Otherwise, his dihybrid crosses would not have produced a $9:3:3:1$ ratio of F_2 phenotypes.
   b. The occurrence of individuals with unexpected phenotypes led him to the discovery of recombination.
   c. It led him to the realization that the behavior of chromosomes during meiosis explained his results.
   d. It meant that the alleles involved were either dominant or recessive, which gave $3:1$ ratios in the F_1 generation.

6. What is meant by the claim that Mendel worked with the simplest possible genetic system?
   a. Discrete traits, two alleles, simple dominance and recessiveness, no sex chromosomes, and unlinked genes are the simplest situation known.
   b. The ability to self-fertilize or cross-pollinate made it simple for Mendel to set up controlled crosses.
   c. Mendel was aware of meiosis and the chromosome theory of inheritance, so it was easy to reach the conclusions he did.
   d. Mendel's experimental designs and his rules of inheritance are actually neither complex nor sophisticated.

7. Mendel's rules do not correctly predict patterns of inheritance for tightly linked genes or the inheritance of alleles that show incomplete dominance. Does this mean that his hypotheses are incorrect?
   a. Yes, because they are relevant to only a small number of organisms and traits.
   b. Yes, because not all data support his hypotheses.
   c. No, because he was not aware of meiosis or the chromosome theory of inheritance.
   d. No, it just means that his hypotheses are limited to certain conditions.

8. The artificial sweetener NutraSweet consists of a phenylalanine molecule linked to aspartic acid. The labels of diet sodas that contain NutraSweet include a warning to people with PKU. Why?
   a. NutraSweet stimulates the same taste receptors that natural sugars do.
   b. People with PKU have to avoid phenylalanine in their diet.
   c. In people with PKU, phenylalanine reacts with aspartic acid to form a toxic compound.
   d. People with PKU cannot lead normal lives, even if their environment is carefully controlled.

9. When Sutton and Boveri published the chromosome theory of inheritance, research on meiosis had not yet established that paternal and maternal homologs of different chromosomes assort independently. Then, in 1913, Elinor Carothers published a paper about a grasshopper species with an unusual karyotype: One chromosome had no homolog (meaning no pairing partner at meiosis I); another chromosome had homologs that could be distinguished under the light microscope. If chromosomes assort independently, how often should Carothers have observed each of the four products of meiosis shown in the following figure?

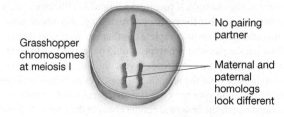

Grasshopper chromosomes at meiosis I — No pairing partner — Maternal and paternal homologs look different

Four types of gametes possible
(each meiotic division can produce only two of the four)

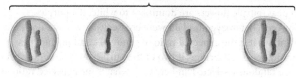

   a. Only the gametes with one of each type of chromosome would occur.
   b. The four types of gametes should be observed to occur at equal frequencies.
   c. The chromosome with no pairing partner would disintegrate, so only gametes with one copy of the other chromosome would be observed.
   d. Gametes with one of each type of chromosome would occur twice as often as gametes with just one chromosome.

10. Which of the following is the strongest evidence that a trait might be influenced by polygenic inheritance?
   a. F_1 offspring of parents with different phenotypes have an intermediate phenotype.
   b. F_1 offspring of parents with different phenotypes have the dominant phenotype.
   c. The trait shows qualitative (discrete) variation.
   d. The trait shows quantitative variation.

The best way to test and extend your knowledge of transmission genetics is to work problems. Most genetics problems are set up as follows: You are given some information about the genotypes or phenotypes of one or both parents, along with data on the phenotypes of F_1 or F_2 offspring. Your task is to generate a set of hypotheses—a genetic model—to explain the results. Your hypotheses should address each of the following questions:

- Is the trait under study discrete or quantitative?
- Is the phenotype a product of one gene or many genes?
- For each gene involved, how many alleles are present—one, two, or many?
- Do the alleles involved show complete dominance, incomplete dominance, or codominance?
- Are the genes involved sex-linked or autosomal?
- If more than one gene is involved, are they linked or unlinked? If they are linked, does crossing over occur frequently?

It's also helpful to ask yourself whether gene interactions or pleiotropy might be occurring and whether it is safe to assume that the experimental design carefully controlled for effects of variation in other genes and in the environment.

In working the problem, be sure to start with the simplest possible explanation. For example, if you are dealing with a discrete trait, you might hypothesize that the cross involves a single autosomal gene with two alleles that show complete dominance. Your next step is to infer what the parental genotypes would be (according to your hypothesis), if they are not already given, and then do a Punnett square to predict what the offspring phenotypes and their frequencies should be based on your hypothesis. Next, check whether these predictions match the observed results given in the problem. If the

answer is yes, you have a valid solution. But if the answer is no, you need to go back and change one of your hypotheses, redo the Punnett square, and check to see if the predictions and observations match. Keep repeating these steps until you have a model that fits the data.

11. Example Problem *Plectritis congesta* plants produce fruits that either have or do not have prominent structures called wings. The alleles involved are $W^{\boxtimes} \boxtimes$ winged fruit; $W^{\boxtimes} \boxtimes$ wingless fruit. Researchers collected an array of individuals from the field and performed a series of crosses. The results are given in the following table. Complete the table by writing down the genotype of the parent or parents involved in each cross.

Parental Phenotype(s)	Number of Offspring with Winged Fruits	Number of Offspring with Wingless Fruits	Parental Genotype(s)
Wingless (self-fertilized)	0	80	
Winged (self-fertilized)	90	30	
Winged ⊠ wingless	46	0	
Winged ⊠ winged	44	0	

A worked solution is available in Appendix A.

12. Example Problem Two black female mice are crossed with a brown male. In several litters, female I produced 9 blacks and 7 browns; female II produced 57 blacks. What deductions can you make concerning the inheritance of black and brown coat color in mice? What are the genotypes of the parents in this case?

A worked solution is available in Appendix A.

13. In peas, purple flowers are dominant to white. If a purple-flowered, heterozygous plant were crossed with a white-flowered plant, what is the expected ratio of genotypes and phenotypes among the F_1 offspring? If two of the purple-flowered F_1 offspring were randomly selected and crossed, what is the expected ratio of genotypes and phenotypes among the F_2 offspring?

14. In garden peas, yellow seeds (Y) are dominant to green seeds (y), and inflated pods (I) are dominant to constricted pods (i). Suppose you have crossed $YYII$ parents with $yyii$ parents.
- Draw the F_1 Punnett square and predict the expected F_1 phenotype(s).
- List the genotype(s) of gametes produced by F_1 individuals.
- Draw the F_2 Punnett square. Based on this Punnett square, predict the expected phenotype(s) in the F_2 generation and the expected frequency of each phenotype.

15. The smooth feathers on the back of the neck in pigeons can be reversed by a mutation to produce a "crested" appearance in which feathers form a distinctive spike at the back of the head. A pigeon breeder examined offspring produced by a single pair of non-crested birds and recorded the following: 22 non-crested and 7 crested. She then made a series of crosses using offspring from the first cross. When she crossed two of the crested birds, all 20 of the offspring were crested. When she crossed a non-crested bird with a crested bird, 7 offspring were non-crested and 6 were crested.

- For these three crosses, provide genotypes for parents and offspring that are consistent with these results.
- Which allele is dominant?

16. A plant with orange, spotted flowers was grown in the greenhouse from a seed collected in the wild. The plant was self-pollinated and gave rise to the following progeny: 88 orange with spots, 34 yellow with spots, 32 orange with no spots, and 8 yellow with no spots. What can you conclude about the dominance relationships of the alleles responsible for the spotted and unspotted phenotypes? For the orange and yellow phenotypes? What can you conclude about the genotype of the original plant that had orange, spotted flowers?

17. As a genetic counselor, you routinely advise couples about the possibility of genetic disease in their offspring based on their family histories. This morning you met with an engaged couple, both of whom are phenotypically normal. The man, however, has a brother who died of Duchenne-type muscular dystrophy, an X-linked condition that results in death before the age of 20. The allele responsible for this disease is recessive. His prospective bride, whose family has no history of the disease, is worried that the couple's sons or daughters might be afflicted.
- How would you advise this couple?
- The sister of this man is planning to marry his fiancée's brother. How would you advise this second couple?

18. Suppose you are heterozygous for two genes that are located on different chromosomes. You carry alleles *A* and *a* for one gene and alleles *B* and *b* for the other. Draw a diagram illustrating what happens to these genes and alleles when meiosis occurs in your reproductive tissues. Label the stages of meiosis, the homologous chromosomes, sister chromatids, nonhomologous chromosomes, genes, and alleles. Be sure to list all the genetically different gametes that could form and indicate how frequently each type should be observed. On the diagram, identify the events responsible for the principle of segregation and the principle of independent assortment.

19. Review the text's description of ABO blood types. Suppose a woman with blood type O married a man with blood type AB. What phenotypes and genotypes would you expect to observe in their offspring, and in what proportions? Answer the same question for a heterozygous mother with blood type A and a heterozygous father with blood type B.

20. An alien friend named Tukan has two sets of eyes, one set forward-looking and one set backward-looking, and smooth skin. His mate, Valco, lacks eyes but has skin covered with tiny hooks that attract all sorts of debris. Tukan and Valco have thrived on earth and have had four children, all with no eyes and smooth skin. Typical of their ways, the children interbred and produced 32 children of their own.
    - Under the models of inheritance proposed by Mendel, identify which alleles are dominant and which are recessive.
    - Provide gene symbols that would reflect the dominant–recessive allelic relationships.
    - Of the 32 children, how many would you expect to have two sets of eyes and smooth skin?

21. Phenylketonuria (PKU) is a genetic disease caused by homozygosity for a recessive mutation in the enzyme that converts the amino acid phenylalanine to tyrosine. In the absence of this enzyme, phenylalanine and some of its derivatives accumulate in the body and cause mental retardation. If individuals are identified soon enough after birth, they can be treated by a low-phenylalanine diet for the early years of their lives. As adults, though, homozygous recessive individuals are allowed to adopt a diet with normal amounts of phenylalanine. Not long after such treatments were initiated, a troubling phenomenon was observed. A high number of children born to treated mothers were mentally retarded even though the children were heterozygous for the PKU gene. Children born of treated PKU males suffered no ill effects.
    - Can you offer an explanation as to why genetically heterozygous children of treated PKU mothers might be prone to mental retardation?
    - Propose a solution to reduce the likelihood of mental retardation in children of treated PKU mothers.

22. The blending-inheritance hypothesis proposed that the genetic material from parents is unavoidably and irreversibly mixed in the offspring. As a result, offspring and later descendants should always appear intermediate in phenotype to their forebears. Mendel, in contrast, proposed that genes are discrete and that their integrity is maintained in the offspring and in subsequent generations. Suppose the year is 1890. You are a horse breeder and have just read Mendel's paper. You don't believe his results,

however, because you often work with cremello (very light-colored) and chestnut (reddish-brown) horses. You know that if you cross a cremello individual from a pure-breeding line with a chestnut individual from a pure-breeding line, the offspring will be palomino—meaning they have an intermediate (golden-yellow) body color. What additional crosses would you do to test whether Mendel's model is valid in the case of genes for horse color? List the crosses and the offspring genotypes and phenotypes you'd expect to obtain. Explain why these experimental crosses would provide a test of Mendel's model.

23. Two mothers give birth to sons at the same time in a busy hospital. The son of couple 1 is afflicted with hemophilia A, which is a recessive X-linked disease. Neither parent has the disease. Couple 2 has a normal son even though the father has hemophilia A. The two couples sue the hospital in court, claiming that a careless staff member swapped their babies at birth. You appear in court as an expert witness. What do you tell the jury? Make a diagram that you can submit to the jury.

24. You have crossed two *Drosophila melanogaster* individuals that have long wings and red eyes—the wild-type phenotype. In the progeny, the mutant phenotypes called curved wings and lozenge eyes appear as follows:

Females	Males
600 long wings, red eyes	300 long wings, red eyes
200 curved wings, red eyes	100 curved wings, red eyes
	300 long wings, lozenge eyes
	100 curved wings, lozenge eyes

    - According to these data, is the curved-wing allele autosomal recessive, autosomal dominant, sex-linked recessive, or sex-linked dominant?
    - Is the lozenge-eyed allele autosomal recessive, autosomal dominant, sex-linked recessive, or sex-linked dominant?
    - What is the genotype of the female parent?
    - What is the genotype of the male parent?

25. In parakeets, two autosomal genes that are located on different chromosomes control the production of feather pigment. Gene *B* codes for an enzyme that is required for the synthesis of a blue pigment, and gene *Y* codes for an enzyme required for the synthesis of a yellow pigment. Recessive mutations that result in no production of the affected pigment are known for both genes. Suppose that a bird breeder has two green parakeets and mates them. The offspring are green, blue, yellow, and albino (unpigmented).
    - Based on this observation, what are the genotypes of the green parents? What is the genotype of each type of offspring? What fraction of the total progeny should exhibit each type of color?
    - Suppose that the parents were the progeny of a cross between two true-breeding strains. What two types of crosses between true-breeding strains could have produced the green parents? Indicate the genotypes and phenotypes for each cross.

26. Recall that hemophilia is an X-linked recessive disease. If a woman with hemophilia had children with a man without hemophilia, what is the chance that their first child will have the disease? What is the chance that their first child will be a carrier?

15 DNA and the Gene: Synthesis and Repair

In this chapter you will learn how

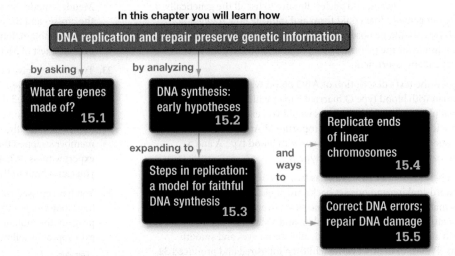

DNA replication and repair preserve genetic information

by asking

What are genes made of? **15.1**

by analyzing

DNA synthesis: early hypotheses **15.2**

expanding to

Steps in replication: a model for faithful DNA synthesis **15.3**

and ways to

Replicate ends of linear chromosomes **15.4**

Correct DNA errors; repair DNA damage **15.5**

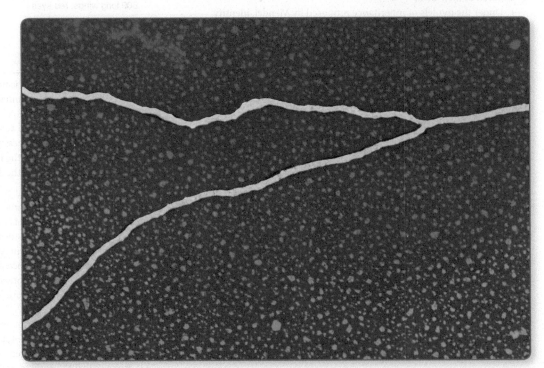

Electron micrograph (with color added) showing DNA in the process of replication. The original DNA double helix (far right) is being replicated into two DNA double helices (on the left). The two helices diverge at the replication fork, which is where DNA synthesis is taking place.

hat are genes made of, and how are they copied so that they are faithfully passed on to offspring? These questions dominated biology during the middle of the twentieth century. Since Mendel's time, the predominant research strategy in genetics had been to conduct a series of experimental crosses, create a genetic model to explain the types and proportions of phenotypes that resulted, and then test the model's predictions through reciprocal crosses, testcrosses, or other techniques. This strategy led to virtually all the discoveries of classical genetics, including Mendel's rules, sex linkage, linkage, and quantitative inheritance (see Chapter 14).

The chemical composition and molecular structure of Mendel's hereditary factors—which came to be called genes—remained a mystery for the first half of the twentieth century. Although biologists knew that genes and chromosomes were replicated during the cell cycle, with copies distributed

This chapter is part of the Big Picture. See how on pages 366–367.

✔ When you see this checkmark, stop and test yourself. Answers are available in Appendix A.

to daughter cells during mitosis and meiosis (see Chapters 12 and 13), no one had the slightest clue about how the copying occurred.

The goal of this chapter is to explore how researchers solved these mysteries. The results provided a link between two of the five attributes of life (introduced in Chapter 1): processing genetic information and replication. (You can see how DNA synthesis and repair fits into the Big Picture of Genetic Information on pages 366–367.)

How are genes copied, so they can be passed on to succeeding generations? Let's begin with studies that identified the nature of the genetic material, then explore how genes are copied during the synthesis phase of the cell cycle, and conclude by analyzing how incorrectly copied or damaged genes are repaired. Once the molecular nature of the gene was known, the nature of biological science changed forever.

15.1 What Are Genes Made Of?

The chromosome theory of inheritance (Chapter 14) proposed that chromosomes contain genes. It had been known since the late 1800s that chromosomes are a complex of DNA and proteins. The question, then, of what genes are made of came down to a simple choice: DNA or protein?

Initially, most biologists backed the hypothesis that genes are made of proteins. The arguments in favor of this hypothesis were compelling. Hundreds, if not thousands, of complex and highly regulated chemical reactions occur in even the simplest living cells. The amount of information required to specify and coordinate these reactions is mind-boggling. With their almost limitless variation in structure and function, proteins are complex enough to contain this much information.

In contrast, DNA was known to be composed of just four types of deoxyribonucleotides (Chapter 4). Early but incorrect evidence suggested that DNA was a simple molecule with some sort of repetitive and uninteresting structure. It seemed impossible that such a simple compound could hold complex information.

DNA or protein? The experiment that settled the question is considered a classic in biological science.

The Hershey–Chase Experiment

In 1952 Alfred Hershey and Martha Chase took up the question of whether genes were made of protein or DNA by studying how a virus called T2 infects and replicates within the bacterium *Escherichia coli*. Nearly 10 years before Hershey and Chase began their study, Oswald Avery and colleagues showed in 1944 that DNA could serve as genetic material, but many scientists remained unconvinced of the finding or its generality. Hershey and Chase knew that T2 infections begin when the virus attaches to the cell wall of *E. coli* and injects its genes into the cell's interior (**FIGURE 15.1a**). These genes then direct the production of a new generation of

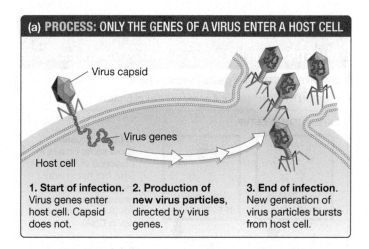

(a) PROCESS: ONLY THE GENES OF A VIRUS ENTER A HOST CELL

Virus capsid

Virus genes

Host cell

1. Start of infection. Virus genes enter host cell. Capsid does not.

2. Production of new virus particles, directed by virus genes.

3. End of infection. New generation of virus particles bursts from host cell.

(b) The virus's capsid stays outside the cell.

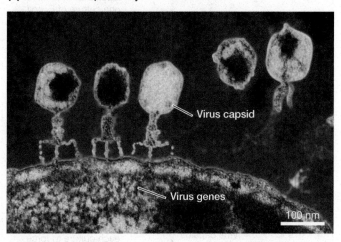

Virus capsid

Virus genes

100 nm

FIGURE 15.1 Viruses Inject Genes into Bacterial Cells and Leave a Capsid Behind. Color has been added to the transmission electron micrograph in (b) to make key structures more visible.

virus particles inside the infected cell, which acts as a host for the virus. (For more information on viruses, see Chapter 36.)

During the infection, the exterior protein coat, or **capsid,** of the original, parent virus is left behind. The capsid remains attached to the exterior of the host cell (**FIGURE 15.1b**). Hershey and Chase also knew that T2 is made up almost exclusively of protein and DNA. Was it protein or DNA that entered the host cell and directed the production of new viruses?

Hershey and Chase's strategy for determining the composition of the viral substance that enters the cell and acts as the hereditary material was based on two biochemical facts: (**1**) Proteins contain sulfur but not phosphorus, and (**2**) DNA contains phosphorus but not sulfur.

As **FIGURE 15.2** (see page 286) shows, the researchers began their work by growing viruses in the presence of either a radioactive isotope of sulfur (^{35}S) or a radioactive isotope of phosphorus (^{32}P). Because these isotopes were incorporated into newly synthesized proteins and DNA, this step produced a population of viruses with radioactive proteins and a population with radioactive DNA.

QUESTION: Do viral genes consist of DNA or protein?

DNA HYPOTHESIS: Viral genes consist of DNA.

PROTEIN HYPOTHESIS: Viral genes consist of protein.

EXPERIMENTAL SETUP:

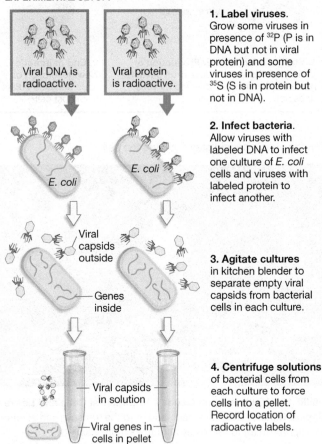

Viral DNA is radioactive.

Viral protein is radioactive.

E. coli

E. coli

Viral capsids outside

Genes inside

Viral capsids in solution

Viral genes in cells in pellet

1. Label viruses. Grow some viruses in presence of ^{32}P (P is in DNA but not in viral protein) and some viruses in presence of ^{35}S (S is in protein but not in DNA).

2. Infect bacteria. Allow viruses with labeled DNA to infect one culture of *E. coli* cells and viruses with labeled protein to infect another.

3. Agitate cultures in kitchen blender to separate empty viral capsids from bacterial cells in each culture.

4. Centrifuge solutions of bacterial cells from each culture to force cells into a pellet. Record location of radioactive labels.

PREDICTION OF DNA HYPOTHESIS: Radioactive DNA will be located within pellet.

PREDICTION OF PROTEIN HYPOTHESIS: Radioactive protein will be located within pellet.

RESULTS:

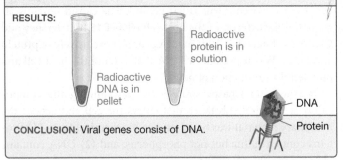

Radioactive protein is in solution

Radioactive DNA is in pellet

DNA

Protein

CONCLUSION: Viral genes consist of DNA.

FIGURE 15.2 Experimental Evidence that DNA Is the Hereditary Material.

SOURCE: Hershey, A. D., and M. Chase. 1952. Independent functions of viral protein and nucleic acid in growth of bacteriophage. *Journal of General Physiology* 36: 39–56.

✔ **QUESTION** What evidence would these investigators have to produce to convince you that the viral capsids were shaken off the bacterial cells by the agitation step?

Hershey and Chase allowed each set of radioactive viruses to infect *E. coli* cells. If genes consist of DNA, then radioactive protein should be found only in the capsids outside the infected host cells, while radioactive DNA should be located inside the cells. But if genes consist of proteins, then radioactive protein—and no radioactive DNA—should be inside the cells.

To test these predictions, Hershey and Chase sheared the capsids off the cells by vigorously agitating each of the cultures in kitchen blenders. When the researchers spun the samples in a centrifuge, the small phage capsids remained in the solution while the cells formed a pellet at the bottom of the centrifuge tube (see **BioSkills 10** in Appendix B to review how centrifugation works).

As predicted by the DNA hypothesis, the biologists found that virtually all the radioactive protein was outside cells in the emptied capsids, while virtually all the radioactive DNA was inside the host cells. Because the injected component of the virus directs the production of a new generation of virus particles, this component must represent the virus's genes.

After these results were published, proponents of the protein hypothesis accepted that DNA, not protein, must be the hereditary material. An astonishing claim—that DNA contained all the information for life's complexity—was correct.

The Secondary Structure of DNA

In 1953, one year after Hershey and Chase's landmark results were published, Watson and Crick proposed a model for the secondary structure of DNA. Recall that DNA is typically double-stranded with each strand consisting of a long, linear polymer made up of monomers called deoxyribonucleotides (Chapter 4).

Each deoxyribonucleotide consists of a deoxyribose sugar, a phosphate group, and a nitrogenous base (**FIGURE 15.3a**). Deoxyribonucleotides link together into a polymer when a phosphodiester bond forms between a hydroxyl group on the 3′ carbon of one deoxyribose and the phosphate group attached to the 5′ carbon of another deoxyribose. The two strands together make up one DNA molecule that functions as the genetic information storage molecule of cells.

As **FIGURE 15.3b** shows, the primary structure of each strand of DNA has two major features: (1) a "backbone" made up of the sugar and phosphate groups of deoxyribonucleotides and (2) a series of bases that project from the backbone. Each strand of DNA has a directionality, or polarity: One end has an exposed hydroxyl group on the 3′ carbon of a deoxyribose, while the other has an exposed phosphate group on a 5′ carbon. Thus, the molecule has distinctly different 3′ and 5′ ends.

As they explored different models for the secondary structure of DNA, Watson and Crick hit on the idea of lining up two of these long strands in opposite directions, or in what is called antiparallel fashion (**FIGURE 15.4a**). They realized that antiparallel strands will twist around each other into a spiral or helix because certain bases fit together snugly in pairs inside the spiral and form hydrogen bonds (**FIGURE 15.4b**). The double-stranded molecule that results is called a **double helix.**

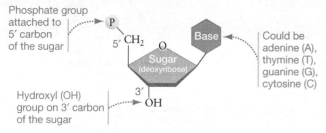

(a) Structure of a deoxyribonucleotide

Phosphate group attached to 5′ carbon of the sugar

P

5′ CH₂ O

Base

Sugar (deoxyribose)

Could be adenine (A), thymine (T), guanine (G), cytosine (C)

3′ OH

Hydroxyl (OH) group on 3′ carbon of the sugar

(b) Primary structure of DNA

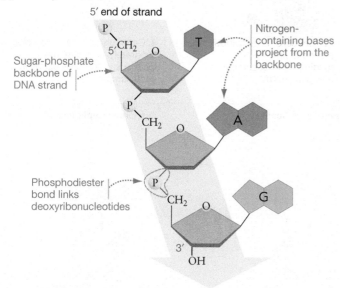

5′ end of strand

Sugar-phosphate backbone of DNA strand

Phosphodiester bond links deoxyribonucleotides

Nitrogen-containing bases project from the backbone

3′ end of strand

FIGURE 15.3 DNA's Primary Structure. (a) Deoxyribonucleotides are monomers that polymerize to form DNA. **(b)** DNA's primary structure is made up of a sequence of deoxyribonucleotides. Notice that the structure has a sugar–phosphate "backbone" with nitrogen-containing bases attached.

✔**EXERCISE** Write the base sequence of the DNA in part (b), in the 5′ → 3′ direction.

The double-helical DNA is stabilized by hydrogen bonds that form between the bases adenine (A) and thymine (T) and between the bases guanine (G) and cytosine (C), along with hydrophobic interactions that the bases experience inside the helix. Hydrogen bonding of particular base pairs is **complementary base pairing.**

15.2 Testing Early Hypotheses about DNA Synthesis

Watson and Crick realized that the A-T and G-C pairing rules suggested a way for DNA to be copied when chromosomes are replicated during S phase of the cell cycle, before mitosis and meiosis. They suggested that the existing strands of DNA served as a template (pattern) for the production of new strands and that deoxyribonucleotides were added to the new strands according to complementary base pairing. For example, if the template

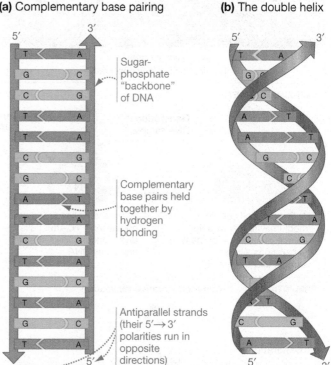

(a) Complementary base pairing   **(b)** The double helix

Sugar-phosphate "backbone" of DNA

Complementary base pairs held together by hydrogen bonding

Antiparallel strands (their 5′→3′ polarities run in opposite directions)

FIGURE 15.4 DNA's Secondary Structure: The Double Helix. (a) DNA normally consists of two strands, each with a sugar–phosphate backbone. Nitrogen-containing bases project from each strand and form hydrogen bonds. Only A-T and G-C pairs fit together in a way that allows hydrogen bonding to occur between the strands. **(b)** Bonding between complementary bases twists the molecule into a double helix.

strand contained a T, then an A would be added to the new strand to pair with that T. Similarly, a G on the template strand would dictate the addition of a C on the new strand.

Complementary base pairing provided a mechanism for DNA to be copied. But many questions remained about how the copying was done.

Three Alternative Hypotheses

Biologists at the time proposed three alternative hypotheses about how the old and new strands might interact during replication:

1. *Semiconservative replication* If the old, **parental strands** of DNA separated, each could then be used as a template for the synthesis of a new, **daughter strand.** This hypothesis is called **semiconservative replication** because each new daughter DNA molecule would consist of one old strand and one new strand.

2. *Conservative replication* If the bases temporarily turned outward so that complementary strands no longer faced each other, they could serve as a template for the synthesis of an entirely new double helix all at once. This hypothesis, called conservative replication, would result in an intact parental

QUESTION: Is replication semiconservative, conservative, or dispersive?

HYPOTHESIS 1:	HYPOTHESIS 2:	HYPOTHESIS 3:
Replication is semiconservative.	Replication is conservative.	Replication is dispersive.

EXPERIMENTAL SETUP:

  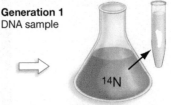 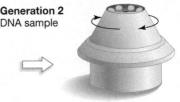

Generation 0 DNA sample

Generation 1 DNA sample

Generation 2 DNA sample

Cell transfer

1. Grow *E. coli* cells in medium with ^{15}N as sole source of nitrogen for many generations. Collect sample and purify DNA.

2. Transfer cells to medium containing ^{14}N. After cells divide once, collect sample and purify DNA.

3. After cells have divided a second time in ^{14}N medium, collect sample and purify DNA.

4. Centrifuge the three samples separately. Compare the locations of the DNA bands in each sample.

PREDICTIONS:

Semiconservative replication	Conservative replication	Dispersive replication

Generation 0

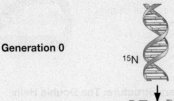 ^{15}N

^{15}N

^{15}N

Generation 1

Hybrid   Hybrid

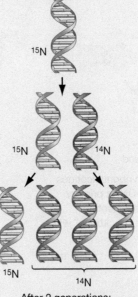 ^{15}N ^{14}N

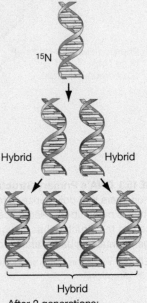 Hybrid   Hybrid

Generation 2

Hybrid ^{14}N Hybrid ^{14}N

^{15}N ^{14}N

Hybrid

After 2 generations:
1/2 low-density DNA (^{14}N)
1/2 intermediate-density DNA (hybrid)

After 2 generations:
1/4 high-density DNA (^{15}N)
3/4 low-density DNA (^{14}N)

After 2 generations:
All intermediate-density DNA (hybrid)

RESULTS:

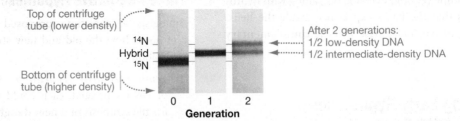

Top of centrifuge tube (lower density)

^{14}N
Hybrid
^{15}N

Bottom of centrifuge tube (higher density)

After 2 generations:
1/2 low-density DNA
1/2 intermediate-density DNA

0   1   2
Generation

CONCLUSION: Data from generation 1 conflict with conservative replication hypothesis. Data from generation 2 conflict with dispersive replication hypothesis. Replication is semiconservative.

FIGURE 15.5 The Meselson–Stahl Experiment.

SOURCE: Meselson, M., and F. W. Stahl. 1958. The replication of DNA in *Escherichia coli*. *Proceedings of the National Academy of Sciences USA* 44: 671–682.

✔**EXERCISE** Meselson and Stahl actually let their experiment run for a fourth generation with cultures growing in the presence of ^{14}N. Explain what data from third- and fourth-generation DNA should look like—that is, where the DNA band(s) should be.

molecule and a daughter DNA molecule consisting entirely of newly synthesized strands.

3. *Dispersive replication* If the parental double helix were cut wherever one strand crossed over another and DNA was synthesized in short sections by extending each of the cut parental strands to the next strand crossover, then there would be a mix of new and old segments along each replicated molecule. This possibility is called dispersive replication—stretches of old DNA would be interspersed with new DNA down the length of each daughter strand.

Matthew Meselson and Franklin Stahl realized that if they could tag or mark parental and daughter strands of DNA in a way that would make them distinguishable from each other, they could determine whether replication was conservative, semiconservative, or dispersive.

The Meselson–Stahl Experiment

Before Meselson and Stahl could do any tagging to distinguish old DNA from new DNA, they needed to choose an organism to study. They decided to work with the bacterium *Escherichia coli*—the same inhabitant of the human gastrointestinal tract that Hershey and Chase used. Because *E. coli* is small and grows quickly and readily in the laboratory, it had become a favored model organism in studies of biochemistry and molecular genetics. (See **BioSkills 13** in Appendix B for more on *E. coli*.)

Like all organisms, bacterial cells copy their entire complement of DNA, or their **genome**, before every cell division. To distinguish parental strands of DNA from daughter strands when *E. coli* replicated, Meselson and Stahl grew the cells for successive generations in the presence of different isotopes of nitrogen: first ^{15}N and later ^{14}N. Because ^{15}N contains an extra neutron, it is heavier than the normal isotope, ^{14}N.

This difference in mass, which creates a difference in density between ^{14}N-containing and ^{15}N-containing DNA, was the key to the experiment summarized in **FIGURE 15.5**. The logic ran as follows:

- If different nitrogen isotopes were available in the growth medium when different generations of DNA were produced, then the parental and daughter strands would have different densities.

- The technique called density-gradient centrifugation separates molecules based on their density (**BioSkills 10** in Appendix B). Low-density molecules cluster in bands high in the centrifuge tube; higher-density molecules cluster in bands lower in the centrifuge tube.

- When intact, double-stranded DNA molecules are subjected to density-gradient centrifugation, DNA that contains ^{14}N should form a band higher in the centrifuge tube; DNA that contains ^{15}N should form a band lower in the centrifuge tube.

In short, DNA containing ^{14}N and DNA containing ^{15}N should form separate bands. How could this tagging system be used to test whether replication is semiconservative, conservative, or dispersive?

Meselson and Stahl began by growing *E. coli* cells with nutrients that contained only ^{15}N. They purified DNA from a sample of these cells and transferred the rest of the culture to a growth medium containing only the ^{14}N isotope. After enough time had elapsed for these cells to divide once—meaning that the DNA had been copied once—they removed a sample and isolated the DNA. After the remainder of the culture had divided again, they removed another sample and isolated its DNA.

As Figure 15.5 shows, the conservative, semiconservative, and dispersive models make distinct predictions about the makeup of the DNA molecules after replication occurs in the first and second generation. Examine the figure carefully to understand these distinct predictions.

The photograph at the bottom of Figure 15.5 shows the experiment's results. After one generation, the density of the DNA molecules was intermediate. These data suggested that the hypothesis of conservative replication was wrong, since it predicted two different densities in the first generation.

After two generations, a lower-density band appeared in addition to the intermediate-density band. This result offered strong support for the hypothesis that DNA replication is semiconservative. Had dispersive replication occurred, the second generation would have produced only a single, intermediate density band. Each newly made DNA molecule comprises one old strand and one new strand—replication is semiconservative.

15.3 A Model for DNA Synthesis

The DNA inside a cell is like an ancient text that has been painstakingly copied and handed down, generation after generation. But while the most ancient of all human texts contain messages that are thousands of years old, the DNA in living cells has been copied and passed down for billions of years. And instead of being copied by monks or clerks, DNA is replicated by molecular scribes. What molecules are responsible for copying DNA, and how do they work?

Meselson and Stahl showed that each strand of DNA is copied in its entirety each time replication occurs, but how does DNA synthesis proceed? Does it require an input of energy in the form of ATP, or it is spontaneous? Is it catalyzed by an enzyme, or does it occur quickly on its own?

The initial breakthrough on DNA replication came with the discovery of an enzyme called **DNA polymerase,** so named because it polymerizes deoxyribonucleotides into DNA. This protein catalyzes DNA synthesis. Follow-up work showed that there are several types of DNA polymerase. DNA polymerase III, for example, is the enzyme that is primarily responsible for copying *E. coli*'s chromosome before cell division.

FIGURE 15.6 (see page 290) illustrates a critical characteristic of DNA polymerases: They can work in only one direction. DNA polymerases can add deoxyribonucleotides only to the 3′ end of a growing DNA chain. As a result, DNA synthesis always proceeds in the 5′ → 3′ direction. ✔ If you understand this

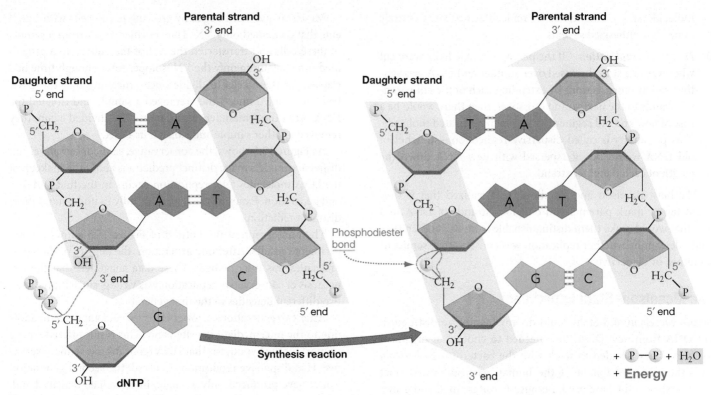

FIGURE 15.6 The DNA Synthesis Reaction. A condensation reaction results in formation of a phosphodiester bond between the 3′ carbon on the end of a DNA strand and the 5′ carbon on an incoming deoxyribonucleoside triphosphate (dNTP) monomer.

concept, you should be able to draw two lines representing a DNA molecule, assign the 3′-to-5′ polarity of each strand, and then label the direction in which DNA synthesis will proceed for each strand.

Figure 15.6 makes another important point about DNA synthesis. You might recall from earlier chapters that polymerization reactions generally are endergonic, meaning they require an input of energy. But for DNA synthesis, the reaction is exergonic (it releases energy) because the monomers that are used in the DNA synthesis reaction are **deoxyribonucleoside triphosphates (dNTPs).** (The *N* in dNTP stands for any of the four bases found in DNA: adenine, thymine, guanine, or cytosine). Because they have three closely spaced phosphate groups, dNTPs have high potential energy—high enough to make the formation of phosphodiester bonds in a growing DNA strand exergonic as two of the phosphates are cleaved off (see Chapter 8).

How Does Replication Get Started?

Another major insight into the mechanism of DNA synthesis emerged when electron microscopy caught DNA replication in action. As **FIGURE 15.7a** shows, a "bubble" forms when DNA is being synthesized. Initially, the replication bubble forms at a specific sequence of bases called the **origin of replication** (**FIGURE 15.7b**). Bacterial chromosomes have only one origin of replication, and thus a single replication bubble forms. Eukaryotes have multiple origins of replication along each chromosome, and thus multiple replication bubbles (**FIGURE 15.7c**).

DNA synthesis is bidirectional—that is, it occurs in both directions at the same time. Therefore, replication bubbles grow in two directions as DNA replication proceeds.

A specific set of proteins are responsible for recognizing sites where replication begins and opening the double helix at those points. These proteins are activated by the proteins that initiate S phase in the cell cycle (see Chapter 12).

Once a replication bubble opens at the origin of replication, a different set of enzymes takes over to start DNA synthesis. Active DNA synthesis takes place at the replication forks of each replication bubble (shown in Figure 15.7c). The **replication fork** is the Y-shaped region where the parent–DNA double helix is split into two single strands and copied.

How Is the Helix Opened and Stabilized?

A large group of enzymes and specialized proteins converge on the point where the double helix opens. The enzyme called **DNA helicase** breaks the hydrogen bonds between the base pairs. This reaction causes the two strands of DNA to separate. **Single-strand DNA-binding proteins (SSBPs)** attach to the separated strands and prevent them from snapping back into a double helix. Working together, DNA helicase and single-strand DNA-binding proteins open up the double helix and maintain the separation of both strands during copying (**FIGURE 15.8**, step 1).

The "unzipping" process that occurs at the replication fork creates tension farther down the helix. To understand why, imagine what would happen if you started to pull apart the twisted

(a) DNA being replicated

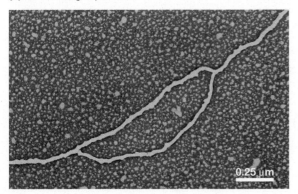

0.25 μm

(b) Bacterial chromosomes have a single origin of replication.

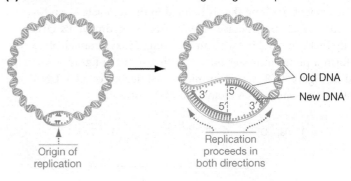

Old DNA

New DNA

Origin of replication

Replication proceeds in both directions

(c) Eukaryotic chromosomes have multiple origins of replication.

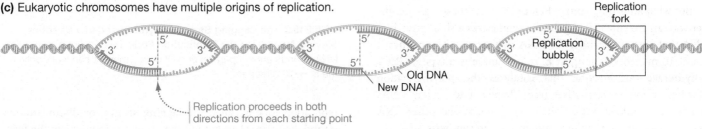

Replication fork

Replication bubble

Old DNA

New DNA

Replication proceeds in both directions from each starting point

FIGURE 15.7 DNA Synthesis Proceeds in Two Directions from an Origin of Replication. Color has been added to the micrograph in part (a).

strands of a rope. The untwisting movements at one end would force the intact section to rotate in response. If the intact end of the rope were fixed in place, it would coil on itself in response to the twisting forces. DNA does not become tightly coiled ahead of the replication fork, because the twisting induced by helicase is relaxed by proteins called topoisomerases. A **topoisomerase** is an enzyme that cuts DNA, allows it to unwind, and rejoins it ahead of the advancing replication fork.

Now, what happens once the DNA helix is open?

How Is the Leading Strand Synthesized?

The keys to understanding what happens at the start of DNA synthesis are to recall that DNA polymerase (**1**) works only in the $5' \rightarrow 3'$ direction and (**2**) requires both a $3'$ end to extend from and a single-stranded template. Both of these properties control how synthesis occurs on both template strands of DNA, and as you'll soon see, they significantly complicate copying one of these. The single-stranded template dictates which

PROCESS: SYNTHESIS OF LEADING STRAND

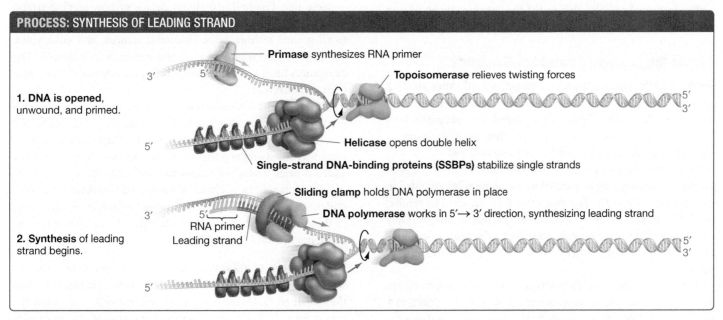

1. DNA is opened, unwound, and primed.

Primase synthesizes RNA primer

Topoisomerase relieves twisting forces

Helicase opens double helix

Single-strand DNA-binding proteins (SSBPs) stabilize single strands

2. Synthesis of leading strand begins.

Sliding clamp holds DNA polymerase in place

DNA polymerase works in $5' \rightarrow 3'$ direction, synthesizing leading strand

RNA primer
Leading strand

FIGURE 15.8 Leading-Strand Synthesis.

deoxyribonucleotide should be added next. A **primer**—a strand a few nucleotides long that is bonded to the template strand—provides DNA polymerase with a free 3′ hydroxyl (⊠ OH) group that can combine with an incoming deoxyribonucleotide to form a phosphodiester bond. As shown in the figure below and in Figure 15.8, step 2, primers used during cellular DNA synthesis are short RNA strands, not DNA strands.

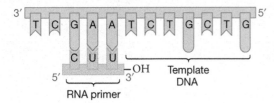

But what adds the primer? Before DNA synthesis can get under way, an enzyme called **primase** synthesizes a short stretch of RNA that acts as a primer for DNA polymerase. The primer is about 10 nucleotides long in *E. coli*. Primase is a type of **RNA polymerase**—an enzyme that catalyzes the polymerization of ribonucleotides into RNA (see Chapter 4 to review RNA's structure). Unlike DNA polymerases, primase and other RNA polymerases do not require a primer to begin synthesis.

Once a primer is present on a single-stranded template, DNA polymerase begins working in the 5′ → 3′ direction and adds deoxyribonucleotides to complete the complementary strand. As Figure 15.8, step 2, shows, DNA polymerase has a shape that grips the DNA strand during synthesis, similar to your hand clasping a rope. Deoxyribonucleotide addition is catalyzed at an active site in a groove between the enzyme's "thumb" and "fingers." As DNA polymerase moves along the DNA molecule, a doughnut-shaped structure behind it, called the sliding clamp, holds the enzyme in place on the template strand.

The enzyme's product is called the **leading strand,** or **continuous strand,** because it leads into the replication fork and is synthesized continuously. ✔ If you understand leading-strand synthesis, you should be able to list the enzymes involved and predict the consequences if any of them are defective.

How Is the Lagging Strand Synthesized?

Synthesis of the leading strand is straightforward. After an RNA primer is in place, DNA polymerase moves along, adding deoxyribonucleotides to the 3′ end of that strand. The enzyme moves into the replication fork, which "unzips" ahead of it. By comparison, events on the opposite strand are more involved.

Recall that the two strands of the DNA double helix are antiparallel—meaning they lie parallel to one another but oriented in opposite directions. The fact that DNA polymerases can synthesize DNA only in the 5′ → 3′ direction creates a paradox. Only one strand of DNA at the replication fork—the leading strand—can be synthesized in a direction that follows the moving replication fork.

The other strand must be synthesized in a direction that runs *away* from the moving replication fork, as illustrated in **FIGURE 15.9**. The strand of DNA that extends in the direction away from the

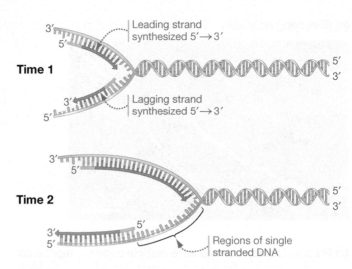

FIGURE 15.9 The Lagging Strand Is Synthesized in a Direction Moving Away from the Replication Fork. This occurs because the DNA strands are antiparallel and DNA polymerase can work only in the 5′ → 3′ direction.

replication fork is called the **lagging strand,** or **discontinuous strand,** because it lags behind the synthesis occurring at the fork. As the replication fork moves, it exposes gaps of single-stranded template DNA (Time 2 in Figure 15.9). How are the growing gaps filled in?

The Discontinuous Replication Hypothesis The puzzle posed by lagging-strand synthesis was resolved when Reiji Okazaki and colleagues tested a hypothesis called discontinuous replication. This hypothesis held that primase synthesizes new RNA primers for lagging strands as the moving replication fork opens single-stranded regions of DNA, and that DNA polymerase uses these primers to synthesize short lagging-strand DNA fragments that are linked together into a continuous strand. These ideas are illustrated in **FIGURE 15.10**.

Note that Figure 15.10 shows details of how lagging-strand synthesis occurs in *E. coli*. The overall process, however, applies to all groups of organisms—bacteria, archaea, and eukaryotes. The basic reactions of lagging-strand synthesis are universal. The differences lie in the names or specific properties of the key proteins and enzymes.

To explore the discontinuous replication hypothesis, Okazaki's group set out to test a key prediction: Could they find short DNA fragments produced during replication? Their critical experiment was based on the pulse–chase strategy (see Chapter 7). They added a brief "pulse" of radioactive deoxyribonucleotides to *E. coli* cells, followed by a "chase" of nonradioactive deoxyribonucleotides. According to the discontinuous replication model, some of these radioactive deoxyribonucleotides should first appear in short, fragments of DNA.

The Discovery of Okazaki Fragments As predicted, the researchers succeeded in finding short DNA fragments when they purified DNA from the experimental cells, separated the two strands of DNA, and analyzed the size of the molecules

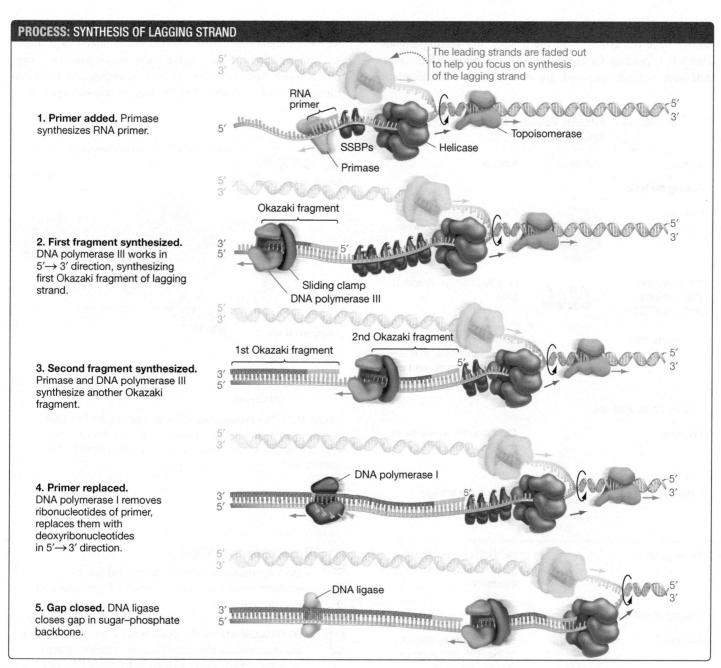

1. Primer added. Primase synthesizes RNA primer.

2. First fragment synthesized. DNA polymerase III works in 5′→ 3′ direction, synthesizing first Okazaki fragment of lagging strand.

3. Second fragment synthesized. Primase and DNA polymerase III synthesize another Okazaki fragment.

4. Primer replaced. DNA polymerase I removes ribonucleotides of primer, replaces them with deoxyribonucleotides in 5′→ 3′ direction.

5. Gap closed. DNA ligase closes gap in sugar–phosphate backbone.

(Labels within figure:) The leading strands are faded out to help you focus on synthesis of the lagging strand; RNA primer; SSBPs; Primase; Helicase; Topoisomerase; Okazaki fragment; Sliding clamp; DNA polymerase III; 1st Okazaki fragment; 2nd Okazaki fragment; DNA polymerase I; DNA ligase

FIGURE 15.10 Lagging-Strand Synthesis.

by centrifugation. A small number of labeled DNA fragments about 1000 base pairs long were present immediately after the pulse. These short DNAs came to be known as **Okazaki fragments** and are shown in steps 2 and 3 of Figure 15.10. These small DNAs became larger during the chase as they were linked together into longer pieces. Subsequent work showed that Okazaki fragments in eukaryotes are even smaller—just 100 to 200 base pairs long.

How are Okazaki fragments connected? First, as step 4 of Figure 15.10 shows, in *E. coli* a specialized DNA polymerase called DNA polymerase I attaches to the 3′ end of an Okazaki fragment. As DNA polymerase I moves along in the 5′ → 3′ direction, it removes that RNA primer ahead of it and replaces the ribonucleotides with the appropriate deoxyribonucleotides.

Once the RNA primer is removed and replaced by DNA, an enzyme called **DNA ligase** catalyzes the formation of a phosphodiester bond between the adjacent fragments (Figure 15.10, step 5). ✔ If you understand lagging-strand synthesis, you should be able to draw what the two newly synthesized molecules of DNA at a single replication fork would look like if DNA ligase were defective.

In eukaryotes, the mechanism for primer removal is different, but the mechanism of synthesizing short Okazaki fragments that are later joined into an unbroken chain of DNA is the same.

Working together, the enzymes that open the replication fork and manage the synthesis of the leading and lagging strands (**TABLE 15.1**) produce faithful copies of DNA before cell division. Although separate enzymes are drawn at different locations around the replication fork in Figures 15.8 and 15.10, in reality, all these enzymes are joined into the **replisome,** a large macromolecular machine. In *E. coli*, the replisome contains two copies of DNA polymerase III that are actively engaged in DNA synthesis. As shown in **FIGURE 15.11**, the lagging strand loops out and

SUMMARY TABLE 15.1   **Proteins Required for DNA Synthesis in Bacteria**

Name	Structure	Function
Opening the helix		
Helicase		Catalyzes the breaking of hydrogen bonds between base pairs to open the double helix
Single-strand DNA-binding proteins (SSBPs)		Stabilizes single-stranded DNA
Topoisomerase		Breaks and rejoins the DNA double helix to relieve twisting forces caused by the opening of the helix
Leading strand synthesis		
Primase		Catalyzes the synthesis of the RNA primer
DNA polymerase III		Extends the leading strand
Sliding clamp		Holds DNA polymerase in place during strand extension
Lagging strand synthesis		
Primase		Catalyzes the synthesis of the RNA primer on an Okazaki fragment
DNA polymerase III		Extends an Okazaki fragment
Sliding clamp		Holds DNA polymerase in place during strand extension
DNA polymerase I		Removes the RNA primer and replaces it with DNA
DNA ligase		Catalyzes the joining of Okazaki fragments into a continuous strand

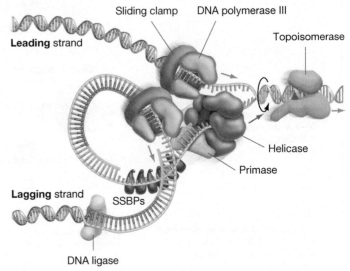

FIGURE 15.11 The Replisome. The enzymes required for DNA synthesis are organized into a macromolecular machine. Note how the lagging strand loops out as the leading strand is being synthesized.

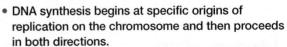

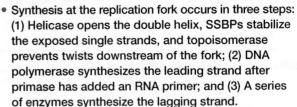

If you understand that . . .

- DNA synthesis begins at specific origins of replication on the chromosome and then proceeds in both directions.
- Synthesis at the replication fork occurs in three steps: (1) Helicase opens the double helix, SSBPs stabilize the exposed single strands, and topoisomerase prevents twists downstream of the fork; (2) DNA polymerase synthesizes the leading strand after primase has added an RNA primer; and (3) A series of enzymes synthesize the lagging strand.
- Lagging-strand synthesis cannot be continuous, because it moves away from the replication fork. In bacteria, enzymes called primase, DNA polymerase III, DNA polymerase I, and ligase work in sequence to synthesize Okazaki fragments and link them into a continuous whole.

✔ **You should be able to . . .**

1. Explain the function of primase.
2. Explain why DNA polymerase I is used predominantly on the lagging strand.

Answers are available in Appendix A.

around the complex, allowing the replisome to move as a single unit as it follows the replication fork. After the DNA polymerase on the lagging strand completes synthesis of an Okazaki fragment, it is released from the DNA and reassembles on the most recently synthesized primer.

15.4 Replicating the Ends of Linear Chromosomes

The circular DNA molecules in bacteria and archaea can be synthesized by the enzymes introduced in Section 15.3, and so can most of the linear DNA molecules found in eukaryotes. But replication at the very ends of linear eukaryotic chromosomes is another story altogether. Replication of chromosome ends requires a specialized DNA replication enzyme that has been the subject of intense research.

The End Replication Problem

The region at the end of a eukaryotic chromosome is called a **telomere** (literally, "end-part"). **FIGURE 15.12** illustrates the problem that arises during the replication of telomeres.

- When the replication fork reaches the end of a linear chromosome, a eukaryotic DNA polymerase synthesizes the leading strand all the way to the end of the parent DNA template (step 1 and step 2, top strand). As a result, leading-strand synthesis results in a double-stranded copy of the DNA molecule.

- On the lagging strand, primase adds an RNA primer close to the tip of the chromosome (see step 2, bottom strand).

- DNA polymerase synthesizes the final Okazaki fragment on the lagging strand (step 3). An enzyme that degrades ribonucleotides removes the primer.

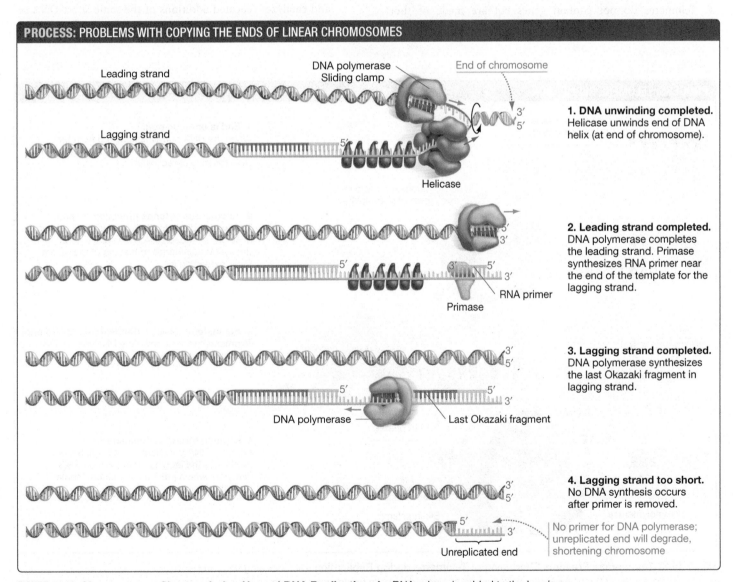

PROCESS: PROBLEMS WITH COPYING THE ENDS OF LINEAR CHROMOSOMES

Leading strand

DNA polymerase
Sliding clamp

End of chromosome

3′
5′

Lagging strand

5′

Helicase

1. DNA unwinding completed. Helicase unwinds end of DNA helix (at end of chromosome).

5′
3′

5′

3′
5′
3′

RNA primer

Primase

2. Leading strand completed. DNA polymerase completes the leading strand. Primase synthesizes RNA primer near the end of the template for the lagging strand.

3′
5′

5′

5′
3′

DNA polymerase

Last Okazaki fragment

3. Lagging strand completed. DNA polymerase synthesizes the last Okazaki fragment in lagging strand.

3′
5′

5′
3′

Unreplicated end

4. Lagging strand too short. No DNA synthesis occurs after primer is removed.

No primer for DNA polymerase; unreplicated end will degrade, shortening chromosome

FIGURE 15.12 Chromosomes Shorten during Normal DNA Replication. An RNA primer is added to the lagging strand near the end of the chromosome. Once the primer is removed, it cannot be replaced with DNA. As a result, the chromosome shortens.

- DNA polymerase is unable to add DNA near the tip of the chromosome, because it cannot synthesize DNA without a primer (step 4). As a result, the single-stranded DNA that is left stays single stranded.

The single-stranded DNA at the end of the lagging strand is eventually degraded, which results in the shortening of the chromosome. If this process were to continue unabated, every chromosome would shorten by about 50 to 100 deoxyribonucleotides each time DNA replication occurred. Over time, linear chromosomes would vanish.

Telomerase Solves the End Replication Problem

How do eukaryotes maintain their chromosomes? One answer emerged after Elizabeth Blackburn, Carol Greider, and Jack Szostak reported two striking discoveries:

1. Telomeres do not contain genes but are made of short stretches of bases that are repeated over and over. In human telomeres, for example, the base sequence TTAGGG is repeated thousands of times.

2. A remarkable enzyme called telomerase that carries its own template is involved in replicating telomeres.

Telomerase is extraordinary because it catalyzes the synthesis of DNA from an RNA template that it contains. Telomerase adds DNA onto the end of a chromosome to prevent it from getting shorter.

FIGURE 15.13 shows one model for how telomerase works to maintain the ends of eukaryotic chromosomes.

Step 1 The unreplicated segment of the telomere at the 3′ end of the template for the lagging strand forms a single-stranded "overhang".

Step 2 Telomerase binds to the overhanging single-stranded DNA and begins DNA synthesis. The template for this reaction is a portion of the RNA held within telomerase.

Step 3 Telomerase synthesizes DNA in the 5′ → 3′ direction and catalyzes repeated additions of the same short DNA sequence to the end of the growing single strand.

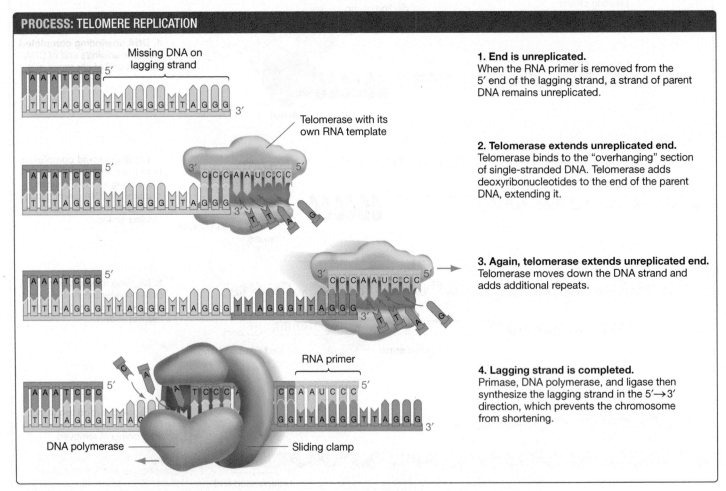

PROCESS: TELOMERE REPLICATION

1. End is unreplicated.
When the RNA primer is removed from the 5′ end of the lagging strand, a strand of parent DNA remains unreplicated.

2. Telomerase extends unreplicated end.
Telomerase binds to the "overhanging" section of single-stranded DNA. Telomerase adds deoxyribonucleotides to the end of the parent DNA, extending it.

3. Again, telomerase extends unreplicated end.
Telomerase moves down the DNA strand and adds additional repeats.

4. Lagging strand is completed.
Primase, DNA polymerase, and ligase then synthesize the lagging strand in the 5′→3′ direction, which prevents the chromosome from shortening.

FIGURE 15.13 Telomerase Prevents Shortening of Telomeres during Replication. By extending the number of repeated sequences in the 5′ → 3′ direction, telomerase provides room for enzymes to add an RNA primer to the lagging-strand template. Normal DNA replication enzymes can then fill in the missing section of the lagging strand.

✔**QUESTION** Would this telomerase work as well if its RNA template had a different sequence?

Step 4 Once the single-stranded overhang on the parent strand is lengthened, the normal enzymes of DNA synthesis use this strand as a template to synthesize a complementary strand. The result is that the lagging strand becomes slightly longer than it was originally.

Telomerase Regulation

The way telomerase is regulated is just as remarkable as the enzyme itself. Telomerase is active in only a limited number of cell types. In humans, for example, active telomerase is found primarily in the cells that produce gametes. Most **somatic cells,** meaning cells that are not involved in gamete formation, lack telomerase activity. As predicted, the chromosomes of somatic cells gradually shorten with each mitotic division, becoming progressively smaller as an individual ages.

These observations led to the hypothesis that the number of cell divisions possible for a somatic cell would be limited by the initial length of its telomeres. Carol Greider and colleagues tested this hypothesis by obtaining cells with a variety of telomere lengths from donors aged newborn to 90 years old and growing these cells in culture. (For an introduction to cell culture, see **BioSkills 12** in Appendix B.) Results of their study are shown in **FIGURE 15.14**. As predicted, there was a positive relationship between initial telomere length and the number of cell divisions before cells stop dividing—longer initial telomere length allowed a greater number of cell divisions, regardless of the donor's age.

You've probably noticed that the data points in Figure 15.14 do not fall perfectly on a line. This scatter or noise is typical in many studies. In interpreting results like these, researchers must consider what might account for the scatter and use statistical tests (see **BioSkills 4** in Appendix B) to determine how reliable the results are likely to be.

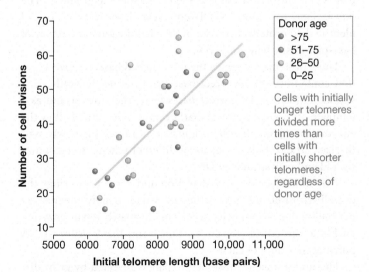

FIGURE 15.14 Telomere Length Predicts the Number of Divisions before Cells Stop Dividing.

DATA: Allsopp, R. C., et al. 1992. *Proceedings of the National Academy of Sciences*, 82: 10114–10118.

If telomere shortening controls the number of divisions possible for a cell, then a related prediction is that by restoring telomerase in somatic cells, these cells should be freed from growth limitations. As predicted, when researchers added telomerase to human cells growing in culture, the cells continued dividing long past the age when otherwise identical cells stop growing. Most biologists are convinced that telomere shortening has a role in limiting the number of cell divisions for somatic cells.

There is a dark side of telomerase activity, however. Unlike the somatic cells they derive from, most cancer cells have active telomerase. Many cancer biologists have proposed that telomerase activity allows the unlimited divisions of cancer cells. A simple prediction is that by inhibiting telomerase, the progression of cancer can be slowed or stopped. When combined with other approaches, could drugs that knock out telomerase be an effective way to fight cancer? Unfortunately, the complexity of cancer often thwarts such simple predictions. So far, answers to this question are unclear. Research continues.

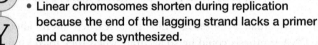

check your understanding

If you understand that . . .

- Linear chromosomes shorten during replication because the end of the lagging strand lacks a primer and cannot be synthesized.
- Shortening is prevented in certain cells—particularly those that produce sperm and egg—because telomerase adds short, repeated DNA sequences to the template strand. Primase can then add an RNA primer to the lagging strand, and DNA polymerase can fill in the missing sections.

✔ **You should be able to . . .**

1. Explain why telomerase is not needed by bacterial cells.
2. Explain why telomerase has to have a built-in template.

Answers are available in Appendix A.

15.5 Repairing Mistakes and DNA Damage

DNA polymerases work fast. In *E. coli*, for example, each replication fork advances about 500 nucleotides per second. But the replication process is also astonishingly accurate. In organisms ranging from *E. coli* to animals, the error rate during DNA replication averages about one mistake per *billion* deoxyribonucleotides.

This level of accuracy is critical. Humans, for example, develop from a fertilized egg that has roughly 12 billion deoxyribonucleotides in its DNA. This DNA is replicated over and over to create the trillions of cells that eventually make up the adult body. If more than one or two mutations occurred during each cell division cycle as a person developed, genes would be riddled with errors by the time the individual reached maturity. Genes that contain errors are often defective.

Based on these observations, it is no exaggeration to claim that the accurate replication of DNA is a matter of life and death. Natural selection favors individuals with enzymes that copy DNA quickly and accurately.

These observations raise a key question. How can the enzymes of DNA replication be as precise as they are?

Correcting Mistakes in DNA Synthesis

As DNA polymerase marches along a DNA template, hydrogen bonding occurs between incoming deoxyribonucleotides and the deoxyribonucleotides on the template strand. DNA polymerases are selective about the bases they add to a growing strand because (1) the correct base pairings (A-T and G-C) are energetically the most favorable, and (2) these correct pairings have a distinct shape. As a result, DNA polymerase inserts an incorrect deoxyribonucleotide (**FIGURE 15.15a**) only about once in every 100,000 bases added.

An error rate of one in 100,000 seems low, but it is much higher than the rate of one in a billion listed at the start of this section. What happens when DNA polymerase makes a mistake?

DNA Polymerase Proofreads Biologists learned more about how DNA synthesis could be so accurate when they found mutant cells in which DNA synthesis was *in*accurate.

Specifically, researchers found *E. coli* mutants with error rates that were 100 times greater than normal. Recall that a mutant is an individual with a novel trait caused by a mutation (see Chapter 14). In the case of *E. coli* mutants with high error rates

(a) DNA polymerase adds a mismatched base...

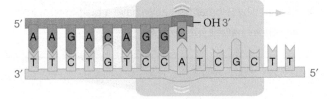

(b) ...but detects the mistake and corrects it.

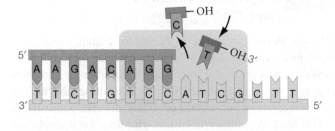

FIGURE 15.15 DNA Polymerase Can Proofread. If a mismatch such as the pairing of A with C occurs **(a)**, DNA polymerase can act as a 3′ → 5′ exonuclease, meaning that it can remove bases in that direction **(b)**. The DNA polymerase then adds the correct base.

in DNA replication, biologists found a defect in a portion of the DNA polymerase III enzyme called the ε (epsilon) subunit. Further analyses showed that the ε subunit acts as an exonuclease—meaning an enzyme that removes deoxyribonucleotides from the ends of DNA strands (**FIGURE 15.15b**).

If a newly added deoxyribonucleotide is not correctly paired with a base on the complementary strand, the positioning of the incorrect deoxyribonucleotide provides a poor substrate for DNA polymerase to extend. This is because the geometry of incorrect base pairs differs from that of the correct A-T and G-C pairs. DNA polymerase's active site can detect these shapes and will add a new deoxyribonucleotide only when the previous base pair is correct. In wild-type *E. coli*, the polymerase pauses when it detects the wrong shape, and the exonuclease activity of the ε subunit removes the mismatched deoxyribonucleotide.

These findings led to the conclusion that DNA polymerase III can **proofread.** If the wrong base is added during DNA synthesis, the enzyme pauses, removes the mismatched deoxyribonucleotide that was just added, and then proceeds again with synthesis.

Eukaryotic DNA polymerases have the same type of proofreading ability. Typically, proofreading reduces the overall error rate of DNA synthesis to about one mistake in 10 million bases added. Is this accurate enough? The answer remains no.

Mismatch Repair If—despite its proofreading ability—DNA polymerase leaves a mismatched base behind in the newly synthesized strand, a battery of enzymes springs into action to correct the problem. **Mismatch repair** occurs when mismatched bases are corrected after DNA synthesis is complete.

The proteins responsible for mismatch repair were discovered in the same way proofreading was—by analyzing *E. coli* mutants. In this case, the mutants had normal DNA polymerase III but abnormally high mutation rates.

The first mutation that caused a deficiency in mismatch repair was identified in the late 1960s and was called *mutS*. (The *mut* is short for "mutator.") Twenty years later, researchers had identified 10 proteins involved in the identification and repair of base-pair mismatches in *E. coli*.

These proteins recognize the mismatched base, remove a section containing the incorrect base from the newly synthesized strand, and fill in the correct bases using the older strand as a template. In *E. coli*, chemical marks on the older strand allow the enzymes to distinguish the original strand from the newly synthesized strand. Eukaryotes use a different scheme to recognize the old and new strands of DNA.

This final layer of error detection and correction brings the overall error rate of DNA synthesis down to roughly one mistake per billion deoxyribonucleotides. The mismatch-repair enzymes are like a copy editor who corrects the errors that a writer—DNA polymerase—did not catch.

The importance of mismatch repair is revealed by grim discoveries: Mutations in components of the mismatch repair system are observed in many common human cancers, where they play an important role in cancer development and progression.

Repairing Damaged DNA

Even after DNA is synthesized and proofread and mismatches repaired, the job of ensuring accuracy doesn't end. Genes are under constant assault. DNA is damaged by sunlight, X-rays, and many chemicals like the hydroxyl (OH) radicals produced during aerobic metabolism, aflatoxin B1 found in moldy peanuts and corn, and benzo[α]pyrene in cigarette smoke. If this damage were ignored, mutations would quickly accumulate to lethal levels. To fix problems caused by chemical attack, radiation, or other events, organisms have evolved a wide array of DNA damage-repair systems. As an example, consider the **nucleotide excision repair** system that works on DNA damage caused by ultraviolet light and many different chemicals.

Ultraviolet (UV) light in sunlight—and tanning booths—can cause a covalent bond to form between adjacent pyrimidine bases within the same DNA strand. The thymine-thymine pair illustrated in **FIGURE 15.16** is a common example. This defect, called a thymine dimer, creates a kink in the structure of DNA. The kink stalls standard DNA polymerases, blocking DNA replication. If the damage is not repaired, the cell may die.

Nucleotide excision repair fixes thymine dimers and many other types of damage that distort the DNA helix. In the first step of excision repair, an enzyme recognizes the kink in the DNA helix (step 1 in **FIGURE 15.17**). Once a damaged region is recognized, another enzyme removes a segment of single-stranded DNA containing the defective sequence (step 2). The intact DNA strand provides a template for synthesis of a corrected strand, and the 3′ hydroxyl of the DNA strand next to the gap serves as a primer (step 3). DNA ligase links the newly synthesized DNA to the original undamaged DNA (step 4). As with mismatch repair, multiple enzymes work together and DNA synthesis plays a central role in repair.

What happens when a human DNA repair system is defective?

Xeroderma Pigmentosum: A Case Study

Xeroderma pigmentosum (XP) is a rare autosomal recessive disease in humans. Individuals with this condition are extremely sensitive to ultraviolet (UV) light. Their skin develops lesions including rough, scaly patches and irregular dark spots after even slight exposure to sunlight.

In 1968 James Cleaver proposed a connection between XP and DNA nucleotide excision repair. He knew that mutants of *E. coli* had defects in nucleotide excision repair that caused an increased sensitivity to radiation. Cleaver's hypothesis was that people with XP have similar mutations. He proposed that they are extremely sensitive to sunlight because they are unable to repair damage induced by UV light.

Cleaver and other researchers made extensive use of cell cultures (**BioSkills 12**, see Appendix B) to study the hypothesized connection between DNA damage, faulty nucleotide excision repair, and XP. They collected skin cells from people with XP and from people with normal UV light sensitivity. When these cells were grown in culture, the biologists exposed them to increasing amounts of UV radiation and recorded how many survived.

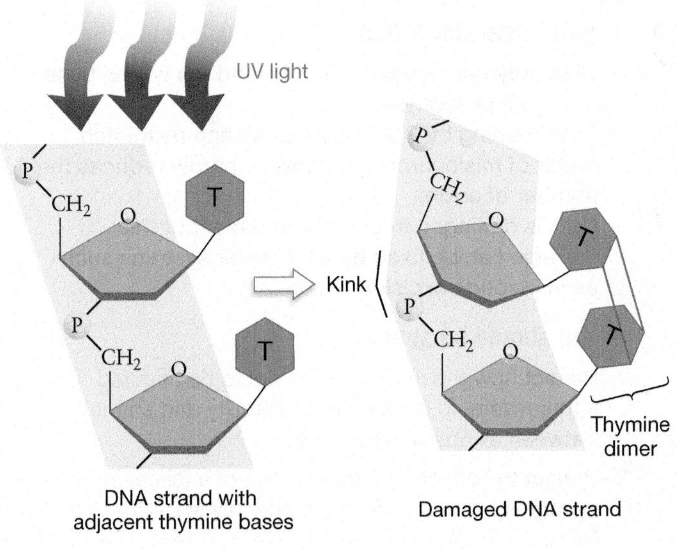

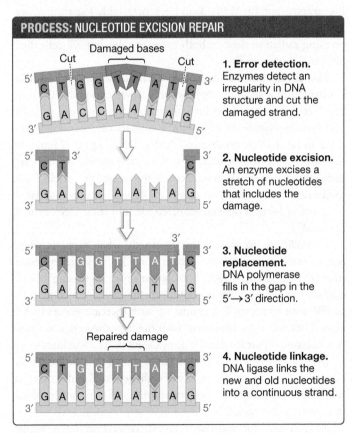

FIGURE 15.16 UV Light Damages DNA. When UV light strikes a section of DNA that has adjacent thymines, the energy can break bonds within each base and lead to the formation of bonds *between* them. The thymine dimer that is produced causes a kink in the DNA.

✔ **QUESTION** Why are infrared wavelengths much less likely than UV to damage DNA? (Hint: See Figure 10.4.)

PROCESS: NUCLEOTIDE EXCISION REPAIR

1. Error detection. Enzymes detect an irregularity in DNA structure and cut the damaged strand.

2. Nucleotide excision. An enzyme excises a stretch of nucleotides that includes the damage.

3. Nucleotide replacement. DNA polymerase fills in the gap in the 5′→3′ direction.

4. Nucleotide linkage. DNA ligase links the new and old nucleotides into a continuous strand.

FIGURE 15.17 In Nucleotide Excision Repair, Defective Bases Are Removed and Replaced.

(a) Vulnerability of cells to UV light damage

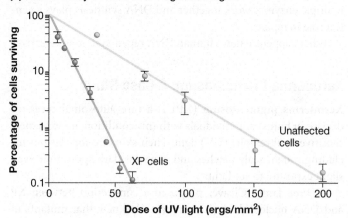

(b) Ability of cells to repair UV light damage

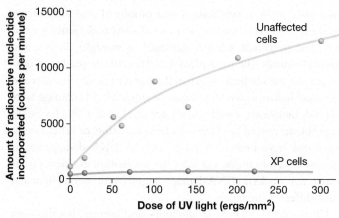

FIGURE 15.18 DNA Damage from UV Light Is Not Repaired Properly in Individuals with XP. (a) When cell cultures from unaffected individuals and XP patients are irradiated with various doses of UV light (expressed here as ergs/mm²), the percentage of cells that survive is strikingly different. **(b)** When cell cultures from unaffected individuals and XP patients are irradiated with various doses of UV light and then provided with a radioactive deoxyribonucleotide, only cells from unaffected individuals incorporate the labeled deoxyribonucleotide into their DNA.

DATA: (a) Cleaver, J. E. 1970. *Int. J. Rad. Biol.* 18: 577–565, Fig 3. (b) Cleaver, J. E. 1972. *J. Invest. Dermatol.* 58: 124–128, Fig 1.

✔**QUESTION** Why are people who cultivate a sun tan increasing their risk of developing cancer? (Hint: Tanning is a response to UV light.)

FIGURE 15.18a shows the results of one such study by Cleaver. Note that the intensity of the radiation is graphed on the *x*-axis, and the percentage of cells surviving is graphed on the *y*-axis. Note, too, that the *y*-axis is logarithmic. (For help with reading graphs, see **BioSkills 3** and for help with logarithms, see **BioSkills 6**, both in Appendix B.) Cell survival declined with increasing radiation dose in both types of cells, but XP cells died off much more rapidly.

The connection to nucleotide excision repair systems was confirmed in a separate study when Cleaver exposed cells from unaffected and XP individuals to various amounts of UV light and then incubated the cells with a radioactive deoxyribonucleotide to label DNA synthesized during DNA repair. If repair is defective in XP individuals, then their cells should incorporate little radioactive deoxyribonucleotide into their DNA. Cells from unaffected individuals, in contrast, should incorporate large amounts of labeled deoxyribonucleotide into their DNA as it is repaired.

As **FIGURE 15.18b** shows, this is exactly what happens. Here the amount of radioactive deoxyribonucleotides incorporated into DNA is graphed against radiation dose. Increasingly large amounts of radioactivity are found in the DNA of healthy cells as UV dose increases, but almost no such increase occurs in XP cells. These data are consistent with the hypothesis that nucleotide excision repair is virtually nonexistent in XP individuals.

Genetic analyses of XP patients have shown that the condition can result from mutations in any of eight genes. This discovery is not surprising in light of the large number of enzymes involved in repairing damaged DNA.

As you saw for mismatch repair, defects in DNA repair genes are frequently associated with cancer. Individuals with xeroderma pigmentosum, for example, are 1000 to 2000 times more likely to get skin cancer than are individuals with intact excision repair systems. To explain this pattern, biologists suggest that if DNA damage in the genes involved in the cell cycle goes unrepaired, mutations will result that may allow the cell to grow in an uncontrolled manner. Tumor formation could result. Recall

check your understanding

If you understand that . . .

- DNA polymerases occasionally add the wrong base during DNA synthesis.
- Proofreading by DNA polymerase and mismatch repair of misincorporated bases sharply reduces the number of errors.
- DNA is damaged frequently, and most of this damage can be fixed by DNA repair systems such as nucleotide excision repair.

✔ **You should be able to . . .**

1. Predict how the mutation rate would be affected if there were no differences in stability and shape between all possible base pairs.
2. Predict the effect on mutation rate of a failure in the system for distinguishing old and newly synthesized DNA.
3. State which nucleotide excision repair enzymes are specific for DNA repair and which work in both normal DNA replication and in DNA repair.

Answers are available in Appendix A.

that most cancers develop only after several genes have been damaged (see Chapter 12). If the overall mutation rate in a cell is elevated because of defects in DNA repair, then mutations that trigger cancer become more likely.

At this point, it's clear that genes are made of DNA and that DNA is accurately copied and passed on to offspring. How can information be stored in DNA, and how can this information be used? (These are the topics of the next two chapters.)

If you understand . . .

15.1 What Are Genes Made Of?

- Experiments on viruses that had labeled proteins or DNA showed that DNA is the hereditary material.

- DNA's primary structure consists of a sugar–phosphate backbone and a sequence of nitrogen-containing bases.

- DNA's secondary structure consists of two strands in an antiparallel orientation. The strands twist into a helix and are held together by complementary pairing between bases.

✔ You should be able to interpret an imaginary experiment like the one done by Hershey and Chase that shows that ^{32}P is found only in the pellet and that ^{35}S is found in both the pellet and the solution.

15.2 Testing Early Hypotheses about DNA Synthesis

- By labeling DNA with ^{15}N or ^{14}N, researchers were able to validate the hypothesis that DNA replication is semiconservative.

- In semiconservative replication, each strand of a parent DNA molecule provides a template for the synthesis of a daughter strand, resulting in two complete DNA double helices.

✔ You should be able to write a sequence of double-stranded DNA that is 10 base pairs long, separate the strands, and, without comparing them, write in the bases that are added during DNA replication.

15.3 A Model for DNA Synthesis

- DNA synthesis requires many different enzymes, and it occurs in one direction only.

- DNA synthesis requires both a template and a primer sequence. It takes place at the replication fork where the double helix is opened.

- Synthesis of the leading strand in the $5' \rightarrow 3'$ direction is continuous, but synthesis of the lagging strand is discontinuous because on that strand, the DNA polymerase moves away from the replication fork.

- On the lagging strand, short DNA fragments called Okazaki fragments form and are joined together. Okazaki fragments are primed by a short strand of RNA.

✔ You should be able to draw and label a diagram of a replication bubble that shows (1) the $5' \rightarrow 3'$ polarity of the two parental DNA strands and (2) the leading and lagging daughter strands at each replication fork.

15.4 Replicating the Ends of Linear Chromosomes

- At the ends of linear chromosomes in eukaryotes, the enzyme telomerase adds short, repeated sections of DNA so that the lagging strand can be synthesized without shortening the chromosome.

- Telomerase is active in reproductive cells that eventually undergo meiosis. As a result, gametes contain chromosomes of normal length.

- Chromosomes in cells without telomerase shorten with continued cell division until their telomeres reach a critical length at which cell division no longer occurs.

✔ You should be able to explain the significance of telomerase reactivation in cancer cells.

15.5 Repairing Mistakes and DNA Damage

- DNA replication is remarkably accurate because (1) DNA polymerase selectively adds a deoxyribonucleotide that correctly pairs with the template strand; (2) DNA proofreads each added deoxyribonucleotide; and (3) mismatch repair enzymes remove incorrect bases once synthesis is complete and replace them with the correct base.

- DNA repair occurs after DNA has been damaged by chemicals or radiation.

- Nucleotide excision repair cuts out damaged portions of DNA and replaces them with correct sequences.

- If DNA repair enzymes are defective, mutation rate increases. Because of this, several types of human cancers are associated with defects in the genes responsible for DNA repair.

✔ You should be able to explain the logical connections between failure of repair systems, increases in mutation rate, and high likelihood of cancer developing.

1. MasteringBiology Assignments

Tutorials and Activities DNA and RNA Structure; DNA Double Helix; DNA Replication; DNA Replication: A Closer Look; DNA Replication: A Review; DNA Replication: An Overview; DNA Synthesis; Experimental Inquiry: Does DNA Replication Follow the Conservative, Semiconservative, or Dispersive Model; Hershey–Chase Experiment

Questions Reading Quizzes, Blue-Thread Questions, Test Bank

2. eText Read your book online, search, take notes, highlight text, and more.

3. The Study Area Practice Test, Cumulative Test, BioFlix® 3-D Animations, Videos, Activities, Audio Glossary, Word Study Tools, Art

You should be able to . . .

✓ TEST YOUR KNOWLEDGE
Answers are available in Appendix A

1. What does it mean to say that strands in a double helix are antiparallel?
   a. Their primary sequences consist of a sequence of *complementary* bases.
   b. They each have a sugar–phosphate backbone.
   c. They each have a $5' \rightarrow 3'$ directionality.
   d. They have opposite directionality, or polarity.

2. Which of the following is *not* a property of DNA polymerase?
   a. It adds dNTPs only in the $5' \rightarrow 3'$ direction.
   b. It requires a primer to work.
   c. It is associated with a sliding clamp only on the leading strand.
   d. Its exonuclease activity is involved in proofreading.

3. The enzyme that removes twists in DNA ahead of the replication fork is _____.

4. What is the function of primase?
   a. synthesis of the short section of double-stranded DNA required by DNA polymerase
   b. synthesis of a short RNA, complementary to single-stranded DNA
   c. closing the gap at the $3'$ end of DNA after excision repair
   d. removing primers and synthesizing a short section of DNA to replace them

5. How are Okazaki fragments synthesized?
   a. using the leading strand template, and synthesizing $5' \rightarrow 3'$
   b. using the leading strand template, and synthesizing $3' \rightarrow 5'$
   c. using the lagging strand template, and synthesizing $5' \rightarrow 3'$
   d. using the lagging strand template, and synthesizing $3' \rightarrow 5'$

6. An enzyme that uses an internal RNA template to synthesize DNA is _____.

✓ TEST YOUR UNDERSTANDING
Answers are available in Appendix A

7. Researchers design experiments so that only one thing is different between the treatments that are being compared. In the Hershey–Chase experiment, what was this single difference?

8. What is the relationship between defective DNA repair and cancer?

9. Why is the synthesis of the lagging strand of DNA discontinuous? How is it possible for the synthesis of the leading strand to be continuous?

10. Explain how telomerase prevents linear chromosomes from shortening during replication.

11. Predict what would occur in a bacterial mutant that lost the ability to chemically mark the template strand of DNA.
    a. The mutation rate would increase.

   b. The ability of DNA polymerase to discriminate between correct and incorrect base pairs would decrease.
   c. The energy differences between correct and incorrect base pairs would decrease.
   d. The energy differences between correct and incorrect base pairs would increase.

12. What aspect of DNA structure makes it possible for the enzymes of nucleotide excision repair to recognize many different types of DNA damage?
    a. the polarity of each DNA strand
    b. the antiparallel orientation of strands in the double helix
    c. the energy differences between correct and incorrect base pairs
    d. the regularity of DNA's overall structure

13. If you could engineer an activity into DNA polymerase to allow both strands to follow the replication fork, what would this additional activity be?
    a. the ability to begin DNA synthesis without a primer
    b. the ability to proofread in the $5' \rightarrow 3'$ direction
    c. the ability to synthesize DNA in the $3' \rightarrow 5'$ direction
    d. the ability to synthesize DNA without using a template

14. In the late 1950s, Herbert Taylor grew bean root-tip cells in a solution of radioactive thymidine and allowed them to undergo one round of DNA replication. He then transferred the cells to a solution without the radioactive deoxyribonucleotide, allowed them to replicate again, and examined their chromosomes for the presence of radioactivity. His results are shown in the following figure, where red indicates a radioactive chromatid.

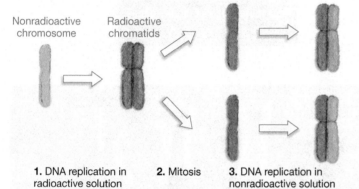

Nonradioactive chromosome   Radioactive chromatids

1. DNA replication in radioactive solution   2. Mitosis   3. DNA replication in nonradioactive solution

    a. Draw diagrams explaining the pattern of radioactivity observed in the sister chromatids after the first and second rounds of replication.
    b. What would the results of Taylor's experiment be if eukaryotes used a conservative mode of DNA replication?

15. The graph that follows shows the survival of four different *E. coli* strains after exposure to increasing doses of ultraviolet light. The wild-type strain is normal, but the other strains have a mutation in either a gene called *uvrA*, a gene called *recA*, or both.

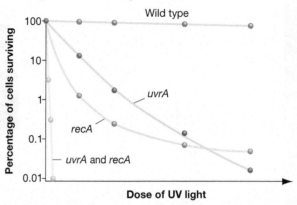

DATA: Howard-Flanders, P., and R. P. Boyce. 1966. *Radiation Research Supplement* 6: 156–184, Fig. 8.

    a. Which strains are most sensitive to UV light? Which strains are least sensitive?
    b. What are the relative contributions of these genes to the repair of UV damage?

16. **QUANTITATIVE** Assuming that each replication fork moves at a rate of 500 base pairs per second, how long would it take to replicate the *E. coli* chromosome (with 4.6 million base pairs) from a single origin of replication?

16 How Genes Work

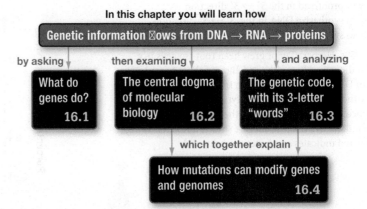

In this chapter you will learn how

Genetic information ⊠ows from DNA → RNA → proteins

by asking ↓

then examining ↓

and analyzing ↓

What do genes do? **16.1**

The central dogma of molecular biology **16.2**

The genetic code, with its 3-letter "words" **16.3**

which together explain ↓

How mutations can modify genes and genomes **16.4**

This image shows a normal human male spectral karyotype—a micrograph of metaphase chromosomes stained to show different homologous chromosome pairs. This chapter explores how DNA sequences in chromosomes are related to phenotypes.

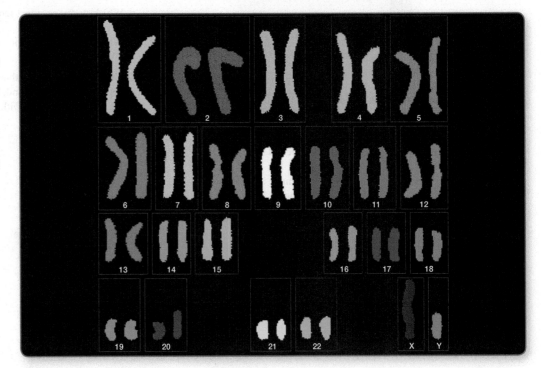

DNA has been called the blueprint of life. If an organism's DNA is like a set of blueprints, then its cells are like construction sites, and the enzymes inside a cell are like construction workers. But how does the DNA inside each cell assemble this team of skilled laborers and specify the materials needed to build and maintain the cell, and remodel it when conditions change?

Mendel provided insights that made the study of these questions possible. He discovered that particular alleles are associated with certain phenotypes and that alleles do not change when transmitted from parent to offspring. Later, the chromosome theory of inheritance established that genes are found in chromosomes, whose movement during meiosis explains Mendel's results.

The science of molecular biology began with the discovery that DNA is the hereditary material and that DNA is a double-helical structure containing sequences of four bases. From these early advances, it was clear that genes are made of DNA and that genes carry the instructions for making and maintaining an individual.

This chapter is part of the Big Picture. See how on pages 366–367.

✔ When you see this checkmark, stop and test yourself. Answers are available in Appendix A.

But biologists still didn't know how the information in DNA is translated into action. How does **gene expression**—the process of converting archived information into molecules that actually do things in the cell—occur?

This chapter introduces some of the most pivotal ideas in all of biology—ideas that connect genotypes to phenotypes by revealing how genes work at the molecular level. They also speak to the heart of a key attribute of life: processing genetic information to produce a living organism. (You can see how these concepts fit into the Big Picture of Genetic Information on pages 366–367.)

Understanding how genes work triggered a major transition in biological science. Instead of thinking about genes solely in relation to their effects on eye color in fruit flies or on seed shape in garden peas, biologists could begin analyzing the molecular composition of genes and their products. The molecular revolution in biology took flight.

16.1 What Do Genes Do?

Although biologists of the early twentieth century made tremendous progress in understanding how genes are inherited, an explicit hypothesis explaining what genes do did not appear until 1941. That year George Beadle and Edward Tatum published a series of breakthrough experiments on a bread mold called *Neurospora crassa*.

Beadle and Tatum's research was inspired by an idea that was brilliant in its simplicity. As Beadle said: "One ought to be able to discover what genes do by making them defective." The idea was to knock out a gene by damaging it and then infer what the gene does by observing the phenotype of the mutant individual.

Today, alleles that do not function at all are called **knock-out, null,** or **loss-of-function alleles.** Creating knock-out mutant alleles and analyzing their effects is still one of the most common research strategies in studies of gene function. But Beadle and Tatum were the pioneers.

The One-Gene, One-Enzyme Hypothesis

To start their work, Beadle and Tatum exposed a large number of *N. crassa* cells to radiation. As described earlier (Chapter 15), radiation can damage the double-helical structure of DNA—often in a way that makes the affected gene nonfunctional.

Their next step was to examine the mutant cells. Eventually they succeeded in finding *N. crassa* mutants that could not make specific compounds. For example, one of the mutants could not make pyridoxine, also called vitamin B_6, even though normal individuals can. Further, Beadle and Tatum showed that the inability to synthesize pyridoxine was due to a defect in a single gene, and that the inability to synthesize other molecules was due to defects in other genes.

These results inspired their **one-gene, one-enzyme hypothesis.** Beadle and Tatum proposed that the mutant *N. crassa* could not make pyridoxine because it lacked an enzyme required to synthesize the compound. They further proposed that the lack of the enzyme was due to a genetic defect. Based on analyses of knock-out mutants, the one-gene, one-enzyme hypothesis claimed that each gene contains the information needed to make an enzyme.

An Experimental Test of the Hypothesis

Three years later, Adrian Srb and Norman Horowitz published a rigorous test of the one-gene, one-enzyme hypothesis. These biologists focused on the ability of *N. crassa* to synthesize the amino acid arginine. In the lab, normal cells of this bread mold grow well on a laboratory culture medium that lacks arginine. This is possible because *N. crassa* cells are able to synthesize their own arginine.

Previous work had shown that organisms synthesize arginine in a series of steps called a **metabolic pathway.** As FIGURE 16.1 shows, compounds called ornithine and citrulline are intermediate products in the metabolic pathway leading to arginine. Specific enzymes are required to synthesize ornithine, convert ornithine to citrulline, and change citrulline to arginine. Srb and Horowitz hypothesized that specific *N. crassa* genes are responsible for producing each of the three enzymes involved.

To test this idea, Srb and Horowitz used radiation to create a large number of mutant cells. However, radiation is equally likely to damage DNA and mutate genes in any part of the organism's genome, and most organisms have thousands or tens of thousands of genes. Of the many mutants the biologists created, how could they find the handful that specifically knocked out a step in the pathway for arginine synthesis?

To find the mutants they were looking for, the researchers performed what is now known as a genetic screen. A **genetic screen** is any technique for picking certain types of mutants out of many randomly generated mutants.

Srb and Horowitz began their screen by raising colonies of irradiated cells on a medium that included arginine. Then they transferred a sample of each colony to a medium that *lacked* arginine. If an individual could grow in the presence of arginine but failed to grow without arginine, they concluded that it couldn't make its own arginine.

FIGURE 16.1 Different Enzymes Catalyze Each Step in the Metabolic Pathway for Arginine.

✓**QUESTION** If a cell lacked enzyme 2 but was placed in growth medium with ornithine, could it grow? Could it grow if it received citrulline instead?

The biologists followed up by confirming that the offspring of these cells also had this defect. Based on these data, they were confident that they had isolated individuals with mutations in one or more of the genes for the enzymes shown in Figure 16.1.

To test the one-gene, one-enzyme hypothesis, the biologists grew each mutant under four different conditions: on normal media without added arginine, and on normal medium supplemented with ornithine, citrulline, or arginine.

As **FIGURE 16.2** shows, the results from these growth experiments were dramatic. Some of the mutant cells were able to grow on some of these media but not on others. More specifically, the mutants fell into three distinct classes, which the researchers called *arg1*, *arg2*, and *arg3*.

As the "Interpretation" section of the figure shows, the data make sense if each type of mutant lacked a different, specific step in a metabolic pathway because of a defect in a particular gene. In short, Srb and Horowitz had documented a correlation between a specific genetic defect and a defect at a specific point in a metabolic pathway. This experiment convinced most investigators that the one-gene, one-enzyme hypothesis was correct.

RESEARCH

QUESTION: What do genes do?

HYPOTHESIS: Each gene contains the information required to make one enzyme.

NULL HYPOTHESIS: Genes do not have a one-to-one correspondence with enzymes.

EXPERIMENTAL STRATEGY: Mutate specific genes. Test to see if each mutant also lacks one of the enzymes required for different steps in the pathway for synthesizing arginine.

EXPERIMENTAL SETUP: Isolate mutant *N. crassa* that cannot synthesize arginine. Grow each type of mutant on normal medium that is:

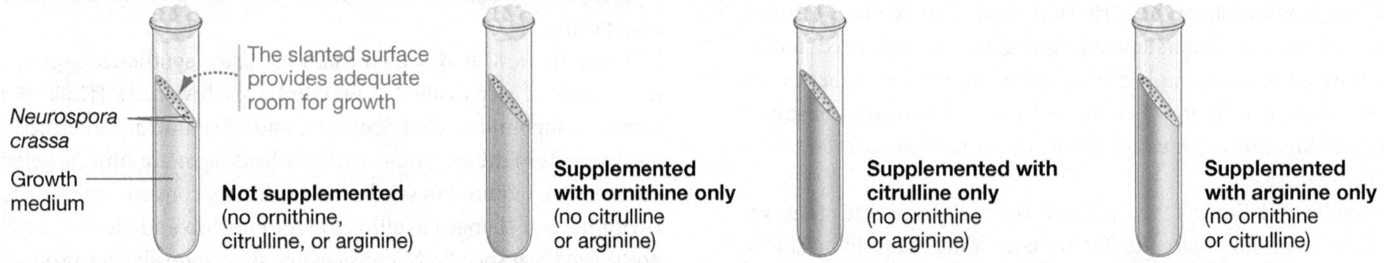

Neurospora crassa

Growth medium

The slanted surface provides adequate room for growth

Not supplemented (no ornithine, citrulline, or arginine)

Supplemented with ornithine only (no citrulline or arginine)

Supplemented with citrulline only (no ornithine or arginine)

Supplemented with arginine only (no ornithine or citrulline)

PREDICTION: There will be three distinct types of mutants, corresponding to defects in enzyme 1, enzyme 2, and enzyme 3 in the pathway for synthesizing arginine. Each type of mutant will be able to grow on different combinations of the four types of media.

PREDICTION OF NULL HYPOTHESIS: There will not be a simple correspondence between a particular mutation and a particular enzyme.

RESULTS: There are three distinct types of mutants, called *arg1*, *arg2*, and *arg3*, each defective in one enzyme.

		None	Ornithine only	Citrulline only	Arginine only
	arg1	no growth	GROWTH	GROWTH	GROWTH
Mutant type	*arg2*	no growth	no growth	GROWTH	GROWTH
	arg3	no growth	no growth	no growth	GROWTH

Supplement type

INTERPRETATION:

Precursor → Ornithine → Citrulline → Arginine

arg1 cells lack enzyme 1

arg2 cells lack enzyme 2

arg3 cells lack enzyme 3

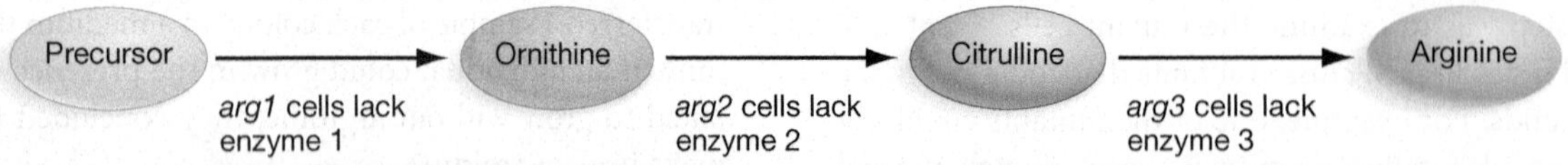

CONCLUSION: The one-gene, one-enzyme hypothesis is supported.

FIGURE 16.2 Experimental Support for the One-Gene, One-Enzyme Hypothesis. The association between specific genetic defects in *N. crassa* and specific defects in the metabolic pathway for arginine synthesis provided evidence that supported the one-gene, one-enzyme hypothesis.

SOURCE: Srb, A. M., and N. H. Horowitz. 1944. The ornithine cycle in *Neurospora* and its genetic control. *Journal of Biological Chemistry* 154: 129–139.

✔**QUESTION** Experimental designs must be repeatable so that other investigators can try the experiment themselves to check the results. Name three things that these researchers would need to describe so that others could repeat this experiment.

Follow-up work showed that genes contain the information for all the proteins produced by an organism—not just enzymes. Biologists finally understood what most genes do: They contain the instructions for making proteins.

In many cases, though, a protein is made up of several different polypeptides, each of which is a product of a different gene. Consequently, for greater accuracy, the one-gene, one-enzyme hypothesis is best called the one-gene, one-polypeptide hypothesis.

16.2 The Central Dogma of Molecular Biology

How does a gene specify the production of a protein? As soon as Beadle and Tatum's hypothesis had been supported in *N. crassa* and a variety of other organisms, this question became a central one.

Part of the answer lay in the molecular structure of the gene. Biochemists knew that the primary components of DNA were four nitrogen-containing bases: the pyrimidines thymine (abbreviated T) and cytosine (C), and the purines adenine (A) and guanine (G). They also knew that these bases were connected in a linear sequence by a sugar–phosphate backbone. Watson and Crick's model for the secondary structure of the DNA molecule (see Chapters 4 and 15) revealed that two strands of DNA are wound into a double helix, held together by hydrogen bonds between the complementary base pairs A-T and G-C.

Given DNA's structure, it appeared extremely unlikely that DNA directly catalyzed the reactions that produce proteins. Its shape was too regular to suggest that it could bind a wide variety of substrate molecules and lower the activation energy for chemical reactions. So how, then, did information translate into action?

The Genetic Code Hypothesis

Crick proposed that the sequence of bases in DNA might act as a code. His idea was that DNA was *only* an information-storage molecule. The instructions it contained would have to be read and then translated into proteins.

Crick offered Morse code as an analogy. Morse code is a message-transmission system using dots and dashes to represent the letters of the alphabet, and in that way it can convey all the complex information of human language. Crick proposed that different combinations of bases could specify the 20 amino acids, just as different combinations of dots and dashes specify the 26 letters of the alphabet. A particular stretch of DNA, then, could contain the information needed to produce the amino acid sequence of a particular polypeptide.

In code form, the tremendous quantity of information required to build and operate a cell could be stored compactly. This information could also be copied through complementary base pairing and transmitted efficiently from one generation to the next.

It soon became apparent, however, that the information encoded in the base sequence of DNA is not translated into the amino acid sequence of proteins directly. Instead, the link between DNA as information repository and proteins as cellular machines is indirect.

RNA as the Intermediary between Genes and Proteins

The first clue that the biological information in DNA must go through an intermediary in order to produce proteins came from knowledge of cell structure. In eukaryotic cells, DNA is enclosed within a membrane-bound organelle called the nucleus (see Chapter 7). But the cells' ribosomes, where protein synthesis takes place, are outside the nucleus, in the cytoplasm.

To make sense of this observation, François Jacob and Jacques Monod suggested that RNA molecules act as a link between genes and the protein-manufacturing centers. Jacob and Monod's hypothesis is illustrated in **FIGURE 16.3**. They predicted that short-lived molecules of RNA, which they called **messenger RNA,** or **mRNA** for short, carry information out of the nucleus from DNA to the site of protein synthesis. Messenger RNA is one of several distinct types of RNA in cells.

Follow-up research confirmed that the messenger RNA hypothesis is correct. One particularly important piece of evidence was the discovery of an enzyme that catalyzes the synthesis of RNA. This protein is called **RNA polymerase** because it polymerizes ribonucleotides into strands of RNA.

RNA polymerase synthesizes RNA molecules according to the information provided by the sequence of bases in a particular stretch of DNA. Unlike DNA polymerase, RNA polymerase

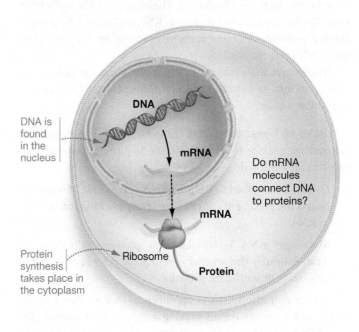

FIGURE 16.3 The Messenger RNA Hypothesis. In cells of eukaryotes such as plants, animals, and fungi, most DNA is found in the nucleus, but proteins are manufactured using ribosomes in the cytoplasm outside the nucleus. Biologists proposed that the information coded in DNA is carried from inside the nucleus out to the ribosomes by messenger RNA (mRNA).

does not require a primer to begin connecting ribonucleotides together to produce a strand of RNA.

To test the mRNA hypothesis, researchers created a reaction mix containing three critical elements: (1) the enzyme RNA polymerase; (2) ribonucleotides containing the bases adenine (A), uracil (U), guanine (G), and cytosine (C); and (3) strands of synthetic DNA that contained deoxyribonucleotides in which the only base was thymine (T).

After allowing the polymerization reaction to proceed, the biologists isolated RNA molecules that contained only the base adenine.

This result supported the hypothesis that RNA polymerase synthesizes RNA according to the rules of complementary base pairing (introduced in Chapter 4), because thymine pairs with adenine. Similar experiments showed that synthetic DNAs containing only cytosine result in the production of RNA molecules containing only guanine.

Dissecting the Central Dogma

Once the mRNA hypothesis was accepted, Francis Crick articulated what became known as the central dogma of molecular biology. The **central dogma** summarizes the flow of information in cells. It simply states that DNA codes for RNA, which codes for proteins:

$$\text{DNA} \longrightarrow \text{RNA} \longrightarrow \text{proteins}$$

Crick's simple statement encapsulates much of the research reviewed in this chapter and the preceding one. DNA is the hereditary material. Genes consist of specific stretches of DNA that code for products used in the cell. The sequence of bases in DNA specifies the sequence of bases in an RNA molecule, which specifies the sequence of amino acids in a protein. In this way, genes ultimately code for proteins.

Proteins are the workers of cells, functioning not only as enzymes but also as motors, structural elements, transporters, and molecular signals.

The Roles of Transcription and Translation
Biologists use specialized vocabulary to summarize the sequence of events captured in the central dogma.

1. DNA is transcribed to RNA by RNA polymerase. **Transcription** is the process of copying hereditary information in DNA to RNA.

2. Messenger RNA is translated to proteins in ribosomes. **Translation** is the process of using the information in nucleic acids to synthesize proteins.

The term transcription is appropriate. In everyday English, transcription simply means making a copy of information. The scientific use is similar because it conveys the idea that DNA acts as a permanent record—an information archive or blueprint. This permanent record is copied, during transcription, to produce the short-lived form called mRNA.

Translation is also an appropriate term. In everyday English, translation refers to converting information from one language

to another. In biology, translation is the transfer of information from one type of molecule to another—from the "language" of nucleic acids to the "language" of proteins. Translation is also referred to simply as protein synthesis.

The following equation summarizes the relationship between transcription and translation as well as the relationships between DNA, RNA, and proteins:

Gene expression occurs via transcription and translation.

Linking Genotypes and Phenotypes
An organism's genotype is determined by the sequence of bases in its DNA, while its phenotype is a product of the proteins it produces.

To appreciate this point, consider that the proteins encoded by genes are what make the "stuff" of the cell and dictate which chemical reactions occur inside. For example, in populations of the oldfield mouse native to southeastern North America, individuals have a gene for a protein called the melanocortin receptor. Melanocortin is a hormone—an important type of molecular signal (discussed in Chapter 11)—that works through the melanocortin receptor to influence how much dark pigment is deposited in fur. An important aspect of a mouse's phenotype—its coat color—is determined in part by the DNA sequence at the gene for this receptor (**FIGURE 16.4a**).

Later work revealed that alleles of a gene differ in their DNA sequence. As a result, the proteins produced by different alleles of the gene may differ in their amino acid sequence. If the primary structures of proteins vary, their functions are likely to vary as well.

To drive this point home, look at the DNA sequence in the portion of the melanocortin receptor gene shown in **FIGURE 16.4b**, and compare it with the sequence in Figure 16.4a. The sequences differ—meaning that they are different alleles. Now look at the protein products of each allele, and note that one of the amino acids in the protein's primary structure differs—one allele specifies an arginine residue; the other specifies a cysteine residue.

At the protein level, the phenotypes associated with these alleles differ. The consequences for the mouse are striking: Melanocortin receptors that have arginine in this location deposit a large amount of pigment, but receptors that have cysteine in this location deposit small amounts of pigment. Whether a mouse is dark or light depends, largely, on a single base change in its DNA sequence. In this case, a tiny difference in genotype produces a large change in phenotype. The central dogma links genotypes to phenotypes.

Exceptions to the Central Dogma
The central dogma provided an important conceptual framework for the burgeoning field of molecular genetics and inspired a series of fundamental questions about how genes and cells work. But important modifications to the central dogma have occurred in the decades since Frances Crick first proposed it:

(a) Genetic information flows from DNA to RNA to proteins.

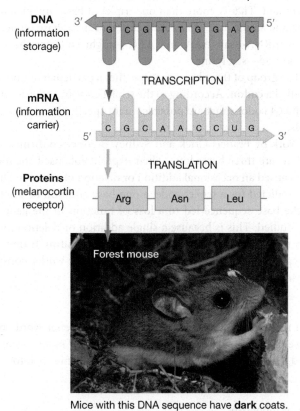

DNA
(information
storage)

3' — G C G T T G G A C — 5'

TRANSCRIPTION

mRNA
(information
carrier)

5' — C G C A A C C U G → 3'

TRANSLATION

Proteins
(melanocortin
receptor)

Arg | Asn | Leu

Forest mouse

Mice with this DNA sequence have **dark** coats.

(b) Differences in genotype may cause differences in phenotype.

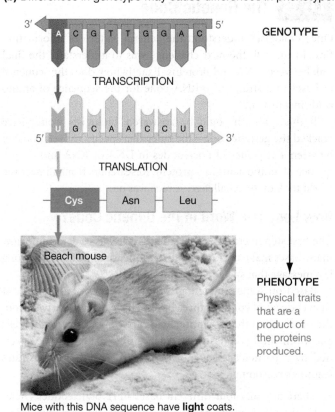

3' — A C G T T G G A C — 5'

GENOTYPE

TRANSCRIPTION

5' — U G C A A C C U G → 3'

TRANSLATION

Cys | Asn | Leu

Beach mouse

Mice with this DNA sequence have **light** coats.

PHENOTYPE
Physical traits
that are a
product of
the proteins
produced.

FIGURE 16.4 The Relationship between Genotype and Phenotype. The central dogma revealed the flow of information within the cell. The DNA sequences given in parts **(a)** and **(b)** are from different alleles (genotypes) that influence coat color (phenotypes) in oldfield mice. Forest-dwelling mice are dark, which camouflages them in their forested habitats. Beach-dwelling mice are light, which camouflages them in their sandy habitat.

- Many genes code for RNA molecules that do not function as mRNAs—they are not translated into proteins.
- In some cases, information flows from RNA back to DNA.

The discovery of a wide array of different RNA types ranks among the most profound advances in the past decade of biological science. Some RNAs form major parts of the ribosome, others help to form mRNA from a much longer precursor RNA (Chapter 17), and yet others regulate which genes are expressed (see Chapter 19). New types of RNA are still being discovered. For the genes coding for these types of RNA, information flow would be diagrammed as simply DNA → RNA.

In the early 1970s, the discovery of "reverse" information flow created the kind of excitement now being generated by the discovery of so many kinds of RNA. Some viruses, for example, have genes consisting of RNA. When some RNA viruses infect a cell, a specialized viral polymerase called **reverse transcriptase** synthesizes a DNA version of the RNA genes. In these viruses, information flows from RNA to DNA.

The human immunodeficiency virus (HIV), which causes AIDS, is an RNA virus that uses reverse transcriptase. Several of the most commonly prescribed drugs for AIDS patients fight the infection by poisoning the HIV reverse transcriptase. The drugs

prevent viruses from replicating efficiently by disrupting reverse information flow.

The punch line? Crick's hypothesis is a central concept in biology, but cells, viruses, and researchers aren't dogmatic about it.

check your understanding

C
Y
U

If you understand that . . .
- Genes code for proteins, but they do so indirectly.
- The sequence of bases in DNA is used to produce RNA, including messenger RNA (mRNA), via transcription. The sequence of bases in an RNA molecule is complementary to one of the DNA strands of a gene.
- Messenger RNAs are translated into proteins.
- Differences in DNA sequence can lead to differences in the amino acid sequence of proteins.

✔ **You should be able to . . .**

List the steps that link a change in the base sequence of a gene to a change in the phenotype of an organism.

Answers are available in Appendix A.

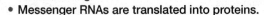

16.3 The Genetic Code

Once biologists understood the general pattern of information flow in the cell, the next challenge was to understand the final link between DNA and proteins. Exactly how does the sequence of bases in a strand of mRNA code for the sequence of amino acids in a protein?

If this question could be answered, biologists would have cracked the **genetic code**—the rules that specify the relationship between a sequence of nucleotides in DNA or RNA and the sequence of amino acids in a protein. Researchers from all over the world took up the challenge. A race was on.

How Long Is a Word in the Genetic Code?

The first step in cracking the genetic code was to determine how many bases make up a "word." In a sequence of mRNA, how long is a message that specifies one amino acid?

Based on some simple logic, George Gamow suggested that each code word contains three bases. His reasoning derived from the observation that 20 amino acids are commonly used in cells and from the hypothesis that each amino acid must be specified by a particular sequence of mRNA. **FIGURE 16.5** illustrates Gamow's reasoning:

- There are only four different bases in ribonucleotides (A, U, G, and C), so a one-base code could specify only four different amino acids.

- A two-base code could represent just 4 × 4, or 16, different amino acids.

- A three-base code could specify 4 × 4 × 4, or 64, different amino acids.

A three-base code provides more than enough words to code for all 20 amino acids. A three-base code is known as a **triplet code.**

Gamow's hypothesis suggested that the genetic code could be redundant. That is, more than one triplet of bases might specify the same amino acid. As a result, different three-base sequences in an mRNA—say, AAA and AAG—might code for the same amino acid—say, lysine.

The group of three bases that specifies a particular amino acid is called a **codon.** According to the triplet code hypothesis, many of the 64 codons that are possible might specify the same amino acids.

Work by Francis Crick and Sydney Brenner confirmed that codons are three bases long. Their experiments used chemicals that caused an occasional addition or deletion of a base in DNA. As predicted for a triplet code, a one-base addition or deletion in the base sequence led to a loss of function in the gene being studied. This is because a single addition or deletion mutation throws the sequence of codons, or the **reading frame,** out of register. To understand how a reading frame works, consider the sentence

"The fat cat ate the rat."

The reading frame of this sentence is a three-letter word and a space. If the fourth letter in this sentence—the *f* in *fat*—were deleted, the reading frame would transform the sentence into

"The atc ata tet her at."

This is gibberish.

When the reading frame in a DNA sequence is thrown out of register by the addition or deletion of a base, the composition of each codon changes just like the letters in each word of the example sentence above. The protein produced from the altered DNA sequence has a completely different sequence of amino acids. In terms of its normal function, this protein is gibberish.

Crick and Brenner were also able to produce DNA sequences that had deletions or additions of two base pairs or three base

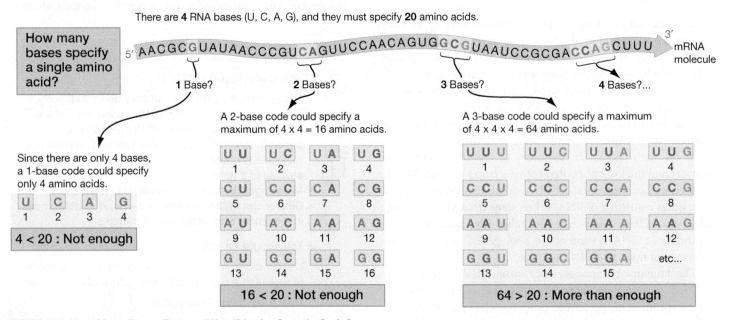

FIGURE 16.5 How Many Bases Form a "Word" in the Genetic Code?

pairs. The only time functional proteins were produced was when three bases were added or removed. In the sentence

"The fat cat ate the rat."

the combination of removing one letter from each of the first three words might result in

"Tha tca ate the rat."

Just as the altered sentence still conveys some meaning, genes with three deletion mutations were able to produce a functional protein.

The researchers interpreted these results as strong evidence in favor of the triplet code hypothesis. Most other biologists agreed.

The confirmation of the triplet code launched an effort to determine which amino acid is specified by each of the 64 codons. Ultimately, it was successful.

How Did Researchers Crack the Code?

The initial advance in deciphering the genetic code came in 1961, when Marshall Nirenberg and Heinrich Matthaei developed a method for synthesizing RNAs of known sequence. They began by creating a long polymer of uracil-containing ribonucleotides. These synthetic RNAs were added to an in vitro system for synthesizing proteins. The researchers analyzed the resulting amino acid chain and determined that it was polyphenylalanine—a polymer consisting of the amino acid phenylalanine.

This result provided evidence that the RNA triplet UUU codes for the amino acid phenylalanine. By complementary base pairing, it was clear that the corresponding DNA sequence would be AAA. This initial work was followed by experiments using RNAs consisting of only A or C. RNAs with only AAAAA . . . produced

polypeptides composed of only lysine; poly-C RNAs (RNAs consisting of only CCCCC . . .) produced polypeptides composed entirely of proline.

Nirenberg and Philip Leder later devised a system for synthesizing specific codons. With these they performed a series of experiments in which they added each codon to a cell extract containing the 20 different amino acids, ribosomes, and other molecules required for protein synthesis. Recall that ribosomes are macromolecular machines that synthesize proteins (Chapter 7). Then the researchers determined which amino acid became bound to the ribosomes when a particular codon was present. For example, when the codon CAC was in the reaction mix, the amino acid histidine would bind to the ribosomes. This result indicated that CAC codes for histidine.

These ribosome-binding experiments allowed Nirenberg and Leder to determine which of the 64 codons coded for each of the 20 amino acids.

Researchers also discovered that certain codons are punctuation marks signaling "start of message" or "end of message." These codons indicate that protein synthesis should start at a given codon or that the protein chain is complete.

- There is one **start codon** (AUG), which signals that protein synthesis should begin at that point on the mRNA molecule. The start codon specifies the amino acid methionine.

- There are three **stop codons,** also called termination codons (UAA, UAG, and UGA). The stop codons signal that the protein is complete, they do not code for any amino acid, and they end translation.

The complete genetic code is given in **FIGURE 16.6**. Deciphering it was a tremendous achievement, requiring more than five years of work by several teams of researchers.

SECOND BASE

FIRST BASE		U	C	A	G	THIRD BASE
U		UUU UUC — Phenylalanine (Phe) UUA UUG — Leucine (Leu)	UCU UCC UCA UCG — Serine (Ser)	UAU UAC — Tyrosine (Tyr) UAA — Stop codon UAG — Stop codon	UGU UGC — Cysteine (Cys) UGA — Stop codon UGG — Tryptophan (Trp)	U C A G
C		CUU CUC CUA CUG — Leucine (Leu)	CCU CCC CCA CCG — Proline (Pro)	CAU CAC — Histidine (His) CAA CAG — Glutamine (Gln)	CGU CGC CGA CGG — Arginine (Arg)	U C A G
A		AUU AUC AUA — Isoleucine (Ile) AUG — Methionine (Met) Start codon	ACU ACC ACA ACG — Threonine (Thr)	AAU AAC — Asparagine (Asn) AAA AAG — Lysine (Lys)	AGU AGC — Serine (Ser) AGA AGG — Arginine (Arg)	U C A G
G		GUU GUC GUA GUG — Valine (Val)	GCU GCC GCA GCG — Alanine (Ala)	GAU GAC — Aspartic acid (Asp) GAA GAG — Glutamic acid (Glu)	GGU GGC GGA GGG — Glycine (Gly)	U C A G

FIGURE 16.6 The Genetic Code. To read a codon in mRNA, locate its first base in the red band on the left; then move rightward to the box under the codon's second base in the blue band along the top. Finally, locate the codon's third base in the green band on the right side to learn the amino acid. By convention, codons are always written in the 5′ → 3′ direction.

(a) Using the genetic code to predict an amino acid sequence

The bottom strand of the DNA sequence...

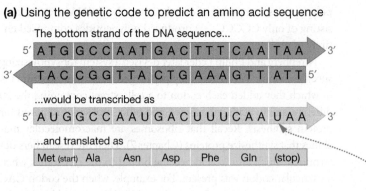

5′ | A T G | G C C | A A T | G A C | T T T | C A A | T A A | 3′

3′ | T A C | C G G | T T A | C T G | A A A | G T T | A T T | 5′

...would be transcribed as

5′ | A U G | G C C | A A U | G A C | U U U | C A A | U A A | 3′

...and translated as

| Met (start) | Ala | Asn | Asp | Phe | Gln | (stop) |

(b) Your turn—a chance to practice using the genetic code

The bottom strand of the DNA sequence...

5′ | A T G | C T G | G A G | G G G | G T T | A G A | C A T | 3′

3′ | T A C | G A C | C T C | C C C | C A A | T C T | G T A | 5′

...would be transcribed as

5′ | | | | | | | | 3′

...and translated as

| | | | | | | |

Remember that RNA contains U (uracil) instead of T (thymine), and that U forms a complementary base pair with A (adenine)

FIGURE 16.7 Using the Genetic Code.

✔**EXERCISE** Fill in the mRNA and amino acid sequences in part (b).

Analyzing the Code Once biologists had cracked the genetic code, they realized that it has a series of important properties.

- *The code is redundant.* All amino acids except methionine and tryptophan are coded by more than one codon.

- *The code is unambiguous.* A single codon never codes for more than one amino acid.

- *The code is non-overlapping.* Once the ribosome locks onto the first codon, it then reads each separate codon one after another.

- *The code is nearly universal.* With a few minor exceptions, all codons specify the same amino acids in all organisms.

- *The code is conservative.* When several codons specify the same amino acid, the first two bases in those codons are almost always identical.

The last point is subtle, but important. Here's the key: If a mutation in DNA or an error in transcription or translation affects the third position in a codon, it is less likely to change the amino acid in the final protein. This feature makes individuals less vulnerable to small, random changes or errors in their DNA sequences. Compared with randomly generated codes, the existing genetic code minimizes the phenotypic effects of small changes in DNA sequence and errors during translation. Stated another way, the genetic code does not represent a random assemblage of bases, like letters drawn from a hat. It has been honed by natural selection and is remarkably efficient.

Using the Code Using the genetic code and the central dogma, biologists can:

1. Predict the codons and amino acid sequence encoded by a particular DNA sequence (see **FIGURE 16.7a**).

2. Determine the set of mRNA and DNA sequences that would code for a particular sequence of amino acids.

Why is a *set* of mRNA or DNA sequences predicted from a given amino acid sequence? The answer lies in the code's redundancy. If a polypeptide contains phenylalanine, you don't know if the codon responsible is UUU or UUC.

✔ If you understand how to read the genetic code, you should be able to do the following tasks: (1) Identify the codons in Figure 16.4 and decide whether they are translated correctly. (2) Complete the exercise for **FIGURE 16.7b**. (3) Write an mRNA that codes for the amino acid sequence Ala-Asn-Asp-Phe-Gln yet is different from the one given in Figure 16.7a. Indicate the mRNA's $5′ \rightarrow 3′$ polarity. Then write the double-stranded DNA that corresponds to this mRNA. Indicate the $5′ \rightarrow 3′$ polarity of both DNA strands.

Once they understood the central dogma and genetic code, biologists were able to explore and eventually understand the molecular basis of mutation. How do novel traits—such as dwarfing in garden peas and white eye color in fruit flies—come to be?

check your understanding

If you understand that . . .

- The sequence of bases in mRNA constitutes a code. Particular combinations of three bases specify specific amino acids in the protein encoded by the gene.

- The genetic code is redundant. It consists of 64 combinations of bases, but only 20 amino acids plus start and stop "punctuation marks" need to be specified.

✔ **You should be able to . . .**

Consider the consequences of a mutation in the DNA template sequence ATA to one of the following sequences: GTA, TTA, or GCA.

1. In each case, specify the resulting change in the mRNA codon.

2. In each case, describe the effect on the resulting protein.

Answers are available in Appendix A.

16.4 How Can Mutation Modify Genes and Chromosomes?

This chapter has explored how the information archived in DNA is put into action in the form of working RNAs and proteins. Now the questions are, what happens if the information in DNA changes? In what ways can this information be changed? What are the consequences for the cell and organism?

A **mutation** is any permanent change in an organism's DNA. It is a modification in a cell's information archive—a change in its genotype. Mutations create new alleles.

Mutations can alter DNA sequences that range in size from a single base pair in DNA to whole sets of chromosomes. Let's look at these different types of mutation and their consequences.

Point Mutation

FIGURE 16.8 shows how a common type of mutation occurs. If a mistake is made during DNA synthesis or DNA repair, a change in the sequence of bases in DNA results. A single-base change such as this is called a **point mutation.**

What happens when point mutations occur in regions of DNA that code for proteins? To answer this question, look back at Figure 16.4 and recall that a change in a single base in DNA is associated with a difference in coat color in populations of oldfield mice. The DNA sequence in Figure 16.4a is found in dark-colored mice that live in forest habitats; the sequence in Figure 16.4b is found in light-colored mice that live in beach habitats.

Because beach-dwelling populations are evolutionarily younger than the nearby forest-dwelling populations, researchers hypothesize the following sequence of events:

1. Forest mice colonized beach habitats.

2. Either before or after the colonization event, a random point mutation occurred in a mouse that altered the melanocortin receptor gene and resulted in some offspring with light coats.

3. Light-colored mice are camouflaged in beach habitats; in sandy environments, they suffer lower predation than dark-colored mice.

4. Over time, the allele created by the point mutation increased in frequency in beach-dwelling populations.

Point mutations that cause these types of changes in the amino acid sequence of proteins are called **missense mutations.** But note that if the same G-to-A change had occurred in the third position of the same DNA codon, instead of the first position, there would have been no change in the protein produced. The mRNA codons CGC and CGU both code for arginine. A point mutation that does not change the amino acid sequence of the gene product is called a **silent mutation.**

Some point mutations disrupt major portions of a protein. Recall that a single addition or deletion mutation throws the sequence of codons out of register and alters the meaning of all subsequent codons. Such mutations are called **frameshift mutations.** Another type of point mutation with a large effect is a **nonsense mutation.** Nonsense mutations occur when a codon that specifies an amino acid is changed by mutation to one that specifies a stop codon. This causes early termination of the polypeptide chain and often results in a non-functional protein.

In terms of the impact on organisms, biologists divide mutations into three categories:

1. **Beneficial** Some mutations increase the fitness of the organism—meaning, its ability to survive and reproduce—in certain environments. The G-to-A mutation is beneficial in beach habitats because it camouflages mice.

2. **Neutral** If a mutation has no effect on fitness, it is termed neutral. Silent mutations are usually neutral.

3. **Deleterious** Because organisms tend to be well adapted to their current habitat, and because mutations are random changes in the genotype, many mutations lower fitness. These mutations are termed harmful or deleterious. The G-to-A mutation would be deleterious in the forest habitat.

Recent studies indicate that the majority of point mutations are slightly deleterious or neutral. **TABLE 16.1** (see page 314) summarizes the types of point mutations that occur in protein-coding sequences of a gene and reviews their consequences for the amino acid sequences of proteins and for fitness.

Point mutations can and do occur in DNA sequences that do not code for proteins. These mutations, however, are not referred to as missense, silent, frameshift, or nonsense mutations

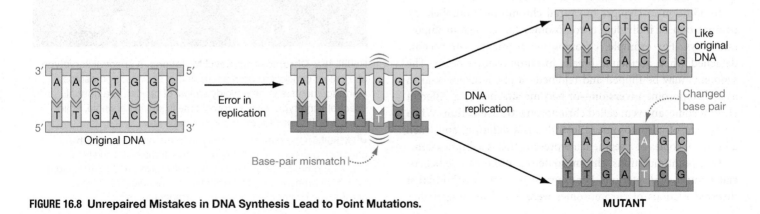

FIGURE 16.8 Unrepaired Mistakes in DNA Synthesis Lead to Point Mutations.

SUMMARY TABLE 16.1 Point Mutations That Alter Codons

Name	Definition	Example	Consequence
		Original DNA sequence — TAT TGG CTA GTA CAT	
		Original mRNA transcript — UAU UGG CUA GUA CAU	
		Tyr – Trp – Leu – Val – His —— Original polypeptide	
Silent	Change in nucleotide sequence that does not change the amino acid specified by a codon	TAC TGG CTA GTA CAT UAC UGG CUA GUA CAU Tyr – Trp – Leu – Val – His	No change in phenotype; neutral with respect to fitness
Missense	Change in nucleotide sequence that changes the amino acid specified by codon	TAT TGT CTA GTA CAT UAU UGU CUA GUA CAU Tyr – Cys – Leu – Val – His	Change in primary structure of protein; may be beneficial, neutral, or deleterious
Nonsense	Change in nucleotide sequence that results in an early stop codon	TAT TGA CTA GTA CAT UAU UGA CUA GUA CAU Tyr STOP	Leads to mRNA breakdown or a shortened polypeptide; usually deleterious
Frameshift	Addition or deletion of a nucleotide	TAT TCG GCT AGT ACA T UAU UCG GCU AGU ACA U Tyr – Ser – Ala – Ser – Thr	Reading frame is shifted, altering the meaning of all subsequent codons; almost always deleterious

because these terms apply only to mutations that can change the protein-coding potential of a gene. If point mutations alter DNA sequences that are important for *gene expression*, they can have important effects on phenotype even though they do not change the amino acid sequence of a protein.

Chromosome Mutations

Besides documenting various types of point mutations, biologists study larger-scale mutations that change chromosomes. You might recall, for example, that polyploidy is an increase in the number of each type of chromosome, while aneuploidy is the addition or deletion of individual chromosomes (Chapter 13).

Polyploidy, aneuploidy, and other changes in chromosome number result from chance mistakes in moving chromosomes into daughter cells during meiosis or mitosis. Polyploidy and aneuploidy are forms of mutation that don't change DNA sequences, but alter the number of chromosome copies.

In addition to changes in overall chromosome number, the composition of individual chromosomes can change in important ways. For example, chromosome segments can become detached when accidental breaks in chromosomes occur. The segments may be flipped and rejoined—a phenomenon known as a chromosome **inversion**—or become attached to a different chromosome, an event called chromosome **translocation.** When a segment of chromosome is lost, this is a **deletion,** and when additional copies of a segment are present, this is a **duplication.**

Like point mutations, chromosome mutations can be beneficial, neutral, or deleterious. For example, more than 200 different inverted sections of chromosomes were found in comparisons

of the DNA from eight phenotypically normal people. These mutations appear to be neutral. Not all chromosome mutations are so harmless, however. Chromosomes of cancer cells exhibit deleterious chromosome mutations that include aneuploidy, inversions, translocations, deletions, and duplications. **FIGURE 16.9**

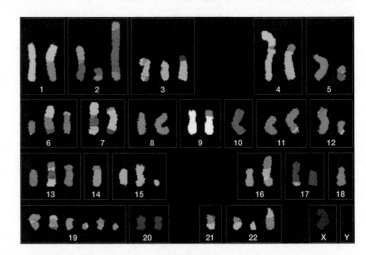

FIGURE 16.9 Chromosome-Level Mutations. A spectral karyotype of a breast cancer cell from a female that shows chromosome rearrangements and aneuploidy typical of cancer. In a normal spectral karyotype, each chromosome is stained a single, solid color, which varies for each chromosome pair.

✔**EXERCISE** Compare this karyotype to the one shown in the chapter-opening image. Remember that females normally have two X chromosomes and males normally have one X chromosome. Which chromosomes show evidence of aneuploidy? Which chromosomes show evidence of rearrangements?

drives this point home by showing the **karyotype**—the complete set of chromosomes in a cell—of a cancerous human cell.

To summarize, point mutations and chromosome mutations are random changes in DNA that can produce new genes, new alleles, and new traits. At the level of individuals, mutations can cause disease or death or lead to increases in fitness. At the level of populations, mutations furnish the heritable variation that Mendel and Morgan analyzed and that makes evolution possible. The central role of mutation in evolution is explored in depth in Unit 5.

CHAPTER 16 REVIEW

For media, go to MasteringBiology

If you understand . . .

16.1 What Do Genes Do?

- Experiments with mutants of the bread mold *N. crassa* led to the one-gene, one-enzyme hypothesis.

- The original one-gene, one-enzyme hypothesis has been broadened to account for genes that code for proteins other than enzymes and for genes that have RNA as a final product.

✔ You should be able to use Figure 16.1 to explain what compounds could be added to the medium to allow the growth of a mutant unable to synthesize citrulline because of a mutation in the gene for enzyme 1.

16.2 The Central Dogma of Molecular Biology

- DNA is transcribed to messenger RNA (mRNA) by RNA polymerase, and then mRNA is translated to proteins by ribosomes. In this way, genetic information is converted from DNA to RNA to protein.

- The flow of information from DNA to RNA to protein is called the central dogma of molecular biology.

- Many RNAs do not code for proteins. Instead, these RNAs perform other important functions in the cell.

- Reverse transcriptase reverses information flow by copying RNA into DNA. Some viruses with an RNA genome use this enzyme during their replication.

✔ You should be able to explain how a compound that blocks RNA synthesis will affect protein synthesis.

16.3 The Genetic Code

- Each amino acid in a protein is specified by a codon—a group of three bases in mRNA.

- By synthesizing RNAs of known base composition and then observing the results of translation, researchers were able to decipher the genetic code.

- The genetic code is redundant—meaning that most of the 20 amino acids are specified by more than one codon.

- Certain codons signal where translation starts and stops.

✔ Using the genetic code shown in Figure 16.6, you should be able to write all possible mRNA sequences that would produce the following sequence of amino acids: Met-Trp-Lys-Gln.

16.4 How Can Mutation Modify Genes and Chromosomes?

- Mutations are random, heritable changes in DNA that range from changes in a single base to changes in the structure and number of chromosomes.

- Point mutations in protein-coding regions may have no effect on the protein (silent mutation), may change a single amino acid (missense mutation), may shorten the protein (nonsense mutation), or may shift the reading frame and cause many amino acids to be wrong (frameshift mutation).

- Mutations can have beneficial, neutral, or harmful effects on organisms.

✔ You should be able to explain how redundancy in the genetic code allows for silent mutations and whether a silent mutation is likely to be beneficial, neutral, or harmful.

MasteringBiology

1. **MasteringBiology Assignments**

   Tutorials and Activities Genetic Code; One-Gene One-Enzyme Hypothesis; Overview of Protein Synthesis; Role of the Nucleus and Ribosomes in Protein Synthesis; Triplet Nature of the Genetic Code

   Questions Reading Quizzes, Blue-Thread Questions, Test Bank

2. **eText** Read your book online, search, take notes, highlight text, and more.

3. **The Study Area** Practice Test, Cumulative Test, BioFlix® 3-D Animations, Videos, Activities, Audio Glossary, Word Study Tools, Art

1. What does the one-gene, one-enzyme hypothesis state?
   a. Genes are composed of stretches of DNA.
   b. Genes are made of protein.
   c. Genes code for ribozymes.
   d. A single gene codes for a single protein.

2. Which of the following is an important exception to the central dogma of molecular biology?
   a. Many genes code for RNAs that function directly in the cell.
   b. DNA is the repository of genetic information in all cells.
   c. Messenger RNA is a short-lived "information carrier."
   d. Proteins are responsible for most aspects of the phenotype.

3. DNA's primary structure is made up of just four different bases, and its secondary structure is regular and highly stable. How can a molecule with these characteristics hold all the information required to build and maintain a cell?
   a. The information is first transcribed, then translated.
   b. The messenger RNA produced from DNA has much more complex secondary structures, allowing mRNA to hold much more information.
   c. A protein coded for in DNA has much more complex primary and secondary structures, allowing it to hold much more information.
   d. The information in DNA is in a code form that is based on the sequence of bases.

4. Why did researchers suspect that DNA does not code for proteins directly?

5. Which of the following describes an important experimental strategy in deciphering the genetic code?
   a. comparing the amino acid sequences of proteins with the base sequence of their genes
   b. analyzing the sequence of RNAs produced from known DNA sequences
   c. analyzing mutants that changed the code
   d. examining the polypeptides produced when RNAs of known sequence were translated

6. What is a stop codon?

7. Explain why Morse code is an appropriate analogy for the genetic code.

8. Draw a hypothetical metabolic pathway in *Neurospora crassa* composed of five substrates, five enzymes, and a product called Biological Sciazine. Number the substrates 1–5, and label the enzymes A–E, in order. (For instance, enzyme A catalyzes the reaction between substrates 1 and 2.)
   - Suppose a mutation made the gene for enzyme C nonfunctional. What molecule would accumulate in the affected cells?
   - Suppose a mutant strain can survive if substrate 5 is added to the growth medium but it cannot grow if substrates 1, 2, 3, or 4 are added. Which enzyme in the pathway is affected in this mutant?

9. How did experiments with *Neurospora crassa* mutants support the one-gene, one-enzyme hypothesis?

10. Why does a single-base deletion mutation within a protein-coding sequence usually have a more severe effect than a deletion of three adjacent bases?
    a. because single-base deletions prevent the ribosome from binding to mRNA
    b. because single-base deletions stabilize mRNA
    c. because single-base deletions change the reading frame
    d. because single-base deletions alter the meaning of individual codons

11. When researchers discovered that a combination of three deletion mutations or three addition mutations would restore the function of a gene, most biologists were convinced that the genetic code was read in triplets. Explain the logic behind this conclusion.

12. Explain why all point mutations change the genotype, but why only some point mutations change the phenotype.

13. Recall that DNA and RNA are synthesized only in the 5′ → 3′ direction and that DNA and RNA sequences are written in the 5′ → 3′ direction, unless otherwise noted. Consider the following DNA sequence:

    5′ TTGAAATGCCCGTTTGGAGATCGGGTTACAGCTAGTCAAAG 3′

    3′ AACTTTACGGGCAAACCTCTAGCCCAATGTCGATCAGTTTC 5′

    - Identify bases in the bottom strand that can be transcribed into start and stop codons.
    - Write the mRNA sequence that would be transcribed between start and stop codons if the bottom strand served as the template for RNA polymerase.
    - Write the amino acid sequence that would be translated from the mRNA sequence you just wrote.

14. What problems would arise if the genetic code contained only 22 codons—one for each amino acid, a start signal, and a stop signal?

15. Scientists say that a phenomenon is a "black box" if they can describe it and study its effects but don't know the underlying mechanism that causes it. In what sense was genetics—meaning the transmission of heritable traits—a black box before the central dogma of molecular biology was understood?

16. **QUANTITATIVE** One of the possibilities that researchers interested in the genetic code considered was that the code was overlapping, meaning that a single base could be part of up to three codons. How many amino acids would be encoded in the sequence 5′ AUGUUACGGAAU 3′ by a non-overlapping and maximally overlapping code?
    a. 4 (non-overlapping) and 16 (overlapping)
    b. 4 and 12
    c. 4 and 10
    d. 12 and 4

17 Transcription, RNA Processing, and Translation

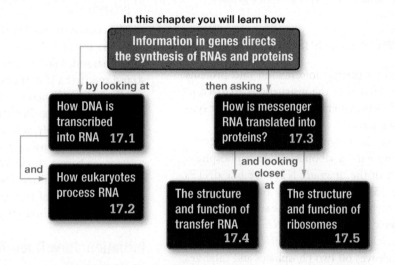

In this chapter you will learn how

Information in genes directs the synthesis of RNAs and proteins

by looking at

then asking

How DNA is transcribed into RNA **17.1**

and

How eukaryotes process RNA **17.2**

How is messenger RNA translated into proteins? **17.3**

and looking closer at

The structure and function of transfer RNA **17.4**

The structure and function of ribosomes **17.5**

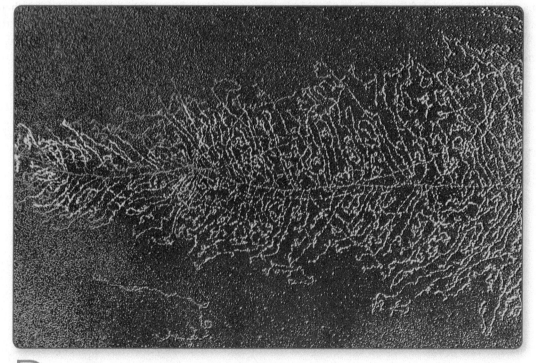

Extensive transcription is occurring along this gene within a frog cell. The horizontal strand in the middle of this micrograph is DNA; the strands that have been colored yellow and red, and that are coming off on either side, are RNA molecules.

This chapter is part of the Big Picture. See how on pages 366–367.

Proteins are the stuff of life. They give shape to our cells, control the chemical reactions that go on inside them, and regulate how materials move into, out of, and through them. Some of these proteins may not be produced at all in some types of cells; others may be present in quantities ranging from millions of copies to fewer than a dozen.

A cell builds the proteins it needs from instructions encoded in its DNA. The central dogma of molecular biology states that the flow of information in cells is from DNA to mRNA to protein (Chapter 16). Once this pattern of information flow had been established, biologists puzzled over how cells actually accomplish the two major steps of the central dogma: transcription and

✔ When you see this checkmark, stop and test yourself. Answers are available in Appendix A.

translation. Specifically, how does RNA polymerase know where to start transcribing a gene, and where to end? And once an RNA message is produced, how is the linear sequence of ribonucleotides translated into the linear sequence of amino acids in a protein?

This chapter delves into the molecular mechanisms of gene expression—the blood and guts of the central dogma. It starts with the monomers that build RNA and ends with a protein.

17.1 An Overview of Transcription

The first step in converting genetic information into proteins is to synthesize an RNA version of the instructions archived in DNA. Enzymes called **RNA polymerases** are responsible for synthesizing mRNA (see Chapter 15).

FIGURE 17.1 shows how the polymerization reaction occurs. Note the incoming monomer—a ribonucleoside triphosphate, or NTP—at the far right of the diagram. NTPs are like dNTPs (introduced in Chapter 15), except that they have a hydroxyl (−OH) group on the 2′ carbon. This makes the sugar in an NTP a ribose instead of the deoxyribose sugar of DNA.

Once an NTP that matches a base on the DNA template is in place, RNA polymerase cleaves off two phosphates and catalyzes the formation of a phosphodiester linkage between the 3′ end of the growing mRNA chain and the new ribonucleoside monophosphate. As this 5′ → 3′ matching-and-catalysis process continues, an RNA that is complementary to the gene is synthesized. This is transcription.

Notice that only one of the two DNA strands is used as a template and transcribed, or "read," by RNA polymerase.

- The strand that is read by the enzyme is the **template strand.**
- The other strand is called the **non-template strand** or **coding strand.** Coding strand is an appropriate name, because, with one exception, its sequence matches the sequence of the RNA that is transcribed from the template strand and codes for a polypeptide.

The coding strand and the RNA don't match exactly, because RNA has uracil (U) rather than the thymine (T) found in the coding strand. Likewise, an adenine (A) in the DNA template strand specifies a U in the complementary RNA strand.

Like DNA polymerases (see Chapter 15), an RNA polymerase performs a template-directed synthesis in the 5′ → 3′ direction. But unlike DNA polymerases, RNA polymerases do not require a primer to begin transcription.

Bacteria have a single RNA polymerase. In contrast, eukaryotes, have at least three distinct types. Let's first take a look at general principles of transcription using bacteria as an example and then examine things that differ in eukaryotes.

Initiation: How Does Transcription Begin in Bacteria?

How does RNA polymerase know where and in which direction to start transcription on the DNA template? The answer to this question defined what biologists call the **initiation** phase of transcription.

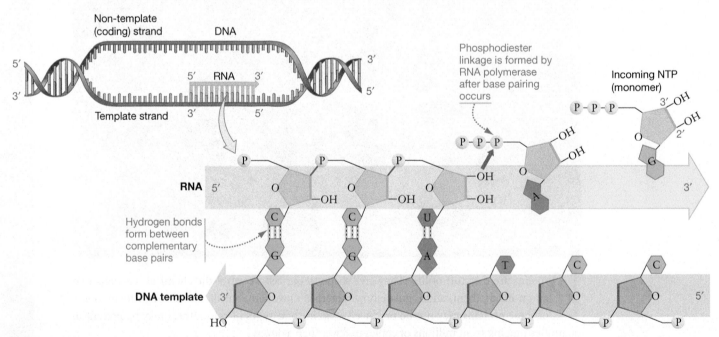

FIGURE 17.1 Transcription Is the Synthesis of RNA from a DNA Template. The reaction catalyzed by RNA polymerase (not shown) results in the formation of a phosphodiester linkage between ribonucleotides. RNA polymerase produces an RNA strand whose sequence is complementary to the bases in the DNA template.

✔**QUESTION** In which direction is RNA synthesized, 5′ → 3′ or 3′ → 5′? In which direction is the DNA template "read"?

Soon after the discovery of bacterial RNA polymerase, researchers found that the enzyme cannot initiate transcription on its own. Instead, a detachable protein subunit called **sigma** must bind to the polymerase before transcription can begin.

Bacterial RNA polymerase and sigma form a **holoenzyme** (literally, "whole enzyme"; **FIGURE 17.2a**). A holoenzyme consists of a **core enzyme** (RNA polymerase, in this case), which contains the active site for catalysis, and other required proteins (such as sigma).

What does sigma do? When researchers mixed the polymerase and DNA together, they found that the core enzyme could bind to any sequence of DNA. When sigma was added to this mixture, the holoenzyme formed and bound only to specific sections of DNA. These binding sites were named **promoters,** because they are sections of DNA that promote the start of transcription.

Most bacteria have alternative sigma proteins that bind to promoters with slightly different DNA base sequences, and may activate a group of genes in response to environmental change. For example, one type of sigma initiates the transcription of genes that help the cell cope with high temperatures. Controlling which sigma proteins are used is one of the ways that bacterial cells regulate which groups of genes are expressed.

The discovery of promoters suggested that sigma was responsible for guiding RNA polymerase to specific locations where transcription should begin. What is the nature of these specific locations? What do promoters look like, and what do they do?

Bacterial Promoters David Pribnow offered an initial answer to these questions in the mid-1970s. When Pribnow analyzed the base sequence of promoters from various bacteria and from viruses that infect bacteria, he found that the promoters were 40–50 base pairs long and had a particular section in common: a series of bases identical or similar to TATAAT. This six-base-pair sequence is now known as the −10 box, because it is centered about 10 bases from the point where bacterial RNA polymerase starts transcription (**FIGURE 17.2b**).

DNA that is located in the direction RNA polymerase moves during transcription is said to be **downstream** from the point of reference; DNA located in the opposite direction is said to be **upstream**. Thus, the −10 box is centered about 10 bases upstream from the transcription start site. The place where transcription begins is called the +1 site.

Soon after the discovery of the −10 box, researchers recognized that the sequence TTGACA also occurred in promoters and was about 35 bases upstream from the +1 site. This second key sequence is called the −35 box. Although all bacterial promoters have a −10 box and a −35 box, the sequences within the promoter but outside these boxes vary.

Events inside the Holoenzyme In bacteria, transcription begins when sigma, as part of the holoenzyme complex, binds to the −35 and −10 boxes. Sigma, and not RNA polymerase, makes the initial contact with DNA of the promoter. Sigma's binding to a promoter determines where and in which direction RNA polymerase will start synthesizing RNA.

Once the holoenzyme is bound to a promoter for a bacterial gene, the DNA helix is opened by RNA polymerase, creating two

(a) RNA polymerase and sigma form a holoenzyme.

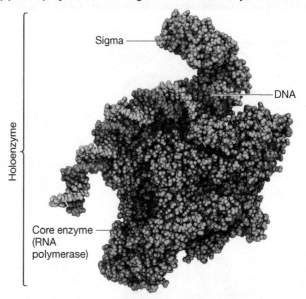

(b) Sigma recognizes and binds to the promoter.

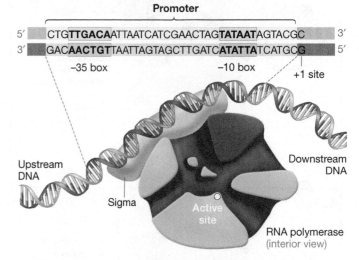

FIGURE 17.2 Sigma Is the Promoter-Recognizing Subunit of Bacterial RNA Polymerase Holoenzyme. (a) A space-filling model of bacterial RNA polymerase holoenzyme. **(b)** A cartoon of bacterial RNA polymerase, showing that sigma binds to the −35 box and −10 box of the promoter.

separated strands of DNA as shown in **FIGURE 17.3** (see page 320), steps 1 and 2. As step 2 shows, the template strand is threaded through a channel that leads to the active site inside RNA polymerase. Ribonucleoside triphosphates (NTPs)—the RNA building blocks—enter a channel in the enzyme and diffuse to the active site.

When an incoming NTP pairs with a complementary base on the template strand of DNA, RNA polymerization begins. The reaction catalyzed by RNA polymerase is exergonic and spontaneous because NTPs have significant potential energy, owing to their three phosphate groups. As step 3 of Figure 17.3 shows, the initiation phase of transcription is complete as RNA polymerase extends the mRNA from the +1 site.

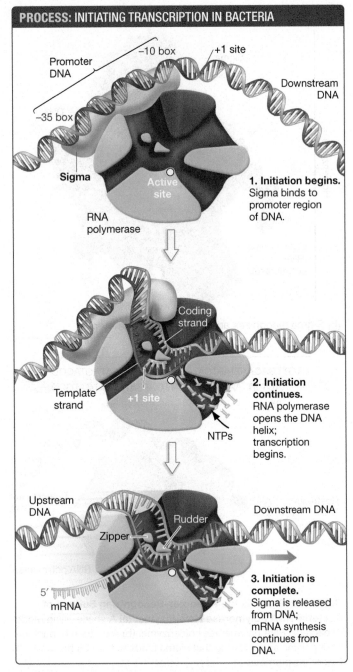

Promoter
DNA

−10 box

+1 site

Downstream
DNA

−35 box

Sigma

Active
site

RNA
polymerase

1. Initiation begins.
Sigma binds to
promoter region
of DNA.

Coding
strand

Template
strand

+1 site

NTPs

**2. Initiation
continues.**
RNA polymerase
opens the DNA
helix;
transcription
begins.

Upstream
DNA

Zipper

Rudder

Downstream DNA

5′
mRNA

**3. Initiation is
complete.**
Sigma is released
from DNA;
mRNA synthesis
continues from
DNA.

**FIGURE 17.3 Sigma Orients the DNA Template inside RNA
Polymerase.** Sigma binds to the promoter, and RNA polymerase
opens the DNA helix and threads the template strand through the
active site.

Elongation and Termination

Once RNA polymerase begins moving along the DNA template
synthesizing RNA, the **elongation** phase of transcription is under way. RNA polymerase is a macromolecular machine with
different parts. In the interior of the enzyme, a group of amino
acids forms a rudder to help steer the template and non-template
strands through channels inside the enzyme (see Figure 17.3,
step 3). Meanwhile, the enzyme's active site catalyzes the addition

of nucleotides to the 3′ end of the growing RNA molecule at the
rate of about 50 nucleotides per second. A group of projecting
amino acids forms a region called the zipper to help separate the
newly synthesized RNA from the DNA template.

During the elongation phase of transcription, all the prominent
channels and grooves in the enzyme are filled (Figure 17.3, step 3).
Double-stranded DNA goes into and out of one groove, ribonucleoside triphosphates enter another, and the growing RNA strand
exits to the rear. The enzyme's structure is critical for its function.

Termination ends transcription. In bacteria, transcription
stops when RNA polymerase transcribes a DNA sequence that
functions as a transcription-termination signal.

The bases that make up the termination signal in bacteria are
transcribed into a stretch of RNA with an important property:
As soon as it is synthesized, this portion of the RNA folds back
on itself and forms a short double helix that is held together by
complementary base pairing (**FIGURE 17.4**). Recall that this type
of RNA secondary structure is called a hairpin (Chapter 4). The
hairpin structure disrupts the interaction between RNA polymerase and the RNA transcript, resulting in the physical separation of the enzyme and its product.

Transcription in Eukaryotes

Fundamental features of transcription are the same in bacteria
and eukaryotes. In fact, these similarities provide compelling
evidence for a common ancestor of all cells. There are, however,
some differences that are worth noting:

- Eukaryotes have three polymerases—RNA polymerase I, II,
  and III—that are often referred to as pol I, pol II, and pol III.
  Each polymerase transcribes only certain types of RNA in eukaryotes. RNA pol II is the only polymerase that transcribes
  protein-coding genes.

- Promoters in eukaryotic DNA are more diverse than bacterial promoters. Most eukaryotic promoters include a sequence
  called the **TATA box,** centered about 30 base pairs upstream
  of the transcription start site, and other important sequences
  that vary more widely.

- Instead of using a sigma protein, eukaryotic RNA polymerases
  recognize promoters using a group of proteins called **basal
  transcription factors.** Basal transcription factors assemble
  at the promoter, and RNA polymerase follows. (This idea, as
  well as the extensive use of other types of transcription factors
  to regulate transcription, will be covered in Chapter 19.)

- Termination of eukaryotic protein-coding genes involves a
  short sequence called the polyadenylation signal or **poly(A)
  signal.** Soon after the signal is transcribed, the RNA is cut
  by an enzyme downstream of the poly(A) signal as the polymerase continues to transcribe the DNA template. Eventually
  RNA polymerase falls off the DNA template and terminates
  transcription. Bacteria end transcription at a distinct site for
  each gene, but in eukaryotes, transcription ends variable distances from the poly(A) signal.

PROCESS: ENDING TRANSCRIPTION IN BACTERIA

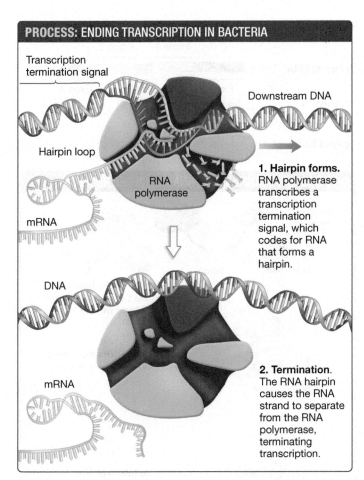

Transcription termination signal

Downstream DNA

Hairpin loop

RNA polymerase

mRNA

DNA

mRNA

1. Hairpin forms. RNA polymerase transcribes a transcription termination signal, which codes for RNA that forms a hairpin.

2. Termination. The RNA hairpin causes the RNA strand to separate from the RNA polymerase, terminating transcription.

FIGURE 17.4 Transcription Terminates When an RNA Hairpin Forms.

17.2 RNA Processing in Eukaryotes

The molecular machinery required for transcription is much more complex in eukaryotes than in bacteria. But these differences are minor when compared with what happens to the eukaryotic RNA after transcription. In bacteria, when transcription terminates, the result is a mature mRNA that's ready to be translated into a protein. In fact, translation often begins while the mRNA is still being transcribed.

The fate of the transcript in eukaryotes is more complicated. When eukaryotic genes of any type are transcribed, the initial product is termed a **primary transcript.** This RNA must undergo multistep processing before it is functional. For protein-coding genes, the primary transcript is called a **pre-mRNA.**

The processing of primary transcripts has important consequences for gene expression in eukaryotes. Let's delve in to see how and why.

The Startling Discovery of Split Eukaryotic Genes

Eukaryotic genes do not consist of one continuous DNA sequence that codes for a product, as do bacterial genes. Instead, the regions in a eukaryotic gene that code for proteins are intermittently interrupted by stretches of hundreds or even thousands of intervening bases.

Although these intervening bases are part of the gene, they do not code for a product. To make a functional RNA, eukaryotic cells must dispose of certain sequences inside the primary transcript and then combine the separated sections into an integrated whole.

What sort of data would provoke such a startling claim? The first evidence came from work that Phillip Sharp and colleagues carried out in the late 1970s to determine the location of genes within the DNA of a virus that infects mammalian cells. Viruses are often used as tools to provide insights into fundamental processes of the cells they infect.

They began one of their experiments by heating the virus' DNA sufficiently to break the hydrogen bonds between complementary bases. This treatment separated the two strands. The single-stranded DNA was then incubated with the mRNA encoded by the virus. The team's intention was to promote base pairing between the mRNA and the single-stranded DNA.

The researchers expected that the mRNA would form base pairs with the DNA sequence that acted as the template for its synthesis—that the mRNA and DNA would match up exactly.

(a) Micrograph of DNA-RNA hybrid

(b) Interpretation of micrograph

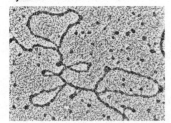

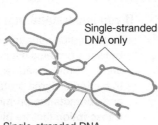

Single-stranded DNA only

Single-stranded DNA base paired with mRNA

FIGURE 17.5 The Discovery of Introns. The loops in the micrograph and drawing represent regions of DNA that are transcribed but are not found in the final mRNA. These regions are introns.

✔**QUESTION** If the noncoding regions of the gene did not exist, what would the micrograph in part (a) look like?

But when the team examined the DNA–RNA hybrid molecules using an electron microscope, they observed the structure shown in **FIGURE 17.5a**. Instead of matching up exactly, parts of the DNA formed loops.

What was going on? As **FIGURE 17.5b** shows, Sharp's group interpreted these loops as stretches of DNA that are present in the template strand but are *not* in the corresponding mRNA.

Sharp's group and a team headed by Richard Roberts then carried out similar studies on eukaryotic genes. The results were the same as for the viral genes. They went on to propose that there is not a one-to-one correspondence between the nucleotide sequence of a eukaryotic gene and its mRNA. As an analogy, it could be said that eukaryotic genes do not carry messages such as "Biology is my favorite course of all time." Instead, they carry messages that read something like:

BIOLτηεπροτεινχοδινγρεγιονσοφγενεσOGY IS MY
FAVORαρειντερρθπτεθβυνονψοθινγθITE COURSE
OF ανθηαωετοβεσπλιχεθτογετηερ ALL TIME

Here the sections of noncoding sequence are represented with Greek letters. They must be removed from the mRNA before it can carry an intelligible message to the translation machinery.

When it became clear that the genes-in-pieces hypothesis was correct, Walter Gilbert suggested that regions of eukaryotic genes that are part of the final mRNA be referred to as **exons** (because they are *ex*pressed) and the sections of primary transcript not in mRNA be referred to as **introns** (because they are *int*ervening). Introns are sections of genes that are not represented in the final RNA product. Because of introns, eukaryotic genes are much larger than their corresponding mature RNAs. Introns were first discovered in genes that produce mRNA, but researchers later found that genes for other types of RNA also could be split.

RNA Splicing

The transcription of eukaryotic genes by RNA polymerase generates a primary transcript (**FIGURE 17.6a**) that contains both exons and introns. As transcription proceeds, the introns are removed

(a) Introns must be removed from eukaryotic RNA transcripts.

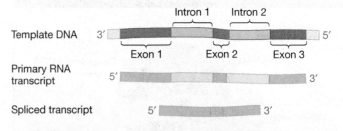

(b) PROCESS: snRNPs SPLICE RNA WITHIN THE NUCLEUS

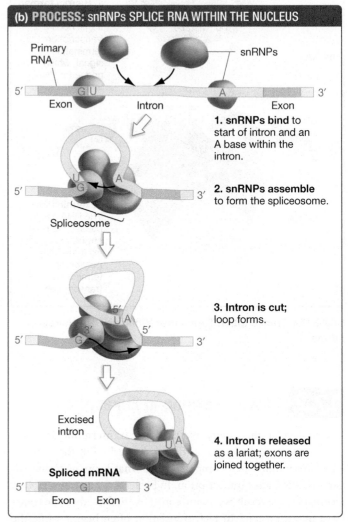

FIGURE 17.6 Introns Are Spliced Out of the Primary Transcript.

from the growing RNA strand by a process known as **splicing.** In this phase of information processing, pieces of the primary transcript are removed and the remaining segments are joined together. Splicing occurs within the nucleus while transcription is still under way and results in an RNA that contains an uninterrupted genetic message.

FIGURE 17.6b provides more detail about how introns are removed from primary transcripts to form mRNA. Splicing of primary transcripts is catalyzed by RNAs called small nuclear RNAs (snRNAs) working with a complex of proteins. These protein-plus-RNA macromolecular machines are known as **small nuclear ribonucleoproteins,** or **snRNPs** (pronounced "snurps").

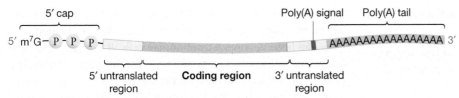

FIGURE 17.7 In Eukaryotes, a Cap and a Tail Are Added to mRNAs. As part of eukaryotic pre-mRNA processing, a cap consisting of a modified guanine (G) nucleotide (symbolized as m^7G) bonded to three phosphate groups is added to the 5′ end, and a tail made up of a long series of adenine (A) residues is added to the 3′ end after cleavage of the primary transcript.

The snRNAs of the snRNPs recognize RNA sequences critical for splicing. Splicing can be broken into four steps:

1. The process begins when snRNPs bind to the 5′ exon–intron boundary, which is marked by the bases GU, and to a key adenine ribonucleotide (A) near the end the intron.

2. Once the initial snRNPs are in place, other snRNPs arrive to form a multipart complex called a **spliceosome**. The spliceosomes found in human cells contain about 145 different proteins and RNAs, making them the most complex macromolecular machines known.

3. The intron forms a loop plus a single-stranded stem (a lariat) with the adenine at its connecting point.

4. The lariat is cut out, and a phosphodiester linkage links the exons on either side, producing a continuous coding sequence—the mRNA.

Splicing is now complete. In most cases, the excised intron is degraded to ribonucleoside monophosphates.

As you'll see later (Chapter 19), for many genes, the RNA can be spliced in more than one way. This allows the production of different, related mRNAs and proteins from one gene.

Current data suggest that both the cutting and rejoining reactions that occur during splicing are catalyzed by the snRNA molecules in the spliceosome—meaning that the reactions are catalyzed by a ribozyme. Section 17.5 will demonstrate that ribozymes also play a key role in translation. As the RNA world hypothesis (Chapter 4) predicts, proteins are not the only important catalysts in cells.

What is the origin of introns? One hypothesis is that introns in eukaryotes arose from an ancient type of DNA sequence that is present in many bacteria and archaea. These ancient sequences are related to viruses (Chapter 36) and, like viruses, can infect cells and insert into their genomes. Remarkably, when this DNA sequence inserts into a gene and is transcribed, the RNA catalyzes its own splicing out of the primary transcript. This is possible in part because these virus-like elements have sequences similar to snRNAs.

The bacterium that was the source of mitochondria (see Chapter 30) likely carried some of these virus-like DNA sequences. When this bacterium was taken up by an ancestral eukaryote, the virus-like sequences are hypothesized to have spread rapidly. Later in evolution, the portion of the sequence that was a precursor to today's snRNA may have separated from the portion of the sequence that was spliced. This spliced sequence is hypothesized to be the ancestor of the modern eukaryotic intron.

Adding Caps and Tails to Transcripts

For pre-mRNAs, intron splicing is accompanied by other important processing steps.

- As soon as the 5′ end of a eukaryotic pre-mRNA emerges from RNA polymerase, enzymes add a structure called the **5′ cap** (**FIGURE 17.7**). The cap consists of a modified guanine (7-methylguanylate) nucleotide with three phosphate groups.

- An enzyme cleaves the 3′ end of the pre-mRNA downstream of the poly(A) signal (introduced in Section 17.1). Another enzyme adds a long row of 100–250 adenine nucleotides that are not encoded on the DNA template strand. This string of adenines is known as the **poly(A) tail**.

With the addition of the cap and tail and completion of splicing, processing of the pre-mRNA is complete. The product is a mature mRNA.

Figure 17.7 also shows that in the mature RNA molecule, the coding sequence for the polypeptide is flanked by sequences that are not destined to be translated. These 5′ and 3′ untranslated regions (or UTRs) help stabilize the mature RNA and regulate its translation. The mRNAs in bacteria also possess 5′ and 3′ UTRs.

Not long after the caps and tails on eukaryotic mRNAs were discovered, evidence began to accumulate that they protect mRNAs from degradation by ribonucleases—enzymes that

check your understanding

If you understand that . . .
- Eukaryotic genes consist of exons, which are parts of the primary transcript that remain in mature RNA, and introns, which are regions of the primary transcript that are removed in forming mature RNA.
- Macromolecular machines, called spliceosomes, splice introns out of pre-mRNAs.
- Enzymes add a 5′ cap and a poly(A) tail to spliced transcripts, producing a mature mRNA that is ready to be translated.

✔ You should be able to . . .
1. Explain why ribonucleoprotein is an appropriate name for the subunits of the spliceosome.
2. Explain the function of the 5′ cap and the poly(A) tail.

Answers are available in Appendix A.

degrade RNA—and enhance the efficiency of translation. For example:

- Experimental mRNAs that have a cap and a tail last longer when they are introduced into cells than do experimental mRNAs that lack a cap or a tail.

- Experimental mRNAs with caps and tails produce more proteins than do experimental mRNAs without caps and tails.

Follow-up work has shown that the 5′ cap and the poly(A) tail are bound by proteins that prevent ribonucleases in the cytoplasm from recognizing and destroying the mRNA. The 5′ cap and the poly(A) tail also are important for initiating translation.

RNA processing is the general term for any of the modifications, such as splicing or poly(A) tail addition, needed to convert a primary transcript into a mature RNA. It is summarized in **TABLE 17.1** along with other important differences in how RNAs are produced in eukaryotes as compared with bacteria.

17.3 An Introduction to Translation

To synthesize a protein, the sequence of bases in a messenger RNA molecule is translated into a sequence of amino acids in a polypeptide. The genetic code specifies the correspondence between each triplet codon in mRNA and the amino acid it codes for (see Chapter 16). But how are the amino acids assembled into a polypeptide according to the information in messenger RNA?

(a) Bacterial ribosomes during translation

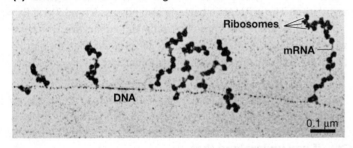

(b) In bacteria, transcription and translation are tightly coupled.

Studies of translation in cell-free systems proved extremely effective in answering this question. Once in vitro translation systems had been developed from human cells, *E. coli*, and a variety of other organisms, biologists could see that the sequence of events is similar in bacteria, archaea, and eukaryotes. As with similarities in transcription across the domains of life, the shared mechanisms of translation argue for a common ancestor of all cells living today.

Ribosomes Are the Site of Protein Synthesis

The first question that biologists answered about translation concerned where it occurs. The answer grew from a simple observation: There is a strong correlation between the number of **ribosomes** in a given type of cell and the rate at which that cell synthesizes proteins. Based on this observation, investigators proposed that ribosomes are the site of protein synthesis.

To test this hypothesis, Roy Britten and collaborators did a pulse–chase experiment similar in design to experiments introduced earlier (Chapter 7). Recall that a pulse–chase experiment labels a population of molecules as they are being produced. The location of the tagged molecules is then followed over time.

In this case, the tagging was done by supplying a pulse of radioactive sulfur atoms that would be incorporated into the amino acids methionine and cysteine, followed by a chase of unlabeled sulfur atoms. If the ribosome hypothesis were correct, the radioactive signal should be associated with ribosomes for a short period of time—when the amino acids are being polymerized into proteins. Later, when translation was complete, all the radioactivity should be found in proteins that are not associated with ribosomes.

This is exactly what the researchers found. Based on these data, biologists concluded that proteins are synthesized at ribosomes and then released.

Translation in Bacteria and Eukaryotes

About a decade after the ribosome hypothesis was confirmed, electron micrographs showed bacterial ribosomes in action (**FIGURE 17.8a**). The images showed that in bacteria, ribosomes

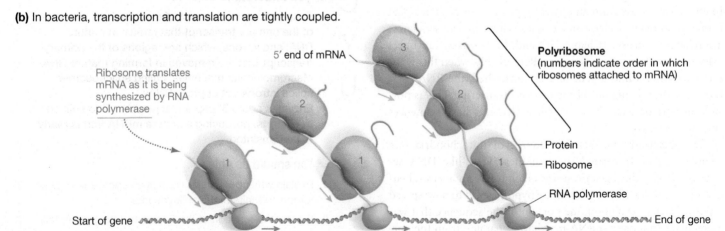

FIGURE 17.8 Transcription and Translation Occur Simultaneously in Bacteria. In bacteria, ribosomes attach to mRNA transcripts and begin translation while RNA polymerase is still transcribing the DNA template strand.

TABLE 17.1 Transcription and RNA Processing in Bacteria and Eukaryotes

Point of Comparison	Bacteria	Eukaryotes
RNA polymerase(s)	One	Three; each produces a different class of RNA
Promoter structure	Typically contains a −35 box and a −10 box	More variable; often includes a TATA box about −30 from the transcription start site
Proteins involved in recognizing promoter	Sigma; different versions of sigma bind to different promoters	Many basal transcription factors
RNA processing	None	Extensive; several processing steps occur in the nucleus before RNA is exported to the cytoplasm: **(1)** Enzyme-catalyzed addition of 5′ cap on mRNAs, **(2)** Splicing (intron removal); by spliceosome to produce mRNA, **(3)** Enzyme-catalyzed addition of 3′ poly(A) tail on mRNAs

attach to mRNAs and begin synthesizing proteins even before transcription is complete. In fact, multiple ribosomes attach to each mRNA, forming a **polyribosome** (**FIGURE 17.8b**). In this way, many copies of a protein can be produced from a single mRNA.

Transcription and translation can occur concurrently in bacteria because there is no nuclear envelope to separate the two processes.

The situation is different in eukaryotes. In these organisms, primary transcripts are processed in the nucleus to produce a mature mRNA, which is then exported to the cytoplasm (**FIGURE 17.9**). This means that in eukaryotes, transcription and translation are separated in time and space. Once mRNAs are outside the nucleus, ribosomes can attach to them and begin translation. As in bacteria, polyribosomes form.

How Does an mRNA Triplet Specify an Amino Acid?

When an mRNA interacts with a ribosome, instructions encoded in nucleic acids are translated into a different chemical language—the amino acid sequences found in proteins. The discovery of the genetic code revealed that triplet codons in mRNA specify particular amino acids in a protein. How does this conversion occur?

One early hypothesis was that mRNA codons and amino acids interact directly. This hypothesis proposed that the bases in a particular codon were complementary in shape or charge to the side group of a particular amino acid (**FIGURE 17.10a**, see page 326). But Francis Crick pointed out that the idea didn't make chemical sense. For example, how could the nucleic acid bases interact with a hydrophobic amino acid side group, which does not form hydrogen bonds?

Crick proposed an alternative hypothesis. As **FIGURE 17.10b** shows, he suggested that some sort of adapter molecule holds amino acids in place while interacting directly and specifically with a codon in mRNA by hydrogen bonding. In essence, Crick predicted the existence of a chemical go-between that produced a physical connection between the two types of molecules. As it turns out, Crick was right.

(a) mRNAs are exported to the cytoplasm.

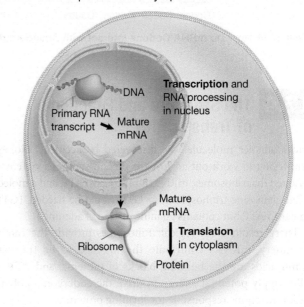

(b) Polypeptides grow from ribosomes translating mRNA.

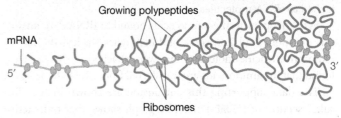

FIGURE 17.9 Transcription and Translation Are Separated in Space and Time in Eukaryotes.

(a) Hypothesis 1: Amino acids interact directly with mRNA codons.

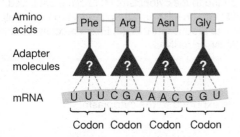

(b) Hypothesis 2: Adapter molecules hold amino acids and interact with mRNA codons.

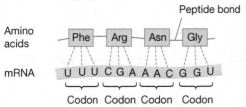

FIGURE 17.10 How Do mRNA Codons Interact with Amino Acids?

17.4 The Structure and Function of Transfer RNA

Crick's adapter molecule was discovered by accident. Biologists were trying to work out an in vitro protein-synthesis system and reasoned that ribosomes, mRNA, amino acids, ATP, and a molecule called guanosine triphosphate, or GTP, would be needed. (GTP is similar to ATP but contains guanine instead of adenine.)

These results were logical: Ribosomes provide the catalytic machinery, mRNAs contribute the message to be translated, amino acids are the building blocks of proteins, and ATP and GTP supply potential energy to drive the endergonic polymerization reactions responsible for forming proteins.

But, in addition, a cellular fraction that contained a previously unknown type of RNA turned out to be indispensable. If this type of RNA is missing, protein synthesis does not occur. What is this mysterious RNA, and why is it essential to translation?

The novel class of RNAs eventually became known as **transfer RNA (tRNA).** The role of tRNA in translation was a mystery until some researchers happened to add a radioactive amino acid—leucine—to an in vitro protein-synthesis system. The treatment was actually done as a control for an unrelated experiment. To the researchers' amazement, some of the radioactive leucine attached to tRNA molecules.

What happens to the amino acids bound to tRNAs? To answer this question, Paul Zamecnik and colleagues tracked the fate of radioactive leucine molecules that were attached to tRNAs. They found that the amino acids are transferred from tRNAs to proteins.

The data supporting this conclusion are shown in the "Results" section of **FIGURE 17.11.** The graph shows that radioactive amino acids are lost from tRNAs and incorporated into polypeptides synthesized by ribosomes. To understand this conclusion:

RESEARCH

QUESTION: What happens to the amino acids attached to tRNAs?

HYPOTHESIS: Aminoacyl tRNAs transfer amino acids to growing polypeptides.

NULL HYPOTHESIS: Aminoacyl tRNAs do not transfer amino acids to growing polypeptides.

EXPERIMENTAL SETUP:

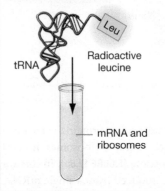

1. Attach radioactive leucine molecules to tRNAs.

2. Add these aminoacyl tRNAs to in vitro translation system. Follow fate of the radioactive amino acids.

PREDICTION: Radioactive amino acids will be found in proteins.

PREDICTION OF NULL HYPOTHESIS: Radioactive amino acids will not be found in proteins.

RESULTS:

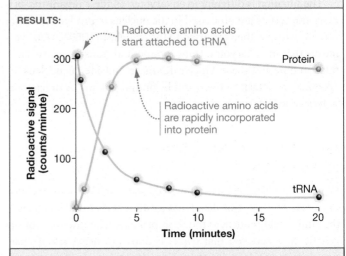

CONCLUSION: Aminoacyl tRNAs transfer amino acids to growing polypeptides.

FIGURE 17.11 Evidence that Amino Acids Are Transferred from tRNAs to Proteins.

SOURCE: Hoagland, M. B., M. L. Stephenson, J. F. Scott, et al. 1958. A soluble ribonucleic acid intermediate in protein synthesis. *Journal of Biological Chemistry* 231: 241–257.

✔ **QUESTION** What would the graphed results look like if the null hypothesis were correct?

1. Put your finger on the point on the *x*-axis that indicates that one minute has passed since the start of the experiment.

2. Read up until you hit the green line and the gray line. The green line represents data from proteins; the gray line represents data from tRNAs.

3. Check the *y*-axis—which indicates the amount of radioactive leucine present—at each point.

4. It should be clear that early in the experiment, almost all the radioactive leucine is attached to tRNA, not protein.

Next, do the same four steps at the point on the *x*-axis labeled 10 minutes (since the start of the experiment). Your conclusion now should be that late in the experiment, almost all the radioactive leucine is attached to proteins, not tRNA.

These results inspired the use of the word transfer in tRNA's name, because amino acids are transferred from the RNA to a growing polypeptide. The experiment also confirmed that tRNAs act as the interpreter during translation: tRNAs are Crick's adapter molecules.

What Do tRNAs Look Like?

Transfer RNAs serve as chemical go-betweens that allow amino acids to interact with an mRNA template. But precisely how does the connection occur?

This question was answered by research on tRNA's molecular structure. The initial studies established the sequence of nucleotides in various tRNAs, or what is termed their primary structure. Transfer RNA sequences are relatively short, ranging from 75 to 85 nucleotides in length.

When biologists studied the primary sequence closely, they noticed that certain parts of the molecules can form secondary structures. Specifically, some sequences of bases in the tRNA molecule can form hydrogen bonds with complementary base sequences elsewhere in the same molecule. As a result, portions of the molecule form stem-and-loop structures (introduced in Chapter 4). The stems are short stretches of double-stranded RNA; the loops are single stranded.

Two aspects of tRNA's secondary structure proved especially important. A CCA sequence at the 3' end of each tRNA molecule offered a site for amino acid attachment, while a triplet on the loop at the other end of the structure could serve as an anticodon. An **anticodon** is a set of three ribonucleotides that forms base pairs with the mRNA codon.

Later, X-ray crystallography studies revealed the tertiary structure of tRNAs. Recall that the tertiary structure of a molecule is the three-dimensional arrangement of its atoms (Chapter 3). As **FIGURE 17.12** shows, tRNAs fold into an L-shaped molecule. The anticodon is at one end of the structure; the CCA sequence and attached amino acid are at the other end.

All the tRNAs in a cell have the same general structure, shaped like an upside-down L. They vary at the anticodon and attached amino acid. The tertiary structure of tRNAs is important because it maintains a precise physical distance between the anticodon and amino acid. As it turns out, this separation is important in positioning the amino acid and the anticodon within the ribosome.

✔ If you understand the structure of tRNAs, you should be able to (1) describe where on the L-shaped structure the amino acid attaches; and (2) explain the relationship between the anticodon of a tRNA and a codon in an mRNA.

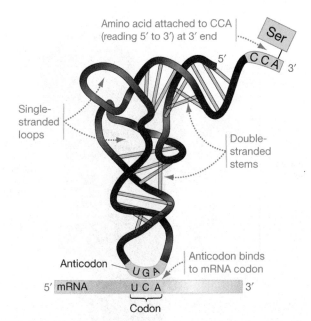

FIGURE 17.12 The Structure of an Aminoacyl Transfer RNA. The anticodon forms complementary base pairs with an mRNA codon.

How Are Amino Acids Attached to tRNAs?

How are amino acids linked to tRNAs? Just as important, what allows the right amino acid for a particular tRNA to be attached?

- An input of energy, in the form of ATP, is required to attach an amino acid to a tRNA.

- Enzymes called **aminoacyl-tRNA synthetases** catalyze the addition of amino acids to tRNAs—what biologists call "charging" a tRNA.

- For each of the 20 major amino acids, there is a different aminoacyl-tRNA synthetase and one or more tRNAs.

Each aminoacyl-tRNA synthetase has a binding site for a particular amino acid and a particular tRNA. Subtle differences in tRNA shape and base sequence allow the enzymes to recognize the correct tRNA for the correct amino acid. The combination of a tRNA molecule covalently linked to an amino acid is called an **aminoacyl tRNA**. **FIGURE 17.13** (see page 328) shows an aminoacyl-tRNA synthetase bound to a tRNA that has just been charged with an amino acid. Note how tightly the two structures fit together—making it possible for the enzyme and its tRNA and amino acid substrates to interact in a precise way.

How Many tRNAs Are There?

After characterizing all the different types of tRNAs, biologists encountered a paradox. According to the genetic code (Chapter 16), the 20 most common amino acids found in proteins are specified by 61 different mRNA codons. Instead of containing 61 different tRNAs with 61 different anticodons, though, most cells contain only about 40. How can all 61 codons be translated with only two-thirds that number of tRNAs?

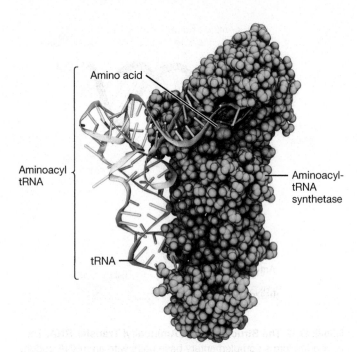

Amino acid

Aminoacyl tRNA

Aminoacyl-tRNA synthetase

tRNA

FIGURE 17.13 Aminoacyl-tRNA Synthetases Couple the Appropriate Amino Acid to the Appropriate tRNA.

To resolve this paradox, Francis Crick proposed what is known as the **wobble hypothesis.** Recall that:

1. Many amino acids are specified by more than one codon.

2. Codons for the same amino acid tend to have the same nucleotides at the first and second positions but a different nucleotide at the third position.

For example, both of the codons CAA and CAG code for the amino acid glutamine. Surprisingly, experimental data have shown that a tRNA with an anticodon of GUU can base-pair with both CAA and CAG in mRNA. The GUU anticodon matches the first two bases (C and A) in both codons, but the U in the anticodon's third position forms a nonstandard base pair with a G in the CAG codon.

Crick proposed that inside the ribosome, certain bases in the third position of tRNA anticodons can bind to bases in the third position of a codon in a manner that does not match Watson–Crick base pairing. If so, this would allow a limited flexibility, or "wobble," in the base pairing.

According to the wobble hypothesis, particular nonstandard base pairs—such as G-U—are acceptable in the third position of a codon and do not change the amino acid that the codon specifies. In this way, wobble in the third position of a codon allows just 40 or so tRNAs to bind to all 61 mRNA codons.

17.5 The Structure and Function of Ribosomes

Recall that protein synthesis occurs when the sequence of bases in an mRNA is translated into a sequence of amino acids in a polypeptide. The translation of each mRNA codon begins when the anticodon of an aminoacyl tRNA binds to the codon. Translation of a codon is complete when a peptide bond forms between the tRNA's amino acid and the growing polypeptide chain.

Both of these events take place inside a ribosome. Biologists have known since the 1930s that ribosomes contain many proteins and **ribosomal RNAs (rRNAs).** Later work showed that ribosomes can be separated into two major substructures, called the large subunit and small subunit. Each ribosome subunit consists of a complex of RNA molecules and proteins. The small subunit holds the mRNA in place during translation; the large subunit is where peptide-bond formation takes place.

FIGURE 17.14 shows two views of how the molecules required for translation fit together. Note that during protein synthesis, three distinct tRNAs are lined up inside the ribosome. All three are bound to their corresponding mRNA codons.

- The tRNA that is on the right in the figure, and colored red, carries an amino acid. This tRNA's position in the ribosome is called the A site—"A" for acceptor or aminoacyl.

- The tRNA that is in the middle (green) holds the growing polypeptide chain and occupies the P site, for peptidyl, inside the ribosome. (Think of "P" for peptide-bond formation.)

- The left-hand (blue) tRNA no longer has an amino acid attached and is about to leave the ribosome. It occupies the ribosome's E site—"E" for exit.

Because all tRNAs have similar secondary and tertiary structure, they all fit equally well in the A, P, and E sites.

The ribosome is a macromolecular machine that synthesizes proteins in a three-step sequence:

1. An aminoacyl tRNA diffuses into the A site; if its anticodon matches a codon in mRNA, it stays in the ribosome.

2. A peptide bond forms between the amino acid held by the aminoacyl tRNA in the A site and the growing polypeptide, which was held by a tRNA in the P site.

3. The ribosome moves down the mRNA by one codon, and all three tRNAs move one position within the ribosome. The tRNA in the E site exits; the tRNA in the P site moves to the E site; and the tRNA in the A site switches to the P site.

The protein that is being synthesized grows by one amino acid each time this three-step sequence repeats. The process occurs up to 20 times per second in bacterial ribosomes and about 2 times per second in eukaryotic ribosomes. Protein synthesis starts at the amino end (N-terminus) of a polypeptide and proceeds to the carboxy end (C-terminus; see Chapter 3).

This introduction to how tRNAs, mRNAs, and ribosomes interact during protein synthesis leaves several key questions unanswered. How do mRNAs and ribosomes get together to start the process? Once protein synthesis is under way, how is peptide-bond formation catalyzed inside the ribosome? And how does protein synthesis conclude when the ribosome reaches the end of the message? Let's consider each question in turn.

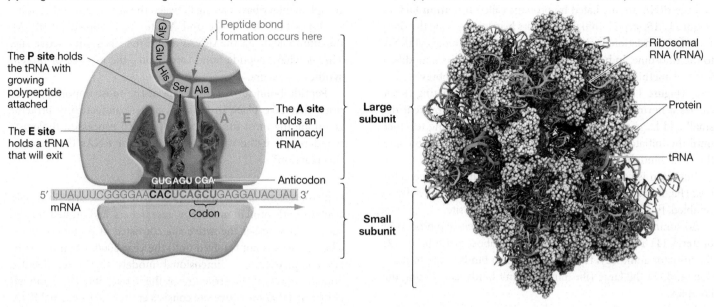

(a) Diagram of ribosome during translation (interior view)

Gly
Glu
His
Ser Ala

Peptide bond formation occurs here

The **P site** holds the tRNA with growing polypeptide attached

The **E site** holds a tRNA that will exit

The **A site** holds an aminoacyl tRNA

E P A

GUGAGU CGA — Anticodon

5′ UUAUUUCGGGGAA**CAC**UCAGCUGAGGAUACUAU 3′
mRNA
Codon

Large subunit

Small subunit

(b) Model of ribosome during translation (exterior view)

Ribosomal RNA (rRNA)

Protein

tRNA

FIGURE 17.14 The Structure of the Ribosome. Ribosomes have three distinct tRNA binding sites in their interior.

Initiating Translation

To translate an mRNA properly, a ribosome must begin at a specific point in the message, translate the mRNA up to the message's termination codon, and then stop. Using the same terminology that they apply to transcription, biologists call these three phases of protein synthesis initiation, elongation, and termination, respectively.

One key to understanding translation initiation is to recall that a start codon (usually AUG) is found near the 5′ end of

all mRNAs and that it codes for the amino acid methionine (Chapter 16).

FIGURE 17.15 shows how translation gets under way in bacteria. The process begins when a section of rRNA in a small ribosomal subunit binds to a complementary sequence on an mRNA. The mRNA region is called the **ribosome binding site,** or **Shine–Dalgarno sequence,** after the biologists who discovered it. The site is about six nucleotides upstream from the start codon.

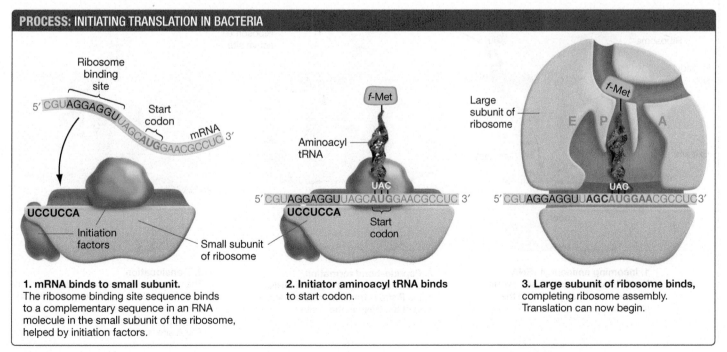

PROCESS: INITIATING TRANSLATION IN BACTERIA

Ribosome binding site

5′ CGU**AGGAGGU**UAGC**AUG**GAACGCCUC 3′

Start codon

mRNA

UCCUCCA

Initiation factors

Small subunit of ribosome

1. mRNA binds to small subunit.
The ribosome binding site sequence binds to a complementary sequence in an RNA molecule in the small subunit of the ribosome, helped by initiation factors.

f-Met

Aminoacyl tRNA

UAC

5′ CGU**AGGAGGU**UAGC**AUG**GAACGCCUC 3′

UCCUCCA

Start codon

2. Initiator aminoacyl tRNA binds to start codon.

f-Met

Large subunit of ribosome

E P A

UAC

5′ CGU**AGGAGGU**U**AGC**AUGGAACGCCUC 3′

3. Large subunit of ribosome binds, completing ribosome assembly. Translation can now begin.

FIGURE 17.15 Initiation of Translation.

The interactions between the small subunit, the message, and the tRNA are mediated by proteins called **initiation factors** (Figure 17.15, step 1). Initiation factors help in preparing the ribosome for translation, including binding the first aminoacyl tRNA to the ribosome. In bacteria this initiator tRNA bears a modified form of methionine called *N*-formylmethionine (abbreviated *f*-met) (Figure 17.15, step 2). In eukaryotes, this initiating tRNA carries a normal methionine. Initiation factors also prevent the small and large subunits of the ribosome from coming together until the initiator tRNA is in place at the AUG start codon, and they help bind the mRNA to the small ribosomal subunit.

Initiation is complete when the large subunit joins the complex (Figure 17.15, step 3). When the ribosome is completely assembled, the tRNA bearing *f*-met occupies the P site.

To summarize, translation initiation is a three-step process in bacteria: **(1)** The mRNA binds to a small ribosomal subunit, **(2)** the initiator aminoacyl tRNA bearing *f*-met binds to the start codon, and **(3)** the large ribosomal subunit binds, completing the complex.

In eukaryotes, the details of initiation are different, but they still involve recognition of a start codon, assembly of the ribosome, assistance from initiation factors, and the positioning of a methionine-carrying tRNA in the P site. The cap and poly(A) tail are also important in assembling the ribosome on the mRNA.

Elongation: Extending the Polypeptide

At the start of elongation, the E and A sites in the ribosome are empty of tRNAs. As a result, an mRNA codon is exposed in the A site. As step 1 in **FIGURE 17.16** illustrates, elongation proceeds when an aminoacyl tRNA binds to the codon in the A site by complementary base pairing between the anticodon and codon.

When both the P site and A site are occupied by tRNAs, the amino acids on the tRNAs are in the ribosome's active site. This is where peptide-bond formation—the essence of protein synthesis—occurs.

Peptide-bond formation is one of the most important reactions that take place in cells because manufacturing proteins is among the most fundamental of all cell processes. Biologists wondered, is it the ribosome's proteins or RNAs that catalyze this reaction?

Is the Ribosome an Enzyme or a Ribozyme? Because ribosomes contain both protein and RNA, researchers had argued for decades over whether the active site consisted of protein or RNA. The debate was not resolved until the year 2000, when researchers completed three-dimensional models that were detailed enough to reveal the structure of the active site. These models confirmed that the active site consists entirely of ribosomal RNA. Based on these results, biologists are now convinced that protein synthesis is catalyzed by RNA. The ribosome is a ribozyme—not a protein-based enzyme.

The observation that protein synthesis is catalyzed by RNA is important because it supports the RNA-world hypothesis (Chapter 4). Recall that proponents of this hypothesis claim that life began with RNA molecules and that the presence of DNA and proteins in cells evolved later. If the RNA-world hypothesis is correct, then it would make sense that the production of proteins is catalyzed by RNA.

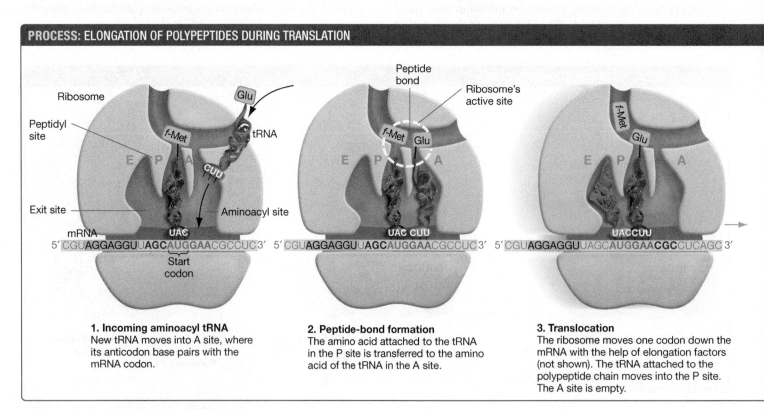

PROCESS: ELONGATION OF POLYPEPTIDES DURING TRANSLATION

1. Incoming aminoacyl tRNA
New tRNA moves into A site, where its anticodon base pairs with the mRNA codon.

2. Peptide-bond formation
The amino acid attached to the tRNA in the P site is transferred to the amino acid of the tRNA in the A site.

3. Translocation
The ribosome moves one codon down the mRNA with the help of elongation factors (not shown). The tRNA attached to the polypeptide chain moves into the P site. The A site is empty.

FIGURE 17.16 The Elongation Phase of Translation.

Moving Down the mRNA What happens after a peptide bond forms? Step 2 in Figure 17.16 shows that when peptide-bond formation is complete, the polypeptide chain is transferred from the tRNA in the P site to the amino acid held by the tRNA in the A site. Step 3 shows the process called **translocation,** which occurs when proteins called **elongation factors** help move the ribosome relative to the mRNA so that translation occurs in the 5′ → 3′ direction. Translocation is an energy-demanding event that requires GTP.

Translocation does several things: It moves the uncharged RNA into the E site; it moves the tRNA containing the growing polypeptide into the P site; and it opens the A site and exposes a new mRNA codon. The empty tRNA that finds itself in the E site is ejected into the cytosol.

The three steps in elongation—(1) arrival of aminoacyl tRNA, (2) peptide-bond formation, and (3) translocation—repeat down the length of the mRNA. Recent three-dimensional models of ribosomes in various stages of translation show that the machine is highly dynamic. The ribosome constantly changes shape as tRNAs come and go and catalysis and translocation occur. The ribosome is a complex and dynamic macromolecular machine.

Terminating Translation

How does protein synthesis end? Recall that the genetic code includes three stop codons: UAA, UAG, and UGA (see Chapter 16). In most cells, no aminoacyl tRNA has an anticodon that binds to these sequences. When the translocating ribosome reaches one of the stop codons, a protein called a **release factor** recognizes the stop codon and fills the A site (**FIGURE 17.17**, see page 333).

Release factors fit tightly into the A site because they have the size and shape of a tRNA coming into the ribosome. However, release factors do not carry an amino acid. When a release factor occupies the A site, the protein's active site catalyzes the hydrolysis of the bond that links the tRNA in the P site to the polypeptide chain. This reaction frees the polypeptide.

The newly synthesized polypeptide and uncharged tRNAs are released from the ribosome, the ribosome separates from the mRNA, and the two ribosomal subunits dissociate. The subunits are ready to attach to the start codon of another message and start translation anew. Termination occurs in very similar ways in bacteria and eukaryotes.

Post-Translational Modifications

Proteins are not fully formed and functional when termination occurs. From earlier chapters, it should be clear that most proteins go through an extensive series of processing steps, collectively called post-translational modification, before they are completely functional. These steps require a wide array of molecules and events and take place in many different locations throughout the cell.

Folding Recall that a protein's function depends on its shape, and that a protein's shape depends on how it folds (see Chapter 3). Although folding can occur spontaneously, it is frequently speeded up by proteins called **molecular chaperones.**

Recent data have shown that in some bacteria, chaperone proteins bind to the ribosome near the "tunnel" where the growing polypeptide emerges from the ribosome. This finding suggests that folding occurs as the polypeptide emerges from the ribosome.

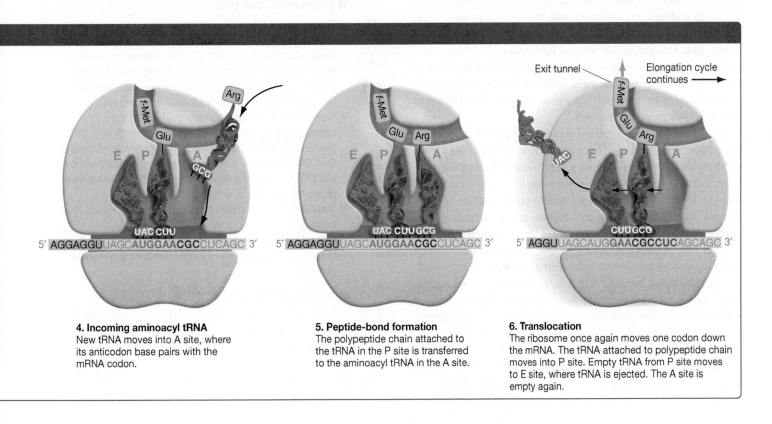

4. Incoming aminoacyl tRNA
New tRNA moves into A site, where its anticodon base pairs with the mRNA codon.

5. Peptide-bond formation
The polypeptide chain attached to the tRNA in the P site is transferred to the aminoacyl tRNA in the A site.

6. Translocation
The ribosome once again moves one codon down the mRNA. The tRNA attached to polypeptide chain moves into P site. Empty tRNA from P site moves to E site, where tRNA is ejected. The A site is empty again.

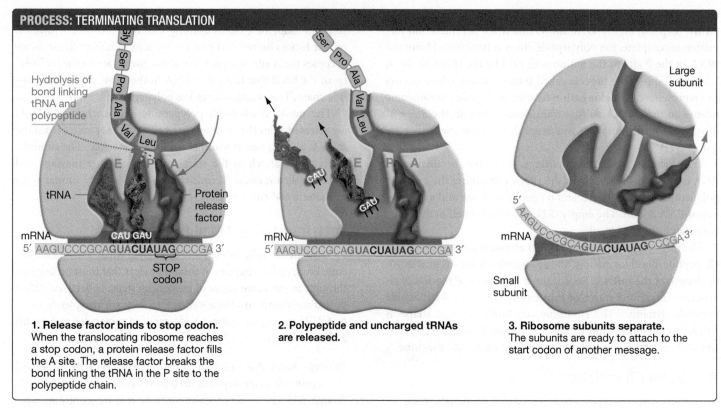

1. Release factor binds to stop codon.
When the translocating ribosome reaches a stop codon, a protein release factor fills the A site. The release factor breaks the bond linking the tRNA in the P site to the polypeptide chain.

2. Polypeptide and uncharged tRNAs are released.

3. Ribosome subunits separate.
The subunits are ready to attach to the start codon of another message.

FIGURE 17.17 Termination of Translation.

Chemical Modifications An earlier chapter pointed out that many eukaryotic proteins are extensively modified after they are synthesized (see Chapter 7). For example, in the organelles called the rough endoplasmic reticulum and the Golgi apparatus, small chemical groups may be added to proteins—often sugar or lipid groups that are critical for normal functioning. In some cases, the proteins receive a sugar-based sorting signal that serves as an address label and ensures that the molecule will be carried to the correct location in the cell. (Other proteins have a sorting signal built into their primary structure.)

In addition, many completed proteins are altered by enzymes that add or remove a phosphate group. Phosphorylation (addition of phosphate) and dephosphorylation (removal of phosphate) of proteins were introduced in previous chapters (Chapters 9 and 11). Recall that because a phosphate group has two negative charges, adding or removing a phosphate group can cause major changes in the shape and chemical reactivity of proteins. These changes have a dramatic effect on the protein's activity—often switching it from an inactive state to an active state, or vice versa.

The take-home message is that gene expression is a complex, multistep process that begins with transcription but may not end with translation. Instead, even completed and folded proteins may be activated or deactivated by events such as phosphorylation. In general, how are genes turned on or off? How does a cell "decide" which of its many genes should be expressed at any time? These questions are the focus of the next two chapters.

check your understanding

C Y U

If you understand that . . .

- Translation begins when (1) the ribosome binding site on an mRNA binds to an rRNA sequence in the small ribosomal subunit, (2) the initiator aminoacyl tRNA binds to the start codon in the mRNA, and (3) the large subunit of the ribosome attaches to the small subunit to complete the ribosome.
- Translation elongation occurs when (1) an appropriate aminoacyl tRNA enters the A site, (2) a peptide bond forms between the amino acid held by that tRNA in the A site and the polypeptide held by the tRNA in the P site, and (3) the ribosome moves down the mRNA one codon.
- Translation ends when the ribosome reaches a stop codon.
- Completed proteins are modified by folding and, in many cases, addition of sugar, lipid, or phosphate groups.

✔ You should be able to . . .

Explain why the E, P, and A sites in the ribosome are appropriately named.

Answers are available in Appendix A.

If you understand . . .

17.1 An Overview of Transcription

- RNA polymerase catalyzes the production of an RNA molecule whose base sequence is complementary to the base sequence of the DNA template strand.

- RNA polymerase binds DNA with the help of other proteins.

- RNA polymerase begins transcription by binding to promoter sequences in DNA.

- In bacteria, this binding occurs in conjunction with a protein called sigma. Sigma associates with RNA polymerase and then recognizes particular sequences within promoters that are centered 10 bases and 35 bases upstream from the start of the actual genetic message.

- Eukaryotic promoters vary more than bacterial promoters.

- In eukaryotes, transcription begins when a large array of proteins called basal transcription factors bind to a promoter. In response, RNA polymerase binds to the site.

- In both bacteria and eukaryotes, the RNA elongates in a $5' \rightarrow 3'$ direction.

- Transcription in bacteria ends when RNA polymerase encounters a stem-loop structure in the just transcribed RNA; in eukaryotes, transcription terminates after the RNA is cleaved downstream of the poly(A) sequence.

✔ You should be able to predict the consequences of a mutation in bacteria that inserts random nucleotides into the hairpin-coding region near the $3'$ end of a transcribed region.

17.2 RNA Processing in Eukaryotes

- In eukaryotes, the primary (initial) transcript must be processed to produce a mature RNA.

- In primary transcripts, stretches of RNA called introns are spliced out and regions called exons are joined together.

- Complex macromolecular machines called spliceosomes splice introns out of pre-mRNA.

- A "cap" is added to the $5'$ end of pre-mRNAs, and a poly(A) tail is added to their $3'$ end.

- The cap and tail serve as recognition signals for translation and protect the message from degradation by ribonucleases.

- RNA processing occurs in the nucleus.

✔ You should be able to predict whether the protein-coding portion of a gene for an identical protein will be of the same or different lengths in a bacterium and a eukaryote.

17.3 An Introduction to Translation

- Ribosomes translate mRNAs into proteins with the help of adaptor molecules called transfer RNAs.

- In bacteria, an RNA is often transcribed and translated at the same time because there is no nucleus.

- In eukaryotes, transcription and translation of an RNA cannot occur together, because transcription and RNA processing occur in the nucleus and translation occurs in the cytoplasm.

- Experiments with radioactively labeled amino acids showed that transfer RNAs (tRNAs) serve as the chemical bridge between the RNA message and the polypeptide product.

✔ You should be able to explain why it is correct to say that transfer RNAs work as molecular adaptors.

17.4 The Structure and Function of Transfer RNA

- Each transfer RNA carries an amino acid corresponding to the tRNA's three-base-long anticodon.

- tRNAs have an L-shaped, tertiary structure. One leg of the L contains the anticodon, which forms complementary base pairs with the mRNA codon. The other leg holds the amino acid appropriate for that codon.

- Enzymes called aminoacyl-tRNA synthetases link the correct amino acid to the correct tRNA.

- Imprecise pairing—or "wobble pairing"—is allowed in the third position of the codon and anticodon, so only about 40 different tRNAs are required to translate the 61 codons that code for amino acids.

✔ You should be able to predict what would occur if a mutation caused an aminoacyl-tRNA synthetase to recognize two different amino acids.

17.5 The Structure and Function of Ribosomes

- Ribosomes are large macromolecular machines made of many proteins and RNAs.

- In the ribosome, the tRNA anticodon binds to a three-base-long mRNA codon to bring the correct amino acid into the ribosome.

- Peptide-bond formation by the ribosome is catalyzed by a ribozyme (RNA), not an enzyme (protein).

- Protein synthesis occurs in three steps: **(1)** an incoming aminoacyl tRNA occupies the A site; **(2)** the growing polypeptide chain is transferred from a peptidyl tRNA in the ribosome's P site to the amino acid bound to the tRNA in the A site, and a peptide bond is formed; and **(3)** the ribosome is translocated to the next codon on the mRNA, accompanied by ejection of the uncharged RNA from the E site.

- Chaperone proteins help fold newly synthesized proteins into their three-dimensional conformation (tertiary structure).

- Most proteins need to be modified after translation (post-translational modification) to activate them or target them to specific locations.

✔ You should be able to create a concept map (see BioSkills 15 in Appendix B) that describes the relationships among the following concepts and structures: translation, initiation, elongation, termination, growing polypeptide in P site, start codon, ribosome subunits.

(MB) MasteringBiology

1. MasteringBiology Assignments

Tutorials and Activities Chromosomal Mutations; Following the Instructions in DNA; Point Mutations Protein Synthesis (1 of 3): Overview; Protein Synthesis (2 of 3): Transcription and RNA Processing; Protein Synthesis (3 of 3): Translation and Protein Targeting Pathways; RNA Processing; RNA Synthesis; Synthesizing Proteins; Transcription; Translation; Types of RNA

Questions Reading Quizzes, Blue-Thread Questions, Test Bank

2. eText Read your book online, search, take notes, highlight text, and more.

3. The Study Area Practice Test, Cumulative Test, BioFlix® 3-D Animations, Videos, Activities, Audio Glossary, Word Study Tools, Art

You should be able to . . .

✔ TEST YOUR KNOWLEDGE
Answers are available in Appendix A

1. How did the A site of the ribosome get its name?
   a. It is where amino acids are joined to tRNAs, producing aminoacyl tRNAs.
   b. It is where the amino group on the growing polypeptide chain is available for peptide-bond formation.
   c. It is the site occupied by incoming aminoacyl tRNAs.
   d. It is surrounded by α-helices of ribosomal proteins.

2. Where is the start codon located?
   a. at the very start (5′ end) of the mRNA
   b. at the downstream end of the 3′ untranslated region (UTR)
   c. at the downstream end of the 5′ untranslated region (UTR)
   d. at the upstream end of the 3′ untranslated region (UTR)

3. What is the function of a molecular chaperone?

4. What does a bacterial RNA polymerase produce when it transcribes a protein-coding gene?

   a. rRNA
   b. tRNA
   c. mRNA
   d. pre-mRNA

5. Where is an amino acid attached to a tRNA?

6. Compared with mRNAs that have a cap and tail, what do researchers observe when eukaryotic mRNAs that lack a cap and poly(A) tail are translated within a cell?
   a. The primary transcript cannot be processed properly.
   b. Translation occurs inefficiently.
   c. Enzymes on the ribosome add back a cap and poly(A) tail.
   d. tRNAs become resistant to degradation (being broken down).

✔ TEST YOUR UNDERSTANDING
Answers are available in Appendix A

7. Explain the relationship between eukaryotic promoter sequences, basal transcription factors, and RNA polymerase. Explain the relationship between bacterial promoter sequences, sigma, and RNA polymerase.

8. According to the wobble rules, the correct amino acid can be added to a growing polypeptide chain even if the third base in the mRNA codon is not complementary to the corresponding base in the tRNA anticodon. How do the wobble rules relate to the redundancy of the genetic code?

9. RNases and proteases are enzymes that destroy RNAs and proteins, respectively. Which of the following enzymes when added to a spliceosome is predicted to prevent recognition of pre-mRNA regions critical for splicing?
   a. an RNase specific for tRNAs
   b. an RNase specific for snRNAs
   c. a protease specific for initiation factors
   d. a protease specific for a release factor

10. Describe the sequence of events that occurs during translation as a protein elongates by one amino acid and the ribosome moves down the mRNA. Your answer should specify what is happening in the ribosome's A site, P site, and E site.

11. **QUANTITATIVE** Controlling the rates of transcription and translation is important in bacteria to avoid collisions between ribosomes and RNA polymerases. Calculate the maximum rate of translation by a ribosome in a bacterial cell, provided in units of amino acids per second, so that the ribosome doesn't overtake an RNA polymerase that is transcribing mRNA at a rate of 60 nucleotides per second. How long would it take for this bacterial cell to translate an mRNA containing 1800 codons?

12. In an aminoacyl tRNA, why is the observed distance between the amino acid and the anticodon important?

✔ **TEST YOUR PROBLEM-SOLVING SKILLS** *Answers are available in Appendix A*

13. The 5′ cap and poly(A) tail in eukaryotic mRNAs protect the message from degradation by ribonucleases. But why do ribonucleases exist? What function would an enzyme that destroys messages serve? Answer this question using the example of an mRNA for a hormone that causes human heart rate to increase.

14. The nucleotide shown below is called cordycepin triphosphate.

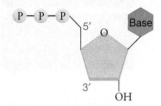

If cordycepin triphosphate is added to a cell-free transcription reaction, the nucleotide is added onto the growing RNA chain but no more nucleotides can be added. The added cordycepin is always found at the 3′ end of an RNA, confirming that synthesis occurs in the 5′ → 3′ direction. Why does cordycepin end transcription?

a. It prevents the association of RNA polymerase and sigma.
b. It irreversibly binds to the active site of RNA polymerase.
c. It cannot be recognized by RNA polymerase.
d. It lacks a 3′ OH.

15. Certain portions of the rRNAs in the large subunit of the ribosome are very similar in all organisms. To make sense of this finding, Carl Woese suggests that the conserved sequences have an important functional role. His logic is that these conserved sequences evolved in a common ancestor of all modern cells and are so important to cell function that any changes in the sequences cause death. In addition to rRNAs, which specific portions of the ribosome would you expect to be identical or nearly identical in all organisms? Explain your logic.

16. Recent structural models show that a poison called α-amanitin inhibits transcription by binding to a site inside eukaryotic RNA polymerase II but not to the active site itself. Based on the model of RNA polymerase in Figure 17.2, predict a place or places where α-amanitin might bind to inhibit transcription.

18 Control of Gene Expression in Bacteria

In this chapter you will learn how

Bacteria turn their genes on and off to adapt to changing environments

surveying

Different ways genes can be regulated **18.1**

and

How mutants help identify regulated genes **18.2**

looking closer at

Negative control of gene expression **18.3**

Positive control of gene expression **18.4**

Ways bacteria regulate many genes together **18.5**

The structures that have been colored blue in this scanning electron micrograph are projections from human intestinal cells; the structures colored yellow are the bacterium *Escherichia coli*. In the intestine, the nutrients available to bacteria constantly change. This chapter explores how changes in gene expression help bacteria respond to environmental changes.

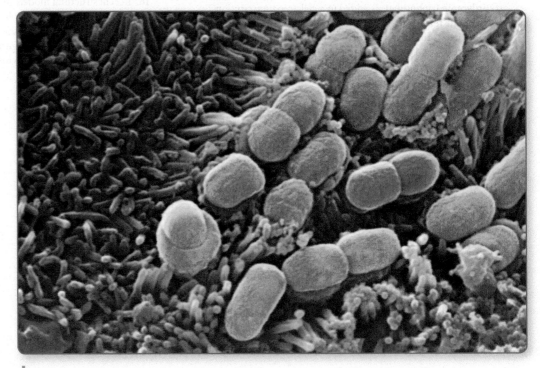

PICTURE

This chapter is part of the Big Picture. See how on pages 366–367.

magine waiting eagerly to hear the opening lines of a wonderfully melodic symphony played by a renowned orchestra. The crowd applauds as the celebrated conductor comes onstage and then hushes as he takes the podium. He cocks the baton; the musicians raise their instruments. As the baton comes down, every instrument begins blaring a different tune at full volume. A tuba plays "Dixie," a violinist renders "In-A-Gadda-Da-Vida," a snare drum lays down beats for Hot Chelle Rae's "Tonight, Tonight," while the bass drum simulates cannons in the "1812 Overture." Instead of music, there is pandemonium. The conductor staggers offstage, clutching his heart.

Cacophony like this would result if a bacterial cell "played" all its genes at full volume all the time. The *Escherichia coli* cells living in your gut right now have over 4300 genes. If all those genes were expressed at the fastest possible rate at all times, the *E. coli* cells would stagger off the stage,

✔ When you see this checkmark, stop and test yourself. Answers are available in Appendix A.

too. But this does not happen. Cells are extremely selective about which genes are expressed, in what amounts, and when.

This chapter explores how bacterial cells control the activity, or expression, of their genes. **Gene expression** is the process of converting information that is archived in DNA into molecules that actually do things in the cell. It occurs when a protein or other gene product is synthesized and active. (You can see on pages 366–367 how gene expression fits into the Big Picture of Genetic Information.)

Previous chapters detailed how genetic information is processed in cells; this chapter focuses on ways to control *when* genetic information is used. Let's begin by reviewing some of the environmental challenges that bacterial cells face and then explore how these organisms meet them.

18.1 An Overview of Gene Regulation and Information Flow

The bacteria that live in and on your body vastly outnumber your own cells. Consider just one of the species present: the gut-dwelling *Escherichia coli*. These cells can use a wide array of carbohydrates to supply the carbon and energy they need. But as your diet changes from day to day, the availability of different sugars in your intestines varies. Each type of nutrient requires a different membrane transport protein to bring the molecule into the cell and a different suite of enzymes to process it. Precise control of gene expression gives *E. coli* the ability to use the available sugars efficiently.

To understand why precise control over gene expression is so important, you have to realize that bacterial cells from an array of species can be densely packed along your intestinal walls. All of these organisms are competing for space and nutrients. In an environment like this, a cell has to use resources efficiently if it's going to be able to survive and reproduce. An individual that synthesizes proteins it doesn't need has fewer resources to devote to making the proteins it does need. Such cells are losers—they compete less successfully for the resources that are required to produce offspring.

Realizing this, biologists predicted that most gene expression is triggered by specific signals from the environment, such as the presence of specific sugars. Did you drink milk at your last meal, or eat French fries and a candy bar? Each type of food contains different sugars. Each sugar should induce a different response from the *E. coli* cells in your intestine. Just as a conductor needs to regulate the orchestra's musicians, cells need to regulate which proteins they produce.

Mechanisms of Regulation

The flow of information from DNA to activation of the final gene product occurs in three steps, represented by arrows in the following diagram:

$$\text{DNA} \longrightarrow \text{mRNA} \longrightarrow \text{protein} \longrightarrow \text{activated protein}$$

Gene expression can be controlled at any of these steps. The arrow from DNA to RNA represents transcription—the making of messenger RNA (mRNA). The arrow from RNA to protein represents translation, in which ribosomes read the information in mRNA and use that information to synthesize a protein. The arrow from protein to activated protein represents post-translational modifications that can lead to changes in shape and activity.

How can a bacterial cell avoid producing proteins that are not needed at a particular time, and thus use resources efficiently? A look at the flow of information from DNA to protein suggests three possible mechanisms:

1. The cell could avoid making the mRNAs for particular enzymes. If there is no mRNA, then ribosomes cannot make the gene product. **Transcriptional control** occurs when regulatory proteins affect RNA polymerase's ability to bind to a promoter and initiate transcription:

$$\text{DNA} \xrightarrow{\;\;\times\;\;} \text{mRNA} \longrightarrow \text{protein} \longrightarrow \text{activated protein}$$

2. If the mRNA for an enzyme has been made, the cell could prevent the mRNA from being translated into protein. **Translational control** occurs when regulatory molecules alter the length of time an mRNA survives, or affect translation initiation or elongation:

$$\text{DNA} \longrightarrow \text{mRNA} \xrightarrow{\;\;\times\;\;} \text{protein} \longrightarrow \text{activated protein}$$

3. Many proteins have to be activated by chemical modification, such as the addition of a phosphate group. Regulating this final step is **post-translational control**:

$$\text{DNA} \longrightarrow \text{mRNA} \longrightarrow \text{protein} \xrightarrow{\;\;\times\;\;} \text{activated protein}$$

Which of these three forms of control occur in bacteria? The short answer is all the above. As **FIGURE 18.1** (see page 338) shows, many factors affect how much active protein is produced from a particular gene.

- Transcriptional control is particularly important due to its efficiency—it saves the most energy for the cell, because it stops the process of gene expression at the earliest possible point.

- Translational control allows a cell to make rapid changes in the amounts of different proteins because the mRNA is already present and available for translation.

- Post-translational control provides the most rapid response of all three mechanisms because only one step is needed to activate an existing protein.

Among these mechanisms of gene regulation, there is a clear trade-off between the speed of response and the conservation of ATP, amino acids, and other resources. Transcriptional control is slow but efficient in resource use; post-translational control is fast but energetically expensive.

Although this chapter focuses almost exclusively on mechanisms of transcriptional control, it is important to keep in mind that bacteria also possess translational and post-translational

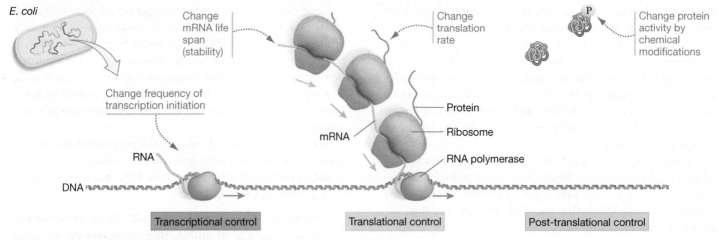

FIGURE 18.1 Gene Expression in Bacteria Can Be Regulated at Three Levels.

✔**EXERCISE** Label the mode of regulation that is slowest in response time and the mode that is fastest. Label the most efficient and least efficient mode in resource use.

controls. Just as important, some genes—such as those that code for the enzymes required for glycolysis—are transcribed all the time, or **constitutively**. Finally, it is critical to realize that gene expression is not an all-or-none proposition. Genes are not just "on" or "off"—instead, the level of expression can vary between these extremes.

The ability to regulate gene expression allows cells to respond to changes in their environment.

Metabolizing Lactose—A Model System

Many of the great advances in genetics have been achieved through the analysis of model systems (see Chapters 14–17). Mendel studied garden peas and discovered the fundamental patterns of gene transmission; Morgan studied fruit flies and confirmed the chromosome theory of inheritance; an array of researchers used *E. coli* and its viruses to work out the mechanisms of DNA synthesis, transcription, and translation. In early studies of gene regulation, a key model system was the metabolism of the sugar lactose in *E. coli*.

Jacques Monod, François Jacob, and many colleagues introduced lactose metabolism in *E. coli* as a model system during the 1950s and 1960s. Although they worked with a single species of bacteria, their results had a profound effect on thinking about gene regulation in all organisms.

E. coli can use a wide variety of sugars for ATP production, via cellular respiration or fermentation. These sugars also serve as raw material in the synthesis of amino acids, vitamins, and other complex compounds. Glucose, however, is *E. coli*'s preferred carbon source—meaning that it is the source of energy and carbon atoms that the organism uses most efficiently.

A preference for glucose makes sense, because glycolysis begins with glucose and is the main pathway for the production of ATP. Lactose, the sugar found in milk, can also be used by *E. coli*, but it is not used until glucose supplies are depleted. Recall that

lactose is a disaccharide made up of one molecule of glucose and one molecule of galactose (see Chapter 5).

To use lactose, *E. coli* must first transport the sugar into the cell. Once lactose is inside the cell, the enzyme ⊠-galactosidase catalyzes a reaction that breaks down the disaccharide into glucose and galactose. The glucose released by this reaction goes directly into the glycolytic pathway; other enzymes convert the galactose to a substance that can also be processed in the glycolytic pathway.

In the early 1950s, biologists discovered that *E. coli* produces high levels of ⊠-galactosidase only when lactose is present in the environment. Based on this observation, researchers proposed that lactose itself regulates the gene for ⊠-galactosidase—meaning that lactose acts as an inducer. An **inducer** is a small molecule that triggers transcription of a specific gene.

In the late 1950s, Jacques Monod wondered how the presence of glucose affects the regulation of the ⊠-galactosidase gene. Would *E. coli* produce high levels of ⊠-galactosidase when both glucose and lactose were present in the surrounding environment? As the experiment summarized in **FIGURE 18.2** shows, the answer was no. Significant amounts of ⊠-galactosidase are produced only when lactose is present and glucose is not present.

Monod teamed up with François Jacob to investigate exactly how lactose and glucose regulate the genes responsible for lactose metabolism—the gene for the membrane protein that imports lactose and the gene for ⊠-galactosidase. Discoveries about how these genes are regulated shed light on how genes in all organisms are controlled. Research on this system is still going strong, over 50 years later.

✔ You should be able to make a chart summarizing the molecules involved in regulating lactose use in *E. coli*. There should be 7 rows and 2 columns. Title the first column "Name" and the second column "Function." The rows are *lacZ*, *lacY*, operator, promoter, repressor, lactose, and glucose. As you read this chapter, fill in the "Function" column.

QUESTION: *E. coli* produces β-galactosidase when lactose is present. Does *E. coli* produce β-galactosidase when both glucose and lactose are present?

HYPOTHESIS: *E. coli* does not produce β-galactosidase when glucose is present, even if lactose is present. (Glucose is the preferred food source.)

NULL HYPOTHESIS: *E. coli* produces β-galactosidase whenever lactose is present, regardless of the presence or absence of glucose.

EXPERIMENTAL SETUP:

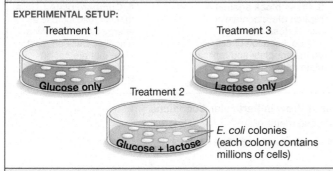

PREDICTION: β-Galactosidase will be produced only in treatment 3.

PREDICTION OF NULL HYPOTHESIS: β-Galactosidase will be produced in treatments 2 and 3.

RESULTS:

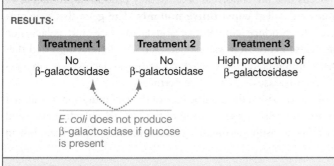

CONCLUSION: Glucose prevents expression of the gene for β-galactosidase. The presence of lactose without glucose stimulates expression of that gene.

FIGURE 18.2 Glucose Affects the Regulation of the β-Galactosidase Gene.

✔**QUESTION** How would you control growth conditions in the three treatments so that the results of this experiment are valid?

SOURCE: Pardee, A. B., F. Jacob, and J. Monod. 1959. The genetic control and cytoplasmic expression of "inducibility" in the synthesis of ⊠-galactosidase by *E. coli*. *Journal of Molecular Biology* 1: 165–178.

18.2 Identifying Regulated Genes

To understand how *E. coli* controls production of ⊠-galactosidase and the transport protein that brings lactose into the cell, Jacob and Monod first had to find the genes that code for these proteins. To do this, they employed the same tactic used in the pioneering studies of DNA replication, transcription, and translation reviewed in earlier chapters: They isolated and analyzed mutants. In this case, their goal was to find *E. coli* cells that could not metabolize lactose. Cells that can't use lactose must lack either ⊠-galactosidase or the lactose transporter protein.

To find mutants that are associated with a particular trait, a researcher has to complete two steps:

1. Generate a large number of individuals with mutations at random locations in their genomes. Monod and colleagues accomplished this step by exposing *E. coli* populations to **mutagens**—X-rays, UV light, or chemicals that damage DNA and increase mutation rates.

2. Screen the treated individuals for mutants with defects in the process or biochemical pathway in question—in this case, defects in lactose metabolism. Recall that a genetic screen is any technique for selecting individuals with certain types of mutations out of a large population, and that a mutant is an individual with a mutation (see Chapter 16).

The researchers were looking for cells that cannot grow in an environment that contains only lactose as an energy source. Normal cells grow well in this environment. How could the researchers select cells on the basis of *lack* of growth?

Replica Plating to Find Lactose Metabolism Mutants

Replica plating and growth on indicator plates were key techniques in the search for mutants with defects in lactose metabolism. **FIGURE 18.3** (see page 6) shows how **replica plating** works.

Step 1 When mutants with defects in lactose metabolism are desired, mutagenized bacteria are spread on a "master plate" filled with a gelatinous growth **medium** containing glucose but no lactose. Growth medium is any liquid or solid that supports the growth of cells. It is important that the mutant cells are capable of growing on the master plate. The bacteria are then allowed to grow, so that each cell produces a colony—a large number of identical cells descended from a single cell.

Step 2 A block covered with a piece of sterilized velvet is pressed onto the master plate. Some cells from each colony on the master plate are transferred to the velvet.

Step 3 The velvet is pressed onto a plate called a replica plate that contains medium that differs from the master plate by a single component. In this case, the second medium has only lactose and no glucose as the source of carbon and energy. Cells from the velvet stick to the replica plate's surface, producing an exact copy of the locations of the colonies on the master plate.

Step 4 After these transferred cells grow, compare the colonies on the replica plate with those on the master plate. In this example, colonies that grow on the master plate but are missing on the replica plate are mutants that cannot metabolize lactose. By picking cells from these colonies on the master plate, researchers build a collection of lactose metabolism mutants.

Several Genes Are Involved in Lactose Metabolism

The initial mutant screen yielded three types of mutants. In one class, the mutant cells were unable to cleave lactose—even when

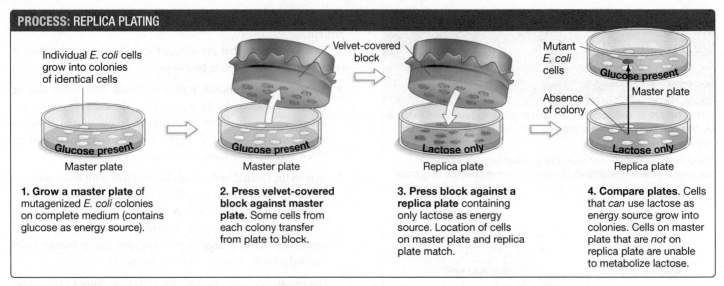

1. **Grow a master plate** of mutagenized *E. coli* colonies on complete medium (contains glucose as energy source).

2. **Press velvet-covered block against master plate.** Some cells from each colony transfer from plate to block.

3. **Press block against a replica plate** containing only lactose as energy source. Location of cells on master plate and replica plate match.

4. **Compare plates.** Cells that *can* use lactose as energy source grow into colonies. Cells on master plate that are *not* on replica plate are unable to metabolize lactose.

FIGURE 18.3 Replica Plating Is a Technique for Identifying Mutants That Cannot Grow in Particular Conditions.
Here, replica plating is used to isolate mutant *E. coli* cells with a deficiency in lactose metabolism.

✔**QUESTION** How would you alter this protocol to isolate mutant cells with a deficiency in the enzymes required to synthesize tryptophan?

lactose was in the medium and transported into cells to induce production of the β-galactosidase protein. Jacob and Monod concluded that these mutants must lack a functioning version of the β-galactosidase protein and, therefore, the gene that encodes β-galactosidase is defective. This gene was designated *lacZ*, and the mutant allele *lacZ*⁻ .

In the second class of mutants, the cells failed to accumulate lactose inside the cell. To explain this result, Jacob and Monod hypothesized that the mutant cells had defective copies of the membrane protein responsible for transporting lactose into the cell. This protein was identified and named galactoside permease; the gene that encodes it was designated *lacY*. **FIGURE 18.4** summarizes the functions of β-galactosidase and galactoside permease.

The third and most surprising class of mutants did not show normal regulation of β-galactosidase and galactoside permease expression. Instead, these mutants made the proteins all the

time—even if no lactose was present. **TABLE 18.1** summarizes these three types of mutants.

Cells that are abnormal because they produce a product at all times are called **constitutive mutants.** The gene that was mutated to produce constitutive β-galactosidase and galactoside permease expression was named *lacI*. The letter I signified that these mutants did not need an inducer—lactose—to express β-galactosidase or galactoside permease.

To understand the significance of the *lacI* mutation, recall that in normal cells, the expression of the *lacZ* (β-galactosidase) and *lacY* (galactoside permease) genes is induced by lactose. But in

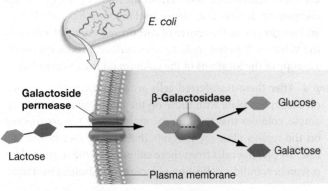

FIGURE 18.4 Two Proteins *E. coli* Needs for Using Lactose.
The membrane protein galactoside permease brings lactose into the cell, and the enzyme β-galactosidase breaks lactose into its glucose and galactose subunits.

TABLE 18.1 Three Types of Lactose Metabolism Mutants in *E. coli*

Observed Phenotype	Interpretation	Genotype
1. Cells cannot cleave lactose, even in the presence of inducer.	No β-galactosidase; gene for β-galactosidase is defective. Call this gene *lacZ*.	*lacZ*⁻
2. Cells cannot accumulate lactose.	No membrane protein (galactoside permease) to import lactose; gene for galactoside permease is defective. Call this gene *lacY*.	*lacY*⁻
3. Cells cleave lactose even if lactose is absent as an inducer.	Constitutive (constant) expression of *lacZ* and *lacY*; gene for regulatory protein that shuts down *lacZ* and *lacY* is defective—it does not need to be induced by lactose. Call this gene *lacI*.	*lacI*⁻

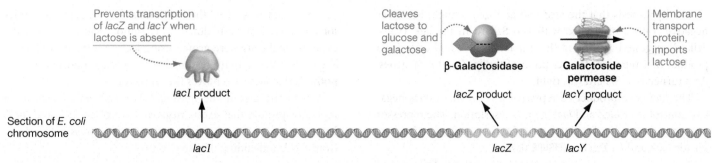

Prevents transcription of *lacZ* and *lacY* when lactose is absent

lacI product

Cleaves lactose to glucose and galactose

β-Galactosidase

lacZ product

Membrane transport protein, imports lactose

Galactoside permease

lacY product

Section of *E. coli* chromosome

lacI

lacZ

lacY

FIGURE 18.5 The *lac* Genes Are in Close Physical Proximity. The associated proteins and their functions are shown above each gene.

cells with a mutant form of *lacI* (*lacI*⊠ mutants), gene expression occurs with or without lactose. This means that *lacI*⊠ mutants have a defect in gene regulation. In these mutants, the gene remains on when it should be turned off.

To pull these observations together, the researchers hypothesized that the normal product of the *lacI* gene prevents the transcription of *lacZ* and *lacY* when lactose is absent. Because lactose triggers production of ⊠-galactosidase, it was reasonable to expect that the *lacI* gene or gene product interacts with lactose in some way. (Later work showed that the inducer is actually a derivative of lactose called *allolactose*. For historical accuracy and simplicity, however, this discussion refers to lactose itself as the inducer.)

Jacob and Monod had succeeded in identifying three genes involved in lactose metabolism: *lacZ*, *lacY*, and *lacI*. They concluded that *lacZ* and *lacY* code for proteins required for the metabolism and import of lactose, while *lacI* is responsible for some sort of regulatory function. When lactose is absent, the *lacI* gene or gene product shuts down the expression of *lacZ* and *lacY*. But when lactose is present, the opposite occurs—transcription of *lacZ* and *lacY* is induced.

✔ If you understand the genes involved in lactose metabolism, you should be able to describe the specific function of *lacZ* and *lacY*. You should also be able to describe the effect of the *lacI* gene product when lactose is present versus absent and explain why these effects are logical.

Jacob and Monod followed up on these experiments by mapping the location of the three genes on the *E. coli* chromosome (**FIGURE 18.5**). They discovered that the genes are close together. This was a crucial finding because it suggested that *lacZ* and *lacY* might be transcribed together. Could the *lacI* regulatory gene govern both the *lacZ* and *lacY* genes? How does *lacI* actually work? And why do lactose and glucose have opposite effects on gene expression?

18.3 Negative Control of Transcription

In principle, there are two general ways that transcription can be regulated: by negative control or positive control.

1. **Negative control** occurs when a regulatory protein called a **repressor** binds to DNA and shuts down transcription (**FIGURE 18.6a**).

2. **Positive control** occurs when a regulatory protein called an **activator** binds to DNA and triggers transcription (**FIGURE 18.6b**).

When you are driving a car, negative control is exerted by setting the parking brake; positive control occurs when you step on the gas pedal. It turned out that the *lacZ* and *lacY* genes in *E. coli* are controlled by engaging or releasing a parking brake—they are under negative control.

(a) Negative control: Regulatory protein *shuts down* transcription.

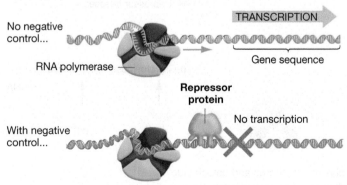

No negative control...

RNA polymerase

TRANSCRIPTION

Gene sequence

Repressor protein

No transcription

With negative control...

(b) Positive control: Regulatory protein *triggers* transcription.

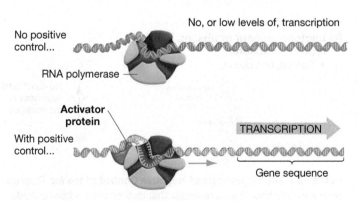

No positive control...

RNA polymerase

No, or low levels of, transcription

Activator protein

With positive control...

TRANSCRIPTION

Gene sequence

FIGURE 18.6 Genes Are Regulated by Negative Control, Positive Control, or Both. (To review transcription initiation, see Figure 17.3.)

The hypothesis that the *lacZ* and *lacY* genes might be under negative control originated with Leo Szilard in the late 1950s. Szilard suggested to Monod that the *lacI* gene could code for a product that represses transcription of the *lacZ* and *lacY* genes. As it turned out, Szilard was right.

The *lacI* gene produces a repressor protein that exerts negative control over *lacZ* and *lacY* gene transcription. The repressor was proposed to bind directly to DNA at or near the promoter for the *lacZ* and *lacY* genes (**FIGURE 18.7a**).

To explain how lactose triggers transcription, Szilard and Monod proposed that lactose interacts with the repressor in a way that makes the repressor release from its binding site (**FIGURE 18.7b**). In negative control, the repressor is the parking brake; lactose releases the brake.

What about the constitutive mutants? **FIGURE 18.7c** shows that constitutive transcription is observed in *lacI*⊠ mutants because a functional repressor is absent—the parking brake is broken.

To test the hypothesis of negative control by a repressor, Jacob, Monod, and co-workers added back a functioning copy of the *lacI* repressor gene to the *lacI*⊠ mutants that made ⊠-galactosidase all the time. If these cells were grown using glucose and no lactose, ⊠-galactosidase production declined and then stopped.

This result supported the hypothesis that the repressor codes for a protein that shuts down transcription. Significantly, if the experimental cells were grown using lactose instead of glucose, ⊠-galactosidase activity resumed. This result supported the hypothesis that lactose removes the repressor.

What's the take-home message? The *lacI* gene codes for a repressor protein that exerts negative control on *lacZ* and *lacY*. Lactose acts as an inducer by causing the repressor to release from DNA and ending negative control.

The Operon Model

Jacob and Monod summarized the results of their experiments with a comprehensive model of negative control that was published in 1961. One of their key conclusions was that the genes for ⊠-galactosidase and galactoside permease are controlled together and transcribed into a single mRNA. To encapsulate this idea, they coined the term **operon** for a set of coordinately regulated bacterial genes that are transcribed together into one mRNA. Logically enough, the group of genes involved in lactose metabolism was termed the **lac operon.**

Later, a gene called *lacA* was found to be adjacent to *lacY* and *lacZ* and transcribed as part of the same operon. The *lacA* gene

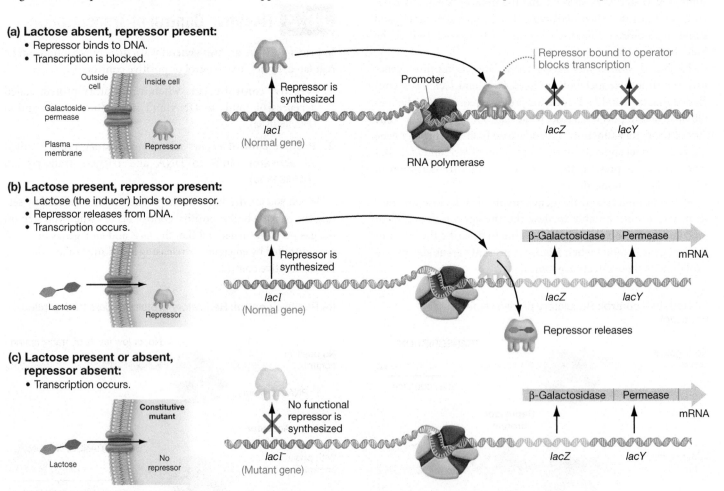

(a) Lactose absent, repressor present:
- Repressor binds to DNA.
- Transcription is blocked.

(b) Lactose present, repressor present:
- Lactose (the inducer) binds to repressor.
- Repressor releases from DNA.
- Transcription occurs.

(c) Lactose present or absent, repressor absent:
- Transcription occurs.

FIGURE 18.7 The Hypothesis of Negative Control of the *lac* Operon. The plasma membrane and galactoside permease are shown as a reminder that lactose comes from outside the cell and controls genes within the *E. coli* chromosome. Repression of the *lac* operon is never complete, so there is always some galactoside permease to transport lactose into the cell and begin induction of the *lac* operon.

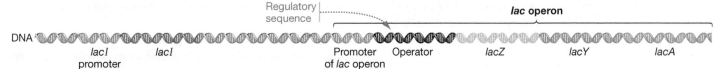

Regulatory sequence   *lac* operon

DNA

lacI   lacI   Promoter   Operator   lacZ   lacY   lacA
promoter   of *lac* operon

FIGURE 18.8 The *lac* Operon and *lacI* Gene. This view emphasizes the arrangement of genes and regulatory sequences and is not drawn to scale.

✔**EXERCISE** Using small, colored bits of candy or paper, add the repressor protein to the figure. Next, add RNA polymerase; then add lactose. At each step, explain what happens after the molecule is added.

codes for the enzyme transacetylase. This enzyme catalyzes reactions that allow certain types of sugars to be exported from the cell when they are too abundant and could harm the cell. The components of the *lac* operon are summarized in **FIGURE 18.8**.

Three hypotheses are central to the Jacob–Monod model of *lac* operon regulation:

1. The *lacZ*, *lacY*, and *lacA* genes are adjacent and are transcribed into one mRNA initiated from the single promoter of the *lac* operon. This is known as cotranscription, and it results in the coordinated expression of the three genes.

2. The repressor is a protein encoded by *lacI* that binds to DNA and prevents transcription of the *lac* operon genes (*lacZ*, *lacY*, and *lacA*). Jacob and Monod proposed that *lacI* is expressed constitutively, and that the repressor binds to a section of DNA in the *lac* operon called the **operator.**

3. The inducer (lactose) binds to the repressor. When it does, the repressor changes shape. The shape change causes the repressor to come off the DNA. Recall that this form of control over protein function is **allosteric regulation** (see Chapter 8). In allosteric regulation, a small molecule binds to a protein and causes it to change its shape and activity. When the inducer binds to the repressor, the repressor can no longer bind to DNA and transcription can proceed.

✔ If you understand negative control of the *lac* operon, you should be able to predict the effect of a mutation in the *lacI* gene that alters the repressor so it cannot bind to lactose, and the effect of a mutation in the operator that prevents repressor binding.

How Does Glucose Regulate the *lac* Operon?

The model of *lac* operon control, summarized in Figure 18.7, is elegant and successful in explaining experimental results. But it is not complete. After studying the model, you may think of an important question that it fails to answer: Where does glucose fit in?

Transcription of the *lac* operon is drastically reduced when glucose is present in the environment—even when lactose is available to induce ⊠-galactosidase expression (see Figure 18.2). This makes sense, given that glucose is *E. coli*'s preferred carbon source. When glucose is already present, the cell doesn't need to cleave lactose as a way of acquiring glucose.

How can glucose prevent expression of the *lac* operon? Researchers recently discovered that glucose inhibits the lactose

transport activity of galactoside permease through a chain of molecular events. When both glucose and lactose are present in the environment, the transport of lactose into the cell is inhibited. Because lactose does not accumulate in the cytoplasm, the repressor remains bound to the operator. Negative control (as in Figure 18.7a) is in place. In contrast, when glucose levels outside the cell are low, galactoside permease is active. If lactose is present, it is transported into the cell and induces *lac* operon expression (as in Figure 18.7b).

The mechanism of glucose preventing the transport of inducer is known as inducer exclusion. Inducer exclusion affects the activity of many different sugar transporters in addition to galactoside permease. It allows *E. coli* to preferentially use glucose, even when other sugars are also present outside the cell.

This understanding of how glucose regulates the *lac* operon is relatively new. For decades, researchers thought that when glucose levels outside the cell declined, an activator protein called CAP bound to a regulatory sequence in DNA just upstream of the promoter to increase the frequency of transcription initiation. There is strong evidence that binding of CAP to the regulatory sequence is important for efficient transcription of the *lac* operon. However, recent results indicate that CAP is always bound to the regulatory sequence, even in the presence of glucose.

Why Has the *lac* Operon Model Been So Important?

The *lac* operon has been an immensely important model system for two reasons. First, follow-up work showed that many bacterial genes and operons are under negative control by repressor proteins. This means that the findings on the *lac* operon are general. Second, the *lac* operon model introduced a fundamentally important idea: Gene expression is regulated by physical contact between regulatory proteins and specific regulatory sites in DNA. Publication of the *lac* operon model was a watershed event in the history of biological science.

Work on the *lac* operon also offered an important example of post-translational control over gene expression. To understand why, you have to realize that the repressor protein is always present; it is transcribed and translated constitutively. When a rapid change in *lac* operon activity is needed, it does not require changes in the transcription or translation of new repressor proteins. Instead, the activity of *existing* repressor proteins is altered.

This is exactly the prediction made at the beginning of this chapter—post-translational control is best when a rapid response is needed. As it turns out, this is a common type of control. In most cases, the activity of key regulatory proteins is controlled by post-translational modifications.

18.4 Positive Control of Transcription

Positive control is an important way of controlling transcription. In positive control, an activator protein binds to a regulatory sequence in DNA when genes are turned on. When bound to DNA, the activator interacts with RNA polymerase to increase the rate of initiating transcription (see Figure 18.6b).

The ***ara* operon** provides an important example of positive control and of the process of science. The *ara* operon wasn't discovered in the laboratory of a famous scientist. Instead, students

working on a project for a laboratory course were the first to uncover it.

This operon contains three genes that allow *E. coli* to use the sugar arabinose. Arabinose is found in many plant cell walls. When you eat vegetables, arabinose is available to the bacteria that inhabit your gut. Without arabinose in the environment, the *ara* operon is not transcribed. But when arabinose is present, transcription of the *ara* operon is turned on by an activator protein called **AraC**. The *ara* operon and an adjacent gene, ***araC***, that codes for the araC activator are shown in **FIGURE 18.9**.

FIGURE 18.10 outlines how AraC controls the *ara* operon. The AraC protein is allosterically regulated by arabinose. When bound to arabinose, two copies of the AraC protein attach to a regulatory sequence of DNA called the *ara* initiator that lies just upstream of the promoter (see Figure 18.10a). Once AraC is bound to DNA, it can also bind to RNA polymerase. This interaction between AraC and the RNA polymerase helps to dock the polymerase to the promoter and accelerate the initiation of transcription.

Continued work on the *ara* operon revealed a surprise—AraC is both an activator and a repressor. In the absence of arabinose, the two copies of the AraC protein remain together; but while one araC copy remains bound to the initiator, the other copy now binds to a different regulatory site in DNA, the *ara* operator, as shown in Figure 18.10b. In this configuration, AraC works as a repressor to prevent the transcription of both the *ara* operon and the *araC* gene.

✔ If you understand positive control by the AraC protein, you should be able to predict the effect of a mutation that removes the part of AraC that binds to RNA polymerase.

18.5 Global Gene Regulation

A theme of this chapter is that cells respond to changing environments. To compete for resources, bacteria must be able to coordinate the expression of large sets of genes. As you've seen for the *lac* and *ara* operons, an effective way to express sets of genes together is to group them into an operon and transcribe them into a single mRNA. But there are limits to the size of operons. How can bacterial cells manage responses that require the expression of dozens or even hundreds of genes?

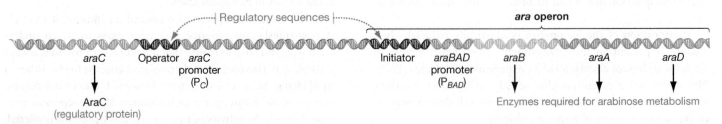

FIGURE 18.9 The *ara* Operon, Regulatory Sequences, and *araC* Gene.

(a) AraC protein is an **activator** when bound to arabinose.

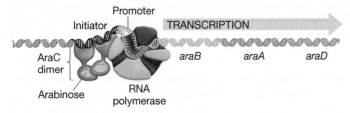

(b) AraC protein is a **repressor** when arabinose is absent.

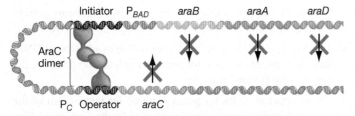

FIGURE 18.10 Positive and Negative Regulation of the *ara* Operon.

Global gene regulation is the coordinated regulation of many genes. You already learned that alternative sigma proteins provide one way for bacteria to turn on large numbers of genes in response to environmental change (Chapter 17). But there are other means of global gene regulation, such as grouping genes into a **regulon**—a set of separate genes or operons that contain the same regulatory sequences and that are controlled by a single type of regulatory protein.

Regulons allow bacteria to respond to challenges that include shortages of nutrients, sudden changes in temperature, exposure to radiation, or shifts in habitat. Let's explore how regulons work in general, and then look at two specific examples.

A general strategy for controlling regulon genes is shown in **FIGURE 18.11**. In this example, the regulon consists of many genes that are scattered across the genome. All of these genes are controlled by the same type of repressor protein that binds to the same operator sequences near the promoter of each gene. When an environmental change triggers the removal of the repressor protein from all the operators, every gene in the regulon is transcribed.

Regulons can be under negative control by a repressor protein or positive control by an activator protein. The regulon in Figure 18.11 is under negative control. The SOS response regulon works exactly this way to allow bacterial cells to repair extensive damage to DNA that can occur when cells are exposed to ultraviolet light, other types of radiation, or some chemicals. Damaged DNA sets off an SOS signal that induces the transcription of more than 40 genes that code for DNA repair enzymes and for DNA polymerases that can use damaged DNA as a template. Without the SOS response, bacteria with massive DNA damage would face almost certain death.

The ToxR regulon of *Vibrio cholera*—the bacterium that causes cholera—is under positive control. This regulon allows *V. cholera* to colonize the human gut and to produce toxins that cause diarrhea. Cholera kills 120,000 people each year and sickens as many as 18 million. ToxR regulon genes are inactive when *V. cholera* lives outside a human host. When bacteria from contaminated drinking water encounter the environment of the human gut, this sets off a signal that activates an activator protein. The activator induces a response by binding to a regulatory DNA sequence near the promoters of all ToxR regulon genes to stimulate their transcription. The diarrhea induced by this regulon is adaptive for *V. cholera* because it spreads more bacteria into the environment to infect new hosts.

What are the general messages of this chapter? Interactions among protein regulators and the DNA sequences they bind produce finely tuned control over gene expression, regulating individual genes, operons, or large sets of genes. With these exquisite controls over gene expression, bacteria have been able to compete, grow, and reproduce for more than 3 billion years of life's history.

Do eukaryotes control their genes the same way as bacteria? If not, what are the differences? These questions are the focus of the next chapter.

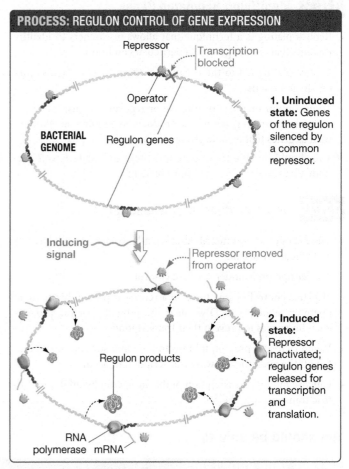

PROCESS: REGULON CONTROL OF GENE EXPRESSION

1. Uninduced state: Genes of the regulon silenced by a common repressor.

2. Induced state: Repressor inactivated; regulon genes released for transcription and translation.

FIGURE 18.11 Genes of a Regulon Are Expressed Together. The "| |" symbols indicate regions of the bacterial genome not shown between regulon genes.

If you understand . . .

18.1   An Overview of Gene Regulation and Information Flow

- Changes in gene expression allow bacterial cells to respond to environmental changes.

- Most gene products are produced or activated only when they are needed.

- Gene expression can be controlled at three levels: transcription, translation, or post-translation (protein activation).

- Transcriptional control can be negative or positive. Negative control occurs when a regulatory protein prevents transcription. Positive control occurs when a regulatory protein increases the frequency of initiating transcription.

✔ You should be able to describe one component of the *lac* operon that is under transcriptional control and one component that is under post-translational control.

18.2   Identifying Regulated Genes

- Replica plating is a technique that allows researchers to identify mutants that cannot grow in a particular condition.

- Replica plating led to the isolation of three types of lactose metabolism mutants.

- Transcription may be constitutive or regulated. Constitutive expression occurs in genes whose products are required at all times, such as genes that encode glycolytic enzymes.

✔ You should be able to propose a strategy to isolate *E. coli* mutants that can grow at 33°C, but not at 42°C.

18.3   Negative Control of Transcription

- The *lac* operon is transcribed efficiently when lactose is present and glucose is absent.

- The *lac* operon is under negative control.

- Negative control occurs because a repressor protein binds to an operator sequence in DNA near the promoter of the protein-encoding genes to prevent their transcription.

- When lactose is present, it binds to the repressor and causes it to fall off the operator, allowing transcription to occur.

- Glucose inhibits transcription of the *lac* operon by inhibiting lactose transport into the cell.

✔ You should be able explain how the operator, repressor, and inducer relate to a car's parking brake.

18.4   Positive Control of Transcription

- Positive control of transcription occurs when a regulatory protein called an activator binds to a regulatory sequence in DNA.

- Activator proteins bind to RNA polymerase in addition to DNA. Binding between the activator and RNA polymerase increases the rate of transcription initiation.

- The *ara* operon codes for genes required for metabolism of the sugar arabinose. The operon is controlled by the AraC regulatory protein. AraC is an activator when bound to arabinose and a repressor when the protein is not bound to arabinose.

✔ You should be able to predict if mutations in the *ara* initiator sequence of the *ara* operon are most likely to affect positive regulation, negative regulation, or both.

18.5   Global Gene Regulation

- Bacterial cells often need to coordinate the expression of large sets of genes in response to changing environments.

- Regulons coordinate the expression of different genes by using a shared regulator that acts on a regulatory sequence found in all genes of the regulon. Regulons can work through negative control using repressors, or through positive control using activators.

✔ You should be able to propose a method that would allow more genes to become part of the SOS regulon.

(MB) **MasteringBiology**

1. **MasteringBiology Assignments**

    Tutorials and Activities The *lac* Operon

    Questions Reading Quizzes, Blue-Thread Questions, Test Bank

2. **eText** Read your book online, search, take notes, highlight text, and more.

3. **The Study Area** Practice Test, Cumulative Test, BioFlix® 3-D animations, Videos, Activities, Audio Glossary, Word Study Tools, Art

You should be able to . . .

✔ TEST YOUR KNOWLEDGE   *Answers are available in Appendix A*

1. Replica plating is used to isolate mutants that
    a. can produce an enzyme.
    b. cannot grow in a particular condition.
    c. can utilize lactose.
    d. turn yellow when lactose is broken down.

2. Why are the genes involved in lactose metabolism considered to be an operon?
   a. They occupy adjacent locations on the *E. coli* chromosome.
   b. They have a similar function.
   c. They are all required for normal cell function.
   d. They are all controlled by the same promoter.

3. In the *lac* operon, the repressor inhibits transcription when
   a. the repressor is bound to the inducer.
   b. the repressor is not bound to the inducer.
   c. the repressor is bound to glucose.
   d. the repressor is not bound to the operator.

4. Activators bind to regulatory sequences in _____ and to _____ polymerase.

5. How does inducer exclusion control gene expression in the *lac* operon?

6. A regulon is a set of genes controlled by
   a. one type of regulator of transcription.
   b. two or more different alternative sigma proteins.
   c. many different types of promoters.
   d. glucose.

7. *E. coli* expresses genes for glycolytic enzymes constitutively. Why?

8. Explain the difference between positive and negative control over transcription.

9. Predict what would happen if the *lac* repressor protein were altered so it could not bind inducer.
   a. The repressor could not bind to DNA.
   b. The repressor would always be bound to DNA.
   c. The repressor could bind to DNA only when cells were grown with glucose.
   d. The repressor could bind to DNA only when cells were grown without glucose.

10. Predict what would happen to regulation of the *lac* operon if the *lacI* gene were moved 50,000 nucleotides upstream of its normal location.

11. If any of the following hypothetical drugs could be developed, which would be most effective in preventing cholera?
    a. a drug that increased the amount of the ToxR activator
    b. a drug that blocked the DNA-binding activity of the activator
    c. a drug that increased rates of transcription in *V. cholerae*
    d. a drug that increased rates of translation in *V. cholerae*

12. IPTG is a molecule with a structure very similar to lactose. IPTG can be transported into cells by galactoside permease and can bind to the *lac* repressor protein. However, unlike lactose, IPTG is not broken down by ⊠-galactosidase. Predict what would occur regarding *lac* operon regulation if IPTG were added to *E. coli* growth medium containing arabinose and no glucose or lactose.

13. You are interested in using bacteria to metabolize wastes at an old chemical plant and convert them into harmless compounds. You find bacteria that are able to tolerate high levels of the toxic compounds toluene and benzene, and you suspect that this is because the bacteria can break down these compounds into less-toxic products. If that is true, these toluene- and benzene-resistant strains will be valuable for cleaning up toxic sites. How could you find out whether these bacteria are metabolizing toluene as a source of carbon compounds?

14. **QUANTITATIVE** Imagine that you are repeating the replica-plating procedure of Jacob and Monod to find mutants that can't grow using lactose. After treating cells with a mutagen, you anticipate a mutation rate of $1 \boxtimes 10^{\boxtimes 4}$ lactose-nonutilizing mutants per mutagen-treated cell. Based on this estimate, how many cells should you replica-plate to have a good chance of finding one mutant?

15. A type of mutation in the *lac* operator known as *lacO^c* prevents repressor binding to DNA and causes constitutive transcription of the *lac* operon. Which of the following secondary mutations might restore normal regulation to the *lac* operon in a *lacO^c* mutant?
    a. a *lacI* mutation that decreases the ability of the repressor to bind the inducer
    b. a *lacI* mutation that produces a repressor than can recognize the mutated *lacO^c* DNA sequence
    c. a promoter mutation that prevents it from being recognized by sigma
    d. an RNA polymerase mutation that allows it to bind to the promoter without using sigma

16. X-gal is a colorless, lactose-like molecule that can be split into two fragments by ⊠-galactosidase. One of these product molecules is blue. The following photograph shows *E. coli* colonies growing in a medium that contains X-gal.

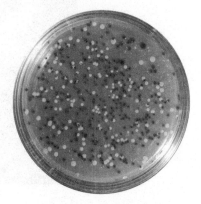

Find three colonies whose cells have functioning copies of ⊠-galactosidase. Find three colonies whose cells might have mutations in the *lacZ* or in the *lacY* genes. Suppose you analyze the protein-coding sequence of the *lacZ* and *lacY* genes of cells from the three mutant colonies and find that these sequences are wild type (normal). What other region of the *lac* operon might be altered to account for the mutant phenotype of these colonies?

19 Control of Gene Expression in Eukaryotes

In this chapter you will learn that

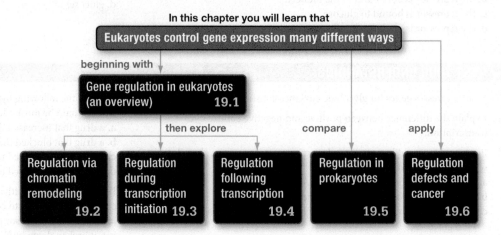

In this chapter you will learn that

Eukaryotes control gene expression many different ways

beginning with

Gene regulation in eukaryotes (an overview) **19.1**

then explore   compare   apply

| Regulation via chromatin remodeling **19.2** | Regulation during transcription initiation **19.3** | Regulation following transcription **19.4** | Regulation in prokaryotes **19.5** | Regulation defects and cancer **19.6** |

A model of eukaryotic DNA in the condensed state. The DNA (shown in red and pink) is wrapped around proteins (in green). The DNA has to be uncoiled before transcription can take place.

This chapter is part of the Big Picture. See how on pages 366–367.

Bacteria regulate gene expression to respond to changes in their environment. *Escherichia coli* thrive best if the genes that are required to import and cleave lactose are expressed only when the cells are relying on lactose as a source of energy (see Chapter 18).

Unicellular eukaryotes face similar challenges. Consider the yeast *Saccharomyces cerevisiae*, which is used extensively in the production of beer, wine, and bread. In nature this species lives on the skins of grapes and other fruits, where the sugars that the cells use as food vary in type and concentration as the fruit ripens, falls, and rots. For yeast cells to grow and reproduce efficiently, gene expression has to be modified in response to these changes.

The cells that make up multicellular eukaryotes face additional challenges. Consider your body, which contains trillions of cells, each with a specialized structure and function. You have heart

✔ When you see this checkmark, stop and test yourself. Answers are available in Appendix A.

muscle cells, lung cells, nerve cells, skin cells, and so on. Even though these cells are different, they contain the same genes. Your bone cells and blood cells aren't different because of a difference in their genes but because they *express* different genes. Your bone cells have blood-cell genes—they just don't transcribe them.

Why not? The answer is that your cells respond to their environment, just as bacteria and unicellular eukaryotes do. But there's a key difference. The cells in a multicellular eukaryote express different genes in response to changes in the *internal* environment—specifically, to signals from other cells. As a human being or an oak tree develops, cells that are located in different parts of the organism are exposed to different cell–cell signals. As a result, they express different genes. **Differential gene expression** is responsible for creating different cell types, arranging them into tissues, and coordinating their activity to form the multicellular society we call an individual.

How does all of this regulation and differentiation happen? Later chapters introduce the signals that trigger the formation of muscle, bone, leaf, and flower cells (see Unit 4). In contrast, this chapter focuses on what happens after a eukaryotic cell receives such a signal. Let's start with an overview of how gene expression can be controlled, and close with a look at how defects in the process can trigger cancer.

19.1 Gene Regulation in Eukaryotes— An Overview

Like bacteria, eukaryotes can control gene expression at the levels of transcription, translation, and post-translation. But as **FIGURE 19.1** shows, three additional levels of control occur in eukaryotes as genetic information flows from DNA to proteins.

The first additional level of control involves the DNA–protein complex at the top of the figure. In eukaryotes, DNA is wrapped around proteins to create a structure called **chromatin.** Eukaryotic genes have promoters, just as bacterial genes do; but before transcription can begin in eukaryotes, the stretch of DNA containing the promoter must be released from tight interactions with proteins, so that RNA polymerase can make contact with the promoter. To capture this idea, biologists say that **chromatin remodeling** must occur before transcription.

The second level of regulation that is unique to eukaryotes is **RNA processing**—the steps required to produce a mature, processed mRNA from a primary RNA transcript. Recall that introns have to be spliced out of primary transcripts (see Chapter 17). In many cases, carefully orchestrated alternative splicing occurs—meaning that different combinations of exons are included in the mRNA. If different cells use different splicing patterns, different gene products result.

Third, mRNA life span is regulated in eukaryotes: mRNAs that remain in the cell for a long time tend to be translated more than mRNAs that have a short life span.

Each of the six potential control points shown in Figure 19.1 is employed in eukaryotic cells. This chapter explores all six—chromatin

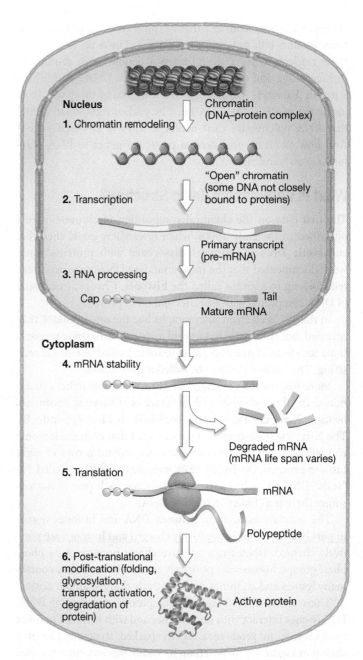

FIGURE 19.1 In Eukaryotes, Gene Expression Can Be Controlled at Many Different Levels.

remodeling, transcription, RNA processing, mRNA stability, translation, and post-translational modification of proteins.

To appreciate the breadth and complexity of gene regulation in eukaryotes, let's follow the series of events that occur as an embryonic cell responds to a developmental signal. Suppose a molecule arrives that specifies the production of a muscle-specific protein. What happens next?

19.2 Chromatin Remodeling

For a molecular signal to trigger the transcription of a particular gene, the chromatin around the target gene must be remodeled.

To appreciate why, consider that a typical cell in your body contains about 6 billion base pairs of DNA. Lined up end to end, these nucleotide pairs would form a double helix about 2 m (6.5 feet) long. But the nucleus that holds this DNA is only about 5 μm in diameter—far less than the thickness of this page. To fit inside the nucleus, the DNA must be packed tightly—so tightly that RNA polymerase can't access it. How is DNA packaged? And how can it be unpacked at particular genes so RNA polymerase can transcribe it?

What Is Chromatin's Basic Structure?

The first data on the chemical composition of chromatin were published in the early 1900s, when researchers established that eukaryotic DNA is intimately associated with proteins. Later work documented that the most abundant DNA-associated proteins belong to a group called the **histones.** Chromatin consists of DNA complexed with histones and other proteins.

In the 1970s electron micrographs like the one in **FIGURE 19.2a** revealed that chromatin has a regular structure. In some preparations for electron microscopy, chromatin looked like beads on a string. The "beads" came to be called **nucleosomes.**

More information emerged in 1984 when researchers determined the three-dimensional structure of eukaryotic chromatin by using X-ray crystallography (see **BioSkills 11** in Appendix B). The X-ray crystallographic data indicated that each nucleosome consists of DNA wrapped almost twice around a core of eight histone proteins. As **FIGURE 19.2b** indicates, a histone called H1 "seals" DNA to each nucleosome. Between each pair of nucleosomes there is a "linker" stretch of DNA.

The intimate association between DNA and histones occurs in part because DNA is negatively charged and histones are positively charged. DNA has a negative charge because of its phosphate groups; histones are positively charged because they contain many lysines and arginines, two positively charged amino acids.

There are additional layers of complexity in packaging DNA. H1 histones interact with one another and with histones in other nucleosomes to produce a tightly packed structure like that shown in Figure 19.2b. Based on its width, this structure is called the 30-nanometer fiber. (Recall that a nanometer is one-billionth of a meter and is abbreviated nm.)

Finally, the 30-nm fibers are attached at intervals along their length to proteins that form a scaffold or framework inside the nucleus. In this way, the entire chromosome is organized and held in place. When chromosomes condense before mitosis or meiosis, the scaffold proteins and 30-nm fibers are folded into still larger and more tightly packed structures.

A eukaryotic chromosome, then, is made up of chromatin that has several layers of organization: The DNA is wrapped around histones to form nucleosomes, nucleosomes are packed into 30-nm fibers, 30-nm fibers are attached to scaffold proteins, and the entire assembly can be folded into the highly condensed structure observed during cell division.

Although research has shown that bacterial DNA interacts with proteins that are organized similarly to nucleosomes,

(a) Nucleosomes in chromatin

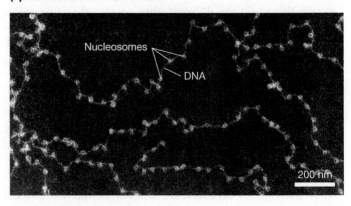

(b) Nucleosome structure

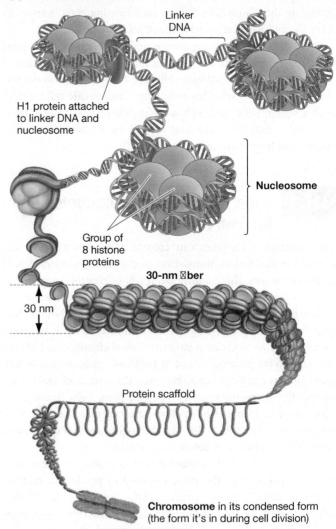

FIGURE 19.2 Chromatin Has Several Levels of Organization.

nothing like the 30-nm fibers or higher-order arrangements has been observed in bacterial chromosomes.

The elaborate structure of eukaryotic chromatin does more than just package DNA so that it fits into the nucleus. Chromatin structure also has profound implications for the control of gene expression. To appreciate this point, consider the 30-nm fiber illustrated in Figure 19.2b. If this tightly packed stretch of DNA contains a promoter, how can RNA polymerase bind to it and initiate transcription?

Evidence that Chromatin Structure Is Altered in Active Genes

Once the nucleosome-based structure of chromatin was established, biologists hypothesized that the close physical interaction between DNA and histones must be altered for RNA polymerase to make contact with DNA. More specifically, biologists hypothesized that a gene could not be transcribed until the condensed chromatin near its promoter was remodeled.

The central idea is that chromatin must be decondensed, to expose the promoter so RNA polymerase can bind to it. If so, then chromatin remodeling would represent the first step in the control of eukaryotic gene expression. Two types of studies have provided strong support for this hypothesis.

DNA in Condensed Chromatin Is Protected from DNase DNases are enzymes that cut DNA. Some DNases cleave DNA at random locations, and these cannot cut efficiently if DNA is tightly wrapped with proteins. As **FIGURE 19.3** shows, this type of DNase works effectively only if DNA is in a decondensed configuration.

Harold Weintraub and Mark Groudine used this observation to test the hypothesis that the DNA of actively transcribed genes is in an open configuration. In chicken blood cells, they compared chromatin structure in two genes: β-globin and ovalbumin. β-globin is a protein that is part of the hemoglobin found in red blood cells; ovalbumin is a protein found in egg white. In blood cells, the β-globin gene is transcribed at high levels, but the ovalbumin gene is not transcribed at all.

After treating blood cells with DNase and then analyzing the state of chromatin at the β-globin and ovalbumin genes, the researchers found that DNase cut the β-globin gene DNA much more readily than DNA of the ovalbumin gene. They interpreted this finding as evidence that in blood cells, chromatin of the

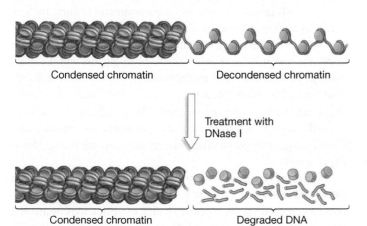

FIGURE 19.3 DNase Assay for Chromatin Structure. DNase is an enzyme that cuts DNA at random locations. It cannot cut condensed chromatin.

actively transcribed β-globin gene was decondensed; and conversely, chromatin of the non-transcribed ovalbumin gene was condensed. Studies using DNase on different genes in different cell types yielded similar results.

Histone Mutants The second type of evidence in support of the chromatin-remodeling hypothesis comes from studies of mutant brewer's yeast cells that do not produce the usual complement of histones. In these mutant cells, many genes that are normally never transcribed are instead always transcribed at high levels.

To interpret this finding, biologists hypothesized that the lack of histone proteins prevented the assembly of normal chromatin. If the absence of normal histone–DNA interactions promotes transcription, then the presence of normal histone–DNA interactions must prevent it.

Taken together, the data suggest that in their normal, or default, state, eukaryotic genes are turned off. This is a new mechanism of negative control—different from repressor proteins (introduced in Chapter 18). When DNA is wrapped into a 30-nm fiber, the parking brake is on. If so, then gene expression depends on chromatin being opened up in the promoter region.

How Is Chromatin Altered?

Research on chromatin remodeling has been proceeding at a furious pace, and biologists have succeeded in identifying some of the key players that work to change the state of chromatin condensation. These include enzymes that add methyl groups to DNA, enzymes that chemically modify histones, and macromolecular machines that actively reshape chromatin. Let's examine each of these in turn.

DNA Methylation A group of enzymes known as **DNA methyltransferases** add methyl groups ($-CH_3$) to cytosine residues in DNA. In mammals, the sequence recognized by these enzymes is a C next to a G in one strand of the DNA. This sequence is abbreviated CpG and is shown below in methylated form within a stretch of DNA.

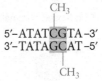

Why is **DNA methylation** important? Methylated CpG sequences are recognized by proteins that trigger chromatin condensation. Actively transcribed genes usually have low levels of methylated CpG near their promoters, and non-transcribed genes usually have high levels of methylated CpG.

Histone Modification DNA methylation is only one part of the chromatin alteration story. A large set of enzymes adds a variety of chemical groups to specific amino acids of histone proteins. These include phosphate groups, methyl groups, short polypeptide chains, and acetyl groups ($-COCH_3$). Addition of these groups to histones promotes condensed or decondensed chromatin depending on the specific set of modifications.

To account for these effects, researchers have proposed the existence of a **histone code.** The histone code hypothesis postulates that particular combinations of histone modifications set the state of chromatin condensation for a particular gene. In turn, this has an important role in regulating transcription. Let's take a closer look at one way histone modifications can control chromatin structure.

As shown in **FIGURE 19.4**, two different types of enzymes can add or remove acetyl groups from histones. **Histone acetyltransferases (HATs)** add acetyl groups to the positively charged lysine residues in histones, and **histone deacetylases (HDACs)** remove them. **Acetylation** of histones usually results in decondensed chromatin, a state associated with active transcription. How can acetylation of histones promote chromatin decondensation? When HATs add acetyl groups, the acetyl groups neutralize the positive charge on lysine residues and loosens the close association of nucleosomes with the negatively charged DNA. The addition of acetyl groups also creates a binding site for other proteins that help open the chromatin.

In contrast, when HDACs remove acetyl groups from histones, this process usually leads to condensed chromatin, a state associated with no transcription. HATs are an on switch for transcription, and HDACs are an off switch.

Chromatin-Remodeling Complexes Other major players in chromatin alteration and gene regulation are enzymes that form macromolecular machines called **chromatin-remodeling complexes.** These machines harness the energy in ATP to reshape chromatin. Chromatin-remodeling complexes cause nucleosomes to slide along the DNA or, in some cases, knock the histones completely off the DNA to open up stretches of chromatin and allow gene transcription.

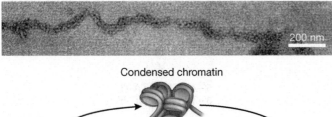

Condensed chromatin

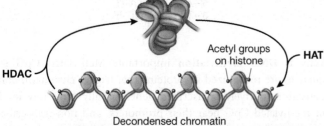

Decondensed chromatin

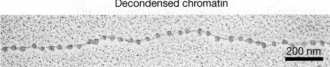

FIGURE 19.4 Acetyl Groups Decondense Chromatin. Histone acetyltransferases (HATs) cause chromatin to decondense; histone deacetylases (HDACs) cause it to condense.

✔ QUESTION Are HAT and HDAC elements in positive control or negative control? Explain your reasoning.

DNA methylation, histone modifications, and chromatin-remodeling complexes work together to fine-tune chromatin condensation at specific genes. The take-home message from work on chromatin remodeling is simple: The condensation state of chromatin is critical in determining whether transcription occurs.

Chromatin Modifications Can Be Inherited

The pattern of chromatin modifications varies from one cell type to another. For example, suppose within an individual you analyzed the same gene in a muscle cell and a brain cell. This and other genes would likely have a different pattern of DNA methylation and histone acetylation in the two cell types.

DNA methylation and histone modifications are an example of **epigenetic inheritance,** the collective term for patterns of inheritance that are due to something other than differences in DNA sequences. The *epi–* of epigenetics comes from the Greek word meaning "upon." It implies another level of inheritance that adds to standard DNA-based mechanisms to explain how different phenotypes are transmitted.

With epigenetic inheritance, if a cell received a "become muscle" signal early in development, it would modify its chromatin in distinctive ways and pass those modifications on to its descendants. Muscle cells are different from brain cells not because they contain different genes, but largely because they have inherited different patterns of DNA methylation and histone modifications during the course of their development.

But the story of epigenetic inheritance involves more than just differentiation of cell types during development. Evidence is emerging that epigenetic mechanisms can record early-life events and that this archive can be difficult to erase. This is the case when prenatal conditions alter the patterns of chromatin modification and the later-life phenotypes of a mother's offspring.

For example, biologists have long known that rats born to mothers fed low-protein diets during pregnancy and while nursing have a greatly increased risk of developing disorders similar to type 2 diabetes. Type 2 diabetes is a serious and increasingly common disease that alters the cellular uptake of glucose (Chapter 44). Both genetic factors and environmental factors, such as diet, play important roles in diabetes development.

One significant gene associated with diabetes is *Hnf4a*. *Hnf4a* codes for a regulator of genes involved in glucose uptake. Rats born to protein-deprived mothers develop symptoms of diabetes later in life, even when these rats are fed a normal, healthy diet from the time they are weaned. These diabetic rats also express the *Hnf4a* regulatory gene at lower levels than normal rats. Could epigenetic mechanisms be at work in silencing *Hnf4a* expression?

One team's approach to probing this question is shown in **FIGURE 19.5.** Using a treatment group and a control group, the researchers measured the types of histone modifications found at a key regulatory region of the *Hnf4a* gene. A regulatory region is a section of DNA that, like prokaryotic operators (Chapter 18), is involved in controlling the activity of a gene. The chromatin at this region has to be opened up for transcription to occur. Levels

QUESTION: Does poor nutrition in a mother produce epigenetic effects in offspring?

HYPOTHESIS: Protein-deprived mothers will produce offspring with abnormal histone modifications.

NULL HYPOTHESIS: Protein-deprived mothers will produce offspring with normal histone modifications.

EXPERIMENTAL SETUP:

1. Provide rat mothers with a normal or a low-protein diet during pregnancy and while nursing.

2. After weaning, feed rat pups a normal diet and raise to old age.

3. Determine types of histone modifications for a regulatory gene involved in diabetes. (Also measure gene transcription.)

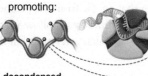

Modifications promoting: Modifications promoting: TRANSCRIPTION

Hnf4a

condensed chromatin   decondensed chromatin

PREDICTION: Offspring of mothers fed a low-protein diet will have abnormal histone modifications.

PREDICTION OF NULL HYPOTHESIS: Offspring of mothers fed a low-protein diet will have normal histone modifications.

RESULTS:

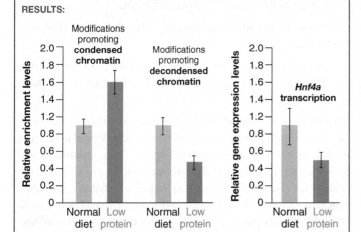

CONCLUSION: A mother's diet influences chromatin modifications and gene expression patterns throughout her offspring's life.

FIGURE 19.5 Events in Early Life Can Be Recorded through Epigenetic Mechanisms.

SOURCE: Sandovici, I., N. H. Smith, and M. D. Nitert. 2011. Maternal diet and aging alter the epigenetic control of a promoter-enhancer interaction at the *Hnf4a* gene in rat pancreatic islets. *Proceedings of the National Academy of Sciences USA* 108: 5449–5454.

✔ **QUESTION** What could researchers do to prove that the histone modifications are causing reduced regulatory gene transcription?

---

of *Hnf4a* transcription in the control and treatment groups were also measured. What did the team learn?

As the graph on the left in the "Results" section of Figure 19.5 shows, they found that histone modifications that lead to condensed chromatin were *elevated* in rats born to malnourished mothers compared to control offspring. Conversely, histone modifications associated with decondensed chromatin were significantly *reduced* in the treatment group. The graph on the right confirms that transcription of *Hnf4a* was much lower in the treatment group than the control group. Together these results demonstrate a correlation between altered histone modifications and decreased levels of *Hnf4a* gene expression.

Remember that in this study, all rats were provided a healthy diet after weaning. This finding implies that a mother's nutritional status during pregnancy and nursing is responsible for the types of chromatin modifications seen in rats that develop diabetes.

Chromatin remodeling must occur before transcription. Now the question is, What happens once a section of chromatin is opened and DNA becomes accessible to RNA polymerase?

check your understanding

C Y U

If you understand that . . .

- Eukaryotic DNA is wrapped tightly around histones, forming nucleosomes, which are then coiled into structures called 30-nm chromatin fibers.
- Before transcription can begin, the DNA–protein complex of chromatin must be decondensed so that RNA polymerase can contact the promoter.
- Methylation of DNA and specific chemical modifications of histones play a key role in determining whether chromatin is opened and a gene is expressed.
- In many cases, the patterns of DNA methylation and histone modification in a cell are passed on to its daughter cells.

✔ You should be able to . . .

1. Predict how gene expression will be affected if a cell is grown with compounds that prevent DNA methylation.

2. Explain how certain patterns of histone acetylation or DNA methylation could influence whether a cell became a muscle cell or a brain cell.

Answers are available in Appendix A.

19.3 Initiating Transcription: Regulatory Sequences and Regulatory Proteins

As in bacteria, the **promoter** is a site in DNA where RNA polymerase binds to initiate transcription. Recent findings from genome sequencing projects (see Chapter 20) have shown that there is still much to be learned about eukaryotic promoters. What is known is that promoters in eukaryotes are more complex than bacterial promoters, often containing two or three conserved sequences that serve as binding sites for proteins needed to start transcription. The most intensively studied of these is a sequence known as the **TATA box.**

Once a promoter that contains a TATA box has been exposed by chromatin remodeling, the first step in initiating transcription is binding of the **TATA-binding protein (TBP).** Proteins related to TBP also work on promoters with other conserved sequences. But the binding of TBP or any of its relatives does not guarantee that a gene will be transcribed. In eukaryotes, a wide array of other DNA sequences and proteins work together to allow transcription.

Promoter-Proximal Elements Are Regulatory Sequences Near the Promoter

The first **regulatory sequences** in eukaryotic DNA were discovered in the late 1970s, when Yasuji Oshima and co-workers set out to understand how yeast cells control the metabolism of the sugar galactose.

When galactose is absent, *S. cerevisiae* cells produce only tiny quantities of the enzymes required to metabolize it. But when galactose is present, transcription of the genes encoding these enzymes increases by a factor of 1000.

The team's first major result was the discovery of mutant cells that failed to produce any of the five enzymes required for galactose metabolism, even if galactose was present. To interpret this observation, they hypothesized that

1. the five genes are regulated together, even though they are not on the same chromosome;

2. normal cells have an activator protein that exerts positive control over the five genes;

3. the mutant cells have a mutation that completely disables the activator protein.

Other researchers were able to isolate the regulatory protein and confirm that it binds to a short stretch of DNA located just upstream from the promoter for all five genes required for galactose use.

In bacteria, genes that need to be regulated together are often clustered into a single operon and transcribed into a single mRNA. In contrast, eukaryotes use the strategy uncovered by Oshima's group for the galactose-metabolizing genes in yeast—co-regulated genes are not clustered together, but instead share a regulatory DNA sequence that binds the same regulatory protein.

Regulatory DNA sequences similar to those first discovered in yeast have now been found in a wide array of eukaryotic genes and species. Regulatory sequences like these that are located close to the promoter and bind regulatory proteins are termed **promoter-proximal elements.**

Unlike the promoter itself, promoter-proximal elements have sequences that are unique to specific sets of genes. In this way, they furnish a mechanism for eukaryotic cells to express certain genes but not others.

The discovery of promoter-proximal elements and a mechanism of positive control suggested a satisfying parallel between gene regulation in bacteria and in eukaryotes. This picture changed, however, when researchers discovered a new class of eukaryotic DNA regulatory sequences—sequences unlike anything in bacteria.

Enhancers Are Regulatory Sequences Far from the Promoter

Susumu Tonegawa and colleagues made a startling discovery while exploring how human cells regulate gene expression. The gene studied by Tonegawa's group was broken into many introns and exons. Recall that introns are transcribed sequences that are spliced out of the primary transcript; exons are transcribed regions that are included in the mature RNA once splicing is complete (Chapter 17). The researchers discovered a regulatory sequence within one of the introns that was required for transcription of the gene.

This finding was remarkable for two reasons: (**1**) The regulatory sequence was thousands of bases away from the promoter, and (**2**) it was downstream of the promoter instead of upstream. Regulatory sequences that are far from the promoter and activate transcription are termed **enhancers.** Follow-up work has shown that enhancers occur in all eukaryotes and that they have several key characteristics:

- Enhancers can be more than 100,000 bases away from the promoter. They can be located in introns or in untranscribed sequences on either the 5′ or 3′ side of the gene (See **FIGURE 19.6**).

- Like promoter-proximal elements, many types of enhancers exist.

- Most genes have more than one enhancer.

- Enhancers usually have binding sites for more than one protein.

- Enhancers can work even if their normal 5′→3′ orientation is flipped, or if they are moved to a new location in the vicinity of the gene.

Enhancers are regulatory DNA sequences unique to eukaryotes. When regulatory proteins called **transcriptional activators** bind to enhancers, transcription begins. Thus, enhancers and activators are like a gas pedal—an element in positive control. Eukaryotes also possess regulatory sequences that are similar in structure and share key characteristics with enhancers but work to inhibit transcription. These DNA sequences are called **silencers.** When regulatory proteins called **repressors** bind to silencers, transcription is shut down. Silencers and repressors are like a brake—an element in negative control.

The Role of Transcription Factors in Differential Gene Expression

Follow-up work supported the hypothesis that enhancers and silencers are binding sites for activators and repressors that regulate transcription. Collectively, these proteins are termed

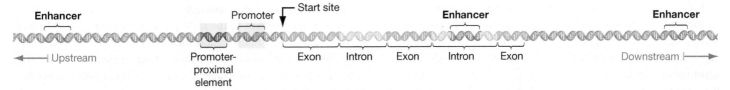

Enhancer   Promoter   Start site   Enhancer   Enhancer

Upstream ◄——   Promoter-proximal element   Exon | Intron | Exon | Intron | Exon   Downstream ——►

FIGURE 19.6 Enhancers and Promoter-Proximal Elements Regulate the Expression of Eukaryotic Genes. Promoter-proximal elements are near the promoter. Enhancers are located farther away, may be upstream or downstream of the promoter, and may even be within introns. Exons and introns are not drawn to scale. They are typically very large compared with regulatory sequences.

✔**EXERCISE** Compare and contrast the structure of this typical eukaryotic gene and the structure of a bacterial operon.

regulatory transcription factors, or often **transcription factors** for short. By analyzing mutant yeast, fruit flies, and roundworms that have defects in the expression of particular genes, biologists have identified a large number of transcription factors that bind to enhancers, silencers, and promoter-proximal elements.

These results support one of the most general statements researchers are able to make about gene regulation in eukaryotes: Different types of cells express different genes because they have different transcription factors. In multicellular species, the transcription factors, in turn, are produced in response to signals that arrive from other cells early in embryonic development.

For example, if a signal that says "become a muscle cell" reaches a cell in the early embryo, it triggers a signal transduction cascade (see Chapter 11) that leads to the production of transcription factors specific to muscle cells. Because different transcription factors bind to specific regulatory sequences, they turn on the production of muscle-specific proteins. But if no "become-a-muscle-cell" signal arrives, then no muscle-specific transcription factors are produced and no muscle-specific gene expression takes place.

Differential gene expression is a result of the production or activation of specific transcription factors. Eukaryotic genes are turned on when transcription factors bind to enhancers and promoter-proximal elements; the genes are turned off when transcription factors bind to silencers or when chromatin is condensed. Distinctive transcription factors are what make a muscle cell a muscle cell and a bone cell a bone cell.

How Do Transcription Factors Recognize Specific DNA Sequences?

Each transcription factor must be able to recognize and bind to a specific DNA sequence. How can it do this?

Recall that DNA bases are partially exposed in the major and minor grooves of the DNA double helix (see Figure 4.7 for a review). The edges of an AT base pair and a GC base pair that project into the grooves of the DNA helix contain different sets of atoms and have different surface shapes (**FIGURE 19.7a**). These differences in composition and shape can be recognized by transcription factors.

(a) AT and CG base pairs present different shapes and chemical groups in the grooves of DNA.

(b) Transcription factors recognize a specific sequence of bases in target DNA.

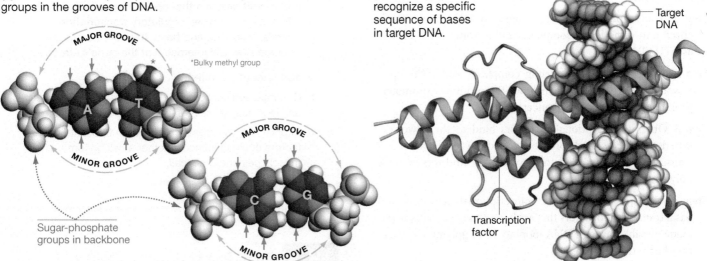

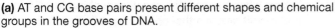

FIGURE 19.7 How Transcription Factors Bind to Regulatory Sequences. (a) The edges of base pairs that project into the major and minor grooves of the double helix present a different structure and set of atoms. Atoms that can participate in hydrogen bonding with amino acids of transcription factors are indicated by arrows. The methyl group on thymine (T) is also important in recognition. **(b)** A transcription factor (green) involved in muscle-cell differentiation binding to a regulatory sequence in DNA. The bases recognized by the protein are highlighted in red.

Just as base pairs come together by complementary molecular interactions, so too can proteins and specific DNA sequences. An example is shown in **FIGURE 19.7b**. In this case, a transcription factor that is essential for the development of muscle cells inserts amino acid side chains into two major grooves of DNA. This particular transcription factor binds to a specific enhancer sequence because of complementary interactions between base pairs and its amino acids. Without such specific interactions between transcription factors and DNA, the development of muscle cells—or any other specialized cell type—would not be possible.

A Model for Transcription Initiation

Although gene expression can be controlled at many levels, regulating the start of transcription is at center stage. For a process so important, many questions remain. What is clear is that transcription factors must interact with regulatory sequences to initiate transcription.

Besides the regulatory transcription factors you've learned about that bind to enhancers, silencers, and promoter-proximal elements, there is another type: **basal transcription factors.** These are proteins that interact with the promoter and are not restricted to particular genes or cell types. The term basal implies that these proteins are necessary for transcription to occur, but they do not provide much in the way of regulation. The promoter-recognized TATA-binding protein (TBP) that you learned about earlier is an example of a basal transcription factor that is common to many genes. ✔ If you understand this concept, you should be able to compare and contrast the regulatory and basal transcription factors found in muscle cells versus nerve cells.

In addition to transcription factors, a large complex of proteins called **Mediator** acts as a bridge between regulatory transcription factors, basal transcription factors, and RNA polymerase II. **FIGURE 19.8** summarizes one model for how transcription is initiated in eukaryotes.

Step 1 Transcriptional activators bind to DNA and recruit chromatin-remodeling complexes and histone acetyltransferases (HATs).

Step 2 The chromatin-remodeling complexes and HATs open a swath of chromatin that includes the promoter, promoter-proximal elements, and enhancers.

Step 3 Other transcriptional activators bind to the newly exposed enhancers and promoter-proximal elements; basal transcription factors bind to the promoter and recruit RNA polymerase II.

Step 4 Mediator connects the transcriptional activators and basal transcription factors that are bound to DNA. This step is made possible through DNA looping. RNA polymerase II can now begin transcription.

✔ If you understand this model, you should be able to explain why DNA forms loops near the promoter in order for transcription to begin.

An important point in this model of transcription initiation is the dual role of transcriptional activators. Activators work not only to stimulate transcription but also to bring chromatin-remodeling proteins to the right place at the right time. None of the proteins that remodel chromatin can recognize specific DNA sequences. It is the transcriptional activators that bind to regulatory sequences at particular genes to recruit the proteins needed to remodel chromatin.

The role of transcriptional activators in bringing in proteins that decondense chromatin leads to a chicken-and-egg paradox: How can an activator bind to DNA in the first place if chromatin is condensed? It turns out that except in its most highly condensed forms, chromatin is dynamic. DNA occasionally dissociates from nucleosomes, exposing regulatory sequences to activators that are present in a particular cell type.

Getting RNA polymerase to initiate transcription requires interactions between many proteins, including transcriptional activators that are bound to enhancers and promoter-proximal elements, Mediator, basal transcription factors, and RNA polymerase itself. The result is a large, macromolecular machine that is positioned at a gene's start site and capable of starting transcription.

Compared with what happens in bacteria, where just three to five proteins may interact at the promoter to initiate transcription, the process in eukaryotes is remarkably complicated.

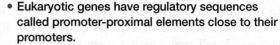

check your understanding

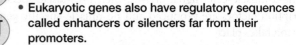

(C)(Y)(U) If you understand that . . .

- Eukaryotic genes have regulatory sequences called promoter-proximal elements close to their promoters.
- Eukaryotic genes also have regulatory sequences called enhancers or silencers far from their promoters.
- Transcription initiation is a multistep process that begins when transcriptional activators bind to DNA and recruit proteins that open chromatin.
- Interactions between regulatory transcription factors, Mediator, and basal transcription factors position RNA polymerase II at the gene's start site.

✔ You should be able to . . .

1. Compare and contrast the nature of regulatory sequences and regulatory proteins in bacteria versus eukaryotes.

2. Explain why the presence of certain transcription factors could influence whether a cell becomes a muscle cell or a brain cell.

Answers are available in Appendix A.

19.4 Post-Transcriptional Control

Chromatin remodeling and transcription are just the opening to the story of gene regulation. Once a gene is transcribed, a series of events has to occur before a final product appears (see Figure 19.1). Each of these events offers an opportunity

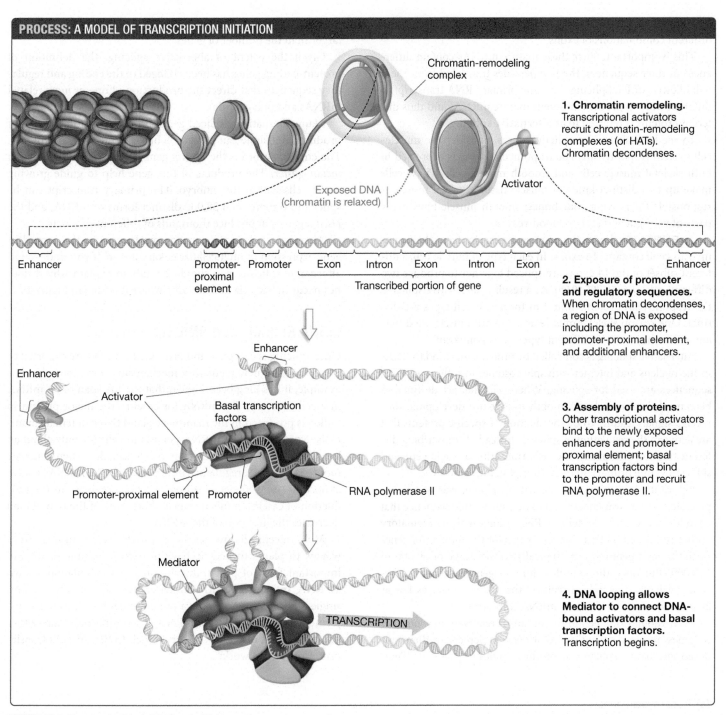

FIGURE 19.8 Transcription Initiation in Eukaryotes.

to regulate gene expression, and each is used in some cells at least some of the time. These control mechanisms include (1) splicing RNAs in various ways, (2) modifying the life span of mRNAs, (3) altering the rate at which translation is initiated, and (4) activating or inactivating proteins after translation has occurred. Let's consider each in turn.

Alternative Splicing of mRNAs

Introns are spliced out in the nucleus as the primary RNA is transcribed. Recall that the mRNA that results from splicing

consists of sequences encoded by exons, and that it is protected by a cap on the 5′ end and a long poly(A) tail on the 3′ end (see Chapter 17). You may also recall that splicing is accomplished by macromolecular machines called **spliceosomes,** and that many primary transcripts can be spliced in more than one way. This turns out to be a major way of regulating eukaryotic gene expression.

During splicing, gene expression is regulated when selected exons are removed from the primary transcript along with the introns. As a result, the same primary RNA transcript can yield more than one kind of mature, processed mRNA, consisting of different combinations of exons.

This is important. Since these mature mRNAs contain differences in their sequences, the polypeptides translated from them will likewise differ. Splicing the same primary RNA transcript in different ways to produce different mature mRNAs and thus different proteins is referred to as **alternative splicing.**

To see how alternative splicing works, consider the muscle-cell protein tropomyosin. The tropomyosin gene is expressed in both skeletal muscle cells and smooth muscle cells. These cells make up two distinct kinds of muscle tissue. Skeletal muscle is responsible for moving your bones; smooth muscle lines many parts of your gut and certain blood vessels.

As **FIGURE 19.9a** shows, the primary transcript from the tropomyosin gene contains 14 exons. In each type of muscle cell, a different subset of the 14 exons are spliced together to produce two different mRNAs (**FIGURE 19.9b**). As a result of alternative splicing, the tropomyosin proteins found in these two cell types are distinct. One reason skeletal muscle and smooth muscle are different is that they contain different types of tropomyosin.

Alternative splicing is controlled by proteins that bind to RNAs in the nucleus and interact with spliceosomes to influence which sequences are used for splicing. When cells that are destined to become skeletal muscle or smooth muscle are developing, they receive signals leading to the production of specific proteins that are active in the regulation of splicing. Instead of transcribing different tropomyosin genes, the cells transcribe a single gene and splice the same primary RNA transcript in different ways.

Before the importance of alternative splicing was widely appreciated, a gene was considered to be a nucleotide sequence that encodes one specific protein or RNA, along with its regulatory sequences. Based on this view, estimates for the number of genes in the human genome were typically in the range of 60,000 to 100,000. But once the complete human genome sequence became available, researchers realized that we may have as few as 20,000 sequences for primary mRNA transcripts.

Even though our genomes contain a relatively low number of genes, recent data indicate that over 90 percent of them undergo alternative splicing to produce multiple products. Thus, the number of different proteins that your cells can produce is far larger than the number of genes.

Given the extent of alternative splicing, the definition of protein-coding genes has been changed to the coding and regulatory sequences that direct the production of one *or more* related mRNAs and polypeptides.

Many alternatively spliced genes produce just a few different products, but some can produce a bewildering array of mRNAs. The current record is the *Dscam* gene of the fruit fly *Drosophila melanogaster*. The products of this gene help to guide growing nerve cells within the embryo. The primary transcript can be spliced into more than 38,000 distinct forms of mRNA, and the *Dscam* gene can produce thousands of different products.

Alternative splicing is a major mechanism in the control of gene expression in multicellular eukaryotes. ✔ If you understand alternative splicing, you should be able to explain why it does not occur in bacteria and describe where it occurs in Figure 19.1.

mRNA Stability and RNA Interference

Once splicing is complete and processed mRNAs are exported to the cytoplasm, new regulatory mechanisms come into play. For example, it has long been known that the life span of an mRNA in a cell can vary. The mRNA for casein—the major protein in milk—is produced in the mammary gland tissue of female mammals. Normally, casein mRNA persists in cells for only about an hour, and little casein protein is produced. But when a female mouse is lactating, regulatory molecules help the mRNAs persist almost 30 times longer—leading to a huge increase in the production of casein. In this instance, shortening of the poly(A) tail decreases the life-span of the mRNA.

More recent discoveries in a variety of organisms, from worms to plants to people, have uncovered a widespread and important form of post-transcriptional gene regulation known as **RNA interference.** RNA interference occurs when a tiny, single-stranded RNA held by a protein complex binds to a complementary sequence in an mRNA. This event unleashes either the destruction of the mRNA or a block to the mRNA's translation. How does it work?

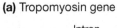

(a) Tropomyosin gene

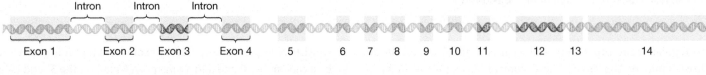

(b) Alternative splicing produces more than one mature mRNA.

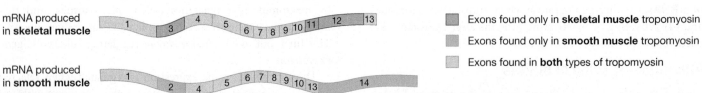

mRNA produced in **skeletal muscle**

mRNA produced in **smooth muscle**

Exons found only in **skeletal muscle** tropomyosin

Exons found only in **smooth muscle** tropomyosin

Exons found in **both** types of tropomyosin

FIGURE 19.9 Alternative Splicing Produces More than One Mature mRNA from the Same Gene.

FIGURE 19.10 walks through the sequence of events.

Step 1 RNA interference begins when RNA polymerase transcribes genes that code for RNAs that double back on themselves to form a hairpin. Hairpin formation occurs because pairs of bases within the RNA transcript are complementary.

Step 2 Some of the RNA is trimmed by enzymes in the nucleus; then the double-stranded hairpin that remains is exported to the cytoplasm.

Step 3 In the cytoplasm, another enzyme cuts out the hairpin loop to form double-stranded RNA molecules that are only about 22 nucleotides long.

Step 4 One of the strands from this short RNA is taken up by a group of proteins called the *RNA-*induced *s*ilencing *c*omplex, or RISC. The RNA strand held by the RISC is a **microRNA (miRNA)**.

Step 5 Once it is part of a RISC, the miRNA binds to its complementary sequences in a target mRNA.

Step 6 If the match between a miRNA and an mRNA is perfect, an enzyme in the RISC destroys the mRNA by cutting it in two. In effect, tight binding by a miRNA is a "kiss of death" for the mRNA. If the match isn't perfect, however, the mRNA is not destroyed. Instead, its translation is inhibited. Either way, miRNAs "interfere" with gene expression.

The first papers on RNA interference were published in the mid-1990s, and the first miRNAs were characterized in 2001. Since then, research on miRNAs and RNA interference has exploded. Current data suggest that a typical animal or plant species has at least 500 genes that code for miRNAs and that each miRNA regulates more than one mRNA. Because of this evidence, it is estimated that a large percentage of all animal and plant genes are controlled by these tiny molecules. miRNAs are critical for normal development, and mutations in miRNA genes are associated with many diseases. RNA interference is increasingly recognized as a key aspect of post-transcriptional control.

Researchers are currently testing whether certain miRNAs could be used to knock out specific genes associated with illness, or to destroy mRNAs produced by viruses during an infection. Research on RNA interference has quickly moved from an exciting new frontier in basic biology to possible applications in medicine.

✔ If you understand RNA interference, you should be able to describe where it occurs in Figure 19.1.

How Is Translation Controlled?

RNA interference is not the only mechanism of gene control that acts on mRNAs and affects whether translation occurs. For example, cells may slow or stop translation in response to a sudden increase in temperature or infection by a virus. The slowdown occurs because regulatory proteins that are activated by the temperature spike or viral invasion add a phosphate group to a protein that is part of the ribosome.

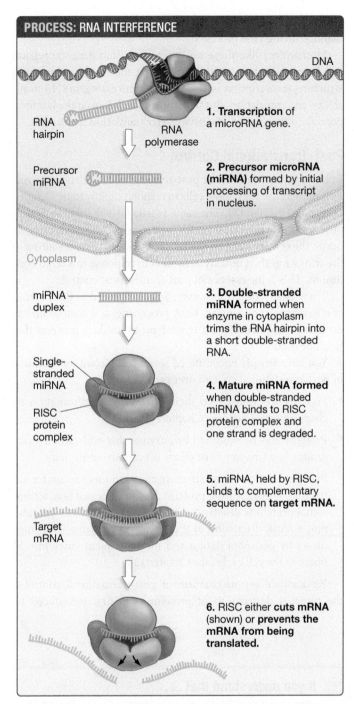

PROCESS: RNA INTERFERENCE

1. **Transcription** of a microRNA gene.

2. **Precursor microRNA (miRNA)** formed by initial processing of transcript in nucleus.

3. **Double-stranded miRNA** formed when enzyme in cytoplasm trims the RNA hairpin into a short double-stranded RNA.

4. **Mature miRNA formed** when double-stranded miRNA binds to RISC protein complex and one strand is degraded.

5. miRNA, held by RISC, binds to complementary sequence on **target mRNA.**

6. RISC either **cuts mRNA** (shown) or **prevents the mRNA from being translated.**

FIGURE 19.10 MicroRNAs Either Target mRNAs for Destruction or Prevent Their Translation. MicroRNAs are held by the RISC protein complex and bind to target mRNAs by complementary base pairing.

You might recall that phosphorylation frequently leads to changes in the shape and chemical reactivity of proteins. In the case of the phosphorylated ribosomal protein, the shape change slows or prevents translation.

For the cell, this dramatic change in gene expression can mean the difference between life and death. High temperatures disrupt protein folding, so shutting down translation prevents the production of improperly folded polypeptides. If the problem is an invading virus, the cell stops the infection because it avoids manufacturing viral proteins.

Mechanisms like these are a reminder that gene expression can be regulated at multiple points: at the level of chromatin structure, transcription initiation, RNA processing, mRNA availability, and translation. But that's not all. Let's look at the last level possible: altering protein activity, after translation is complete.

Post-Translational Control

In bacteria, mechanisms of post-translational regulation are important because they allow cells to respond rapidly to new conditions (see Chapter 18). The same is true for eukaryotes. Instead of waiting for transcription, RNA processing, and translation to occur, the cell can keep an existing but inactive protein waiting in the wings and then quickly activate it in response to altered conditions. This is the essence of post-translational control.

There is a trade-off, however: Speed is gained at the expense of efficiency. Transcription, RNA processing, and translation use up energy and materials; it is wasteful to produce proteins that won't be used.

You have already encountered several important mechanisms of post-translational control over gene expression.

- Proteins are folded into their final, active conformation by chaperone proteins (see Chapters 3 and 17).

- Proteins may be modified by enzymes that add carbohydrate groups (see Chapter 7) or cleave off certain amino acids.

- Phosphorylation is an extremely common mechanism for activating or deactivating proteins. You just learned how a ribosomal protein is deactivated by adding a phosphate. You also might recall discussion of the activation of cyclin–Cdk complexes by phosphorylation and the subsequent entry into M phase of the cell cycle (see Chapter 12).

Yet another key mechanism of post-translational control—the targeted destruction of proteins—was first introduced by

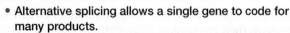
check your understanding

If you understand that . . .

C
Y
U

- Alternative splicing allows a single gene to code for many products.
- RNA interference is one of several mechanisms for controlling an mRNA's life span and translation rate.
- Ubiquitin tagging and destruction by proteasomes is one of many mechanisms for controlling a protein's life span.

✔ **You should be able to . . .**

1. Explain why the discovery of alternative splicing forced biologists to change their definition of the gene.

2. Explain why RNA interference is aptly named.

Answers are available in Appendix A.

describing the short life span of cyclin proteins. When a protein such as a cyclin needs to be destroyed, enzymes mark it by adding many copies of a small polypeptide called ubiquitin. Ubiquitin got its name because it is ubiquitous in cells. A macromolecular machine called the **proteasome** recognizes proteins that have a ubiquitin tag and cuts them into short segments.

As you can see, the regulation of gene expression in eukaryotes includes everything from opening chromatin in the nucleus to controlling the life span of proteins.

Do bacteria use the same range of regulatory mechanisms? Let's explore this question next.

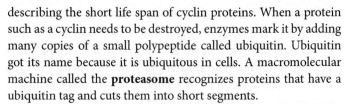

19.5 How Does Gene Expression Compare in Bacteria and Eukaryotes?

Almost as soon as biologists knew that information in DNA is transcribed into RNA and then translated into proteins, they began asking questions about how that flow of information is regulated. **TABLE 19.1** summarizes what biologists have learned over the past half century about how bacterial and eukaryotic gene expression is controlled—organized by the six steps in gene expression introduced in Figure 19.1.

How does the regulation of gene expression differ in bacteria and eukaryotes? Biologists point to five fundamental differences in the control of gene expression in bacteria and eukaryotes:

1. **DNA Packaging** The chromatin of eukaryotic DNA must be decondensed for basal and regulatory transcription factors to gain access to genes and for RNA polymerase to initiate transcription. The tight packaging of eukaryotic DNA means that the default state of transcription in eukaryotes is "off." In contrast, the default state of transcription in bacteria, which lack histone proteins and have freely accessible promoters, is "on." Chromatin structure provides a mechanism of negative control that does not exist in bacteria.

2. **Complexity of transcription** Transcriptional control is much more complex in eukaryotes than in bacteria. The sheer number of eukaryotic proteins involved in regulating transcription dwarfs that in bacteria, as does the complexity of their interactions.

3. **Coordinated transcription** In bacteria, genes that take part in the same cellular response are often organized into operons and transcribed together from a single promoter. In contrast, operons are rare in eukaryotes. Instead, for coordinated gene expression, eukaryotes rely on the strategy used in bacterial regulons—physically scattered genes are expressed together when the same regulatory transcription factors trigger the transcription of genes with the same DNA regulatory sequences.

4. **Greater reliance on post-transcriptional control** Eukaryotes make greater use of post-transcriptional control, such as alternative splicing. Alternative splicing allows eukaryotes to regulate the production of many proteins from each gene.

Level of Regulation	Bacteria	Eukaryotes
Chromatin remodeling	• Limited packaging of DNA • Remodeling not a major issue in regulating gene expression.	• Extensive packaging of DNA • Chromatin must be decondensed for transcription to begin.
Transcription	• Positive and negative control by regulatory proteins that act at sites close to the promoter • Sigma interacts with promoter.	• Positive and negative control by regulatory proteins that act at sites close to *and* far from promoter • Large set of basal transcription factors interact with promoter. • Mediator required.
RNA processing	• Rare	• Extensive processing: alternative splicing of introns
mRNA stability	• Rarely used for control	• Commonly used: RNA interference limits life span or translation rate of many mRNAs.
Translation	• Regulatory proteins bind to mRNAs and ribosomes and affect translation rate.	• Regulatory proteins bind to mRNAs and ribosomes and affect translation rate.
Post-translational modification	• Folding by chaperone proteins • Chemical modification (e.g., phosphorylation) changes protein activity.	• Folding by chaperone proteins • Chemical modification (e.g., phosphorylation) changes protein activity. • Ubiquitination targets proteins for destruction by proteasome.

Alternative splicing, microRNAs, and regulation of mRNA stability are seldom seen in bacteria, but these constitute major elements of control in eukaryotes.

To date, biologists do not have a good explanation for why gene expression is so much more complex in eukaryotes than it is in bacteria. After decades of research, the debate continues.

For multicellular eukaryotes, one hypothesis is that the requirement for complex regulation of gene expression during development has driven the evolution of such complicated and multilayered means of controlling genes.

Normal regulation of gene expression results in the orderly development of an embryo and appropriate responses to environmental change in adults. What happens when gene expression goes awry? Unfortunately, one answer is uncontrolled cell growth and the set of diseases called cancer. Understanding how changes in gene expression can lead to cancer is one of today's great research frontiers.

19.6 Linking Cancer with Defects in Gene Regulation

All cancers involve uncontrolled cell division. What allows this unbridled increase in cell number? Each type of cancer is caused by a different set of mutations that lead to cancer when they affect one of two classes of genes: (1) genes that stop or slow the cell cycle, and (2) genes that trigger cell growth and division by initiating specific phases in the cell cycle. Many of the genes that are mutated in cancer influence gene regulation. Let's take a closer look at how altered gene regulation can cause uncontrolled cell growth.

The Genetic Basis of Uncontrolled Cell Growth

As you learned in the chapter on the cell cycle (Chapter 12), proteins that stop or slow the cell cycle when conditions are unfavorable for cell division are called tumor suppressors. Logically enough, the genes that code for these proteins are called **tumor suppressor** genes. If the function of a tumor suppressor gene is lost because of mutation, then a key brake on the cell cycle is eliminated.

Genes that stimulate cell division are called **proto-oncogenes** (literally, "first cancer genes"). In normal cells, the proteins produced from proto-oncogenes are active only when conditions are appropriate for growth. In cancerous cells, defects in the regulation of proto-oncogenes can cause these genes to stimulate growth at all times. (In the context of cancer, cell growth refers to an increase in cell numbers, not an increase in the size of individual cells.) In such cases, a mutation has converted the proto-oncogene into an **oncogene**—an allele that promotes cancer development.

For cancers to develop, many mutations are required within a single cell, and these alter both tumor suppressor genes and proto-oncogenes.

The *p53* Tumor Suppressor: A Case Study

To gain a deeper understanding of how defects in gene expression can lead to cancer, consider research on the gene that is most often defective in human cancers. The gene is called *p53* because

(a) Normal cell

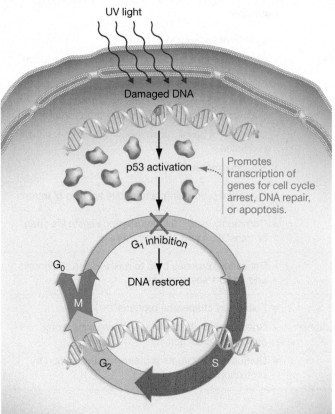

(b) p53 mutant cell

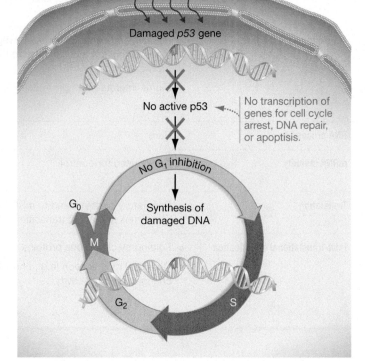

FIGURE 19.11 Consequences of *p53* Mutation.

the protein it codes for has a molecular weight of approximately 53 kilodaltons. Sequencing studies have revealed that mutant, nonfunctional forms of *p53* are found in over half of all human cancers. The *p53* gene codes for a regulatory transcription factor.

Researchers began to understand what *p53* does when they exposed normal, noncancerous human cells to UV radiation and noticed that levels of active *p53* protein increased markedly. Recall that UV radiation damages DNA (see Chapter 15). Follow-up studies confirmed that there is a close correlation between DNA damage and the amount of *p53* in a cell. In addition, analyses of the protein's primary structure suggested that it might contain a DNA-binding region similar to the one shown for the muscle-specific transcription factor in Figure 19.7.

These observations inspired the hypothesis that *p53* is a regulatory transcription factor that serves as a master brake on the cell cycle. In this model, shown in **FIGURE 19.11**, *p53* is activated by DNA damage. Activated *p53* binds to the enhancers of genes that arrest the cell cycle, repair DNA damage, and when all else fails, trigger apoptosis (cell death). Expression of these genes allows the cell to halt the cell cycle in order to repair its DNA, if this is possible, or commit suicide if the DNA damage is too severe. In mutant cells that lack a form of *p53* that can bind to enhancers, DNA damage cannot arrest the cell cycle, the cell cannot kill

check your understanding

C Y U

If you understand that . . .

- Many mutations associated with cancer alter gene regulation.
- Cancer is associated with mutations that lead to loss of control over the cell cycle.
- Uncontrolled cell growth may result when a mutation in a regulatory gene creates a protein that activates the cell cycle constitutively.
- Uncontrolled cell growth may result when a mutation prevents a tumor suppressor protein from shutting down the cell cycle in damaged cells.

✔ **You should be able to . . .**

1. Explain why cancer has a common pattern of uncontrolled cell growth, but not a common cause. Your answer should refer to the six levels of gene regulation outlined in Figure 19.1.

2. Explain why loss-of-function mutations in *p53* are observed in so many cancers.

Answers are available in Appendix A.

itself, and damaged DNA is replicated. This situation leads to mutations that can move the cell farther down the road to cancer. The *p53* protein is like a quality control officer. If it is missing, errors are made and things go downhill.

Here are some of the results that support this model of *p53* function:

- *p53* activates many different genes, including genes for cell cycle regulation, DNA repair, and apoptosis.

- X-ray crystallography studies show that *p53* binds directly to DNA regulatory sequences of the genes it controls.

- Virtually all the *p53* mutations associated with cancer are located in the protein's DNA-binding region and alter amino acids that interfere with *p53*'s ability to bind to regulatory DNA sequences.

The role of *p53* in preventing cancer is so important that biologists call this gene "the guardian of the genome." Today, biologists are searching for molecules that can restore *p53* activity to protect the genome and act against cancer.

CHAPTER 19 REVIEW

For media, go to MasteringBiology

If you understand . . .

19.1 Gene Regulation in Eukaryotes— An Overview

- Changes in gene expression allow eukaryotic cells to respond to changes in the environment and cause distinct cell types to develop.

- In a multicellular eukaryote, cells are different because they express different genes, not because they have different genes.

- Gene expression is regulated at six levels: Chromatin has to be remodeled, the transcription of specific genes may be initiated or repressed, mRNAs may be spliced in different ways to produce a different product, the life span of specific mRNAs may be extended or shortened, translation rate may be increased or decreased, and the life span or activity of particular proteins may be altered.

✔ You should be able to describe how the presence of the nuclear envelope, and the physical separation of transcription and translation, influences the levels of gene regulation observed in eukaryotes versus bacteria and archaea.

19.2 Chromatin Remodeling

- Eukaryotic DNA is packaged with proteins into chromatin that must be opened before transcription can occur.

- Eukaryotic DNA is wrapped around histone proteins to form bead-like nucleosomes that are then coiled into 30-nm fibers and higher-order chromatin structures.

- Transcription cannot be initiated until chromatin around regulatory regions is decondensed.

- The state of chromatin condensation depends on the methylation of cytosines in DNA, acetylation and other modifications of histones, and the action of molecular machines called chromatin-remodeling complexes.

- Patterns of DNA methylation and histone modifications can be passed from mother cells to daughter cells.

- Epigenetic inheritance is the inheritance of different phenotypes due to anything other than differences in alleles; transmitting patterns of chromatin condensation from mother to daughter cells or from parent to offspring is a mechanism of epigenetic inheritance.

✔ You should be able to explain why chromatin remodeling has to be the first step in gene activation.

19.3 Initiating Transcription: Regulatory Sequences and Regulatory Proteins

- In eukaryotes, transcription is triggered by regulatory proteins called transcription factors that bind to sequences both close to and far from the promoter.

- Regulatory transcription factors can be activators or repressors; these bind to regulatory sequences called (1) promoter-proximal sequences that are near promoters or (2) enhancers and silencers that are often located at a distance from gene promoters.

- Amino acids on regulatory transcription factors interact with the projections of base pairs in the grooves of the DNA helix to allow binding to specific regulatory sequences.

- The first regulatory transcription factors that bind to DNA recruit proteins that loosen the interaction between nucleosomes and DNA, making the promoter, promoter-proximal elements, and enhancers accessible to other transcription factors.

- Interactions between regulatory and basal transcription factors occur through a complex of proteins called Mediator and lead to the positioning of RNA polymerase at the promoter and the start of transcription.

✔ You should be able to draw a model of a eukaryotic gene undergoing transcription. Label enhancers, promoter-proximal elements, the promoter, activators, basal transcription factors, Mediator, and RNA polymerase.

19.4 Post-Transcriptional Control

- Once transcription is complete, gene expression is controlled by (1) alternative splicing, (2) RNA interference, and (3) activation or inactivation of protein products.

- Alternative splicing allows a single gene to produce more than one version of an mRNA and more than one kind of protein. It is regulated by proteins that interact with potential splice sites in the primary transcript to control which ones the spliceosome uses.

- RNA interference occurs when tiny strands of complementary RNA bind to mRNAs in association with the protein complex called RISC. This marks the mRNAs for destruction or prevents their translation. If the short RNA strands come from a transcribed cellular gene, they are known as microRNAs (miRNAs).

- Once translation occurs, proteins may be activated or inactivated by the addition or removal of chemical groups such as phosphates, or marked for destruction in the proteasome by adding polypeptides known as ubiquitin.

- ✓ You should be able to explain why humans can have so few genes.

19.5 How Does Gene Expression Compare in Bacteria and Eukaryotes?

- Examine Table 19.1 Regulating Gene Expression in Bacteria and Eukaryotes.

- ✓ You should be able to compare and contrast how bacteria and eukaryotes regulate the transcription of genes that need to be turned on together.

19.6 Linking Cancer with Defects in Gene Regulation

- If mutations alter regulatory proteins that promote or inhibit progression through the cell cycle, then uncontrolled cell growth and tumor formation may result.
- ✓ You should be able to explain why mutations of *p53* that prevent the protein from binding to DNA set the stage for cancer.

MB MasteringBiology

1. MasteringBiology Assignments

Tutorials and Activities Control of Gene Expression; Control of Transcription; DNA Packing; Overview: Control of Gene Expression; Post-Transcriptional Control Mechanisms; Regulation of Gene Expression in Eukaryotes; Transcription Initiation in Eukaryotes

Questions Reading Quizzes, Blue-Thread Questions, Test Bank

2. eText Read your book online, search, take notes, highlight text, and more.

3. The Study Area Practice Test, Cumulative Test, BioFlix® 3-D Animations, Videos, Activities, Audio Glossary, Word Study Tools, Art

---

You should be able to . . .

✓ TEST YOUR KNOWLEDGE

Answers are available in Appendix A

1. What is chromatin?
   a. the histone-containing protein core of the nucleosome
   b. the 30-nm fiber
   c. the complex of DNA and proteins found in eukaryotes
   d. the histone *and* non-histone proteins in eukaryotic nuclei

2. What is a tumor suppressor?

3. Which of the following statements about enhancers is correct?
   a. They contain a unique base sequence called a TATA box.
   b. They are located only in 5'-flanking regions.
   c. They are located only in introns.
   d. They are found in a variety of locations and are functional in any orientation.

4. In eukaryotes, what allows only certain genes to be expressed in certain types of cells?

5. What is alternative splicing?
   a. phosphorylation events that lead to different types of post-translational regulation
   b. mRNA processing events that lead to different combinations of exons being spliced together
   c. folding events that lead to proteins with alternative conformations
   d. action by regulatory proteins that leads to changes in the life span of an mRNA

6. What types of proteins bind to promoter-proximal elements?
   a. the basal transcription complex
   b. the basal transcription complex plus RNA polymerase
   c. basal transcription factors such as TBP
   d. regulatory transcription factors such as activators

7. Compare and contrast (a) enhancers and the *E. coli araC* binding site (see Chapter 18), (b) promoter-proximal elements and the operator of the *lac* operon, and (c) basal transcription factors and sigma.

8. Explain how alternative splicing could play a role in changing eukaryotic gene expression in response to changes in the environment.

9. Compare and contrast (a) enhancers and silencers; (b) promoter-proximal elements and enhancers; and (c) regulatory transcription factors and Mediator.

10. Predict how a drug that inhibits histone deacetylase will alter gene expression.

11. Relative to the genetic code, the histone code
    a. has more triplets.
    b. is much simpler to read because of complementary base pairing.
    c. does not depend on particular base sequences.
    d. requires methylated Cs rather than standard Cs in DNA.

12. Predict how a mutation that caused continuous production of active *p53* would affect the cell.

13. In the follow-up work to the experiment shown in Figure 19.5, the researchers used a technique that allowed them to see if two DNA sequences are in close physical proximity (association). They applied this method to examine how often an enhancer and the promoter of the *Hnf4a* regulatory gene were near each other. A logical prediction is that compared with rats born to mothers fed a healthy diet, the *Hnf4a* gene in rats born to mothers fed a protein poor diet would
    a. show no difference in how often the promoter and enhancer associated.
    b. never show any promoter–enhancer association.
    c. show a lower frequency of promoter–enhancer association.
    d. show a higher frequency of promoter–enhancer association.

14. QUANTITATIVE Imagine repeating the experiment on epigenetic inheritance that is shown in Figure 19.5. You measure the amount of radioactive uridine (U) incorporated into *Hnf4a* mRNA in counts per minute (cpm) to determine the level of *Hnf4a* gene transcription in rats born to mothers fed either a normal diet or a low protein diet. The results are 11,478 cpm for the normal diet

and 7368 cpm for the low-protein diet conditions. You should prepare a graph similar to the one at the bottom of Figure 19.5 that shows the normalized results relative to the normal diet condition. Normalizing values means that value obtained from one condition is expressed as 1.0 (the norm; the normal diet in this case) and the values obtained from any other conditions (low-protein diet in this case) are expressed as decimal values relative to the norm.

15. After DNA damage, levels of activated p53 protein in the cytoplasm increase. Design an experiment to determine whether this increase is due to increased transcription of the *p53* gene or to activation of preexisting p53 proteins by a post-translational mechanism such as phosphorylation.

16. Researchers have discovered that if a single-stranded mRNA produced by a virus is used as a template to create a double-stranded RNA, that this double-stranded RNA often blocks infection by the virus. Propose an explanation for how infection can be blocked by this type of double-stranded RNA.

The Big Picture

Copying, using, and transmitting genetic information is fundamental to life. Cells use the genetic information archived in their DNA to respond to changes in the environment and, in multicellular organisms, to develop into specific cell types.

Hereditary information is transmitted to offspring with random changes called mutations. Thus, genetic information is dynamic—both within generations and between generations.

Note that each box in the concept map indicates the chapter and section where you can go for review. Also, be sure to do the blue exercises in the Check Your Understanding box below.

GENETIC INFORMATION

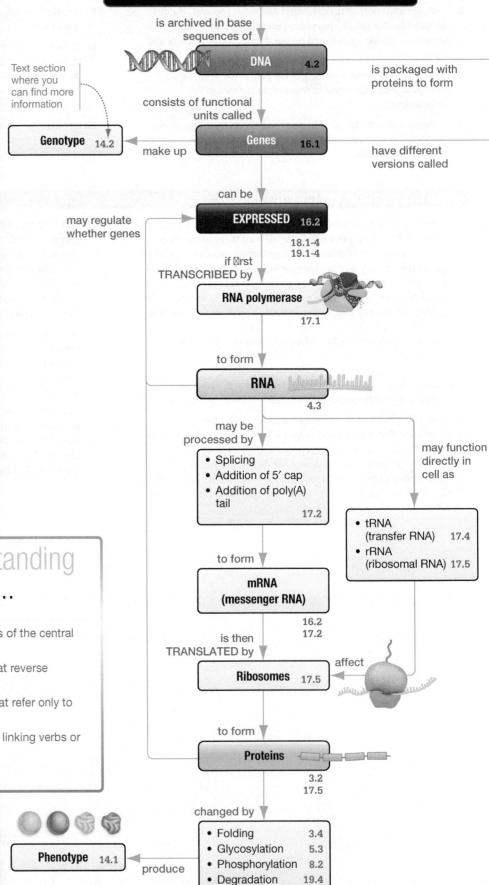

is archived in base sequences of

DNA 4.2

Text section where you can find more information

consists of functional units called

Genotype 14.2 ← make up — **Genes** 16.1

is packaged with proteins to form

have different versions called

can be

EXPRESSED 16.2

18.1-4
19.1-4

may regulate whether genes

if first TRANSCRIBED by

RNA polymerase 17.1

to form

RNA 4.3

may be processed by

- Splicing
- Addition of 5′ cap
- Addition of poly(A) tail
  17.2

may function directly in cell as

- tRNA (transfer RNA) 17.4
- rRNA (ribosomal RNA) 17.5

to form

mRNA (messenger RNA) 16.2 17.2

is then TRANSLATED by

Ribosomes 17.5

affect

to form

Proteins 3.2 17.5

changed by

- Folding 3.4
- Glycosylation 5.3
- Phosphorylation 8.2
- Degradation 19.4

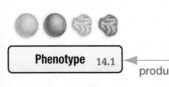

Phenotype 14.1 ← produce

check your understanding

If you understand the big picture . . .
✔ You should be able to . . .

1. Draw stars next to the three elements of the central dogma of molecular biology.

2. Add arrows and labels indicating what reverse transcriptase does.

3. Draw an E in the corners of boxes that refer only to eukaryotes, not prokaryotes.

4. Fill in the blue ovals with appropriate linking verbs or phrases.

Answers are available in Appendix A.

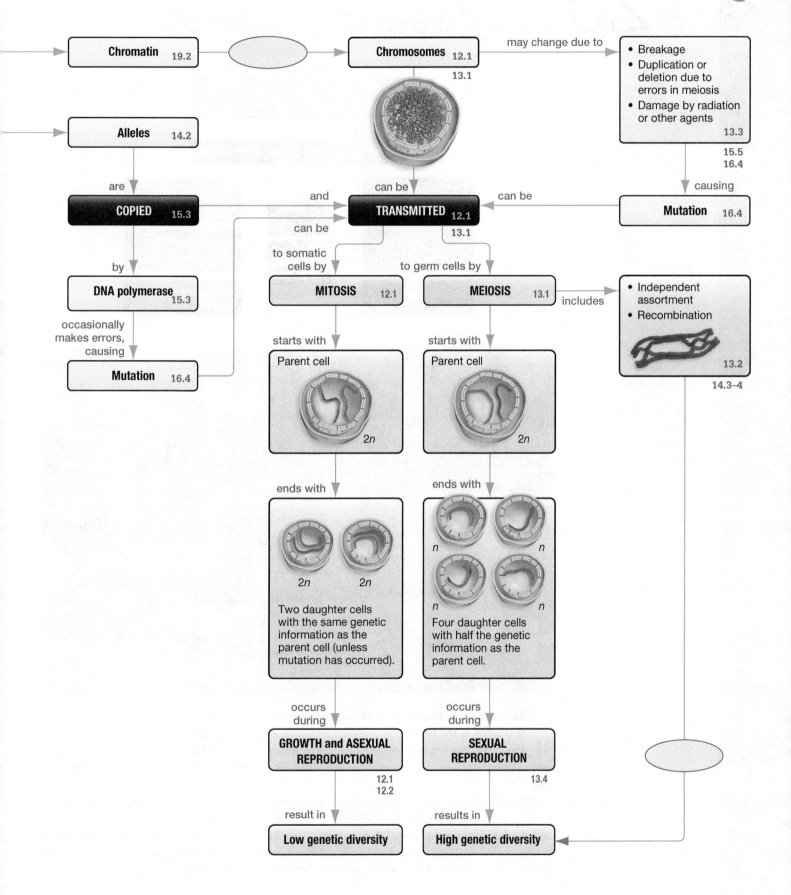

Chromatin 19.2

Chromosomes 12.1 13.1

may change due to
- Breakage
- Duplication or deletion due to errors in meiosis
- Damage by radiation or other agents

13.3

15.5
16.4

Alleles 14.2

can be

COPIED 15.3

and

TRANSMITTED 12.1 13.1

can be

can be

Mutation 16.4

causing

by

DNA polymerase 15.3

occasionally makes errors, causing

Mutation 16.4

to somatic cells by

MITOSIS 12.1

to germ cells by

MEIOSIS 13.1

includes
- Independent assortment
- Recombination

13.2

14.3–4

starts with

Parent cell

$2n$

starts with

Parent cell

$2n$

ends with

$2n$ $2n$

Two daughter cells with the same genetic information as the parent cell (unless mutation has occurred).

ends with

n n

n n

Four daughter cells with half the genetic information as the parent cell.

occurs during

GROWTH and ASEXUAL REPRODUCTION

12.1
12.2

occurs during

SEXUAL REPRODUCTION

13.4

result in

Low genetic diversity

results in

High genetic diversity

20 Analyzing and Engineering Genes

In this chapter you will learn that

Biotechnology depends on methods to analyze and alter genomes

by exploring ↓

Case studies of key genetic technologies

applied to

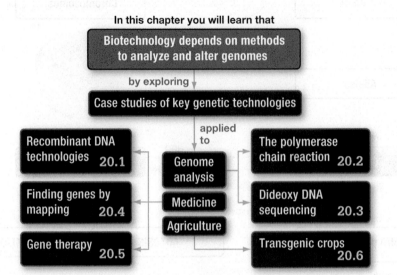

The rice plants in these bottles have been genetically engineered—using techniques introduced in this chapter—to produce a molecule needed for a key vitamin.

The molecular revolution in biological science got its start when researchers confirmed that DNA is the hereditary material and succeeded in describing the molecule's secondary structure. But when biologists discovered how to remove DNA sequences from an organism, manipulate them, and insert them into different individuals, the molecular revolution really took off.

Efforts to manipulate DNA sequences in organisms are often referred to as genetic engineering. Genetic engineering became possible with the discovery of enzymes that cut DNA at specific sites and of other enzymes that paste DNA sequences together. These new molecular tools were extremely powerful. Biologists no longer had to rely solely on controlled breeding experiments to change the genetic characteristics of individuals. Instead, they could mix and match specific DNA sequences in

✔ When you see this checkmark, stop and test yourself. Answers are available in Appendix A.

the lab. Because successful efforts to manipulate genes usually result in novel combinations of DNA, techniques used to engineer genes are often referred to as **recombinant DNA technology.**

This chapter uses a series of case histories to introduce basic molecular biology techniques in the context of solving problems. It also considers the ethical and economic issues raised by efforts to manipulate genes. What are the potential perils and benefits of introducing recombinant genes into human beings, food plants, and other organisms? This question, one of the great ethical challenges of the twenty-first century, is a recurrent theme in the following pages.

20.1 Case 1–The Effort to Cure Pituitary Dwarfism: Basic Recombinant DNA Technologies

To understand the basic techniques and tools of genetic engineering, let's consider the role they played in developing a treatment for pituitary dwarfism in humans.

The pituitary gland is a structure at the base of the mammalian brain that produces several important biomolecules, including a protein that stimulates growth. This protein, which was found to be just 191 amino acids long, was named human growth hormone (HGH). In humans, the gene that codes for it is called *GH1*.

The discovery of growth hormone led researchers immediately to suspect that at least some forms of inherited dwarfism might be caused by a defect in the *GH1* gene. This hypothesis was confirmed by studies showing that people with certain types of dwarfism produce little growth hormone or none at all. These people have defective copies of *GH1* and exhibit pituitary dwarfism, type I (**FIGURE 20.1a**).

By studying the pedigrees of families in which dwarfism was common, several teams of researchers established that pituitary dwarfism, type I, is an autosomal recessive trait (see Chapter 14). In other words, affected individuals have two copies of the defective allele. Individuals who are affected by pituitary dwarfism have normal body proportions but grow more slowly than average people, reach puberty from two to 10 years later than average, and are short in stature as adults—typically no more than 120 cm (4 feet) tall (**FIGURE 20.1b**).

Why Did Early Efforts to Treat the Disease Fail?

Once the molecular basis of pituitary dwarfism was understood, physicians began treating the disease with injections of naturally produced growth hormone. This approach was inspired by the spectacular success that had been achieved in treating type I diabetes mellitus. This form of diabetes is caused by a deficiency of the peptide hormone insulin, and clinicians had been able to alleviate the disease's symptoms by injecting patients with insulin from pigs.

Early trials showed that people with pituitary dwarfism could be treated successfully with growth hormone therapy, but only if the protein came from humans. Growth hormones isolated from pigs, cows, or other animals were ineffective. Until the 1980s, however, the only source of human growth hormone was pituitary glands from human cadavers. As a result, the drug was extremely scarce and expensive.

It turned out that meeting demand was the least of the problems with growth hormone therapy. To understand why, recall that infectious proteins called prions can cause degenerative brain disorders in mammals (see Chapter 3). When some of the children treated with human growth hormone developed a prion disease in their teens and twenties, physicians realized that the supply of growth hormone was contaminated with a prion protein from

(a) *GH1* codes for a pituitary growth hormone.

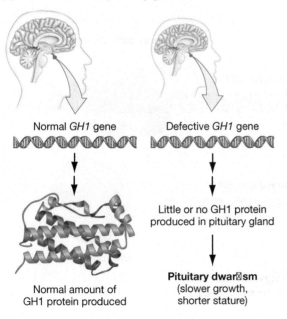

Normal *GH1* gene

Defective *GH1* gene

Little or no GH1 protein produced in pituitary gland

Normal amount of GH1 protein produced

Pituitary dwarfism (slower growth, shorter stature)

(b) Normal versus GH1-deficient

FIGURE 20.1 Pituitary Dwarfism Is a Genetic Disease. (a) If mutations in the human *GH1* sequence are severe enough to inactivate the gene, pituitary dwarfism may result. **(b)** William Harrison and Charles Stratton, in a photo taken about 1860. Harrison and Stratton were both celebrated comedians and performers. Stratton, whose stage name was Tom Thumb, enjoyed audiences in the White House with Abraham Lincoln and Buckingham Palace with Queen Victoria. Stratton had pituitary dwarfism; Harrison had normal height.

some of the cadavers supplying the hormone. In 1984, the use of growth hormone isolated from cadavers was banned.

Steps in Engineering a Safe Supply of Growth Hormone

To replace natural sources of growth hormone, researchers turned to genetic engineering. Their plan was to insert fully functional copies of human *GH1* into the bacterium *Escherichia coli*, which they hoped would then produce huge quantities of recombinant progeny. If the plan worked, the recombinant cells would produce uncontaminated growth hormone in sufficient quantities to meet demand at an affordable price.

The plan required investigators to find *GH1*, obtain many copies of the gene, and insert them into *E. coli* cells. Their ability to do these things hinged on using basic tools of molecular biology.

Using Reverse Transcriptase to Produce cDNAs An enzyme called reverse transcriptase (Chapter 16) is responsible for an exception to the central dogma of molecular biology: It allows information to flow from RNA to DNA. More specifically, reverse transcriptase catalyzes the synthesis of DNA from an RNA template.

DNA that is produced from RNA is called **complementary DNA,** or **cDNA.** Although reverse transcriptase initially produces a single-stranded cDNA, it is also capable of synthesizing the complementary strand to yield a double-stranded DNA. In many cases, however, researchers add a chemically synthesized primer to single-stranded cDNAs and use DNA polymerase to synthesize the second strand (**FIGURE 20.2**).

Reverse transcriptase played a key role in the search for the growth hormone gene. Knowing that *GH1* is actively transcribed in the pituitary gland, researchers isolated mRNAs from pituitary-gland cells and used the enzyme to reverse-transcribe those mRNAs to cDNAs. These reaction products contained double-stranded cDNAs corresponding to each gene that is actively expressed in pituitary cells.

The next move? Isolating each of the cDNAs and making many identical copies of them.

Using Plasmids in Cloning Producing many copies of a gene is referred to as **DNA cloning.** If a researcher says that she has cloned a gene, it means that she has isolated it and then produced many identical copies.

In many cases, researchers can clone a gene by inserting it into a small, circular DNA molecule called a **plasmid.** You might recall that plasmids are common in bacterial cells (see Chapter 7). They are physically separate from the bacterial chromosome and are not required for normal growth and reproduction. Most replicate independently of the chromosome. Some plasmids carry genes for antibiotic resistance or other traits that increase the cell's ability to grow in a particular environment.

Researchers realized that if they could splice a loose piece of DNA into a plasmid and then insert the modified plasmid into a bacterial cell, the engineered plasmid would be replicated and passed on to daughter cells as the bacterium grew and divided. If this recombinant bacterium were then placed in a nutrient broth and allowed to grow and reproduce overnight, billions of copies of the original cell, each containing identical modified plasmid DNA, would result. When a plasmid is used in this way—to make copies of a foreign DNA sequence—it is called a **cloning vector,** or simply a **vector.**

Biologists harvest the recombinant genes by breaking the bacteria open, isolating all the DNA, and then separating the plasmids from the main chromosomes. But how do they insert a gene into a plasmid in the first place?

Using Restriction Endonucleases and DNA Ligase to Cut and Paste DNA To cut a gene out for later insertion into a cloning vector, researchers use enzymes called restriction endonucleases. A **restriction endonuclease** is a bacterial enzyme that cuts DNA molecules at specific base sequences. In bacterial cells, these enzymes cut up DNA from invading viruses and prevent a fatal infection.

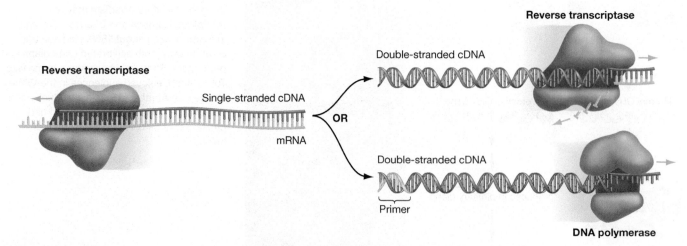

FIGURE 20.2 Reverse Transcriptase Catalyzes the Synthesis of DNA from RNA. The single-stranded DNA produced by reverse transcriptase is complementary to the RNA template. The cDNA can be made double stranded by reverse transcriptase or DNA polymerase. DNA polymerase requires a primer.

More than 800 restriction endonucleases are known, and many of them cut DNA only at sequences that form palindromes. In English, a word or sentence is a palindrome if it reads the same way backward as it does forward. "Madam, I'm Adam" is an example. In biology, a stretch of double-stranded DNA forms a palindrome if the 5′→3′ sequence of one strand is identical to the 5′→3′ sequence on the antiparallel, complementary strand.

To insert the pituitary-gland cDNAs into plasmids, researchers performed the sequence of steps outlined in **FIGURE 20.3**.

Step 1 The left side of the figure shows a plasmid containing a palindromic sequence, or recognition site, that is cut by a specific restriction endonuclease. As the right side of the figure shows, the researchers attached the same palindromic sequence to the ends of each cDNA in their sample.

Step 2 They cut the recognition sites in each plasmid (left) and at the ends of each cDNA (right) with a restriction endonuclease called EcoRI. (The name comes from the fact that this

enzyme was the first (Roman numeral *I*) restriction endonuclease discovered in *E. coli* strain RY13.)

Step 3 Like most restriction endonucleases, EcoRI makes a staggered cut in the palindrome. The resulting DNA fragments are described as having **sticky ends,** because the single-stranded bases on one fragment are complementary to the single-stranded bases on the other fragment. As a result, the two ends can pair up and hydrogen-bond to each other: The complementary sequences in the sticky ends of the plasmid (in grey) will bind to the sticky ends in the cDNA (in red) by complementary base pairing.

Step 4 Finally, researchers used **DNA ligase**—the enzyme that connects Okazaki fragments during DNA replication (see Chapter 15)—to seal the pieces of DNA together at the arrows marked in green.

The creation of sticky ends in DNA is important. If restriction sites in different DNA sequences are cut with the same restriction

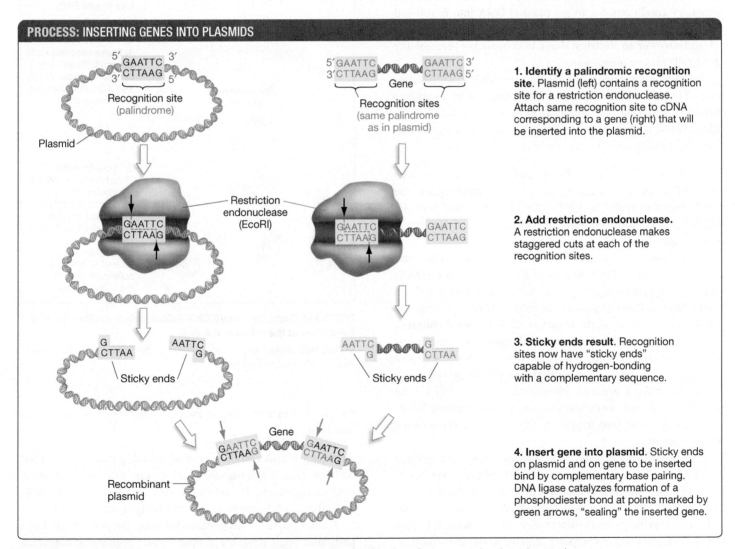

PROCESS: INSERTING GENES INTO PLASMIDS

1. Identify a palindromic recognition site. Plasmid (left) contains a recognition site for a restriction endonuclease. Attach same recognition site to cDNA corresponding to a gene (right) that will be inserted into the plasmid.

2. Add restriction endonuclease. A restriction endonuclease makes staggered cuts at each of the recognition sites.

3. Sticky ends result. Recognition sites now have "sticky ends" capable of hydrogen-bonding with a complementary sequence.

4. Insert gene into plasmid. Sticky ends on plasmid and on gene to be inserted bind by complementary base pairing. DNA ligase catalyzes formation of a phosphodiester bond at points marked by green arrows, "sealing" the inserted gene.

FIGURE 20.3 Genes Can Be Inserted into Plasmids in Preparation for Cloning. Once a gene has been inserted into a plasmid, the recombinant plasmid can be introduced into bacterial cells that grow and divide to produce many identical copies of the gene.

endonuclease, the presence of the same sticky ends in both samples of DNA promotes joining of the resulting fragments. This is the essence of recombinant DNA technology—the ability to create novel combinations of DNA sequences by cutting specific sequences and pasting them into new locations.

After performing this procedure, the researchers who were hunting for the growth hormone gene had a set of recombinant plasmids. Each contained a cDNA made from one of the many human pituitary-gland mRNAs. But the *GH1* gene was still not cloned.

Transformation: Introducing Recombinant Plasmids into Bacterial Cells

If a recombinant plasmid can be inserted into a bacterial or yeast cell, the foreign DNA will be copied and transmitted to new cells as the host cell grows and divides. In short, it can be cloned. In this way, researchers can obtain millions or billions of copies of specific genes. How is the insertion brought about?

Cells that take up DNA from the environment and incorporate it into their genomes are said to undergo **transformation.** Most bacterial cells do not take up DNA on their own under laboratory conditions. So, to get plasmid DNA into *E. coli* and other common laboratory species, researchers use simple chemical treatments or an electrical shock to increase the permeability of the cell's plasma membrane.

Typically, just a single plasmid enters the cell during this treatment. The cells are then spread out on plates under conditions that allow only cells with plasmids to grow into colonies. Each colony contains millions of identical cells, each with many identical copies of the recombinant plasmid.

Producing a cDNA Library

FIGURE 20.4 summarizes the steps covered thus far in the hunt for the growth hormone gene. The result, shown in step 5, is a collection of transformed bacterial cells. Each of the cells contains a plasmid with one cDNA from a pituitary gland mRNA.

A collection of DNA sequences, each of which is inserted into a vector, is called a **DNA library.** If the sequences are cDNAs made from a particular cell type or tissue, the library is called a **cDNA library.** If the sequences are fragments of DNA from the genome of an individual, the library is called a **genomic library.**

DNA libraries are made up of cloned genes. Each gene can be produced in large quantity and isolated in pure form. ✔ If you understand this concept, you should be able to describe how you could make a genomic library starting with DNA from your own cells and using the restriction endonuclease EcoRI to cut the genome into fragments that can be inserted into a plasmid vector.

DNA libraries are important because they provide researchers a way to store DNA fragments from a particular cell type or genome in a form that is accessible for gene cloning. But like a college library, a DNA library isn't very useful unless there is a way to retrieve specific pieces of information. At your school's library, you use call numbers or computer searches to retrieve a particular book or article. How do you go about retrieving a particular gene from a DNA library? For example, how did researchers find

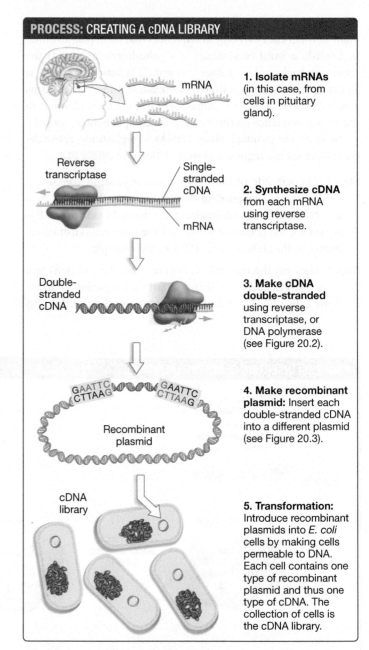

PROCESS: CREATING A cDNA LIBRARY

mRNA

1. **Isolate mRNAs** (in this case, from cells in pituitary gland).

Reverse transcriptase

Single-stranded cDNA

mRNA

2. **Synthesize cDNA** from each mRNA using reverse transcriptase.

Double-stranded cDNA

3. **Make cDNA double-stranded** using reverse transcriptase, or DNA polymerase (see Figure 20.2).

GAATTC CTTAAG   GAATTC CTTAAG

Recombinant plasmid

4. **Make recombinant plasmid:** Insert each double-stranded cDNA into a different plasmid (see Figure 20.3).

cDNA library

5. **Transformation:** Introduce recombinant plasmids into *E. coli* cells by making cells permeable to DNA. Each cell contains one type of recombinant plasmid and thus one type of cDNA. The collection of cells is the cDNA library.

FIGURE 20.4 Complementary DNA (cDNA) Libraries Represent a Collection of the mRNAs in a Cell.

✔**QUESTION** Would each type of cDNA in the library be represented just once? Why or why not?

the growth hormone gene in the cDNA library of the human pituitary gland?

Screening a DNA Library

Molecular biologists are often faced with the task of finding one specific gene in a large collection of DNA fragments. To do this requires a **probe**—a marked molecule that binds to the molecule the biologist is looking for.

A DNA probe is a single-stranded fragment that will bind to a particular single-stranded complementary sequence in a mixture of DNAs. By binding to the target sequence, the probe marks the fragment containing that sequence, distinguishing it from all the other DNA fragments in the sample. As **FIGURE 20.5** shows, a DNA probe must be labeled in some way so that it can be found after it has bound to the complementary sequence in the large sample of fragments.

✔ If you understand the concept of a DNA probe, you should be able to explain why the probe must be single stranded and labeled in order to work, and why it binds to just one specific fragment. You should also be able to indicate where a probe with the sequence AATCG (recall that sequences are always written $5' \rightarrow 3'$) will bind to a target DNA with the sequence TTTTACCCATTTACGATTGGCCT (again written $5' \rightarrow 3'$).

To find an appropriate probe for the human growth hormone gene, researchers began by using the genetic code to predict possible DNA sequences of *GH1*. They could do this because they knew the sequence of amino acids in the polypeptide, which they could use to infer the codons that coded for each amino acid. You made similar inferences in some of the exercises in earlier chapters. But recall that there is more than one codon for most amino acids (see Chapter 16). As a result, the researchers could not infer a unique sequence for the growth hormone gene. Instead, they deduced a set of possible sequences that could encode the *GH1* gene.

The next step was to chemically synthesize the set of short, single-stranded DNAs that were complementary to the possible *GH1* sequences. Because one of these sequences would bind to single-stranded fragments from the actual gene by complementary base pairing, it could act as a probe. In this case, the label the researchers attached to the probe was a radioactive atom.

FIGURE 20.6 shows how researchers used this probe to find the plasmid in the cDNA library that contained *GH1*. (For more information on how to use probes, see **BioSkills 9** in Appendix B.) As predicted, the labeled probe bound to its complementary sequence in the cDNA library—identifying the recombinant cell that contained the human growth hormone cDNA.

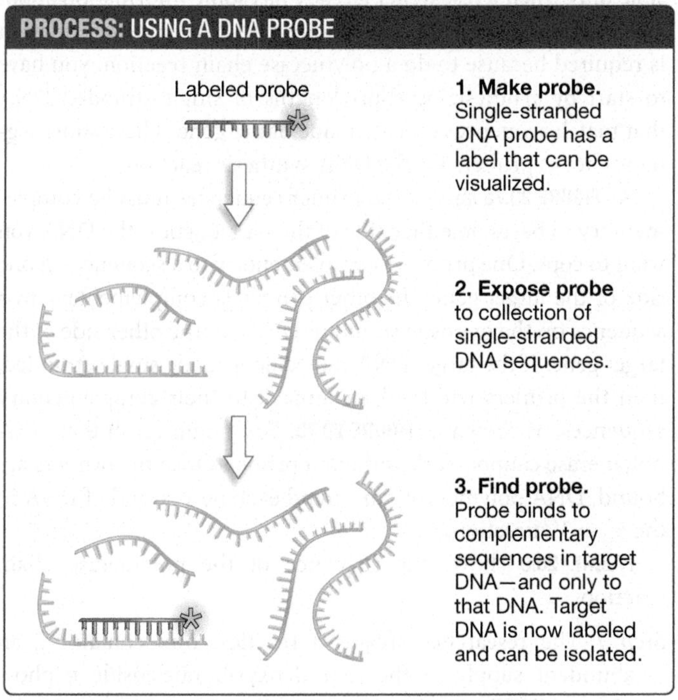

Mass-Producing Growth Hormone To accomplish their goal of producing large quantities of the human growth hormone, the investigators used recombinant DNA techniques to transfer the growth hormone cDNA to a new plasmid. The plasmid in question contained a promoter sequence recognized by *E. coli*'s RNA polymerase holoenzyme (see Chapter 17). The recombinant plasmids were then introduced into *E. coli* cells.

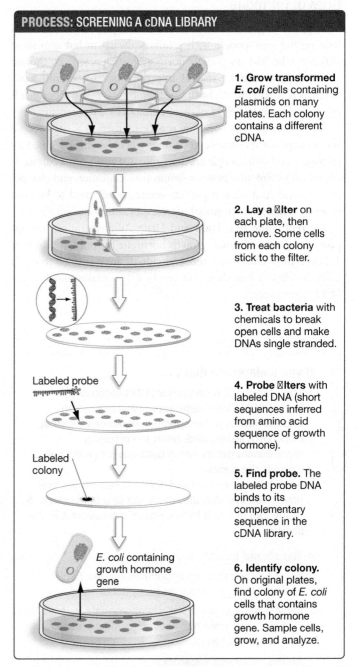

PROCESS: SCREENING A cDNA LIBRARY

1. **Grow transformed** *E. coli* cells containing plasmids on many plates. Each colony contains a different cDNA.

2. **Lay a filter** on each plate, then remove. Some cells from each colony stick to the filter.

3. **Treat bacteria** with chemicals to break open cells and make DNAs single stranded.

4. **Probe filters** with labeled DNA (short sequences inferred from amino acid sequence of growth hormone).

Labeled probe

5. **Find probe.** The labeled probe DNA binds to its complementary sequence in the cDNA library.

Labeled colony

6. **Identify colony.** On original plates, find colony of *E. coli* cells that contains growth hormone gene. Sample cells, grow, and analyze.

E. coli containing growth hormone gene

FIGURE 20.6 Finding Specific Genes by Probing a cDNA Library.

PROCESS: USING A DNA PROBE

Labeled probe

1. **Make probe.** Single-stranded DNA probe has a label that can be visualized.

2. **Expose probe** to collection of single-stranded DNA sequences.

3. **Find probe.** Probe binds to complementary sequences in target DNA—and only to that DNA. Target DNA is now labeled and can be isolated.

FIGURE 20.5 DNA Probes Bind to and Identify Specific Target Sequences.

The resulting transformed *E. coli* cells now contained a gene for human growth hormone attached to a promoter. These cells began to transcribe and translate the human growth hormone gene. Human growth hormone accumulated in the cells and was subsequently isolated and purified.

Today, bacterial cells containing the human growth hormone gene are grown in huge quantities. These cells have proved to be a safe and reliable source of the human growth hormone protein. The effort to cure pituitary dwarfism using recombinant DNA technology was a spectacular success—a triumph of applied biology, or **biotechnology.**

Ethical Concerns over Recombinant Growth Hormone

As supplies of growth hormone increased, physicians used it in treating not only people with pituitary dwarfism but also short children who had no growth hormone deficiency. Even though the treatment requires several injections per week until adult height is reached, growth hormone therapy was popular because it often increased the height of these children by a few centimeters.

In essence, growth hormone was being used as a cosmetic—a way to improve appearance in cultures where height is deemed attractive. But if short people are discriminated against in a culture, is a medical treatment a better solution than education and changes in attitudes? And what if parents wanted a tall child to be even taller, to enhance her potential success as, say, a basketball player?

Currently, the U.S. Food and Drug Administration has approved the use of human growth hormone for only the shortest 1.2 percent of children. These individuals are projected to reach adult heights of less than 160 cm (5′3″) in males and 150 cm (4′11″) in women.

check your understanding

If you understand that . . .

- The essence of recombinant DNA technology is to cut DNA into fragments with a restriction endonuclease, paste specific sequences together using DNA ligase, and insert the resulting recombinant genes into a bacterial (or yeast) cell to express the genes.
- A DNA library consists of different sequences that have been inserted into plasmids or other vectors. A probe can be used to find specific sequences in the library.

✔ You should be able to . . .

1. Explain why restriction endonucleases like EcoRI create DNA fragments with sticky ends.
2. Explain why the word probe is appropriate to describe a labeled sequence that is used to find a particular gene in a DNA library.

Answers are available in Appendix A.

Growth hormone has also become a popular performance-enhancing drug for athletes, because it improves the maintenance of bone density and muscle mass. Part of its popularity stems from the fact that it is difficult to detect in current drug tests.

Should athletes be able to enhance their physical skills by taking hormones or other types of drugs? Is the drug safe at the dosages athletes are using? These questions are being debated by physicians, researchers, agencies that govern sports, and legislative bodies.

In the meantime, it is clear that while solving one important problem, recombinant DNA technology created others. One of this chapter's recurring themes is that genetic engineering has costs that must be carefully weighed against its benefits.

20.2 Case 2–Amplification of Fossil DNA: The Polymerase Chain Reaction

Inserting a gene into a bacterial plasmid is one method for cloning DNA. The polymerase chain reaction is another.

The **polymerase chain reaction (PCR)** is an in vitro DNA synthesis reaction that uses DNA polymerase to replicate a specific section of DNA over and over. It generates many identical copies of a particular region of DNA.

Requirements of PCR

Although PCR is much faster and technologically easier than cloning genes into a DNA library, there is a catch: PCR is possible only when a researcher already has some information about DNA sequences near the gene in question. Sequence information is required because to do a polymerase chain reaction, you have to start by synthesizing short lengths of single-stranded DNA that match sequences on either side of the gene. These short segments act as primers for the DNA synthesis reaction.

As **FIGURE 20.7a** shows, the primer sequences must be complementary to bases on either side of the target gene—the DNA you want to copy. One primer is complementary to a sequence on one side of the target gene; the other primer is complementary to a sequence on the opposite strand of DNA, on the other side of the target gene. If the target DNA molecule is made single stranded, then the primers will bind, or anneal, to their complementary sequences, as shown in **FIGURE 20.7b**. You might recall that DNA polymerase cannot work without a primer. Once the primers are bound, DNA polymerase can extend each new strand of DNA in the 5′ →3′ direction.

FIGURE 20.8 shows the sequence of the polymerase chain reaction.

Step 1 The researcher creates a reaction mix containing an abundant supply of the four deoxyribonucleoside triphosphates (dNTPs; see Chapter 15), a DNA sample that includes the gene of interest, many copies of the two primers, and a heat-resistant DNA polymerase called *Taq* polymerase.

(a) PCR primers must bind to sequences on either side of the target sequence, on opposite strands.

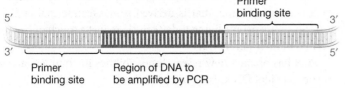

(b) When target DNA is made single stranded, primers bind and allow DNA polymerase to work.

FIGURE 20.7 The Polymerase Chain Reaction Requires Appropriate Primers. (a) To design an appropriate primer, the base sequence at the primer binding sites must be known. **(b)** The primers bind by complementary base pairing to single-stranded target DNA.

✔**EXERCISE** Indicate where DNA polymerase would begin to work on each strand; add an arrow indicating the direction of DNA synthesis.

Step 2 The reaction mix is heated to 95°C. At this temperature, the double-stranded template DNA denatures. This means that the two DNA strands separate, forming single-stranded templates.

Step 3 The mixture is allowed to cool to 50–60°C. In this temperature range, the primers bind, or anneal, to complementary portions of the single-stranded template DNA. This step is called primer annealing.

Step 4 The reaction mix is heated to 72°C. At this temperature, *Taq* polymerase efficiently synthesizes the complementary DNA strand from the dNTPs, starting at the primer. This step is called *extension*.

Step 5 Repeat steps 2 through 4.

Step 6 Continue repeating steps 2 through 4 until the necessary number of copies is obtained.

The temperature changes required in each step are controlled by automated PCR machines, and there is no need to add more components once the reaction starts.

Taq polymerase is a DNA polymerase found in the thermophilic ("heat-loving") bacterium *Thermus aquaticus*, which was discovered in a hot spring in Yellowstone National Park. Researchers use *Taq* polymerase because the PCR mixture has to be heated, and *Taq* polymerase is heat stable. Enzymes from most organisms are destroyed at high temperature, but *Taq* polymerase functions normally even when heated to 95°C.

The denaturation, primer annealing, and extension steps constitute a single PCR cycle. If one copy of the template sequence existed in the original sample, then two copies are present at the

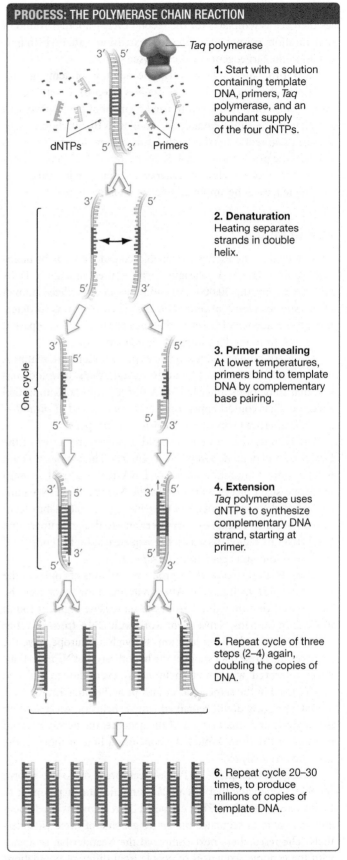

FIGURE 20.8 The Polymerase Chain Reaction Produces Many Copies of a Specific Sequence. Each PCR cycle (denaturation, primer annealing, and extension) results in a doubling of the number of target sequences.

end of the first cycle (see step 4 in Figure 20.8). These two copies then act as templates for the second cycle—another round of denaturation, primer annealing, and extension—after which four copies of the target gene are present (see step 5).

Each time the cycle repeats, the amount of template sequence in the reaction mixture doubles (step 6). Doubling occurs because each newly synthesized segment of DNA serves as a template in the subsequent cycle, along with the previously synthesized segments. Starting with a single copy, successive cycles result in the production of 2, 4, 8, 16, 32, 64, 128, 256 copies, and so on. A total of n cycles can generate 2^n copies. In just 20 cycles, one sequence can be amplified to over a million copies.

PCR in Action

To understand why PCR is so valuable, consider a study by biologist Svante Pääbo and colleagues, who wanted to analyze DNA recovered from the 30,000-year-old bones of a fossilized human of the species *Homo neanderthalensis*. Their goal was to determine the sequence of bases in the ancient DNA and compare it with DNA from modern humans (*Homo sapiens*).

If modern humans have sequences that are identical or almost identical to the sequences found in Neanderthals, it would suggest that some of us inherited DNA directly from a Neanderthal ancestor. That could happen only if *H. sapiens* and *H. neanderthalensis* interbred while they coexisted in Europe.

The Neanderthal bone was so old, however, that most of the DNA in it had degraded into tiny fragments. The biologists could recover only a minute amount of DNA that was still in even moderate-sized pieces. Fortunately, the Neanderthal DNA sample included a few fragments of the gene region that Pääbo's team wanted to study. The researchers were able to design primers that bracketed this region, based on the sequence of highly conserved sections of the same gene from *H. sapiens*.

Using PCR, the researchers produced millions of copies of the Neanderthal DNA fragment. After analyzing these sequences, the team found that they differ from the same gene segment found in modern humans. Subsequent work with DNA from 14 other Neanderthal fossils, from locations throughout Europe, gave the same result. These data support the hypothesis that Neanderthals never interbred with modern humans—even though the two species lived in the same areas of Europe at the same time.

But a nagging doubt remained—the conclusion was based on the analysis of a small region of the genome, the best that could be done at the time. Would the conclusion hold if more of the genome was analyzed?

To answer this question, Pääbo's team went on to use a form of DNA sequencing that has a DNA amplification step similar to PCR (see Section 20.3). They extracted DNA from fossilized bones and were able to sequence the entire genome of three Neanderthals. The researchers next compared the Neanderthal sequence with the genome sequences of people from different populations living today.

Their conclusion? For African populations there was no evidence of inbreeding with Neanderthals. The story is different,

however, for non-African populations. People from these groups have a small amount of DNA, roughly 1 percent to 4 percent of each person's genome, that is derived from Neanderthal ancestors. So, many people living today can claim just a touch of Neanderthal in their family tree.

PCR has opened new research possibilities in countless areas beyond ancient DNA. For example:

- Forensic scientists, who use biological analyses to help solve crimes, clone DNA from tiny drops of blood or hair. The copied DNA can then be analyzed to identify victims, implicate perpetrators, or exonerate the falsely accused.

- Genetic counselors, who advise couples on how likely their offspring are to suffer from inherited diseases, can use PCR to find out if an embryo conceived by the couple has alleles associated with deadly illness.

Because the complete genomes of a wide array of organisms have now been sequenced, researchers can easily find appropriate primer sequences to use in cloning almost any target gene by PCR. The polymerase chain reaction is now one of the most basic and widely used techniques in biology.

check your understanding

If you understand that . . .

- PCR is a technique for amplifying a specific region of DNA into millions of copies, which can then be sequenced or used for other types of analyses.

✔ You should be able to . . .

1. Explain the purpose of the denaturation, annealing, and extension steps in a PCR cycle, and why "chain reaction" is an appropriate part of the term PCR.

2. Write down the sequence of a double-stranded DNA that is 50 base pairs long. Then design 21-base-pair-long primers that would allow you to amplify the segment by PCR.

Answers are available in Appendix A.

20.3 Case 3–Sanger's Breakthrough: Dideoxy DNA Sequencing

Once researchers have cloned a gene from a DNA library or by PCR, determining the gene's base sequence is usually one of the first things they want to do. Learning a gene's sequence is valuable for a variety of reasons. For example:

- Once a gene's sequence is known, the amino acid sequence of its product can be inferred from the genetic code. Knowing a protein's primary structure often provides clues to its function.

- Comparing sequences is fundamental to understanding why alleles vary in function—for example, why one allele causes disease and another doesn't.

- Researchers can infer evolutionary relationships by comparing the sequences of the same gene in different species (see Chapter 1). This information can be used to study an array of questions, ranging from how new traits evolve to where new diseases come from.

How do researchers sequence DNA? In 1977 Frederick Sanger published a technique called dideoxy sequencing that is still in use today.

The Logic of Dideoxy Sequencing

As **FIGURE 20.9** shows, **dideoxy sequencing** is a clever variation on the basic in vitro DNA synthesis reaction. But saying "clever" is an understatement. Sanger had to link three important insights to make his sequencing strategy work.

Dideoxynucleotides Terminate DNA Synthesis Sanger's first insight was to use monomers for DNA synthesis called dideoxyribonucleoside triphosphates (ddNTPs) along with the normal deoxyribonucleoside triphosphates (dNTPs) (Chapter 15) in the reaction mix. The ddNTPs are identical to dNTPs except that they lack a hydroxyl group at their 3′ carbon. Four types of ddNTPs are used in dideoxy sequencing, each named according to whether it contains adenine (ddATP), thymine (ddTTP), cytosine (ddCTP), or guanine (ddGTP). The use of ddNTPs inspired the name dideoxy sequencing.

Sanger realized that if a ddNTP were added to a growing DNA strand, it would terminate synthesis. Why? After a ddNTP is added, no hydroxyl group is available on a 3′ carbon to link to the 5′ carbon on an incoming dNTP monomer. As a result, DNA polymerization stops once a ddNTP is added.

Fragment Length Correlates with the Location of Each Base Sanger linked the ability of ddNTPs to stop DNA synthesis to a second fundamental insight: Every time a ddNTP is added to a growing strand, the result is a fragment with a length corresponding to the position in the template of a base complementary to the ddNTP. To produce these fragments, biologists create a reaction mix containing **(1)** many copies of the template DNA with **(2)** a primer, **(3)** DNA polymerase, **(4)** a large supply of the four dNTPs, and **(5)** a small amount of the four ddNTPs (Figure 20.9, step 1). Each of the four ddNTPs carries a different fluorescent tag. (In the figure, ddGTP is purple, ddCTP is blue, ddATP is green, and ddTTP is orange.) Fluorescent molecules absorb light at one wavelength and reemit the light at a longer wavelength. As described in **BioSkills 10** (see Appendix B), fluorescent tags provide a very sensitive way of detecting molecules.

Under these conditions, many daughter strands of different lengths are synthesized. All fragments that are the same length end in the same kind of ddNTP.

Step 2 in Figure 20.9 shows why:

- DNA polymerase synthesizes a complementary strand from each template in the reaction mix.

- The synthesis of each one of these complementary strands starts at the same point—the primer.

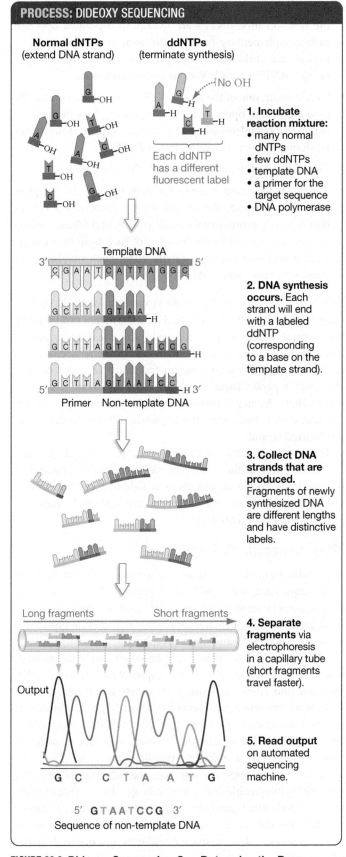

FIGURE 20.9 Dideoxy Sequencing Can Determine the Base Sequence of DNA.

- Because there are many dNTPs and relatively few ddNTPs in the reaction mix, dNTPs are usually incorporated opposite each complementary base on the template strand as DNA polymerase works its way along the template strand. Incorporating a dNTP allows DNA synthesis to continue.

- Occasionally, one of the few ddNTPs is incorporated into the growing strand, opposite the corresponding base in the template. The complementary base in the template strand pairs randomly with either a ddNTP or a dNTP.

- The addition of the ddNTP stops further elongation.

- "Stops" of this kind happen for each base in the template strand. As a result, the overall reaction produces a collection of newly synthesized strands (fragments) whose various lengths correspond to the location of each base in the template strand (see step 3 in Figure 20.9). Each fragment will fluoresce in the color of its ddNTP.

DNA Sequence Can Be Read from Fragments Lined Up by Size
Sanger's third insight? When the DNA fragments produced by the synthesis reactions are lined up by size, the dideoxy monomers on the successive fragments reveal the sequence of bases in the template DNA. To line up fragments in order of size, biologists separate them using gel electrophoresis (step 4 in Figure 20.9). As step 5 shows, a machine can read the pattern of fluorescence, indicating the sequence of bases in the newly synthesized strand.

Dideoxy sequencing ranks among the greatest of all technological advances in the history of biological science. Its impact is comparable to the development of light and electron microscopes, microelectrodes for recording membrane potentials, and recombinant gene technology.

"Next Generation" Sequencing

Sequencing technology is advancing at a blindingly fast pace. Dideoxy sequencing is still performed, particularly when relatively long sequences need to be read with great accuracy. But new, "next generation" sequencing approaches now make it possible to sequence much faster and more cheaply.

Most of the newer methods are based on amplification steps related to PCR. These create many copies of each template DNA molecule and allow sequencing of minute quantities of DNA. Even more important, millions of different DNAs can be amplified and sequenced in a single run. Methods that allow simultaneous sequencing or analysis of huge numbers of different molecules are called massively parallel approaches. These sequencing technologies are opening research possibilities that were barely imaginable only a few years ago. Today, instead of sequencing individual genes, researchers often obtain the sequence of entire genomes. A case in point is the sequencing of the Neanderthal genome—this was made possible using a massively parallel approach.

The project to sequence the human genome for the first time took 10 years and cost $3 billion U.S. dollars. Now researchers could sequence your genome in a day for less than $5,000.

20.4 Case 4—The Huntington's Disease Story: Finding Genes by Mapping

Mendel had no idea what a "hereditary determinant" actually was. But now we know. Biology's molecular revolution has allowed researchers to find and characterize individual genes—to explore the connection between genotype and phenotype as explicitly and directly as possible. The question is, How do researchers find the genes associated with certain traits in the first place? How do you find the gene responsible for seed shape in peas, or white eyes in flies, or DNA polymerase III in *E. coli*?

One widely used approach is conceptually simple: You begin with a map of known sites in the genome and then look for an association between one of those known sites and the phenotype you're interested in. The gene that affects the phenotype is probably close to the known site.

In practice, the process is not so simple. As an example of how this type of gene hunt is done, let's consider one of the first successful searches ever conducted for a human gene—the gene associated with Huntington's disease.

How Was the Huntington's Disease Gene Found?

Huntington's disease is a rare but devastating illness. Typically, affected individuals first show symptoms between the ages of 35 and 45. At onset, an individual appears to be clumsier than normal and tends to develop small tics and abnormal movements. As the disease progresses, uncontrollable movements become more pronounced. Eventually the affected individual twists and writhes involuntarily. Personality and intelligence are also compromised—to the extent that the early stage of this disease is sometimes misdiagnosed as the brain disorder schizophrenia. The illness may continue to progress for 10 to 20 years and is eventually fatal.

Because Huntington's disease runs in families, physicians suspected that it was a genetic disease. An analysis of pedigrees from families affected by Huntington's disease suggested that the trait was due to a single, autosomal dominant allele (see Chapter 14). To understand the molecular basis for the disease, researchers used many of the tools and techniques of genetic engineering that are shown in **TABLES 20.1** and **20.2** (see pages 380–381) as they set out to locate and identify the gene or genes involved. It took over 10 years of intensive effort to reach this goal.

The search for the Huntington's disease gene was led by Nancy Wexler, whose mother had died of the disease. If the trait was indeed due to an autosomal dominant allele, it meant that Wexler had a 50 percent chance of receiving the allele from her mother and would begin to show symptoms when she reached middle age.

Using Genetic Markers To locate the gene or genes associated with a particular phenotype, such as a disease, researchers traditionally start with a **genetic map,** also known as a **linkage map** (see Chapter 14). Recall that a genetic map shows the relative positions of genes on the same chromosome, determined by analyzing the frequency of recombination between pairs of genes. Biologists also use **physical maps** of the genome. A physical map shows the absolute position of a gene—in numbers of base pairs—along a chromosome. Genome sequencing (see Chapter 21) has produced physical maps for a wide array of species.

A genetic map is valuable in gene hunts because it contains **genetic markers**—easily identified genes or DNA sequences that have known locations. Each genetic marker provides a landmark—a position along a chromosome that is known relative to other markers. The key is to find where the unknown gene lies relative to the established genetic markers.

To understand how genetic markers can be used, let's use a hypothetical example. Suppose that you knew the position of a hair-color gene in humans relative to other genetic markers. Suppose too that various alleles of this gene contributed to the development of black hair, red hair, blond hair, and brown hair in the group of people you were studying. This variation in phenotype associated with the marker is crucial. To be useful in a gene hunt, a genetic marker has to be **polymorphic,** meaning that the phenotype associated with the marker varies. In our hypothetical example, hair color is a polymorphic genetic marker.

Now suppose that the genetic disease called cystic fibrosis is common among the individuals you were studying and that your goal is to find the gene associated with cystic fibrosis. Further, suppose that people who have cystic fibrosis almost always have black hair—even though they are just as likely as unaffected individuals to have any other inherited trait observed in the study population, such as the presence or absence of a widow's peak or detached earlobes.

If you observe that a certain form of a marker and a certain disease are almost always inherited together, this means that the marker gene and disease gene are physically close to each other on the same chromosome—they are closely linked. If they were not closely linked, then crossing over in between them would be common and they would *not* be inherited together. In this hypothetical study, you could infer that the gene for cystic fibrosis is very close to the hair-color gene. ✔ If you understand this concept, you should be able to explain why it's helpful to hunt for genes using a genetic map with many genetic markers rather than only a few.

Gene hunts in humans boil down to this: Researchers have to find a large number of people who are affected and unaffected. Then they must attempt to locate a genetic marker that almost always occurs in one form in the affected individuals but only rarely in unaffected people. If such a marker is found, the disease gene is almost guaranteed to be nearby.

The types of genetic markers used in gene mapping have changed over time. Today, researchers often have a large catalog of polymorphic genetic markers available, including the particularly abundant markers known as **single nucleotide polymorphisms** (**SNPs,** pronounced *snips*). A SNP is a site in DNA that varies between alleles at a single base pair. Below is an example of a SNP:

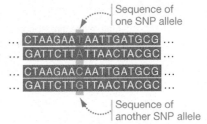

To date, roughly 10 million human SNPs have been identified.

In the late 1970s and early 1980s, when biologists were searching for the Huntington's disease gene, SNPs were unknown. The best genetic markers available were restriction sites—short stretches of DNA where restriction endonucleases cut the double helix. These sequences are also known as restriction endonuclease recognition sites.

The restriction sites that Wexler's team used were polymorphic: Some alleles had a sequence that allowed cuts to occur; but in other alleles, the DNA sequence at the same site varied slightly, and no cuts occurred. Thus, just as an individual might have an A instead of a C at a certain SNP, an individual might have a restriction site allele that allowed cutting or not. Wexler's team was looking for restriction site alleles that were almost always present in diseased individuals but not found any more often than predicted by chance in healthy individuals (**FIGURE 20.10**).

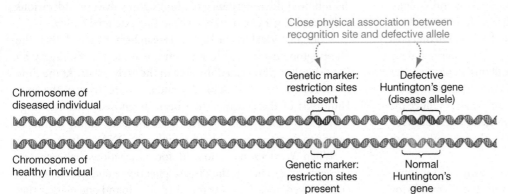

FIGURE 20.10 Genetic Markers Can be Used to Locate Disease Alleles. Because of genetic recombination, genetic markers that are far from the gene of interest are equally likely to be found in both affected and unaffected individuals—there will be no association between particular forms of the marker and either the normal or the disease-causing allele.

Tool	Description	How Used	Illustration
Reverse transcriptase	Enzyme that catalyzes synthesis of a complementary DNA (cDNA) from an RNA template.	Many applications, including making cDNAs used in constructing a genetic library.	cDNA RNA
Restriction endonucleases	Enzymes that cut DNA at a specific sequence—often a palindromic sequence that is six base pairs long.	Allows researchers to cut DNA at specific locations. Cuts in palindromic sites create "sticky ends."	GAATTC CTTAAG
DNA ligase	An enzyme that catalyzes the formation of a phosphodiester bond between nucleotides on the same DNA strand.	Ligates (joins) sequences that were cut with a restriction endonuclease. Gives researchers the ability to splice fragments of DNA together.	GAATTC CTTAAG
Plasmids	Small, extrachromosomal circles of DNA found in many bacteria and in some yeast.	After a target gene is inserted into a plasmid, the recombinant plasmid serves as a vector for transferring the gene into a bacterial or yeast cell, so the gene can be cloned.	GAATTC CTTAAG GAATTC CTTAAG
Taq polymerase	DNA polymerase from the bacterium *Thermus aquaticus*. Catalyzes synthesis of DNA from a primed DNA template; remains stable at 95°C.	Responsible for the "primer extension" step in the polymerase chain reaction. Heat stability allows enzyme to be active even after the 95°C denaturation step of PCR.	
Single nucleotide polymorphisms (SNPs)	Sites in DNA where the identity of a single base pair varies between alleles.	An important type of polymorphic DNA sequence that is useful in creating the genetic maps required for gene hunts.	... CTAAGAAT AATTGATGCG ... ... GATTCTTA TTAACTACGC ... ... CTAAGAAC AATTGATGCG ... ... GATTCTTG TTAACTACGC ... Base pairs vary

A Linkage Study

Once a genetic map containing many genetic markers has been assembled, to find the gene in question, biologists need help from groups of people that include individuals affected by an inherited disease. Recall that the fundamental goal is to find a genetic marker that is almost always inherited along with the disease-causing allele. Biologists call this a linkage study. Gene hunts based on linkage studies are more likely to be successful if large groups are involved. Large sample sizes reduce the possibility that researchers will observe an association between one or more markers and the disease just by chance, rather than because they are closely linked.

Huntington's disease is rare, but Wexler's team was fortunate to find a large, extended family affected with the disease living along the shores of Lake Maracaibo, Venezuela. The researchers followed the inheritance of Huntington's disease and various polymorphic genetic markers within this extended family.

From historical records, the researchers deduced that the Huntington's disease allele was introduced to this family by an English sailor who visited the area in the early 1800s. At the time of the study, over 3000 of his descendants were living in the area. Hundreds of these people had been diagnosed with Huntington's disease. To help in the search for the gene, family members agreed to donate skin or blood samples for DNA analysis.

When Wexler's team looked for associations between the presence or absence of the disease phenotype and genetic markers observed in each family member, they found one marker that

Technique	Description	How Used	Illustration
Recombinant DNA technology	Taking a copy of a gene from one individual and placing it in the genome of a different individual (usually of a different species).	Many applications, including DNA cloning, gene therapy (see Section 20.5), and biotechnology (see Sections 20.1 and 20.6).	Inserted gene
DNA libraries	A collection of all DNA sequences present in a particular source. The library consists of individual DNA fragments that are isolated and inserted into a plasmid or other vector, so they can be cloned.	cDNA libraries allow researchers to catalog the genes being expressed in a particular cell type and to work with coding sequences uninterrupted by introns. Genomic libraries allow researchers to archive all the DNA sequences present in a genome. Libraries can be screened to find a particular target gene.	Stored cDNA
Probing/screening a DNA library	Use of a labeled, known DNA fragment to hybridize (by complementary base pairing) with a collection of unlabeled, unknown fragments.	Allows a researcher to find a particular DNA sequence in a large collection of sequences.	Labeled probe
Polymerase chain reaction (PCR)	A DNA synthesis reaction that uses known primer sequences on either side of a target gene. Reaction is based on many cycles of DNA denaturation, primer annealing, and primer extension.	Produces many identical copies of a target sequence. A shortcut method for DNA cloning.	
Dideoxy sequencing	In vitro DNA synthesis reaction that includes dideoxyribonucleoside triphosphates (ddNTPs) as monomers.	Determining the base sequence of a gene or other section of DNA.	G C C T A A T G
Genetic mapping	Creation of a map showing the relative positions of genes or specific DNA sequences on chromosomes. Done by analyzing the frequency of recombination between sequences.	Many applications, including use of mapped genetic markers in genetic association studies to find unknown genes associated with diseases or other distinctive phenotypes.	Yellow body / White eyes 1.4 / Ruby eyes 6.1

turned out to be especially important. Four different restriction site alleles (*A, B, C,* and *D*) were present at this location in the genome. The key finding was that the *C* form of the marker was almost always found in diseased individuals. Almost certainly, the English sailor who introduced the Huntington's disease allele had the *C* form of the marker in his DNA. The marker and the Huntington's disease gene are so close together that recombination in between them has been extremely rare. No other genetic marker showed this tight association with Huntington's disease.

From the human genetic map that was available at the time, Wexler's team knew that the marker they had identified was on chromosome 4. Eventually the team succeeded in narrowing down the location of the marker, and thus the Huntington's disease gene, to a region about 500,000 base pairs long. Because the haploid human genome contains over 3 billion base pairs, this was a huge step in focusing the search for the gene.

Pinpointing the Defect Once the general location of the Huntington's disease gene was known, biologists looked in that region for exons that encode an mRNA. Then they used dideoxy sequencing to determine the sequence of exons from diseased and normal individuals, compared the data, and pinpointed specific bases that differed between the two groups.

When this analysis was complete, the research team found that individuals with Huntington's disease have an unusually large number of CAG codons near the 5' end of one gene. CAG codes for glutamine. Healthy individuals have 11–25 copies of the CAG codon at that location, while affected individuals have 42 or more copies.

When the Huntington's disease research team confirmed that the increased number of CAG codons was always observed in affected individuals, they concluded that the long search for the Huntington's disease gene was over. They named the newly discovered gene *IT15* and its protein product huntingtin. The huntingtin protein is involved in the development of nerve cells. Only later in life do the mutant forms of the protein cause disease.

What Are the Benefits of Finding a Disease Gene?

How have efforts to find disease genes improved human health and welfare? Has the effort to locate the Huntington's disease gene helped researchers and physicians understand and treat the illness? Biomedical researchers point to three major benefits of disease-gene discovery.

Improved Understanding of the Phenotype
Once a disease gene is found and its sequence is known, researchers can usually figure out why its product causes disease. In the case of *IT15*, autopsies of Huntington's patients had shown that their brains decrease in size, and that the brain tissue contains clumps, or aggregates of the protein now called huntingtin.

Huntingtin aggregates are a direct consequence of the increased number of CAG repeats in the *IT15* gene. Long stretches of glutamine are known to promote protein aggregations. The leading hypothesis to explain Huntington's disease proposes that a gradual buildup of huntingtin aggregates triggers neurons to undergo apoptosis, or programmed cell death.

These results explained why Huntington's disease is pleiotropic (see Chapter 14). Patients suffer from abnormal movements *and* personality changes because neurons throughout the brain are killed. The results also help explain why the disease takes so long to appear, and why it is progressive: The defective huntingtin proteins take time to build up to harmful levels and then continue to increase over time. Finally, understanding the molecular mechanism responsible for the illness explained why the disease allele is dominant. One copy of the defective gene is enough to produce fatal concentrations of huntingtin aggregates.

Therapy
Once *IT15* was found, biologists began a search for new therapies for Huntington's disease by introducing the defective allele into mice, using the types of genetic engineering techniques discussed in Section 20.5. These mice with alleles that have been modified by genetic engineering are called **transgenic** (literally, "across-genes").

Transgenic mice that produce defective versions of the huntingtin protein develop a version of Huntington's disease, exhibiting tremors and abnormal movements, higher-than-normal levels of aggression toward litter and cage mates, and a loss of neurons in the brain. Laboratory animals with disease symptoms that parallel those of a human disease provide an **animal model** of the disease (see **BioSkills 13** in Appendix B).

Animal models are valuable in disease research because they can be used to test potential treatments. For example, research groups are using transgenic mice to test drugs that may prevent or reduce the aggregation of the huntingtin protein.

Genetic Testing
When the Huntington's gene was found and sequenced, biologists used the knowledge to develop a test for the presence of the defective allele. The test consists of obtaining a DNA sample from an individual and using the polymerase chain reaction to amplify the chromosome region that contains the CAG repeats responsible for the disease. If the number of CAG repeats is 35 or less, the individual is not considered at risk. Forty or more repeats results in a positive diagnosis for Huntington's.

Thanks to genetic maps based on SNPs, gene hunts are increasingly successful. Biologists have recently documented alleles associated with a predisposition to developing type I and type II diabetes, breast and ovarian cancer, obesity, coronary heart disease, bipolar disorder, Crohn's disease, and rheumatoid arthritis. Genetic testing for these alleles is now available for both prenatal and adult screens.

Ethical Concerns over Genetic Testing

Knowing the genetic basis of human diseases offers hope, but it also raises difficult ethical issues.

Genetic testing, for example, can create serious moral and legal dilemmas as well as harrowing personal choices. Consider that some people maintain that it is morally wrong to terminate any pregnancy, even if the fetus is certain to be born with a debilitating or fatal genetic disease. Think too about Nancy Wexler's position soon after the discovery of *IT15*: Would you choose to be tested for the defective allele and risk finding out that you were almost certain to develop an incurable disease such as Huntington's?

There are other, equally serious, questions. Should people be tested for any disease that has no cure? Should it be legal for insurance companies to test clients? If so, can companies refuse to insure people at risk for diseases that require expensive treatments? What about employers?

These questions are being debated by political and religious leaders, health-care workers, philosophers, and the public at large. In many cases, we've yet to find answers.

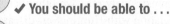

check your understanding

If you understand that . . .
- Genes for particular traits can be located if they are inherited together with a known genetic marker.

✔ **You should be able to . . .**

Describe how you would design a study aimed at identifying alleles associated with alcoholism.

Answers are available in Appendix A.

20.5 Case 5–Severe Immune Disorders: The Potential of Gene Therapy

For physicians who treat inherited disorders such as Huntington's disease, sickle-cell anemia, and cystic fibrosis, the ultimate goal is to cure the disease. This may be done by replacing or augmenting defective copies of the gene with normal alleles. This approach to treatment is called **gene therapy.**

For gene therapy to succeed, two crucial requirements must be met. First, the sequence of the allele associated with the healthy phenotype must be known. Second, a method must be available for introducing this allele into affected individuals and having it be expressed in the correct tissues, in the correct amount, and at the correct time. If the defective allele is dominant, then the introduction step may be even more complicated: In at least some cases, the introduced allele must physically replace or block the expression of the undesirable dominant allele.

How Can Genes Be Introduced into Human Cells?

Section 20.1 reviewed how recombinant DNA sequences are packaged into plasmids and taken up by *E. coli* cells. However, humans and other mammals lack plasmids. How can foreign genes be introduced into human cells?

Researchers have focused on packaging foreign genes into viruses for transport into human cells. These viruses have been engineered so they can deliver genes to cells but cannot replicate to produce new viruses. Viral infection begins when a virus particle attaches to a cell and delivers its genome into the cell (Chapter 36). For some viruses, the viral DNA becomes integrated into a host-cell chromosome. This trait makes it possible to use these viruses as vectors to carry engineered genes into the chromosomes of target cells. Potentially, the genes delivered by the virus could be expressed and produce a product capable of curing a genetic disease.

Vectors used today in gene therapy are often modified retroviruses. Retroviruses have genomes made of single-stranded RNA. When a **retrovirus** infects a human cell, a reverse transcriptase encoded by the virus catalyzes the production of a DNA copy of the virus's RNA genome. Other viral enzymes catalyze the insertion of the viral DNA into a host-cell chromosome. If an RNA version of a human gene can be packaged into a recombinant retrovirus, then the virus will insert a DNA copy of the human gene into a chromosome in a target cell (**FIGURE 20.11**).

Unfortunately, there are problems associated with using retroviruses as agents in gene therapy. For example, if the virus happens to insert the recombinant human gene in a position that disrupts the function of an important gene in the target cell, the consequences may be serious. Despite these risks, modified retroviruses are still among the best vectors currently available for human gene therapy.

Using Gene Therapy to Treat X-Linked Immune Deficiency

In 2000, a research team reported the successful use of gene therapy to treat an illness called severe combined immunodeficiency (SCID). Children who are born with SCID lack a normal immune system and are unable to fight off infections.

The type of SCID the team treated is designated SCID-X1, because it is caused by mutations in a gene on the X chromosome.

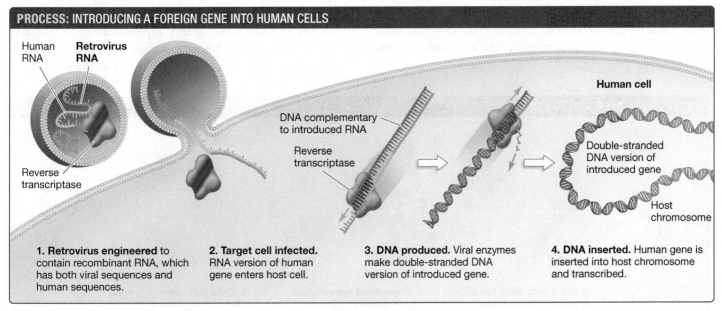

PROCESS: INTRODUCING A FOREIGN GENE INTO HUMAN CELLS

Human RNA / Retrovirus **RNA**

Reverse transcriptase

DNA complementary to introduced RNA

Reverse transcriptase

Human cell

Double-stranded DNA version of introduced gene

Host chromosome

1. Retrovirus engineered to contain recombinant RNA, which has both viral sequences and human sequences.

2. Target cell infected. RNA version of human gene enters host cell.

3. DNA produced. Viral enzymes make double-stranded DNA version of introduced gene.

4. DNA inserted. Human gene is inserted into host chromosome and transcribed.

FIGURE 20.11 Modified Retroviruses Can Insert a Foreign Gene into a Host-Cell Chromosome. (Many details have been omitted for conceptual clarity.)

✔**QUESTION** What happens if the recombinant DNA is inserted in the middle of a gene that is critical to normal cell function?

FIGURE 20.12 A "Bubble Child." Children with SCID cannot fight off bacterial or viral infections. As a result, such children must live in a sterile environment.

The gene codes for a receptor protein necessary for the development of immune system cells, called T cells, that develop in bone marrow (Chapter 51).

Traditionally, physicians have treated SCID-X1 by keeping the patient in a sterile environment, isolated from any direct human contact, until the person could receive a transplant of bone-marrow tissue from a close relative (FIGURE 20.12). In most cases, the T cells that the patient needs are produced by the transplanted bone-marrow cells and allow the individual to live normally. In some cases, though, no suitable donor is available. Could gene therapy cure this disease by furnishing functioning copies of the defective gene?

After extensive testing suggested that their treatment plan was safe and effective, the research team gained approval to treat 10 boys, each less than 1 year old, who had SCID-X1 but no suitable bone-marrow donor. The researchers removed bone marrow from each child, collected the stem cells that produce mature T cells, and infected those cells with an engineered retrovirus that delivered the normal receptor gene. Cells that began to produce normal receptor protein were then isolated and transferred back into the patients (FIGURE 20.13).

Within four months after reinsertion of the transformed marrow cells, nine of the boys had normal levels of functioning T cells. These patients were removed from germ-free isolation rooms and began residing at home, where they grew and developed normally.

Subsequently, however, four of the boys developed a cancer characterized by unchecked growth of T cells. Follow-up analyses of their bone-marrow cells showed that the normal receptor gene had been inserted either near a gene for a transcription factor that triggers T-cell growth, or near a gene for a cyclin that drives the cell cycle (see Chapter 12). The inserted receptor gene provided an enhancer that led to constitutive (constant) expression of the transcription factor or cyclin.

Three of the four boys responded to cancer chemotherapy and are healthy. The fourth did not respond to treatment and died of cancer.

The tenth boy to receive gene therapy never produced T cells. For unknown reasons, his recombinant stem cells failed to function normally when they were transplanted back into his bone marrow. Fortunately, physicians were later able to find a bone-marrow donor whose cells matched the boy's closely enough to make a successful transplant possible.

Ethical Concerns over Gene Therapy

Throughout the history of medicine, efforts to test new drugs, vaccines, and surgical protocols have always carried a risk for the patients involved. Gene therapy experiments are no different. The researchers who run gene therapy trials must explain the risks clearly and make every effort to minimize them.

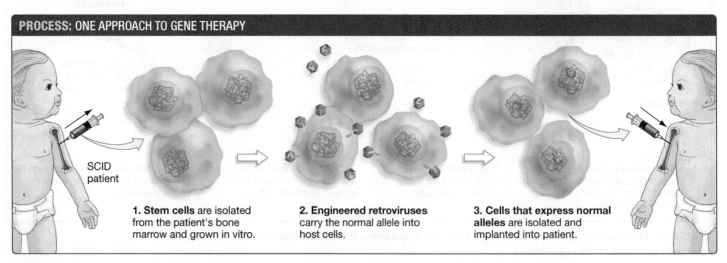

PROCESS: ONE APPROACH TO GENE THERAPY

SCID patient

1. **Stem cells** are isolated from the patient's bone marrow and grown in vitro.

2. **Engineered retroviruses** carry the normal allele into host cells.

3. **Cells that express normal alleles** are isolated and implanted into patient.

FIGURE 20.13 Gene Therapy Can Cure a Genetic Disorder. For gene therapy to work in the case of a loss-of-function allele, copies of a normal allele have to be introduced into a patient's cells and be expressed.

The initial report on the development of cancer in the boys who received gene therapy for SCID-X1 concluded with the following statement: "We have proposed . . . a halt to our trial until further evaluation of the causes of this adverse event and a careful reassessment of the risks and benefits of continuing our study of gene therapy."

When recombinant DNA technology first became possible, many researchers thought they would live to see most or all of the serious inherited diseases caused by single-gene mutations cured by gene therapy. After several decades of rare successes punctuated by tragic failures, that optimism was tempered. In the past few years, however, renewed hope has emerged for gene therapy. Improved vectors have been used successfully to treat two different forms of blindness, a brain disorder, and another type of SCID. Perhaps gene therapy is finally poised to deliver on some of its promises.

20.6 Case 6–The Development of Golden Rice: Biotechnology in Agriculture

Progress in transforming crop plants with recombinant genes has been breathtaking. In 2010, a total 10 percent of all farmland worldwide was planted with transgenic crops—and this number is predicted to show double-digit growth over the foreseeable future. In the same year, roughly 90 percent of soybeans, cotton, and corn grown in the United States were genetically engineered. You almost certainly have eaten food from a genetically modified plant sometime, if not today.

Transgenic crops have been engineered largely to meet three objectives:

1. **Reducing losses from herbivore damage** For instance, researchers have transferred a gene from the bacterium *Bacillus thuringiensis* into corn; the presence of the "Bt toxin" encoded by this gene protects the plant from corn borers and other caterpillar pests.

2. **Reducing competition with weeds** An example is the genetic engineering of soybeans for resistance to an herbicide—a molecule that kills plants—called glyphosate. Soybean fields with the engineered strain can be sprayed with glyphosate to kill weeds without harming the soybeans.

3. **Improving food quality** An important example is engineering soybeans and canola to produce a higher percentage of unsaturated fatty acids relative to saturated fatty acids (Chapter 6). Reducing the amounts of saturated fatty acids helps prevent heart disease, so these crops produce healthier vegetable oils.

How is this work done?

Rice as a Target Crop

Almost half the world's population depends on rice as its staple food. Unfortunately, rice is a poor source of some vitamins and essential nutrients—including vitamin A. Vitamin A deficiency causes blindness in 250,000 Southeast Asian children each year. It also increases susceptibility to diarrhea, respiratory infections, and childhood diseases such as measles.

Humans and other mammals synthesize vitamin A from a precursor molecule known as β-carotene (beta-carotene). β-carotene belongs to a family of orange, yellow, and red plant pigments called the carotenoids (Chapter 10).

Rice plants synthesize β-carotene in their chloroplasts but not in the carbohydrate-rich seed tissue called endosperm—the part of the rice seed that you eat. Could genetic engineering produce a strain of rice plants that synthesizes β-carotene in the endosperm?

Synthesizing β-Carotene in Rice

To explore the possibility of genetically engineering rice, a research team searched for compounds in rice endosperm that could serve as precursors for the synthesis of β-carotene. They found that maturing rice endosperm contains a molecule that could be converted to β-carotene in three enzyme-catalyzed reactions. The researchers reasoned that if genes that encode these enzymes could be introduced into rice plants along with regulatory sequences that would trigger their synthesis in endosperm, it should be possible to create a transgenic strain of rice that would contain β-carotene.

Fortunately, genes that encode two of the required enzymes had already been isolated from daffodils, and the gene for the third enzyme had been purified from a bacterium. These genes had been cloned in bacteria. To each of the coding sequences, biologists added regulatory sequences from an endosperm-specific protein. This segment would promote transcription of the recombinant sequences in endosperm cells.

Next, the three sets of sequences had to be inserted into rice plants. How are foreign genes introduced into plants?

The *Agrobacterium* Transformation System

Agrobacterium tumefaciens is a bacterium that infects plant tissues and triggers formation of tumorlike growths called galls. When researchers looked into how these infections occur, they found that a plasmid carried by the *Agrobacterium* cells, called a **Ti (tumor-inducing) plasmid,** plays a key role (**FIGURE 20.14**, see page 386).

Ti plasmids contain several sets of genes. One set encodes products that allow the bacterium to bind to the cell walls of a host. Another set, referred to as the virulence genes, encodes the proteins required to transfer part of the Ti DNA, called T-DNA (transferred DNA), into the plant cell. The T-DNA then travels to the nucleus and integrates into host-cell chromosomes (Figure 20.14, step 1). T-DNA genes are expressed and their products induce the infected cell to grow and divide. This results in the formation of a gall that houses a growing population of *Agrobacterium* cells (Figure 20.14, step 2).

Researchers soon realized that the Ti plasmid offers an efficient way to introduce recombinant genes into plant cells. Follow-up experiments confirmed that recombinant genes could be

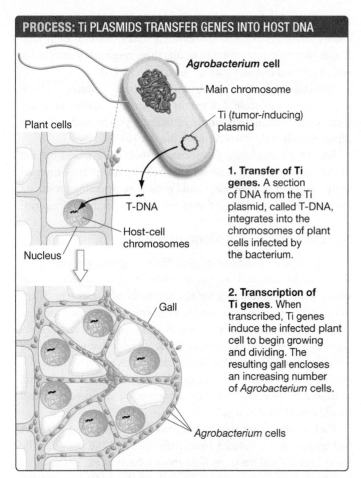

1. Transfer of Ti genes. A section of DNA from the Ti plasmid, called T-DNA, integrates into the chromosomes of plant cells infected by the bacterium.

2. Transcription of Ti genes. When transcribed, Ti genes induce the infected plant cell to begin growing and dividing. The resulting gall encloses an increasing number of *Agrobacterium* cells.

FIGURE 20.14 *Agrobacterium* Infections Introduce Genes into a Plant Host-Cell Chromosome. Ti plasmids of *Agrobacterium* cells induce gall formation—a tumorlike growth.

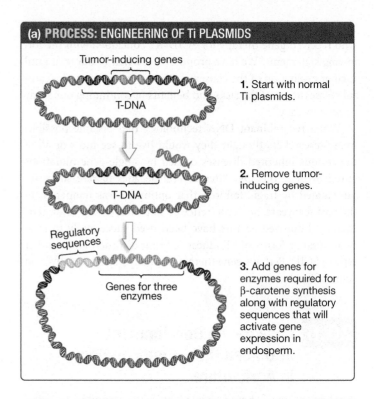

1. Start with normal Ti plasmids.

2. Remove tumor-inducing genes.

3. Add genes for enzymes required for β-carotene synthesis along with regulatory sequences that will activate gene expression in endosperm.

(b) Golden rice (right) is engineered to synthesize β-carotene.

FIGURE 20.15 Constructing a Ti Plasmid to Produce "Golden Rice." Golden rice is a transgenic strain capable of synthesizing ⬚-carotene in the endosperm of its seeds.

added to the T-DNA that integrates into the host chromosome, that the gall-inducing genes could be removed from the T-DNA, and that the resulting sequence is efficiently transferred and expressed in its new host plant.

Using the Ti Plasmid to Produce Golden Rice

To generate a strain of rice that produces all three enzymes needed to synthesize β-carotene in endosperm, the researchers exposed embryos to *Agrobacterium* cells containing genetically modified Ti plasmids (**FIGURE 20.15**). When the transgenic rice plants grew and produced seeds, the researchers found that some rice grains contained so much β-carotene that they were yellow. The biologists called the engineered plants "golden rice."

Follow-up experiments used gene sequences from corn, rather than daffodil, to produce 23 times more β-carotene in rice than the original transformants contained.

Will golden rice help solve a serious public health problem? The answer is not clear. Many environmental groups are strongly opposed to golden rice and any other engineered crops. Regulatory agencies in an array of countries would need to approve the use of golden rice—but there is strong resistance in some nations—and seed would have to be made available to farmers at an affordable price. The barriers to answering the question of whether golden rice can solve health problems are more societal than scientific.

It's important to recognize that each solution offered by genetic engineering introduces new issues to resolve. Biology students and others who are well informed about the techniques and issues involved will be important participants in this debate.

If you understand . . .

20.1 Basic Recombinant DNA Technologies

- In genetic engineering, DNA is added to a cell either to modify the cell's properties or to clone (obtain many identical copies of) the DNA.

- Restriction endonucleases cut DNA at specific locations. The resulting DNA fragments can be inserted into plasmids or other vectors with the help of DNA ligase.

- In many cases, the DNA fragments are inserted into vectors containing regulatory sequences that control expression of inserted genes.

✔ You should be able to explain why a plasmid is needed for gene cloning.

20.2 The Polymerase Chain Reaction

- The polymerase chain reaction (PCR) produces many identical copies of a gene without using cells for cloning.

- PCR depends on having primers that bracket a target stretch of DNA. These allow *Taq* polymerase, a heat-stable DNA polymerase, to amplify a single target DNA sequence to millions of identical copies.

✔ You should be able to list the advantages and disadvantages of cloning in cells versus using PCR to obtain many copies of genes.

20.3 Dideoxy DNA Sequencing

- Dideoxy sequencing determines the sequence of bases in DNA.

- Dideoxy sequencing is based on an in vitro DNA synthesis reaction in which dideoxyribonucleotides stop different DNA replication reactions at different bases in the sequence.

- The DNA fragments of different lengths that are generated by a dideoxy sequencing reaction are separated via gel electrophoresis to determine the sequence of bases.

✔ You should be able to explain how the newly synthesized DNA fragments—when they are lined up by size—can be used to determine the sequence of bases in the template DNA.

20.4 Finding Genes by Mapping

- Genetic maps are often used to find genes associated with phenotypes such as diseases.

- If individuals with a certain phenotype share a particular form of a polymorphic genetic marker (a mapped site with two or more forms in DNA that is unrelated to the phenotype), the gene responsible for the phenotype is likely to be near that marker.

- Once the general area of a gene is known, DNA in the region can be sequenced to determine exactly where the gene is located.

✔ You should be able to explain why genetic markers that are not polymorphic (come in only one form) are not useful in gene hunts.

20.5 The Potential of Gene Therapy

- Researchers are working to cure genetic diseases by gene therapy. This involves inserting normal copies of the defective gene into patients.

- In humans, genes used for gene therapy are often introduced using modified viruses.

- Gene therapy has faced many difficulties but recently has met with some notable successes.

✔ You should be able to describe what makes retroviruses well suited for gene therapy and what the concerns are about their use.

20.6 Biotechnology in Agriculture

- Many important crop plants are genetically engineered for traits that include pest and herbicide resistance, and improved food quality.

- Genes are often introduced into crops by infecting plant cells with bacteria that integrate their plasmid genes into the host-plant genome. By adding recombinant genes to these plasmids, researchers have been able to introduce genes that improve crops.

✔ You should be able to explain how genes are inserted into plants.

(MB) **MasteringBiology**

1. MasteringBiology Assignments

Tutorials and Activities Analyzing DNA Fragments Using Gel Electrophoresis; Cloning a Gene in Bacteria; Gel Electrophoresis of DNA; Making Decisions about DNA Technology: Golden Rice; Producing Human Growth Hormone; Restriction Enzymes; Restriction Enzymes, Recombinant DNA, and Gene Cloning; The Polymerase Chain Reaction

Questions Reading Quizzes, Blue-Thread Questions, Test Bank

2. eText Read your book online, search, take notes, highlight text, and more.

3. The Study Area Practice Test, Cumulative Test, BioFlix® 3-D Animations, Videos, Activities, Audio Glossary, Word Study Tools, Art

You should be able to . . .

1. What do restriction endonucleases do?

2. What is a plasmid?
   a. an organelle found in many bacteria and certain eukaryotes
   b. a circular DNA molecule that often replicates independently of the main chromosome(s)
   c. a type of virus that has a DNA genome and that infects certain types of human cells, including lung and respiratory tract tissue
   d. a type of virus that has an RNA genome, codes for reverse transcriptase, and inserts a cDNA copy of its genome into host cells

3. When present in a DNA synthesis reaction mixture, a ddNTP molecule is added to the growing chain of DNA. No further nucleotides can be added afterward. Why?

4. Once the gene that causes Huntington's disease was found, researchers introduced the defective allele into mice to create an animal model of the disease. Why was this model valuable?
   a. It allowed the testing of potential drug therapies without endangering human patients.
   b. It allowed the study of how the gene is regulated.
   c. It allowed the production of large quantities of the huntingtin protein.
   d. It allowed the study of how the gene was transmitted from parents to offspring.

5. To begin the hunt for the human growth hormone gene, researchers created a cDNA library from cells in the pituitary gland. What did this library contain?
   a. only the sequence encoding growth hormone
   b. DNA versions of all the mRNAs in the pituitary-gland cells
   c. all the coding sequences in the human genome, but no introns
   d. all the coding sequences in the human genome, including introns

6. What does it mean to say that a genetic marker and a disease gene are closely linked?
   a. The marker lies within the coding region for the disease gene.
   b. The sequence of the marker and the sequence of the disease gene are extremely similar.
   c. The marker and the disease gene are on different chromosomes.
   d. The marker and the disease gene are in close physical proximity and tend to be inherited together.

7. Explain how restriction endonucleases and DNA ligase are used to insert foreign genes into plasmids and create recombinant DNA. Make a drawing that shows why sticky ends are sticky and that identifies the location where DNA ligase catalyzes a key reaction.

8. **QUANTITATIVE** If a particular sequence of DNA were amplified using 25 PCR cycles, then the amount of this DNA would be predicted to increase by _____ -fold.

9. What is a cDNA library? Would you expect the cDNA library from a human muscle cell to be different from the cDNA library from a human nerve cell in the same individual? Explain why or why not.

10. What are genetic markers, and how are they used to create a genetic map?

11. Researchers added regulatory sequences from an endosperm-specific gene to the Ti plasmids used in creating golden rice. This was important to
    a. allow inserted genes to integrate into the plant genome.
    b. increase the endosperm growth rate.
    c. prevent the introduced plasmid from harming the endosperm.
    d. promote expression of introduced genes in the rice grain.

12. Compare and contrast PCR with the DNA synthesis that occurs in cells (see Chapter 15).

13. Suppose you had a large amount of sequence data, similar to the data that Nancy Wexler's team had in the region of the Huntington's disease gene, and that you knew that mRNAs of the species being studied typically contain protein-coding regions about 1500 bases long. How would you use the genetic code (see Chapter 16) and information on the structure of promoters (see Chapters 17 and 18) to find the precise location of one or more genes in your sequence?

14. Modifying germ-line or somatic cells for gene therapy involves the same ethical concerns. True or false?

15. Describe similarities between how researchers screen a DNA library and how they perform a genetic screen—for example, for mutant *E. coli* cells that cannot metabolize lactose (see Chapter 18).

16. A friend of yours is doing a series of PCRs and comes to you for advice. She purchased two sets of primers, hoping that one set would amplify the template sequence shown here. (The dashed lines in the template sequence stand for a long sequence of unspecified bases.) Neither of the primer pairs produced any product DNA, however.

	Primer a		Primer b
Primer Pair 1:	5' CAAGTCC 3'	&	5' GCTGGAC 3'
Primer Pair 2:	5' GGACTTG 3'	&	5' GTCCAGC 3'
Template:	5' ATTCGGACTTG---GTCCAGCTAGAGG 3'		
	3' TAAGCCTGAAC---CAGGTCGATCTCC 5'		

a. Explain why each primer pair didn't work. Indicate whether both primers are at fault, or just one of them.
b. Your friend doesn't want to buy new primers. She asks you whether she can salvage this experiment. What do you tell your friend to do?

21 Genomics and Beyond

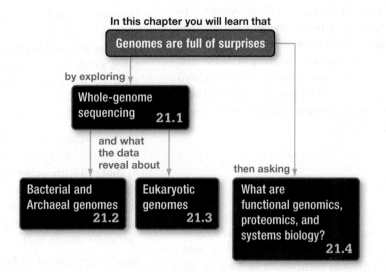

In this chapter you will learn that

Genomes are full of surprises

by exploring

Whole-genome sequencing 21.1

and what the data reveal about

Bacterial and Archaeal genomes 21.2

Eukaryotic genomes 21.3

then asking

What are functional genomics, proteomics, and systems biology? 21.4

A high-throughput robotic genome sequencer. Advances in DNA sequencing technologies are opening new questions to biologists and deepening the understanding of life and its evolution.

The first data sets describing the complete DNA sequence, or **genome,** of humans were published in February 2001. These papers were immediately hailed as a landmark in the history of science. In just 50 years, biologists had gone from not understanding the molecular nature of the gene to knowing the molecular makeup of every gene present in our species.

Years later, knowledge continues to stream from the multinational effort called the **Human Genome Project** and its many spinoffs. It's important to recognize, though, that research on *Homo sapiens* is part of a much larger, ongoing effort to gain insights from the genome sequences of an array of other eukaryotes, bacteria, and archaea. The pace of progress in this field is nothing short of explosive.

The effort to sequence, interpret, and compare whole genomes is **genomics.** While whole-genome sequencing supplies a list of the genes present in an organism, **functional genomics**

✔ When you see this checkmark, stop and test yourself. Answers are available in Appendix A.

answers questions about the functioning of that genome, such as what particular genes do and how they're expressed.

Genomics has spawned a host of related fields. These are often referred to as the *–omics*—proteomics, metabolomics, and transcriptomics—but also include emerging areas like systems biology. Like genomics, these fields take a holistic approach to learning about the entire set of proteins, metabolites, or RNA transcripts present in a given cell or tissue type at a given time.

As an introductory biology student, you are part of the first generation trained in the genome era. Genomics and the related fields it has generated are revolutionizing biological science. They will almost certainly be an important part of your personal and professional life. Let's delve in.

21.1 Whole-Genome Sequencing

Genomics has moved to the cutting edge of research in biology, largely because of technological advances. These began with the development of dideoxy sequencing and progressed to next-generation sequencing techniques (introduced in Chapter 20). These technical breakthroughs have enabled obtaining immense quantities of high-quality sequence data rapidly and at low cost.

As technology continues to become faster and less expensive, the pace of genome sequencing accelerates. The result is that an almost mind-boggling number of sequences of genes and whole genomes are now being generated. As this book goes to press, the primary international repository for DNA sequence data contained over 425 *billion* nucleotides. By way of comparison, a haploid human genome contains about 3 billion nucleotides on each strand of the DNA double helix.

FIGURE 21.1 gives a visual sense of the growth in sequence data by plotting the number of nucleotides, in billions, versus time. There are three large international online repositories for

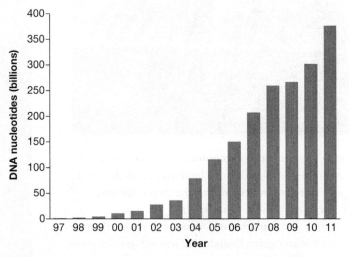

FIGURE 21.1 The Total Number of Bases Sequenced Is Growing Rapidly. Data from the EMBL Nucleotide Sequence Database (also known as EMBL-Bank).

DATA: European Nucleotide Archive/EMBL-Bank Release Notes. Release 110, December 2011. www.ebi.ac.uk/embl/.

sequence data; the numbers plotted here were compiled from one of them. Over 15 years, this database has grown at a staggering average rate of about 46 percent per year.

How Are Complete Genomes Sequenced?

Genomes range in size from about a half million base pairs to several billion. But even under the best conditions, a single dideoxy sequencing reaction can analyze only about 1000 nucleotides. Reads from next-generation sequencing are even shorter. How do investigators break a genome into sequencing-sized pieces and then figure out how the thousands or millions of pieces go back together?

Shotgun Sequencing When researchers first set out to sequence the genome of a species, they usually rely on an approach known as **shotgun sequencing.** In shotgun sequencing, a genome is broken up into a set of overlapping fragments that are small enough to be sequenced completely. The regions of overlap are then used as guides for putting the sequenced fragments back into the correct order (**FIGURE 21.2**).

Step 1 Application of high-frequency sound waves, or sonication, is used to break a genome randomly into pieces about 160 kilobases (kb) long (1 kb = 1000 bases).

Step 2 Each 160-kb piece is inserted into a type of cloning vector called a **bacterial artificial chromosome (BAC).** BACs are able to replicate large segments of DNA. Each BAC is then inserted into a different *Escherichia coli* cell (using techniques introduced in Chapter 20), creating a **BAC library.** A BAC library is a genomic library: a set of all the DNA sequences in a particular genome, split into small segments and inserted into cloning vectors. By allowing each cell to grow into a colony, researchers can isolate large numbers of each 160-kb fragment.

Step 3 After many copies of each 160-kb fragment have been produced, each cloned DNA is again broken into fragments—but this time, into segments about 1 kb long.

Step 4 These small fragments are then inserted into plasmids and placed inside bacterial cells. (Note that by this point the genome has been broken down twice, into increasingly manageable pieces: 160-kb fragments in BACs and 1-kb segments in plasmids.) The plasmids are copied many times as each bacterial cell grows into a large population. Cloned 1-kb fragments are then available for sequencing reactions.

Step 5 Next, the cloned 1-kb fragments from each 160-kb BAC clone are sequenced, and computer programs analyze regions where the ends of different 1-kb segments overlap. Overlaps occur because many copies were made of each 160-kb segment, and these copies were fragmented randomly by sonication.

Step 6 A computer program searches for overlaps between 1-kb fragments from a single BAC clone and stitches the sequences together until a continuous sequence across the BAC has been reconstructed.

Step 7 The ends of the reconstructed BACs are analyzed in a similar way. The goal is to link sequences from each 160-kb

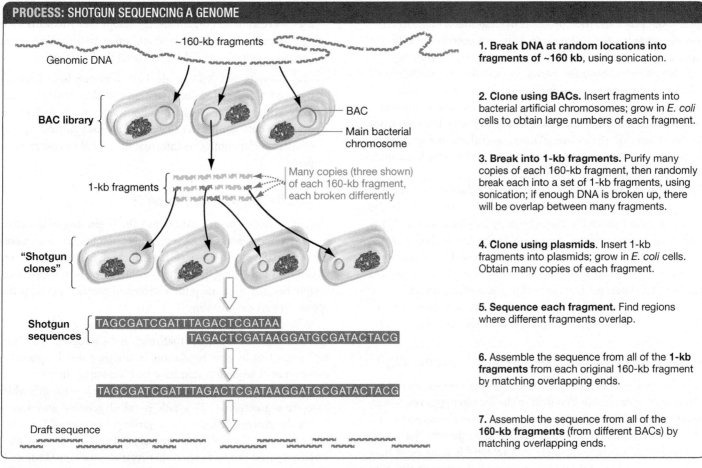

~160-kb fragments

Genomic DNA

BAC library

BAC

Main bacterial chromosome

1-kb fragments

Many copies (three shown) of each 160-kb fragment, each broken differently

"Shotgun clones"

Shotgun sequences

TAGCGATCGATTTAGACTCGATAA
TAGACTCGATAAGGATGCGATACTACG

TAGCGATCGATTTAGACTCGATAAGGATGCGATACTACG

Draft sequence

1. **Break DNA at random locations into fragments of ~160 kb**, using sonication.

2. **Clone using BACs.** Insert fragments into bacterial artificial chromosomes; grow in *E. coli* cells to obtain large numbers of each fragment.

3. **Break into 1-kb fragments.** Purify many copies of each 160-kb fragment, then randomly break each into a set of 1-kb fragments, using sonication; if enough DNA is broken up, there will be overlap between many fragments.

4. **Clone using plasmids.** Insert 1-kb fragments into plasmids; grow in *E. coli* cells. Obtain many copies of each fragment.

5. **Sequence each fragment.** Find regions where different fragments overlap.

6. Assemble the sequence from all of the **1-kb fragments** from each original 160-kb fragment by matching overlapping ends.

7. Assemble the sequence from all of the **160-kb fragments** (from different BACs) by matching overlapping ends.

FIGURE 21.2 Shotgun Sequencing Breaks Large Genomes into Many Short Segments.

✔ **QUESTION** A shotgun blast produces many small, scattered pieces of shot. Why is "shotgun" an appropriate way to describe this sequencing strategy?

segment based on regions of overlap until the sequence of an entire chromosome is assembled.

In essence, the shotgun strategy consists of breaking a genome into many small fragments, sequencing each fragment, and then putting the sequence data back in the correct order.

✔ If you understand shotgun sequencing, you should be able to explain why it is essential for fragments to have regions of overlap.

The Impact of Next-Generation Sequencing Today, there are approaches that are much faster and cheaper than dideoxy sequencing (see Chapter 20). These next-generation methods are massively parallel, meaning that millions of DNA fragments can be sequenced simultaneously in one run of a sequencing machine. The downside of these methods is that they produce sequence reads of only about 50–200 nucleotides, depending on the particular technology. This is in contrast to the roughly 1000 nucleotides obtained by dideoxy sequencing. For piecing together a whole genome, especially one with many repetitive sequences such as those present in most eukaryotes, these read lengths are too short.

But if a complete genome is already available for the organism, next-generation sequencing offers a remarkably quick and inexpensive way to sequence the entire genome from a particular individual—with all the tiny fragments arranged in the correct order by being compared with the "master genome." This sequencing power has opened up possibilities that were unimaginable even a few years ago.

Consider what was involved in sequencing the human genome. The Human Genome Project required more than 15 years and about $3 billion to assemble the first human genome sequence. In 2011, ten years after the first human genome sequence was available, more than 2700 individual human genomes had been sequenced at a cost as low as $5000 per genome. This is a 2700-fold increase in output and a 600,000-fold drop in price.

What's important is not only the numbers, but what can be done with the information. One illustration is an offshoot of the Human Genome Project, the 1000 Genomes Project. This effort has already sequenced the genomes of over 1000 people selected from diverse populations spread across the planet. An important goal is to assess the genetic similarities and differences among people in order to understand our own evolution. Many similarly ambitious and exciting genomics projects are under way.

Bioinformatics How do researchers piece together the millions of fragments produced by shotgun sequencing? Once a complete genome is assembled, how are the raw sequence data and information about genes and their products made available to the international community of researchers? How can genomes of different species be compared to learn about evolutionary relationships?

The answer is **bioinformatics**—a field that fuses mathematics, computer science, and biology in an effort to manage and analyze sequence data. Researchers in bioinformatics have created searchable databases. These vast repositories hold sequence information that allows investigators to evaluate the similarities between newly discovered genes and genes that have been studied previously in the same or other species.

The World Wide Web has put sequence databases at the fingertips of anyone with an Internet connection. For example, the U.S. National Center for Biotechnology Information (NCBI) is only a click away on your computer. At this free and publicly accessible site, you can search billions of nucleotides by using programs such as BLAST, which can quickly find DNA sequences related to any new gene uncovered in a genomics project.

The vast quantity of data generated by genome sequencing centers makes bioinformatics an indispensable element of genomics.

Which Genomes Are Being Sequenced, and Why?

The first genome to be sequenced from an organism—not a virus—came from a bacterium that lives in the human upper respiratory tract. *Haemophilus influenzae* has one circular chromosome and a total of 1.8 million base pairs of DNA. Its genome was small enough to sequence completely in a reasonable amount of time and within a reasonable budget, given the technology available in the early 1990s. *H. influenzae* was an important research subject because it causes earaches and respiratory tract infections in children. One strain is also capable of infecting the membranes surrounding the brain and spinal cord, causing meningitis.

Publication of the *H. influenzae* genome in 1995 was quickly followed by publication of complete genomes sequenced from an assortment of bacteria and archaea. Sequencing of the first eukaryotic genome, from the yeast *Saccharomyces cerevisiae*, was finished in 1996. Today, the genomes of more than 2000 species from all domains of life have been sequenced. That number is certain to continue climbing in the coming years.

Most of the organisms that have been selected for whole-genome sequencing have interesting biological properties, represent a particular branch of life informative for evolutionary investigations, or cause disease. For example:

- Genomes of bacteria and archaea from hot environments have been sequenced in the hopes of discovering enzymes useful for high-temperature industrial applications.

- A set of more than 50 genomes of diverse bacteria and archaea was sequenced to explore patterns of evolution that are impossible to study by other means.

- Genomes such as those of rice and maize (corn) have been sequenced for crop improvement applications.

- The fruit fly *Drosophila melanogaster*, the roundworm *Caenorhabditis elegans*, the house mouse *Mus musculus*, and the mustard plant *Arabidopsis thaliana* were analyzed because they serve as model organisms in biology (see **BioSkills 13** in Appendix B). Data from these and other well-studied organisms have helped researchers interpret the human genome.

- The platypus and African elephant genomes have been sequenced to reveal evolutionary relationships among mammals. Although the elephant genomes are not complete, the available data confirmed that there are two distinct species of African elephant. This information is vital to conservation plans.

Which Sequences Are Genes?

Obtaining raw sequence data is just the beginning of the effort to understand a genome. As researchers point out, raw sequence data are analogous to the parts list for a house. The list, however, would read something like "windowwabeborogovestaircasedoorjubjub" because it has no punctuation and contains portions that appear to have no meaning.

Where do the genes for "window," "staircase," and "door" start and end? Are the segments that read "wabeborogove" and "jubjub" important in gene regulation, or are they simply spacers or other types of sequences that have no function at all?

The most basic task in interpreting a genome is to identify which bases constitute genes. This task is called **genome annotation.** Recall the current definition of a gene: A segment of DNA that codes for a functional RNA or protein product—or a series of alternatively spliced products—and that regulates their production. In bacteria and archaea, identifying genes is relatively straightforward. The task is much more difficult in eukaryotes.

Identifying Genes in Bacterial and Archaeal Genomes To interpret bacterial and archaeal genomes, biologists begin with computer programs that scan the sequence of a genome in both directions. These programs identify each reading frame that is possible on the two strands of the DNA. Recall that a reading frame is a continuous sequence of non-overlapping codons (see Chapter 16).

Codons consist of three bases, so three reading frames are possible on each DNA strand, for a total of six possible reading frames (**FIGURE 21.3**). Because randomly generated sequences contain a stop codon at about 1 in every 20 codons on average, a long stretch of codons that lacks a stop codon is a good indication of a protein-coding sequence. The computer programs draw attention to any "gene-sized" stretches of sequence that lack an internal stop codon and are flanked by a stop codon and a start codon. Because polypeptides range in size from a few dozen amino acids to many hundreds of amino acids, gene-sized stretches of sequence range from several hundred bases to thousands of bases. In addition, the computer programs look for sequences typical of promoters, ribosome binding sites, or other regulatory sites. DNA segments that are identified in this way are called **open reading frames,** or **ORFs.**

Once an ORF is found, a computer program compares its sequence with the sequences of known genes from another species.

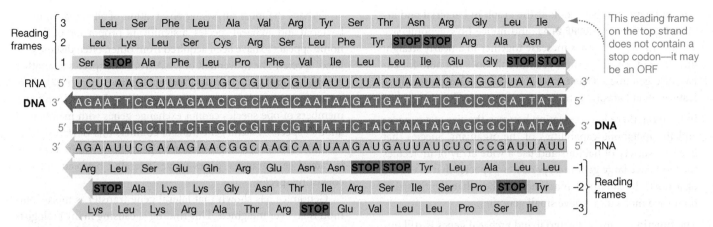

FIGURE 21.3 **Open Reading Frames Can Identify Genes.** Computer programs use the genetic code to translate the three possible reading frames on each strand of DNA. A long stretch of codons that lacks a stop codon may be an open reading frame (ORF) and identify a gene.

✔QUESTION To predict the mRNA codons that would be produced by a particular reading frame, a computer analyzes the DNA in the 3′-to-5′ direction. Why?

If the ORF is unlike any gene that has so far been described in any species, further research is required before it can actually be considered a gene. In contrast, if an ORF shares a significant amount of sequence with a known gene from another species, then it is very likely to be a gene.

Similarities between genes in different species are usually due to **homology.** If genes are homologous, it means they are similar because they are related by descent from a common ancestor. Homologous genes have similar base sequences and frequently the same or a similar function. For example, consider the genes that code for enzymes involved in repairing mismatches in DNA (introduced in Chapter 15). The mismatch-repair genes in *E. coli*, yeast, and humans are similar in DNA sequence and function. To explain this similarity, biologists hypothesize that the common ancestor of all cells living today had mismatch-repair genes—thus, the descendants of this ancestral species also have versions of these genes.

Identifying Genes in Eukaryotic Genomes Mining eukaryotic sequence data for protein-coding genes is complicated. For example, because coding regions are broken up by introns, it is not possible to scan for long ORFs. Instead, researchers combine an array of approaches.

Perhaps the most productive gene-finding strategy has been to isolate mRNAs from cells, use reverse transcriptase to produce a cDNA version of each mRNA, and sequence a portion of the resulting molecule to produce an **expressed sequence tag,** or **EST.** ESTs represent protein-coding genes. To locate the gene, researchers use the EST to find the matching sequence in genomic DNA.

Although ESTs and many other gene-finding strategies have been fruitful, it will likely be many years before biologists are convinced they have identified all the genes in even a single eukaryotic genome. As gene identification efforts continue, researchers are analyzing the data and making some remarkable discoveries. Let's first consider what genome sequencing has revealed about the nature of bacterial and archaeal genomes and then move on to eukaryotes. Is the effort to sequence whole genomes paying off?

21.2 Bacterial and Archaeal Genomes

Biologists have obtained the genome sequences of thousands of distinct bacterial and archaeal species or strains. For example, researchers have sequenced the genome of a laboratory population of *Escherichia coli*—derived from the harmless strain that lives in your gut—as well as the genome of a form that causes severe disease in humans. As a result, researchers can identify genes that differ between these strains and begin experiments to learn what accounts for the infectious properties of some strains.

What general observations have biologists been able to make about the nature of all these bacterial and archaeal genomes?

The Natural History of Prokaryotic Genomes

In a sense, biologists who are working in genomics can be compared to the naturalists of the eighteenth and nineteenth centuries. These early biologists explored the globe, collecting the plants and animals they encountered. Their goals were to describe what existed and identify any patterns. Similarly, the first task of a genome sequencer is to catalog what is in a genome—specifically, the number, type, and organization of genes—and then look for patterns within and between different genomes. Here are some principles that have emerged from analysis of prokaryotic genomes:

- Bacterial and archaeal genomes are compact. They have uninterrupted coding sequences, little space between genes, extensive use of operons, and relatively few regulatory sequences. This structure leads to a linear relationship between genome size and gene number. Look at the graph of bacterial and ar-chaeal genomes in **FIGURE 21.4a**, and notice how genome size and the number of genes increase together in a nearly straight line. In contrast, this simple relationship does not hold for eu-karyotic genomes (**FIGURE 21.4b**). Section 21.3 explores these features of eukaryotic genome organization in detail.

- In bacteria, there is a correlation between the size of a genome and the metabolic capabilities of the organism. Species that live in a variety of habitats and use a wide array of molecules for food have large genomes; parasites—species that make use of a host's biochemical machinery rather than synthesizing their own molecules—have small genomes.

- The function of many bacterial and archaeal genes is still un-known. Across a wide range of species, a function cannot yet be assigned to 15 to 30 percent of genes.

- Most of the genes found in one species are not shared widely with others. In a study that sampled the genomes of diverse prokaryotes, every time a new genome was sequenced, more than 1000 new genes were discovered. Only a small set of genes involved in processes such as DNA replication, tran-scription, and translation are similar across a wide range of bacteria or archaea.

- The content of genomes varies widely even within species. For example, sequencing of 17 different *E. coli* strains revealed a total of about 13,000 different genes. The genome of any one strain has only about 4400 genes, and roughly 2200 of these are shared by all strains. The remaining genes in each genome are found only in some strains but not in others.

- Prokaryotic genomes are frequently rearranged during evolu-tion. Even closely related species show little similarity in gene order.

Perhaps the most surprising observation of all is that in many bacterial and archaeal species, a significant proportion of the ge-nome appears to have been acquired from other, often distantly re-lated, species. The movement of DNA from one species to another is called **lateral gene transfer**. As you'll learn (Chapter 27), there are many ways to define a species. But in all traditional definitions, members of one species cannot exchange genes with members of another species. Lateral gene transfer counters this view: Instead of moving vertically from generation to generation within a species, in lateral gene transfer, genes move "laterally" between different coexisting species.

Genomics has shown that lateral gene transfer is more com-mon than ever imagined. This finding is causing many biologists to wonder if conventional evolutionary trees capture the way bacteria and archaea have evolved.

Lateral Gene Transfer in Bacteria and Archaea

The extent of lateral gene transfer is still debated, but genomic data indicate that all bacterial and archaeal species have experi-enced lateral gene transfer. Lateral gene transfer is a major force in the evolution of bacteria and archaea.

One illustration is the bacterium *Thermotoga maritima*. This species thrives in high-temperature environments near deep-sea vents. Almost 25 percent of the genes in this species are closely related to genes found in archaea that live in the same habitats. The archaea-like genes occur in well-defined clusters within the *T. maritima* genome. These observations support the hypothesis that these sequences were transferred in large pieces from an ar-chaean to a bacterium—organisms in two different domains of life.

How are laterally transferred genes identified? Biologists pri-marily use two criteria: (**1**) A gene is much more similar to genes in distantly related species than to those in closely related species,

(a) In bacteria (○) and archaea (●), genome size and number of genes increase together in a linear relationship.

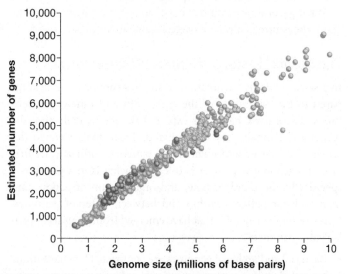

(b) The same relationship does not hold true for eukaryotes (●).

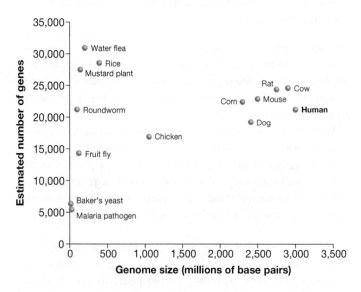

FIGURE 21.4 Relationship Between Genome Size and Gene Number.

DATA: (a) Hou, Y., and S. Lin. 2009. *PLoS ONE* 4(9): e6978, Supplemental Table S1. (b) KEGG: Kyoto Encyclopedia of Genes and Genomes, KEGG Organisms: Complete Genomes. www.genome.jp/kegg/.

and (2) the proportion of G-C base pairs to A-T base pairs in a particular gene or series of genes is markedly different from the base composition of the rest of the genome. This second criterion works because the proportion of G-C base pairs in a genome is characteristic of the particular genus or species.

How can genes move from one species to another? In some cases, plasmids are responsible. For example, most of the genes that are responsible for conferring resistance to antibiotics are found on plasmids. Researchers have documented the transfer of plasmid-borne antibiotic-resistance genes between distantly related bacteria. In many cases of lateral gene transfer, genes from plasmids become integrated into the main chromosome of a bacterium through genetic recombination.

Lateral gene transfer may also occur by transformation—when bacteria and archaea take up raw pieces of DNA from the environment—and by viruses that pick up DNA from one cell and transfer it to another cell.

There is no doubt that lateral gene transfer occurs even between distantly related organisms. What is still debated, however, is how much this shakes the tree of life. If lateral gene transfer is rare, then evolutionary paths in the bacteria and archaea form a set of branches that begin at common ancestors and spread out to descendants. If lateral gene transfer is as widespread as some biologists believe, then evolutionary paths must form a complex interconnected network that links species in a web of vertical and lateral gene transfers. These alternative views are shown in **FIGURE 21.5**.

In light of new genomics findings, will a tree of life stand for bacteria and archaea? Or are the evolutionary relationships in these domains of life best viewed as a web? Stay tuned.

Metagenomics

Biologists continue to gain important insights from sequencing the genomes of individual species and strains. But more recently, some research groups have taken a different approach: cataloging all the genes present in a community of bacteria and archaea. This type of research is called **metagenomics,** or **environmental sequencing.** The subject of these studies is genes—not organisms.

The first environmental sequencing study was conducted in the Sargasso Sea, near the Caribbean island of Bermuda. Researchers chose the spot because it is extremely nutrient poor and species poor—a desert in the ocean. This is a common strategy

in biological science: Start by studying a simple system, then go on to more complex situations. To inventory the complete array of bacterial genes present, the research group collected cells from different water depths and locations, isolated DNA from the samples, and sequenced the DNA.

After analyzing over 1 billion nucleotides, the team concluded that at least 1800 bacterial species were present, of which 148 were previously undiscovered. They also identified more than 1.2 million genes that had never before been characterized. These genes included over 780 sequences that code for proteins similar to the rhodopsin found in the cells of your retina—a molecule that is absorbing the light entering your eye right now. Follow-up work suggests that most of the Sargasso Sea rhodopsin-like molecules are also absorbing light, and that bacterial cells use the energy of the light to pump protons across their plasma membranes—creating a chemiosmotic gradient that can synthesize ATP (see Chapter 9).

Many metagenomics studies are going on today, including one that examined microbes of the human gut (Chapter 29). All these investigations are providing new insights about the living world, from how rhodopsin-like proteins help bacteria thrive in a desert to how your lunch is being digested.

check your understanding

If you understand that . . .
- The size of bacterial and archaeal genomes correlates with the cell's metabolic capabilities.
- Lateral gene transfer—movement of DNA from one species to another—is extensive in prokaryotes.
- Environmental sequencing catalogs all the genes found in a particular habitat.

✔ **You should be able to . . .**
1. Explain why it is logical to observe that parasitic bacteria have small genomes.
2. Explain the logic behind claiming that a gene's similarity to a gene in a distantly related species, and dissimilarity to the same gene in closely related species, is evidence for lateral gene transfer.

Answers are available in Appendix A.

21.3 Eukaryotic Genomes

DNA sequencing has revealed some extraordinary features of eukaryotic genome organization. Genome size varies widely, but the number of genes is much more similar. For example, the genomes shown in Figure 21.4b vary roughly 250-fold in size (from 12 to 3000 million base pairs) but less than sixfold in the number of genes (from 5400 to 30,900). How can gene number be so similar among organisms with vastly different genome sizes and that range in complexity from single-celled parasites to large multicellular plants and animals?

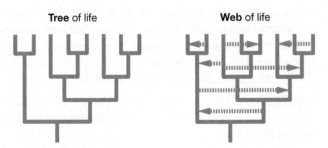

FIGURE 21.5 Tree of Life and Web of Life Views of Evolution. The broken horizontal arrows indicate lateral gene transfer events.

Before exploring possible answers, let's consider two daunting challenges in sequencing eukaryotic genomes. The first is size. The largest bacterial genome, that of *Sorangium cellulosum,* is slightly more than 13 million base pairs. However, as Figure 21.4b shows, even modest-sized eukaryotic genomes are much larger. The 3-billion-base-pair human genome dwarfs those of bacteria but is miniscule compared with the genome of the Japanese flower *Paris japonica.* This plant's genome contains 149 billion base pairs of DNA—that's 50 times the size of the human genome!

The second challenge in sequencing eukaryotic genes is coping with sequences that are repeated many times. Many eukaryotic genomes are dominated by repeated DNA sequences that occur between genes or inside introns and do not code for products used by the organism. These repeated sequences greatly complicate the work of aligning and interpreting sequence data. They also explain some of the paradox of the immense variation in eukaryotic genome sizes. If repeated sequences don't code for products needed by cells, what do they do?

Transposable Elements and Other Repeated Sequences

In many eukaryotes, the exons and regulatory sequences associated with genes make up a relatively small percentage of the genome. Over 90 percent of a bacterial or archaeal genome consists of genes, but about 50 percent of an average eukaryotic genome consists of repeated sequences that do not code for a product used by the cell.

When repeated sequences were discovered, they were initially considered "junk DNA" that was nonfunctional and probably unimportant and uninteresting. But subsequent work has shown that many of the repeated sequences observed in eukaryotes are actually derived from sequences known as transposable elements.

Transposable elements are segments of DNA that are capable of being inserted into new locations, or transposing, in a genome. They were first discovered in corn by Barbara McClintock and later shown to be present in organisms from every domain of life. Transposable elements behave similarly to some viruses that insert into the genome. In contrast to viruses, however, transposable elements seldom leave their host cell—instead, they make copies of themselves that become inserted in new locations. Transposable elements are passed from mother to daughter cell and from parents to offspring, generation after generation, because they are part of the genome.

A transposable element is an example of what biologists call selfish DNA: a DNA sequence that has invaded a host and persists and reproduces using the resources of the host. Selfish or not, transposable elements play a big role in a species as they move from place to place and cause mutation. Like any mutation, a transposable element insertion into a new site in the genome can have negative, neutral, or positive effects on fitness. Transposable elements are a significant part of almost all cellular genomes and play a major role in evolution. Transposable elements have many effects, disrupting the coding sequence of genes, changing patterns of gene regulation, and promoting gene

duplication and loss. They are genome invaders that also shape the structure and function of genomes in profound ways.

How Do Transposable Elements Work? Transposable elements come in a wide variety of types and spread through genomes in a variety of ways. Different organisms—*E. coli*, fruit flies, yeast, and humans, for example—contain distinct types of transposable elements. Bacterial and archaeal genomes, however, have far fewer transposable elements compared with most eukaryotes. This observation has inspired the hypothesis that bacteria and archaea either have efficient means of removing parasitic sequences or can somehow thwart insertion events.

As an example of how these selfish DNA sequences work, consider a well-studied type of transposable element called a **long interspersed nuclear element (LINE).** LINEs are found in humans and other animals. Because LINEs have a reverse transcriptase like retroviruses (introduced in Chapter 20), biologists hypothesize that they are derived from them evolutionarily. Your genome contains nearly 1 million LINEs, each between 1000 and 5000 bases long. Transposable elements of different types make up over 45 percent of the human genome and 85 percent of the corn (maize) genome. **FIGURE 21.6** illustrates the steps that allow an active LINE to transpose.

Most of the LINEs observed in the human genome do not actually function, however, because they don't contain a promoter or the genes for either reverse transcriptase or integrase. To make sense of this observation, researchers hypothesize that the insertion process illustrated in steps 6 and 7 of Figure 21.6 is often disrupted in some way, leaving the inserted replica of the original LINE incomplete.

Research on transposable elements and lateral gene transfer has revolutionized how biologists view the genome. Many genomes are riddled with transposable elements, and others have undergone radical change in response to lateral gene transfer events. In other words, genomes are much more dynamic and complex than previously thought. Their size and composition can change dramatically over time.

Repeated Sequences and DNA Fingerprinting In addition to containing repeated sequences from transposable elements, many eukaryotic genomes have several thousand loci of relatively short DNA sequences. They are repeated in tandem, one after another, contiguously along part of a chromosome.

These tandem repetitive DNA sequences fall into two major classes:

1. Repeating units that are just 2 to about 6 bases long. These are **microsatellites,** also known as **short tandem repeats (STRs)** or **simple sequence repeats.** The most common type of microsatellite in humans is a repeated stretch of the dinucleotide AC, giving the sequence ACACACAC . . . .

2. Repeating units that are longer, from about 6 to 100 bases long. These are **minisatellites,** or **variable number tandem repeats (VNTRs).**

Microsatellite sequences are thought to originate when DNA polymerase skips or mistakenly adds extra bases during replication;

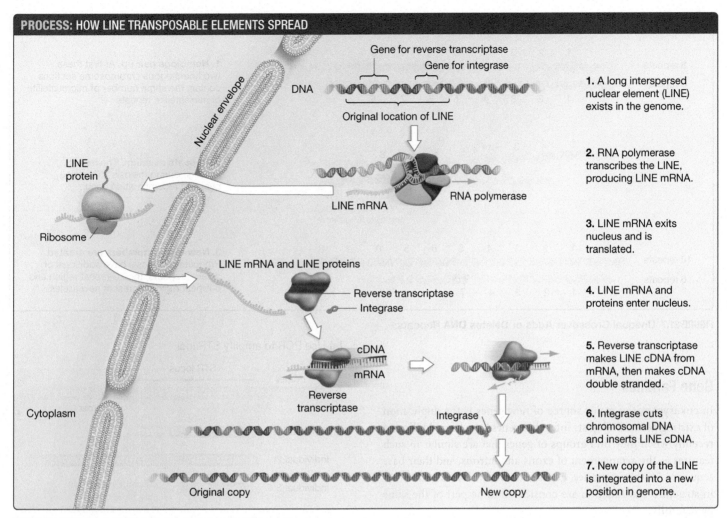

FIGURE 21.6 Transposable Elements Spread within a Genome.

the origin of minisatellites is still unclear. Together, the two types of repeated sequences make up 3 percent of the human genome.

Soon after these sequences were first characterized, Alec Jeffreys and co-workers established that microsatellite and minisatellite loci are "hypervariable," meaning that they vary among individuals much more than any other type of sequence does.

FIGURE 21.7 (see page 398) illustrates one mechanism to explain why microsatellites and minisatellites have so many different alleles: a process called **unequal crossover**. Here's how it works: Homologous chromosomes sometimes align incorrectly during prophase of meiosis I. Instead of lining up in exactly the same location, the two chromosomes pair in a way that matches up bases in different DNA repeats. When crossover occurs, the resulting chromosomes have different numbers of repeats.

Repeated sequences are particularly prone to unequal crossover, because their homologs are so similar that they are likely to misalign. If the region in question has a unique number of repeats, it represents a unique allele. Like any other alleles, microsatellite and minisatellite alleles are transmitted from parents to offspring.

The variation in repeat number among individuals is more than a curious feature of genome organization—it is the basis

of most DNA fingerprinting. **DNA fingerprinting** refers to any technique for identifying individuals based on the unique features of their genomes. Because microsatellite and minisatellite sequences vary so much, they are now the sequences of choice for DNA fingerprinting. How can these sequences be used for DNA fingerprinting?

Investigators obtain a DNA sample and perform the polymerase chain reaction (PCR), using primers that flank a region containing an STR (**FIGURE 21.8**; see page 398). Once the region has been amplified, it can be analyzed to determine the number of repeats present. Primers are now available that allow the analysis of many different STR loci.

These advances have profound impacts on society. Police use DNA fingerprinting to put people behind bars, and DNA fingerprinting has been used to show that people who were accused of crimes were actually innocent. Beyond criminal investigations, DNA fingerprinting has also been used to assign paternity and to identify remains.

Now that some characteristics of eukaryotic genomes have been reviewed, let's consider the genes they contain. Let's start with the most basic question of all: Where do eukaryotic genes come from?

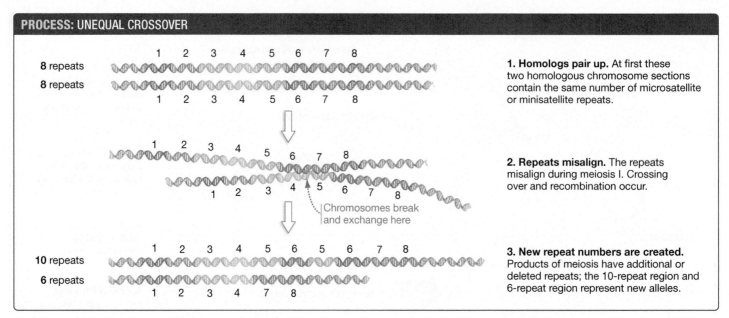

8 repeats
8 repeats

1. **Homologs pair up.** At first these two homologous chromosome sections contain the same number of microsatellite or minisatellite repeats.

2. **Repeats misalign.** The repeats misalign during meiosis I. Crossing over and recombination occur.

Chromosomes break and exchange here

10 repeats
6 repeats

3. **New repeat numbers are created.** Products of meiosis have additional or deleted repeats; the 10-repeat region and 6-repeat region represent new alleles.

FIGURE 21.7 Unequal Crossover Adds or Deletes DNA Repeats.

Gene Families

In eukaryotes, the major source of new genes is the duplication of existing genes. Biologists infer that genes have been duplicated recently when they find groups of genes that are similar in such features as the arrangement of exons and introns, and their base sequence. Within a species, genes that are similar to each other in structure and function are considered to be part of the same **gene family.**

The degree of sequence similarity among members of a gene family varies. In the genes that code for ribosomal RNAs (rRNAs) in vertebrates, the sequences are virtually identical—meaning that each individual has many exact copies of the same gene. In other cases, though, 50 percent or less of the bases are identical.

How Do Gene Families Arise? Genes that make up gene families are hypothesized to have arisen from a common ancestral sequence through gene duplication. When **gene duplication** occurs, an extra copy of a gene is added to the genome.

The most common type of gene duplication results from unequal crossover during meiosis—the same process that resulted in extra microsatellite and minisatellite repeats in Figure 21.7. Gene-sized segments of chromosomes can be deleted or duplicated if homologous chromosomes misalign during prophase of meiosis I and an unequal crossover occurs. Like microsatellites or minisatellites, the duplicated segments are arranged in tandem—one after the other.

New Genes—New Functions? Gene duplication is important because the original gene is still functional and produces a normal product. As a result, the new, duplicated stretches of sequence are redundant. If mutations in the duplicated sequence alter the protein product so that it performs a valuable new function, then an important new gene has been created.

(a) Use PCR to amplify STR loci.

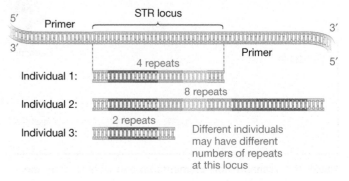

STR locus

Primer

Primer

Individual 1:   4 repeats

Individual 2:   8 repeats

Individual 3:   2 repeats

Different individuals may have different numbers of repeats at this locus

(b) Compare number of STR repeats in alleles to test paternity.

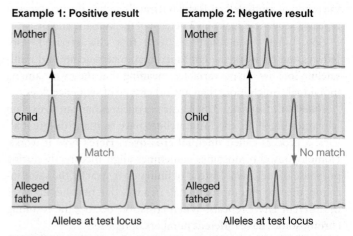

Example 1: Positive result

Mother

Child

Match

Alleged father

Alleles at test locus

Example 2: Negative result

Mother

Child

No match

Alleged father

Alleles at test locus

FIGURE 21.8 DNA Fingerprinting Can Be Used to Identify Parents.
(a) The lengths of STR loci vary. Only one allele is shown for each individual. Individuals are often heterozygous, so the repeat number varies within and between individuals. **(b)** Here, the position of each peak indicates the number of repeats at a particular locus. Each individual is heterozygous and thus shows two peaks. One of the peaks from the mother and one of the peaks from the father should line up with a peak in the child. Typically 6 to 16 loci are tested to determine paternity.

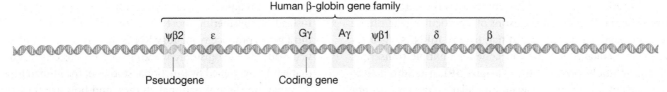

Human β-globin gene family

ψβ2   ε   Gγ   Aγ   ψβ1   δ   β

Pseudogene   Coding gene

FIGURE 21.9 Gene Families Are Closely Related Genes. The ▯-globin gene family is shown with coding genes in red and pseudogenes in yellow.

✔ **EXERCISE** Suppose that during prophase of meiosis I, the ▯ locus on one chromosome aligned with the ▯▯2 locus on another chromosome. Then crossing over occurred in the noncoding sequences just to the left (as oriented in the figure) of this ▯-▯▯2 pairing. List the order of the ▯-globin-family genes that would result on each chromosome.

As an example of a gene family, consider the human globin genes diagrammed in **FIGURE 21.9**. Collectively, this set of genes is known as the ▯-globin gene family, and they code for proteins that form part of hemoglobin—the oxygen-carrying molecule in your red blood cells. Each coding gene in the family serves a slightly different function. For example, some genes are transcribed only in the fetus or the adult. The product of the fetal gene binds oxygen more tightly than the proteins expressed in adults. Consequently, oxygen moves from the mother's blood, where it is not as tightly bound to hemoglobin, to the fetus's blood (see Chapter 45).

In addition to creating genes with new functions, mutations in duplicated regions often make gene expression impossible. For example, a mutation could produce a stop codon in the middle of an exon. A member of a gene family that resembles a working gene but does not code for a functional product because of a mutation is a **pseudogene.** Pseudogenes do not function. Note that the ▯-globin gene family contains pseudogenes along with several genes that code for oxygen-transporting proteins. The number of pseudogenes is remarkable. In the human genome, for example, there are roughly as many pseudogenes as functional genes.

Lateral Gene Transfer in Eukaryotes   Genome sequencing projects are revealing more and more instances of lateral gene transfer in eukaryotes. What is the role of lateral gene transfer in the evolution of eukaryotes?

There are some clear examples of lateral gene transfer playing pivotal roles in eukaryote evolution. One key example is the capture of bacterial cells that were predecessors of today's mitochondria and chloroplasts and the subsequent transfer of many bacterial genes to the host genome (see Chapter 30). But in general, lateral gene transfer seems to be relatively rare in eukaryotes compared with prokaryotes. While biologists debate whether a tree or a web of life best describes evolution in bacteria and archaea, the eukaryotic tree remains rooted in what appear to be more modest rates of lateral gene transfer.

Insights from the Human Genome Project

More than 10 years ago, President Clinton announced the completion of the human genome sequence as "the most wondrous map ever produced by humankind." What has analysis of human genome sequence revealed? Let's first explore what types of DNA sequences make up the human genome and then examine some questions raised by this wondrous map.

Given biologists' focus on protein-coding genes, the composition of the human genome was unexpected. As **FIGURE 21.10** reveals, less than 2 percent of the genome consists of protein-coding exons, and nearly half is made of transposable elements. Introns make up over one-quarter of the genome and are 17 times more abundant than protein-coding exons.

Of all the observations stemming from the human genome, perhaps the most striking is that organisms with complex morphology, biochemistry, and behavior do not have particularly large numbers of genes. Notice in Figure 21.4b that the total number of genes in humans is only 50 percent more than the number in fruit flies, is about the same as in roundworms, and is substantially lower than the number of genes in water fleas, rice, and the mustard plant *Arabidopsis thaliana*.

Before the human genome was sequenced, many biologists expected that humans would have at least 100,000 genes. But we may only have a fifth of that number. How can this be?

In prokaryotes there is a correlation between genome size, gene number, a cell's metabolic capabilities, and the cell's ability to live in a variety of habitats. But why isn't there a stronger correlation between gene number and morphological, biochemical, and behavioral complexity in eukaryotes?

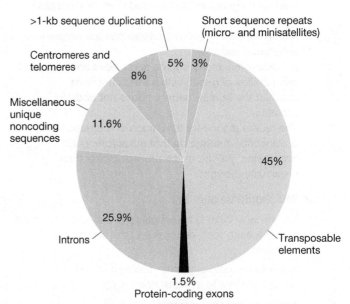

FIGURE 21.10 Composition of the Human Genome.
DATA: Gregory, T. R. 2005. *Nature Reviews Genetics* 6: 699–708.

One hypothesis to explain this observation is based on **alternative splicing.** Recall that the exons of a particular gene can be spliced in ways that produce distinct, mature mRNAs. As a result, a single eukaryotic gene can code for multiple transcripts and thus multiple proteins (see Chapter 19). The alternative-splicing hypothesis claims that multicellular eukaryotes do not need enormous numbers of distinct genes. Instead, more extensive use of alternative splicing in these organisms creates different proteins from the same gene.

In support of the alternative-splicing hypothesis, researchers have analyzed the mRNAs produced by human genes. They estimate that at least 90 percent of genes produce transcripts that are alternatively spliced, with an average of more than three distinct transcripts per gene. This means that the number of different proteins that can be produced is more than triple the gene number. Because of extensive alternative splicing, the number of genes and number of proteins do not have to be tightly linked.

There is likely more to the story, however, than extensive alternative splicing. Accompanying the rapid advances in sequencing technology have been equally dramatic advances in methods for studying how the genome functions. Some of these methods are described later, in Section 21.4. But what's important here are the findings.

Roughly 90 percent of the human genome is transcribed. This is far more than believed even a few years ago. Some of these transcripts code for regulatory RNAs with known roles, such as microRNAs (Chapter 19). Many of these transcripts, however, have no currently known roles. If many of these newly discovered RNAs have a function, then the human genome and the genomes of other complex organisms may not be so gene poor after all. If so,

this would require an adjustment in how we view a typical gene. Instead of considering most genes to code for proteins, perhaps most genes produce regulatory RNAs that are never translated. As you read this, biologists are working hard on this central question that has been opened by functional studies of the human genome.

What are these functional studies, and how are they carried out? The following section considers these questions.

21.4 Functional Genomics, Proteomics, and Systems Biology

Genomics researcher Eric Lander has compared the sequencing of the human genome to the establishment of the periodic table of the elements in chemistry. Once the periodic table was validated, chemists focused on understanding how the elements combine to form molecules. Similarly, biologists now want to understand how the elements of the human genome combine to produce an individual.

Remember that a genome sequence is essentially a parts list. Once that list is assembled, researchers delve deeper to understand how genes interact to produce an organism.

What Is Functional Genomics?

For decades, biologists have worked at understanding how and when individual genes are expressed. Research on the *lac* operon is typical of this type of study (see Chapter 18). But now researchers can ask how and when *all* the genes in an organism are expressed.

Large-scale analysis of gene expression is part of functional genomics—research on how genes work together to produce a phenotype. The effort is motivated by the realization that gene products do not exist in a vacuum. Instead, groups of RNAs and proteins act together to respond to environmental challenges such as extreme heat or drought. Similarly, distinct groups of genes are transcribed at different stages as a multicellular eukaryote grows and develops.

A basic tool of functional genomics is a microarray. A **DNA microarray** consists of as many as 1 million different single-stranded DNA segments that are permanently attached at one end to a glass slide or silicon chip. Each DNA sequence is linked to the slide or chip in a known location and serves as a probe for a specific transcript. For example, the slide pictured in **FIGURE 21.11** contains thousands of spots, each one containing single-stranded DNA from a unique exon found in the human genome.

Microarrays can be used for many applications. The most common use is to learn which genes are expressed as RNAs in a particular cell type under particular conditions. A typical experiment done with a DNA microarray would follow the protocol outlined in **FIGURE 21.12**. For example, if the researchers' goal was to learn how a cell alters its gene expression to meet the challenges of heat stress, the first step would be to isolate mRNAs produced in control cells functioning at normal temperature and in cells of the same kind exposed to high temperatures.

check your understanding

C Y U
If you understand that . . .

- Eukaryotic genomes are riddled with transposable elements.
- Relatively short repeated sequences are common in eukaryotic genomes.
- In eukaryotes, many coding sequences are organized into families of genes with related functions.
- Much of the human genome does not code for proteins.
- The recent discovery that much of the genome is transcribed suggests that eukaryotic gene expression may be much more complex than previously thought.

✔ You should be able to . . .

1. Explain why there is no simple relationship between the size of a eukaryotic genome and the complexity of the organism.
2. Estimate the ratio of protein-coding portions of the human genome to all transcribed regions of the genome.

Answers are available in Appendix A.

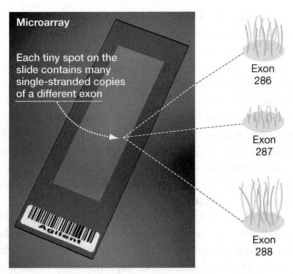

FIGURE 21.11 A DNA Microarray. To create this microarray, thousands of short, single-stranded DNA sequences were synthesized in defined positions on a glass plate. In this microarray, the synthesized DNAs represent portions of all exons from a particular species.

Once they had purified mRNAs from the two populations of cells (step 1), investigators would use reverse transcriptase to make a single-stranded cDNA version of each RNA in each of the two samples (see Chapter 20). In addition to the four standard dNTPs, one of the DNA building blocks used in synthesizing the cDNA would carry a fluorescent label (step 2). The label used for the cDNA of the control cells would glow one color (let's say green), while the label chosen for the cDNA of the heat-stressed cells would glow another color (let's say red). The labeled cDNAs of both colors would then be used to bind to the complementary DNA probes on the microarray (step 3). This step is called hybridization because hybrids between probe DNAs and cDNAs will form.

Out of all the exons in the genome, then, only the exons that are being expressed by the two populations of cells will be labeled on the microarray. In this example, genes that are expressed by the control cells under normal conditions will be labeled green, while those expressed by the cells during heat stress will be labeled red. If an exon in the microarray is expressed under both sets of conditions, then both green- and red-labeled cDNAs will bind to the DNA in that spot and make it appear yellow (step 4).

A microarray lets researchers study the expression of thousands of genes at a time. As a result, they can identify which sets of genes are expressed in concert under specific sets of conditions.

Researchers can use microarrays to establish which genes are transcribed in different organs and tissues, in cancers, or—as you saw in Figure 21.12—in response to changes in environmental conditions such as heat stress. ✔ If you understand how microarrays are used, you should be able to explain how you would use a DNA microarray to compare the genes expressed in brain cells versus liver cells of an adult human.

Besides using microarrays, investigators are now able to assess gene expression by directly sequencing cDNAs using next-generation sequencing technologies. For example, if biologists

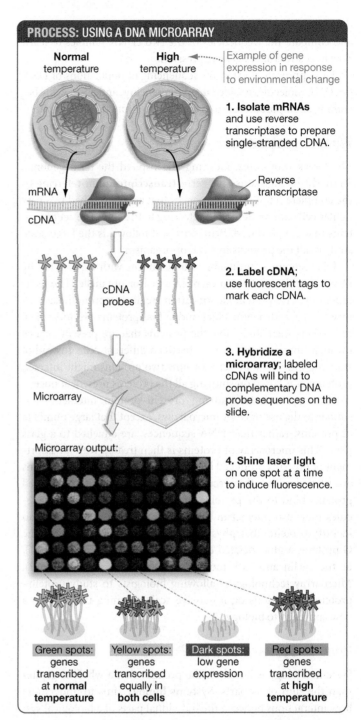

FIGURE 21.12 DNA Microarrays Can Be Used to Study Changes in Gene Expression. By probing a microarray with labeled cDNAs synthesized from mRNAs, researchers can identify which sequences are being transcribed. Here mRNAs from cells growing at normal temperature are detected by green color, while mRNAs from cells growing at high temperature are detected by red color.

wanted to learn about gene expression changes induced by heat stress, they would start as they did for the microarray by preparing two different sets of cDNAs, one from control and one from heat-stressed cells. But instead of using these cDNAs to hybridize with microarray probes, biologists would sequence millions of cDNAs from each treatment type. Using bioinformatics tools, they would then determine the frequency of each type of cDNA and compare the frequencies of the two cDNA samples to learn how heat stress alters gene expression.

This approach of extensive sequencing of populations of DNA or cDNA molecules is called **deep sequencing,** and it is quickly becoming an important research approach for functional genomics.

What Is Proteomics?

The Greek root *-ome*, meaning all, inspired the term genome. Similarly, biologists use the term **transcriptome** in referring to the complete set of DNA sequences that are transcribed in a particular cell, and **proteome** in referring to the complete set of proteins that are produced. **Proteomics,** it follows, is the large-scale study of all the proteins in a cell or organism.

Like genomics, proteomic studies begin with a parts list by identifying the proteins present in a cell or organelle. The techniques used for protein identification are distinct from those used in working with DNA. Once individual proteins are identified, researchers then study how the proteins that are present change through time, interact, or vary between different cells. Instead of studying individual proteins or how two proteins might interact, proteomics is based on studying all the proteins present at once.

One approach to studying protein–protein interactions is similar to the use of DNA microarrays, except that large numbers of proteins, rather than DNA sequences, are attached to a glass plate. This microarray of proteins is then treated with an assortment of proteins produced by the same organism. These proteins are labeled with a fluorescent or radioactive tag. If any labeled proteins bind to the proteins in the microarray, the two molecules may also interact in the cell. In this way, researchers can identify proteins that physically bind to one another—like the G proteins and associated enzymes (introduced in Chapter 11), or the cyclin and Cdk molecules (introduced in Chapter 12). Microarray technology is allowing biologists to study protein–protein interactions on a massive scale, opening the door to a new approach to biology.

What Is Systems Biology?

Systems biology is based on the premise that a whole is greater than the sum of its parts. **Systems biology** aims to understand how interactions between the individual parts of a biological system create new properties. For example, how does metabolism come about from the interaction of proteins within a cell? How does cancer arise from the interplay of individual genes? Complex properties that arise from the interaction of simpler elements are **emergent properties.**

DNA replication, metabolism, cancer, and the development of an organism all are emergent properties because they come about from the interactions of simpler elements—genes and proteins. ✔ If you understand this concept, you should be able to explain why cell replication is an emergent property.

Many systems biology investigations focus on mapping the interactions between genes or proteins. Genomics and proteomics provide the parts list needed to start these systems biology studies. It's the job of a systems biologist to learn how these parts are linked together into networks and how new properties emerge from these interactions.

Let's look at how a systems biology approach was taken to predict all possible interactions between proteins in *Schizosaccharomyces pombe*, a species of yeast. An interaction can mean either that two proteins bind to one another to form a stable complex or that one protein acts on another protein. An example of the first type of interaction is cyclin binding to a cyclin-dependent kinase (Cdk); an example of the second interaction type is when the cyclin–Cdk complex acts as a kinase to add a phosphate to a target protein (see Chapter 12).

To begin their study, the researchers used existing databases of known protein–protein interactions to make predictions about the fission yeast protein interaction network. Then they verified some of the predicted interactions experimentally to show that their prediction method worked. Once they had shown that their prediction method was accurate, they mapped 37,325 possible interactions between 3438 different proteins. If you look at the interaction network in **FIGURE 21.13**, you will see how clusters of interacting proteins emerge from the tangle. These clusters reveal highly connected portions of the network.

The significance? Some of the predicted interactions in this yeast may have implications for human disease. For example, some of the key players in the cluster associated with signal transduction point to previously unexplored relationships that could be important in understanding cancer and neurodegenerative disorders, such as Huntington's disease (see Chapter 20), and for targeted drug design.

Work in genomics, proteomics, and systems biology is opening the door to knowing how cells work in health and disease. These new areas of biology also lay the foundation for understanding one of the most wondrous aspects of life—how a single cell develops into a complete organism. This topic is explored in the unit ahead.

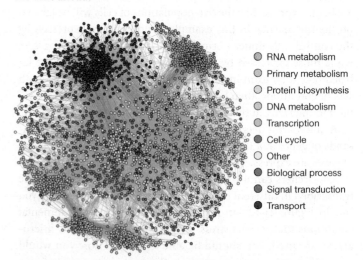

- RNA metabolism
- Primary metabolism
- Protein biosynthesis
- DNA metabolism
- Transcription
- Cell cycle
- Other
- Biological process
- Signal transduction
- Transport

FIGURE 21.13 Yeast Protein Interaction Network. Each circle represents a different protein, with each protein color-coded according to its cellular function. Lines that connect a pair of proteins indicate an interaction.

DATA: V. Pancaldi et al. 2012. *G3: Genes, Genomes, Genetics* 2: 453–467.

If you understand . . .

21.1 Whole-Genome Sequencing

- Advances in DNA sequencing technologies have allowed investigators to sequence DNA more rapidly and cheaply, resulting in a flood of genome data.

- Thousands of genomes have been sequenced to date for many different purposes.

- Bioinformatics is the application of computer science to genome analysis and is essential for genome research.

- Researchers annotate genome sequences by finding genes and determining their function.

- To identify genes in bacteria and archaea, researchers use computers to scan the genome for start and stop codons that are in the same reading frame and that are separated by gene-sized stretches of sequence.

- Genes are also identified based on their homology (similarity due to evolutionary relatedness) to previously identified genes in other species.

- To find genes in eukaryotes, researchers couple the use of computers and study of RNAs to identify transcribed sequences.

✔ You should be able to describe how a research group that discovered a gene for coat color in mice would determine whether a homologous gene exists in the human genome.

21.2 Bacterial and Archaeal Genomes

- Bacterial and archaeal genomes are small relative to many eukaryotic genomes and have tightly spaced genes.

- There is a linear relationship between bacterial and archaeal gene number and genome size, and a similar correspondence in the relationship between metabolic capacity and genome size.

- The function of many of the genes identified in bacteria and archaea is still unknown.

- There is a huge amount of genetic diversity in bacterial and archaeal genomes, even among different strains of the same species.

- Lateral gene transfer is common in bacteria and archaea. It is an important source of new genes in many species.

- Metagenomics allows the analysis of all the genes of all the bacteria or archaea in a community.

✔ You should be able to propose genome characteristics you would look for to distinguish a bacterial parasite from a nonparasitic bacterial species that is found in a range of environments.

21.3 Eukaryotic Genomes

- Eukaryotic genomes tend to be large and complex. They include many sequences that have little to no effect on the fitness of the organism, and many transcribed sequences whose function is not known.

- There is no correlation between morphological complexity and gene number in eukaryotes.

- Because of alternative splicing, the number of distinct transcripts produced in many eukaryotes is much larger than the gene number.

- Gene duplication has been an important source of new genes in eukaryotes.

- Lateral gene transfer occurs in eukaryotes, but appears to play a smaller role than in bacteria and archaea.

- Recent findings show that much more of the eukaryotic genome is transcribed than previously believed, and the function of many noncoding transcripts is unknown.

✔ You should be able to explain what features of eukaryotic genomes result in a lack of correspondence between genome size, gene number, and morphological complexity.

21.4 Functional Genomics, Proteomics, and Systems Biology

- Functional genomics uses tools such as DNA microarrays to learn patterns of gene expression and gene function.

- Proteomics is similar to genomics but works to identify the complete set of proteins expressed in a cell, how this set changes under different conditions, and how it relates to phenotype.

- Systems biology starts with genomics and proteomics data and studies the set of interactions between different genes or proteins to understand how biological systems work.

✔ You should be able to explain how Figure 21.13 indicates that there are networks within networks for interacting proteins associated with particular functions.

(MB) **MasteringBiology**

1. MasteringBiology Assignments

Tutorials and Activities DNA Fingerprinting; Human Genome Project: Genes on Human Chromosome 17; Human Genome Sequencing Strategies; Shotgun Approach to Whole-Genome Sequencing

Questions Reading Quizzes, Blue-Thread Questions, Test Bank

2. eText Read your book online, search, take notes, highlight text, and more.

3. The Study Area Practice Test, Cumulative Test, BioFlix® 3-D Animations, Videos, Activities, Audio Glossary, Word Study Tools, Art

You should be able to . . .

1. What is an open reading frame in bacteria?
   a. a gene whose function is already known
   b. a DNA section that is thought to code for a protein because it is similar to a complementary DNA (cDNA)
   c. a DNA section that is thought to code for a protein because it has a start codon and a stop codon flanking hundreds of nucleotides
   d. any member of a gene family

2. What best describes the logic behind shotgun sequencing?
   a. Break the genome into tiny pieces. Sequence each piece. Use overlapping ends to assemble the pieces in the correct order.
   b. Start with one end of each chromosome. Sequence straight through to the other end of the chromosome.
   c. Use a variety of techniques to identify genes and ORFs. Sequence these segments—not the noncoding and repeated sequences.
   d. Break the genome into pieces. Map the location of each piece. Then sequence each piece.

3. A _____ is a 2- to 6-base-pair repeated sequence in DNA.
   a. LINE
   b. restriction site
   c. gene duplication
   d. microsatellite

4. What is a leading hypothesis to explain the paradox that large, morphologically complex eukaryotes such as humans have relatively small numbers of genes?
   a. lateral transfer of genes from other species
   b. alternative splicing of mRNAs
   c. polyploidy, or the doubling of the genome's entire chromosome complement
   d. expansion of gene families through gene duplication

5. What evidence do biologists use to infer that a gene is part of a gene family?

6. What are some characteristics of a pseudogene?

7. Explain how open reading frames are identified in the genomes of bacteria and archaea. Why is it more difficult to find open reading frames in eukaryotes?

8. In a genomics-based search for mutations that caused a patient's cancer, which of the following would provide the most informative comparison with the cancer cell?
   a. the average human DNA sequence available from a database
   b. the DNA sequence of a noncancerous cell from another person
   c. the DNA sequence of a noncancerous cell from the patient
   d. the DNA sequence of a different tumor type from another cancer patient

9. **QUANTITATIVE** Gene density is the number of genes per unit length of DNA. Most often, gene density is expressed as the number of genes per million base pairs (Mbp). Go to Figure 21.4b and find the approximate number of genes estimated in water fleas and in humans and the size of each genome. What is the gene density per Mbp in water fleas? What is the gene density per Mbp in humans? How much greater is the gene density in water fleas relative to humans?

10. In DNA fingerprinting, why is it an advantage to analyze an STR locus with many different repeat length alleles versus an STR locus with only a few different repeat length alleles?

11. Explain how microarrays of short, single-stranded DNAs that represent many or all of the exons in a genome are used to document changes in the transcription of genes over time or in response to environmental challenges.

12. Explain the concept of homology and how identifying homologous genes helps researchers identify the function of unknown genes.

13. Parasites lack genes for many of the enzymes found in their hosts. Most parasites, however, have evolved from free-living ancestors that had larger genomes. Based on these observations, W. Ford Doolittle claims that the loss of genes in parasites represents an evolutionary trend. He summarizes his hypothesis with the quip "use it or lose it." What does he mean?

14. According to eyewitness accounts, communist revolutionaries executed Nicholas II, the last czar of Russia, along with his wife and five children, the family physician, and about a dozen servants. Many decades after this event, a grave purported to hold the remains of the royal family was discovered. Biologists were asked to analyze DNA from each adult and juvenile skeleton and determine whether the bodies were indeed those of several young siblings, two parents, and several unrelated adults. If the remains of the family were in this grave, predict how similar the DNA fingerprints would be between the parents, the children, and the unrelated individuals in the grave.

15. Pleiotropy (a concept presented in Chapter 14) occurs when a mutation in one gene results in many different phenotypes.

In a study of a gene interaction network, similar to the protein interaction network shown in Figure 21.13, which type of gene would you predict to exhibit the greatest degree of pleiotropy when mutated?
   a. a gene that interacts with one neighbor
   b. a gene that has a duplicate copy
   c. a gene that is the center of interactions with functionally related genes
   d. a gene that is the center of interactions with genes of many different functions

16. One hypothesis for differences between humans and chimps involves differences in gene regulation. A recent study used microarrays to compare the patterns of expression of genes that are active in the brain, liver, and blood of chimpanzees and humans. The overall patterns of gene expression were similar in the liver and blood of the two species, but the expression patterns were strikingly different in the brain. How do these results relate to the hypothesis?

25 Evolution by Natural Selection

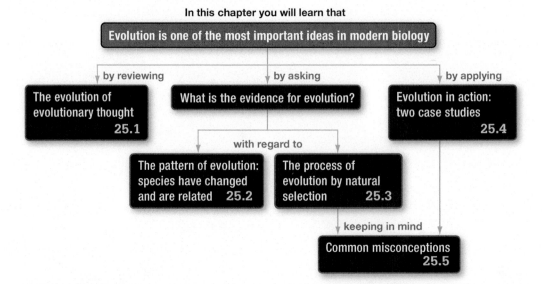

In this chapter you will learn that

Evolution is one of the most important ideas in modern biology

by reviewing → The evolution of evolutionary thought **25.1**

by asking → What is the evidence for evolution?

with regard to

The pattern of evolution: species have changed and are related **25.2**

The process of evolution by natural selection **25.3**

by applying → Evolution in action: two case studies **25.4**

keeping in mind

Common misconceptions **25.5**

Natural selection acts on individuals in populations such as these sea stars, but only populations evolve. One of Darwin's greatest contributions to science was the introduction of population thinking to the theory of evolution.

This chapter is part of the Big Picture. See how on pages 526–527.

This chapter is about one of the great ideas in science. The theory of evolution by natural selection, formulated independently by Charles Darwin and Alfred Russel Wallace, explains how organisms have come to be adapted to environments ranging from arctic tundra to tropical wet forest. It revealed one of the five key attributes of life: Populations of organisms evolve—meaning that they change through time (Chapter 1).

As an example of a revolutionary breakthrough in our understanding of the world, the theory of evolution by natural selection ranks alongside Copernicus's theory of the Sun as the center of our solar system, Newton's laws of motion and theory of gravitation, the germ theory of disease, the theory of plate tectonics, and Einstein's general theory of relativity. These theories are the foundation stones of modern science; all are accepted on the basis of overwhelming evidence.

✔ When you see this checkmark, stop and test yourself. Answers are available in Appendix A.

Evolution by natural selection is one of the best supported and most important theories in the history of scientific research. But like most scientific breakthroughs, this one did not come easily. When Darwin published his theory in 1859 in a book called *On the Origin of Species by Means of Natural Selection*, it unleashed a firestorm of protest throughout Europe. At that time, the leading explanation for the diversity of organisms was an idea called special creation.

Special creation held that: **(1)** All species are independent, in the sense of being unrelated to each other; **(2)** life on Earth is young—perhaps just 6000 years old; and **(3)** species are immutable, or incapable of change. These beliefs were explained by the instantaneous and independent creation of living organisms by a supernatural being.

Darwin's theory was radically different. How did it differ? Scientific theories usually have two components: a pattern and a process (see Chapter 1):

1. The *pattern component* is a statement that summarizes a series of observations about the natural world. The pattern component is about facts—about how things *are* in nature.

2. The *process component* is a mechanism that produces that pattern or set of observations.

Let's begin with an overview of the evolution of evolutionary thought, and then examine the pattern and process components of the theory of evolution by natural selection.

25.1 The Evolution of Evolutionary Thought

People often use the word revolutionary to describe the theory of evolution by natural selection. Revolutions overturn things—they replace an existing entity with something new and often radically different. A political revolution removes the ruling class or group and replaces it with another. The industrial revolution replaced small shops for manufacturing goods by hand with huge, mechanized assembly lines.

A scientific revolution, in contrast, overturns an existing idea about how nature works and replaces it with another, radically different, idea. The idea that Darwin and Wallace overturned—that species were supernaturally, not naturally, created—had dominated thinking about the nature of organisms in Western civilization for over 2000 years.

Plato and Typological Thinking

The Greek philosopher Plato claimed that every organism was an example of a perfect essence, or type, created by God, and that these types were unchanging. Plato acknowledged that the individual organisms present on Earth might deviate slightly from the perfect type, but he said this deviation was similar to seeing the perfect type in a shadow on a wall. The key to understanding life, in Plato's mind, was to ignore the shadows and focus on understanding each type of unchanging, perfect essence.

Today, philosophers and biologists refer to ideas like this as typological thinking. Typological thinking is based on the idea that species are unchanging types and that variations within species are unimportant or even misleading. Typological thinking also occurs in the Bible's book of Genesis, where God creates each type of organism.

Aristotle and the Great Chain of Being

Not long after Plato developed his ideas, Aristotle ordered the types of organisms known at the time into a linear scheme called the great chain of being, also called the scale of nature (**FIGURE 25.1**). Aristotle proposed that species were organized into a sequence based on increased size and complexity, with humans at the top. He also claimed that the characteristics of species were fixed—they did not change through time.

In the 1700s Aristotle's ideas were still popular in scientific and religious circles. The central claims were that **(1)** species are fixed types, and **(2)** some species are higher—in the sense of being more complex or "better"—than others.

Lamarck and the Idea of Evolution as Change through Time

Typological thinking eventually began to break down. In 1809 the biologist Jean-Baptiste de Lamarck proposed a formal theory of **evolution**—that species are not static but change through time. However, the pattern component of Lamarck's theory was initially based on the great chain of being.

When he started his work on evolution, Lamarck claimed that simple organisms originate at the base of the chain by

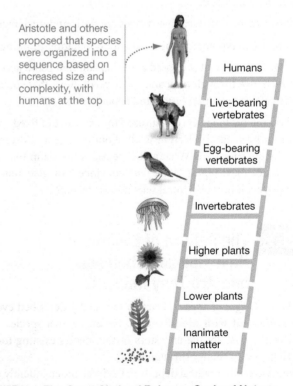

FIGURE 25.1 The Great Chain of Being, or Scale of Nature.

spontaneous generation (see Chapter 1) and then evolve by moving up the chain over time. Thus, Lamarckian evolution is progressive in the sense of always producing larger and more complex, or "better," species. To capture this point, biologists often say that Lamarck turned the ladder of life into an escalator.

Lamarck also contended that species change through time via the inheritance of acquired characters. The idea here is that as an individual develops in response to challenges posed by the environment, its phenotype changes, and it passes on these phenotypic changes to offspring. A classic Lamarckian scenario is that giraffes develop long necks as they stretch to reach leaves high in treetops, and they then produce offspring with elongated necks.

Darwin and Wallace and Evolution by Natural Selection

As his thinking matured, Lamarck eventually abandoned his linear and progressive view of life. Darwin and Wallace concurred. But more important, they emphasized that the process responsible for change through time—evolution—occurs because traits vary among the individuals in a population, and because individuals with certain traits leave more offspring than others do. A **population** consists of individuals of the same species that are living in the same area at the same time.

Darwin and Wallace's proposal was a radical break from the typological thinking that had dominated scientific thought since Plato. Darwin claimed that instead of being unimportant or an illusion, variation among individuals in a population was the key to understanding the nature of species. Biologists refer to this view as **population thinking.**

The theory of evolution by natural selection was revolutionary for several reasons:

1. It overturned the idea that species are static and unchanging.

2. It replaced typological thinking with population thinking.

3. It was scientific. It proposed a mechanism that could account for change through time and made predictions that could be tested through observation and experimentation.

Plato and his followers emphasized the existence of fixed types; evolution by natural selection is all about change and diversity. Now the questions are: What evidence backs the claim that species are not fixed types? What data convince biologists that the theory of evolution by natural selection is correct?

25.2 The Pattern of Evolution: Have Species Changed, and Are They Related?

In *On the Origin of Species*, Darwin repeatedly described evolution as **descent with modification.** He meant that species that lived in the past are the ancestors of the species existing today, and that species change through time.

This view was a radical departure from the independently created and immutable species embodied in Plato's work and in the idea of special creation. In essence, the pattern component of the theory of evolution by natural selection makes two predictions about the nature of species:

1. Species change through time.

2. Species are related by common ancestry.

Let's consider the evidence for each of these predictions in turn.

Evidence for Change through Time

When Darwin began his work, biologists and geologists had just begun to assemble and interpret the fossil record. A **fossil** is any trace of an organism that lived in the past. These traces range from bones and branches to shells, tracks or impressions, and dung. The **fossil record** consists of all the fossils that have been found on Earth and described in the scientific literature.

Why did data in the fossil record support the hypothesis that species have changed through time? And what data from **extant species**—those living today—support the claim that they are modified forms of ancestral species?

The Vastness of Geologic Time   Initially, fossils were organized according to their *relative* ages based on a series of principles derived from observations about rock formation. **Sedimentary rocks,** for example, form from sand or mud or other materials deposited at locations such as beaches or river mouths. Sedimentary rocks, along with rocks derived from volcanic ash or lava, are known to form in layers—younger layers are deposited on top of older layers.

Researchers used this information to place fossils in a younger-to-older sequence, based on the fossils' relative position in layers of sedimentary rock (**FIGURE 25.2**). As the scientists observed similarities in rocks and fossils at different sites, they began to create a **geologic time scale:** a sequence of named intervals called eons, eras, and periods that represented the major events in Earth history (see Chapter 28). They also realized that vast amounts of time were required to form the thick layers of sedimentary rock that they were studying, because erosion and deposition of sediments are such slow processes.

This was an important insight. The geologic record indicated that the Earth was much, much older than the 6000 years claimed by proponents of special creation.

After the discovery of radioactivity in the late 1800s, researchers realized that radioactive decay—the steady rate at which unstable or "parent" atoms are converted into more stable "daughter" atoms—furnished a way to assign *absolute* ages, in years, to the relative ages in the geologic time scale.

Radiometric dating is based on three pieces of information:

1. Observed decay rates of parent to daughter atoms

2. The ratio of parent to daughter atoms present in newly formed rocks—such as the amount of uranium atoms versus lead atoms when uranium-containing molten rock first cools (Uranium decays to form lead.)

3. The ratio of parent to daughter atoms present in a particular rock sample

Younger rock layers　　　　　　**Younger fossils**

Tracks from a mammal-like reptile

Fern

Trilobite

Older rock layers　　　　　　**Older fossils**

FIGURE 25.2 Sedimentary Rocks Reveal the Vastness of Geologic Time. The relative ages of sedimentary rocks are used to determine the relative ages of fossil organisms because younger layers are deposited on top of older ones. The deepest rock layer in the Grand Canyon is over a billion years old, and the top layer is 270 million years old.

Combining information from these two ratios with information on the decay rate allows researchers to estimate how long ago a rock formed. According to data from radiometric dating, Earth is about 4.6 billion years old, and the earliest signs of life appear in rocks that formed 3.4–3.8 billion years ago.

Data from relative and absolute dating techniques agree: Life on Earth is ancient. A great deal of time has gone by for change to occur.

Extinction Changes the Species Present over Time　In the early nineteenth century, researchers began discovering fossil bones, leaves, and shells that were unlike structures from any known animal or plant. At first, many scientists insisted that living examples of these species would be found in unexplored regions of the globe. But as research continued and the number and diversity of fossil collections grew, the argument became less and less plausible.

The issue was finally settled in 1812 when Baron Georges Cuvier published a detailed analysis of an **extinct species**—that is, a species that no longer exists—called the Irish "elk." Scientists accepted the fact of extinction because this gigantic deer was judged to be too large to have escaped discovery and too

FIGURE 25.3 Evidence of Extinction. The skeleton of the Irish "elk" dwarfs a human. Scientists agreed that the deer was too large and unique to be overlooked if it were alive; it must have gone extinct.

distinctive to be classified as a large-bodied population of an existing species (**FIGURE 25.3**).

Advocates of special creation argued that fossil species were victims of the flood at the time of Noah. Darwin, in contrast, interpreted extinct forms as evidence that species are not static, immutable entities, unchanged since the moment of special creation. His reasoning was that if species have gone extinct, then the array of species living on Earth has changed through time.

Recent analyses of the fossil record suggest that over 99 percent of all the species that have ever lived are now extinct. The data also indicate that species have gone extinct continuously throughout Earth's history—not just in one or even a few catastrophic events.

Transitional Features Link Older and Younger Species　Long before Darwin published his theory, researchers reported striking resemblances between the fossils found in the rocks underlying certain regions and the living species found in the same geographic areas. The pattern was so widespread that it became known as the "law of succession." The general observation was that extinct species in the fossil record were succeeded, in the same region, by similar species.

Early in the nineteenth century, the pattern was simply reported and not interpreted. But later, Darwin pointed out that it provided strong evidence in favor of the hypothesis that species had changed through time. His idea was that the extinct forms and living forms were related—that they represented ancestors and descendants.

As the fossil record expanded, researchers discovered species with characteristics that broadened the scope of the law of succession. A **transitional feature** is a trait in a fossil species that is intermediate between those of ancestral (older) and derived (younger) species. For example, intensive work over the past several decades has yielded fossils that document a gradual change over time from aquatic animals that had fins to terrestrial animals that had limbs (**FIGURE 25.4**). Over a period of about 25 million years, the fins of species similar to today's lungfish changed into limbs similar to those found in today's amphibians, reptiles, and mammals—a group called the tetrapods (literally, "four-footed").

These observations support the hypothesis that an ancestral lungfish-like species first used stout, lobed fins to navigate in shallow aquatic habitats. Then they moved onto land, where their descendants became more and more like today's tetrapods in appearance and lifestyle. Lungfish and tetrapod species have clearly changed through time.

Similar sequences of transitional features document changes that led to the evolution of feathers and flight in birds; stomata and vascular tissue in plants; upright posture, flattened faces, and large brains in humans; jaws in vertebrates (animals with backbones); the loss of limbs in snakes; and other traits. Data like these are consistent with predictions from the theory of evolution: If the traits observed in more recent species evolved from traits in more ancient species, then transitional forms are expected to occur in the appropriate time sequence.

The fossil record provides compelling evidence that species have evolved. What data from extant forms support the hypothesis that the characteristics of species change through time?

Vestigial Traits Are Evidence of Change through Time Darwin was the first to provide a widely accepted interpretation of vestigial traits. A **vestigial trait** is a reduced or incompletely developed structure that has no function, or reduced function, but is clearly similar to functioning organs or structures in closely related species.

Biologists have documented thousands of examples of vestigial traits.

- Some whales and snakes have tiny hip and leg bones that do not help them swim or slither.
- Ostriches and kiwis have reduced wings and cannot fly.
- Eyeless, blind cave-dwelling fish have eye sockets.
- Even though marsupial mammals give birth to live young, an eggshell forms briefly early in their development; in some species, newborns have a nonfunctioning "egg tooth" similar to those used by birds and reptiles to break open their shells.
- Monkeys and many other primates have long tails; but our coccyx, illustrated in **FIGURE 25.5**, is too small to help us maintain balance or grab tree limbs for support.
- Many mammals, including primates, are able to erect their hair when they are cold or excited. This behavior manifests itself as goose bumps in humans, but goose bumps are largely ineffective in warming us or signalling our emotional state.

FIGURE 25.4 Transitional Features during the Evolution of the Tetrapod Limb. Fossil species similar to today's lungfish and tetrapods have fin and limb bones that are transitional features. *Eusthenopteron* was aquatic; *Tulerpeton* was probably semiaquatic (mya = million years ago).

✔ **QUESTION** How would observations of transitional features be explained under special creation?

 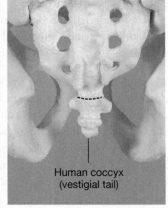

FIGURE 25.5 Vestigial Traits Are Reduced Versions of Traits in Other Species. The tailbone is a human trait that has reduced function. It is no longer useful for balance and locomotion.

✔ **QUESTION** How would observations of vestigial traits be explained if evolution occurred via inheritance of acquired characters?

The existence of vestigial traits is inconsistent with the idea of special creation, which maintains that species were perfectly designed by a supernatural being and that the characteristics of species are static. Instead, vestigial traits are evidence that the characteristics of species have changed over time.

Current Examples of Change through Time Biologists have documented hundreds of contemporary populations that are changing in response to changes in their environment. Bacteria have evolved resistance to drugs; insects have evolved resistance to pesticides; weedy plants have evolved resistance to herbicides; the timing of bird migrations, the emergence of insects, and the blooming of flowering plants have evolved in response to climate change. Section 25.4 provides a detailed analysis of research on two examples of evolution in action.

To summarize, change through time continues and can be measured directly. Evidence from the fossil record and living species indicates that life is ancient, that species have changed through the course of Earth's history, and that species continue to change. The take-home message is that species are dynamic—not static, unchanging, and fixed types, as claimed by Plato, Aristotle, and advocates of special creation.

Evidence of Descent from a Common Ancestor

Data from the fossil record and contemporary species refute the hypothesis that species are immutable. What about the claim that species were created independently—meaning that they are un-related to each other?

Similar Species Are Found in the Same Geographic Area Charles Darwin began to realize that species are related by common an-cestry during a five-year voyage he took aboard the English naval ship HMS *Beagle*. While fulfilling its mission to explore and map the coast of South America, the *Beagle* spent a few weeks in the Galápagos Islands off the coast of present-day Ecuador. Darwin had taken over the role of ship's naturalist and, as the first scien-tist to study the area, gathered extensive collections of the plants and animals found in these islands. Most famous among the birds he collected were the Galápagos finches (featured in Section 25.4) and the Galápagos mockingbirds, pictured in **FIGURE 25.6a**.

Several years after Darwin returned to England, a colleague pointed out that the mockingbirds collected on different islands were distinct species, based on differences in coloration and beak size and shape. This struck Darwin as remarkable. Why would species that inhabit neighboring islands be so similar, yet clearly

(a) Pattern: Although the Galápagos mockingbirds are extremely similar, distinct species are found on different islands.

Nesomimus parvulus *Nesomimus trifasciatus* *Nesomimus melanotis* *Nesomimus macdonaldi*

(b) Recent data support Darwin's hypothesis that the Galápagos mockingbirds share a common ancestor.

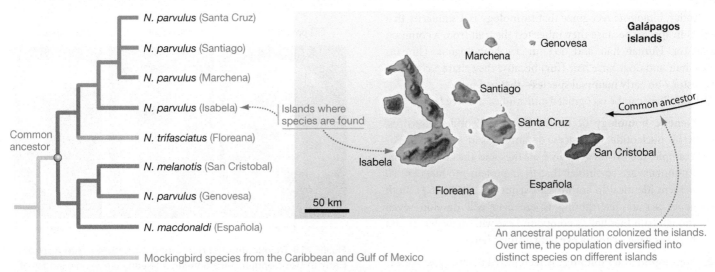

N. parvulus (Santa Cruz)
N. parvulus (Santiago)
N. parvulus (Marchena)
N. parvulus (Isabela)
N. trifasciatus (Floreana)
N. melanotis (San Cristobal)
N. parvulus (Genovesa)
N. macdonaldi (Española)

Common ancestor

Islands where species are found

Mockingbird species from the Caribbean and Gulf of Mexico

50 km

Galápagos islands
Genovesa
Marchena
Santiago
Santa Cruz
Common ancestor
Isabela
San Cristobal
Floreana
Española

An ancestral population colonized the islands. Over time, the population diversified into distinct species on different islands

FIGURE 25.6 Close Relationships among Island Forms Argue for Shared Ancestry.

Gene:	Amino acid sequence (single-letter abbreviations):
Aniridia (Human)	LQRNRTSFTQEQIEALEKEFERTHYPDVFARERLAAKIDLPEARIQVWFSNRRAKWRREE
eyeless (Fruit fly)	LQRNRTSFTNDQIDSLEKEFERTHYPDVFARERLAGKIGLPEARIQVWFSNRRAKWRREE

FIGURE 25.7 Genetic Homology: Genes from Different Species May Be Similar in DNA Sequence or Other Attributes. Amino acid sequences from a portion of the *Aniridia* gene product found in humans are 90 percent identical to those found in the *Drosophila eyeless* gene product. (For a key to the single-letter abbreviations used for the amino acids, see Figure 3.2.)

distinct? This turns out to be a widespread pattern: In island groups across the globe, it is routine to find similar but distinct species on neighboring islands.

Darwin realized that this pattern—puzzling when examined as a product of special creation—made perfect sense when interpreted in the context of evolution, or descent with modification. The mockingbirds were similar, he proposed, because they had descended from the same common ancestor. That is, instead of being created independently, mockingbird populations that colonized different islands had changed through time and formed new species (**FIGURE 25.6b**).

Recent analyses of DNA sequences in these mockingbirds support Darwin's hypothesis. Researchers have used the DNA sequence comparisons to place the mockingbirds on a **phylogenetic tree**—a branching diagram that describes the ancestor–descendant relationships among species or other taxa (see Chapter 28). As Figure 25.6b shows, the Galápagos mockingbirds are each others' closest living relatives. As Darwin predicted, they share a single common ancestor. (For help with reading phylogenetic trees, see **BioSkills 7** in Appendix B.)

Similar Species Share Homologies Translated literally, homology means "the study of likeness." When biologists first began to study the anatomy of humans and other vertebrates, they were struck by the remarkable similarity of their skeletons, muscles, and organs. But because the biologists who did these early studies were advocates of special creation, they could not explain why striking similarities existed among certain organisms but not others.

Today, biologists recognize that **homology** is a similarity that exists in species because they inherited the trait from a common ancestor. Human hair and dog fur are homologous. Humans have hair and dogs have hair (fur) because they share a common ancestor—an early mammal species—that had hair.

Homology can be recognized and studied at three levels:

1. **Genetic homology** occurs in DNA nucleotide sequences, RNA nucleotide sequences, or amino acid sequences. For example, the *eyeless* gene in fruit flies and the *Aniridia* gene in humans are so similar that their protein products are 90 percent identical in amino acid sequence (**FIGURE 25.7**). Both genes act in determining where eyes will develop—even though fruit flies have a compound eye with many lenses and humans have a camera eye with a single lens.

2. **Developmental homology** is recognized in embryos. For example, early chick, human, and cat embryos have tails and

structures called gill pouches (**FIGURE 25.8**). Later, gill pouches are lost in all three species and tails are lost in humans. But in fish, the embryonic gill pouches stay intact and give rise to functioning gills in adults. To explain this observation, biologists hypothesize that gill pouches and tails exist in chicks, humans, and cats because they existed in the fishlike species that was the common ancestor of today's vertebrates. Embryonic gill pouches are a vestigial trait in chicks, humans, and cats; embryonic tails are a vestigial trait in humans.

3. **Structural homology** is a similarity in adult **morphology,** or form. A classic example is the common structural plan observed in the limbs of vertebrates (**FIGURE 25.9**). In Darwin's own words, "What could be more curious than that the hand of a man, formed for grasping, that of a mole for digging, the leg of the horse, the paddle of the porpoise, and the wing of the bat, should all be constructed on the same pattern, and should include the same bones, in the same relative positions?" An engineer would never use the same underlying structure to design a grasping tool, a digging implement, a walking device, a propeller, and a wing. Instead, the structural homology exists because mammals evolved from the lungfish-like ancestor in Figure 25.4, which had the same general arrangement of bones in its fins.

The three levels of homology interact. Genetic homologies cause the developmental homologies observed in embryos, which then lead to the structural homologies recognized in adults. Perhaps the most fundamental of all homologies is the genetic code.

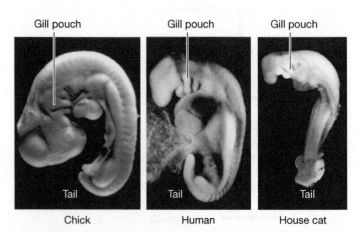

FIGURE 25.8 Developmental Homology: Structures That Appear Early in Development Are Similar. The early embryonic stages of a chick, a human, and a cat show a strong resemblance.

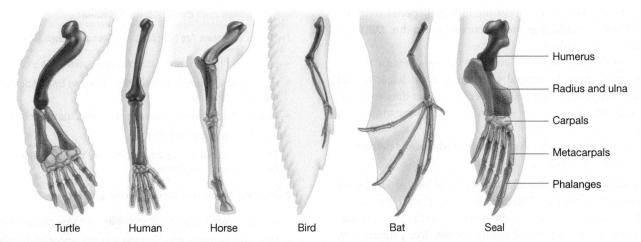

Turtle   Human   Horse   Bird   Bat   Seal

Humerus
Radius and ulna
Carpals
Metacarpals
Phalanges

FIGURE 25.9 Structural Homology: Limbs with Different Functions Have the Same Underlying Structure. Even though their function varies, all vertebrate limbs are modifications of the same number and arrangement of bones. (These limbs are not drawn to scale.)

With a few minor exceptions, all organisms use the same rules for transferring the information coded in DNA into proteins (see Chapter 16).

In some cases, hypotheses about homology can be tested experimentally. For example, researchers (1) isolated a mouse gene that was thought to be homologous to the fruit fly *eyeless* gene, (2) inserted the mouse gene into fruit fly embryos, (3) stimulated expression of the foreign gene in locations that normally give rise to appendages, and (4) observed formation of eyes on legs and antennae (**FIGURE 25.10**). The function of the inserted gene was identical to that of *eyeless*. This result was strong evidence that the fruit fly and mouse genes are homologous, as predicted from their sequence similarity.

Homology is a key concept in contemporary biology:

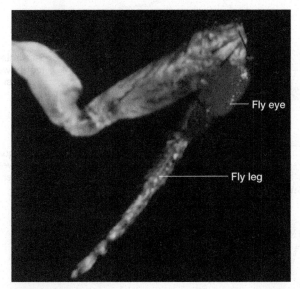

Fly eye

Fly leg

FIGURE 25.10 Evidence for Homology: A Mouse Gene Expressed in Fruit Flies. As an embryo, this fruit fly received a mouse gene that signals where eyes should form. A fruit fly eye formed in the location where the mouse gene was expressed.

- Chemicals that cause cancer in humans can often be identified by testing their effects on mutation rates in bacteria, yeast, zebrafish, mice, and other model organisms because the molecular machinery responsible for copying and repairing DNA is homologous in all organisms (see Chapter 15).

- Drugs intended for human use can be tested on mice or rabbits if the molecules targeted by the drugs are homologous.

- Unknown sequences in the human, rice, or other genomes can be identified if they are homologous to known sequences in yeast, fruit flies, or other well-studied model organisms (see Chapter 21 and **BioSkills 13** in Appendix B).

The theory of evolution by natural selection predicts that homologies will occur. If species were created independently of one another, as special creation claims, these types of similarities would not occur.

Current Examples of Descent from a Common Ancestor Biologists have documented dozens of contemporary populations that are undergoing speciation—a process that results in one species splitting into two or more descendant species. Some populations have served as particularly well-studied examples of speciation in action (see Chapter 27). In most cases, the identity of the ancestral species and the descendant species is known—meaning that biologists have established a direct link between ancestral and descendant species. In addition, the reason for the splitting event is usually known.

The contemporary examples of new species being formed are powerful evidence that species living today are the descendants of species that lived in the past. They support the claim that all organisms are related by descent from a common ancestor.

Evolution's "Internal Consistency"— The Importance of Independent Data Sets

Biologists draw upon data from several sources to challenge the hypothesis that species are immutable and were created independently. The data support the idea that species have descended, with modification, from a common ancestor. **TABLE 25.1** summarizes this evidence.

Perhaps the most powerful evidence for any scientific theory, including evolution by natural selection, is what scientists call internal consistency. This is the observation that data from independent sources agree in supporting predictions made by a theory.

As an example, consider the evolution of whales and dolphins—a group called the cetaceans.

- The fossil record contains a series of species that are clearly identified as cetaceans based on the unusual ear bones found only in this group. Some of the species have the long legs and compact bodies typical of mammals that live primarily on land; some are limbless and have the streamlined bodies typical of aquatic mammals; some have intermediate features.

- A phylogeny of the fossil cetaceans, estimated on the basis of similarities and differences in morphological traits other than limbs and overall body shape, indicates that a gradual transition occurred between terrestrial forms and aquatic, whalelike forms (**FIGURE 25.11**).

SUMMARY TABLE 25.1 Evidence for Evolution

Prediction 1: Species Are Not Static, but Change through Time

- Life on Earth is ancient. Most species have gone extinct.
- Fossil (extinct) species frequently resemble living species found in the same area.
- Transitional features document change in traits through time.
- Vestigial traits are common.
- The characteristics of populations vary within species and can be observed changing today.

Prediction 2: Species Are Related, Not Independent

- Closely related species often live in the same geographic area.
- Homologous traits are common and are recognized at three levels:
  1. genetic (gene structure and the genetic code)
  2. developmental (embryonic structures and processes)
  3. structural (morphological traits in adults)
- The formation of new species, from preexisting species, can be observed today.

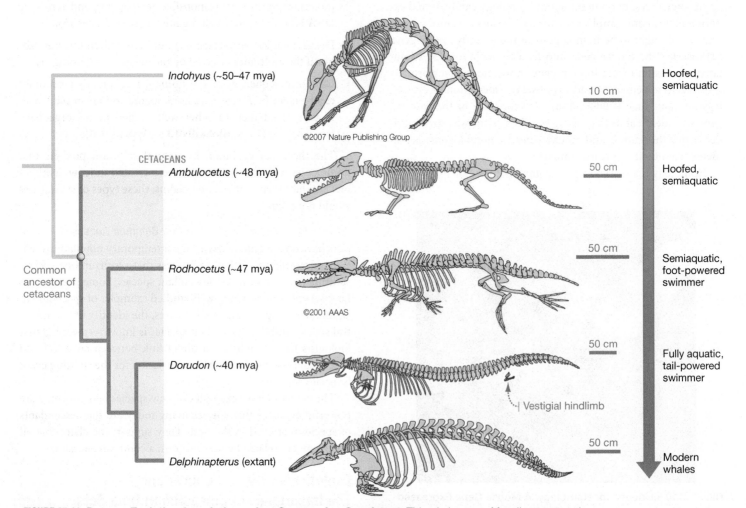

FIGURE 25.11 Data on Evolution from Independent Sources Are Consistent. This phylogeny of fossil cetaceans is consistent with data from relative dating, absolute dating, and phylogenies estimated from molecular traits in living species—all agree that whales evolved from terrestrial ancestors that were related to today's hippos.

- Relative dating, based on the positions of sedimentary rocks where the fossils were found, agrees with the order of species indicated in the phylogeny.

- Absolute dating, based on analyses of radioactive atoms in rocks in or near the layers where the fossils were found, also agrees with the order of species indicated in the phylogeny.

- A phylogeny of living whales and dolphins, estimated from similarities and differences in DNA sequences, indicates that hippos—which spend much of their time in shallow water—are the closest living relative of cetaceans. This observation supports the hypothesis that cetaceans and hippos shared a common ancestor that was semiaquatic.

- Some whales have vestigial hip and limb bones as adults, and some dolphin embryos have vestigial hindlimb buds—outgrowths where legs form in other mammals.

The general message here is that many independent lines of evidence converge on the same conclusion: Whales gradually evolved from a terrestrial ancestor about 50 million years ago.

As you evaluate the evidence supporting the pattern component of the theory of evolution, though, it's important to recognize that no single observation or experiment instantly "proved" the fact of evolution and swept aside belief in special creation. Rather, data from many different sources are much more consistent with evolution than with special creation. Descent with modification is a successful and powerful scientific theory because it explains observations—such as vestigial traits and the close relationships among species on neighboring islands—that special creation does not.

What about the process component of the theory of evolution by natural selection? If the limbs of bats and humans were not created independently and recently, how did they come to be?

check your understanding

If you understand that . . .
- Species are not static, but change through time.
- Species are related by common ancestry.

✔ **You should be able to . . .**

1. Determine what kind of evidence would support the hypothesis that birds evolved from dinosaurs.

2. Explain why the DNA sequences of chimpanzees and humans are about 96 percent similar.

Answers are available in Appendix A.

25.3 The Process of Evolution: How Does Natural Selection Work?

Darwin's greatest contribution did not lie in recognizing the fact of evolution. Lamarck and other researchers had proposed evolution long before Darwin began his work. Instead, Darwin's

crucial insight lay in recognizing a process, called natural selection, that could explain the pattern of descent with modification.

Darwin's Inspiration

How did Darwin arrive at his insight? In part, he turned to pigeon breeding—a model system that would be easier to study and manipulate than populations in the wild. Pigeon breeding was popular in England at the time, offering a wealth of experience for Darwin to tap into. Also, pigeons could be maintained easily, and in Darwin's words, "the diversity of the breeds is something astonishing" (see examples in **FIGURE 25.12**).

Darwin crossbred pigeons and observed how characteristics were passed on to offspring. He could choose certain individuals with desirable traits to reproduce, thus manipulating the composition of the population by a process called **artificial selection.** It was clear to Darwin and other breeders that the diverse varieties were all descended from the wild rock pigeons.

Another influence on Darwin was the fortuitous publication of a book by Thomas Robert Malthus, *An Essay on the Principle of Population*, which inspired a great deal of discussion in England at the time. Malthus's studies of human populations in England and elsewhere led him to a startling conclusion: Since many more individuals are born than can survive, a "struggle for existence" occurs as people compete for food and places to live.

Darwin combined his observations of artificial selection with this notion of "struggle for existence" in natural populations, which he knew—from his extensive studies—contained variation. From this synthesis arose his concept of natural selection. Although both Darwin and Wallace arrived at the same idea, Darwin's name is more closely associated with the concept of natural selection because he thought of it first and provided extensive evidence for it in *On the Origin of Species*.

FIGURE 25.12 Diversity of Pigeon Breeds in Captivity. Darwin used the breeding of pigeons as a model system to study how the characteristics of populations can change over time.

Darwin's Four Postulates

Darwin broke the process of evolution by natural selection into four simple postulates (criteria) that form a logical sequence:

1. The individual organisms that make up a population vary in the traits they possess, such as their size and shape.

2. Some of the trait differences are heritable, meaning that they are passed on to offspring. For example, tall parents tend to have tall offspring.

3. In each generation, many more offspring are produced than can possibly survive. Thus, only some individuals in the population survive long enough to produce offspring, and among the individuals that produce offspring, some will produce more than others.

4. The subset of individuals that survive best and produce the most offspring is not a random sample of the population. Instead, individuals with certain heritable traits are more likely to survive and reproduce. **Natural selection** occurs when individuals with certain characteristics produce more offspring than do individuals without those characteristics. The individuals are selected naturally—meaning, by the environment.

Because the selected traits are passed on to offspring, the frequency of the selected traits increases from one generation to the next. We now know that traits are determined by alleles, particular versions of genes (see Chapter 14). Thus, the outcome of evolution by natural selection is a change in allele frequencies in a population over time.

In studying these criteria, you should realize that variation among individuals in a population is essential if evolution is to occur. Darwin had to introduce population thinking into biology because it is populations that change over time. To come up with these postulates and understand their consequences, Darwin had to think in a revolutionary way.

Today, biologists usually condense Darwin's four postulates into a two-part statement that communicates the essence of evolution by natural selection more forcefully: Evolution by natural selection occurs when **(1)** heritable variation leads to **(2)** differential reproductive success.

The Biological Definitions of Fitness, Adaptation, and Selection

To explain the process of natural selection, Darwin referred to successful individuals as "more fit" than other individuals. In doing so, he gave the word fitness a definition different from its everyday English usage. Biological **fitness** is the ability of an individual to produce surviving, fertile offspring relative to that ability in other individuals in the population.

Note that fitness is a measurable quantity. When researchers study a population in the lab or in the field, they can estimate the relative fitness of individuals by counting the number of surviving offspring each individual produces and comparing the data.

The concept of fitness, in turn, provides a compact way of formally defining adaptation. The biological meaning of adaptation,

like the biological meaning of fitness, is different from its normal English usage. In biology, an **adaptation** is a heritable trait that increases the fitness of an individual in a particular environment relative to individuals lacking the trait. Adaptations increase fitness—the ability to produce viable, fertile offspring. You can see the Big Picture of how adaptation and fitness relate to natural selection on pages 526–527.

Lastly, the term selection has a commonsense meaning in the context of artificial selection. Breeders *choose* which characteristics they want to keep or get rid of in their plant and animal breeds. However, the term selection has a very different meaning in the biological context of natural selection. Here, it refers to a passive process—differential reproduction as a result of heritable variation—not a purposeful choice.

25.4 Evolution in Action: Recent Research on Natural Selection

The theory of evolution by natural selection is testable. If the theory is correct, biologists should be able to test the validity of each of Darwin's postulates—documenting heritable variation and differential reproductive success in a wide array of natural populations.

This section summarizes two examples in which evolution by natural selection is being observed in nature. Literally hundreds of other case studies are available, involving a wide variety of traits and organisms. To begin, let's explore the evolution of drug resistance, one of the great challenges facing today's biomedical researchers and physicians.

Case Study 1: How Did *Mycobacterium tuberculosis* Become Resistant to Antibiotics?

Mycobacterium tuberculosis, the bacterium that causes **tuberculosis**, or TB, has long been a scourge of humankind. It usually infects the lungs and causes fever, coughing, sweats, weight loss, and often death. In Europe and the United States, TB was once as great a public health issue as cancer is now. It receded in importance during the early 1900s, though, for two reasons:

1. Advances in nutrition made people better able to fight off most *M. tuberculosis* infections quickly.

2. The development of antibiotics allowed physicians to stop even advanced infections.

In the late 1980s, however, rates of *M. tuberculosis* infection surged in many countries, and in 1993 the World Health Organization declared TB a global health emergency. Physicians were particularly alarmed because the strains of *M. tuberculosis* responsible for the increase were largely or completely resistant to antibiotics that were once extremely effective.

How and why did the evolution of drug resistance occur? The case of a single patient—a young man who lived in Baltimore—illustrates what is happening all over the world.

A Patient History The story begins when the individual was admitted to the hospital with fever and coughing. Chest X-rays, followed by bacterial cultures of fluid coughed up from the lungs, showed that he had an active TB infection. He was given several antibiotics for 6 weeks, followed by twice-weekly doses of the antibiotic rifampin for an additional 33 weeks. Ten months after therapy started, bacterial cultures from the patient's chest fluid indicated no *M. tuberculosis* cells. His chest X-rays were also normal. The antibiotics seemed to have cleared the infection.

Just two months after the TB tests proved normal, however, the young man was readmitted to the hospital with a fever, severe cough, and labored breathing. Despite being treated with a variety of antibiotics, including rifampin, he died of respiratory failure 10 days later. Samples of material from his lungs showed that *M. tuberculosis* was again growing actively there. But this time the bacterial cells were completely resistant to rifampin.

Drug-resistant *M. tuberculosis* cells had killed this patient. Where did they come from? Could a strain that was resistant to antibiotic treatment have evolved *within* him? To answer this question, a research team analyzed DNA from the drug-resistant strain and compared it with stored DNA from *M. tuberculosis* cells that had been isolated a year earlier from the same patient. After examining extensive stretches from each genome, the biologists were able to find only one difference: a point mutation in a gene called *rpoB*.

A Mutation in a Bacterial Gene Confers Resistance The *rpoB* gene codes for a component of RNA polymerase. This enzyme transcribes DNA to mRNA, so it is essential to the survival and reproduction of bacterial cells (see Chapter 17). In this case, the point mutation in the *rpoB* gene changed a cytosine to a thymine, forming a new allele for the *rpoB* gene (see Chapter 16). This missense mutation caused a change in the amino acid sequence of the RNA polymerase (from a serine to a leucine at the 153rd amino acid)—and a change in its shape.

This shape change proved critical. Rifampin, the antibiotic that was being used to treat the patient, works by binding to the RNA polymerase of *M. tuberculosis* and interfering with transcription. Bacterial cells with the C → T mutation continue to produce offspring efficiently even in the presence of the drug because the drug cannot bind efficiently to the mutant RNA polymerase.

These results suggest the steps that led to this patient's death (**FIGURE 25.13**).

1. By chance, one or a few of the bacterial cells present in the patient, before drug therapy started, happened to have the *rpoB* allele with the C → T mutation. Under normal conditions, mutant forms of RNA polymerase do not work as well as the more common form, so cells with the C → T mutation would not produce many offspring and would stay at low frequency—even while the overall population grew to the point of inducing symptoms that sent the young man to the hospital.

2. Therapy with rifampin began. In response, cells in the population with normal RNA polymerase began to grow much more slowly or to die outright. As a result, the overall bacterial population declined in size so drastically that the patient appeared to be cured—his symptoms began to disappear.

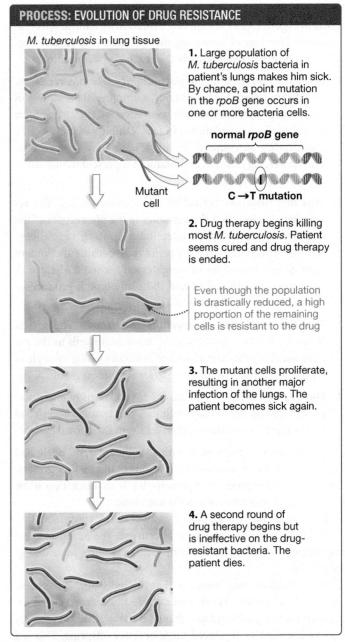

PROCESS: EVOLUTION OF DRUG RESISTANCE

M. tuberculosis in lung tissue

1. Large population of *M. tuberculosis* bacteria in patient's lungs makes him sick. By chance, a point mutation in the *rpoB* gene occurs in one or more bacteria cells.

normal *rpoB* gene

Mutant cell

C → T mutation

2. Drug therapy begins killing most *M. tuberculosis*. Patient seems cured and drug therapy is ended.

Even though the population is drastically reduced, a high proportion of the remaining cells is resistant to the drug

3. The mutant cells proliferate, resulting in another major infection of the lungs. The patient becomes sick again.

4. A second round of drug therapy begins but is ineffective on the drug-resistant bacteria. The patient dies.

FIGURE 25.13 Alleles That Confer Drug Resistance Increase in Frequency When Drugs Are Used.

3. Cells with the C → T mutation continued to increase in number after therapy ended. Eventually the *M. tuberculosis* population regained its former abundance, and the patient's symptoms reappeared.

4. Drug-resistant *M. tuberculosis* cells now dominated the population, so the second round of rifampin therapy was futile.

✔ If you understand these concepts, you should be able to explain: (1) Why the relapse in step 3 occurred, and (2) whether a family member or health-care worker who got TB from this patient at step 3 or step 4 would respond to drug therapy.

Testing Darwin's Postulates Does the sequence of events illustrated in Figure 25.13 indicate that evolution by natural selection occurred? One way of answering this question is to review Darwin's four postulates and test whether each one was verified:

1. *Did variation exist in the population?* The answer is yes. Due to mutation, both resistant and nonresistant strains of TB were present before administration of the drug. Most *M. tuberculosis* populations, in fact, exhibit variation for the trait; studies on cultured *M. tuberculosis* show that a mutation conferring resistance to rifampin is present in one out of every 10^7 to 10^8 cells.

2. *Was this variation heritable?* The answer is yes. The researchers showed that the variation in the phenotypes of the two strains—from drug susceptibility to drug resistance—was due to variation in their genotypes. Because the mutant *rpoB* gene is passed on to daughter cells when a *Mycobacterium* replicates, the allele and the phenotype it produces—drug resistance—are passed on to offspring.

3. *Was there variation in reproductive success?* The answer is yes. Only a tiny fraction of *M. tuberculosis* cells in the patient survived the first round of antibiotics long enough to reproduce. Most cells died and left no or almost no offspring.

4. *Did selection occur?* The answer is yes. When rifampin was present, certain cells—those with the drug-resistant allele—had higher reproductive success than cells with the normal allele.

M. tuberculosis individuals with the mutant *rpoB* allele had higher fitness in an environment where rifampin was present. The mutant allele produces a protein that is an adaptation when the cell's environment contains the antibiotic.

This study verified all four postulates and confirmed that evolution by natural selection had occurred. The *M. tuberculosis* population evolved because the mutant *rpoB* allele increased in frequency.

It is critical to note, however, that the individual cells themselves did not evolve. When natural selection occurred, the individual bacterial cells did not change through time; they simply survived or died, or produced more or fewer offspring. This is a fundamentally important point: Natural selection acts on individuals, because individuals experience differential reproductive success. But only populations evolve. Allele frequencies change in populations, not in individuals. Understanding evolution by natural selection requires population thinking.

Drug Resistance: A Widespread Problem The events reviewed for this single patient have occurred many times in other patients. Recent surveys indicate that drug-resistant strains now account for about 10 percent of the *M. tuberculosis*–causing infections throughout the world.

Unfortunately, the emergence of drug resistance in TB is far from unusual. Resistance to a wide variety of insecticides, fungicides, antibiotics, antiviral drugs, and herbicides has evolved in hundreds of insects, fungi, bacteria, viruses, and plants. In every case, evolution has occurred because individuals with the

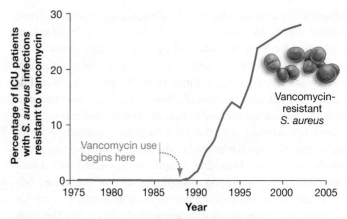

FIGURE 25.14 Trends in Infections Due to Antibiotic-resistant Bacteria. The line indicates changes in the percentage of *S. aureus* infections, acquired in hospitals, that are resistant to the antibiotic vancomycin.

DATA: Centers for Disease Control, 2004.

heritable ability to resist some chemical compound were present in the original population. As the susceptible individuals die from the pesticide, herbicide, or drug, the alleles that confer resistance increase in frequency.

To drive home the prevalence of evolution in response to drugs and other human-induced changes in the environment, consider the data in **FIGURE 25.14**. The graph shows changes through time in the percentage of infections, in intensive care units in the United States, caused by strains of the bacterium *Staphylococcus aureus* that are resistant to the antibiotic vancomycin. Most of these *S. aureus* cells are also resistant to methicillin and other antibiotics—a phenomenon known as multidrug resistance. In some cases, physicians have no effective antibiotics available to treat these infections. ✔ If you understand antibiotic resistance, you should be able to explain why the overprescription of antibiotics by doctors, or the overuse of everyday soaps and cleaners laced with antibiotics, can be a health risk.

Case Study 2: Why Are Beak Size, Beak Shape, and Body Size Changing in Galápagos Finches?

Can biologists study evolution in response to natural environmental change—when humans are not involved? The answer is yes. As an example, consider research led by Peter and Rosemary Grant. For over four decades, these biologists have been investigating changes in beak size, beak shape, and body size that have occurred in finches native to the Galápagos Islands.

Because the island of Daphne Major of the Galápagos is so small—about the size of 80 football fields—the Grants' team has been able to catch, weigh, and measure all the medium ground finches in the island's population (**FIGURE 25.15**) and mark each one with a unique combination of colored leg bands. The medium ground finch makes its living by eating seeds. Finches crack seeds with their beaks.

Early studies of the finch population established that beak size and shape and body size vary among individuals, and that beak

Medium ground finch
(*Geospiza fortis*)

Daphne Major

FIGURE 25.15 Studying Evolution in Action on the Galápagos.

morphology and body size are heritable. Stated another way, parents with particularly deep beaks tend to have offspring with deep beaks. Large parents also tend to have large offspring. Beak size and shape and body size are traits with heritable variation.

Selection during Drought Conditions   Not long after the team began to study the finch population, a dramatic selection event occurred. In the annual wet season of 1977, Daphne Major received just 24 millimeters (mm) of rain instead of the 130 mm that normally falls. During the drought, few plants were able to produce seeds, and 84 percent (about 660 individuals) of the medium ground finch population disappeared.

Two observations support the hypothesis that most or all of these individuals died of starvation:

1. The researchers found 38 dead birds, and all were emaciated.

2. None of the missing individuals were spotted on nearby islands, and none reappeared once the drought had ended and food supplies returned to normal.

The research team realized that the die-off was a **natural experiment.** Instead of comparing groups created by direct manipulation under controlled conditions, natural experiments allow researchers to compare treatment groups created by an unplanned change in conditions. In this case, the Grants' team could test whether natural selection occurred by comparing the population before and after the drought.

Were the survivors different from nonsurvivors? The histograms in **FIGURE 25.16** show the distribution of beak sizes in the population before and after the drought. Notice the different scales of the *y*-axes of the two graphs. (For more on how histograms are constructed, see **BioSkills 3** in Appendix B.) On average, survivors tended to have much deeper beaks than did the birds that died.

RESEARCH

QUESTION: Did natural selection on ground ☐nches occur when the environment changed?

HYPOTHESIS: Beak characteristics changed in response to a drought.

NULL HYPOTHESIS: No changes in beak characteristics occurred in response to a drought.

EXPERIMENTAL SETUP:

Weigh and measure all birds in the population before and after the drought.

PREDICTION:

PREDICTION OF NULL HYPOTHESIS:

RESULTS:

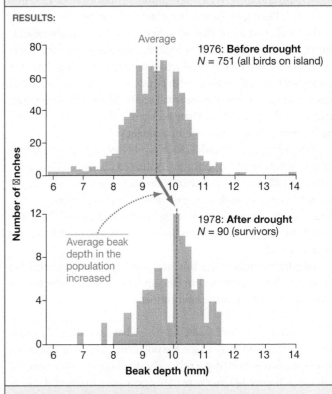

CONCLUSION: Natural selection occurred. The characteristics of the population have changed.

FIGURE 25.16 A Natural Experiment: Changes in a Medium Ground Finch Population in Response to a Change in the Environment (a Drought). The results show the distribution of beak depth in the population of medium ground finches on Daphne Major before and after the drought of 1977. *N* is the population size.

SOURCE: Boag, P. T., and P. R. Grant. 1981. Intense natural selection in a population of Darwin's finches (Geospizinae) in the Galápagos. *Science* 214: 82–85.

✔**EXERCISE** Fill in the predictions made by the two hypotheses.

Why were deeper beaks adaptive? At the peak of the drought, most seed sources were absent and the tough fruits of a plant called *Tribulus cistoides* served as the finches' primary food source. These fruits are so difficult to crack that finches ignore them in years when food supplies are normal. The Grants hypothesized that individuals with particularly large and deep beaks were more likely to crack these fruits efficiently enough to survive.

At this point, the Grants had shown that natural selection led to an increase in average beak depth in the population. When breeding resumed in 1978, the offspring produced had beaks that were half a millimeter deeper, on average, than those in the population that existed before the drought. This result confirmed that evolution had occurred.

In only one generation, natural selection led to a measurable change in the characteristics of the population. Alleles that led to the development of deep beaks had increased in frequency in the population. Large, deep beaks were an adaptation for cracking large fruits and seeds.

Continued Changes in the Environment, Continued Selection, Continued Evolution

In 1983, the environment on the Galápagos Islands changed again. Over a seven-month period, a total of 1359 mm of rain fell. Plant growth was luxuriant, and finches fed primarily on the small, soft seeds that were being produced in abundance. During this interval, small individuals with small, pointed beaks had exceptionally high reproductive success—meaning that they had higher fitness than those with large, deep beaks—because they were better able to harvest the small seeds. As a result, the characteristics of the population changed again. Alleles associated with small, pointed beaks increased in frequency.

Over subsequent decades, the Grants have documented continued evolution in response to continued changes in the environment. **FIGURE 25.17** documents changes that have occurred in average body size, beak size, and beak shape over 35 years. From 1972 to 2006, average body size got smaller and average beak size initially increased and then declined. In addition, finch beaks got much pointier.

Long-term studies like this are proving to be powerful because they have succeeded in documenting natural selection in response to changes in the environment.

Which Genes Are under Selection?

Characteristics like body size, beak size, and beak shape are polygenic, meaning that many genes—each one exerting a relatively small effect—influence the trait (see Chapter 14). Because many genes are involved, it can be difficult for researchers to know exactly which alleles are changing in frequency when polygenic traits evolve.

To explore which of the medium ground finch's genes might be under selection, researchers in Clifford Tabin's lab began studying beak development in an array of Galápagos finch species. More specifically, they looked for variation in the pattern of expression of cell–cell signals that had already been identified as important in the development of chicken beaks. The hope was that homologous genes might affect beak development in finches.

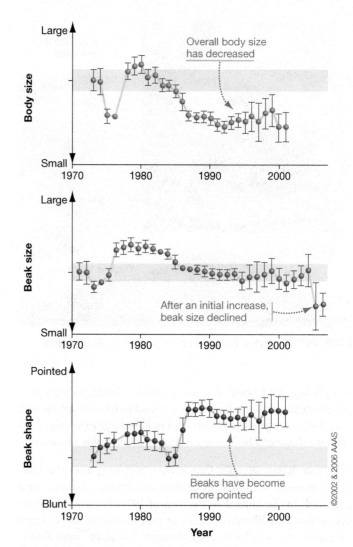

FIGURE 25.17 Body Size, Beak Size, and Beak Shape in Finches Changed over a 35-Year Interval.

DATA: Grant, P. R., and B. R. Grant. 2002. *Science* 296: 707–711; Grant, P. R., and B. R. Grant. 2006. *Science* 313: 224–226.

The researchers struck pay dirt when they carried out in situ hybridization (a technique featured in Chapter 22) showing where a cell–cell signal gene called *Bmp4* is expressed.

- There is a strong correlation between the amount of *Bmp4* expression when beaks are developing in young Galápagos finches and the width and depth of adult beaks (**FIGURE 25.18**).

- When the researchers experimentally increased *Bmp4* expression in young chickens, they found that beaks got wider and deeper than normal.

Similar experiments suggest that variation in alleles for a molecule called calmodulin, which is involved in calcium signaling during development, affects beak length. Based on these data, biologists suspect that alleles associated with *Bmp4* and calmodulin expression may be under selection in the population of medium ground finches that the Grants are studying. If so, the research community will have made a direct connection between natural selection on phenotypes and evolutionary change in genotypes.

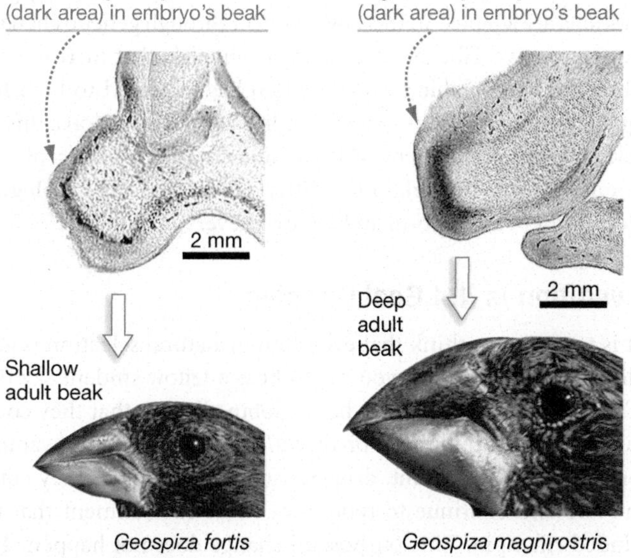

Lower *Bmp4* expression (dark area) in embryo's beak

Higher *Bmp4* expression (dark area) in embryo's beak

2 mm

2 mm

Shallow adult beak

Deep adult beak

Geospiza fortis

Geospiza magnirostris

FIGURE 25.18 Changes in *Bmp4* Expression Change Beak Depth and Width. These micrographs are in situ hybridizations (see Chapter 22) showing the location and extent of *Bmp4* expression in young *Geospiza fortis* and *G. magnirostris*. In these and four other species that were investigated, the amount of Bmp4 protein produced correlates with the depth and width of the adult beak.

check your understanding

C Y U

If you understand that . . .

- If individuals with certain alleles produce the most offspring in a population, then those alleles increase in frequency over time. Evolution results from this process of natural selection on heritable variation.

✔ You should be able to . . .

1. List Darwin's four postulates in your own words and indicate which are related to heritable variation and which are related to differential reproductive success.

2. Explain how data on beak size and shape of Galápagos finch populations provide examples of heritable variation and differential reproductive success.

Answers are available in Appendix A.

25.5 Common Misconceptions about Natural Selection and Adaptation

Evolution by natural selection is a simple process—just the logical outcome of some straightforward postulates. Ironically, it can be extremely difficult to understand.

Research has verified that evolution by natural selection is often misunderstood. To help clarify how the process works, let's consider four of the most common types of misconceptions about natural selection, summarized in **TABLE 25.2** (on page 460).

Selection Acts on Individuals, but Evolutionary Change Occurs in Populations

Perhaps the most important point to clarify about natural selection is that during the process, individuals do not change—only the population does. During the drought, the beaks of individual finches did not become deeper. Rather, the average beak depth in the population increased over time because deep-beaked individuals produced more offspring than shallow-beaked individuals did. Natural selection acted on individuals, but the evolutionary change occurred in the characteristics of the population.

In the same way, individual *M. tuberculosis* cells did not change when rifampin was introduced to their environment. Each of these bacterial cells had the same RNA polymerase alleles throughout its life. But because the mutant allele increased in frequency in the population over time, the average characteristics of the bacterial population changed.

Natural Selection Is Not "Lamarckian" Inheritance There is a sharp contrast between evolution by natural selection and evolution by the inheritance of acquired characters—the hypothesis promoted by Jean-Baptiste de Lamarck. If you recall, Lamarck proposed that (1) individuals change in response to challenges posed by the environment (such as giraffes stretching their necks to reach leaves high in the treetops), and (2) the changed traits are then passed on to offspring. The key claim is that the important evolutionary changes occur in individuals.

In contrast, Darwin realized that individuals do not change when they are selected. Instead, they simply produce more or less offspring than other individuals do. When this happens, alleles found in the selected individuals become more or less frequent in the population.

Darwin was correct: There is no mechanism that makes it possible for natural selection to change the nature of an allele inside an individual. An individual's heritable characteristics don't change when natural selection occurs. Natural selection just sorts existing variants—it doesn't change them.

Acclimatization Is *Not* Adaptation The issue of change in individuals is tricky because individuals often *do* change in response to changes in the environment. For example, if you were to travel to the Tibetan Plateau in Asia, your body would experience oxygen deprivation due to the low partial pressure of oxygen at high elevations (see Figure 45.2). As a result, your body would produce more of the oxygen-carrying pigment hemoglobin and more hemoglobin-carrying red blood cells. Your body does not normally produce more red blood cells than it needs, because viscous (thick) blood can cause a disease—chronic mountain sickness—that can lead to heart failure.

The increase in red blood cells is an example of what biologists call **acclimatization**—a change in an individual's phenotype that occurs in response to a change in natural environmental conditions. (When this process occurs in study organisms in a laboratory, it is called **acclimation**.) Phenotypic changes due to acclimatization are not passed on to offspring, because no alleles have changed. As a result, acclimatization does not cause evolution.

Misconception	Example
"Evolutionary change occurs in organisms" CORRECTION: • Natural selection just sorts existing variants in organisms; it doesn't change them • Evolutionary change occurs only in populations • Acclimatization ≠ adaptation Selection does not cause neck length to increase in individual giraffes, only in populations	
"Adaptations occur because organisms want or need them" CORRECTION: • Mutation, the source of new alleles, occurs by chance • Evolution is not goal directed or progressive • There is no such thing as a higher or lower organism Tapeworms are not "lower" than their human hosts, just adapted to a different environment	
"Organisms sacri☐ce themselves for the good of the species" CORRECTION: • Individuals with alleles that cause self-sacrificing behavior die and do not produce offspring, so these alleles are eliminated from the population Lemmings do not jump off cliffs into the sea to save the species	
"Evolution perfects organisms" CORRECTION: • Some traits are nonadaptive • Some traits cannot be optimized due to fitness trade-offs • Some traits are limited by genetic or historical constraints Finch beaks cannot be both deep and narrow, due to genetic constraints	

In contrast, populations that have lived in Tibet for many generations are adapted to this environment through genetic changes. Among native Tibetans, for example, an allele that increases the ability of hemoglobin to hold oxygen has increased to high frequency. In populations that do not live at high elevations, this allele is rare or nonexistent. ✔ If you understand this concept, you should be able to explain the difference between the biological definition of adaptation and its use in everyday English.

Evolution Is Not Goal Directed

It is tempting to think that evolution by natural selection is goal directed. For example, you might hear a fellow student say that Tibetans "needed" the new hemoglobin allele so that they could survive at high altitudes, or that *M. tuberculosis* cells "wanted" or "needed" the mutant, drug-resistant allele so that they could survive and continue to reproduce in an environment that included rifampin. This purposeful change does not happen. The mutations that created the mutant alleles in both examples occurred randomly, due to errors in DNA synthesis, and they just happened to be advantageous when the environments changed.

Stated another way, mutations do not occur to solve problems. Mutations just happen. Every mutation is equally likely to occur in every environment. There is no mechanism that enables the environment to direct which mistakes DNA polymerase makes when copying genes. Adaptations do not occur because organisms want or need them.

Evolution Is Not Progressive   It is often appealing to think that evolution by natural selection is progressive—meaning organisms have gotten "better" over time. (In this context, *better* usually means bigger, stronger, or more complex.) It is true that the groups appearing later in the fossil record are often more morphologically complex than closely related groups that appeared earlier. Flowering plants are considered more complex than mosses, and most biologists would agree that the morphology of mammals is more complex than that of the first vertebrates in the fossil record. But there is nothing predetermined or absolute about this tendency.

In fact, complex traits are routinely lost or simplified over time as a result of evolution by natural selection. You've already analyzed evidence documenting limb loss in snakes (Chapter 22) and whales (this chapter). Populations that become parasitic are particularly prone to loss of complex traits. For example, the tapeworm parasites of humans and other mammals have lost their sophisticated digestive tracts and mouths as a result of natural selection—tapeworms simply absorb nutrients directly from their environment.

There Is No Such Thing as a Higher or Lower Organism   The nonprogressive nature of evolution by natural selection contrasts sharply with Lamarck's conception of the evolutionary process, in which organisms progress over time to higher and higher levels on a chain of being (see Figure 25.1).

Under Aristotle's and Lamarck's hypothesis, it is sensible to refer to "higher" and "lower" organisms. But under evolution by natural selection, there is no such thing as a higher or lower organism (**FIGURE 25.19**). Mosses may be a more ancient group than flowering plants, but neither group is higher or lower than the other. Mosses simply have a different suite of adaptations than do flowering plants, so they thrive in different types of environments. A human is no higher than its tapeworm parasite; each is well adapted to its environment.

Organisms Do Not Act for the Good of the Species

Consider the widely circulated story that rodents called lemmings sacrifice themselves for the good of their species. The story claims that when lemming populations are high, overgrazing is so extensive that the entire species is threatened with starvation and extinction. In response, some individuals throw themselves into the sea and drown. This lowers the overall population size and allows the vegetation to recover enough to save the species. Even though individuals suffer, the good-of-the-species hypothesis maintains that the behavior evolved because the group benefits.

The lemming suicide story is false. Although lemmings do disperse from areas of high population density to find habitats with higher food availability, they do not throw themselves into the sea.

To understand why this type of self-sacrificing behavior does not occur, suppose that certain alleles predispose lemmings to sacrifice themselves for others. But consider what happens if alleles exist that prevent this type of behavior—what biologists call

a "selfish" allele. Individuals with self-sacrificing alleles die and do not produce offspring. But individuals with selfish, cheater alleles survive and produce offspring. As a result, selfish alleles increase in frequency while self-sacrificing alleles decrease in frequency. Thus, it is not possible for self-sacrificing alleles to evolve by natural selection.

There Are Constraints on Natural Selection

Although organisms are often exquisitely adapted to their environment, adaptation is far from perfect. A long list of circumstances limits the effectiveness of natural selection; only a few of the most important are discussed here.

Nonadaptive Traits   Vestigial traits such as the human coccyx (tailbone) and goose bumps do not increase the fitness of individuals with those traits. The structures are not adaptive. They exist because they were present in the ancestral population.

Vestigial traits are not the only types of structures with no or reduced function. Some adult traits exist as holdovers from structures that appear early in development. For example, human males have nipples despite the absence of mammary glands. Nipples exist in men because they form in the human embryo before sex hormones begin directing the development of male organs instead of female organs.

Perhaps the best example of nonadaptive traits involves evolutionary changes in DNA sequences. A mutation may change a base in the third position of a codon without changing the amino acid sequence of the protein encoded by that gene. Changes such as these are said to be silent. They occur due to the redundancy of the genetic code (see Chapter 16). Silent changes in DNA sequences are extremely common. But because they don't change the phenotype, they can't be acted on by natural selection and are not adaptive.

Genetic Constraints   The Grants' team analyzed data on the characteristics of finches that survived the 1977 drought in the Galápagos, and the team made an interesting observation: Although individuals with deep beaks survived better than individuals with shallow beaks, birds with particularly narrow beaks survived better than individuals with wider beaks.

This observation made sense because finches crack *Tribulus* fruits by twisting them. Narrow beaks concentrate the twisting force more efficiently than wider beaks, so they are especially useful for cracking the fruits. But narrower beaks did not evolve in the population.

To explain why, the biologists noted that parents with deep beaks tend to have offspring with beaks that are both deep and wide. This is a common pattern. Many alleles that affect body size have an effect on all aspects of size—not just one structure or dimension. As a result, selection for increased beak depth overrode selection for narrow beaks, even though a deep and narrow beak would have been more advantageous.

The general point here is that selection was not able to optimize all aspects of a trait due to **genetic correlation.** Genetic correlations occur because of pleiotropy, in which a single allele affects multiple traits (see Chapter 14). In this case, selection on

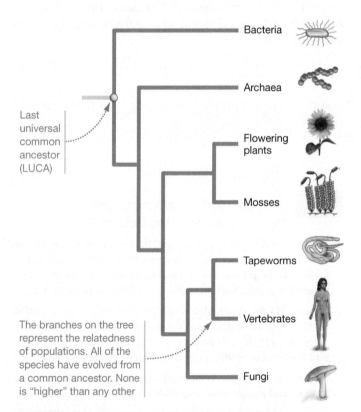

FIGURE 25.19 Evolution Produces a Tree of Life, Not a Progressive Ladder of Life. Under evolution by natural selection, species are related by common ancestry and all have evolved through time. (Not all branches of the tree of life are shown.)

Bacteria

Archaea

Flowering plants

Mosses

Tapeworms

Vertebrates

Fungi

Last universal common ancestor (LUCA)

The branches on the tree represent the relatedness of populations. All of the species have evolved from a common ancestor. None is "higher" than any other alleles for one trait (increased beak depth) caused a correlated, though suboptimal, increase in another trait (beak width).

Genetic correlations are not the only genetic constraint on adaptation. Lack of genetic variation is also important. Consider that salamanders have the ability to regrow severed limbs. Some eels and sharks can sense electric fields. Birds can see ultraviolet light. Even though these traits would possibly confer increased reproductive success in humans, they do not exist—because humans lack the requisite genes.

Fitness Trade-offs   In everyday English, the term trade-off refers to a compromise between competing goals. It is difficult to design a car that is both large and fuel efficient, a bicycle that is both rugged and light, or a plane that is both fast and maneuverable.

In nature, selection occurs in the context of fitness trade-offs. A **fitness trade-off** is a compromise between traits, in terms of how those traits perform in the environment. During the drought in the Galápagos, for example, medium ground finches with large bodies had an advantage because they were able to chase off smaller birds from the few remaining sources of seeds. But individuals with large bodies require large amounts of food to maintain their mass; they also tend to be slower and less nimble than smaller individuals. When food is scarce, large individuals are more prone to starvation. Even if large size is advantageous in an environment, there is always counteracting selection that prevents individuals from getting even bigger.

Biologists have documented trade-offs between the size of eggs or seeds that an individual makes and the number of offspring it can produce, between rapid growth and long life span, and between bright coloration and tendency to attract predators.

The message of this research is simple: Because selection acts on many traits at once, every adaptation is a compromise.

Historical Constraints   In addition to being constrained by genetic correlations, lack of genetic variation, and fitness trade-offs, adaptations are constrained by history. The reason is simple: All traits have evolved from previously existing traits.

Natural selection acts on structures that originally had a very different function. For example, the tiny incus, malleus, and stapes bones found in your middle ear evolved from bones that were part of the jaw and jaw support in the ancestors of mammals. These bones now function in transmitting and amplifying sound from your outer ear to your inner ear. Biologists routinely interpret these bones as adaptations that improve your ability to hear airborne sounds. But are the bones a "perfect" solution to the problem of transmitting sound from the outside of the ear to the inside? The answer is no. They are the best solution possible, given an important historical constraint. Other vertebrates have different structures involved in transmitting sound to the ear. In at least some cases, those structures may be more efficient than our incus, malleus, and stapes.

To summarize, not all traits are adaptive, and even adaptive traits are constrained by genetic and historical factors. In addition, natural selection is not the only process that causes evolutionary change. Three other processes—genetic drift, gene flow, and mutation—change allele frequencies over time (see Chapter 26). Compared with natural selection, these processes have very different consequences. You can see the Big Picture of how natural selection relates to other evolutionary processes on pages 526–527.

CHAPTER 25   REVIEW

 For media, go to MasteringBiology

If you understand . . .

25.1 The Evolution of Evolutionary Thought

- Plato, Aristotle, and the Bible's book of Genesis consider species as unchanging types. This view is called typological thinking.

- Lamarck proposed a theory of evolution—that species are not static but change through time. He proposed that evolution occurs by the inheritance of acquired characteristics.

- Darwin and Wallace proposed that evolution occurs by natural selection. This was the beginning of population thinking, whereby variation among individuals is the key to understanding evolution.

✔ You should be able to compare and contrast typological thinking and population thinking.

25.2 The Pattern of Evolution: Have Species Changed, and Are They Related?

- Data on (1) the age of the Earth and the fact of extinction; (2) the resemblance of modern to fossil forms; (3) transitional features in fossils; (4) the presence of vestigial traits; and (5) change in contemporary populations show that species change through time.

- Data on (1) the geographic proximity of closely related species; (2) the existence of structural, developmental, and genetic homologies; and (3) the contemporary formation of new species support the consensus that species are related by common ancestry.

- Evidence for evolution is internally consistent, meaning that data from several independent sources are mutually reinforcing.

✔ You should be able to cite examples in support of the statement that species have changed through time and are related by common ancestry.

25.3 The Process of Evolution: How Does Natural Selection Work?

- Darwin developed four postulates that outline the process of evolution by natural selection. These postulates can be summarized by the following statement: Heritable variation leads to differential reproductive success.

- Alleles or traits that increase the reproductive success of an individual are said to increase the individual's fitness. A trait that leads to higher fitness, relative to individuals without the trait, is an adaptation. If a particular allele increases fitness and leads to adaptation, the allele will increase in frequency in the population.

✔ You should be able to explain the difference between the biological and everyday English definitions of fitness.

25.4 Evolution in Action: Recent Research on Natural Selection

- Selection by drugs on the TB bacterium and changes in the size and shape of finch beaks in the Galápagos as a result of seed availability are well-studied examples of evolution by natural selection.

- Both examples demonstrate that evolution can be observed and measured. Evolution by natural selection has been confirmed by a wide variety of studies and has long been considered to be the central organizing principle of biology.

✔ You should be able to predict how changes in *Mycobacterium tuberculosis* populations would be explained under special creation and under evolution by inheritance of acquired characters.

25.5 Common Misconceptions about Natural Selection and Adaptation

- Natural selection acts on individuals, but evolutionary change occurs in populations. Nonheritable changes that occur in individuals are not adaptations and do not result in evolution.

- Evolution is not goal directed and does not lead to perfection. There is no such thing as a higher or lower organism.

- Organisms do not act for the good of the species.

- Not all traits are adaptive, and even adaptive traits are limited by genetic and historical constraints.

✔ You should be able to discuss how adaptations such as the large brains of *Homo sapiens* and the ability of falcons to fly very fast are constrained.

(MB) MasteringBiology

1. MasteringBiology Assignments

Tutorials and Activities Darwin and the Galápagos Islands; Experimental Inquiry: Did Natural Selection of Ground Finches Occur When the Environment Changed?; Natural Selection for Antibiotic Resistance; The Voyage of the *Beagle*: Darwin's Trip Around the World; Reconstructing Forelimbs

Questions Reading Quizzes, Blue-Thread Questions, Test Bank

2. eText Read your book online, search, take notes, highlight text, and more.

3. The Study Area Practice Test, Cumulative Test, BioFlix® 3-D Animations, Videos, Activities, Audio Glossary, Word Study Tools, Art

You should be able to . . .

✔ TEST YOUR KNOWLEDGE

Answers are available in Appendix A

1. How can biological fitness be estimated?
   a. Document how long different individuals in a population survive.
   b. Count the number of healthy, fertile offspring produced by different individuals in a population.
   c. Determine which individuals are strongest.
   d. Determine which phenotype is the most common one in a given population.

2. True or false? Some traits are considered vestigial because they existed long ago.

3. What is an adaptation?
   a. a trait that improves the fitness of its bearer, compared with individuals without the trait
   b. a trait that changes in response to environmental influences within the individual's lifetime
   c. an ancestral trait—one that was modified to form the trait observed today
   d. the ability to produce offspring

4. Why does the presence of extinct forms and transitional features in the fossil record support the pattern component of the theory of evolution by natural selection?
   a. It supports the hypothesis that individuals change over time.
   b. It supports the hypothesis that weaker species are eliminated by natural selection.
   c. It supports the hypothesis that species evolve to become more complex and better adapted over time.
   d. It supports the hypothesis that species change over time.

5. Traits that are derived from a common ancestor, like the bones of human arms and bird wings, are said to be _____.

6. According to data presented in this chapter, which of the following statements is correct?
   a. When individuals change in response to challenges from the environment, their altered traits are passed on to offspring.
   b. Species are created independently of each other and do not change over time.
   c. Populations—not individuals—change when natural selection occurs.
   d. The traits of populations become more perfect over time.

7. Some biologists summarize evolution by natural selection with the phrase "mutation proposes, selection disposes." Mutation is a process that creates heritable variation. Explain what the phrase means.

8. Explain how artificial selection differs from natural selection.

9. Why don't the biggest and strongest individuals in a population always produce the most offspring?
   a. The biggest and strongest individuals always have higher fitness.
   b. In some environments, being big and strong lowers fitness.
   c. Sometimes the biggest and strongest individuals may choose to have fewer offspring.
   d. Sometimes the number of offspring is not related to fitness.

10. **QUANTITATIVE** The graphs in Figure 25.16 show that the average beak depth of medium ground finches increased after the drought.

However, more finches had deep beaks before the drought than after. Explain this seeming contradiction by calculating the percent of finches that survived the drought.

11. Review the section on the evolution of drug resistance in *Mycobacterium tuberculosis*.
    - What evidence do researchers have that a drug-resistant strain evolved in the patient analyzed in their study, and wasn't instead transmitted from another infected individual?
    - If the antibiotic rifampin were banned, would the mutant *rpoB* gene have lower or higher fitness in the new environment? Would strains carrying the mutation continue to increase in frequency in *M. tuberculosis* populations?

12. Describe how Darwin's four postulates would apply to a population of rabbits sharing a meadow with foxes.

13. Scientists have observed white deer mice living on coastal beaches in Florida and brown deer mice living in nearby forests. Compare and contrast how the theory of evolution by natural selection, special creation, and evolution by inheritance of acquired characters might explain this observation.

14. The average height of humans in industrialized nations has increased steadily for the past 100 years. This trait has clearly changed over time. Most physicians and human geneticists hypothesize that the change is due to better nutrition and a reduced incidence of disease. Has human height evolved?
    a. Yes, because average height has changed over time.
    b. No, because changes in height due to nutrition and reduced incidence of disease are not heritable.
    c. Yes, because height is a heritable trait.
    d. No, because height is not a heritable trait.

15. Scientists hypothesize that humans and chimpanzees diverged from a common ancestor that lived in Africa about 6–7 million years ago. What evidence would support this hypothesis?

16. The geneticist James Crow wrote that successful scientific theories have the following characteristics: (1) They explain otherwise puzzling observations; (2) they provide connections between otherwise disparate observations; (3) they make predictions that can be tested; and (4) they are heuristic, meaning that they open up new avenues of theory and experimentation. Crow added two other elements of scientific theories that he considered important on a personal, emotional level: (5) They should be elegant, in the sense of being simple and powerful; and (6) they should have an element of surprise. How well does the theory of evolution by natural selection fulfill these six criteria?

APPENDIX A Answers

CHAPTER 1

IN-TEXT QUESTIONS AND EXERCISES

p. 4 Fig. 1.2 `analyze` If Pasteur had done any of the things listed, he would have had more than one variable in his experiment. This would allow critics to claim that he got different results because of the differences in broth types, heating, or flask types—not the difference in exposure to preexisting cells. The results would not be definitive.
p. 6 `apply` The average kernel protein content would decline, from 11 percent to a much lower value over time.
p. 6 CYU `apply` The data points would all be about 11 percent, indicating no change in average kernel protein content over time.
p. 7 Fig. 1.4 `apply` Molds and other fungi are more closely related to green algae because they differ from plants at two positions (5 and 8 from left) but differ from green algae at only one position (8).
p. 8 Fig. 1.6 `apply` The eukaryotic cell is roughly 10 times the size of the prokaryotic cell.
p. 9 CYU `evaluate` From the sequence data provided, species A and B differ only in one ribonucleotide of the rRNA sequence (position 10 from left). Species C differs from species A and B in four ribonucleotides (positions 1, 2, 9, and 10). A correctly drawn phylogenetic tree would indicate that species A and B appear to be closely related, and species C is more distantly related. See **FIGURE A1.1**.
p. 13 (1) `analyze` You could conclude that the ants weren't navigating normally, because they had been caught and released and transferred to a new channel. **(2)** `analyze` You could conclude that the ants can't navigate normally on their manipulated legs.
p. 13 CYU The key here is to test predation rates during the hottest part of the day (when desert ants actually feed) versus other parts of the day. The experiment would best be done in the field, where natural predators are present. One approach would be to capture a large number of ants, divide the group in two, and measure predation rates (number of ants killed per hour) when they are placed in normal habitat during the hottest part of the day versus an hour before (or after). **(1)** `analyze` The control group here is the normal condition—ants out during the hottest part of the day. If you didn't include a control, a critic could argue that predation did or did not occur because of your experimental setup or manipulation, not because of differences in temperature. **(2)** `analyze` You would need to make sure that there is no difference in body size, walking speed, how they were captured and maintained, or other traits that might make the ants in the two groups more or less susceptible to predators. They should also be put out in the same habitat, so the presence of predators is the same in the two treatments.
p. 13 Fig. 1.10 `analyze` The interpretation of the experiment would not likely change, but your confidence in the conclusions drawn would be reduced if you used just one ant.

IF YOU UNDERSTAND . . .

1.1. `understand` Dead cells cannot regulate the passage of materials between exterior and interior spaces, replicate, use energy, or process information. **1.2** `understand` Observations on thousands of diverse species supported the claim that all organisms consist of cells. The hypothesis that all cells come from preexisting cells was supported when Pasteur showed that new cells do not arise and grow in a boiled liquid unless they are introduced from the air. **1.3** `understand` If seeds with higher protein content leave the most

offspring, then individuals with low protein in their seeds will become rare over time. **1.4** `understand` A newly discovered species can be classified as a member of the Bacteria if the sequence of its rRNA contains some features found only in Bacteria. The same logic applies to classifying a new species in the Archaea or Eukarya. **1.5** `understand` (1) A hypothesis is an explanation of how the world works; a prediction is an outcome you should observe if the hypothesis is correct. (2) Experiments are convincing because they measure predictions from two opposing hypotheses. Both predicted actions cannot occur, so one hypothesis will be supported while the other will not.

YOU SHOULD BE ABLE TO . . .

✔ Test Your Knowledge

1. `remember` d **2.** `understand` d **3.** `remember` populations **4.** `understand` b **5.** `understand` An individual's ability to survive and reproduce **6.** `understand` c

✔ Test Your Understanding

7. `evaluate` That the entity they discovered replicates, processes information, acquires and uses energy, is cellular, and that its populations evolve. **8.** `understand` a **9.** `understand` Over time, traits that increased the fitness of individuals in this habitat became increasingly frequent in the population. **10.** `understand` Individuals with certain traits are selected, in the sense that they produce the most offspring. **11.** `analyze` Yes. If evolution is defined as "change in the characteristics of a population over time," then those organisms that are most closely related should have experienced less change over time. On a phylogenetic tree, species with substantially similar rRNA sequences would be diagrammed with a closer common ancestor—one that had the sequences they inherited—than the ancestors shared between species with dissimilar rRNA sequences. **12.** `understand` A null hypothesis specifies what a researcher should observe when the hypothesis being tested isn't correct.

✔ Test Your Problem-Solving Skills

13. `analyze` A scientific theory is not a guess—it is an idea whose validity can be tested with data. Both the cell theory and the theory of evolution have been validated by large bodies of observational and experimental data. **14.** `apply` If all eukaryotes living today have a nucleus, then it is logical to conclude that the nucleus arose in a common ancestor of all eukaryotes, indicated by the arrow you should have added to the figure. See **FIGURE A1.2**. If it had arisen in a common ancestor of Bacteria or Archaea, then species in those groups would have had to lose the trait—an unlikely event. **15.** `evaluate` The data set was so large and diverse that it was no longer reasonable to argue that noncellular lifeforms would be discovered. **16.** `apply` b

BIG PICTURE Doing Biology

p. 16 CYU (1) `understand` Biologists design and carry out a study, either observational or experimental, to test their ideas. As part of this process, they state their ideas as a hypothesis and null hypothesis and make predictions. They analyze and interpret the data they have gathered, and determine whether the data support their ideas. If not, they revisit their ideas and come up with an alternative hypothesis and design another study to test these new predictions. **(2)** `understand` There are many

possible examples. Consider, for example, the experiment on navigation in foraging desert ants (Chapter 1). In addition to testing how the ants use information on stride length and number to calculate how far they are from the nest (multicellular organism and population levels), researchers also could test how the "pedometer" works at the level of cells and molecules. **(3)** `analyze` A hypothesis is a testable statement to explain a specific phenomenon or a set of observations. The word theory refers to proposed explanations for very broad patterns in nature that are supported by a wide body of evidence. A theory serves as a framework for the development of new hypotheses. **(4)** `analyze` The next step is to relate your findings to existing theories and the current scientific literature, and then to communicate your findings to colleagues through informal conversations, presentations at scientific meetings, and eventually publication in peer-reviewed journals.

CHAPTER 2

IN-TEXT QUESTIONS AND EXERCISES

p. 20 Fig. 2.3 `apply` There are 15 electrons in phosphorus, so there must be 15 protons, which is the atomic number. Since the mass number is 31, then the number of neutrons is 16.
p. 23 `understand` *Water:* arrows pointing from hydrogens to oxygen atom; *ammonia:* arrows pointing from hydrogens to nitrogen atom; *methane:* double arrows between carbons and hydrogens; *carbon dioxide:* arrows pointing from carbon to oxygens; *molecular nitrogen:* double arrows between nitrogens.
p. 23 Fig. 2.7 `understand` Oxygen and nitrogen have high electronegativities. They hold shared electrons more tightly than C, H, and many other atoms, resulting in polar bonds.
p. 24 CYU `evaluate` See **FIGURE A2.1**.

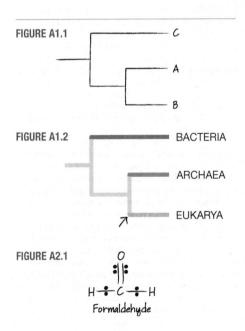

FIGURE A1.1   C

A

B

FIGURE A1.2   BACTERIA

ARCHAEA

EUKARYA

FIGURE A2.1   Formaldehyde

p. 25 (1) [evaluate] δ^+H—O$^{\delta-}$—H$^{\delta+}$ **(2)** [apply] If water were linear, the partial negative charge on oxygen would have partial positive charges on either side. Compared to the actual, bent molecule, the partial negative charge would be much less exposed and less able to participate in hydrogen bonding.

p. 26 Fig. 2.14 [understand] Oils are nonpolar. They have long chains of carbon atoms bonded to hydrogen atoms, which share electrons evenly because their electronegativities are similar. When an oil and water are mixed, the polar water molecules interact with each other via hydrogen bonding rather than with the nonpolar oil molecules, which interact with themselves instead.

p. 28 Table 2.2 [understand] "Cause" (Row 1): electrostatic attractions between partial charges on water and opposite charges on ions; hydrogen bonds; water and other polar molecules. "Biological Consequences" (Row 2): ice to float; freezing solid. "Cause" (Row 4): lots of heat energy; break hydrogen bonds and change water to a gas.

p. 29 [apply] The proton concentration would be 3.2×10^{-9} M.

p. 29 Fig. 2.17 [apply] The concentration of protons would decrease because milk is more basic (pH 6.5) than black coffee (pH 5).

p. 30 [apply] The bicarbonate concentration would increase. The protons (H^+) released from carbonic acid would react with the hydroxide ions (OH^-) dissociated from NaOH to form H_2O, leaving fewer protons free to react with bicarbonate to reform carbonic acid.

p. 32 CYU (1) [apply] The reaction would be spontaneous based on the change in potential energy; the reactants have higher chemical energy than the products. The entropy, however, is not increased based on the number of molecules, although heat given off from the reaction still results in increased entropy. **(2)** [understand] The electrons are shifted farther from the nuclei of the carbon and hydrogen atoms and closer to the nuclei of the more electronegative oxygen atoms.

p. 32 Fig. 2.19 [remember] See FIGURE A2.2.

p. 33 Fig. 2.21 [analyze] The water-filled flask is the ocean; the gas-filled flask is the atmosphere; the condensed water droplets are rain; the electrical sparks are lightning.

p. 37 Table 2.3 [understand] All the functional groups in Table 2.3, except the sulfhydryl group (—SH), are highly polar. The sulfhydryl group is only very slightly polar.

IF YOU UNDERSTAND . . .

2.1. [understand] The bonds in methane and ammonia are all covalent, but differ in polarity: Methane has nonpolar covalent bonds while ammonia has polar covalent bonds. Sodium chloride does not have covalent bonds; instead, ionic bonds hold the ionized sodium and chloride together. **2.2** [understand] Assuming neutral pH, amino and hydroxyl groups would interact with the partial negative charge on water's oxygen, because they both carry a positive charge (partial for the hydrogen in the hydroxyl). The carboxyl group would interact with the partial positive charges on water's hydrogens, since it would carry a negative charge after losing the proton from its hydroxyl. **2.3** [understand] Like solar radiation, the energy in electricity generates free radicals that would promote the reaction. **2.4** [understand] "Top-down" approach: The reaction responsible for synthesizing acetic acid is observed in cells and can serve as an intermediate for the formation of a more complex molecule (acetyl CoA) that is used by cells throughout the tree of life. "Bottom-up" approach: This reaction can also occur under conditions that mimic the early Earth environment in deep-sea vents. **2.5** [apply] The hydroxyls would increase the solubility of octane by introducing polar covalent bonds, which would make the molecule more hydrophilic. The high electronegativity of oxygen would decrease the potential energy of the modified molecule.

YOU SHOULD BE ABLE TO . . .

✔ **Test Your Knowledge**

1. [understand] b **2.** [remember] a **3.** [remember] c **4.** [remember] d **5.** [remember] Potential energy and entropy. **6.** [remember] The prebiotic soup model and the surface metabolism model.

✔ **Test Your Understanding**

7. [apply] c. Acetic acid has more highly electronegative oxygen atoms than the other molecules. When bonded to carbon or hydrogen, each oxygen will result in a polar covalent bond. **8.** [apply] Relative electronegativities would be F > O > H > Na. One bond would form with sodium, and it would be ionic. **9.** [understand] When oxygen is covalently bonded to hydrogen, the difference in electronegativities between the atoms causes the electrons to spend more time near the oxygen. In contrast, the atoms in H_2 and O_2 have the same electronegativities, so they equally share electrons in their covalent bonds. **10.** [apply] See FIGURE A2.3. **11.** [apply] The dissociation reaction of carbonic acid lowers the pH of the solution by releasing extra H^+ into the solution. If additional CO_2 is added, the sequence of reactions would be driven to the right, which would make the ocean more acidic. **12.** [understand] The carbon framework determines the overall shape of an organic molecule. The functional groups attached to the carbons determine the molecule's chemical behavior, because these groups are likely to interact with other molecules.

✔ **Test Your Problem-Solving Skills**

13. [analyze] b. **14.** [analyze] No, they don't conflict. Shells that are farther from the protons (positive charges) in the nucleus house electrons that have greater potential energy than shells closer to the nucleus. **15.** [analyze] One possible concept map relating the structure of water to its properties is shown below (see FIGURE A2.4). **16.** [create] In hot weather, water absorbs large amounts of heat due to its high specific heat and high heat of vaporization. In cold weather, water releases the large amount of heat that it has absorbed.

FIGURE A2.2

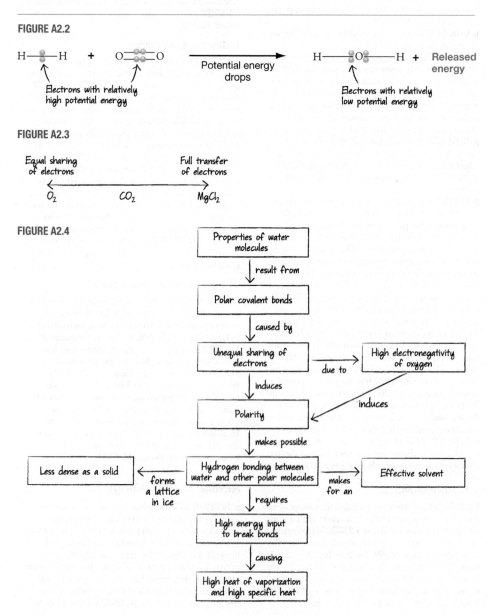

FIGURE A2.3

FIGURE A2.4

CHAPTER 3

IN-TEXT QUESTIONS AND EXERCISES

p. 43 Fig. 3.2 `understand` The green R-groups contain mostly C and H, which have roughly equal electronegativities. Electrons are evenly shared in C−H bonds and C−S bonds, so the groups are nonpolar. Cysteine has a sulfur that is slightly more electronegative than hydrogen, so it will be less nonpolar than the other green groups. All of the pink R-groups have a highly electronegative oxygen atom with a partial negative charge, making them polar.

p. 44 `apply` From most hydrophilic to most hydrophobic: (1) aspartate, (2) asparagine, (3) tyrosine, (4) valine. The most hydrophilic amino acids will have side chains with full charges (ionized), like aspartate, followed by those with the largest number of highly electronegative atoms, like oxygen or nitrogen. Highly electronegative atoms produce polar covalent bonds with carbon or hydrogen. The most hydrophobic will not have oxygen or nitrogen in their side chains, but instead will have the largest number of C−H bonds, which are nonpolar covalent.

p. 47 CYU `understand` See **FIGURE A3.1**.

p. 52 CYU (1) `understand` Secondary, tertiary, and quaternary structure all depend on bonds and other interactions between amino acids that are linked in a chain in a specific order (primary structure). **(2)** `apply` There would be 20^5 different peptides, or 3.2×10^6 different primary sequences.

p. 55 CYU `apply` Amino acid changes would be expected to be in the active site or in regions that affect the folded structure of this site. Either of these changes could result in a different active site that either binds a new substrate or catalyzes a different reaction.

IF YOU UNDERSTAND . . .

3.1. `understand` Look at the R-group of the amino acid. If there is a positive charge, then it is basic. If there is a negative charge, then it is acidic. If there is not a charge, but there is an oxygen atom, then it is polar uncharged. If there is no charge or oxygen, then it is nonpolar. **3.2** `apply` Nonpolar amino acid residues would be found in the interior of a globular protein, grouped with other nonpolar residues due to hydrophobic interactions. **3.3** `analyze` Both calmodulin and infectious prions require some form of induction to achieve their active conformations. Calcium ions are required for calmodulin to fold into its functional structure while prions are induced to change their shape by other, improperly folded prion proteins. **3.4** `analyze` *Catalysis:* Proteins are made of amino acids, which have many reactive functional groups, and can fold into different shapes that allow the formation of active sites. *Defense:* Similar to catalysis, the chemical properties and capacity for different shapes allows proteins to be made that can attach to virtually any type of invading virus or cell. *Signaling:* The flexibility in protein structure allows protein activities to be quickly turned on or off based on binding to signal molecules or ions.

YOU SHOULD BE ABLE TO . . .

✔ Test Your Knowledge

1. `remember` d **2.** `remember` The atoms and functional groups found in the side chains. **3.** `remember` b **4.** `remember` b **5.** `understand` The order and type of amino acids (i.e., the primary structure) contains the information that directs folding. **6.** `understand` a

✔ Test Your Understanding

7. `understand` Because the nonpolar amino acid residues are not able to interact with the water solvent, they are crowded together in the interior of a protein and surrounded by a network of hydrogen-bonded water molecules. This crowding leads to the development of van der Waals interactions that help glue the nonpolar side chains together. **8.** `understand` No, polymerization is a nonspontaneous reaction because the product molecules have lower entropy than the free form of the reactants and there would be nothing to prevent hydrolysis from reversing the reaction. **9.** `understand` Many possible correct answers, including (1) the presence of an active site in an enzyme that is precisely shaped to fit a substrate or substrates in the correct orientation for a reaction to occur; (2) the doughnut shape of porin that allows certain substances to pass through it; (3) the cable shape of collagen to provide structural support for cells and tissues. **10.** `create` Proteins are highly variable in overall shape and chemical properties due to variation in the composition of R-groups and the array of secondary through quaternary structures that are possible. This variation allows them to fulfill many different roles in the cell. Diversity in the shape and reactivity of active sites also makes them effective catalysts. **11.** `understand` c **12.** `create` In many proteins, especially those involved in cell signaling, their structure is affected by binding to other molecules or ions. Since the shape of the protein is directly involved in its function, the protein's activity is regulated by controlling how it is folded. If proteins were inflexible, this type of control could not occur.

✔ Test Your Problem-Solving Skills

13. `analyze` The side chain of proline is a cyclic structure that is covalently bonded to the nitrogen in the core amino group. This restricts the movement of the side chain relative to the core nitrogen, which further restricts the backbone when the nitrogen participates in a peptide bond with a neighboring amino acid. **14.** `create` See **FIGURE A3.2 15.** `apply` b. Phosphates have a negative charge, so they are most likely to form ionic bonds with the positively-charged side chains of basic amino acid residues. **16.** `apply` The inherited forms likely have some alteration in the primary structure such that the infectious form is spontaneously generated at a higher rate than normal. The amino acid sequence in these prions would likely differ from those transmitted between animals.

CHAPTER 4

IN-TEXT QUESTIONS AND EXERCISES

p. 59 `understand` See **FIGURE A4.1**.

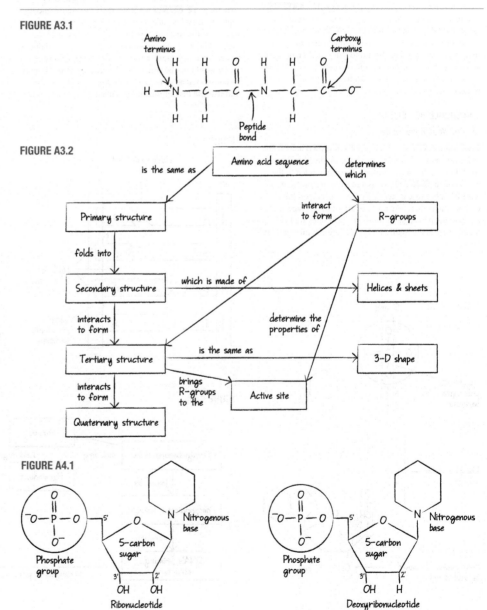

FIGURE A3.1

FIGURE A3.2

FIGURE A4.1

p. 60 Fig. 4.3 understand 5′-UAGC-′3
p. 61 CYU understand See FIGURE A4.2.
p. 63 understand If the two strands were parallel, the G-C pairing would align N—H groups together and C=H groups together, which would not allow hydrogen bonds to form.
p. 64 Fig. 4.8 analyze It is not spontaneous—energy must be added (as heat) for the reaction to occur.
p. 65 CYU remember See FIGURE A4.3.

IF YOU UNDERSTAND . . .

4.1. understand Cells activate nucleotides by linking additional phosphates to an existing 5′ phosphate. Activation increases the chemical energy in the nucleotides enough to offset the decrease in entropy that will result from the polymerization reaction. **4.2** understand C-G pairs involve three hydrogen bonds, so they are more stable than A-T pairs with just two hydrogen bonds. **4.3** analyze A single-stranded RNA molecule has unpaired bases that can pair with other bases on the same RNA strand, thereby folding the molecule into stem-and-loop configurations. These secondary structures can further fold on themselves, giving the molecule a tertiary structure. Because DNA molecules are double stranded, with no unpaired bases, further internal folding is not possible. **4.4** understand Examples would include (1) the production of nucleotides, and (2) polymerization of RNA. It is thought that nucleotides were scarce during chemical evolution, so their catalyzed synthesis by a ribozyme would have been advantageous. Catalysis by an RNA replicase would have dramatically increased the reproductive rate of RNA molecules.

YOU SHOULD BE ABLE TO . . .

✔ Test Your Knowledge

1. remember c **2.** remember c **3.** remember a **4.** remember d **5.** remember One end has a free phosphate group on the 5′ carbon; the other end has a free hydroxyl group bonded to the 3′ carbon. **6.** understand DNA is a more stable molecule than RNA because it lacks a hydroxyl group on the 2′ carbon and is therefore more resistant to cleavage, and because the two sugar-phosphate backbones are held together by many hydrogen bonds between nitrogenous bases.

✔ Test Your Understanding

7. apply In DNA, the secondary structure requires that every guanine pairs with a cytosine and every thymine pairs with an adenine, resulting in consistent ratios between the nucleotides. Chargaff's rules do not apply to RNA, since it is single-stranded and the pairing is not consistent throughout the molecules. **8.** apply a; if 30 percent is adenine, then 30 percent would be thymine, since they are base-paired together. This means that 40 percent consists of G-C base pairs, which would be equally divided between the two bases. **9.** apply The DNA sequence of the new strand would be 5′-ATCGATATC-3′. The RNA sequence would be the same, except each T would be replaced by a U. **10.** understand DNA has limited catalytic ability because it (1) lacks functional groups that can participate in catalysis and (2) has a regular structure that is not conducive to forming shapes required for catalysis. RNA molecules can catalyze some reactions because they (1) have exposed hydroxyl functional groups and (2) can fold into shapes that can function in catalysis. **11.** apply No. Catalytic activity in ribozymes depends on the tertiary structure generated from single-stranded molecules. Double-stranded nucleic acids do not form tertiary structures. **12.** understand An RNA replicase would undergo replication and be able to evolve. It would process information in the sense of copying itself, and it would use energy to drive polymerization reactions. It would not be bound by a membrane and considered a cell, however, and it would not be able to acquire energy. It would best be considered as an intermediate step between nonlife and true life (as outlined in Chapter 1).

✔ Test Your Problem-Solving Skills

13. create See FIGURE A4.4 **14.** apply Yes—if the complementary bases lined up over the entire length of the two strands, they would twist into a double helix analogous to a DNA molecule. The same types of hydrogen bonds and hydrophobic interactions would occur as observed in the "stem" portion of hairpins in single-stranded RNA. **15.** apply In a triple helix, the bases are unlikely to align properly for hydrogen bonding to occur, so hydrophobic interactions would probably be more important. **16.** apply b; the high temperature would make it more likely that the secondary and tertiary structures would be denatured in the ribozymes. To overcome this effect, you would expect the hairpins to possess more G-C pairs, since they consist of three hydrogen bonds compared to the two found in A-T pairs.

CHAPTER 5

IN-TEXT QUESTIONS AND EXERCISES

p. 73 Fig. 5.2 understand See the structure of mannose in FIGURE A5.1.
p. 75 CYU apply See FIGURE A5.2.
p. 78 CYU remember They could differ in (1) location of linkages (e.g., 1,4 or 1,6); (2) types of linkages (e.g., α or β); (3) the sequence of the monomers (e.g., two galactose and then two glucose, versus alternating galactose and glucose); and/or (4) whether the four monomers are linked in a line or whether they branch.
p. 79 Fig. 5.6 apply The percentage of inhibition would not change for the intact glycoprotein bar. The purified

FIGURE A4.2

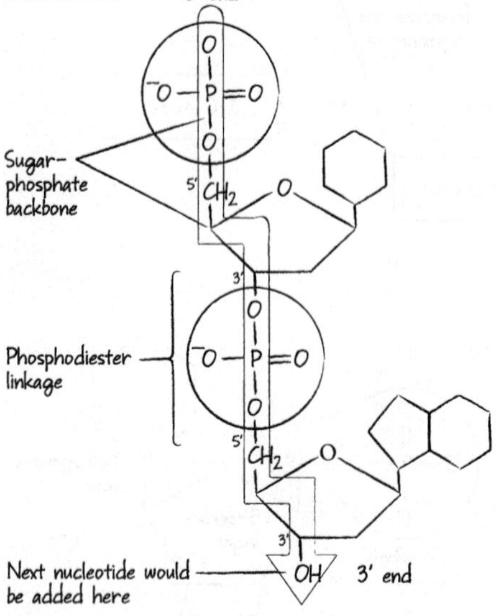

FIGURE A4.3

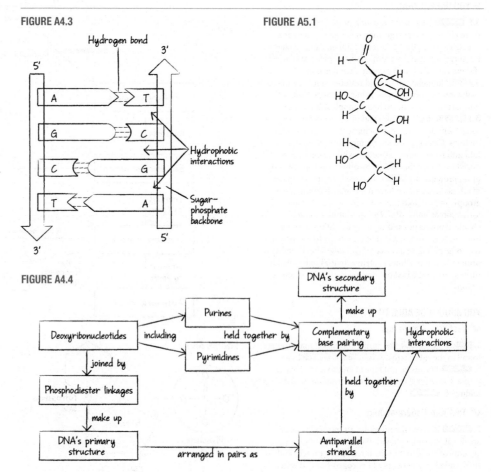

FIGURE A4.4

carbohydrate bar would be at zero inhibition, and the glycoprotein with digested carbohydrate bar would be similar to the intact glycoprotein bar.

p. 80 Fig. 5.7 (understand) All of the C—C and C—H bonds should be circled.

p. 81 CYU (1) (understand) *Aspect 1:* The β-1,4-glycosidic linkages in these molecules result in insoluble fibers that are difficult to degrade. *Aspect 2:* When individual molecules of these carbohydrates align, bonds form between them and produce fibers or sheets that resist pulling and pushing forces. **(2)** (apply) Most are probably being broken down into glucose, some of which in turn is being broken down in reactions that lead to the synthesis of ATP. Some will be resistant to digestion, such as the insoluble cellulose that makes up dietary fiber. This will help retain water and support the digestion and passage of fecal material.

IF YOU UNDERSTAND . . .

5.1. (understand) Molecules have to interact in an extremely specific orientation in order for a reaction to occur. Changing the location of a functional group by even one carbon can mean that the molecule will undergo completely different types of reactions. **5.2** (analyze) Glycosidic linkages can vary more in location and geometry than linkages between amino acids and nucleotides do. This variability increases the structural diversity possible in carbohydrates compared to proteins and nucleic acids. **5.3** (understand) (1) Polysaccharides used for energy storage are formed entirely from glucose monomers joined by α-glycosidic linkages; structural polysaccharides are made up of glucose or other sugars joined by β-glycosidic linkages. (2) The monomers in energy-storage polysaccharides are linked in a helical arrangement; the monomers in structural polysaccharides are linked in a linear arrangement. (3) Energy-storage polysaccharides may branch; structural polysaccharides do not. (4) Individual chains of energy-storage polysaccharides do not associate with each other; adjacent chains of structural polysaccharides are linked by hydrogen bonds or covalent bonds.

YOU SHOULD BE ABLE TO . . .

✔ Test Your Knowledge

1. (remember) d **2.** (remember) Monosaccharides can differ from one another in three ways: (1) the location of their carbonyl group; (2) the number of carbon atoms they contain; and (3) the orientations of their hydroxyl groups. **3.** (remember) a **4.** (remember) c **5.** (remember) a **6.** (understand) The electrons in the C=O bonds of carbon dioxide molecules are held tightly by the highly electronegative oxygen atoms, so they have low potential energy. The electrons in the C—C and C—H bonds of carbohydrates are shared equally, so they have much higher potential energy.

✔ Test Your Understanding

7. (understand) c. **8.** (apply) a; lactose is a disaccharide formed from a β-1,4-glycosidic linkage, so if two glucose molecules were linked with this bond, they would resemble units of cellulose and not be digested by human infants or adults. **9.** (understand) Carbohydrates are ideal for displaying the identity of the cell because they are so diverse structurally. This diversity enables them to serve as very specific identity tags for cells. **10.** (understand) When you compare the glucose monomers in an α-1,4-glycosidic linkage versus in a β-1,4-glycosidic linkage, the linkages are located on opposite sides of the plane of the glucose rings, and the glucose monomers are linked in the same orientation versus having every other glucose flipped in orientation. β-1,4-glycosidic linkages are much more likely to form linear fibers and sheets, so they resist degradation. **11.** (remember) Because (1) no mechanism is

known for the prebiotic polymerization of sugars; (2) no catalytic carbohydrates have been discovered that can perform polymerization reactions; and (3) sugar residues in a polysaccharide are not capable of complementary base pairing. **12.** (understand) Starch and glycogen both consist of glucose monomers joined by α-1,4-glycosidic linkages, and both function as storage carbohydrates. Starch is a mixture of unbranched and branched polysaccharides—called amylose and amylopectin, respectively. All glycogen polysaccharides are branched.

✔ Test Your Problem-Solving Skills

13. (analyze) Carbohydrates are energy-storage molecules, so minimizing their consumption may reduce total energy intake. Lack of available carbohydrate also forces the body to use fats for energy, reducing the amount of fat that is stored. **14.** (apply) d; lactose is a disaccharide of glucose and galactose, which can be cleaved by enzymes expressed in the human gut to release galactose. **15.** (analyze) Amylase breaks down the starch in the cracker into glucose monomers, which stimulate the sweet receptors in your tongue. **16.** (apply) When bacteria contact lysozyme, the peptidoglycan in their cell walls begins to degrade, leading to the death of the bacteria. Lysozyme therefore helps protect humans against bacterial infections.

CHAPTER 6

IN-TEXT QUESTIONS AND EXERCISES

p. 87 (understand) Fatty acids are amphipathic because their hydrocarbon tails are hydrophobic but their carboxyl functional groups are hydrophilic.

p. 87 Fig. 6.4 (apply) At the polar hydroxyl group in cholesterol and the polar head group in phospholipids.

p. 88 CYU (1) (analyze) Fats consist of three fatty acids linked to glycerol; steroids have a distinctive four-ring structure with variable side groups attached; phospholipids have a hydrophilic, phosphate-containing "head" region and a hydrocarbon tail. **(2)** (understand) In cholesterol, the hydrocarbon steroid rings and isoprenoid chain are hydrophobic; the hydroxyl group is hydrophilic. In phospholipids, the phosphate-containing head group is hydrophilic; the hydrocarbon chains are hydrophobic.

p. 89 (apply) Amino acids have amino and carboxyl groups that are ionized in water and nucleotides have negatively charged phosphates. Due to their charge and larger size, both would be placed below the small ions at the bottom of the scale (permeability<10^{-12} cm/sec).

p. 90 CYU (create) See TABLE A6.1.

p. 91 Fig. 6.10 (apply) Increasing the number of phospholipids with polyunsaturated tails would increase permeability of the liposomes. Starting from the left, the first line (no cholesterol) would represent liposomes with 50% polyunsaturated phospholipids, the second line would be 20% polyunsaturated phospholipids, and the third line would contain only saturated phospholipids.

p. 92 (apply) If there is a difference in temperature, then there would be a difference in thermal motion. The solute concentration on the side with a higher temperature would decrease because the solute particles would be moving faster and hence be more likely to move to the cooler side of the membrane, where they would slow down.

p. 93 Fig. 6.13 (apply) Higher, because less water would have to move to the right side to achieve equilibrium.

FIGURE A5.2

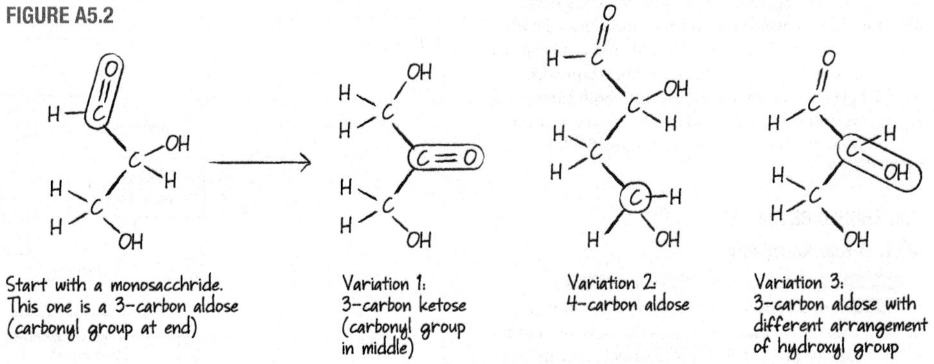

Start with a monosaccharide. This one is a 3-carbon aldose (carbonyl group at end)

Variation 1: 3-carbon ketose (carbonyl group in middle)

Variation 2: 4-carbon aldose

Variation 3: 3-carbon aldose with different arrangement of hydroxyl group

TABLE A6.1

Factor	Effect on permeability	Reason
Temperature	Decreases as temperature decreases.	Lower temperature slows movement of hydrocarbon tails, allowing more interactions (membrane is more dense).
Cholesterol	Decreases as cholesterol content increases.	Cholesterol molecules fill in the spaces between the hydrocarbon tails, making the membrane more tightly packed.
Length of hydrocarbon tails	Decreases as length of hydrocarbon tails increases.	Longer hydrocarbon tails have more interactions (membrane is more dense).
Saturation of hydrocarbon tails	Decreases as degree of saturation increases.	Saturated fatty acids have straight hydrocarbon tails that pack together tightly, leaving few gaps.

p. 94 CYU create See **FIGURE A6.1**.

p. 96 Fig. 6.18 create Repeat the procedure using a lipid bilayer that is free of membrane proteins, such as synthetic liposomes constructed from only phospholipids. If proteins were responsible for the pits and mounds, then this control would not show these structures.

p. 97 apply Your arrow should point out of the cell. There is no concentration gradient for chloride, but the outside has a net positive charge, which favors outward movement of negative ions.

p. 97 Fig. 6.21 analyze No—the 10 replicates where no current was recorded probably represent instances where the CFTR protein was damaged and not functioning properly. (In general, no experimental method works "perfectly.")

p. 101 CYU understand Passive transport does not require an input of energy—it happens as a result of energy already present in existing concentration or electrical gradients. Active transport is active in the sense of requiring an input of energy from, for example, ATP. In cotransport, a second ion or molecule is transported against its concentration gradient along with (i.e., "co") an ion that is transported along its concentration gradient.

p. 101 Fig. 6.26 understand *Diffusion:* description as given; no proteins involved. *Facilitated diffusion:* Passive movement of ions or molecules that cannot cross a phospholipid bilayer readily along a concentration gradient; facilitated by channel or carrier proteins. *Active transport:* Active movement of ions or molecules that will build a gradient; facilitated by pump proteins powered by an energy source such as ATP.

IF YOU UNDERSTAND . . .

6.1. analyze Adding H_2 increases the saturation of the oil by converting C=C bonds into C—C bonds with added hydrogens. Lipids with more C—H bonds tend to be solid at room temperature. **6.2** understand Highly permeable and fluid bilayers possess short, unsaturated hydrocarbon tails while those that are highly impermeable and less fluid contain long, saturated hydrocarbon tails. **6.3** apply (1) The solute will diffuse until both sides are at equal concentrations. (2) Water will diffuse toward the side with the higher solute concentration. **6.4** apply See **FIGURE A6.2**.

YOU SHOULD BE ABLE TO . . .

✔ Test Your Knowledge

1. understand c **2.** remember a **3.** understand b **4.** understand d
5. understand For osmosis to occur, a concentration gradient and membrane that allows water to pass, but not the solute, must be present. **6.** analyze Channel proteins form pores in the membrane and carrier proteins undergo conformational changes to shuttle molecules or ions across the membrane.

✔ Test Your Understanding

7. apply b **8.** analyze No, because they have no polar end to interact with water. Instead, these lipids would float on the surface of water, or collect in droplets suspended in water, reducing their interaction with water to a minimum. **9.** understand Hydrophilic, phosphate-containing head groups interact with water; hydrophobic hydrocarbon tails associate with each other. A bilayer is more stable than are independent phospholipids in solution. **10.** apply Ethanol's polar hydroxyl group reduces the speed at which it can cross a membrane, but its small size and lack of charge would allow it to slowly cross membranes—between the rates of water and glucose transport. **11.** understand Only nonpolar, hydrophobic amino acid residues would be found in the portion of the protein that crosses the membrane. In the interior of the bilayer, these residues would be hidden from the water solvent and interact with the nonpolar lipid tails. **12.** apply Chloride ions from sodium chloride will move from the left side to the right through the CFTR. Water

will initially move from the right side to the left by osmosis, but as chloride ions move to the right, water will follow. Na^+ and K^+ ions will not move across the membrane.

✔ Test Your Problem-Solving Skills

13. apply c **14.** create Flip-flops should be rare, because they require a polar head group to pass through the hydrophobic portion of the lipid bilayer. To test this prediction, you could monitor the number of dyed phospholipids that transfer from one side of the membrane to the other in a given period of time. **15.** apply Organisms that live in very cold environments are likely to have highly unsaturated phospholipids. The kinks in unsaturated hydrocarbon tails keep membranes fluid and permeable, even at low temperature. Organisms that live in very hot environments would likely have phospholipids with saturated tails, to prevent membranes from becoming too fluid and permeable. **16.** analyze Adding a methyl group makes a drug more hydrophobic and thus more likely to pass through a lipid bilayer. Adding a charged group makes it hydrophilic and reduces its ability to pass through the lipid bilayer. These modifications would help target the drug to either the inside or outside of cells, respectively.

BIG PICTURE Chemistry of Life

p. 104 CYU (1) understand Oxygen is much more electronegative than hydrogen, so within water, the electrons are unequally shared in the O—H covalent bonds. The resulting partial negative charge around the oxygen and partial positive charges around the hydrogen atoms allow for hydrogen bonds to form among water molecules. **(2)** analyze Unlike other macromolecules, nucleic acids can serve as templates for their own replication. RNA is generally single-stranded and can adopt many different

three-dimensional structures. The flexibility in structure, combined with the presence of reactive hydroxyl groups, contribute to the formation of active sites that catalyze chemical reactions. One or more of these catalytic RNA molecules may have evolved the ability to self-replicate. DNA is not likely to have catalyzed its own replication, as it is most often double-stranded, with no clear tertiary structure, and it lacks the reactive hydroxyl groups. **(3)** remember In the amino acid, the nitrogen in the amino (NH_3^+) group and the carbon in the carboxyl (COO^-) group should be circled. In the nucleotide, the oxygen in the hydroxyl (OH) group and the phosphorus in the phosphate (PO_4^{2-}) group on the nucleotide should be circled. **(4)** understand A line representing a protein should be drawn such that it completely crosses the lipid bilayer at least once. The protein could be involved in a variety of different roles, including transport of substances across the membrane in the form of a channel, carrier, or pump.

CHAPTER 7

IN-TEXT QUESTIONS AND EXERCISES

p. 110 CYU remember (1) The nucleoid compacts the chromosome to fit inside the cell via supercoiling while still keeping it accessible for replication and transmission of information. (2) Photosynthetic membranes increase food production by providing a large surface area to hold the pigments and enzymes required for photosynthesis. (3) Flagella propel cells through liquid, often toward a food source. (4) The layer of thick, strong material stiffens the cell wall and provides protection from mechanical damage.

p. 114 Fig. 7.12 create Storing the toxins in vacuoles prevents the toxins from damaging the plant's own organelles and cells.

FIGURE A6.1

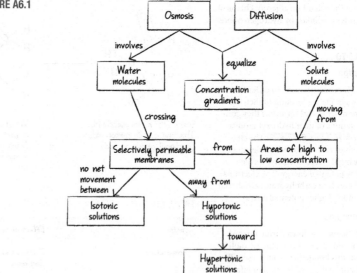

FIGURE A6.2

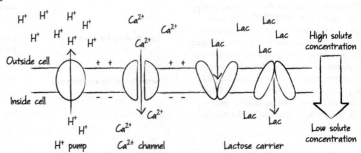

p. 116 CYU (1) understand Both organelles contain specific sets of enzymes. Lysosomal enzymes digest macromolecules in the acidic lumen of this organelle, releasing monomers that can be recycled into new macromolecules. Peroxisomes contain catalase and other enzymes that process fatty acids and toxins via oxidation reactions. (2) understand From top to bottom: administrative/information hub, protein factory, large molecule manufacturing and shipping (protein synthesis and folding center, lipid factory, protein finishing and shipping line, waste processing and recycling center), warehouse, fatty-acid processing and detox center, power station, food-manufacturing facility, support beams, perimeter fencing with secured gates, and leave blank.
p. 118 Fig. 7.16 remember See FIGURE A7.1.
p. 121 analyze (1) Nucleotides are small enough that they would diffuse through the nuclear pore complex along their gradients—a passive process that would not require

energy. (2) Large proteins must be escorted through the nuclear pore complex, which is directional and requires energy, since the protein is concentrated inside the nucleus.
p. 121 Fig. 7.18 apply "Prediction": The labeled tail region fragments or the labeled core region fragments of the nucleoplasmin protein will be found in the cell nucleus. "Prediction of null hypothesis": Either both the fragments (no required signal) or neither of them (whole protein signal) will be found in the nucleus of the cell. "Conclusion": The send-to-nucleus signal is in the tail region of the nucleoplasmin protein.
p. 123 apply During the chase period, proteins appear to have first entered the Golgi after 7 minutes and then started to move into secretory granules after 37 minutes. This means that in this experiment, it took approximately 30 minutes for the fastest-moving proteins to pass through the Golgi.

p. 126 apply In receptor-mediated endocytosis, the conversion of a late endosome to a lysosome is dependent on receiving acid hydrolases from the Golgi. If this receptor is not present, then the enzymes will not be sent and the late endosome will not mature into a lysosome to digest the endocytosed products.
p. 126 CYU (1) apply Proteins that enter the nucleus are fully synthesized and have an NLS that interacts with another protein to get it into the organelle. The NLS is not removed. Proteins that enter the ER have a signal sequence that interacts with the SRP during translation. The ribosome is moved to the ER and synthesis continues, moving the protein into the ER. The signal is removed once it enters the organelle. (2) apply The protein would be in the lysosome. The ER signal would direct the protein into the ER before it is completely synthesized. The M-6-P tag will direct the protein from the Golgi to the late endosome to the lysosome. Thus the complete protein is never free in the cytosol, where the NLS could direct it into the nucleus.
p. 132 CYU analyze Actin filaments are made up of two strands of actin monomers, microtubules are made up of tubulin protein dimers that form a tube, and intermediate filaments are made up of a number of different protein subunits. Actin filaments and microtubules exhibit polarity (or directionality), and new subunits are constantly being added or subtracted at either end (but added faster to the plus end). All three elements provide structural support, but only actin filaments and microtubules serve as tracks for motors involved in movement and cell division.
p. 132 Fig. 7.30 apply The microtubule doublets of the axoneme would slide past each other completely, but the axoneme would not bend.

IF YOU UNDERSTAND . . .

7.1 understand (1) Cells will be unable to synthesize new proteins and will die. (2) In many environments, cells will be unable to resist the osmotic pressure of water entering the cytoplasm and will burst. (3) The cell shape will be different, and cells will not be able to divide. 7.2 understand (1) The cell will be unable to produce a sufficient amount of ATP and will die. (2) Reactive molecules, like hydrogen peroxide, will damage the cell, and it will likely die. (3) Nothing will happen, since plants do not have centrioles. 7.3 analyze The liver cell would be expected to have more peroxisomes and less rough endoplasmic reticulum than the salivary cells would. 7.4 create The addition or removal of phosphates would change the folded structure of the protein, exposing the NLS for nuclear transport. 7.5 create As a group, proteins have complex and highly diverse shapes and chemical properties that allow them to recognize a great number of different zip codes in a very specific manner. 7.6 apply The Golgi is positioned near the microtubule organizing center, which has microtubules running from the minus end out to the plus end (near the plasma membrane). Kinesin would be used to move these vesicles as it walks toward the plus end.

YOU SHOULD BE ABLE TO . . .

✔ Test Your Knowledge

1. understand b 2. remember They have their own small, circular chromosomes; they produce their own ribosomes; and they divide in a manner that is similar to bacterial fission, independent of cellular division. 3. remember c 4. remember b 5. remember a 6. understand The phosphate links to the motor protein and causes it to change shape, which results in the protein moving along the filament.

✔ Test Your Understanding

7. analyze All cells are bound by a plasma membrane, are filled with cytoplasm, carry their genetic information (DNA) in chromosomes, and contain ribosomes

FIGURE A7.1

(a) Animal pancreatic cell: Exports digestive enzymes.

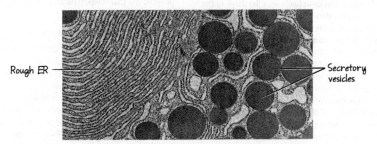

Rough ER

Secretory vesicles

(b) Animal testis cell: Exports lipid-soluble signals.

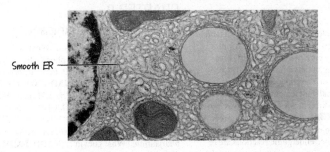

Smooth ER

(c) Plant leaf cell: Manufactures ATP and sugar.

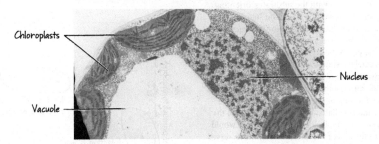

Chloroplasts

Nucleus

Vacuole

(d) Brown fat cells: Burn fat to generate heat in lieu of ATP.

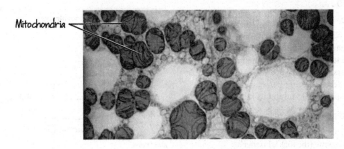

Mitochondria

(the sites of protein synthesis). Some prokaryotes have organelles not found in plants or animals, such as a magnetite-containing structure. Plant cells have chloroplasts, vacuoles, and a cell wall. Animal cells contain lysosomes and lack a cell wall. **8.** [analyze] a; the endoplasmic reticulum is responsible for synthesizing the membrane proteins required for the transport of solutes across the plasma membrane. **9.** [create] The NLS will be used to actively import the protein into the nucleus, leaving very little of the protein in the cytoplasm. Diffusion alone would not drive all the protein into the nucleus. **10.** [create] Ribosome in cytoplasm (signal is synthesized) → Ribosome at rough ER (protein is completed, folded, and glycosylated) → Transport vesicle → Golgi apparatus (protein is processed; has molecular zip code indicating destination) → Transport vesicle → Plasma membrane → Extracellular space. **11.** [create] This occurs in microfilaments and microtubules because they have ends that differ structurally and functionally—they have different filament growth rates. Intermediate filaments have identical ends, so there is no difference in the rate of assembly between the two ends. **12.** [understand] Polarized cytoskeletal filaments (microtubules or microfilaments) are present between the organelles. End-directed motor proteins use ATP to move these transport vesicles between them.

✔ **Test Your Problem-Solving Skills**

13. [understand] b; fimbriae are involved in bacterial attachment to surfaces and other cells, which would be important in the ability to grow on teeth. **14.** [create] The proteins must receive a molecular zip code that binds to a receptor on the surface of peroxisomes. They could diffuse randomly to peroxisomes or be transported in a directed way by motor proteins. **15.** [create] The tails cleaved from nucleoplasmin could be attached to the gold particles that were excluded from crossing the pore complex owing to their size. If these modified particles entered the nucleus, then the tail is not limited to the nucleoplasmin transport alone. **16.** [apply] The proteins would likely be found in the cytoplasm (e.g., actin and myosin) or imported into the mitochondria. Since there is a high energy demand, you would predict that there are many active mitochondria.

CHAPTER 8

IN-TEXT QUESTIONS AND ANSWERS

p. 139 [apply] (1) If ΔS is positive (products have more disorder than reactants), then according to the free energy equation, ΔG is more likely to be negative as temperature (T) increases even if ΔH is positive. The increased temperature represents added heat energy that may be used to drive an endothermic reaction to completion, making the reaction spontaneous. (2) Exothermic reactions may be nonspontaneous if they result in a decrease in entropy—meaning that the products are more ordered than the reactants (ΔS is negative).
p. 139 CYU (1) [understand] Gibbs equation: $\Delta G = \Delta H - T \Delta S$. ΔG symbolizes the change in the Gibbs free energy. ΔH represents the difference in enthalpy (heat, pressure, and volume) between the products and the reactants. T represents the temperature (in degrees Kelvin) at which the reaction is taking place. ΔS symbolizes the change in entropy (amount of disorder). (2) [understand] When ΔH is negative—meaning that the reactants have lower enthalpy than the products—and when ΔS is positive, meaning that the products have higher entropy (are more disordered) than the reactants.
p. 140 Fig. 8.4 [understand] Each point represents the data from a single test, not an average of many experiments, so it is not possible to calculate the standard error of the average.
p. 144 [analyze] Redox reactions transfer energy between molecules or atoms via electrons. When oxidized molecules are reduced, their potential energy increases. ATP

hydrolysis is often coupled with the phosphorylation of another molecule. This phosphorylation increases the potential energy of the molecule.
p. 144 CYU (1) [understand] Electrons in C–H bonds are not held as tightly as electrons in C–O bonds, so they have higher potential energy. **(2)** [understand] In part, because its three phosphate groups have four negative charges in close proximity. The electrons repulse each other, raising their potential energy.
p. 144 Fig. 8.9 [understand] The ΔG in the uncoupled reaction would be positive (>0), and each of the steps in the coupled reaction would have a negative (<0) ΔG.
p. 147 [remember] (1) binding substrates, (2) transition state, (3) R-groups, (4) structure
p. 146 Fig. 8.12 [understand] No—a catalyst affects only the activation energy, not the overall change in free energy.
p. 147 Fig. 8.14 [analyze] See FIGURE A8.1.
p. 149 CYU (1) [create] The rate of the reaction is based primarily on the activity of the enzyme. Once the temperature reaches a level that causes unfolding and inactivation of the enzyme, the rate decreases to the uncatalyzed rate. **(2)** [apply] The shape change would most likely alter the shape of the active site. If phosphorylation activates catalytic activity, the change to the active site would allow substrates to bind and be brought to their transition state. If phosphorylation inhibits catalytic activity, the shape change to the active site would likely prevent substrates from binding or no longer orient them correctly for the reaction to occur.
p. 150 [apply] The concentration of A and B would be higher than in the fully functional pathway since they are not depleted to produce C. If D is not being depleted by other reactions, then equilibrium would be established between C and D, resulting in lower concentrations of both.

IF YOU UNDERSTAND . . .

8.1 [understand] Reactions are spontaneous when the free energy in the products is lower than that of the reactants (ΔG is negative). Enthalpy and entropy are measures used to determine free-energy changes. Enthalpy measures the potential energy of the molecules, and entropy measures the disorder. For exergonic, spontaneous reactions, disorder normally increases and the potential energy stored in the products normally decreases relative to the reactants. **8.2** [understand] Energetic coupling transfers free energy released from exergonic reactions to drive endergonic reactions. Since endergonic reactions are required for sustaining life, without energetic coupling, life would not exist. **8.3** [understand] Amino acid R-groups lining the active site interact with the substrates, orienting them in a way that stabilizes the transition state, thereby lowering the activation energy needed for the reaction to proceed. **8.4** [analyze] Allosteric regulation and phosphorylation cause changes in the conformation of the enzyme that affects its catalytic function. Allosteric regulation involves non-covalent bonding, while phosphorylation is a covalent modification of the enzyme's primary structure. **8.5** [apply] In the first step of the pathway, the rate would increase as the intermediate, which is the product of the first reaction, is removed. In the last step, the rate would decrease due to the loss of the intermediate, which serves as the substrate for the last reaction.

YOU SHOULD BE ABLE TO . . .

✔ **Test Your Knowledge**

1. [remember] c **2.** [remember] a **3.** [remember] a **4.** [remember] The enzyme changes shape, but the change is not permanent. The enzyme shape will return to its original conformation after releasing the products. **5.** [remember] d **6.** [remember] When the product of a pathway feeds back to interact with an enzyme early in the same pathway to inhibit its function.

✔ **Test Your Understanding**

7. [understand] The shape of reactant molecules (the key) fits into the active site of an enzyme (the lock). Fischer's

original model assumed that enzymes were rigid; in fact, enzymes are flexible and dynamic. **8.** [understand] d. Energy, such as the thermal energy in fire, must be provided to overcome the activation energy barrier before the reaction can proceed. **9.** [understand] The phosphorylation reaction is exergonic because the electrons in ADP and the phosphate added to the substrate experience less electrical repulsion, and thus have less potential energy, than they did in ATP. A phosphorylated reactant (i.e., an activated intermediate) gains enough potential energy to shift the free energy change for the reaction from endergonic to exergonic. **10.** [apply] For the coupled reaction, step 1 has a ΔG of about −3 kcal/mol and step 2 has a ΔG of about −3 kcal/mol. The uncoupled reaction has a ΔG of about +1.3 kcal/mol. **11.** [analyze] Both are mechanisms that regulate enzymes; the difference is whether the regulatory molecule binds at the active site (competitive inhibition) or away from the active site (allosteric regulation). **12.** [apply] Catabolic reactions will often have a negative ΔG based on a decrease in enthalpy and increase in entropy. Anabolic reactions are the opposite—a positive ΔG that is based on an increase in enthalpy and decrease in entropy.

✔ **Test Your Problem-Solving Skills**

13. [create] See FIGURE A8.2. **14.** [apply] Without the coenzyme, the free-radical-containing transition state would not be stabilized and the reaction rate would drop dramatically. **15.** [analyze] The data suggest that the enzyme and substrate form a transition state that requires a change in the shape of the active site, and that each movement corresponds to one reaction. **16.** [apply] b. The sugar likely functions as an allosteric regulator to activate the enzyme.

CHAPTER 9

IN-TEXT QUESTIONS AND EXERCISES

p. 156 Fig. 9.2 [remember] Glycolysis: "What goes in" = glucose, NAD^+, ADP, inorganic phosphate; "What comes out" = pyruvate, NADH, ATP. Pyruvate processing: "What goes in" = pyruvate, NAD^+; "What comes out" = NADH, CO_2, acetyl CoA. Citric acid cycle: "What goes in" = acetyl CoA, NAD^+, FAD, GDP or ADP, inorganic phosphate; "What comes out" = NADH, $FADH_2$, ATP or GTP, CO_2. Electron transport and oxidative phosphorylation: "What goes in" = NADH, $FADH_2$, O_2, ADP, inorganic phosphate; "What comes out" = ATP, H_2O, NAD^+, FAD.

FIGURE A8.1

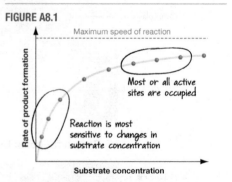

FIGURE A8.2

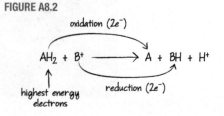

p. 161 apply If the regulatory site had a higher affinity for ATP than the active site, then ATP would always be bound at the regulatory site, and glycolysis would always proceed at a very slow rate.

p. 161 Fig. 9.9 remember "Positive control": AMP, NAD⁺, CoA (reaction substrates). "Negative control by feedback inhibition": acetyl CoA, NADH, ATP (reaction products).

p. 165 CYU remember (1) and (2) are combined with the answer to p. 171 CYU (3) Start with 12 triangles on glucose. (These triangles represent the 12 pairs of electrons that will be moved to electron carriers during redox reactions throughout glycolysis and the citric acid cycle.) Move two triangles to the NADH circle generated by glycolysis and the other 10 triangles to the pyruvate circle. Then move these 10 triangles through the pyruvate dehydrogenase square, placing two of them in the NADH circle next to pyruvate dehydrogenase. Add the remaining eight triangles in the acetyl CoA circle. Next move the eight triangles in the acetyl CoA circle through the citric acid cycle, placing six of them in the NADH circle and two in the FADH₂ circle generated during the citric acid cycle. (4) These boxes are marked with stars in the diagram.

p. 165 Fig. 9.13 apply NADH would be expected to have the highest amount of chemical energy since its production is correlated with the largest drop in free energy in the graph.

p. 167 Fig. 9.15 understand The proton gradient arrow should start above in the inner membrane space and point down across the membrane into the mitochondrial matrix. *Complex I:* "What goes in" = NADH; "What comes out" = NAD⁺, e⁻, transported H⁺. *Complex II:* "What goes in" = FADH₂; "What comes out" = FAD, e⁻, H⁺. *Complex III:* "What goes in" = e⁻, H⁺; "What comes out" = e⁻, transported H⁺. *Complex IV:* "What goes in" = e⁻, H⁺, O₂; "What comes out" = H₂O, transported H⁺.

p. 169 explain "Indirect" is accurate because most of the energy released during glucose oxidation is not used to produce ATP directly. Instead, this energy is stored in reduced electron carriers that are used by the ETC to generate a proton gradient across a membrane. These protons then diffuse down their concentration gradient across the inner membrane through ATP synthase, which drives ATP synthesis.

p. 169 Fig. 9.17 create They could have placed the vesicles in an acidic solution that has a pH below that of the solution in the vesicle. This would set up a proton gradient across the membrane to test for ATP synthesis.

p. 171 CYU understand See FIGURE A9.1. To illustrate the chemiosmotic mechanism, take the triangles (electrons) piled on the NADH and FADH₂ circles and move them through the ETC. While moving these triangles, also move dimes from the mitochondrial matrix to the intermembrane space. As the triangles exit the ETC, add them to the oxygen to water circle. Once all the dimes have been pumped by the ETC into the intermembrane space, move them through ATP synthase back into the mitochondrial matrix to fuel the formation of ATP.

p. 173 CYU understand Electron acceptors such as oxygen have a much higher electronegativity than pyruvate. Donating an electron to O₂ causes a greater drop in potential energy, making it possible to generate much more ATP per molecule of glucose.

IF YOU UNDERSTAND . . .

9.1 understand The radioactive carbons in glucose can be fully oxidized by the central pathways to generate CO₂, which would be radiolabeled. Other molecules, like lipids and amino acids, would also be expected to be radiolabeled since they are made using intermediates from the central pathways in other anabolic pathways. **9.2** apply See FIGURE A9.2. **9.3** understand Pyruvate dehydrogenase accomplishes three different tasks that would be expected to require multiple enzymes and active sites: CO₂ release, NADH production, and linking of an acetyl group to CoA. **9.4** apply NADH would decrease if a drug poisoned the acetyl CoA and oxaloacetate-to-citrate enzyme, since the citric acid cycle would no longer be able to produce NADH in the steps following this reaction in the pathway. **9.5** apply The ATP synthase allows protons to reenter the mitochondrial matrix after they have been pumped out by the ETC. By blocking ATP synthase, you would expect the pH of the matrix to increase (decreased proton concentration). **9.6** understand Organisms that produce ATP by fermentation would be expected to grow more slowly than those that produce ATP via cellular respiration simply because fermentation produces fewer ATP molecules per glucose molecule than cellular respiration does.

YOU SHOULD BE ABLE TO . . .

✔ Test Your Knowledge

1. understand Glycolysis → Pyruvate processing → citric acid cycle → ETC and chemiosmosis. The first three steps are responsible for glucose oxidation; the final step produces the most ATP. **2.** remember b **3.** understand d **4.** understand Most of the energy is stored in the form of NADH. **5.** remember c **6.** remember a

✔ Test Your Understanding

7. understand Stored carbohydrates can be broken down into glucose that enters the glycolytic pathway. If carbohydrates are absent, products from fat and protein catabolism can be used to fuel cellular respiration or fermentation. If ATP is plentiful, anabolic reactions use

FIGURE A9.1

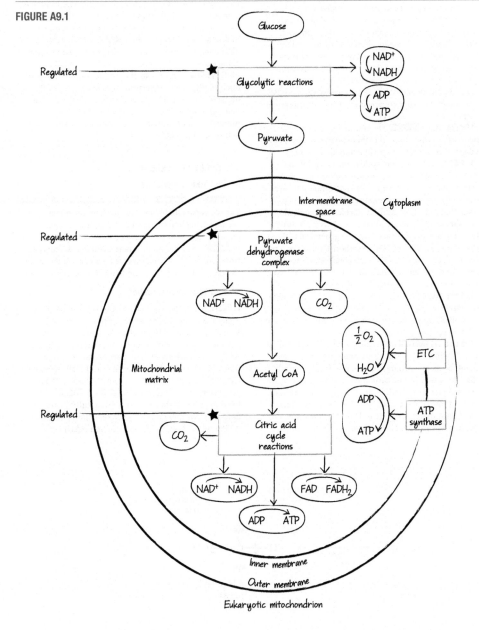

Eukaryotic mitochondrion

FIGURE A9.2

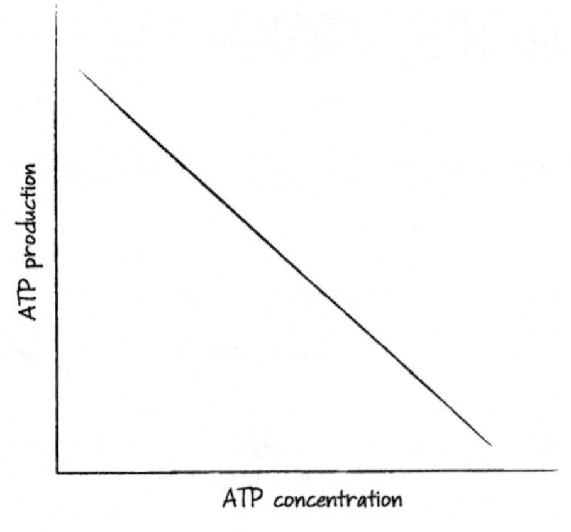

intermediates of the glycolytic pathway and the citric acid cycle to synthesize carbohydrates, fats, and proteins. **8.** `analyze` Both processes produce ATP from ADP and P_i, but substrate-level phosphorylation occurs when enzymes remove a "high-energy" phosphate from a substrate and directly transfer it to ADP, while oxidative phosphorylation occurs when electrons move through an ETC and produce a proton-motive force that drives ATP synthase. **9.** `understand` Aerobic respiration is much more productive because oxygen has extremely high electronegativity compared with other electron acceptors, resulting in a greater release of energy during electron transport and more proton pumping. **10.** `apply` b **11.** `analyze` Both phosphofructokinase and isocitrate dehydrogenase are regulated by feedback inhibition, where the product of the reaction or series of reactions inhibits the enzyme activity. They differ in that phosphofructokinase is regulated by allosteric inhibition while isocitrate dehydrogenase is controlled by competitive inhibition. **12.** `understand` Oxidative phosphorylation is possible via a proton gradient that is established by redox reactions in the ETC. ATP synthase consists of a membrane-associated F_o unit and a F_1 unit joined by a rotor shaft. When protons flow through the F_o unit, it spins the rotor shaft within the fixed F_1 unit. This spinning shaft causes structural changes in the F_1 that drives the synthesis of ATP from ADP and P_i.

✔ Test Your Problem-Solving Skills

13. `create` When complex IV is blocked, electrons can no longer be transferred to oxygen, the final acceptor, and cellular respiration stops. Fermentation could keep glycolysis going, but it is inefficient and unlikely to fuel a cell's energy needs over the long term. Cells that lack the enzymes required for fermentation would die first. **14.** `apply` Because mitochondria with few cristae would have fewer electron transport chains and ATP synthase molecules, they would produce much less ATP than mitochondria with numerous cristae. **15.** `apply` For each glucose molecule, two ATP are produced in glycolysis and two ATP are produced in the citric acid cycle via substrate-level phosphorylation. A total of 10 NADH and 2 $FADH_2$ molecules are produced from glycolysis, pyruvate oxidation, and the citric acid cycle. If each NADH were to yield 3 ATP, and each $FADH_2$ were to yield 2 ATP, then a total of 34 ATP would be produced via oxidative phosphorylation. Adding these totals would result in 38 ATP. A cell will not produce this much ATP, because the proton-motive force is used in other transport steps and because of other issues that may reduce the overall efficiency. **16.** `apply` b

CHAPTER 10

IN-TEXT QUESTIONS AND EXERCISES

p. 177 `understand` See **FIGURE A10.1**. This reaction is endergonic because there are more high-energy chemical bonds in the products compared with the reactants, and there is a decrease in entropy.
p. 177 Fig. 10.1 `apply` See **FIGURE A10.1**.
p. 180 Fig. 10.6 `apply` See **FIGURE A10.2**.

p. 182 Fig. 10.9 `apply` The energy state corresponding to a photon of green light would be located between the energy states corresponding to red and blue photons.
p. 183 CYU `apply` The outer pigments would be more likely to absorb blue photons (short wavelength, high energy), and interior pigments would absorb red photons (long wavelength, low energy). This establishes a pathway to direct photon energy toward the reaction center since resonance energy is transferred from higher to lower energy levels.
p. 184 Fig. 10.11 `understand` Yes—otherwise, changes in the production of oxygen could be due to differences in the number of chloroplasts, not differences in the rate of photosynthesis.
p. 186 `analyze` Light → Antenna complex → Reaction center → Pheophytin → ETC → Proton gradient → ATP synthase. Electrons from water are donated to the reaction center to replace those that were transferred to pheophytin.
p. 188 `remember` (1) Plastocyanin transfers electrons that move through the cytochrome complex in the ETC to the reaction center of photosystem (PS) I. (2) After they are excited by a photon and donated to the initial electron acceptor.
p. 190 CYU `analyze` In mitochondria, high-energy electrons are donated by NADH or $FADH_2$ (primary donors) and passed through an ETC to generate a proton-motive force. The low-energy electrons at the end of the chain are accepted by O_2 (terminal acceptor) to form water. In chloroplasts, low-energy electrons are donated by H_2O (primary donor), energized by photons or resonance energy, and passed through an ETC to generate a proton-motive force. These electrons are then excited a second time by photons or resonance energy, and the high-energy electrons are accepted by $NADP^+$ (terminal acceptor) to form NADPH.
p. 190 Fig. 10.18 `understand` The researchers didn't have any basis on which to predict these intermediates. They needed to perform the experiment to identify them.
p. 192 `apply` Each complete cycle requires 3 ATP and 2 NADPH molecules. To complete 6 runs through the cycle, a total of 18 ATP and 12 NADPH molecules are needed. By following the number of carbons, it is apparent that only three RuBP molecules are required, since they are fully regenerated every 3 cycles: 3 RuBP (15 carbons) fix and reduce 3 CO_2 to generate 6 G3P (18 carbons), yielding 1 G3P (3 carbons); the other 5 are used to regenerate 3 RuBP (15 carbons). The regeneration of RuBP means that only three would be required for continued runs through the Calvin cycle.
p. 194 Fig. 10.24 `apply` The morning would have the highest concentration of organic acids in the vacuoles of CAM plants, since these acids are made during the night and used up during the day.
p. 195 CYU (1) `understand` (a) C_4 plants use PEP carboxylase to fix CO_2 into organic acids in mesophyll cells. These organic acids are then transported into bundle-sheath cells, where they release carbon dioxide to rubisco. (b) CAM plants take in CO_2 at night and have enzymes that fix it into organic acids stored in the central vacuoles of photosynthesizing cells. During the day, the organic acids are processed to release CO_2 to rubisco.

(c) By diffusion through a plant's stomata when they are open. **(2)** `apply` The concentration of starch would be highest at the end of the day and lowest at the start of the day. Starch is made and stored in the chloroplasts of leaves during periods of high photosynthetic activity during the day. At night, it is broken down to make sucrose, which is transported throughout the plant to drive cellular respiration. (Cellular respiration also occurs during the day, but the impact is minimized due to the photosynthetic production of sugar.)

IF YOU UNDERSTAND . . .

10.1 `understand` The Calvin cycle depends on the ATP and NADPH produced by the light-capturing reactions, so it is not independent of light. **10.2** `understand` Most of the energy captured by pigments in chloroplasts is converted into chemical energy by reducing electron acceptors in ETCs. When pigments are extracted, the antenna complexes, reaction centers, and ETCs have been disassembled, so the energy is given off as fluorescence and heat. **10.3** `understand` Oxygen is produced by a critical step in photosynthesis: splitting water to provide electrons to PS II. If oxygen production increases, it means that more electrons are moving through the photosystems. **10.4** `apply` Each CO_2 that is fixed and reduced by the Calvin cycle requires 2 NADPH, which means that 12 NADPH molecules are required for a 6-carbon glucose. Each NADPH is made when two high-energy electrons reduce $NADP^+$. Each of these high-energy electrons originates from H_2O only after being excited by 2 photons (one in PS II and one in PS I). This means that 48 photons are required to produce 24 high-energy electrons to reduce 12 $NADP^+$ molecules for the fixation and reduction of 6 CO_2 to make glucose. Photorespiration would increase the number of photons required, since some of the CO_2 that is fixed would be released.

YOU SHOULD BE ABLE TO . . .

✔ Test Your Knowledge

1. `remember` d **2.** `understand` c **3.** `remember` c **4.** `understand` b **5.** `remember` The conversion of light energy to chemical energy occurs when electrons are transferred from excited pigments to an electron carrier in the photosystems. **6.** `remember` The electron transport chain that accepts electrons from PS II. Plastocyanin is the molecule that transfers electrons from this chain to the PS I reaction center.

✔ Test Your Understanding

7. `understand` The electrons taken from water in PS II are excited twice by either photons or resonance energy. When excited in PS II, the electrons are transferred to PQ and used to build a proton-motive force that makes ATP. After reaching PS I, they are excited a second time and will either be used to reduce $NADP^+$ to make NADPH (noncyclic) or be transported back to PQ to produce more ATP (cyclic). **8.** `analyze` c **9.** `understand` The fixation phase is when CO_2 is fixed to RuBP by rubisco to form 3-phosphoglycerate. The reduction phase uses ATP to phosphorylate the carbons and NADPH to

---

FIGURE A10.1

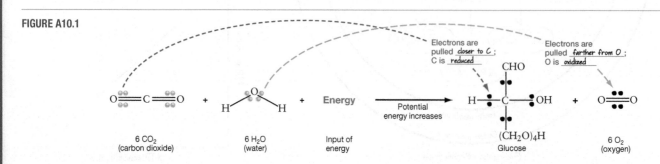

O=C=O + H–O–H + Energy → Potential energy increases → H–C–OH + O=O

6 CO₂ (carbon dioxide)   6 H₂O (water)   Input of energy   Glucose $(CH_2O)_4H$ 6 O₂ (oxygen)

Electrons are pulled closer to C; C is reduced
Electrons are pulled farther from O; O is oxidized
CHO

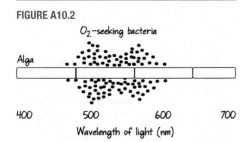

O_2-seeking bacteria

Alga

400   500   600   700

Wavelength of light (nm)

reduce them with high-energy electrons to form G3P. The regeneration phase uses more ATP to convert some of the G3P to RuBP to continue the cycle. **10.** understand Photorespiration occurs when levels of CO_2 are low and O_2 are high. Less sugar is produced because (1) CO_2 doesn't participate in the initial reaction catalyzed by rubisco and (2) when rubisco catalyzes the reaction with O_2 instead, one of the products is eventually broken down to CO_2 in a process that uses ATP. **11.** understand In both C_4 and CAM plants, atmospheric CO_2 is brought in through stomata and first captured by fixing it to a 3-carbon molecule by PEP carboxylase. The C_4 pathway and CAM differ in the timing of this first fixation step—it occurs during the day in C_4 plants and during the night in CAM plants. They also differ in the location of the Calvin cycle with respect to this first fixation step. In C_4 plants, the two processes occur in different cells, while in CAM plants they occur in the same cell, but at different times (Calvin cycle during the day). **12.** analyze Photosynthesis in chloroplasts produces sugar, which is used as a source of carbon for building organic molecules and energy for cellular respiration. Mitochondria harvest the energy stored in sugar to produce ATP, which is used to drive many cellular activities.

✔ Test Your Problem-Solving Skills

13. apply (1) O_2, ATP, and NADPH would be formed by noncyclic electron flow. (2) No O_2 or NADPH would be formed, but ATP may be made by cyclic electron flow. (3) Initially, O_2 and NADPH would be formed by noncyclic electron flow, but no ATP would be made. Without ATP, the Calvin cycle would halt and, once all the NADP$^+$ is used up, noncyclic electron flow would switch to cyclic electron flow. **14.** evaluate Because rubisco evolved in a high CO_2, low O_2 environment, which would minimize the impact of photorespiration, the hypothesis is credible. But once O_2 levels increased, any change in rubisco that minimized photorespiration would give individuals a huge advantage over organisms with "old" forms of rubisco. There has been plenty of time for such changes to occur, making the "holdover" hypothesis less credible. **15.** analyze b; the wavelength of light could excite PS I, but not PS II, resulting in cyclic electron flow since no electrons could be harvested from water by PS II. **16.** create No—they are unlikely to have the same complement of photosynthetic pigments. Different wavelengths of light are available in various layers of a forest and water depths. It is logical to predict that plants and algae have pigments that absorb the available wavelengths efficiently. One way to test this hypothesis would be to isolate pigments from species in different locations and test the absorbance spectra of each.

BIG PICTURE Energy

p. 198 CYU (1) understand Photosynthesis uses H_2O as a substrate and releases O_2 as a by-product; cellular respiration uses O_2 as a substrate and releases H_2O as a by-product. **(2)** understand Photosynthesis uses CO_2 as a substrate; cellular respiration releases CO_2 as a by-product. **(3)** analyze CO_2 fixation would essentially stop; CO_2 would continue to be released by cellular respiration. CO_2

levels in the atmosphere would increase rapidly, and production of new plant tissue would cease—meaning that most animals would quickly starve to death. **(4)** analyze ATP "is used by" the Calvin cycle; photosystem I "yields" NADPH.

CHAPTER 11

IN-TEXT QUESTIONS AND EXERCISES

p. 204 CYU analyze Plant cell walls and animal ECMs are both fiber composites. In plant cell walls the fiber component consists of cross-linked cellulose fibers, and the ground substance is pectin. In animal ECMs the fiber component consists of collagen fibrils, and the ground substance is proteoglycan.
p. 207 apply Developing muscle cells could not adhere normally, and muscle tissue would not form properly. The embryo would die.
p. 207 Fig. 11.9 apply "Prediction": Cells treated with an antibody that blocks membrane proteins involved in adhesion will not adhere. "Prediction of null hypothesis": All cells will adhere normally.
p. 209 CYU (1) analyze The three structures differ in composition, but their function is similar. The middle lamella in plants is composed of pectins that glue adjacent cells together. Tight junctions are made up of membrane proteins that line up and "stitch" adjacent cells together. Desmosomes are "rivet-like" structures composed of proteins that link the cytoskeletons of adjacent cells.
(2) understand The plasma membranes of adjacent plant cells are continuous at plasmodesmata and share portions of the smooth endoplasmic reticulum. Gap junctions connect adjacent animal cells by forming protein-lined pores. Both structures result in openings between the cells that allow cytosol, including ions and small molecules, to be shared.
p. 211 Fig. 11.12 create The steroid hormone likely changes the structure of the receptor such that it now exposes a nuclear localization signal, which is required for the protein to be transported into the nucleus.
p. 213 analyze The spy is the signaling molecule that arrives at the cell surface (the castle gate). The guard is the G-protein-coupled receptor in the plasma membrane, and the queen is the G protein. The commander of the guard is the enzyme that is activated by the G protein to produce second messengers (the soldiers).
p. 214 apply **(1)** The red dominos (RTK components) would be the first two dominos in the chain, followed by the black domino (Ras). This black domino would start two or more new branches, each one represented by a single domino of one color (e.g., green) to represent the activation of one type of kinase. Each of these green dominos would then again branch out, knocking down two or more branches consisting of single dominos of a different color (blue). The same branching pattern would result from each blue domino knocking down two or more yellow dominos. **(2)** Each single black domino (Ras) would require 10 green dominos, 100 blue dominos, and 1000 yellow dominos.
p. 215 CYU (1) understand Each cell–cell signaling molecule binds to a specific receptor protein. A cell can respond to a signal only if it has the appropriate receptor. Only certain cell types will have the appropriate receptor for a given signaling molecule. **(2)** understand Signals are amplified if one or more steps in a signal transduction pathway, involving either second messengers or a phosphorylation cascade, result in the activation of multiple downstream molecules.
p. 215 Fig. 11.16 apply **(1)** cell responses A and C **(2)** cell responses A, B, and C **(3)** cell responses B and C.

IF YOU UNDERSTAND . . .

11.1 apply **(1)** Cells without functional integrin molecules would likely die as a result of not being able to send the

appropriate anchorage-dependent survival signals. **(2)** Cells would be more sensitive to pulling or shearing forces; both cells and tissues would be weaker and more susceptible to damage. **11.2** apply Cells would not be co-ordinated in their activity, so the heart tissue would not contract in unison and the heart would not beat.
11.3 analyze Adrenalin binds to both heart and liver cells, but the activated receptors trigger different signal transduction pathways and lead to different cell responses.
11.4 analyze The signal transduction pathways are similarly organized in both unicellular and multicellular organisms—consisting of signaling molecules, receptors, and second messengers. There is more variety in the means of transmitting the signal between cells in multicellular organisms compared to unicellular organisms. For example, there are no direct connections such as gap junctions or plasmodesmata in unicellular organisms.

YOU SHOULD BE ABLE TO . . .

✔ Test Your Knowledge

1. remember Fiber composites consist of cross-linked fiber components that withstand tension and a ground substance that withstands compression. The cellulose microfibrils in plants and collagen fibrils in animals functionally resemble the steel rods in reinforced concrete. The pectin in plants and proteoglycan in animals functionally resemble the concrete ground substance. **2.** remember b **3.** remember b **4.** understand a **5.** remember d **6.** remember Responses that affect which proteins are produced and those that affect the activity of existing proteins.

✔ Test Your Understanding

7. understand b **8.** understand If each enzyme in the cascade phosphorylates many copies of the enzyme in the next step of the cascade, the initial signal will be amplified many times over. **9.** analyze All three are made up of membrane-spanning proteins that directly interact between adjacent cells. Tight junctions seal adjacent animal cells together; gap junctions allow a flow of material from the cytosol of one to the other. Desmosomes firmly secure adjacent cells to one another but do not affect the movement of substances between cells or into the cells.
10. understand When dissociated cells from two sponge species were mixed, the cells sorted themselves into distinct aggregates that contained only cells of the same species. By blocking membrane proteins with antibodies and isolating cells that would not adhere, researchers found that specialized groups of proteins, including cadherins, are responsible for selective adhesion. **11.** create Signaling molecule crosses plasma membrane and binds to intracellular receptor (reception) → Receptor changes conformation, and the activated receptor complex moves to target site (processing) → Activated receptor complex binds to a target molecule (e.g., a gene or membrane pump), which changes its activity (response) → Signaling molecule falls off receptor or is destroyed; receptor changes to inactive conformation (deactivation).
12. understand Information from different signals may conflict or be reinforcing. "Crosstalk" between signaling pathways allows cells to integrate information from many signals at the same time instead of responding to each signal in isolation.

✔ Test Your Problem-Solving Skills

13. apply d **14.** analyze (a) The response would have to be extremely local—the activated receptor complex would have to affect nearby proteins. (b) No amplification could occur, because the number of signaling molecules dictates the amount of the response. (c) The only way to regulate the response would be to block the receptor or make it more responsive to the signaling molecule.
15. create Chitin forms chains that can cross-link with one another. This fungal cell wall would likely need to be either relaxed or destroyed, and new cell wall synthesis

would be coordinated with the directional growth.
16. create Antibody binding to the two parts of the receptor may be causing them to dimerize. Since dimerization normally results after the signaling molecule binds to the receptor, the antibodies could be activating the receptor by mimicking this interaction. The result would be signal transduction even in the absence of the signaling molecule.

CHAPTER 12

IN-TEXT QUESTIONS AND EXERCISES

p. 223 understand **(1)** Genes are segments of chromosomes that code for RNAs and proteins. **(2)** Chromosomes are made of chromatin. **(3)** Sister chromatids are identical copies of the same chromosome, joined together.
p. 224 Fig. 12.5 apply **(1)** prophase cells would have 4 chromosomes with $2x$ DNA. **(2)** Anaphase cells would have 8 chromosomes and $2x$ DNA. **(3)** Each daughter cell will have 4 chromosomes with x DNA.
p. 226 apply See **TABLE A12.1.**
p. 227 Fig. 12.6 apply The chromosome and black bar would move at the same rate toward the spindle pole.
p. 229 CYU (1) apply See **FIGURE A12.1. (2)** apply Loss of the motors would result in two problems: (1) It would reduce the ability of chromosomes to attach to microtubules via their kinetochores; (2) cytokinesis would be inhibited since the Golgi-derived vesicles would not be moved to the center of the spindle to build the cell plate.
p. 230 Fig. 12.10 create Inject cytoplasm from an M-phase frog egg into a somatic cell that is in interphase. If the somatic cell starts mitosis, then the meiotic factor is not limited to gametes.
p. 230 Fig. 12.11 analyze In effect, MPF turns itself off after it is activated. If this didn't happen, the cell might undergo mitosis again before the cell has replicated its DNA.

p. 231 understand MPF activates proteins that get mitosis under way. MPF consists of a cyclin and a Cdk, and it is turned on by phosphorylation at the activating site and dephosphorylation at the inhibitory site. Enzymes that degrade cyclin reduce MPF levels.
p. 232 CYU (1) remember $G_1 \rightarrow S \rightarrow G_2 \rightarrow M$. Checkpoints occur at the end of G_1 and G_2 and during M phase. **(2)** understand Cdk levels are fairly constant throughout the cycle, but cyclin increases during interphase and peaks in M phase. This accumulation of cyclin is a prerequisite for MPF activity, which turns on at the end of G_2, initiating M phase, and declines at the end of M phase.

IF YOU UNDERSTAND . . .

12.1 understand The G_1 and G_2 phases give the cell time to replicate organelles and grow before division as well as perform the normal functions required to stay alive. Chromosomes replicate during S phase and are separated from one another during M phase. Cytokinesis also occurs during M phase, when the parent cell divides into two daughter cells. **12.2** apply In cells that do not dissolve the nuclear envelope, the spindle must be constructed inside the nucleus to attach to the chromosomes and separate them. **12.3** apply Cells would prematurely enter M phase, shortening the length of G_2 and resulting in the daughter cells' being smaller than normal. **12.4** analyze The absence of growth factors in normal cells would cause them to arrest in the G_1 phase—eventually all the cells in the culture would be in G_1. The cancerous cells are not likely to be dependent on these growth factors, so the cells would not arrest and would continue through the cell cycle.

YOU SHOULD BE ABLE TO . . .

✔ Test Your Knowledge

1. remember b **2.** remember d **3.** remember d **4.** remember c
5. understand Daughter chromosomes were observed to move toward the pole faster than do the marked regions of fluorescently labeled kinetochore microtubules.
6. remember The cycle would arrest in M phase, and cytokinesis would not occur.

✔ Test Your Understanding

7. apply For daughter cells to have identical complements of chromosomes, all the chromosomes must be replicated during the S phase, the spindle apparatus must connect with the kinetochores of each sister chromatid in prometaphase, and the sister chromatids of each replicated chromosome must be partitioned in anaphase and fully separated into daughter cells by cytokinesis. **8.** create One possible concept map is shown in **FIGURE A12.2. 9.** understand Microinjection experiments suggested that something in the cytoplasm of M-phase cells activated the transition from interphase to M phase. The control for this experiment was to inject cytoplasm from a G_2-arrested oocyte into another G_2-arrested oocyte. **10.** apply Protein kinases phosphorylate proteins. Phosphorylation changes a protein's shape, altering its function (activating or inactivating it). As a result, protein kinases regulate the function of proteins. **11.** understand Cyclin concentrations change during the cell cycle. At high concentration, cyclins bind to a specific cyclin-dependent kinase (or Cdk), forming a dimer. This dimer becomes active MPF by changing its shape through the phosphorylation (activating site) and dephosphorylation (inhibitory site) of Cdk. **12.** analyze b.

✔ Test Your Problem-Solving Skills

13. analyze a; adding up each phase allows you to determine that the cell cycle is 8.5 hours long. After 9 hours, the radiolabeled cells would have passed through a full cycle and be in either S phase or G_2—none would have entered M phase. **14.** apply The embryo passes through multiple rounds of the cell cycle, but cytokinesis does

---

FIGURE A12.1

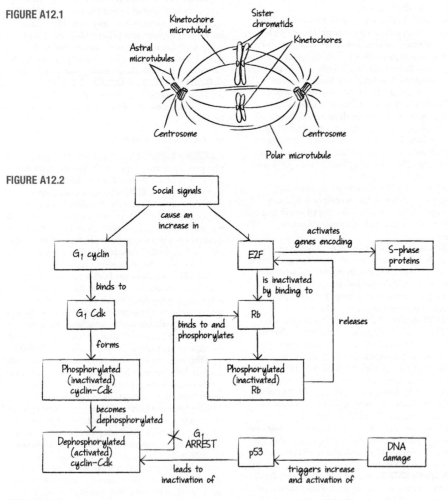

FIGURE A12.2

TABLE A12.1

	Prophase	Prometaphase	Metaphase	Anaphase	Telophase
Spindle apparatus	Starts to form	Contacts and moves chromosomes	Anchors poles to membrane and produces tension at kinetochores	Pulls chromatids apart	Defines site of cytokinesis
Nuclear envelope	Present	Disintegrates	Nonexistent	Nonexistent	Re-forms
Chromosomes	Condense	Attach to microtubules	Held at metaphase plate	Sister chromatids separate into daughter chromosomes	Collect at opposite poles

not occur during M phases. **15.** [apply] Early detection of cancers leads to a greater likelihood of survival. The widespread implementation of breast and prostate exams allows for the identification and removal of benign tumors before they become malignant. **16.** [analyze] Cancer requires many defects. Older cells have had more time to accumulate defects. Individuals with a genetic predisposition to cancer start out with some cancer-related defects, but this does not mean that the additional defects required for cancer to occur will develop.

CHAPTER 13

IN-TEXT QUESTIONS AND EXERCISES

p. 239 [apply] $n = 4$; the organism is diploid with $2n = 8$.
p. 240 [remember] See **FIGURE A13.1**. Because the two sister chromatids are identical and attached, it is sensible to consider them as parts of a single chromosome.
p. 242 [apply] There will be four DNA molecules in each gamete because the 8 replicated chromosomes in a diploid cell are reduced to 4 replicated chromosomes per cell at the end of meiosis I. In meiosis II, the sister chromatids of each replicated chromosome are separated. Each cell now contains 4 unreplicated chromosomes, each with a single molecule of DNA.
p. 245 [apply] Crossing over would not occur and the daughter cells produced by meiosis would be diploid, not haploid. There would be no reduction division.
p. 246 CYU (1) [understand] Use four long and four short pipe cleaners (or pieces of cooked spaghetti) to represent the chromatids of two replicated homologous chromosomes (four total chromosomes). Mark two long and two short ones with a colored marker pen to distinguish maternal and paternal copies of these chromosomes. Twist identical pipe cleaners (e.g., the two long colored ones) together to simulate replicated chromosomes. Arrange the pipe cleaners to depict the different phases of meiosis I as follows: *Early prophase I:* Align sister chromatids of each homologous pair to form two tetrads. *Late prophase I:* Form one or more crossovers between non-sister chromatids in each tetrad. (This is hard to simulate with pipe cleaners—you'll have to imagine that each chromatid now contains both maternal and paternal segments.) *Metaphase I:* Line up homologous pairs (the two pairs of short pipe cleaners and the two pairs of long pipe cleaners) at the metaphase plate. *Anaphase I:* Separate homologs. Each homolog still consists of sister chromatids joined at the centromere. *Telophase I and cytokinesis:* Move homologs apart to depict formation of two haploid cells, each containing a single replicated copy of two different chromosomes. **(2)** [understand] During anaphase I, homologs (not sister chromatids, as in mitosis) are separated, making the cell products of meiosis I haploid. **(3)** [understand] The pairing of homologs in metaphase I and their separation in anaphase I so that one goes to one daughter cell and the other to the other daughter cell means that each daughter cell obtains precisely one copy of each type of chromosome.
p. 248 [apply] Each gamete would inherit either all maternal or all paternal chromosomes. This would limit genetic variation in the offspring by precluding the many possible gametes containing various combinations of maternal and paternal chromosomes.
p. 248 CYU (1) [apply] See **FIGURE A13.2**. Maternal chromosomes are white and paternal chromosomes are black. Daughter cells with other possible combinations of chromosomes than shown could result from meiosis of this parent cell. **(2)** [understand] Crossing over would increase the genetic diversity of these gametes by creating many different combinations of maternal and paternal alleles along each of the chromosomes. **(3)** [analyze] Asexual reproduction generates no appreciable genetic diversity. Self-fertilization is preceded by meiosis so it generates gametes, through crossing over and independent

assortment, that have combinations of alleles not present in the parent. Outcrossing generates the most genetic diversity among offspring because it produces new combinations of alleles from two different individuals.
p. 249 Fig. 13.11 [apply] See **FIGURE A13.3**.
p. 251 Fig. 13.14 [apply] Asexually: 64 (16 individuals from generation three produce 4 offspring per individual). Sexually: 16 (8 individuals from generation three form 4 couples; each couple produces 4 offspring).
p. 252 Fig. 13.15 [apply] The rate of outcrossing is predicted to rise initially, as the pathogen selects for resistant roundworms, and then to fall as the roundworms in the population gain resistance and take advantage of the increased numbers of offspring offered by having more hermaphrodites that can reproduce by self-fertilization.

IF YOU UNDERSTAND . . .

13.1 [remember] See the right panel of Figure 13.7 and note how the cells transition from diploid to haploid in meiosis I. Also note that each chromosome contains two sister chromatids before and after meiosis I.
13.2 [understand] (a) See Figure 13.10 and note how the two different ways of aligning two homologous pairs of chromosomes at metaphase I of meiosis can create four different combinations of maternal and paternal chromosomes in daughter cells. (b) See Figure 13.11. Note that for each homologous pair with one crossover, two chromatids are recombinant and two are unaltered. Since each chromatid will produce a chromosome at the end of meiosis II, your drawing should show that two out of four of these chromosomes are recombinant.
13.3 [apply] (a) Your model should show events similar to those of Figure 13.12. (b) Your model should show two cells with one of each type of chromosome (n), one cell with an extra copy of one chromosome ($n + 1$), and one gamete without any copies of one chromosome ($n - 1$).
13.4 [remember] Sexual reproduction will likely occur during times when conditions are changing rapidly, because genetically diverse offspring may have an advantage in the new conditions.

YOU SHOULD BE ABLE TO . . .

✔ Test Your Knowledge
1. [remember] b **2.** [remember] a **3.** [remember] b **4.** [understand] b
5. [remember] 1/2 **6.** [remember] mitosis.

✔ Test Your Understanding
7. [remember] Homologous chromosomes are similar in size, shape, and gene content, and originate from different parents. Sister chromatids are exact copies of a chromosome that are generated when chromosomes are replicated (S phase of the cell cycle). **8.** [understand] Refer to Figure 13.7 as a guide for this exercise. The four pens represent the chromatids in one replicated homologous pair; the four pencils, the chromatids in a different homologous pair. To simulate meiosis II, make two "haploid cells"—each with a pair of pens and a pair of pencils representing two replicated chromosomes (one of each type in this species). Line them up in the middle of the cell; then separate the two pens and the two pencils in each cell such that one pen and one pencil go to each of four daughter cells. **9.** [understand] Meiosis I is a reduction division because homologs separate—daughter cells have just one of each type of chromosome instead of two. Meiosis II is not a reduction division because sister chromatids separate— daughter cells have unreplicated chromosomes instead of replicated chromosomes, but still just one of each type. **10.** [apply] b. **11.** [apply] Tetraploids produce diploid gametes, which combine with a haploid gamete from a diploid individual to form a triploid offspring. Mitosis proceeds normally in triploid cells because mitosis doesn't require forming pairs of chromosomes. But during meiosis in a triploid, homologous chromosomes can't pair up correctly. The third set of chromosomes does not have a homologous partner to pair with. **12.** [understand] Asexually produced individuals are genetically identical, so if one is susceptible to a new disease, all are. Sexually produced individuals are genetically unique, so if a new disease strain evolves, at least some plants are likely to be resistant.

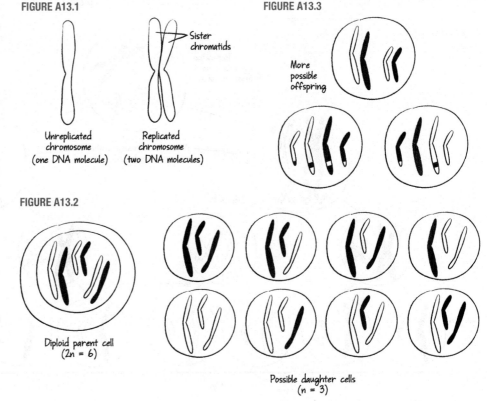

FIGURE A13.1

Unreplicated chromosome (one DNA molecule)

Replicated chromosome (two DNA molecules)

Sister chromatids

FIGURE A13.2

Diploid parent cell ($2n = 6$)

Possible daughter cells ($n = 3$)

FIGURE A13.3

More possible offspring

13. apply The gibbon would have 22 chromosomes in each gamete, and the siamang would have 25. Each somatic cell of the offspring would have 47 chromosomes. The offspring should be sterile because it has some chromosomes that would not form homologous pairs at prophase I of meiosis. **14.** apply c **15.** apply Aneuploidy is the major cause of spontaneous abortion. If spontaneous abortion is rare in older women, it would result in a higher incidence of aneuploid conditions such as Down syndrome in older women, as recorded in the Figure 13.13. **16. (a)** create Such a study might be done in the laboratory, controlling conditions in identical dishes. A population of rotifers infected with fungus could be established in each dish. One dish of rotifers would be kept moist; the other dishes of rotifers would be allowed to dry out. After various periods of time, water would be added to each dish and then the rotifers would be observed to see if fungal infections reappeared. **(b)** create Wind disperses the rotifer to new and often pathogen-free environments. In this case, the ticket to a sex-free existence is not genetic diversity but the evolution of an alternative means of evading pathogens made possible by fungus-infected rotifers ridding themselves of the pathogen when they dry.

CHAPTER 14

IN-TEXT QUESTIONS AND EXERCISES

p. 260 Fig. 14.3 evaluate An experiment is a failure if you didn't learn anything from it. That is not the case here.
p. 261 Table 14.2 analyze Row 6: 3.14 : 1; Row 7: 266.
p. 262 apply Filling in the top and side of a Punnett square requires writing out the types and ratios of gametes. For a cross involving one gene (monohybrid cross), this amounts to applying the principle of segregation as one allele is segregated from another. The phenotype ratios are 1 : 1 round : wrinkled; the genotype ratios are 1 : 1 *Rr* : *rr*.
p. 262 Fig. 14.4 understand No—the outcome (the expected offspring genotypes that the Punnett square generates) will be the same.

p. 263 CYU (1) apply See answer to Problem 13 in Test Your Problem-Solving Skills, below. **(2)** apply See answer to Problem 15 in Test Your Problem-Solving Skills.
p. 265 apply *AABb* → *AB* and *Ab*. *PpRr* → *PR*, *Pr*, *pR*, and *pr*. *AaPpRr* → *APR*, *APr*, *ApR*, *Apr*, *aPR*, *apR*, *apr*, and *aPr*.
p. 265 CYU (1) apply See answer to Problem 14 in Test Your Problem-Solving Skills. **(2)** apply See answer to Problem 16 in Test Your Problem-Solving Skills.
p. 269 CYU (1) understand See **FIGURE A14.1**. Segregation of alleles occurs when homologs that carry those alleles are separated during anaphase I. One allele ends up in each daughter cell. **(2)** understand See **FIGURE A14.2**. Independent assortment occurs because homologous pairs line up randomly at the metaphase plate during metaphase I. The figure shows two alternative arrangements of homologs in metaphase I. As a result, it is equally possible for a gamete to receive the following four combinations of alleles: *YR*, *Yr*, *yR*, *yr*.
p. 270 Fig. 14.12 apply *XWY*, *XWy*, *XwY*, *Xwy*.

p. 271 Fig. 14.13 analyze Random chance (or perhaps red-eyed, gray-bodied males don't survive well).
p. 273 Fig. 14.16 analyze The gene colored orange is *ruby*; the gene colored blue is *miniature wings*.
p. 275 Fig. 14.19 understand In this case of gene-by-gene interaction, the 9 : 3 : 3 : 1 ratio comes from four different forms of one trait (comb shape), whereas in a standard dihybrid cross, the four different phenotypes come from two different phenotypes for each of two genes.
p. 276 CYU (1) apply The comb phenotype results from interactions between alleles at two different genes, not a single gene. Matings between rose- and pea-comb chickens produce F₂ offspring that may have a new combination of alleles and thus new phenotypes. **(2)** apply Kernel color in wheat is influenced by alleles at many different genes, not a single gene. F₂ offspring have a normal distribution of phenotypes, not a 3 : 1 ratio.
p. 276 Fig. 14.21 understand Because there are many different genotypes that can produce intermediate coloration and fewer that can produce the extremes of coloration.

FIGURE A14.1

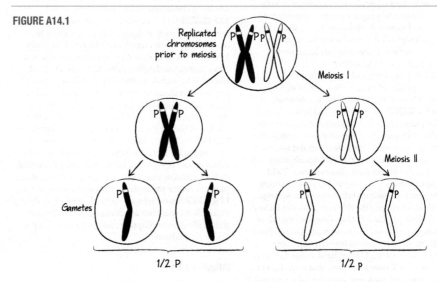

FIGURE A14.2

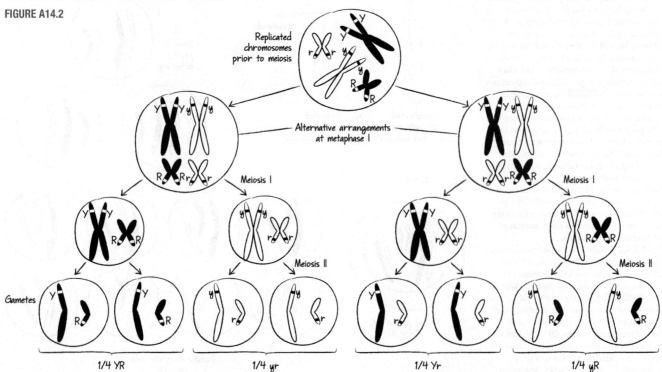

p. 279 Fig. 14.23 apply A heterozygous female and a color-blind male. 1 color-blind male : 1 color-blind female.

IF YOU UNDERSTAND . . .

14.1 understand Because crosses within a pure line never produce individuals with a different phenotype, this indicates that there must be only one allele in pure-line individuals. **14.2** apply B and b. **14.3** apply BR, Br, bR, and br, in equal proportions. The B and b alleles are located on different but homologous chromosomes, which separate into different daughter cells during meiosis I. The $BbRr$ notation indicates that the B and R genes are on different chromosomes. As a result, the chromosomes line up independently of each other in metaphase of meiosis I. The B allele is equally likely to go to a daughter cell with R as with r; likewise, the b allele is equally likely to go to a daughter cell with R as with r. **14.4** apply There are many ways to show this. If eye color in *Drosophila* is chosen as an example, then a pair of Punnett squares like those in Figure 14.11 illustrate how reciprocal crosses involving an X-linked recessive gene give different results. **14.5** understand Linkage refers to the physical connection of two alleles on the same chromosome. Crossing over breaks this linkage between particular alleles as segments of maternal and paternal homologs are exchanged. **14.6** apply See **FIGURE A14.3** for the pedigree. Note that the birth order of daughters and sons is arbitrary; other birth orders are equally valid. A Punnett square will show that all the sons are predicted to be X^+Y and all the daughters X^+X^c, where X^+ shows the dominant, X-linked allele for normal color vision and X^c shows the X-linked recessive color blindness allele.

YOU SHOULD BE ABLE TO . . .

✔ Test Your Understanding

1. understand d 2. understand b 3. understand a 4. understand d
5. understand a 6. understand a 7. evaluate d 8. remember b 9. apply b
10. understand d

✔ Test Your Problem-Solving Skills

11. apply **Example Solution** Here you're given offspring phenotypes and you're asked to infer parental genotypes. To do this you have to propose hypothetical parental genotypes to test, make a Punnett square to predict the offspring genotypes, and then see if the predicted offspring phenotypes match the data. In this case, coming up with a hypothesis for the parental genotypes is relatively straightforward because the problem states that the trait is due to one gene and two alleles. No information on sex is given, so assume the gene is autosomal (the simplest case). Now look at the second entry in the chart. It shows a 3 : 1 ratio of offspring from a winged individual that self-fertilizes. This result is consistent with the hypothesis that W^+ is dominant and W^- recessive and that this parent's genotype is W^+W^-. Now let's look at the first cross in the chart. If W^+ is dominant, then a wingless parent must be W^-W^-. When you do the Punnett square to predict offspring genotypes from selfing, you find that all the offspring will produce wingless fruits, consistent with the data. In the third cross, all the offspring make winged fruits even though one of the parents produces wingless

FIGURE A14.3

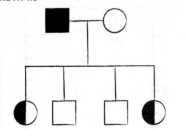

fruits and thus is W^-W^-. This would happen only if the winged parent is W^+W^+. (If this reasoning isn't immediately clear to you, work the Punnett square.) In the fourth cross, you could get offspring that all make winged fruits if the parents were W^+W^+ and W^+W^+, or if the parents were W^+W^+ and W^+W^-. Either answer is correct. Again, you can write out the Punnett squares to see that this statement is correct.

12. apply **Example Solution** Here you are given parental and offspring phenotypes and are asked to infer the parental genotypes. As a starting point, assume that the coat colors are due to the simplest genetic system possible: one autosomal gene with two alleles, where one allele is dominant and the other recessive. Because female II produces only black offspring, it's logical to suppose that black is dominant to brown. Let's use B for black and b for brown. Then the male parent is bb. To produce offspring with a 1 : 1 ratio of black : brown coats, female I must be Bb. But to produce all black offspring, female II must be BB. This model explains the data, so you can accept it as correct.

13. apply 3/4; 1/256 (see BioSkills 5 in Appendix B); 1/2 (the probabilities of transmitting the alleles or having sons does not change over time). **14.** apply Your answer to the first three parts should conform to the F_1 and F_2 crosses diagrammed in Figure 14.5b, except that different alleles and traits are being analyzed. The recombinant gametes would be Yi and yI. Yes—there would be some individuals with yellow seeds and constricted pods and with green seeds and inflated pods. **15.** apply Cross 1: non-crested (Cc) × non-crested (Cc) = 22 non-crested ($C\_$); 7 crested (cc). Cross 2: crested (cc) × crested (cc) = 20 crested (cc). Cross 3: non-crested (Cc) × crested (cc) = 7 non-crested (Cc); 6 crested (cc). Non-crested (C) is the dominant allele. **16.** apply This is a dihybrid cross that yields progeny phenotypes in a 9 : 3 : 3 : 1 ratio. Let O stand for the allele for orange petals and o the allele for yellow petals; let S stand for the allele for spotted petals and s the allele for unspotted petals. Start with the hypothesis that O is dominant to o, that S is dominant to s, that the two genes are found on different chromosomes so they assort independently, and that the parent individual's genotype is $OoSs$. If you do a Punnett square for the $OoSs \times OoSs$ mating, you'll find that progeny phenotypes should be in the observed 9 : 3 : 3 : 1 proportions. **17.** analyze Let D stand for the normal allele and d for the allele responsible for Duchenne-type muscular dystrophy. The woman's family has no history of the disease, so her genotype is almost certainly DD. The man is not afflicted, so he must be DY. (The trait is X-linked, so he has only one allele; the "Y" stands for the Y chromosome.) Their children are not at risk. The man's sister could be a carrier, however—meaning she has the genotype Dd. If so, then half of the second couple's male children are likely to be affected. **18.** understand Your stages of meiosis should look like a simplified version of Figure 13.7, except with $2n = 4$ instead of $2n = 6$. The A and a alleles could be on the red and blue versions of the longest chromosome, and the B and b alleles could be on the red and blue versions of the smallest chromosome, similar to the way the hair- and eye-color genes are shown in Figure 13.10. The places you draw them are the locations of the A and B genes, but each chromosome has only one allele. Each pair of red and blue chromosomes is a homologous pair. Sister chromatids bear the same allele (e.g., both sister chromatids of the long blue chromosomes might bear the a allele). Chromatids from the longest and shortest chromosomes are not homologous. To identify the events that result in the principles of segregation and independent assortment, see Figures 14.7 and 14.8 and substitute A, a, and B, b for R, r and Y, y. **19.** apply Half their offspring should have the genotype iI^A and the type A blood phenotype. The other half of their offspring should have the genotype iI^B and the type B blood

phenotype. Second case: the genotype and phenotype ratios would be 1 : 1 : 1 : 1 I^AI^B (type AB) : I^Ai (type A) : I^Bi (type B) : ii (type O). **20.** apply Because the children of Tukan and Valco had no eyes and smooth skin, you can conclude that the allele for eyelessness is dominant to eyes and the allele for smooth skin is dominant to hooked skin. E = eyeless, e = two eye sets, S = smooth skin, s = hooked skin. Tukan is $eeSS$; Valco is $EEss$. The children are all $EeSs$. Grandchildren with eyes and smooth skin are $eeS\-$. Assuming that the genes are on different chromosomes, one-fourth of the children's gametes are ee and three-fourths are $S\-$. So 1/4 $ee \times$ 3/4 $S\- \times 32 = 6$ children would be expected to have two sets of eyes and smooth skin. **21.** create Although the mothers were treated as children by a reduction of dietary phenylalanine, they would have accumulated phenylalanine and its derivatives once they went off the low-phenylalanine diet as young adults. Children born of such mothers were therefore exposed to high levels of phenylalanine during pregnancy. For this reason, a low-phenylalanine diet is recommended for such mothers throughout the pregnancy. **22.** apply According to Mendel's model, palomino individuals should be heterozygous at the locus for coat color. If you mated palomino individuals, you would expect to see a combination of chestnut, palomino, and cremello offspring. If blending inheritance occurred, however, all the offspring should be palomino. **23.** apply Because this is an X-linked trait, the father who has hemophilia could not have passed the trait on to his son. Thus, the mother in couple 1 must be a carrier and must have passed the recessive allele on to her son, who is XY and affected. To educate a jury about the situation, you should draw what happens to the X and Y during meiosis and then make a drawing showing the chromosomes in couple 1 and couple 2, with a Punnett square showing how these chromosomes are passed to the affected and unaffected children. **24.** apply The curved-wing allele is autosomal recessive; the lozenge-eyed allele is sex-linked (specifically, X-linked) recessive. Let L be the allele for long wings and l be the allele for curved wings; let X^R be the allele for red eyes and X^r the allele for lozenge eyes. The female parent is LlX^RX^r; the male parent is LlX^RY. **25.** apply Albinism indicates the absence of pigment, so let b stand for an allele that gives the absence of blue and y for an allele that gives the absence of yellow pigment. If blue and yellow pigment blend to give green, then both green parents are $BbYy$. The green phenotype is found in $BBYY$, $BBYy$, $BbYY$, and $BbYy$ offspring. The blue phenotype is found in $BByy$ or $Bbyy$ offspring. The yellow phenotype is observed in $bbYY$ or $bbYy$ offspring. Albino offspring are $bbyy$. The phenotypes of the offspring should be in the ratio 9 : 3 : 3 : 1 as green : blue : yellow : albino. Two types of crosses yield $BbYy$ F_1 offspring: $BByy \times bbYY$ (blue × yellow) and $BBYY \times bbyy$ (green × albino). **26.** apply The chance that their first child will have hemophilia is 1/2. This is because all sons will have the disease and there is a 1/2 chance of having a firstborn son. The chance of having a carrier as their first child is also 1/2. This is because all daughters and none of the sons will be carriers and there is a 1/2 chance of having a firstborn daughter. (Recall that males cannot carry an X-linked recessive trait—with only one X chromosome, males either have the trait or not.) **27.** apply Autosomal dominant.

CHAPTER 15

IN-TEXT QUESTIONS AND EXERCISES

p. 286 Fig. 15.2 analyze The lack of radioactive protein in the pellet (after centrifugation) is strong evidence; they could also make micrographs of infected bacterial cells before and after agitation.
p. 287 Fig. 15.3 apply 5'-TAG-3'.
p. 288 Fig. 15.5 apply The same two bands should appear, but the upper band (DNA containing only ^{14}N) should get bigger and darker and the lower band (hybrid DNA)

should get smaller and lighter in color since each suc-ceeding generation has relatively less heavy DNA.

p. 290 `apply` See **FIGURE A15.1**. The new strands grow in opposite directions, each in the $5' \rightarrow 3'$ direction.

p. 292 `apply` Helicase, topoisomerase, single-strand DNA-binding proteins, primase, and DNA polymerase are all required for leading-strand synthesis. If any one of these proteins is nonfunctional, DNA replication will not occur.

p. 293 `apply` See **FIGURE A15.2**. If DNA ligase were defective, then the leading strand would be continuous, and the lagging strand would have gaps in it where the Okazaki fragments had not been joined.

p. 294 CYU (1) `understand` DNA polymerase adds nucleotides only to the free $3' - OH$ on a strand. Primase synthesizes a short RNA sequence that provides the free $3'$ end necessary for DNA polymerase to start working. **(2)** `understand` The need to begin DNA synthesis many times on the lagging strand requires many new primers. Since DNA polymerase I is needed to remove primers, it is required predominantly on the primer-rich lagging strand.

p. 296 Fig. 15.13 `apply` As long as the RNA template could bind to the "overhanging" section of single-stranded DNA, any sequence could produce a longer strand. For example, 5'-CCCAUUCCC-3' would work just as well.

p. 297 CYU (1) `understand` This is because telomerase is needed only to replicate one end of a linear DNA and bacterial DNAs lack ends because they are circular. **(2)** `understand` Since telomerase works by extending one strand of DNA without any external template and because DNA synthesis requires a template, telomerase must contain an internal template to allow it to extend a DNA chain.

p. 299 Fig. 15.16 `analyze` They are lower in energy and not absorbed effectively by the DNA bases.

p. 300 CYU (1) `apply` The mutation rate would be predicted to rise because differences in base-pair stability and shape make it possible for DNA polymerase to distinguish correct from incorrect base pairs during DNA replication. **(2)** `apply` The mutation rate should increase because without a way to distinguish which strand to use as a template for repair, about half of mismatches on average would be repaired using the incorrect strand as a template. **(3)** `remember` The enzyme that removes the dimer and surrounding DNA is specific to nucleotide excision repair. DNA polymerase and DNA ligase work in both nucleotide excision repair and normal DNA synthesis.

p. 300 Fig. 15.18 `apply` Exposure to UV radiation can cause formation of thymine dimers. If thymine dimers are not repaired, they represent mutations. If such mutations occur in genes controlling the cell cycle, cells can grow abnormally, resulting in cancers.

IF YOU UNDERSTAND . . .

15.1 `apply` These results would not allow distinguishing whether DNA or protein was the genetic material.

15.2 `understand` The bases added during DNA replication are shown in red type.

Original DNA:	**CAATTACGGA**
	GTTAATGCCT
Replicated DNA:	**CAATTACGGA**
	GTTAATGCCT
	CAATTACGGA
	GTTAATGCCT

15.3 `understand` See **FIGURE A15.3**. **15.4** `understand` Because cancer cells divide nearly without limit, it's important for these cells to have active telomerase so that chromosomes don't shorten to the point where cell division becomes impossible. **15.5** `understand` If errors in DNA aren't corrected, they represent mutations. When DNA repair systems fail, the mutation rate increases. As the mutation rate increases, the chance that one or more cell-cycle genes will be mutated increases. Mutations in these genes often result in uncontrolled cell division, ultimately leading to cancer.

YOU SHOULD BE ABLE TO . . .

✔ **Test Your Knowledge**

1. `remember` d **2.** `understand` a **3.** `remember` topoisomerase
4. `remember` b **5.** `remember` c **6.** `remember` telomerase

✔ **Test Your Understanding**

7. `remember` Labeling DNA or labeling proteins. **8.** `understand` DNA is constantly damaged, and many pathways have evolved to repair this onslaught of damage. If a DNA repair pathway is inactivated by mutation, damage is inefficiently repaired. Consequently mutation rates increase, and the increased number of mutations increases the probability that cancer-causing mutations will occur.
9. `understand` On the lagging strand, DNA polymerase moves away from the replication fork. When helicase unwinds a new section of DNA, primase must build a new primer on the template for the lagging strand (closer to the fork) and another polymerase molecule must begin synthesis at this point. This makes the lagging-strand synthesis discontinuous. On the leading strand, DNA polymerase moves in the same direction as helicase, so synthesis can continue, without interruption, from a single primer (at the origin of replication).
10. `understand` Telomerase binds to the overhang at the end of a chromosome. Once bound, it begins catalyzing the addition of deoxyribonucleotides to the overhang in the

$5' \rightarrow 3'$ direction, lengthening the overhang. This allows primase, DNA polymerase, and ligase to catalyze the addition of deoxyribonucleotides to the lagging strand in the $5' \rightarrow 3'$ direction, restoring the lagging strand to its original length. **11.** `apply` a (Because the ability to distinguish which strand contains the incorrect base would be lost). **12.** `analyze` d (The regularity of DNA's structure allows enzymes to recognize any type of damage that distorts this regular structure.)

✔ **Test Your Problem-Solving Skills**

13. `analyze` c (If DNA polymerase could synthesize DNA $3' \rightarrow 5'$ as well as the normal $5' \rightarrow 3'$, then both newly synthesized DNA strands could be extended to follow the replication fork.) **14.** `apply` (a) In **FIGURE A15.4**, the gray lines represent DNA strands containing radioactivity. (b) After one round of replication in radioactive solution, one double-stranded DNA would be radioactive in both strands and the other would not be radioactive in either strand. After another round of DNA synthesis, this time in nonradioactive solution, one of the four DNA molecules would be radioactive in both strands and the other three DNA molecules would contain no radioactivity in any strand. **15.** `analyze` (a) The double mutant of both *uvrA* and *recA* is most sensitive to UV light; the single mutants are in between; and the wild type is

---

FIGURE A15.1

FIGURE A15.2

FIGURE A15.3

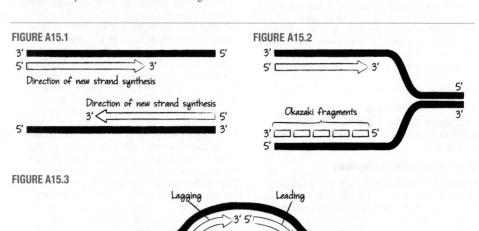

FIGURE A15.4

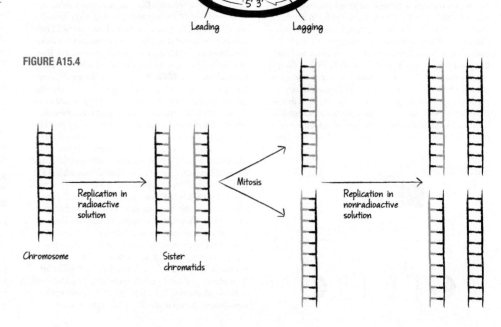

least sensitive. (b) The *recA* gene contributes more to UV repair through most of the UV dose levels. But at very high UV doses, the *uvrA* gene is somewhat more important than the *recA* gene. **16.** apply About 4600 seconds or 77 minutes. This answer comes from knowing that replication proceeds bidirectionally, so replication from each fork is predicted to replicate half the chromosome. This is 4.6 million base pairs/2 = 2.3 million base pairs. At 500 base pairs per second, this requires 2.3 million base pairs/500 base pairs per second = 4600 seconds. To obtain the time in minutes, divide 4600 seconds by 60 seconds per minute.

CHAPTER 16

IN-TEXT QUESTIONS AND EXERCISES

p. 305 Fig. 16.1 apply No, it could not make citrulline from ornithine without enzyme 2. Yes, it would no longer need enzyme 2 to make citrulline.

p. 306 Fig. 16.2 create Many possibilities: strain of fungi used, exact method for creating mutants and harvesting spores to grow, exact growing conditions (temperature, light, recipe for growth medium—including concentrations of supplements), objective criteria for determining growth or no growth.

p. 309 CYU remember Change in DNA sequence, change in sequence of transcribed mRNA, potential change in amino acid sequence of protein, likely altered protein function (if amino acid sequence was altered), likely change in phenotype.

p. 312 analyze (1) The codons in Figure 16.4 are translated correctly. (2) See **FIGURE A16.1**. (3) There are many possibilities (just pick alternative codons for one or more of the amino acids); one is an mRNA sequence (running 5′ → 3′): 5′ GCG-AAC-GAU-UUC-CAG 3′. To get the corresponding DNA sequence, write this sequence but substitute Ts for Us: 5′ GCG-AAC-GAT-TTC-CAG 3′. Now write the complementary bases, which will be in the 3′ → 5′ direction: 3′ CGC-TTG-CTA-AAG-GTC 5′. When this second strand is transcribed by RNA polymerase, it will produce the mRNA given with the proper 5′ → 3′ orientation.

p. 312 CYU (1) apply Note the 3′ → 5′ polarity of the DNA sequences in the accompanying table, and in the subsequent answer. This means that the complementary mRNA codon will read 5′ → 3′. U (rather than T) is the base transcribed from A.

DNA	mRNA Codon	Amino Acid
ATA	UAU	Tyrosine
ATG	UAC	Tyrosine
ATT	UAA	Stop
GCA	UGC	Cysteine

(2) understand The ATA → ATG mutation would have no effect on the protein. The ATA → ATT mutation introduces a stop codon, so the resulting polypeptide would be shortened. This would result in synthesis of a mutant protein much shorter than the original protein. The ATA → GCA mutation might have a profound effect on the protein's conformation because cysteine's structure is different from tyrosine's.

p. 312 Fig. 16.7 apply See **FIGURE A16.1**.

p. 314 Fig. 16.9 analyze Chromosomes 2, 3, 6, 10, 13, 14, 15, 18, 19, 21, 22, and the X chromosome show aneuploidy. Virtually every chromosome has structural rearrangements, and translocations are the most obvious. These are seen when two or more different colors occur on the same chromosome.

IF YOU UNDERSTAND . . .

16.1 understand Ornithine, citrulline or arginine could be added to allow growth. As Figure 16.1 shows, these compounds are made after the steps catalyzed by the enzymes 1, 2, and 3 that are needed to produce arginine. **16.2** understand An inhibitor of RNA synthesis will eventually prevent the synthesis of new proteins because newly synthesized mRNA is needed for translation. **16.3** apply AUG UGG AAA/AAG CAA/CAG **16.4** understand Since redundancy is having more than one codon specify a particular amino acid, redundancy makes it possible for there to be a point mutation without altering the amino acid. This is a silent mutation. A silent mutation is likely to be neutral because there is no change in amino acid sequence.

YOU SHOULD BE ABLE TO . . .

✔ Test Your Knowledge

1. remember d **2.** understand a **3.** understand d **4.** remember Because there is no chemical complementarity between nucleotides and amino acids; and because in eukaryotes, DNA is in the nucleus but translation occurs in the cytoplasm. **5.** understand d **6.** remember A codon that signals the end of translation.

✔ Test Your Understanding

7. understand Because the Morse code and genetic code both use simple elements (dots and dashes; 4 different bases) in different orders to encode complex information (words; amino acid sequences).

8.

Substrate 1 $\xrightarrow{A}$ Substrate 2 $\xrightarrow{B}$ Substrate 3 $\xrightarrow{C}$
Substrate 4 $\xrightarrow{D}$ Substrate 5 $\xrightarrow{E}$ Biological Sciazine

apply Substrate 3 would accumulate. Hypothesis: The individuals have a mutation in the gene for enzyme D. **9.** understand They supported an important prediction of the hypothesis: Losing a gene (via mutation) resulted in loss of an enzyme. **10.** understand c **11.** understand In a triplet code, addition or deletion of 1–2 bases disrupts the reading frame "downstream" of the mutation site(s), resulting in a dysfunctional protein. But addition or deletion of 3 bases restores the reading frame—the normal sequence is disrupted only between the first and third mutation. The resulting protein is altered but may still be able to function normally. Only a triplet code would show these patterns. **12.** understand A point mutation changes the nucleotide sequence of an existing allele, creating a new one, so it always changes the genotype. But because the genetic code is redundant, and because point mutations can occur in DNA sequences that do not code for amino acids, these point mutations do not change the protein product and therefore do not change the phenotype.

✔ Test Your Problem-Solving Skills

13. apply See **FIGURE A16.2**. **14.** analyze Every copying error would result in a mutation that would change the amino acid sequence of the protein and would likely affect its function. **15.** analyze Before the central dogma was understood, DNA was known to be the hereditary material, but no one knew how particular sequences of bases resulted in the production of RNA and protein products. The central dogma clarified how genotypes produce phenotypes. **16.** analyze c

CHAPTER 17

IN-TEXT QUESTIONS AND EXERCISES

p. 318 Fig. 17.1 remember RNA is synthesized in the 5′ → 3′ direction; the DNA template is "read" 3′ → 5′.

p. 321 CYU (1) apply Transcription would be reduced or absent because the missing nucleotides are in the −10 region, one of the two critical parts of the promoter. **(2)** understand NTPs are required because the three phosphate groups raise the monomer's potential energy enough to make the polymerization reaction exergonic.

p. 322 Fig. 17.5 apply There would be no loops—the molecules would match up exactly.

p. 323 CYU (1) understand The subunits contain both RNA (the *ribonucleo*– in the name) and proteins. **(2)** understand The cap and tail protect mRNAs from degradation and facilitate translation.

p. 326 Fig. 17.11 analyze If the amino acids stayed attached to the tRNAs, the gray line in the graph would stay high and the green line low. If the amino acids were transferred to some other cell component, the gray line would decline but the green line would be low.

p. 327 understand (1) The amino acid attaches on the top right of the L-shaped structure. (2) The anticodon is antiparallel in orientation to the mRNA codon, and it contains the complementary bases.

p. 332 CYU understand E is for exit—the site where uncharged tRNAs are ejected; P is for peptidyl (or peptide bond)—the site where peptide bond formation takes place; A is for aminoacyl—the site where aminoacyl tRNAs enter.

IF YOU UNDERSTAND . . .

17.1 apply Transcription would continue past the normal point because the insertion of nucleotides would disrupt the structure of the RNA hairpin that functions as a terminator. **17.2** understand The protein-coding segment of the gene is predicted to be longer in eukaryotes because of the presence of introns. **17.3** understand The tRNAs act as adaptors because they couple the information contained in the nucleotides of mRNA to that contained in the amino acid sequence of proteins. **17.4** apply An incorrect amino acid would appear often in proteins. This is because the altered synthetase would sometimes add the correct amino acid for a particular tRNA and at other

---

FIGURE A16.1

mRNA sequence:
5′ AUG-CUG-GAG-GGG-GUU-AGA-CAU 3′

Amino acid sequence:
Met-Leu-Glu-Gly-Val-Arg-His

FIGURE A16.2

Bottom DNA strand:
3′ AACTT-TAC(start)-GGG-CAA-ACC-TCT-AGC-CCA-ATG-TCG-ATC(stop)-AGTTTC 5′

mRNA sequence:
5′ AUG-CCC-GUU-UGG-AGA-UCG-GGU-UAC-AGC-UAG 3′

Amino acid sequence:
Met-Pro-Val-Trp-Arg-Ser-Gly-Tyr-Ser

times add the incorrect amino acid. **17.5** create One possible concept map is shown in **FIGURE A17.1**.

YOU SHOULD BE ABLE TO . . .

✔ Test Your Knowledge

1. understand c **2.** remember c **3.** understand To speed the correct folding of newly synthesized proteins **4.** remember d **5.** remember At the 3′ end **6.** apply b

✔ Test Your Understanding

7. understand Basal transcription factors bind to promoter sequences in eukaryotic DNA and facilitate the binding of RNA polymerase. As part of the RNA polymerase holoenzyme, sigma binds to a promoter sequence in bacterial DNA and to allow RNA polymerase to initiate at the start of genes. **8.** analyze The wobble rules allow a single tRNA to pair with more than one type of mRNA codon. This is distinct from redundancy, in which more than one codon can specify a single amino acid. If the wobble rules did not exist, there would need to be one tRNA for each amino-acid-specifying codon in the redundant genetic code. **9.** apply b **10.** apply After a peptide bond forms between the polypeptide and the amino acid held by the tRNA in the A site, the ribosome moves down the mRNA. As it does, an uncharged tRNA leaves the E site. The now-uncharged tRNA that was in the P site enters the E site; the tRNA holding the polypeptide chain moves from the A site to the P site, and a new aminoacyl tRNA enters the A site. **11.** apply The ribosome's active site is made up of RNA, not protein. **12.** understand The separation allows the aminoacyl tRNA to place the amino acid into the ribosome's active site while reaching to the distant codon on the mRNA.

✔ Test Your Problem-Solving Skills

13. create Ribonucleases degrade mRNAs that are no longer needed by the cell. If an mRNA for a hormone that increased heart rate were never degraded, the hormone would be produced continuously and heart rate would stay elevated—a dangerous situation. **14.** apply d **15.** analyze The regions most crucial to the ribosome's function should be the most highly conserved: the active site, the E, P, and A sites, and the site where mRNAs initially bind. **16.** analyze The most likely locations are one of the grooves or channels where RNA, DNA, and ribonucleotides move through the enzyme—plugging one of them would prevent transcription.

CHAPTER 18

IN-TEXT QUESTIONS AND EXERCISES

p. 338 understand See **TABLE A18.1**.
p. 338 Fig. 18.1 analyze Write "Slowest response, most efficient resource use" next to the transcriptional control label. Write "Fastest response, least efficient resource use" next to the post-translational control label.
p. 339 Fig. 18.2 apply Plates from all three treatments must be identical and contain identical growth medium, except for the presence of the sugars labeled in the figure. Also, all plates must be grown under the same physical conditions (temperature, light) for the same time.
p. 340 Fig. 18.3 apply Use a medium with all 20 amino acids when producing a master plate of mutagenized *E. coli* colonies; then use a replica plate that contains all the amino acids except tryptophan. Choose cells from the master plate that did *not* grow on the replica plate.
p. 341 understand *lacZ* codes for the β-galactosidase enzyme, which breaks the disaccharide lactose into glucose and galactose. *lacY* codes for the galactoside permease enzyme, which transports lactose into the bacterial cell. *lacI* codes for a protein that shuts down production of the other *lac* products. When lactose is absent, the *lacI* product prevents transcription. This is logical because there is no reason for the cell to make β-galactosidase

and galactoside permease if there is no lactose to metabolize. But when lactose is present, it interacts with *lacI* in some way so that *lacZ* and *lacY* are induced (their transcription can occur). When lactose is present, the enzymes that metabolize it are expressed.
p. 343 apply A mutation that prevents lactose binding to repressor is predicted to prevent transcription of the *lac* operon under any condition. This is because the repressor would never come off the operator. A mutation in the operator that prevents repressor binding is predicted to lead to constitutive expression of the *lac* operon.
p. 343 Fig. 18.8 understand Put the "Repressor protein" on the operator. No transcription will take place. Then put the "RNA polymerase" on the promoter. No transcription will take place. Finally, put "lactose" on the repressor protein and then remove the resulting lactose–repressor complex from the operon. Transcription will begin.
p. 344 CYU (1) understand It is logical that the genes for metabolizing lactose should be expressed only when lactose is available. **(2)** understand See **FIGURE A18.1**.
p. 344 apply This mutation is predicted to lower rates of transcription initiation because AraC's binding to

RNA polymerase is essential for AraC to work as an activator.

IF YOU UNDERSTAND . . .

18.1 understand Production of β-galactosidase and galactosidase permease are under transcriptional control—transcription depends on the action of regulatory proteins. The activity of the repressor is under post-translational control. **18.2** apply Treat *E. coli* cells with a mutagen, and create a master plate that is grown at 33°C. Replica-plate this master plate and grow the replica plate at 42°C. Look for colonies that are on the master plate at 33°C but not on the replica plate at 42°C. **18.3** understand The operator is the parking brake; the repressor locks it in place, and the inducer releases it. **18.4** apply *ara* initiator mutations are likely to affect positive and negative control because AraC must bind to the *ara* initiator sequence for both forms of control. **18.5** create Mutations that create operators for the SOS regulon repressor protein would put new genes under control of the repressor and incorporate them into the regulon.

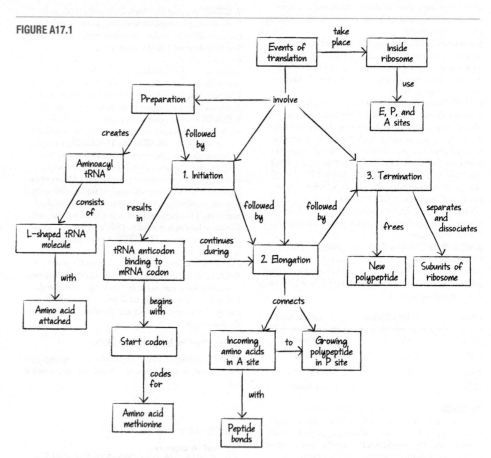

FIGURE A17.1

TABLE A18.1

Name	Function
lacZ	Gene for β-galactosidase
lacY	Gene for galactoside permease
Operator	Binding site for repressor
Promoter	Binding site for RNA polymerase
Repressor	Shuts down transcription
Lactose	Binds to repressor and stimulates transcription (removes negative control)
Glucose	At low concentration, increases transcription

✔ **Test Your Knowledge**

1. `remember` b **2.** `understand` d **3.** `apply` b **4.** `remember` DNA; RNA;
5. `understand` When glucose and another sugar are present in the environment, inducer exclusion prevents the use of the other sugar and allows only use of glucose.
6. `remember` a

✔ **Test Your Understanding**

7. `understand` The glycolytic enzymes are always needed in the cell because they are required to produce ATP, and ATP is always needed. **8.** `understand` Positive control means that a regulatory protein, when present, causes transcription to increase. Negative control means that a regulatory protein, when present, prevents transcription. **9.** `apply` b. **10.** `apply` Regulation of the *lac* operon should be normal. The location of the *lacI* gene isn't important, because the gene produces a protein that diffuses within the cell to the operator. **11.** `analyze` b (since the activator needs to bind to regulatory sequences to activate gene expression, preventing DNA binding would cripple the regulon and prevent cholera).**12.** `analyze` The *lac* operon would be strongly induced. Once inside the cell, the IPTG will bind to the repressor, causing it to release from DNA. IPTG cannot be broken down, so its concentration will remain high. Finally, since glucose is absent, there will be no inducer exclusion to inhibit IPTG transport through the galactoside permease transporter.

✔ **Test Your Problem-Solving Skills**

13. `create` Set up cultures with individuals that all come from the same colony of toluene-tolerating bacteria. Half the cultures should have toluene as the only source of carbon; half should have glucose or another common source of carbon. The glucose-containing medium serves as a control to ensure that cells can be grown in the lab. Cells will grow in both cultures if they are able to use toluene as a source of carbon; they will grow only in glucose-containing medium if toluene cannot be used as a carbon source. **14.** `apply` At a rate of 1×10^{-4} mutants per cell, you would on average find one mutant in every 10,000 (1×10^4) cells. Therefore, you should screen a bit more (~ 2–3 times more) than 10,000 cells to be reasonably sure of finding at least one mutant. **15.** `apply` b **16.** `analyze` Cells with functioning β-galactosidase will produce blue colonies; cells with *lacZ* mutations or *lacY* mutations will not produce β-galactosidase and will produce white colonies. The *lac* promoter could be mutated so that RNA polymerase cannot bind.

CHAPTER 19

IN-TEXT QUESTIONS AND EXERCISES

p. 352 Fig. 19.4 `analyze` Acetylation of histones decondenses chromatin and allows transcription to begin, so HATs are elements in positive control. Deacetylation condenses chromatin and inactivates transcription, so HDACs are elements in negative control.
p. 353 CYU (1) `apply` Many more genes than normal are predicted to be expressed because the inability to methylate DNA would lead to more decondensed chromatin.
(2) `understand` Addition of acetyl groups to histones or methyl groups to DNA can cause chromatin to decondense or condense, respectively. Different patterns of acetylation or methylation will determine which genes in muscle cells versus brain cells can be transcribed and which are not available for transcription.
p. 353 Fig. 19.5 `create` They could do something to change histone modifications to see how this affects gene transcription instead of just making the observation that certain histone modifications and low rates of transcription go together.
p. 355 Fig. 19.6 `analyze` A typical eukaryotic gene usually contains introns and is regulated by multiple enhancers. Bacterial operons lack introns and enhancers. The

promoter-proximal element found in some eukaryotic genes is comparable to the *araC* binding site in the *ara* operon of bacteria. Bacterial operons have a single promoter but code for more than one protein; eukaryotic genes code for a single product.
p. 356 `analyze` The basal transcription factors found in muscle and nerve cells are similar or identical; the regulatory transcription factors found in each cell type are different.
p. 356 `understand` DNA forms loops when distant regulatory regions, such as silencers and enhancers, are brought close to the promoter through binding of regulatory transcription factors to mediator.
p. 356 CYU (1) `analyze` Bacterial regulatory sequences are found close to the promoter; eukaryotic regulatory sequences can be close to the promoter or far from it. Bacterial regulatory proteins interact directly with RNA polymerase to initiate or prevent transcription; eukaryotic regulatory proteins influence transcription by altering chromatin structure or binding to the basal transcription complex through mediator proteins.
(2) `understand` Certain regulatory proteins decondense chromatin at muscle- or brain-specific genes and then activate or repress the transcription of cell-type-specific genes. Muscle-specific genes are expressed only if muscle-specific regulatory proteins are produced and activated.
p. 358 `understand` Alternative splicing does not occur in bacteria because bacterial genes do not contain introns—in bacteria, each gene codes for a single product. Alternative splicing is part of step 3 in Figure 19.1.

p. 359 `remember` Step 4 and step 5. RNA interference either **(1)** decreases the life span of mRNAs or **(2)** inhibits translation.
p. 360 CYU (1) `understand` It became clear that a single gene can code for multiple products instead of a single one.
(2) `understand` The miRNAs interfere with mRNAs by targeting them for destruction or preventing them from being translated.
p. 362 CYU (1) `understand` Many different types of mutations can disrupt control of the cell cycle and initiate cancer. These mutations can affect any of the six levels of control over gene regulation outlined in Figure 19.1.
(2) `understand` The p53 protein is responsible for shutting down the cell cycle in cells with damaged DNA. If the protein does not function, then cells with damaged DNA—and thus many mutations—continue to divide. If these cells have mutations in genes that regulate the cell cycle, then they may continue to divide in an uncontrolled fashion.

IF YOU UNDERSTAND . . .

19.1 `understand` Because eukaryotic RNAs are not translated as soon as transcription occurs, it is possible for RNA processing to occur, which creates variation in the mRNAs produced from a primary RNA transcript and in their life spans. **19.2** `understand` The default state of eukaryotic genes is "off," because the highly condensed state of the chromatin makes DNA unavailable to RNA polymerase. **19.3** `understand` See **FIGURE A19.1**. **19.4** `understand` Alternative splicing makes it possible for a single gene to

FIGURE A18.1

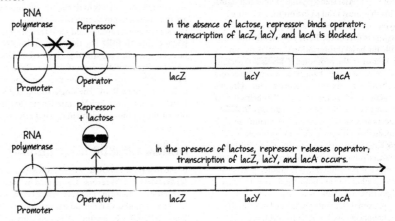

In the absence of lactose, repressor binds operator; transcription of lacZ, lacY, and lacA is blocked.

In the presence of lactose, repressor releases operator; transcription of lacZ, lacY, and lacA occurs.

FIGURE A19.1

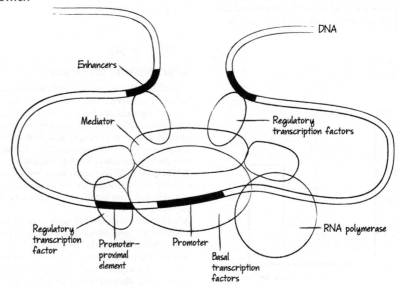

code for multiple products. **19.5** analyze One difference is that, in bacteria, genes that need to be turned on together are often clustered together in operons. Eukaryotes do not use operons. A similarity is in the way eukaryotes turn on many genes together and the strategy of bacterial regulons. Here, genes that are in many different locations share a DNA regulatory sequence and are activated when a regulatory transcription factor binds to the regulatory sequence. **19.6** understand In mutant cells that lack a form of p53 that can bind to enhancers, DNA damage cannot arrest the cell cycle, the cell cannot kill itself, and damaged DNA is replicated. This leads to mutations that can move the cell farther down the road to cancer.

YOU SHOULD BE ABLE TO . . .

✓ Test Your Knowledge

1. remember c **2.** remember A tumor suppressor is a gene or protein that holds cell division in check unless conditions are right for the cell to divide. **3.** understand d **4.** remember The set of regulatory transcription factors present in a particular cell, not differences in DNA sequence, are largely responsible for which genes are expressed. **5.** remember b **6.** remember d

✓ Test Your Understanding

7. analyze (a) Enhancers and the *araC* site are similar because both are sites in DNA where regulatory proteins bind. They are different because enhancers generally are located at great distances from the promoter, whereas the *araC* site is located nearer the promoter. (b) Promoter-proximal elements and the *lac* operon operator are both regulatory sites in DNA located close to the promoter. (c) Basal transcription factors and sigma are proteins that must bind to the promoter before RNA polymerase can initiate transcription. They differ because sigma is part of the RNA polymerase holoenzyme, while the basal transcription complex recruits RNA polymerase to the promoter. **8.** understand If changes in the environment cause changes in how spliceosomes function, then the RNAs and proteins produced from a particular gene could change in a way that helps the cell cope with the new environmental conditions. **9.** analyze (a) Enhancers and silencers are both regulatory sequences located at a distance from the promoter. Enhancers bind regulatory transcription factors that activate transcription; silencers bind regulatory proteins that shut down transcription. (b) Promoter-proximal elements and enhancers are both regulatory sequences that bind positive regulatory transcription factors. Promoter-proximal elements are located close to the promoter; enhancers are far from the promoter. (c) Transcription factors bind to regulatory sites in DNA; mediator does not bind to DNA but instead forms a bridge between regulatory transcription factors and

basal transcription factors. **10.** apply Inhibition of a histone deacetylase is predicted to leave acetyl groups on histones longer than normal. This is predicted to keep gene transcription going longer than normal, leading to higher levels of particular proteins and a change in the phenotype of the cell. **11.** analyze c; this is because there are many more modifications in the histone code relative to the genetic code. **12.** apply The cell is predicted to arrest in the cell cycle and most likely will commit suicide through activation of apoptosis genes because of the continually active *p53*.

✓ Test Your Problem-Solving Skills

13. apply c; This is because promoters and enhancers are brought into close physical proximity when transcription begins (see Figure 19.8). Since rats of malnourished mothers initiate *Hnf4a* gene transcription infrequently, the promoter and enhancer will be together less often in these animals compared with rats born to well-nourished mothers. **14.** understand See **FIGURE A19.2**. The value for the normal diet should be shown as 1.0 and the value for the low-protein diet should be shown as 0.64 (0.64 comes from the ratio of the cpm of the low-protein diet divided by the cpm of the normal diet, or 7368/11,478). **15.** create You could treat a culture of DNA-damaged cells with a drug that stops transcription and then compare them with untreated DNA-damaged cells. If transcriptional control regulates p53 levels, then the p53 level would be lower in the treated cells versus control cells. If control of p53 levels is post-translational, then in both cultures the p53 level would be the same. *Other approaches:* Add labeled NTPs to damaged cells and see if they are incorporated into mRNAs for p53; or add labeled amino acids to damaged cells and see if they are incorporated into completed p53 proteins; or add labeled phosphate groups and see if they are added to p53 proteins. **16.** create The double-stranded RNA could be cut by the same enzyme that creates double-stranded miRNAs from miRNA precursors. This double-stranded RNA may be incorporated into RISC and converted into a single-stranded RNA. The single-stranded RNA held by RISC would work in RNA interference to trigger the destruction of the complementary viral mRNA.

BIG PICTURE Genetic Information

p. 366 CYU (1) remember Star = DNA, mRNA, proteins. **(2)** understand RNA "is reverse transcribed by" reverse transcriptase "to form" DNA. **(3)** analyze E = splicing, etc.; E = meiosis and sexual reproduction (along with their links). **(4)** analyze Chromatin "makes up" chromosomes; independent assortment and recombination "contribute to" high genetic diversity.

CHAPTER 20

IN-TEXT QUESTIONS AND EXERCISES

p. 372 understand Isolate the DNA and cut it into small fragments with EcoRI, which leaves sticky ends. Cut copies of a plasmid or other vector with EcoRI. Mix the fragments and plasmids under conditions that promote complementary base pairing by sticky ends of fragments and plasmids. Use DNA ligase to catalyze formation of phosphodiester bonds and seal the sequences.
p. 372 Fig. 20.4 apply No—many times, because many copies of each type of mRNA were present in the pituitary cells, and many pituitary cells were used to prepare the library.
p. 373 apply The probe must be single stranded so that it will bind by complementary base pairing to the target DNA, and it must be labeled so that it can be detected. The probe will base-pair only with fragments that include a sequence complementary to the probe's sequence. A probe with the sequence 5′ AATCG 3′ will

bind to the region of the target DNA that has the sequence 5′ CGATT 3′ as shown here:

5′ AATCG 3′
3′ TCCGGTTAGCATTACCATTTT 5′

p. 374 CYU (1) understand When the endonuclease makes a staggered cut in a palindromic sequence and the strands separate, the single-stranded bases that are left will bind ("stick") to the single-stranded bases left where the endonuclease cut the same palindrome at a different location. **(2)** understand The word probe means to examine thoroughly. A DNA probe "examines" a large set of sequences thoroughly and binds to one—the one that has a complementary base sequence.
p. 375 Fig. 20.7 analyze The polymerase will begin at the 3′ end of each primer. On the top strand in part (b), it will move to the left; on the bottom strand, it will move to the right. As always, synthesis is in the 5′-to-3′ direction.
p. 376 CYU (1) understand Denaturation makes DNA single stranded so the primer can bind to the sequence during the annealing step. Once the primer is in place, *Taq* polymerase can synthesize the rest of the strand during the extension step. It is a "chain reaction" because the products of each reaction cycle are used in the next reaction cycle—this is why the number of copies doubles in each cycle. **(2)** apply One of many possible answers is shown in **FIGURE A20.1**.
p. 378 CYU understand If ddNTPs were present at high concentration, they would almost always be incorporated—meaning that only fragments from the first complementary base in the sequence would be produced.
p. 379 understand Using a map with many markers makes it more likely that there will be one marker that is very tightly linked to the gene of interest—meaning that a form of the marker will almost always be associated with the phenotype you are tracking.
p. 382 CYU create Start with a genetic map with as many polymorphic markers as possible. Determine the genotype at these markers for a large number of individuals who have the same type of alcoholism—one that is thought to have a genetic component—as well as a large number of unaffected individuals. Look for particular versions of a marker that is almost always found in affected individuals. Genes that contribute to a predisposition to alcoholism will be near that marker.
p. 383 Fig. 20.11 apply The insertion will probably disrupt the gene and have serious consequences for the cell and potentially the individual.

IF YOU UNDERSTAND . . .

20.1 understand Special features of DNA are needed to allow replication in a cell. It is unlikely that any DNA fragment generated by cutting the DNA of one species with a restriction enzyme would replicate when inserted into a bacterial cell. By placing DNA fragments within plasmids that normally replicate in a bacterial cell, the inserted DNA can be replicated along with the plasmid. **20.2** analyze Advantages of cloning in cells: No knowledge of the sequence is required. Disadvantages of cloning in cells: It is slower and technically more difficult than PCR. PCR advantages: It is fast and easy, and it can amplify a DNA sequence that is rare in the sample. PCR disadvantage: It requires knowledge of sequences on either side of the target gene, so primers can be designed. **20.3** understand The length of each fragment is dictated by where a ddNTP was incorporated into the growing strand, and each ddNTP corresponds to a base on the template strand. Thus the sequence of fragment sizes corresponds to the sequence on the template DNA. **20.4** understand In this case, both affected and unaffected individuals would have the same marker, so there would be no way to associate a particular form of the marker with the gene and phenotype you are interested in. **20.5** understand An advantage of using retrovirus vectors is that any foreign genes they carry are integrated into

FIGURE A19.2

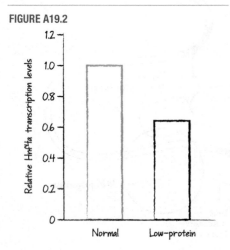

human chromosomes, so delivered genes become a permanent feature of the cell's genome. The concern is that they may integrate at sites that alter gene function in ways that harm cell function, or even worse, lead to cancer. **20.6** understand Genes can be inserted into the Ti plasmids carried by *Agrobacterium*, and the recombinant plasmids transferred to plant cells infected by the bacterium.

YOU SHOULD BE ABLE TO . . .

✔ Test Your Knowledge

1. understand They cut DNA at specific sites, known as recognition sites, to produce DNA fragments useful for cloning. **2.** remember b **3.** understand ddNTPs lack the −OH (hydroxyl) group on the 3′ carbon of deoxyribose sugar that is required to extend the DNA chain during synthesis. **4.** understand a **5.** remember b **6.** understand d

✔ Test Your Understanding

7. understand When a restriction endonuclease cuts a "foreign gene" sequence and a plasmid, the same sticky ends are created on the excised foreign gene and the cut plasmid. After the sticky ends on the foreign gene and the plasmid anneal, DNA ligase catalyzes closure of the DNA backbone, sealing the foreign gene into the plasmid DNA (see **FIGURE A20.2**). **8.** apply If the DNA at each cycle steadily doubles, it is predicted to yield a 33.6 million-fold increase (a 2^{25}-fold increase). **9.** understand A cDNA library is a collection of complementary DNAs made from all the mRNAs present in a certain group of cells. A cDNA library from a human nerve cell would be different from one made from a human muscle cell, because nerve cells and muscle cells express many different genes that are specific to their cell type. **10.** remember Genetic markers are genes or other loci

that have known locations in the genome. When these locations are diagrammed, they represent the physical relationships between landmarks—in other words, they form a map. **11.** understand d; these regulatory sequences promote expression of introduced genes in the endosperm—the rice grain eaten as food. **12.** analyze PCR and cellular DNA synthesis are similar in the sense of producing copies of a template DNA. Both rely on primers and DNA polymerase. The major difference between the two is that PCR copies only a specific target sequence, but the entire genome is copied during cellular DNA synthesis.

✔ Test Your Problem-Solving Skills

13. create You could use a computer program to identify likely promoter sequences in the sequence data and then look for sequences just downstream that have an AUG start codon and codons that could be part of the protein-coding exons of a potential protein about 500 amino acids (500 codons or 1500 bases) long. **14.** analyze False. Since somatic-cell modifications cannot be passed on to future generations, but germ-line modifications may be passed on to offspring, germ-line modification opens a new set of ethical questions. **15.** analyze In both techniques, researchers use an indicator to identify either a gene of interest or a colony of bacteria with a particular trait. The problem is the same—picking one particular thing (a certain gene or a cell with a particular mutation) out of a large collection. **16.** analyze (a) Primer 1b binds to the top right strand and would allow DNA polymerase to synthesize the top strand across the target gene. Primer 1a, however, binds to the upper left strand and would allow DNA polymerase to synthesize the upper strand *away* from the target gene. Primer 2a binds to the bottom left strand and would allow DNA polymerase to synthesize the bottom strand across the target gene. Primer 2b, however, binds

to the bottom right strand and would allow DNA polymerase to synthesize away from the target gene. (b) She could use primer 1b with primer 2a.

CHAPTER 21

IN-TEXT QUESTIONS AND EXERCISES

p. 391 understand If no overlap occurred, there would be no way of ordering the fragments correctly. You would be able to put fragments only in random order—not the correct order.
p. 391 Fig. 21.2 understand Shotgun sequencing is based on fragmenting the genome into many small pieces.
p. 393 Fig. 21.3 understand Because the mRNA codons that match up with each strand are oriented in the 5′-to-3′ direction.
p. 395 CYU (1) understand Parasites don't need genes that code for enzymes required to synthesize molecules they acquire from their hosts. **(2)** understand If two closely related species inherited the same gene from a common ancestor, the genes should be similar. But if one species acquired the same gene from a distantly related species via lateral gene transfer, then the genes should be much less similar.
p. 399 Fig. 21.9 understand
Chromosome 1:
ψβ2-ε-Gγ-Aγ-ψβ1-δ-ψβ2-ε-Gγ-Aγ-ψβ1-δ-β
Chromosome 2: β
p. 400 CYU (1) understand Eukaryotic genomes have vastly different numbers of transposable elements and other repeated sequences that don't directly contribute to phenotype. So genome size can vary widely without changing the number of coding genes or the complexity of the organism. **(2)** apply Because most of the genome is transcribed, this number is very close to the percentage of the genome that codes for exons. In humans, the ratio would be roughly 2%.
p. 401 understand Start with a microarray containing exons from a large number of human genes. Isolate mRNAs from brain tissue and liver tissue, and make labeled cDNAs from each. Probe the microarray with cDNA made from each type of tissue, and record where binding occurs. Binding events identify exons that are transcribed in each type of tissue. Compare the results to identify genes that are expressed in brain but not liver, or in liver but not brain.
p. 402 understand Cell replication is an emergent property because it is due to the interaction of proteins working in a network, yet is a property that could not be predicted from the analysis of any one of these proteins.

IF YOU UNDERSTAND . . .

21.1 understand If a search of human gene sequence databases revealed a gene that was similar in base sequence, and if follow-up work confirmed that the mouse and human genes were similar in their pattern of exons and introns and regulatory sequences, then the researchers could claim that they are homologous. **21.2** understand The genome of a parasite is predicted to be smaller and to have fewer genes, particularly for metabolism, than the genome of a nonparasite. **21.3** understand These features include variable numbers of transposable elements; noncoding repeated sequences; and noncoding, nonrepetitive DNA. These add to genome size without adding genes that directly influence phenotype. Additionally, mechanisms such as alternative splicing and the possibility of many noncoding regulatory RNAs can create situations in which few protein-coding genes but many different proteins are expressed in intricately regulated ways—features that would increase morphological complexity without increasing gene number. **21.4** understand Color-coded clusters shown in Figure 21.13 represent networks of interacting proteins that work together to carry out a particular cellular function. But it's clear from the figure that smaller, clusters are also connected into larger networks.

FIGURE A20.1

5′ CATGACTATTACGTATCGGGTACTATGCTATCGATCTAGCTACGCTAGCT 3′
3′ GTACTGATAATGCATAGCCCATGATACGATAGCTAGATCGATGCGATCGA 5′

Primer #1, which will anneal to the 3′ end of the top strand:

5′ AGCTAGCGTAGCTAGATCGAT 3′

Primer #2, which will anneal to the 3′ end of the bottom strand:

5′ CATGACTATTACGTATCGGGT 3′

The primers will bind to the separated strands of the parent DNA sequence as follows:

5′ CATGACTATTACGTATCGGGTACTATGCTATCGATCTAGCTACGCTAGCT 3′
                                    3′ TAGCTAGATCGATGCGATCGA 5′

5′ CATGACTATTACGTATCGGGT 3′
3′ GTACTGATAATGCATAGCCCATGATACGATAGCTAGATCGATGCGATCGA 5′

FIGURE A20.2

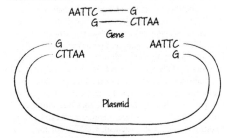

Sticky ends on cut plasmid and gene to be inserted are complementary and can base pair

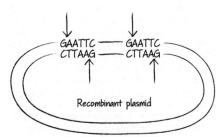

DNA ligase forms four phosphodiester bonds between gene and plasmid DNA at the points indicated by arrows

YOU SHOULD BE ABLE TO . . .

✔ Test Your Knowledge

1. remember c 2. understand a 3. remember d 4. remember b 5. understand Finding two or more genes of similar sequence in the genome. 6. remember Having a sequence that is clearly related to a functional gene but with a crippling mutation such as a stop codon or deletion.

✔ Test Your Understanding

7. analyze Computer programs are used to scan sequences in both directions to find ATG start codons, a gene-sized logical sequence with recognizable codons, and then a stop codon. One can also look for characteristic promoter, operator, and other regulatory sites. It is more difficult to identify open reading frames in eukaryotes because their genomes are so much larger and because of the presence of introns and repeated sequences.

8. evaluate c 9. apply Water flea gene density is about 31,000 genes/200 Mbp = 155 genes/Mbp. In humans, gene density is about 21,000 genes/3000 Mbp = 7 genes/Mbp. The relative gene density of water flea/human = 155/7 = 22. 10. analyze Because with many different alleles, the chance that a match is coincidental is low relative to the chance that they match by identity (they come from the same person). 11. understand A DNA microarray experiment identifies which genes are being expressed in a particular cell at a particular time. If a series of experiments shows that different genes are expressed in cells at different times or under different conditions, it implies that expression was turned on or off in response to changes in age or changes in conditions. 12. understand Homology is a similarity among different species that is due to their inheritance from a common ancestor. If a newly sequenced gene is found to be homologous with a known gene of a different species, it is assumed that the gene products have similar function.

✔ Test Your Problem-Solving Skills

13. analyze If "gene A" is not necessary for existence, it can be lost by an event like unequal crossing over (on the chromosome with deleted segments) with no ill effects on the organism. In fact, individuals who have lost unnecessary genes are probably at a competitive advantage, because they no longer have to spend time and energy copying and repairing unused genes.
14. apply If the grave were authentic, it might include two very different parental patterns along with five children whose patterns each represented a mix between the two parents. The other unrelated individuals would have patterns not shared by anyone else in the grave. 15. apply d; mutation of such a central gene is likely to influence the phenotypes associated with all the genes it interacts with. If these interacting genes are involved in many different functions, the effects of mutation of a central gene are likely to be widespread, or pleiotropic. 16. apply You would expect that the livers and blood of chimps and humans would function similarly, but that strong differences occur in brain function. The microarray data support this prediction and suggest chimp and human brains are different because certain genes are turned on or off at different times and expressed in different amounts.

CHAPTER 25

IN-TEXT QUESTIONS AND ANSWERS

p. 448 Fig. 25.4 analyze Under special creation, fossils with transitional features would be explained as separate types, unrelated to other organisms and just coincidentally having intermediate features.

p. 448 Fig. 25.5 analyze If vestigial traits result from inheritance of acquired characteristics, some individuals must have lost the traits during their own lifetimes and passed

the reduced traits on to their offspring. For example, a certain monkey's long tail might have been bitten off by a predator. The new traits would then somehow have passed to the individual's eggs or sperm, resulting in shorter-tailed offspring, until humans with a coccyx resulted.

p. 453 CYU (1) evaluate If birds evolved from dinosaurs you would expect to find transitional fossil dinosaurs with feathers. Such fossils have been found. (2) analyze The DNA sequences of chimpanzees and humans are so similar because we share a recent common ancestor.

p. 455 (1) understand Relapse occurred because the few bacteria remaining after drug therapy were not eliminated by the patient's weakened immune system and began to reproduce quickly. (2) understand No—almost all of the cells present at the start of step 3 would have been resistant to the drug.

p. 456 understand When antibiotics are overused, some bacteria will be killed, including the bacteria that are harmless or beneficial to us. However, bacteria that are resistant to these antibiotics will flourish and multiply, reducing the likelihood that antibiotic treatment will be effective in the future.

p. 457 Fig. 25.16 analyze "Prediction": Beak measurements were different before and after the drought. "Prediction of null hypothesis": No difference was found in beak measurements before and after the drought.

p. 459 CYU (1) understand Postulate 1: Traits vary within a population. Postulate 2: Some of the trait variation is heritable. Postulate 3: There is variation in reproductive success (some individuals produce more offspring than others). Postulate 4: Individuals with certain heritable traits produce the most offspring. The first two postulates describe heritable variation; the second two describe differential reproductive success. (2) understand Beak size and shape and body size vary among individual finches, in part because of differences in their genotypes (some alleles lead to deeper or shallower beaks, for example). When a drought hit, individuals with deep beaks survived better and produced more offspring than individuals with shallow beaks.

p. 460 analyze In biology, an adaptation is any heritable trait that increases an individual's ability to produce offspring in a particular environment. In everyday English, adaptation is often used to refer to an individual's nonheritable adjustment to meet an environmental challenge, a phenomenon that biologists call acclimatization. The phenotypic changes resulting from acclimatization are not passed on to offspring.

IF YOU UNDERSTAND . . .

25.1 analyze Typological thinking is based on the idea that species are unchanging types and that variations within species are unimportant or even misleading. Population thinking recognizes the variation that occurs within a species as critically important. 25.2 remember Many answers are possible. For example, the evolution of an antibiotic-resistant TB bacterium demonstrates that species change through time. The homologous sequences in human and fruit fly genes demonstrate that these species are related by common ancestry. 25.3 analyze In biology, fitness is the ability of an individual to produce viable, fertile offspring, relative to that ability in other individuals in the population. In everyday English, fitness is a physical attribute that is acquired as a result of practice or exercise. 25.4 apply Under special creation, changes in Mycobacterium tuberculosis populations would be explained as individual creative events governed by an intelligent creator. Under the theory of evolution by inheritance of acquired characters, changes in M. tuberculosis populations would be explained by the cells trying to transcribe genes in the presence of the drug, and their rpoB gene becoming altered as a

result. 25.5 understand Brain size in H. sapiens might be constrained by the need for babies to pass through the mother's birth canal, by the energy required to maintain a large brain as an adult, or by lack of genetic variation for even larger brain size. Flying speed in falcons might be constrained by loss of maneuverability (and thus less success in hunting), the energy demands of extremely rapid flight, or lack of genetic variation for even faster flight.

YOU SHOULD BE ABLE TO . . .

✔ Test Your Knowledge

1. remember b 2. remember False 3. remember a 4. understand d
5. remember homologous 6. remember c

✔ Test Your Understanding

1. understand Mutation produces new genetic variations, at random, without any forethought as to which variations might prove adaptive in the future. Individuals with mutations that are disadvantageous won't produce many offspring, but individuals with beneficial mutations will produce many offspring. The beneficial mutations will thus increase in frequency through selection. 2. analyze Artificial selection is determined by human choice and is goal directed, whereas natural selection is the unplanned differential reproductive success of individuals that vary in their heritable traits. 3. analyze b (In some environments, being big and strong lowers fitness.) 4. analyze There were 751 finches before the drought and 90 finches afterward, so only 90/751 = 0.12, or 12 percent, survived. There were more finches with deep beaks before the drought only because the population was much larger, but the average beak depth increased after the drought. 5. analyze The evidence for within-patient evolution is that DNA sequences at the start and end of treatment were identical except for a single nucleotide change in the rpoB gene. If rifampin were banned, rpoB mutant strains likely would have had lower fitness in the drug-free environment and would not continue to increase in frequency in M. tuberculosis populations. 6. apply (1) Traits vary within rabbit populations, such as fur color and hearing ability. (2) Some of this variation is heritable. (3) More rabbits are produced than can survive. (4) Rabbits with certain heritable traits, such as the ability to camouflage in their environment or hear the approach of foxes, produce more offspring.

✔ Test Your Problem-Solving Skills

1. analyze The theory of evolution by natural selection predicts that white and brown deer mice are descendants of an ancestral population that varied in color. The white mice had higher fitness in the beach environment, where they were more likely to escape the notice of predators. Likewise, the brown mice had a higher fitness in the shady forest environment. Over time, the average color of each population changed. Special creation claims that the two colors of mice do not change and were created by divine intervention. Evolution by inheritance of acquired characteristic predicts that the mice in the different environments needed to change color, so they did so and then passed their traits onto their offspring. 2. analyze b (No, because changes in height due to nutrition and reduced incidence of disease are not heritable.) 3. evaluate Evidence to support a common ancestor of humans and chimpanzees about 6–7 million years ago includes the following: fossils from Africa that date from 6–7 million years ago with primate characteristics that are common to chimps and humans, and DNA sequence comparisons showing homologies between chimps and humans (the rate of change of some genes can be used to estimate time of divergence). 4. evaluate The theory of evolution fits the six criteria as follows: (1) and (2): It provides a common underlying mechanism responsible for puzzling observations such as homology, geographic

proximity of similar species, the law of succession in the fossil record, vestigial traits, and extinctions. (3) and (4): It suggests new lines of research to test predictions about the outcome of changing environmental conditions in populations, about the presence of transitional forms in the fossil record, and so on. (5): It is a simple idea that explains the tremendous diversity of living and fossil organisms and why species continue to change today. (6): The realization that all organisms are related by common descent and that none are higher or lower than others was a surprise.

Bioskills

BIOSKILLS 1; p. B:2 CYU (1) apply 3.1 miles **(2)** apply 37°C **(3)** apply Multiply your weight in pounds by 1/2.2 (0.45). **(4)** apply 4 **(5)** apply 4 **(6)** Two significant figures. When you multiply, the answer can have no more significant figures than the least accurate measurement—in this case, 1.6.

BIOSKILLS 2; p. B:3 CYU (1) apply "different-yoked-together" **(2)** apply "sugary-loosened" **(3)** apply "study-of-form" **(4)** apply "three-bodies"

BIOSKILLS 3; p. B:6 CYU (1) apply about 18% **(2)** apply a dramatic drop (almost 10%) **(3)** understand No—the order of presentation in a bar chart does not matter (though it's convenient to arrange the bars in a way that reinforces the overall message). **(4)** apply 11 **(5)** apply 68 inches

BIOSKILLS 4; p. B:7 CYU apply Test 2, the estimate based on the larger sample—the more replicates or observations you have, the more precise your estimate of the average should be.

BIOSKILLS 5; p. B:8 CYU (1) apply $1/2 \times 1/2 \times 1/2 \times 1/2 = 1/16$ **(2)** apply $1/6 + 1/6 + 1/6 = 1/2$

BIOSKILLS 6; p. B:9 CYU (1) understand exponential **(2)** apply $\ln N_t = \ln N_0 + rt$

BIOSKILLS 7; p. B:9 Fig. B7.1. analyze See **FIGURE BA.1.**

FIGURE BA.1
p. B:10 Fig. B7.2. analyze See **FIGURE BA.2.**
FIGURE BA.2
p. B:11 Fig. B7.3. analyze Figure B7.3d is different.

BIOSKILLS 8; p. B:12 Fig. B8.1. apply See **FIGURE BA.3.**

FIGURE BA.3

BIOSKILLS 9; p. B:13 Fig. B9.1 understand DNA and RNA are acids that tend to drop a proton in solution, giving them a negative charge.
p. B:15 CYU analyze The lane with no band comes from a sample where RNA X is not present. The same size RNA X is present in the next two lanes, but the faint band has very few copies while the dark band has many. In the fourth lane, the band is formed by a smaller version of RNA X, and relatively few copies are present.

BIOSKILLS 10; p. B:17 CYU (1) understand size and/or density. **(2)** apply Mitochondria, because they are larger in size compared with ribosomes.

BIOSKILLS 11; p. B:19 CYU (1) analyze No—it's just that no mitochondria happened to be present in this section sliced through the cell. **(2)** explain Understanding a molecule's structure is often critical to understanding how it functions in cells.

BIOSKILLS 12; p. B:21 CYU (1) analyze It may not be clear that the results are relevant to noncancerous cells that are not growing in cell culture—that is, that the artificial conditions mimic natural conditions. **(2)** analyze It may not be clear that the results are relevant to individuals that developed normally, from an embryo—that is, that the artificial conditions mimic natural conditions.

BIOSKILLS 13; p. B:23 Fig. B13.1 analyze This is human body temperature—the natural habitat of *E. coli*.

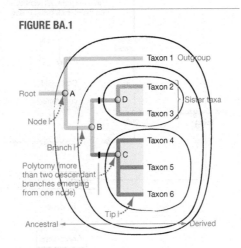

FIGURE BA.1

FIGURE BA.2

p. B:24 CYU (1) analyze *Caenorhabditis elegans* would be a good possibility, because the cells that normally die have already been identified. You could find mutant individuals that lacked normal cell death; you could compare the resulting embryos to normal embryos and be able to identify exactly which cells change as a result. **(2)** analyze Any of the multicellular organisms in the list would be a candidate, but *Dictyostelium discoideum* might be particularly interesting because cells stick to each other only during certain points in the life cycle. **(3)** analyze *Mus musculus*—as the only mammal in the list, it is the organism most likely to have a gene similar to the one you want to study.

BIOSKILLS 14; p. B:26 CYU synthesize Many examples are possible. See Figure 1.9 in Chapter 1, as an example of the format to use for your Research Box.

BIOSKILLS 15; p. B:27 CYU (1) analyze See **FIGURE BA.4.** **(2)** analyze See **FIGURE BA.4.**

FIGURE BA.3

Molecular formula: CO_2

Structural formula: $O = C = O$

Ball–and–stick model:

Space–filling model:

FIGURE BA.4

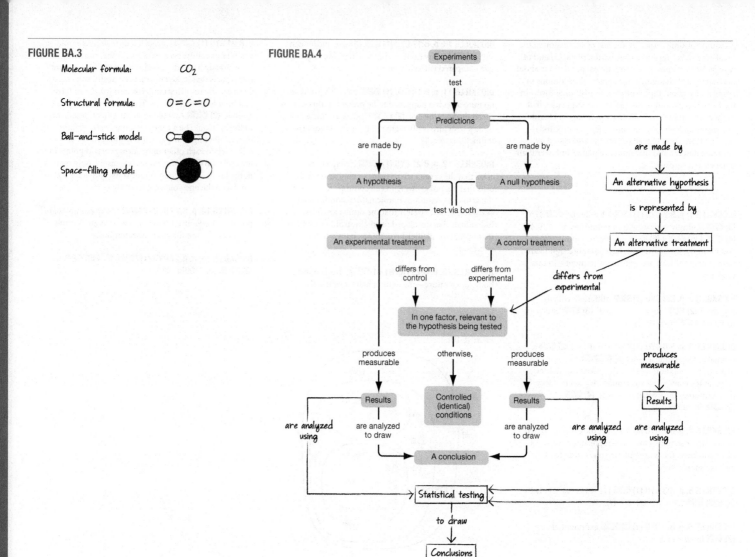

BioSkills

Scientists ask questions that can be answered by observing or measuring things—by collecting data. What units are used to make measurements? When measurements are reported, how can you tell how reliable the data are?

The Metric System

The metric system is the system of units of measure used in every country of the world but three (Liberia, Myanmar, and the United States). It is also the basis of the SI system—the International System of Units (abbreviated from the French, *Système international d'unités*)—used in scientific publications.

The popularity of the metric system is based on its consistency and ease of use. These attributes, in turn, arise from the

system's use of the base 10. For example, each unit of length in the system is related to all other measures of length in the system by a multiple of 10. There are 10 millimeters in a centimeter; 100 centimeters in a meter; 1000 meters in a kilometer.

Measures of length in the English system, in contrast, do not relate to each other in a regular way. Inches are routinely divided into 16ths; there are 12 inches in a foot; 3 feet in a yard; 5280 feet (or 1760 yards) in a mile.

If you have grown up in the United States and are accustomed to using the English system, it is extremely important to begin developing a working familiarity with metric units and values. **Tables B1.1** and **B1.2** (see B:2) should help you get started with this process.

As an example, consider the following question: An American football field is 120 yards long, while rugby fields are 144 meters

TABLE B1.1 **Metric System Units and Conversions**

Measurement	Unit of Measurement and Abbreviation	Metric System Equivalent	Converting Metric Units to English Units
Length	kilometer (km)	1 km = 1000 m = 10^3 m	1 km = 0.62 mile
	meter (m)	1 m = 100 cm	1 m = 1.09 yards = 3.28 feet = 39.37 inches
	centimeter (cm)	1 cm = 0.01 m = 10^{-2} m	1 cm = 0.3937 inch
	millimeter (mm)	1 mm = 0.001 m = 10^{-3} m	1 mm = 0.039 inch
	micrometer (μm)	1 μm = 10^{-6} m = 10^{-3} mm	
	nanometer (nm)	1 nm = 10^{-9} m = 10^{-3} μm	
Area	hectare (ha)	1 ha = 10,000 m^2	1 ha = 2.47 acres
	square meter (m^2)	1 m^2 = 10,000 cm^2	1 m^2 = 1.196 square yards
	square centimeter (cm^2)	1 cm^2 = 100 mm^2 = 10^{-4} m^2	1 cm^2 = 0.155 square inch
Volume	liter (L)	1 L = 1000 mL	1 L = 1.06 quarts
	milliliter (mL)	1 mL = 1000 μL = 10^{-3} L	1 mL = 0.034 fluid ounce
	microliter (μL)	1 μL = 10^{-6} L	
Mass	kilogram (kg)	1 kg = 1000 g	1 kg = 2.20 pounds
	gram (g)	1 g = 1000 mg	1 g = 0.035 ounce
	milligram (mg)	1 mg = 1000 μg = 10^{-3} g	
	microgram (μg)	1 μg = 10^{-6} g	
Temperature	Kelvin (K)*		K = °C + 273.15
	degrees Celsius (°C)		°C = $\frac{5}{9}$ (°F − 32)
	degrees Fahrenheit (°F)		°F = $\frac{9}{5}$°C + 32

*Absolute zero is −273.15 °C = 0 K.

TABLE B1.2 Prefixes Used in the Metric System

Prefix	Abbreviation	Definition
nano–	n	$0.000\ 000\ 001 = 10^{-9}$
micro–	µ	$0.000\ 001 = 10^{-6}$
milli–	m	$0.001 = 10^{-3}$
centi–	c	$0.01 = 10^{-2}$
deci–	d	$0.1 = 10^{-1}$
–	–	$1 = 10^{0}$
kilo–	k	$1000 = 10^{3}$
mega–	M	$1\ 000\ 000 = 10^{6}$
giga–	G	$1\ 000\ 000\ 000 = 10^{9}$

long. In yards, how much longer is a rugby field than an American football field? To solve this problem, first convert meters to yards: 144 m × 1.09 yards/m = 157 yards (note that the unit "m" cancels out). The difference in yards is thus: 157 – 120 = 37 yards. If you did these calculations on a calculator, you might have come up with 36.96 yards. Why has the number of yards been rounded off? The answer lies in significant figures. Let's take a closer look.

Significant Figures

Significant figures or "sig figs"—the number of digits used to report the measurement—are critical when reporting scientific data. The number of significant figures in a measurement, such as 3.524, is the number of digits that are known with some degree of confidence (3, 5, and 2) plus the last digit (4), which is an estimate or approximation. How do scientists know how many digits to report?

Rules for Working with Significant Figures

The rules for counting significant figures are summarized here:

- All nonzero numbers are always significant.

- Leading zeros are never significant; these zeros do nothing but set the decimal point.

- Embedded zeros are always significant.

- Trailing zeros are significant *only* if the decimal point is specified (Hint: Change the number to scientific notation. It is easier to see the "trailing" zeros.)

Table B1.3 provides examples of how to apply these rules. The bottom line is that significant figures indicate the precision of measurements.

Precision versus Accuracy

If biologists count the number of bird eggs in a nest, they report the data as an exact number—say, 3 eggs. But if the same biologists are measuring the diameter of the eggs, the numbers will be inexact. Just how inexact they are depends on the equipment used to make the measurements. For example, if you measure the width of your textbook with a ruler several times, you'll get essentially the same measurement again and again. Precision refers to how closely individual measurements agree with each other. So, you have determined the length with precision, but how do you know if the ruler was accurate to begin with?

Accuracy refers to how closely a measured value agrees with the correct value. You don't know the accuracy of a measuring device unless you calibrate it, by comparing it against a ruler that is known to be accurate. As the sensitivity of equipment used to

check your understanding

If you understand BioSkill 1

✓ **You should be able to . . .**

1. **QUANTITATIVE** Calculate how many miles a runner completes in a 5.0-kilometer run.

2. **QUANTITATIVE** Calculate your normal body temperature in degrees Celsius (Normal body temperature is 98.6°F.).

3. **QUANTITATIVE** Calculate your current weight in kilograms.

4. **QUANTITATIVE** Calculate how many liters of milk you would need to buy to get approximately the same volume as a gallon of milk.

5. **QUANTITATIVE** Multiply the measurements 2.8723 and 1.6. How many significant figures does your answer have? Why?

TABLE B1.3 Rules for Working with Significant Figures

Example	Number of Significant Figures	Scientific Notation	Rule
35,200	5	3.52×10^{4}	All nonzero numbers are always significant
0.00352	3	3.52×10^{-3}	Leading zeros are not significant
1.035	4	$1.035\ (\times 10^{0})$	Imbedded zeros are always significant
200	1	2×10^{2}	Trailing zeros are significant only if the decimal point is specified
200.0	4	2.000×10^{2}	Trailing zeros are significant only if the decimal point is specified

make a measurement increases, the number of significant figures increases. For example, if you used a kitchen scale to weigh out some sodium chloride, it might be accurate to 3 ± 1 g (1 significant figure); but an analytical balance in the lab might be accurate to 3.524 ± 0.001 g (4 significant figures).

In science, only the numbers that have significance—that are obtained from measurement—are reported. It is important to follow the "sig fig rules" when reporting a measurement, so that data do not appear to be more accurate than the equipment allows.

Combining Measurements

How do you deal with combining measurements with different degrees of accuracy and precision? The simple rule to follow is that the accuracy of the final answer can be no greater than the least accurate measurement. So, when you multiply or divide measurements, the answer can have no more significant figures than the least accurate measurement. When you add or subtract measurements, the answer can have no more decimal places than the least accurate measurement.

As an example, consider that you are adding the following measurements: 5.9522, 2.065, and 1.06. If you plug these numbers into your calculator, the answer your calculator will give you is 9.0772. However, this is incorrect—you must round your answer off to the nearest value, 9.08, to the least number of decimal places in your data.

It is important to nail down the concept of significant figures and to practice working with metric units and values. The Check Your Understanding questions in this BioSkill should help you get started with this process.

BIOSKILL 2 some common Latin and Greek roots used in biology

Greek or Latin Root	English Translation	Example Term
a, an	not	anaerobic
aero	air	aerobic
allo	other	allopatric
amphi	on both sides	amphipathic
anti	against	antibody
auto	self	autotroph
bi	two	bilateral symmetry
bio	life, living	bioinformatics
blast	bud, sprout	blastula
co	with	cofactor
cyto	cell	cytoplasm
di	two	diploid
ecto	outer	ectoparasite
endo	inner, within	endoparasite
epi	outer, upon	epidermis
exo	outside	exothermic
glyco	sugary	glycolysis
hetero	different	heterozygous
homo	alike	homozygous
hydro	water	hydrolysis
hyper	over, more than	hypertonic
hypo	under, less than	hypotonic
inter	between	interspecific
intra	within	intraspecific
iso	same	isotonic
logo, logy	study of	morphology
lyse, lysis	loosen, burst	glycolysis
macro	large	macromolecule

Greek or Latin Root	English Translation	Example Term
meta	change, turning point	metamorphosis
micro	small	microfilament
morph	form	morphology
oligo	few	oligopeptide
para	beside	parathyroid gland
photo	light	photosynthesis
poly	many	polymer
soma	body	somatic cells
sym, syn	together	symbiotic, synapsis
trans	across	translation
tri	three	trisomy
zygo	yoked together	zygote

check your understanding

C Y U

If you understand BioSkill 2

✔ **You should be able to . . .**

Provide literal translations of the following terms:

1. heterozygote

2. glycolysis

3. morphology

4. trisomy

Graphs are the most common way to report data, for a simple reason. Compared to reading raw numerical values in a table or list, a graph makes it much easier to understand what the data mean.

Learning how to read and interpret graphs is one of the most basic skills you'll need to acquire as a biology student. As when learning piano or soccer or anything else, you need to understand a few key ideas to get started and then have a chance to practice—a lot—with some guidance and feedback.

Getting Started

To start reading a graph, you need to do three things: read the axes, figure out what the data points represent—that is, where they came from—and think about the overall message of the data. Let's consider each step in turn.

What Do the Axes Represent?

Graphs have two axes: one horizontal and one vertical. The horizontal axis of a graph is also called the *x*-axis or the abscissa. The vertical axis of a graph is also called the *y*-axis or the ordinate. Each axis represents a variable that takes on a range of values. These values are indicated by the ticks and labels on the axis. Note that each axis should *always* be clearly labeled with the unit or treatment it represents.

FIGURE B3.1 shows a scatterplot—a type of graph where continuous data are graphed on each axis. Continuous data can take an array of values over a range. In contrast, discrete data can take only a restricted set of values. If you were graphing the average height of men and women in your class, height is a continuous variable, but gender is a discrete variable.

For the example in this figure, the *x*-axis represents time in units of generations of maize; the *y*-axis represents the average percentage of the dry weight of a maize kernel that is protein.

To create a graph, researchers plot the independent variable on the *x*-axis and the dependent variable on the *y*-axis (Figure B3.1a). The terms independent and dependent are used because the values on the *y*-axis depend on the *x*-axis values. In our example, the researchers wanted to show how the protein content of maize kernels in a study population changed over time. Thus, the protein concentration plotted on the *y*-axis depended on the year (generation) plotted on the *x*-axis. The value on the *y*-axis always depends on the value on the *x*-axis, but not vice versa.

In many graphs in biology, the independent variable is either time or the various treatments used in an experiment. In these cases, the *y*-axis records how some quantity changes as a function of time or as the outcome of the treatments applied to the experimental cells or organisms.

(a) Read the axes—what is being plotted?

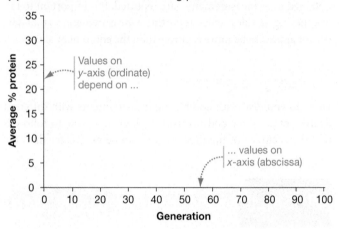

(b) Look at the bars or data points—what do they represent?

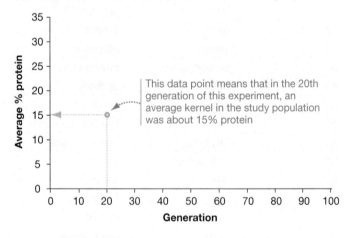

(c) What's the punchline?

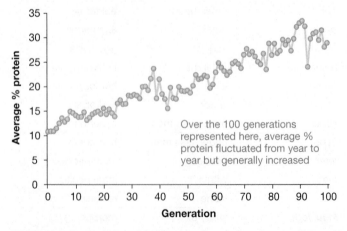

FIGURE B3.1 Scatterplots Are Used to Graph Continuous Data.

What Do the Data Points Represent?

Once you've read the axes, you need to figure out what each data point is. In our maize kernel example, the data point in Figure B3.1b represents the average percentage of protein found in a sample of kernels from a study population in a particular generation.

If it's difficult to figure out what the data points are, ask yourself where they came from—meaning, how the researchers got them. You can do this by understanding how the study was done and by understanding what is being plotted on each axis. The y-axis will tell you what they measured; the x-axis will usually tell you when they measured it or what group was measured. In some cases—for example, in a plot of average body size versus average brain size in primates—the x-axis will report a second variable that was measured.

In other cases, a data point on a graph may represent a relative or arbitrary unit of measurement. The data point shows the ratio of the amount of a substance, intensity, or other quantities, relative to a predetermined reference measurement. For example, the y-axis might show the percentage of relative activity of an enzyme—the rate of the enzyme-catalyzed reaction, scaled to the highest rate of activity observed (100 percent)—in experiments conducted under conditions that are identical except for one variable, such as pH or temperature (see Figure 8.14).

What Is the Overall Trend or Message?

Look at the data as a whole, and figure out what they mean. Figure B3.1c suggests an interpretation of the maize kernel example. If the graph shows how some quantity changes over time, ask yourself if that quantity is increasing, decreasing, fluctuating up and down, or staying the same. Then ask whether the pattern is the same over time or whether it changes over time.

When you're interpreting a graph, it's extremely important to limit your conclusions to the data presented. Don't extrapolate beyond the data, unless you are explicitly making a prediction based on the assumption that present trends will continue. For example, you can't say that the average percentage of protein content was increasing in the population before the experiment started, or that it will continue to increase in the future. You can say only what the data tell you.

Types of Graphs

Many of the graphs in this text are scatterplots like the one shown in Figure B3.1c, where individual data points are plotted. But you will also come across other types of graphs in this text.

Scatterplots, Lines, and Curves

Scatterplots sometimes have data points that are by themselves, but at other times data points will be connected by dot-to-dot lines to help make the overall trend clearer, as in Figure B3.1c, or may have a smooth line through them.

A *smooth line* through data points—sometimes straight, sometimes curved—is a mathematical "line of best fit." A line of best fit represents a mathematical function that summarizes the relationship between the x and y variables. It is "best" in the sense of fitting the data points most precisely. The line may pass through some of the points, none of the points, or all of the points.

Curved lines often take on characteristic shapes depending on the relationships between the x and y variable. For example, a bell-shaped curve depicts a normal distribution in which most data points are clumped near the middle, while a sigmoid or S-shaped curve exhibits small changes at first, which then accelerate and approach maximal value over time. Data from studies on population growth (see Chapter 54), enzyme kinetics (see Chapter 8), and oxygen–hemoglobin dissociation (see Chapter 45) typically fall on a curved line.

Bar Charts, Histograms, and Box-and-Whisker Plots

Scatterplots, or line-of-best-fit graphs, are the most appropriate type of graph when the data have a continuous range of values and you want to show individual data points. But other types of graphs are used to represent different types of distributions:

- *Bar charts* plot data that have discrete or categorical values instead of a continuous range of values. In many cases the bars might represent different treatment groups in an experiment, as in **FIGURE B3.2a** (see B:6). In this graph, the height of the bar indicates the average value. Statistical tests can be used to determine whether a difference between treatment groups is significant (see **BIOSKILLS 4**).

- *Histograms* illustrate frequency data and can be plotted as numbers or percentages. **FIGURE B3.2b** shows an example where height is plotted on the x-axis, and the number of students in a population is plotted on the y-axis. Each rectangle indicates the number of individuals in each interval of height, which reflects the relative frequency, in this population, of people whose heights are in that interval. The measurements could also be recalculated so that the y-axis would report the proportion of people in each interval. Then the sum of all the bars would equal 100 percent. Note that if you were to draw a smooth curve connecting the top of the bars on this histogram, the smooth curve would represent the shape of a bell.

- *Box-and-whisker plots* allow you to easily see where most of the data fall. Each box indicates where half of the data numbers are. The whiskers indicate the lower extreme and the upper extreme of the data. The vertical line inside each box indicates the median—meaning that half of the data are above this value and half are below (see Figure 1.9 for an example).

When you are looking at a bar chart that plots values from different treatments in an experiment, ask yourself if these values are the same or different. If the bar chart reports averages over discrete ranges of values, ask what trend is implied—as you would for a scatterplot.

(a) Bar chart

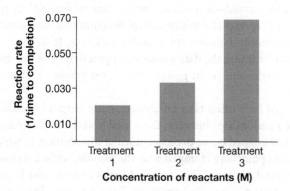

(b) Histogram

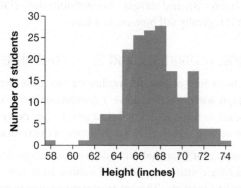

FIGURE B3.2 **Bar Charts and Histograms. (a)** Bar charts are used to graph data that are discontinuous or categorical. **(b)** Histograms show the distribution of frequencies or values in a population.

When you are looking at a histogram, ask whether there is a "hump" in the data—indicating a group of values that are more frequent than others. Is the hump in the center of the distribution of values, toward the left, or toward the right? If so, what does it mean?

Similarly, when you are looking at a box-and-whisker plot, ask yourself what information the graph gives you. What is the range of values for the data? Where are half the data points? Below what value is three quarters of the data?

Getting Practice

Working with this text will give you lots of practice with reading graphs—they appear in almost every chapter. In many cases we've inserted an arrow to represent your instructor's hand at the whiteboard, with a label that suggests an interpretation or draws your attention to an important point on the graph. In other cases, you should be able to figure out what the data mean on your own or with the help of other students or your instructor.

check your understanding

C
Y
U

If you understand BioSkill 3

✔ **You should be able to . . .**

1. **QUANTITATIVE** Determine the total change in average percentage of protein in maize kernels, from the start of the experiment until the end.

2. **QUANTITATIVE** Determine the trend in average percentage of protein in maize kernels between generation 37 and generation 42.

3. Explain whether the conclusions from the bar chart in Figure B3.2a would be different if the data and label for Treatment 3 were put on the far left and the data and label for Treatment 1 on the far right.

4. **QUANTITATIVE** Determine approximately how many students in this class are 70 inches tall, by using Figure B3.2b.

5. **QUANTITATIVE** Determine the most common height in the class graphed in Figure B3.2b.

BIOSKILL 4   using statistical tests and interpreting standard error bars

When biologists do an experiment, they collect data on individuals in a treatment group and a control group, or several such comparison groups. Then they want to know whether the individuals in the two (or more) groups are different. For example, in one experiment student researchers measured how fast a product formed when they set up a reaction with three different concentrations of reactants (introduced in Chapter 8). Each treatment—meaning, each combination of reactant concentrations—was replicated many times.

FIGURE B4.1 graphs the average reaction rate for each of the three treatments in the experiment. Note that Treatments 1, 2, and 3 represent increasing concentrations of reactants. The thin

"I-beams" on each bar indicate the standard error of each average. The standard error is a quantity that indicates the uncertainty in the calculation of an average.

For example, if two trials with the same concentration of reactants had a reaction rate of 0.075 and two trials had a reaction rate of 0.025, then the average reaction rate would be 0.050. In this case, the standard error would be large. But if two trials had a reaction rate of 0.051 and two had a reaction rate of 0.049, the average would still be 0.050, but the standard error would be small.

In effect, the standard error quantifies how confident you are that the average you've calculated is the average you'd observe if

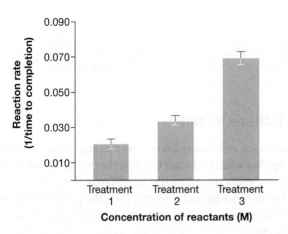

FIGURE B4.1 Standard Error Bars Indicate the Uncertainty in an Average.

you did the experiment under the same conditions an extremely large number of times. It is a measure of precision (see **BIOSKILLS 1**).

Once they had calculated these averages and standard errors, the students wanted to answer a question: Does reaction rate increase when reactant concentration increases?

After looking at the data, you might conclude that the answer is yes. But how could you come to a conclusion like this objectively, instead of subjectively?

The answer is to use a statistical test. This can be thought of as a three-step process.

1. Specify the null hypothesis, which is that reactant concentration has no effect on reaction rate.

2. Calculate a test statistic, which is a number that characterizes the size of the difference among the treatments. In this case, the test statistic compares the actual differences in reaction rates among treatments to the difference predicted by the null hypothesis. The null hypothesis predicts that there should be no difference.

3. The third step is to determine the probability of getting a test statistic at least as large as the one calculated just by chance. The answer comes from a reference distribution—a mathematical function that specifies the probability of getting various values of the test statistic if the null hypothesis is correct. (If you take a statistics course, you'll learn which test

statistics and reference distributions are relevant to different types of data.)

You are very likely to see small differences among treatment groups just by chance—even if no differences actually exist. If you flipped a coin 10 times, for example, you are unlikely to get exactly five heads and five tails, even if the coin is fair. A reference distribution tells you how likely you are to get each of the possible outcomes of the 10 flips if the coin is fair, just by chance.

In this case, the reference distribution indicated that if the null hypothesis of no actual difference in reaction rates is correct, you would see differences at least as large as those observed only 0.01 percent of the time just by chance. By convention, biologists consider a difference among treatment groups to be statistically significant if there is less than a 5 percent probability of observing it just by chance. Based on this convention, the student researchers were able to claim that the null hypothesis is not correct for reactant concentration. According to their data, the reaction they studied really does happen faster when reactant concentration increases.

You'll likely be doing actual statistical tests early in your undergraduate career. To use this text, though, you only need to know what statistical testing does. And you should take care to inspect the standard error bars on graphs in this book. As a *very* rough rule of thumb, averages often turn out to be significantly different, according to an appropriate statistical test, if there is no overlap between two times the standard errors.

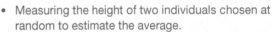

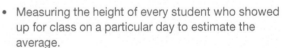 **If you understand BioSkill 4**

✔ **You should be able to . . .**

QUANTITATIVE Determine which of the following tests used to estimate the average height of individuals in a class is likely to have the smallest standard error, and why.

- Measuring the height of two individuals chosen at random to estimate the average.

- Measuring the height of every student who showed up for class on a particular day to estimate the average.

In several cases in this text, you'll need to combine probabilities from different events in order to solve a problem. One of the most common applications is in genetics problems. For example, Punnett squares work because they are based on two fundamental rules of probability. Each rule pertains to a distinct situation.

The Both-And Rule

The both-and rule—also known as the product rule or multiplication rule—applies when you want to know the probability that two or more independent events occur together. Let's use the rolling of two dice as an example. What is the probability of rolling two sixes? These two events are independent, because the probability of rolling a six on one die has no effect on the probability of rolling a six on the other die. (In the same way, the probability of getting a gamete with allele R from one parent has no effect on the probability of getting a gamete with allele R from the other parent. Gametes fuse randomly.)

The probability of rolling a six on the first die is 1/6. The probability of rolling a six on the second die is also 1/6. The probability of rolling a six on *both* dice, then, is $1/6 \times 1/6 = 1/36$. In other words, if you rolled two dice 36 times, on average you would expect to roll two sixes once.

In the case of a cross between two parents heterozygous at the R gene, the probability of getting allele R from the father is 1/2 and the probability of getting R from the mother is 1/2. Thus, the probability of getting both alleles and creating an offspring with genotype RR is $1/2 \times 1/2 = 1/4$.

The Either-Or Rule

The either-or rule—also known as the sum rule or addition rule—applies when you want to know the probability of an event happening when there are several different ways for the same event or outcome to occur. In this case, the probability that the event will occur is the sum of the probabilities of each way that it can occur.

For example, suppose you wanted to know the probability of rolling either a one or a six when you toss a die. The probability of drawing each is 1/6, so the probability of getting one or the other is $1/6 + 1/6 = 1/3$. If you rolled a die three times, on average you'd expect to get a one or a six once.

In the case of a cross between two parents heterozygous at the R gene, the probability of getting an R allele from the father and an r allele from the mother is $1/2 \times 1/2 = 1/4$. Similarly, the probability of getting an r allele from the father and an R allele from the mother is $1/2 \times 1/2 = 1/4$. Thus, the combined probability of getting the Rr genotype in either of the two ways is $1/4 + 1/4 = 1/2$.

check your understanding

If you understand BioSkill 5

✔ **You should be able to . . .**

1. **QUANTITATIVE** Calculate the probability of getting four "tails" if four students each toss a coin.

2. **QUANTITATIVE** Calculate the probability of getting a two, a three, or a six after a single roll of a die.

You have probably been introduced to logarithms and logarithmic notation in algebra courses, and you will encounter logarithms at several points in this course. Logarithms are a way of working with powers—meaning, numbers that are multiplied by themselves one or more times.

Scientists use exponential notation to represent powers. For example,

$$a^x = y$$

means that if you multiply a by itself x times, you get y. In exponential notation, a is called the base and x is called the exponent. The entire expression is called an exponential function.

What if you know y and a, and you want to know x? This is where logarithms come in. You can solve for exponents using logarithms. For example,

$$x = \log_a y$$

This equation reads, x is equal to the logarithm of y to the base a. Logarithms are a way of working with exponential functions. They are important because so many processes in biology (and chemistry and physics, for that matter) are exponential. To understand what's going on, you have to describe the process with an exponential function and then use logarithms to work with that function.

Although a base can be any number, most scientists use just two bases when they employ logarithmic notation: 10 and e (sometimes called Euler's number after Swiss mathematician Leonhard Euler). What is e? It is a rate of exponential growth shared by many natural processes, where e is the limit of $(1 + \frac{1}{n})^n$ (as n tends to infinity). Mathematicians have shown that the base e is an irrational number (like π) that is approximately equal to 2.718. Like 10, e is just a number; $10^0 = 1$ and, likewise, $e^0 = 1$. But both 10 and e have qualities that make them convenient to use in biology (as well as chemistry and physics).

Logarithms to the base 10 are so common that they are usually symbolized in the form $\log y$ instead of $\log_{10} y$. A logarithm to the base e is called a natural logarithm and is symbolized ln (pronounced *EL-EN*) instead of log. You write "the natural logarithm of y" as $\ln y$.

Most scientific calculators have keys that allow you to solve problems involving base 10 and base e. For example, if you know y, they'll tell you what $\log y$ or $\ln y$ are—meaning that they'll solve for x in our first example equation. They'll also allow you to find a number when you know its logarithm to base 10 or base

e. Stated another way, they'll tell you what y is if you know x, and y is equal to e^x or 10^x. This is called taking an antilog. In most cases, you'll use the inverse or second function button on your calculator to find an antilog (above the log or ln key).

To get some practice with your calculator, consider this equation:

$$10^2 = 100$$

If you enter 100 in your calculator and then press the log key, the screen should say 2. The logarithm tells you what the exponent is. Now press the antilog key while 2 is on the screen. The calculator screen should return to 100. The antilog solves the exponential function, given the base and the exponent.

If your background in algebra isn't strong, you'll want to get more practice working with logarithms—you'll see them frequently during your undergraduate career. Remember that once you understand the basic notation, there's nothing mysterious about logarithms. They are simply a way of working with exponential functions, which describe what happens when something is multiplied by itself a number of times—like cells that divide and then divide again and then again.

Using logarithms will also come up when you are studying something that can have a large range of values, like the concentration of hydrogen ions in a solution or the intensity of sound that the human ear can detect. In cases like this, it's convenient to express the numbers involved as exponents. Using exponents makes a large range of numbers smaller and more manageable. For example, instead of saying that hydrogen ion concentration in a solution can range from 1 to 10^{-14}, the pH scale allows you to simply say that it ranges from 1 to 14. Instead of giving the actual value, you're expressing it as an exponent. It just simplifies things.

check your understanding

If you understand BioSkill 6

✓ **You should be able to . . .**

Use the equation $N_t = N_0 e^{rt}$ (see Chapter 54).

1. Explain what type of function this equation describes.

2. **QUANTITATIVE** Determine how you would write the equation, after taking the natural logarithm of both sides.

Phylogenetic trees show the evolutionary relationships among species, just as a genealogy shows the relationships among people in your family. They are unusual diagrams, however, and it can take practice to interpret them correctly.

To understand how evolutionary trees work, consider **FIGURE B7.1**. Notice that a phylogenetic tree consists of a root (the most ancestral branch in the tree), branches, nodes, and tips.

- Branches represent populations through time. In this text, branches are drawn as horizontal lines. In most cases the length of the branch is arbitrary and has no meaning, but in some cases branch lengths are proportional to time or the extent of genetic difference among populations (if so, there will be a scale at the bottom of the tree). The vertical lines on the tree represent splitting events, where one group broke into two independent groups. Their length is arbitrary—chosen simply to make the tree more readable.

- Nodes (also called forks) occur where an ancestral group splits into two or more descendant groups (see point A in Figure B7.1). Thus, each node represents the most recent common ancestor of the two or more descendant populations that emerge from it. If more than two descendant groups emerge from a node, the node is called a polytomy (see node C). A polytomy usually means that the populations split from one another so quickly that it is not possible to tell which split off earlier or later.

- Tips (also called terminal nodes) are the tree's endpoints, which represent groups living today or a dead end—a branch

ending in extinction. The names at the tips can represent species or larger groups such as mammals or conifers.

Recall that a taxon (plural: taxa) is any named group of organisms (see Chapter 1). A taxon could be a single species, such as *Homo sapiens*, or a large group of species, such as Primates. Tips connected by a single node on a tree are called sister taxa.

The phylogenetic trees used in this text are all rooted. This means that the first, or most basal, node on the tree—the one on the far left in this book—is the most ancient. To determine where the root on a tree occurs, biologists include one or more outgroup species when they are collecting data to estimate a particular phylogeny. An outgroup is a taxonomic group that is known to have diverged before the rest of the taxa in the study. Outgroups are used to establish whether a trait is ancestral or derived. An ancestral trait is a characteristic that existed in an ancestor; a derived trait is a characteristic that is a modified form of the ancestral trait, found in a descendant.

In Figure B7.1, Taxon 1 is an outgroup to the monophyletic group consisting of taxa 2–6. A monophyletic group consists of an ancestral species and all of its descendants. The root of a tree is placed between the outgroup and the monophyletic group being studied. This position in Figure B7.1 is node A. Note that black hash marks are used to indicate a derived trait that is shared among the red branches, and another derived trait that is shared among the orange branches.

Understanding monophyletic groups is fundamental to reading and estimating phylogenetic trees. Monophyletic groups may also be called lineages or clades and can be identified using the "one-snip test": If you cut any branch on a phylogenetic tree, all of the branches and tips that fall off represent a monophyletic group. Using the one-snip test, you should be able to convince yourself that the monophyletic groups on a tree are nested. In Figure B7.1, for example, the monophyletic group comprising node A and taxa 1–6 contains a monophyletic group consisting of node B and taxa 2–6, which includes the monophyletic group represented by node C and taxa 4–6.

To put all these new terms and concepts to work, consider the phylogenetic tree in **FIGURE B7.2**, which shows the relationships between common chimpanzees and six human and humanlike species that lived over the past 5–6 million years. Chimps functioned as an outgroup in the analysis that led to this tree, so the root was placed at node A. The branches marked in red identify a monophyletic group called the hominins.

To practice how to read a tree, put your finger at the tree's root, at the far left, and work your way to the right. At node A, the ancestral population split into two descendant populations. One of these populations eventually evolved into today's chimps; the other gave rise to the six species of hominins pictured. Now

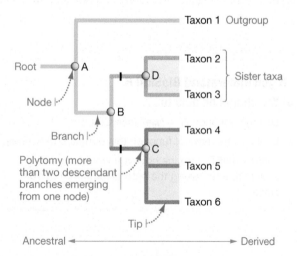

FIGURE B7.1 Phylogenetic Trees Have Roots, Branches, Nodes, and Tips.

✔**EXERCISE** Circle all four monophyletic groups present.

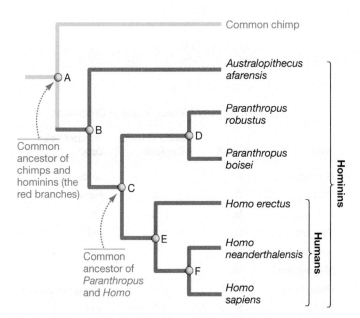

FIGURE B7.2 **An Example of a Phylogenetic Tree.** A phylogenetic tree showing the relationships of species in the monophyletic group called hominins.

✔**EXERCISE** All of the hominins walked on two legs—unlike chimps and all of the other primates. Add a mark on the phylogeny to show where upright posture evolved, and label it "origin of walking on two legs." Circle and label a pair of sister species. Label an outgroup to the monophyletic group called humans (species in the genus *Homo*).

continue moving your finger toward the tips of the tree until you hit node C. It should make sense to you that at this splitting event, one descendant population eventually gave rise to two *Paranthropus* species, while the other became the ancestor of humans—species in the genus *Homo*. As you study Figure B7.2, consider these two important points:

1. There are many equivalent ways of drawing this tree. For example, this version shows *Homo sapiens* on the bottom. But the tree would be identical if the two branches emerging from node E were rotated 180°, so that the species appeared in the order *Homo sapiens*, *Homo neanderthalensis*, *Homo erectus*. Trees are read from root to tips, not from top to bottom or bottom to top.

2. No species on any tree is any higher or lower than any other. Chimps and *Homo sapiens* have been evolving exactly the same amount of time since their divergence from a common ancestor—neither species is higher or lower than the other. It is legitimate to say that more ancient groups like *Australopithecus afarensis* have traits that are ancestral or more basal—meaning, that appeared earlier in evolution—compared to traits that appear in *Homo sapiens*, which are referred to as more derived.

FIGURE B7.3 presents a chance to test your tree-reading ability. Five of the six trees shown in this diagram are identical in terms of the evolutionary relationships they represent. One differs. The key to understanding the difference is to recognize that the ordering of tips does not matter in a tree—only the ordering of nodes (branch points) matters. You can think of a tree as being like a mobile: The tips can rotate without changing the underlying relationships.

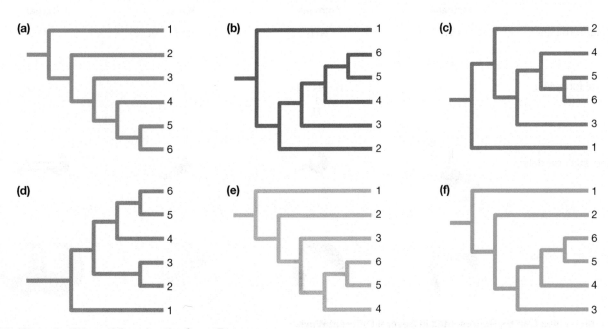

FIGURE B7.3 **Alternative Ways of Drawing the Same Tree.**

✔**QUESTION** Five of these six trees describe exactly the same relationships among taxa 1 through 6. Identify the tree that is different from the other five.

If you haven't had much chemistry yet, learning basic biological chemistry can be a challenge. One stumbling block is simply being able to read chemical structures efficiently and understand what they mean. This skill will come much easier once you have a little notation under your belt and you understand some basic symbols.

Atoms are the basic building blocks of everything in the universe, just as cells are the basic building blocks of your body. Every atom has a one- or two-letter symbol. **Table B8.1** shows the symbols for most of the atoms you'll encounter in this book. You should memorize these. The table also offers details on how the atoms form bonds as well as how they are represented in some visual models.

When atoms attach to each other by covalent bonding, a molecule forms. Biologists have a couple of different ways of representing molecules—you'll see each of these in the book and in class.

- Molecular formulas like those in **FIGURE B8.1a** simply list the atoms present in a molecule. Subscripts indicate how many of each atom are present. If the formula has no subscript, only one atom of that type is present. A methane (natural gas) molecule, for example, can be written as CH_4. It consists of one carbon atom and four hydrogen atoms.

TABLE B8.1 **Some Attributes of Atoms Found in Organisms**

Atom	Symbol	Number of Bonds It Can Form	Standard Color Code*
Hydrogen	H	1	white
Carbon	C	4	black
Nitrogen	N	3	blue
Oxygen	O	2	red
Sodium	Na	1	—
Magnesium	Mg	2	—
Phosphorus	P	5	orange or purple
Sulfur	S	2	yellow
Chlorine	Cl	1	—
Potassium	K	1	—
Calcium	Ca	2	—

*In ball-and-stick or space-filling models.

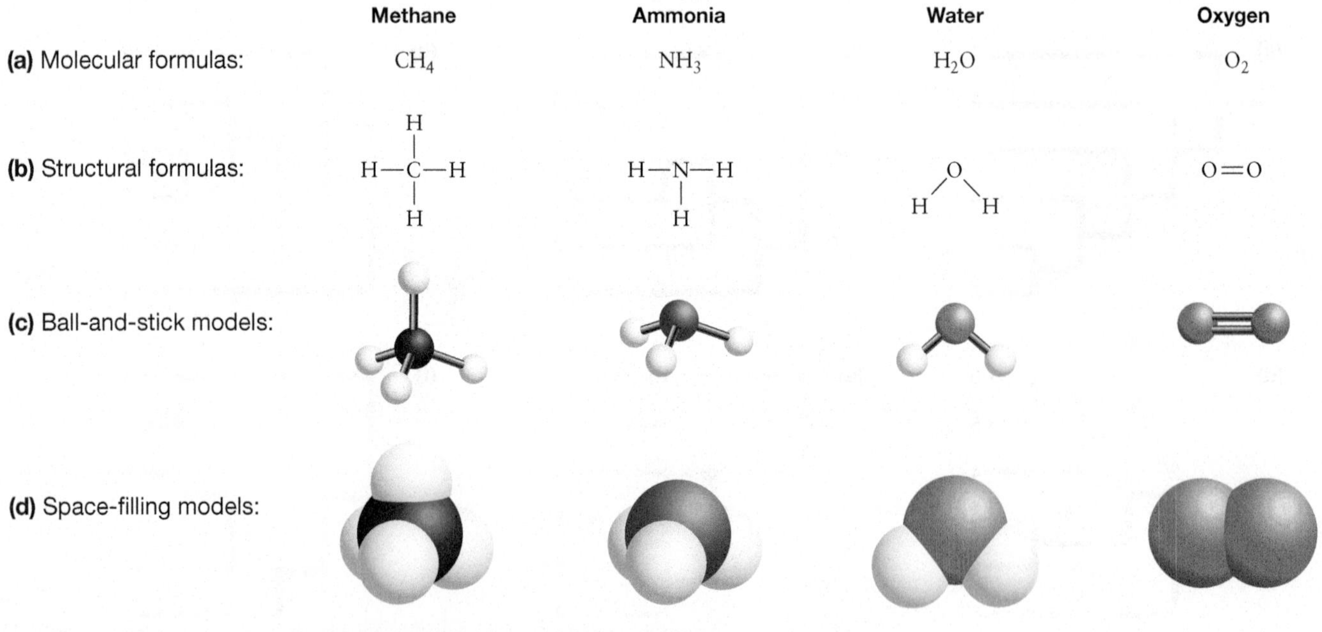

- Structural formulas like those in **FIGURE B8.1b** show which atoms in the molecule are bonded to each other. Each bond is indicated by a dash. The structural formula for methane in-

	Methane	Ammonia	Water	Oxygen
(a) Molecular formulas:	CH_4	NH_3	H_2O	O_2

(b) Structural formulas:

(c) Ball-and-stick models:

(d) Space-filling models:

FIGURE B8.1 Molecules Can Be Represented in Several Different Ways.

✔**EXERCISE** Carbon dioxide consists of a carbon atom that forms a double bond with each of two oxygen atoms, for a total of four bonds. It is a linear molecule. Write carbon dioxide's molecular formula and then draw its structural formula, a ball-and-stick model, and a space-filling model.

dicates that each of the four hydrogen atoms forms one covalent bond with carbon, and that carbon makes a total of four covalent bonds. Single covalent bonds are symbolized by a single dash; double bonds are indicated by two dashes.

Even simple molecules have distinctive shapes, because different atoms make covalent bonds at different angles. Ball-and-stick and space-filling models show the geometry of the bonds accurately.

- In a ball-and-stick model, a stick is used to represent each covalent bond (see **FIGURE B8.1c**).
- In space-filling models, the atoms are simply stuck onto each other in their proper places (see **FIGURE B8.1d**).

To learn more about a molecule when you look at a chemical structure, ask yourself three questions:

1. *Is the molecule polar—meaning that some parts are more negatively or positively charged than others?* Molecules that contain nitrogen or oxygen atoms are often polar, because these atoms have such high electronegativity (see Chapter 2). This trait is important because polar molecules dissolve in water.

2. *Does the structural formula show atoms that might participate in chemical reactions?* For example, are there charged atoms or amino or carboxyl ($-COOH$) groups that might act as a base or an acid?

3. *In ball-and-stick and especially space-filling models of large molecules, are there interesting aspects of overall shape?* For example, is there a groove where a protein might bind to DNA, or a cleft where a substrate might undergo a reaction in an enzyme?

BIOSKILL 9 separating and visualizing molecules

To study a molecule, you have to be able to isolate it. Isolating a molecule is a two-step process: the molecule has to be separated from other molecules in a mixture and then physically picked out or located in a purified form. **BIOSKILLS 9** focuses on the techniques that biologists use to separate nucleic acids and proteins and then find the particular one they are interested in.

Using Electrophoresis to Separate Molecules

In molecular biology, the standard technique for separating proteins and nucleic acids is called gel electrophoresis or, simply, electrophoresis (literally, "electricity-moving"). You may be using electrophoresis in a lab for this course, and you will certainly be analyzing data derived from electrophoresis in this text.

The principle behind electrophoresis is simple. Proteins (when denatured and coated with a special detergent) and nucleic acids carry a charge. As a result, these molecules move when placed in an electric field. Negatively charged molecules move toward the positive electrode; positively charged molecules move toward the negative electrode.

To separate a mixture of macromolecules so that each one can be isolated and analyzed, researchers place the sample in a gelatinous substance. More specifically, the sample is placed in a "well"—a slot in a sheet or slab of the gelatinous substance. The "gel" itself consists of long molecules that form a matrix of fibers. The gelatinous matrix has pores that act like a sieve through which the molecules can pass.

When an electrical field is applied across the gel, the molecules in the well move through the gel toward an electrode. Molecules that are smaller or more highly charged for their size move faster than do larger or less highly charged molecules. As they move, then, the molecules separate by size and by charge. Small and highly charged molecules end up at the bottom of the gel; large, less-charged molecules remain near the top.

An Example "Run"

FIGURE B9.1 (see B:14) shows the electrophoresis setup used in an experiment investigating how RNA molecules polymerize. In this case, the investigators wanted to document how long RNA molecules became over time, when ribonucleoside triphosphates were present in a particular type of solution.

Step 1 shows how they loaded samples of macromolecules, taken on different days during the experiment, into wells at the top of the gel slab. This is a general observation: Each well holds a different sample. In this and many other cases, the researchers also filled a well with a sample containing fragments of known size, called a size standard or "ladder."

In step 2, the researchers immersed the gel in a solution that conducts electricity and applied a voltage across the gel. The molecules in each well started to run down the gel, forming a lane. After several hours of allowing the molecules to move, the researchers removed the electric field (step 3). By then, molecules of different size and charge had separated from one another. In this case, small RNA molecules had reached the bottom of the gel. Above them were larger RNA molecules, which had run more slowly.

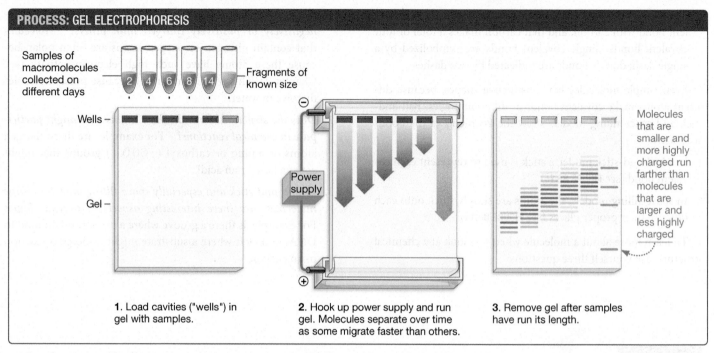

PROCESS: GEL ELECTROPHORESIS

Samples of macromolecules collected on different days

2 4 6 8 14

Fragments of known size

Wells —

Gel —

Power supply

⊖

⊕

Molecules that are smaller and more highly charged run farther than molecules that are larger and less highly charged

1. Load cavities ("wells") in gel with samples.

2. Hook up power supply and run gel. Molecules separate over time as some migrate faster than others.

3. Remove gel after samples have run its length.

FIGURE B9.1 Macromolecules Can Be Separated via Gel Electrophoresis.

✔**QUESTION** DNA and RNA run toward the positive electrode. Why are these molecules negatively charged?

Why Do Separated Molecules Form Bands?

When researchers visualize a particular molecule on a gel, using techniques described in this section, the image that results consists of bands: shallow lines that are as wide as a lane in the gel. Why?

To understand the answer, study **FIGURE B9.2**. The left panel shows the original mixture of molecules. In this cartoon, the size of each dot represents the size of each molecule. The key is to realize that the original sample contains many copies of each specific molecule, and that these copies run down the length of the gel together—meaning, at the same rate—because they have the same size and charge.

It's that simple: Molecules that are alike form a band because they stay together.

Using Thin Layer Chromatography to Separate Molecules

Gel electrophoresis is not the only way to separate molecules. Researchers also use a method called thin layer chromatography. This method was developed in the early 1900s by botanists who were analyzing the different-colored pigments from leaves of a plant (see Chapter 10), hence the name chromatography from the Greek words khroma for "color" and graphein, "to write."

In this method, rather than loading the sample into the well of a gel, the samples are deposited or "spotted" near the bottom of a stiff support, either glass or plastic, that is coated with a thin layer of silica gel, cellulose, or a similar porous material. The coated support is placed in a solvent solution. As the solvent

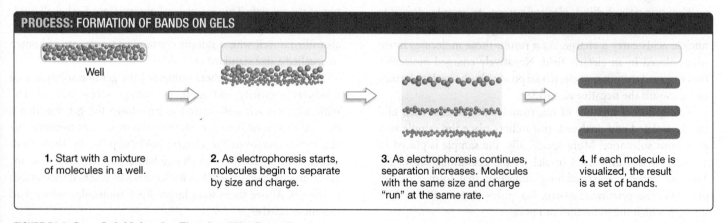

PROCESS: FORMATION OF BANDS ON GELS

Well

1. Start with a mixture of molecules in a well.

2. As electrophoresis starts, molecules begin to separate by size and charge.

3. As electrophoresis continues, separation increases. Molecules with the same size and charge "run" at the same rate.

4. If each molecule is visualized, the result is a set of bands.

FIGURE B9.2 On a Gel, Molecules That Are Alike Form Bands.

wicks upward through the coating by capillary action, it carries the molecules in the mixture with it. Molecules are carried at different rates, based on their size and solubility in the solvent.

Visualizing Molecules

Once molecules have been separated using electrophoresis or thin layer chromatography, they have to be detected. Unfortunately, although plant pigments are colored, proteins and nucleic acids are invisible unless they are tagged in some way. Let's first look at two of the most common tagging systems and then consider how researchers can tag and visualize specific molecules of interest and not others.

Using Radioactive Isotopes and Autoradiography

When molecular biology was getting under way, the first types of tags in common use were radioactive isotopes—forms of atoms that are unstable and release energy in the form of radiation.

In the polymerization experiment diagrammed in Figure B9.1, for example, the researchers had attached a radioactive phosphorus atom to the monomers—ribonucleoside triphosphates—used in the original reaction mix. Once polymers formed, they contained radioactive atoms. When electrophoresis was complete, the investigators visualized the polymers by laying X-ray film over the gel. Because radioactive emissions expose film, a black dot appears wherever a radioactive atom is located in the gel. So many black dots occur so close together that the collection forms a dark band.

This technique for visualizing macromolecules is called autoradiography. The autoradiograph that resulted from the polymerization experiment is shown in **FIGURE B9.3**. The samples, taken on days 2, 4, 6, 8, and 14 of the experiment, are noted along the bottom. The far right lane contains macromolecules of known size; this lane is used to estimate the size of the molecules in the experimental samples. The bands that appear in each sample lane represent the different polymers that had formed.

Reading a Gel

One of the keys to interpreting or "reading" a gel, or the corresponding autoradiograph, is to realize that darker bands contain more radioactive markers, indicating the presence of many radioactive molecules. Lighter bands contain fewer molecules.

To read a gel, then, you look for (1) the presence or absence of bands in some lanes—meaning, some experimental samples—versus others, and (2) contrasts in the darkness of the bands—meaning, differences in the number of molecules present.

For example, several conclusions can be drawn from the data in Figure B9.3. First, a variety of polymers formed at each stage. After the second day, for example, polymers from 12 to 18 monomers long had formed. Second, the overall length of polymers produced increased with time. At the end of the fourteenth day, most of the RNA molecules were between 20 and 40 monomers long.

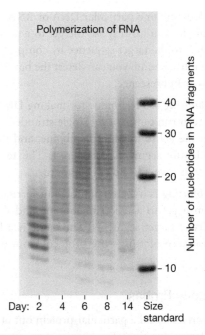

FIGURE B9.3 Autoradiography Is a Technique for Visualizing Macromolecules. The molecules in a gel can be visualized in a number of ways. In this case, the RNA molecules in the gel exposed an X-ray film because they had radioactive atoms attached. When developed, the film is called an autoradiograph.

Starting in the late 1990s and early 2000s, it became much more common to tag nucleic acids with fluorescent tags. Once electrophoresis is complete, fluorescence can be detected by exposing the gel to an appropriate wavelength of light; the fluorescent tag fluoresces or glows in response (fluorescence is explained in Chapter 10).

Fluorescent tags have important advantages over radioactive isotopes: (1) They are safer to handle. (2) They are faster—you don't have to wait hours or days for the radioactive isotope to expose a film. (3) They come in multiple colors, so you can tag several different molecules in the same experiment and detect them independently.

Using Nucleic Acid Probes

In many cases, researchers want to find one specific molecule—a certain DNA sequence, for example—in the collection of molecules on a gel. How is this possible? The answer hinges on using a particular molecule as a probe.

You'll learn in more detail about how probes work in this text (Chapter 20). Here it's enough to get the general idea: A probe is a marked molecule that binds specifically to your molecule of interest. The "mark" is often a radioactive atom, a fluorescent tag, or an enzyme that catalyzes a color-forming or light-emitting reaction.

If you are looking for a particular DNA or RNA sequence on a gel, for example, you can expose the gel to a single-stranded probe that binds to the target sequence by complementary base pairing. Once it has bound, you can detect the band through autoradiography or fluorescence.

- *Southern blotting* is a technique for making DNA fragments that have been run out on a gel single stranded, transferring them from the gel to a nylon membrane, and then probing them to identify segments of interest. The technique was named after its inventor, Edwin Southern.

- *Northern blotting* is a technique for transferring RNA fragments from a gel to a nylon membrane and then probing them to detect target segments. The name is a lighthearted play on Southern blotting—the protocol from which it was derived.

Using Antibody Probes

How can researchers find a particular protein out of a large collection of different proteins? The answer is to use an antibody. An antibody is a protein that binds specifically to a section of a different protein (see Chapter 51 if you want more detail on the structure of antibodies and their function in the immune system).

To use an antibody as a probe, investigators attach a tag molecule—often an enzyme that catalyzes a color-forming reaction—to the antibody and allow it to react with proteins in a mixture. The antibody will stick to the specific protein that it binds to and then can be visualized thanks to the tag it carries.

If the proteins in question have been separated by gel electrophoresis and transferred to a membrane, the result is called a western blot. The name western is an extension of the Southern and northern patterns.

Using Radioimmunoassay and ELISA to Measure Amounts of Molecules

Another important method that makes use of antibodies is called a radioimmunoassay. This method is used when investigators want to measure tiny amounts of a molecule, such as a hormone in the blood. In this case, a known quantity of a hormone is labeled with a radioactive tag. This tagged hormone is then mixed with a known amount of antibody, and the two bind to one another. Next, a sample of blood, containing an unknown quantity of that same hormone, is added. The hormone from the blood and the radiolabeled hormone compete for antibody binding sites. As the concentration of unlabeled hormone increases, more of it binds to the antibody, displacing more of the radiolabeled hormone. The amount of unbound radiolabeled hormone is then measured. Using known standards as a reference, the amount of hormone in the blood can be determined.

Another commonly used technique based on similar principles is called ELISA (enzyme-linked immunosorbent assay). In this case, the amount of a particular molecule is measured using colorimetric signals instead of a radioactive signal.

check your understanding

If you understand BioSkill 9

✔You should be able to . . .

Interpret a gel that has been stained for "RNA X." One lane contains no bands. Two lanes have a band in the same location, even though one of the bands is barely visible and the other is extremely dark. The fourth lane has a faint band located below the bands in the other lanes.

Biologists use a technique called differential centrifugation to isolate specific cell components. Differential centrifugation is based on breaking cells apart to create a complex mixture and then separating components in a centrifuge. A centrifuge accomplishes this task by spinning cells in a solution that allows molecules and other cell components to separate according to their density or size and shape. The individual parts of the cell can then be purified and studied in detail, in isolation from other parts of the cell.

The first step in preparing a cell sample for centrifugation is to release the cell components by breaking the cells apart. This can be done by putting them in a hypotonic solution, by exposing them to high-frequency vibration, by treating cells with a detergent, or by grinding them up. Each of these methods breaks apart plasma membranes and releases the contents of the cells.

The resulting pieces of plasma membrane quickly reseal to form small vesicles, often trapping cell components inside. The solution that results from the homogenization step is a mixture of these vesicles, free-floating macromolecules released from the cells, and organelles. A solution like this is called a cell extract or cell homogenate.

When a cell homogenate is placed in a centrifuge tube and spun at high speed, the components that are in solution tend to move outward, along the red arrow in **FIGURE B10.1a**. The effect is similar to a merry-go-round, which seems to push you outward in a straight line away from the spinning platform. In response to this outward-directed force, the cell homogenate exerts a centripetal (literally, "center-seeking") force that pushes the homogenate away from the bottom of the tube. Larger, denser molecules or particles resist this inward force more readily than do smaller, less dense ones and so reach the bottom of the centrifuge tube faster.

To separate the components of a cell extract, researchers often perform a series of centrifuge runs. Steps 1 and 2 of

(a) How a centrifuge works

When the centrifuge spins, the macromolecules tend to move toward the bottom of the centrifuge tube (red arrow)

The solution in the tube exerts a centripetal force, which resists movement of the molecules to the bottom of the tube (blue arrow)

Very large or dense molecules overcome the centripetal force more readily than smaller, less dense ones. As a result, larger, denser molecules move toward the bottom of the tube faster.

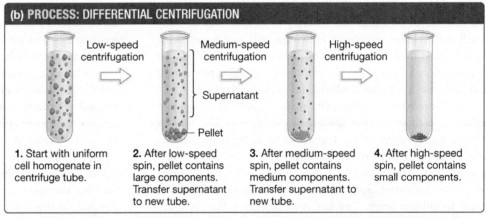

(b) PROCESS: DIFFERENTIAL CENTRIFUGATION

Low-speed centrifugation → Medium-speed centrifugation → High-speed centrifugation

Supernatant

Pellet

1. Start with uniform cell homogenate in centrifuge tube.

2. After low-speed spin, pellet contains large components. Transfer supernatant to new tube.

3. After medium-speed spin, pellet contains medium components. Transfer supernatant to new tube.

4. After high-speed spin, pellet contains small components.

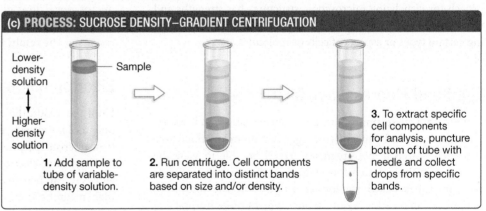

(c) PROCESS: SUCROSE DENSITY–GRADIENT CENTRIFUGATION

Lower-density solution

Higher-density solution

Sample

1. Add sample to tube of variable-density solution.

2. Run centrifuge. Cell components are separated into distinct bands based on size and/or density.

3. To extract specific cell components for analysis, puncture bottom of tube with needle and collect drops from specific bands.

FIGURE B10.1 Cell Components Can Be Separated by Centrifugation. (a) The forces inside a centrifuge tube allow cell components to be separated. **(b)** Through a series of centrifuge runs made at increasingly higher speeds, an investigator can separate fractions of a cell homogenate by size via differential centrifugation. **(c)** A high-speed centrifuge run can achieve extremely fine separation among cell components by sucrose density–gradient centrifugation.

FIGURE B10.1b illustrate how an initial treatment at low speed causes larger, heavier parts of the homogenate to move below smaller, lighter parts. The material that collects at the bottom of the tube is called the pellet, and the solution and solutes left behind form the supernatant ("above-swimming"). The supernatant is placed in a fresh tube and centrifuged at increasingly higher speeds and longer durations. Each centrifuge run continues to separate cell components based on their size and density.

To accomplish separation of macromolecules or organelles, researchers frequently follow up with centrifugation at extremely high speeds. One strategy is based on filling the centrifuge tube with a series of sucrose solutions of increasing density (**FIGURE B10.1c**). The density gradient allows cell components to separate on the basis of small differences in size, shape, and density. When the centrifuge run is complete, each cell component occupies a distinct band of material in the tube, based on how quickly each component moves through the increasingly

dense gradient of sucrose solution during the centrifuge run. A researcher can then collect the material in each band for further study.

BIOSKILL 11 biological imaging: microscopy and x-ray crystallography

A lot of biology happens at levels that can't be detected with the naked eye. Biologists use an array of microscopes to study small multicellular organisms, individual cells, and the contents of cells. And to understand what individual macromolecules or macromolecular machines like ribosomes look like, researchers use data from a technique called X-ray crystallography.

You'll probably use dissecting microscopes and compound light microscopes to view specimens during your labs for this course, and throughout this text you'll be seeing images generated from other types of microscopy and from X-ray crystallographic data. Among the fundamental skills you'll be acquiring as an introductory student, then, is a basic understanding of how these techniques work. The key is to recognize that each approach for visualizing microscopic structures has strengths and weaknesses. As a result, each technique is appropriate for studying certain types or aspects of cells or molecules.

Light and Fluorescence Microscopy

If you use a dissecting microscope during labs, you'll recognize that it works by magnifying light that bounces off a whole specimen—often a live organism. You'll be able to view the specimen in three dimensions, which is why these instruments are sometimes called stereomicroscopes, but the maximum magnification possible is only about 20 to 40 times normal size (20× to 40×).

To view smaller objects, you'll probably use a compound microscope. Compound microscopes magnify light that is passed *through* a specimen. The instruments used in introductory labs are usually capable of 400× magnifications; the most sophisticated

compound microscopes available can achieve magnifications of about 2000×. This is enough to view individual bacterial or eukaryotic cells and see large structures inside cells, like condensed chromosomes (see Chapter 12). To prepare a specimen for viewing under a compound light microscope, the tissues or cells are usually sliced to create a section thin enough for light to pass through efficiently. The section is then dyed to increase contrast and make structures visible. In many cases, different types of dyes are used to highlight different types of structures.

To visualize specific proteins, researchers use a technique called immunostaining. After preparing tissues or cells for viewing, the specimen is stained with fluorescently tagged antibodies. In this case, the cells are viewed under a fluorescence microscope. Ultraviolet or other wavelengths of light are passed through the specimen. The fluorescing tag emits visible light in response. The result? Beautiful cells that glow green, red, or blue.

Electron Microscopy

Until the 1950s, the compound microscope was the biologist's only tool for viewing cells directly. But the invention of the electron microscope provided a new way to view specimens. Two basic types of electron microscopy are now available: one that allows researchers to examine cross sections of cells at extremely high magnification, and one that offers a view of surfaces at somewhat lower magnification.

Transmission Electron Microscopy

The transmission electron microscope (TEM) is an extraordinarily effective tool for viewing cell structure at high magnification. TEM forms an image from electrons that pass through a specimen, just as a light microscope forms an image from light rays that pass through a specimen.

Biologists who want to view a cell under a transmission electron microscope begin by "fixing" the cell, meaning that they treat it with a chemical agent that stabilizes the cell's structure and contents while disturbing them as little as possible. Then the researcher permeates the cell with an epoxy plastic that stiffens the structure. Once this epoxy hardens, the cell can be cut into extremely thin sections with a glass or diamond knife. Finally, the sectioned specimens are impregnated with a metal—often lead. (The reason for this last step is explained shortly.)

FIGURE B11.1a outlines how the transmission electron microscope works. A beam of electrons is produced by a tungsten filament at the top of a column and directed downward. (All of the air is pumped out of the column, so that the electron beam isn't scattered by collisions with air molecules.) The electron beam passes through a series of lenses and through the specimen. The lenses are actually electromagnets, which alter the path of the beam much like a glass lens in a dissecting or compound microscope bends light. The electromagnet lenses magnify and focus the image on a screen at the bottom of the column. There the electrons strike a coating of fluorescent crystals, which emit visible light in response—just like a television screen. When the microscopist moves the screen out of the way and allows the electrons to expose a sheet of black-and-white film or to be detected by a digital camera, the result is a micrograph—a photograph of an image produced by microscopy.

The image itself is created by electrons that pass through the specimen. If no specimen were in place, all the electrons would pass through and the screen (and micrograph) would be uniformly bright. Unfortunately, cell materials by themselves would also appear fairly uniform and bright. This is because an atom's ability to deflect an electron depends on its mass. In turn, an atom's mass is a function of its atomic number. The hydrogen, carbon, oxygen, and nitrogen atoms that dominate biological molecules have low atomic numbers. This is why cell biologists must saturate cell sections with lead solutions. Lead has a high atomic number and scatters electrons effectively. Different macromolecules take up lead atoms in different amounts, so the metal acts as a "stain" that produces contrast. With TEM, areas of dense metal scatter the electron beam most, producing dark areas in micrographs.

The advantage of TEM is that it can magnify objects up to 250,000×—meaning that intracellular structures are clearly visible. The downsides are that researchers are restricted to observing dead, sectioned material, and they must take care that the preparation process does not distort the specimen.

Scanning Electron Microscopy

The scanning electron microscope (SEM) is the most useful tool biologists have for looking at the surfaces of structures. Materials are prepared for scanning electron microscopy by coating their surfaces with a layer of metal atoms. To create an image of this surface, the microscope scans the surface with a narrow beam of electrons. Electrons that are reflected back from the surface or that are emitted by the metal atoms in response to the beam then strike a detector. The signal from the detector controls a second electron beam, which scans a TV-like screen and forms an image magnified up to 50,000 times the object's size.

Because SEM records shadows and highlights, it provides images with a three-dimensional appearance (**FIGURE B11.1b**). It cannot magnify objects nearly as much as TEM can, however.

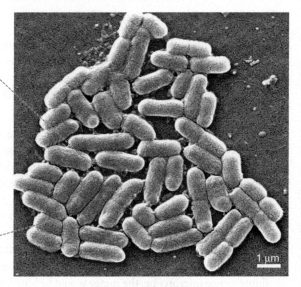

(a) Transmission electron microscopy: High magnification of cross sections

Tungsten filament (source of electrons)

Condenser lens

Specimen

Objective lens

Projector lens

Image on fluorescent screen

0.2 μm

Cross section of *E. coli* bacterium

(b) Scanning electron microscopy: Lower magnification of surfaces

1 μm

Surface view of *E. coli* bacteria

FIGURE B11.1 There Are Two Basic Types of Electron Microscopy.

Studying Live Cells and Real-Time Processes

Until the 1960s, biologists were unable to get clear, high-magnification images of living cells. But a series of innovations over the past 50 years has made it possible to observe organelles and subcellular structures in action.

The development of video microscopy, where the image from a light microscope is captured by a video camera instead of by an eye or a film camera, proved revolutionary. It allowed specimens to be viewed at higher magnification, because video cameras are more sensitive to small differences in contrast than are the human eye or still cameras. It also made it easier to keep live specimens functioning normally, because the increased light sensitivity of video cameras allows them to be used with low illumination, so specimens don't overheat. And when it became possible to digitize video images, researchers began using computers to remove out-of-focus background material and increase image clarity.

A more recent innovation was the use of a fluorescent molecule called green fluorescent protein, or GFP, which allows researchers to tag specific molecules or structures and follow their movement in live cells over time. This was a major advance over immunostaining, in which cells have to be fixed. GFP is naturally synthesized in jellyfish that fluoresce, or emit light. By affixing GFP to another protein (using genetic engineering techniques described in Chapter 20) and then inserting it into a live cell, investigators can follow the protein's fate over time and even videotape its movement. For example, researchers have videotaped GFP-tagged proteins being transported from the rough ER through the Golgi apparatus and out to the plasma membrane. This is cell biology: the movie.

GFP's influence has been so profound that the researchers who developed its use in microscopy were awarded the 2008 Nobel Prize in Chemistry.

Visualizing Structures in 3-D

The world is three-dimensional. To understand how microscopic structures and macromolecules work, it is essential to understand their shape and spatial relationships. Consider three techniques currently being used to reconstruct the 3-D structure of cells, organelles, and macromolecules.

- *Confocal microscopy* is carried out by mounting cells that have been treated with one or more fluorescing tags on a microscope slide and then focusing a beam of ultraviolet or other wavelengths of light at a specific depth within the specimen. The fluorescing tag emits visible light in response. A detector for this light is then set up at exactly the position where the emitted light comes into focus. The result is a sharp image of a precise plane in the cell being studied (**FIGURE B11.2a**). Note that if you viewed the same specimen under a conventional fluorescence microscope, the image would be blurry because it results from light emitted by the entire cell (**FIGURE B11.2b**). By altering the focal plane, a researcher can record images from

(a) Confocal fluorescence image of single cell

(b) Conventional fluorescence image of same cell

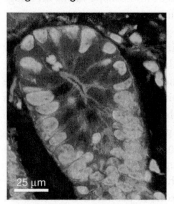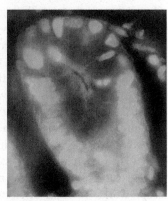

25 μm

FIGURE B11.2 Confocal Microscopy Provides Sharp Images of Living Cells. (a) The confocal image of this mouse intestinal cell is sharp, because it results from light emitted at a single plane inside the cell. **(b)** The conventional image of this same cell is blurred, because it results from light emitted by the entire cell.

an array of depths in the specimen; a computer can then be used to generate a 3-D image of the cell.

- *Electron tomography* uses a transmission electron microscope to generate a 3-D image of an organelle or other subcellular structure. The specimen is rotated around a single axis while the researcher takes many "snapshots." The individual images are then pieced together with a computer. This technique has provided a much more accurate view of mitochondrial structure than was possible using traditional TEM (see Chapter 7).

- *X-ray crystallography, or X-ray diffraction analysis*, is the most widely used technique for reconstructing the 3-D structure of molecules. As its name implies, the procedure is based on bombarding crystals of a molecule with X-rays. X-rays are scattered in precise ways when they interact with the electrons surrounding the atoms in a crystal, producing a diffraction pattern that can be recorded on X-ray film or other types of detectors (**FIGURE B11.3**). By varying the orientation of the X-ray beam as it strikes a crystal and documenting the

check your understanding

If you understand BioSkill 11

✔ You should be able to . . .

1. Interpret whether the absence of mitochondria in a transmission electron micrograph of a cancerous human liver means that the cell lacks mitochondria.

2. Explain why the effort to understand the structure of biological molecules is worthwhile even though X-ray crystallography is time consuming and technically difficult. What's the payoff?

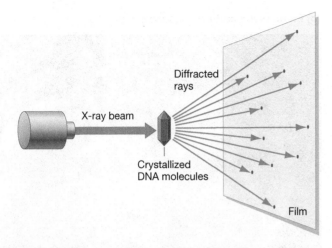

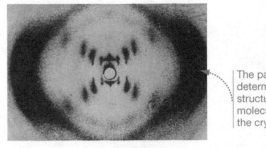

The patterns are determined by the structure of the molecules within the crystal

FIGURE B11.3 X-Ray Crystallography. When crystallized molecules are bombarded with X-rays, the radiation is scattered in distinctive patterns. The photograph at the right shows an X-ray film that recorded the pattern of scattered radiation from DNA molecules.

diffraction patterns that result, researchers can construct a map representing the density of electrons in the crystal. By relating these electron-density maps to information about the primary structure of the nucleic acid or protein, a 3-D model of the molecule can be built. Virtually all of the molecular models used in this book were built from X-ray crystallographic data.

BIOSKILL 12 cell and tissue culture methods

For researchers, there are important advantages to growing plant and animal cells and tissues outside the organism itself. Cell and tissue cultures provide large populations of a single type of cell or tissue and the opportunity to control experimental conditions precisely.

Animal Cell Culture

The first successful attempt to culture animal cells occurred in 1907, when a researcher cultivated amphibian nerve cells in a drop of fluid from the spinal cord. But it was not until the 1950s and 1960s that biologists could routinely culture plant and animal cells in the laboratory. The long lag time was due to the difficulty of re-creating conditions that exist in the intact organism precisely enough for cells to grow normally.

To grow in culture, animal cells must be provided with a liquid mixture containing the nutrients, vitamins, and hormones that stimulate growth. Initially, this mixture was serum, the liquid portion of blood; now, serum-free media are available for certain cell types. Serum-free media are preferred because they are much more precisely defined chemically than serum.

In addition, many types of animal cells will not grow in culture unless they are provided with a solid surface that mimics the types of surfaces that enable cells in the intact organisms to adhere. As a result, cells are typically cultured in flasks (**FIGURE B12.1a**, left; see B:22).

Even under optimal conditions, though, normal cells display a finite life span in culture. In contrast, many cultured cancerous cells grow indefinitely. This characteristic correlates with a key feature of cancerous cells in organisms: Their growth is continuous and uncontrolled.

Because of their immortality and relative ease of growth, cultured cancer cells are commonly used in research on basic aspects of cell structure and function. For example, the first human cell type to be grown in culture was isolated in 1951 from a malignant tumor of the uterine cervix. These cells are called HeLa cells in honor of their donor, Henrietta Lacks, who died soon thereafter from her cancer. HeLa cells continue to grow in laboratories around the world (Figure B12.1a, right).

Plant Tissue Culture

Certain cells found in plants are totipotent—meaning that they retain the ability to divide and differentiate into a complete, mature plant, including new types of tissue. These cells, called parenchyma cells, are important in wound healing and asexual reproduction. But they also allow researchers to grow complete adult plants in the laboratory, starting with a small number of parenchyma cells.

Biologists who grow plants in tissue culture begin by placing parenchyma cells in a liquid or solid medium containing all the

(a) Animal cell culture: immortal HeLa cancer cells

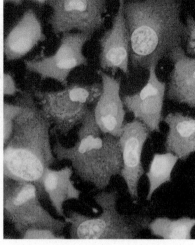

(b) Plant tissue culture: tobacco callus

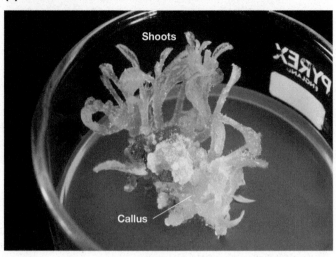

FIGURE B12.1 Animal and Plant Cells Can Be Grown in the Lab.

nutrients required for cell maintenance and growth. In the early days of plant tissue culture, investigators found not only that specific growth signals called hormones were required for successful growth and differentiation but also that the relative abundance of hormones present was critical to success.

The earliest experiments on hormone interactions in tissue cultures were done with tobacco cells in the 1950s by Folke Skoog and co-workers. These researchers found that when the hormone called auxin was added to the culture by itself, the cells enlarged but did not divide. But if the team added roughly equal amounts of auxin and another growth signal called cytokinin to the cells, the cells began to divide and eventually formed a callus, or an undifferentiated mass of parenchyma cells.

By varying the proportion of auxin to cytokinins in different parts of the callus and through time, the team could stimulate the growth and differentiation of root and shoot systems and produce whole new plants (**FIGURE B12.1b**). A high ratio of auxin to cytokinin led to the differentiation of a root system, while a high ratio of cytokinin to auxin led to the development of a shoot system. Eventually Skoog's team was able to produce a complete plant from just one parenchyma cell.

The ability to grow whole new plants in tissue culture from just one cell has been instrumental in the development of genetic engineering (see Chapter 20). Researchers insert recombinant genes into target cells, test the cells to identify those that successfully express the recombinant genes, and then use tissue culture techniques to grow those cells into adult individuals with a novel genotype and phenotype.

check your understanding

If you understand BioSkill 12

✔ **You should be able to . . .**

1. Identify a limitation of how experiments on HeLa cells are interpreted.

2. State a disadvantage of doing experiments on plants that have been propagated from single cells growing in tissue culture.

Research in biological science starts with a question. In most cases, the question is inspired by an observation about a cell or an organism. To answer it, biologists have to study a particular species. Study organisms are called model organisms, because investigators hope that they serve as a model for what is going on in a wide array of species.

Model organisms are chosen because they are convenient to study and because they have attributes that make them appropriate for the particular research proposed. They tend to have some common characteristics:

- **Short generation time and rapid reproduction** This trait is important because it makes it possible to produce offspring quickly and perform many experiments in a short amount of time—you don't have to wait long for individuals to grow.

- **Large numbers of offspring** This trait is particularly important in genetics, where many offspring phenotypes and genotypes need to be assessed to get a large sample size.

- **Small size, simple feeding and habitat requirements** These attributes make it relatively cheap and easy to maintain individuals in the lab.

The following notes highlight just a few model organisms supporting current work in biological science.

Escherichia coli

Of all model organisms in biology, perhaps none has been more important than the bacterium *Escherichia coli*—a common inhabitant of the human gut. The strain that is most commonly worked on today, called K-12 (**FIGURE B13.1a**; see B:24), was originally isolated from a hospital patient in 1922.

During the last half of the twentieth century, key results in molecular biology originated in studies of *E. coli*. These results include the discovery of enzymes such as DNA polymerase, RNA polymerase, DNA repair enzymes, and restriction endonucleases; the elucidation of ribosome structure and function; and the initial characterization of promoters, regulatory transcription factors, regulatory sites in DNA, and operons. In many cases, initial discoveries made in *E. coli* allowed researchers to confirm that homologous enzymes and processes existed in an array of organisms, often ranging from other bacteria to yeast, mice, and humans.

The success of *E. coli* as a model for other species inspired Jacques Monod's claim that "Once we understand the biology of *Escherichia coli*, we will understand the biology of an elephant." The genome of *E. coli* K-12 was sequenced in 1997, and the strain continues to be a workhorse in studies of gene function, biochemistry, and particularly biotechnology. Much remains to

be learned, however. Despite over 60 years of intensive study, the function of about a third of the *E. coli* genome is still unknown.

In the lab, *E. coli* is usually grown in suspension culture, where cells are introduced to a liquid nutrient medium, or on plates containing agar—a gelatinous mix of polysaccharides. Under optimal growing conditions—meaning before cells begin to get crowded and compete for space and nutrients—a cell takes just 30 minutes on average to grow and divide. At this rate, a single cell can produce a population of over a million descendants in just 10 hours. Except for new mutations, all of the descendant cells are genetically identical.

Dictyostelium discoideum

The cellular slime mold *Dictyostelium discoideum* is not always slimy, and it is not a mold—meaning a type of fungus. Instead, it is an amoeba. Amoeba is a general term that biologists use to characterize a unicellular eukaryote that lacks a cell wall and is extremely flexible in shape. *Dictyostelium* has long fascinated biologists because it is a social organism. Independent cells sometimes aggregate to form a multicellular structure.

Under most conditions, *Dictyostelium* cells are haploid (n) and move about in decaying vegetation on forest floors or other habitats. They feed on bacteria by engulfing them whole. When these cells reproduce, they can do so sexually by fusing with another cell then undergoing meiosis, or asexually by mitosis, which is more common. If food begins to run out, the cells begin to aggregate. In many cases, tens of thousands of cells cohere to form a 2-mm-long mass called a slug (**FIGURE B13.1b**). (This is not the slug that is related to snails.)

After migrating to a sunlit location, the slug stops and individual cells differentiate according to their position in the slug. Some form a stalk; others form a mass of spores at the tip of the stalk. (A spore is a single cell that develops into an adult organism, but it is not formed from gamete fusion like a zygote is.) The entire structure, stalk plus mass of spores, is called a fruiting body. Cells that form spores secrete a tough coat and represent a durable resting stage. The fruiting body eventually dries out, and the wind disperses the spores to new locations, where more food might be available.

Dictyostelium has been an important model organism for investigating questions about eukaryotes:

- Cells in a slug are initially identical in morphology but then differentiate into distinctive stalk cells and spores. Studying this process helped biologists better understand how cells in plant and animal embryos differentiate into distinct cell types.

(a) Bacterium *Escherichia coli* (strain K-12)

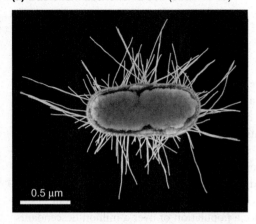

0.5 μm

(b) Slime mold *Dictyostelium discoideum*

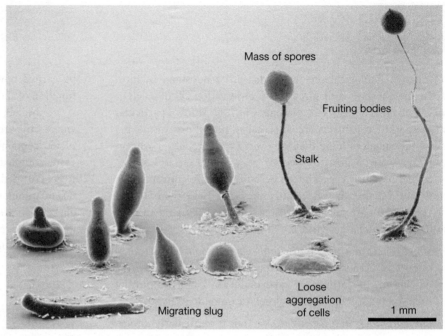

Mass of spores

Fruiting bodies

Stalk

Migrating slug

Loose aggregation of cells

1 mm

(c) Thale cress *Arabidopsis thaliana*

5 cm

(e) Fruit fly *Drosophila melanogaster*

0.5 mm

(f) Roundworm *Caenorhabditis elegans*

0.1 mm

(d) Yeast *Saccharomyces cerevisiae*

5 μm

(g) Mouse *Mus musculus*

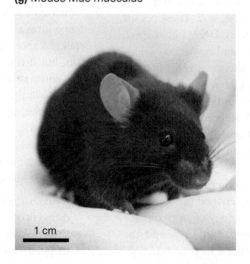

1 cm

FIGURE B13.1 Model Organisms.

✔ **QUESTION** *E. coli* is grown at a temperature of 37°C. Why?

- The process of slug formation has helped biologists study how animal cells move and how they aggregate as they form specific types of tissues.
- When *Dictyostelium* cells aggregate to form a slug, they stick to each other. The discovery of membrane proteins responsible for cell–cell adhesion helped biologists understand some of the general principles of multicellular life (highlighted in Chapter 11).

Arabidopsis thaliana

In the early days of biology, the best-studied plants were agricultural varieties such as maize (corn), rice, and garden peas. When biologists began to unravel the mechanisms responsible for oxygenic photosynthesis in the early to mid-1900s, they relied on green algae that were relatively easy to grow and manipulate in the lab—often the unicellular species *Chlamydomonas reinhardii*—as an experimental subject.

Although crop plants and green algae continue to be the subject of considerable research, a new model organism emerged in the 1980s and now serves as the preeminent experimental subject in plant biology. That organism is *Arabidopsis thaliana*, commonly known as thale cress or wall cress (**FIGURE B13.1c**).

Arabidopsis is a member of the mustard family, or Brassicaceae, so it is closely related to radishes and broccoli. In nature it is a weed—meaning a species that is adapted to thrive in habitats where soils have been disturbed.

One of the most attractive aspects of working with *Arabidopsis* is that individuals can grow from a seed into a mature, seed-producing plant in just four to six weeks. Several other attributes make it an effective subject for study: It has just five chromosomes, has a relatively small genome with limited numbers of repetitive sequences, can self-fertilize as well as undergo cross-fertilization, can be grown in a relatively small amount of space and with a minimum of care in the greenhouse, and produces up to 10,000 seeds per individual per generation.

Arabidopsis has been instrumental in a variety of studies in plant molecular genetics and development, and it is increasingly popular in ecological and evolutionary studies. In addition, the entire genome of the species has now been sequenced, and studies have benefited from the development of an international "*Arabidopsis* community"—a combination of informal and formal associations of investigators who work on *Arabidopsis* and use regular meetings, e-mail, and the Internet to share data, techniques, and seed stocks.

Saccharomyces cerevisiae

When biologists want to answer basic questions about how eukaryotic cells work, they often turn to the yeast *Saccharomyces cerevisiae*.

S. cerevisiae is unicellular and relatively easy to culture and manipulate in the lab (**FIGURE B13.1d**). In good conditions, yeast cells grow and divide almost as rapidly as bacteria. As a result, the species has become the organism of choice for experiments on control of the cell cycle and regulation of gene expression in eukaryotes. For example, research has confirmed that several of the genes controlling cell division and DNA repair in yeast have homologs in humans; and when mutated, these genes contribute to cancer. Strains of yeast that carry these mutations are now being used to test drugs that might be effective against cancer.

S. cerevisiae has become even more important in efforts to interpret the genomes of organisms like rice, mice, zebrafish, and humans. It is much easier to investigate the function of particular genes in *S. cerevisiae* by creating mutants or transferring specific alleles among individuals than it is to do the same experiments in mice or zebrafish. Once the function of a gene has been established in yeast, biologists can look for the homologous gene in other eukaryotes. If such a gene exists, they can usually infer that it has a function similar to its role in *S. cerevisiae*. It was also the first eukaryote with a completely sequenced genome.

Drosophila melanogaster

If you walk into a biology building on any university campus around the world, you are almost certain to find at least one lab where the fruit fly *Drosophila melanogaster* is being studied (**FIGURE B13.1e**).

Drosophila has been a key experimental subject in genetics since the early 1900s. It was initially chosen as a focus for study by T. H. Morgan, because it can be reared in the laboratory easily and inexpensively, matings can be arranged, the life cycle is completed in less than two weeks, and females lay a large number of eggs. These traits made fruit flies valuable subjects for breeding experiments designed to test hypotheses about how traits are transmitted from parents to offspring (see Chapter 14).

More recently, *Drosophila* has also become a key model organism in the field of developmental biology. The use of flies in developmental studies was inspired largely by the work of Christianne Nüsslein-Volhard and Eric Wieschaus, who in the 1980s isolated flies with genetic defects in early embryonic development. By investigating the nature of these defects, researchers have gained valuable insights into how various gene products influence the development of eukaryotes (see Chapter 22). The complete genome sequence of *Drosophila* has been available to investigators since the year 2000.

Caenorhabditis elegans

The roundworm *Caenorhabditis elegans* emerged as a model organism in developmental biology in the 1970s, due largely to work by Sydney Brenner and colleagues. (*Caenorhabditis* is pronounced *see-no-rab-DIE-tiss*.)

C. elegans was chosen for three reasons: (**1**) Its cuticle (soft outer layer) is transparent, making individual cells relatively easy to observe (**FIGURE B13.1f**); (**2**) adults have exactly 959 nonreproductive cells; and, most important, (**3**) the fate of each cell in an embryo can be predicted because cell fates are invariant among individuals. For example, when researchers examine a 33-cell *C. elegans* embryo, they know exactly which of the 959 cells in the adult will be derived from each of those 33 embryonic cells.

In addition, *C. elegans* are small (less than 1 mm long), are able to self-fertilize or cross-fertilize, and undergo early development in just 16 hours. The entire genome of *C. elegans* has now been sequenced.

Mus musculus

The house mouse *Mus musculus* is the most important model organism among mammals. For this reason, it is especially prominent in biomedical research, where researchers need to work on individuals with strong genetic and developmental similarities to humans.

The house mouse was an intelligent choice of model organism in mammals because it is small and thus relatively inexpensive to maintain in captivity, and because it breeds rapidly. A litter can contain 10 offspring, and generation time is only 12 weeks—meaning that several generations can be produced in a year. Descendants of wild house mice have been selected for docility and other traits that make them easy to handle and rear; these populations are referred to as laboratory mice (**FIGURE B13.1g**).

Some of the most valuable laboratory mice are strains with distinctive, well-characterized genotypes. Inbred strains are

virtually homogenous genetically (see Chapter 26) and are useful in experiments where gene-by-gene or gene-by-environment interactions have to be controlled. Other populations carry mutations that knock out genes and cause diseases similar to those observed in humans. These individuals are useful for identifying the cause of genetic diseases and testing drugs or other types of therapies.

BIOSKILL 14 — primary literature and peer review

As part of the process of doing science, biologists communicate their results to the scientific community through publications in scientific journals that report on their original research discoveries (see Chapter 1). These published reports are referred to, interchangeably, as the primary literature, research papers, or primary research articles.

What Is the Primary Literature?

Scientists publish "peer-reviewed" papers. This means that several experts in the field have carefully read the paper and considered its strengths and weaknesses. Reviewers write a critique of the paper and make a recommendation to the journal editor as to whether the paper should be published. Often reviewers will suggest additional experiments that need to be completed before a paper is considered acceptable for publication. The peer review process means that research discoveries are carefully vetted before they go to press.

A primary research paper can be distinguished from secondary sources—such as review articles, textbooks, and magazine articles—by looking for key characteristics. A primary research paper includes a detailed description of methods and results,

written by the researchers who did the work. A typical paper contains a Title, Abstract, Introduction, Materials and Methods (or Experimental Design), Results and Discussion (**Table B14.1**), although the order and name of the sections varies among journals.

Getting Started

At first, trying to read the primary literature may seem like a daunting task. A paper may be peppered with unfamiliar terms and acronyms. If you tried to read a research paper from start to finish, like you might read a chapter in this textbook, it would be a frustrating experience. But, with practice, the scientific literature becomes approachable, and it is well worth the effort. The primary literature is the cutting edge, the place to read firsthand about the process of doing science. Becoming skilled at reading and evaluating scientific reports is a powerful way to learn how to think critically—to think like a biologist.

To get started, try breaking down reading the primary research article into a series of steps:

1. Read the authors' names. Where are they from? Are they working as a team or alone? After delving into the literature,

TABLE B14.1 Sections of a Primary Research Paper

Section	Characteristics
Title	Short, succinct, eye-catching
Abstract	Summary of Methods, Results, Discussion. Explains why the research was done and why the results are significant.
Introduction	Background information (what past work was done, why the work was important). States the objectives and hypotheses of the study and explains why the study is important.
Materials and Methods	Explains how the work was done and where it was done.
Results	Explains what the data show.
Discussion	Explains why the data show what they show, how the analysis relates to the objectives from the Introduction, and the significance of findings and how they advance the field.

certain familiar names will crop up again and again. You'll begin to recognize the experts in a particular field.

2. Read the title. It should summarize the key finding of the paper and tell you what you can expect to learn from the paper.

3. Read the abstract. The abstract summarizes the entire paper in a short paragraph. At this point, it might be tempting to stop reading. But sometimes authors understate or overstate the significance and conclusions of their work. You should never cite an article as a reference after having read only the abstract.

4. Read the Introduction. The first couple of paragraphs should make it clear what the objectives or hypotheses of the paper are; the remaining paragraphs will give you the background information you need to understand the point of the paper.

5. Flip through the article and look at the figures, illustrations, and tables, including reading the legends.

6. Read the Results section carefully. Ask yourself these questions: Do the results accurately describe the data presented in the paper? Were all the appropriate controls carried out in an experiment? Are there additional experiments that you think should have been performed? Are the figures and tables clearly labeled?

7. Consult the Materials and Methods section to help understand the research design and the techniques used.

8. Read the Discussion. The first and last paragraphs usually summarize the key findings and state their significance. The Discussion is the part of the paper where the results are explained in the context of the scientific literature. The authors should explain what their results mean.

Getting Practice

The best way to get practice is to start reading the scientific literature as often as possible. You could begin by reading some of the references cited in this textbook. You can get an electronic copy of most articles through online databases such as PubMed, ScienceDirect, or Google Scholar, or through your institution's library.

After reading a primary research paper, you should be able to paraphrase the significance of the paper in a few sentences, free of technical jargon. You should also be able to both praise and criticize several points of the paper. As you become more familiar with reading the scientific literature, you're likely to start thinking about what questions remain to be answered. And, you may even come up with "the next experiment."

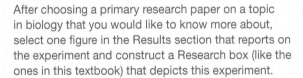

check your understanding

If you understand BioSkill 14

✔ **You should be able to . . .**

After choosing a primary research paper on a topic in biology that you would like to know more about, select one figure in the Results section that reports on the experiment and construct a Research box (like the ones in this textbook) that depicts this experiment.

A concept map is a graphical device for organizing and expressing what you know about a topic. It has two main elements: **(1)** concepts that are identified by words or short phrases and placed in a box or circle, and **(2)** labeled arrows that physically link two concepts and explain the relationship between them. The concepts are arranged hierarchically on a page with the most general concepts at the top and the most specific ideas at the bottom.

The combination of a concept, a linking word, and a second concept is called a proposition. Good concept maps also have cross-links—meaning, labeled arrows that connect different elements in the hierarchy as you read down the page.

Concept maps, initially developed by Joseph Novak in the early 1970s, have proven to be an effective studying and learning tool. They can be particularly valuable if constructed by a group, or when different individuals exchange and critique concept maps they have created independently. Although concept maps vary widely in quality and can be graded using objective criteria, there are many equally valid ways of making a high-quality concept map on a particular topic.

When you are asked to make a concept map in this text, you will usually be given at least a partial list of concepts to use. As an example, suppose you were asked to create a concept map on experimental design and were given the following concepts: results, predictions, control treatment, experimental treatment, controlled (identical) conditions, conclusions, experiment, hypothesis to be tested, null hypothesis. One possible concept map is shown in **FIGURE B15.1**.

Good concept maps have four qualities:

1. They exhibit an organized hierarchy, indicating how each concept on the map relates to larger and smaller concepts.

2. The concept words are specific—not vague.

3. The propositions are accurate.

4. There is cross-linking between different elements in the hierarchy of concepts.

As you practice making concept maps, go through these criteria and use them to evaluate your own work as well as the work of fellow students.

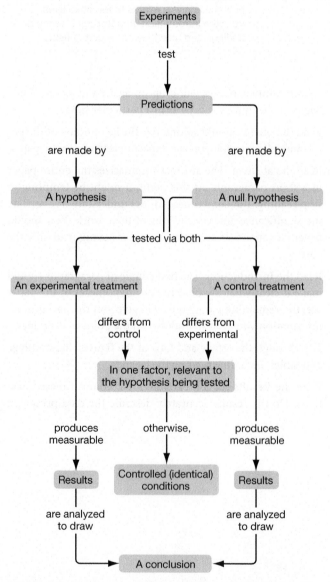

FIGURE B15.1 A Concept Map on Principles of Experimental Design.

check your understanding

If you understand BioSkill 15
✔ **You should be able to . . .**

1. Add an "Alternative hypothesis" concept to the map in Figure B15.1, along with other concepts and labeled linking arrows needed to indicate its relationship to other information on the map. (Hint: Recall that investigators often contrast a hypothesis being tested with an alternative hypothesis that does not qualify as a null hypothesis.)

2. Add a box for the concept "Statistical testing" (see **BIOSKILLS 4**) along with appropriately labeled linking arrows.

Most students have at one time or another wondered why a particular question on an exam seemed so hard, while others seemed easy. The explanation lies in the type of cognitive skills required to answer the question. Let's take a closer look.

Categories of Human Cognition

Bloom's Taxonomy is a classification system that instructors use to identify the cognitive skill levels at which they are asking students to work, particularly on practice problems and exams. Bloom's Taxonomy is also a very useful tool for students to know—it can help you to figure out the appropriate level at which you should be studying to succeed in a course.

Bloom's Taxonomy distinguishes six different categories of human thinking: remember, understand, apply, analyze, evaluate, and create. One of the most useful distinctions lies not in the differences among the six categories, but rather in the difference between high-order cognitive (HOC) and low-order cognitive (LOC) skills. **FIGURE B16.1** shows how the different levels of the taxonomy can be broken into HOC and LOC skills.

Skills that hallmark LOCs include recall, explanation, or application of knowledge in the exact way that you have before (remember, understand, apply), while skills that typify HOCs include the application of knowledge in a new way, as well as the breakdown, critique, or creation of information (analyze, evaluate, and create). Most college instructors will assume students are proficient at solving LOC questions and will expect you to frequently work at the HOC levels. HOC problems usually require use of basic vocabulary and applying knowledge—working at this level helps students to master the LOC levels.

Six Study Steps to Success

Bloom's Taxonomy provides a useful guide for preparing for an exam, using the following six steps:

1. *Answer in-chapter questions while reading the chapter.* All questions in this book have been assigned Bloom's levels, so you can review the question answers and the Bloom's level while you study.

2. *Identify the Bloom's level(s) of the questions that you are having greatest difficulty answering.* While working through

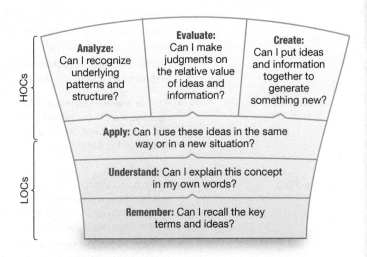

FIGURE B16.1 Bloom's Taxonomy.

the text, take note of the content and Bloom's level(s) that you find the most challenging.

3. *Use the Bloom's Taxonomy Study Guide* (**Table B16.1;** see **B:30**) *to focus your study efforts at the appropriate Bloom's level.* Table B16.1 lists specific study methods that can help you practice your understanding of the material at both the LOC and HOC levels, whether you are studying alone or with a study group.

4. *Complete the end-of-chapter questions as if you're taking an exam, without looking for the answers.* If you look at the chapter text or jump to the answers, then you really aren't testing your ability to work with the content and have reduced the questions to the lowest Bloom's level of remember.

5. *Grade your answers and note the Bloom's level of the questions you got wrong.* At what level of Bloom's Taxonomy were the questions you missed?

6. *Use the Bloom's Taxonomy Study Guide to focus your study efforts at the appropriate Bloom's level.* If you missed a lot of questions, then spend more time studying the material and find other resources for quizzing yourself.

By following these steps and studying at the HOC levels, you should succeed in answering questions on in-class exams.

	Individual Study Activities	Group Study Activities
Create (HOC) Generate something new	• Generate a hypothesis or design an experiment based on information you are studying • Create a model based on a given data set • Create summary sheets that show how facts and concepts relate to each other • Create questions at each level of Bloom's Taxonomy as a practice test and then take the test	• Each student puts forward a hypothesis about biological process and designs an experiment to test it. Peers critique the hypotheses and experiments • Create a new model/summary sheet/concept map that integrates each group member's ideas
Evaluate (HOC) Defend or judge a concept or idea	• Provide a written assessment of the strengths and weaknesses of your peers' work or understanding of a given concept based on previously determined criteria	• Provide a verbal assessment of the strengths and weaknesses of your peers' work or understanding of a given concept based on previously described criteria, and have your peers critique your assessment
Analyze (HOC) Distinguish parts and make inferences	• Analyze and interpret data in primary literature or a textbook without reading the author's interpretation and then compare the authors' interpretation with your own • Analyze a situation and then identify the assumptions and principles of the argument • Compare and contrast two ideas or concepts • Construct a map of the main concepts by defining the relationships of the concepts using one- or two-way arrows	• Work together to analyze and interpret data in primary literature or a textbook without reading the author's interpretation, and defend your analysis to your peers • Work together to identify all of the concepts in a paper or textbook chapter, construct individual maps linking the concepts together with arrows and words that relate the concepts, and then grade each other's concept maps
Apply (HOC or LOC) Use information or concepts in new ways (HOC) or in the same ways (LOC)	• Review each process you have learned and then ask yourself: What would happen if you increase or decrease a component in the system, or what would happen if you alter the activity of a component in the system? • If possible, graph a biological process and create scenarios that change the shape or slope of the graph	• Practice writing out answers to old exam questions on the board, and have your peers check to make sure you don't have too much or too little information in your answer • Take turns teaching your peers a biological process while the group critiques the content
Understand (LOC) Explain information or concepts	• Describe a biological process in your own words without copying it from a book or another source • Provide examples of a process • Write a sentence using the word • Give examples of a process	• Discuss content with peers • Take turns quizzing each other about definitions, and have your peers check your answer
Remember (LOC) Recall information	• Practice labeling diagrams • List characteristics • Identify biological objects or components from flash cards • Quiz yourself with flash cards • Take a self-made quiz on vocabulary • Draw, classify, select, or match items • Write out the textbook definitions	• Check a drawing that another student labeled • Create lists of concepts and processes that your peers can match • Place flash cards in a bag and take turns selecting one for which you must define a term • Do the preceding activities, and have peers check your answers

Periodic Table of Elements

Key (sample cell):
- 1 — Atomic number
- H — Atomic symbol
- Hydrogen — Name
- 1.008 — Atomic weight*

Legend:
- Most common elements in living things
- Other major elements (minerals) found in living things
- Important trace elements (minerals) found in living things
- Elements mostly found in non-living things
- Elements not found in nature (synthesized by scientists)

Groups 1–18 main table:

1	2	3	4	5	6	7	8	9	10	11	12	13	14	15	16	17	18
1 H Hydrogen 1.008																	2 He Helium 4.003
3 Li Lithium 6.941	4 Be Beryllium 9.012											5 B Boron 10.81	6 C Carbon 12.01	7 N Nitrogen 14.01	8 O Oxygen 16.00	9 F Fluorine 19.00	10 Ne Neon 20.18
11 Na Sodium 22.99	12 Mg Magnesium 24.31											13 Al Aluminum 26.98	14 Si Silicon 28.09	15 P Phosphorus 30.97	16 S Sulfur 32.07	17 Cl Chlorine 35.45	18 Ar Argon 39.95
19 K Potassium 39.10	20 Ca Calcium 40.08	21 Sc Scandium 44.96	22 Ti Titanium 47.87	23 V Vanadium 50.94	24 Cr Chromium 52.00	25 Mn Manganese 54.94	26 Fe Iron 55.85	27 Co Cobalt 58.93	28 Ni Nickel 58.69	29 Cu Copper 63.55	30 Zn Zinc 65.38	31 Ga Gallium 69.72	32 Ge Germanium 72.64	33 As Arsenic 74.92	34 Se Selenium 78.96	35 Br Bromine 79.90	36 Kr Krypton 83.80
37 Rb Rubidium 85.47	38 Sr Strontium 87.61	39 Y Yttrium 88.91	40 Zr Zirconium 91.22	41 Nb Niobium 92.91	42 Mo Molybdenum 95.96	43 Tc Technetium [98]†	44 Ru Ruthenium 101.1	45 Rh Rhodium 102.9	46 Pd Palladium 106.4	47 Ag Silver 107.9	48 Cd Cadmium 112.4	49 In Indium 114.8	50 Sn Tin 118.7	51 Sb Antimony 121.8	52 Te Tellurium 127.6	53 I Iodine 126.9	54 Xe Xenon 131.3
55 Cs Cesium 132.9	56 Ba Barium 137.3	*	72 Hf Hafnium 178.5	73 Ta Tantalum 180.9	74 W Tungsten 183.8	75 Re Rhenium 186.2	76 Os Osmium 190.2	77 Ir Iridium 192.2	78 Pt Platinum 195.1	79 Au Gold 197.0	80 Hg Mercury 200.6	81 Tl Thallium 204.4	82 Pb Lead 207.2	83 Bi Bismuth 209.0	84 Po Polonium [209]	85 At Astatine [210]	86 Rn Radon [222]
87 Fr Francium [223]	88 Ra Radium [226]	**	104 Rf Rutherfordium [265]	105 Db Dubnium [268]	106 Sg Seaborgium [271]	107 Bh Bohrium [270]	108 Hs Hassium [277]	109 Mt Meitnerium [276]	110 Ds Darmstadtium [281]	111 Rg Roentgenium [280]	112 Cn Copernicium [285]	113 Uut Ununtrium [284]	114 Fl Flerovium [289]	115 Uup Ununpentium [288]	116 Lv Livermorium [293]	117 UUs Ununseptium [294]	118 UUo Ununoctium [294]

*Lanthanides:

57 La Lanthanum 138.9	58 Ce Cerium 140.1	59 Pr Praseodymium 140.9	60 Nd Neodymium 144.2	61 Pm Promethium [145]	62 Sm Samarium 150.4	63 Eu Europium 152.0	64 Gd Gadolinium 157.3	65 Tb Terbium 158.9	66 Dy Dysprosium 162.5	67 Ho Holmium 164.9	68 Er Erbium 167.3	69 Tm Thulium 168.9	70 Yb Ytterbium 173.1	71 Lu Lutetium 175.0

**Actinides:

89 Ac Actinium [227]	90 Th Thorium 232.0	91 Pa Protactinium 231.0	92 U Uranium 238.0	93 Np Neptunium [237]	94 Pu Plutonium [244]	95 Am Americium [243]	96 Cm Curium [247]	97 Bk Berkelium [247]	98 Cf Californium [251]	99 Es Einsteinium [252]	100 Fm Fermium [257]	101 Md Mendelevium [258]	102 No Nobelium [259]	103 Lr Lawrencium [262]

DATA: Wieser, M. E., and M. Berglund. 2009. *Pure and Applied Chemistry* 81: 2131–2156.

*Atomic weights are reported to four significant figures.

†For elements with a variable number of protons and/or neutrons, the mass number of the longest-lived isotope of the element is reported in brackets.

(handwritten: Pinguin Pro Basic Chemistry Concepts)

Glossary

5′ cap A modified guanine (G) nucleotide (7-methylguanylate) added to the 5′ end of eukaryotic mRNAs. Helps protect the mRNA from being degraded and promotes efficient initiation of translation.

abdomen A region of the body; in insects, one of the three prominent body regions called tagmata.

abiotic Not alive (e.g., air, water, and some components of soil). Compare with **biotic**.

aboveground biomass The total mass of living plants in an area, excluding roots.

abscisic acid (ABA) A plant hormone that inhibits growth; it stimulates stomatal closure and triggers dormancy.

abscission In plants, the normal (often seasonal) shedding of leaves, fruits, or flowers.

abscission zone The region at the base of a petiole where cell wall degradation occurs; results in the dropping of leaves.

absorption In animals, the uptake of ions and small molecules, derived from food, across the lining of the intestine and into the bloodstream.

absorption spectrum The amount of light of different wavelengths absorbed by a pigment. Usually depicted as a graph of light absorbed versus wavelength. Compare with **action spectrum**.

acclimation A change in a study organism's phenotype that occurs in response to laboratory conditions.

acclimatization A change in an individual's phenotype that occurs in response to a change in natural environmental conditions.

acetyl CoA A molecule produced by oxidation of pyruvate (the final product of glycolysis) in a reaction catalyzed by pyruvate dehydrogenase. Can enter the citric acid cycle and is used as a carbon source in the synthesis of fatty acids, steroids, and other compounds.

acetylation Addition of an acetyl group ($-COCH_3$) to a molecule. Acetylation of histone proteins is important in controlling chromatin condensation.

acetylcholine (Ach) A neurotransmitter, released by nerve cells at neuromuscular junctions, that triggers contraction of skeletal muscle cells but slows the rate of contraction in cardiac muscle cells. Also used as a neurotransmitter between neurons.

acid Any compound that gives up protons or accepts electrons during a chemical reaction or that releases hydrogen ions when dissolved in water.

acid-growth hypothesis The hypothesis that auxin triggers elongation of plant cells by increasing the activity of proton pumps, making the cell wall more acidic and leading to expansion of the cell wall and an influx of water.

acoelomate A bilaterian animal that lacks an internal body cavity (coelom). Compare with **coelomate** and **pseudocoelomate**.

acquired immune deficiency syndrome (AIDS) A human disease characterized by death of immune system cells (in particular helper T cells) and subsequent vulnerability to other infections. Caused by the human immunodeficiency virus (HIV).

acrosome A caplike structure, located on the head of a sperm cell, that contains enzymes capable of dissolving the outer coverings of an egg.

ACTH See **adrenocorticotropic hormone**.

actin A globular protein that can be polymerized to form filaments. Actin filaments are part of the cytoskeleton and constitute the thin filaments in skeletal muscle cells.

actin filament A long fiber, about 7 nm in diameter, composed of two intertwined strands of polymerized actin protein; one of the three types of cytoskeletal fibers. Involved in cell movement. Also called a *microfilament*. Compare with **intermediate filament** and **microtubule**.

action potential A rapid, temporary change in electrical potential across a membrane, from negative to positive and back to negative. Occurs in cells, such as neurons and muscle cells, that have an excitable membrane.

action spectrum The relative effectiveness of different wavelengths of light in driving a light-dependent process such as photosynthesis. Usually depicted as a graph of some measure of the process versus wavelength. Compare with **absorption spectrum**.

activation energy The amount of energy required to initiate a chemical reaction; specifically, the energy required to reach the transition state.

activator A protein that binds to a DNA regulatory sequence to increase the frequency of transcription initiation by RNA polymerase.

active site The location in an enzyme molecule where substrates (reactant molecules) bind and react.

active transport The movement of ions or molecules across a membrane against an electrochemical gradient. Requires energy (e.g., from hydrolysis of ATP) and assistance of a transport protein (e.g., pump).

adaptation Any heritable trait that increases the fitness of an individual with that trait, compared with individuals without that trait, in a particular environment.

adaptive immune response See **adaptive immunity**.

adaptive immunity Immunity to a particular pathogen or other antigen conferred by activated B and T cells in vertebrates. Characterized by specificity, diversity, memory, and self–nonself recognition. Also called *adaptive immune response*. Compare with **innate immunity**.

adaptive radiation Rapid evolutionary diversification within one lineage, producing many descendant species with a wide range of adaptive forms.

adenosine triphosphate (ATP) A molecule consisting of an adenine base, a sugar, and three phosphate groups that can be hydrolyzed to release energy. Universally used by cells to store and transfer energy.

adhesion The tendency of certain dissimilar molecules to cling together due to attractive forces. Compare with **cohesion**.

adipocyte A fat cell.

adrenal gland Either of two small endocrine glands, one above each kidney. The outer portion (cortex) secretes several steroid hormones; the inner portion (medulla) secretes epinephrine and norepinephrine.

adrenaline See **epinephrine**.

adrenocorticotropic hormone (ACTH) A peptide hormone, produced and secreted by the anterior pituitary, that stimulates release of steroid hormones (e.g., cortisol, aldosterone) from the adrenal cortex.

adult A sexually mature individual.

adventitious root A root that develops from a plant's shoot system instead of from the plant's root system.

aerobic Referring to any metabolic process, cell, or organism that uses oxygen as an electron acceptor. Compare with **anaerobic**.

afferent division The part of the nervous system that transmits information about the internal and external environment to the central nervous system. Consists mainly of sensory neurons. Compare with **efferent division**.

age class All the individuals of a specific age in a population.

age-specific fecundity The average number of female offspring produced by a female in a certain age class.

age structure The proportion of individuals in a population that are of each possible age.

agglutination Clumping together of cells or viruses by antibodies or other cross-linking molecules.

aggregate fruit A fruit (e.g., raspberry) that develops from a single flower that has many separate carpels. Compare with **multiple** and **simple fruit**.

AIDS See **acquired immune deficiency syndrome**.

albumen A solution of water and protein (particularly albumins), found in amniotic eggs, that nourishes the growing embryo. Also called *egg white*.

alcohol fermentation Catabolic pathway in which pyruvate produced by glycolysis is converted to ethanol in the absence of oxygen.

aldosterone A hormone that stimulates the kidney to conserve salt and water and promotes retention of sodium; produced in the adrenal cortex.

allele A particular version of a gene.

allergen Any molecule (antigen) that triggers an allergic response (an allergy).

allergy An IgE-mediated abnormal response to an antigen, usually characterized by dilation of blood vessels, contraction of smooth muscle cells, and increased activity of mucus-secreting cells.

allopatric speciation Speciation that occurs when populations of the same species become geographically isolated, often due to dispersal or vicariance. Compare with **sympatric speciation**.

allopatry Condition in which two or more populations live in different geographic areas. Compare with **sympatry**.

allopolyploidy (adjective: allopolyploid) The state of having more than two full sets of chromosomes (polyploidy) due to hybridization between different species. Compare with **autopolyploidy**.

allosteric regulation Regulation of a protein's function by binding of a regulatory molecule, usually to a specific site distinct from the active site, that causes a change in the protein's shape.

α-amylase See **amylase**.

α-helix (alpha-helix) A protein secondary structure in which the polypeptide backbone coils into a spiral shape stabilized by hydrogen bonding.

alternation of generations A life cycle involving alternation of a multicellular haploid stage (gametophyte) with a multicellular diploid stage (sporophyte). Occurs in most plants and some protists.

alternative splicing In eukaryotes, the splicing of primary RNA transcripts from a single gene in different ways to produce different mature mRNAs and thus different polypeptides.

altruism Any behavior that has a fitness cost to the individual (lowered survival and/or reproduction) and a fitness benefit to the recipient. See **reciprocal altruism**.

alveolus (plural: alveoli) Any of the tiny air-filled sacs of a mammalian lung.

ambisense RNA virus A ssRNA virus whose genome consists of at least one strand that contains both positive-sense and negative-sense regions.

aminoacyl tRNA A transfer RNA molecule that is covalently bound to an amino acid.

aminoacyl-tRNA synthetase An enzyme that catalyzes the addition of a particular amino acid to its corresponding tRNA molecule.

ammonia (NH_3) A small molecule, produced by the breakdown of proteins and nucleic acids, that is very toxic to cells. Is a strong base that gains a proton to form the ammonium ion (NH_4^+).

amnion The innermost of the membranes surrounding the embryo in an amniotic egg.

amniotes A major lineage of vertebrates (Amniota) that reproduce with amniotic eggs. Includes all reptiles (including birds) and mammals—all tetrapods except amphibians.

amniotic egg An egg that has a watertight shell or case enclosing a membrane-bound water supply (the amnion), food supply (yolk sac), and waste sac (allantois).

amoeboid motion See **cell crawling**.

amphibians A lineage of vertebrates, many of which breathe through their skin and feed on land but lay their eggs in water. Represent the earliest tetrapods; include frogs, salamanders, and caecilians.

amphipathic Containing hydrophilic and hydrophobic regions.

ampullae of Lorenzini Structures on the heads of sharks that contain cells with electroreceptors.

amylase Any enzyme that can break down starch by catalyzing hydrolysis of the glycosidic linkages between the glucose residues.

amyloplasts Starch-storing organelles (plastids) in plants. In root cap cells, they settle to the bottom of the cell and may be used as gravity detectors.

anabolic pathway Any set of chemical reactions that synthesizes large molecules from smaller ones. Generally requires an input of energy. Compare with **catabolic pathway**.

anadromous Having a life cycle in which adults live in the ocean (or large lakes) but migrate up freshwater streams to breed and lay eggs.

anaerobic Referring to any metabolic process, cell, or organism that uses an electron acceptor other than oxygen, including fermentation or anaerobic respiration. Compare with **aerobic**.

anaphase A stage in mitosis or meiosis during which chromosomes are moved to opposite poles of the spindle apparatus.

anatomy The study of the physical structure of organisms.

ancestral trait A trait found in the ancestors of a particular group.

aneuploidy (adjective: aneuploid) The state of having an abnormal number of copies of a certain chromosome.

angiosperm A flowering vascular plant that produces seeds within mature ovaries (fruits). The angiosperms form a single lineage. Compare with **gymnosperm**.

animal A member of a major lineage of eukaryotes (Animalia) whose members typically have a complex, large, multicellular body; eat other organisms; and are mobile.

animal model Any disease that occurs in a non-human animal and has parallels to a similar disease of humans. Studied by medical researchers in hopes that findings may apply to human disease.

anion A negatively charged ion.

annelids Members of the phylum Annelida (segmented worms). Distinguished by a segmented body and a coelom that functions as a hydrostatic skeleton. Annelids belong to the lophotrochozoan branch of the protostomes.

annual Referring to a plant whose life cycle normally lasts only one growing season—less than one year. Compare with **perennial**.

anoxygenic Referring to any process or reaction that does not produce oxygen. Photosynthesis in purple sulfur and purple nonsulfur bacteria, which does not involve photosystem II, is anoxygenic. Compare with **oxygenic**.

antagonistic muscle group A set of two or more muscles that reextend one another by transmitting their forces via the skeleton.

antenna (plural: antennae) A long appendage of the head that is used to touch or smell.

antenna complex Part of a photosystem, containing an array of chlorophyll molecules and accessory pigments, that receives energy from light and directs the energy to a central reaction center during photosynthesis.

anterior Toward an animal's head and away from its tail. The opposite of posterior.

anterior pituitary The part of the pituitary gland containing endocrine cells that produce and release a variety of peptide hormones in response to other hormones from the hypothalamus. Compare with **posterior pituitary**.

anther The pollen-producing structure at the end of a stamen in flowering plants (angiosperms).

antheridium (plural: antheridia) The sperm-producing structure in most land plants except angiosperms.

anthropoids One of the two major lineages of primates, including apes, humans, and all monkeys. Compare with **prosimians**.

antibiotic Any substance, such as penicillin, that can kill or inhibit the growth of bacteria.

antibody A protein produced by B cells that can bind to a specific part of an antigen, tagging it for removal by the immune system. All monomeric forms of antibodies consist of two light chains and two heavy chains, which vary between different antibodies. Also called *immunoglobulin*.

anticodon The sequence of three bases (a triplet) in a transfer RNA molecule that can bind to an mRNA codon with a complementary sequence.

antidiuretic hormone (ADH) A peptide hormone, secreted from the posterior pituitary gland, that stimulates water retention by the kidney. Also called *vasopressin*.

antigen Any foreign molecule, often a protein, that can stimulate an innate or adaptive response by the immune system.

antigen presentation Process by which small peptides, derived from ingested particulate antigens (e.g., bacteria) or intracellular antigens (e.g., viruses in infected cell) are complexed with MHC proteins and transported to the cell surface, where they are displayed and can be recognized by T cells.

antiparallel Describing the opposite orientation of nucleic acid strands that are hydrogen bonded to one another, with one strand running in the $5' \rightarrow 3'$ direction and the other in the $3' \rightarrow 5'$ direction.

antiporter A carrier protein that allows an ion to diffuse down an electrochemical gradient, using the energy of that process to transport a different substance in the opposite direction *against* its concentration gradient. Compare with **symporter**.

antiviral Any drug or other agent that can interfere with the transmission or replication of viruses.

aorta In terrestrial vertebrates, the major artery carrying oxygenated blood away from the heart.

aphotic zone Deep water receiving no sunlight. Compare with **photic zone**.

apical Toward the top. In plants, at the tip of a branch. In animals, on the side of an epithelial layer that faces the environment and not other body tissues. Compare with **basal**.

apical–basal axis The shoot-to-root axis of a plant.

apical bud A bud at the tip of a stem or branch, where growth occurs to lengthen the stem or branch.

apical dominance Inhibition of lateral bud growth by the apical meristem at the tip of a plant branch.

apical meristem A group of undifferentiated plant cells, at the tip of a shoot or root, that is responsible for primary growth. Compare with **cambium**.

apodeme Any of the chitinous ingrowths of the exoskeleton to which muscles attach.

apomixis The formation of mature seeds without fertilization occurring; a type of asexual reproduction.

apoplast In plants, the region outside plasma membranes consisting of the porous cell walls and the intervening extracellular air space. Compare with **symplast**.

apoptosis Series of tightly controlled changes that lead to the self-destruction of a cell. Occurs frequently during embryological development and as part of the immune response to remove infected or cancerous cells. Also called *programmed cell death*.

appendix A blind sac (having only one opening) that extends from the cecum in some mammals.

aquaporin A type of channel protein through which water can move by osmosis across a plasma membrane.

aquifer An underground layer of porous rock, sand, or gravel that is saturated with water.

ara operon A set of three genes in *E. coli* that are transcribed into a single mRNA and required for metabolism of the sugar arabinose. Transcription of the *ara* operon is controlled by the AraC regulatory protein.

araC The regulatory gene (written as *araC*) or regulatory protein (when written as AraC) of the *E. coli ara* operon.

arbuscular mycorrhizal fungi (AMF) Fungi from the Glomeromycota lineage whose hyphae enter the root cells of their host plants. Also called *endomycorrhizal fungi*.

Archaea One of the three taxonomic domains of life, consisting of unicellular prokaryotes distinguished by cell walls made of certain polysaccharides not found in bacterial or eukaryotic cell walls, plasma membranes composed of unique isoprene-containing phospholipids, and ribosomes and RNA polymerase similar to those of eukaryotes. Compare with **Bacteria** and **Eukarya**.

archegonium (plural: archegonia) The egg-producing structure in most land plants except angiosperms.

arteriole Any of the many tiny vessels that carry blood from arteries to capillaries.

arteriosclerosis Hardening and loss of elasticity of arteries.

artery Any thick-walled blood vessel that carries blood (oxygenated or not) under relatively high pressure away from the heart to organs throughout the body. Compare with **vein**.

arthropods Members of the phylum Arthropoda. Distinguished by a segmented body; a hard, jointed exoskeleton; paired, jointed appendages; and an extensive body cavity called a hemocoel. Arthropods belong to the ecdysozoan branch of the protostomes.

articulation A movable point of contact between two rigid components of a skeleton, such as between bones of a vertebrate endoskeleton or between segments of cuticle in an arthropod exoskeleton. See **joint**.

artificial selection Deliberate manipulation by humans, as in animal and plant breeding, of the genetic composition of a population by allowing only individuals with desirable traits to reproduce.

ascus (plural: asci) Specialized spore-producing cell found at the ends of hyphae in "sac fungi" (Ascomycota).

asexual reproduction Any form of reproduction where offspring inherit DNA from only one parent. Includes binary fission, budding, and parthenogenesis. Compare with **sexual reproduction**.

astral microtubules Mitotic and meiotic microtubules that have arisen from the two spindle poles and interact with proteins on the plasma membrane.

asymmetric competition Ecological competition between two species in which one species suffers a much greater fitness decline than the other. Compare with **symmetric competition**.

atomic number The number of protons in the nucleus of an atom, giving the atom its identity as a particular chemical element.

atomic weight The average mass of an element that is based on the relative proportions of all the naturally occurring isotopes.

ATP synthase A large membrane-bound protein complex that uses the energy of protons flowing through it to synthesize ATP.

ATP See **adenosine triphosphate**.

atrioventricular (AV) node A region of the heart between the right atrium and right ventricle where electrical signals from the atrium are slowed briefly before spreading to the ventricle. This delay allows the ventricle to fill with blood before contracting. Compare with **sinoatrial (SA) node**.

atrium (plural: atria) A thin-walled chamber of the heart that receives blood from veins and pumps it to a neighboring chamber (the ventricle).

autocrine Relating to a chemical signal that affects the same cell that produced and released it.

autoimmunity A pathological condition in which the immune system attacks self cells or tissues of an individual's own body.

autonomic nervous system The part of the peripheral nervous system that controls internal organs and involuntary processes, such as stomach contraction, hormone release, and heart rate. Includes parasympathetic and sympathetic nerves. Compare with **somatic nervous system**.

autophagy The process by which damaged organelles are surrounded by a membrane and delivered to a lysosome to be recycled.

autopolyploidy (adjective: autopolyploid) The state of having more than two full sets of chromosomes (polyploidy) due to a mutation that doubled the chromosome number. All the chromosomes come from the same species. Compare with **allopolyploidy**.

autosomal inheritance The inheritance patterns that occur when genes are located on autosomes rather than on sex chromosomes.

autosome Any chromosome other than a sex chromosome (i.e,. any chromosome other than the X or Y in mammals).

autotroph Any organism that can synthesize reduced organic compounds from simple inorganic sources such as CO_2 or CH_4. Most plants and some bacteria and archaea are autotrophs. Also called *primary producer*. Compare with **heterotroph**.

auxin Indoleacetic acid (IAA), a plant hormone that stimulates phototropism and cell elongation.

axillary bud A bud that forms at a node and may develop into a lateral (side) branch. Also called *lateral bud*.

axon A long projection of a neuron that can propagate an action potential.

axon hillock The site in a neuron where an axon joins the cell body and where action potentials are first triggered.

axoneme A structure found in eukaryotic cilia and flagella and responsible for their motion; composed of two central microtubules surrounded by nine doublet microtubules (9 + 2 arrangement).

B cell A type of lymphocyte that matures in the bone marrow and, with T cells, is responsible for adaptive immunity. Produces antibodies and also functions in antigen presentation. Also called *B lymphocyte*.

B-cell receptor (BCR) An immunoglobulin protein embedded in the plasma membrane of mature B cells and to which antigens bind. Apart from the transmembrane domain, it is identical in structure to antibodies.

BAC library A collection of all the sequences found in the genome of a species, inserted into **bacterial artificial chromosomes (BACs)**.

background extinction The average rate of low-level extinction that has occurred continuously throughout much of evolutionary history. Compare with **mass extinction**.

Bacteria One of the three taxonomic domains of life, consisting of unicellular prokaryotes distinguished by cell walls composed largely of peptidoglycan, plasma membranes similar to those of eukaryotic cells, and ribosomes and RNA polymerase that differ from those in archaeans or eukaryotes. Compare with **Archaea** and **Eukarya**.

bacterial artificial chromosome (BAC) An artificial version of a bacterial chromosome that can be used as a cloning vector to produce many copies of large DNA fragments.

bacteriophage Any virus that infects bacteria.

baculum A bone inside the penis; usually present in mammals with a penis that lacks erectile tissue.

balancing selection A mode of natural selection in which no single allele is favored in all populations of a species at all times. Instead, there is a balance among alleles in terms of fitness and frequency.

ball-and-stick model A representation of a molecule where atoms are shown as balls—colored and scaled to indicate the atom's identity—and covalent bonds are shown as rods or sticks connecting the balls in the correct geometry.

bar coding The use of well-characterized gene sequences to identify species.

bark The protective outer layer of woody plants, composed of cork cells, cork cambium, and secondary phloem.

baroreceptors Specialized nerve cells in the walls of the heart and certain major arteries that detect changes in blood pressure and trigger appropriate responses by the brain.

basal Toward the base. In plants, toward the root or at the base of a branch where it joins the stem. In animals, on the side of an epithelial layer that abuts underlying body tissues. Compare with **apical**.

basal body The microtubule organizing center for cilia and flagella in eukaryotic cells. Consists of nine triplets of microtubules arranged in a circle and establishes the structure of axonemes. Structurally identical with a centriole.

basal lamina A thick, collagen-rich extracellular matrix that underlies most epithelial tissues in animals and connects it to connective tissue.

basal metabolic rate (BMR) The total energy consumption by an organism at rest in a comfortable environment. For aerobes, often measured as the amount of oxygen consumed per hour.

basal transcription factor Proteins, present in all eukaryotic cells, that bind to promoters and help initiate transcription. Compare with **regulatory transcription factor**.

base Any compound that acquires protons or gives up electrons during a chemical reaction or accepts hydrogen ions when dissolved in water.

basidium (plural: basidia) Specialized spore-producing cell at the ends of hyphae in club fungi, members of the Basidiomycota.

basilar membrane The membrane on which the bottom portion of hair cells sits in the vertebrate cochlea.

basolateral Toward the bottom and sides. In animals, the side of an epithelial layer that faces other body tissues and not the environment.

Batesian mimicry A type of mimicry in which a harmless or palatable species resembles a dangerous or poisonous species. Compare with **Müllerian mimicry**.

beak A structure that exerts biting forces and is associated with the mouth; found in birds, cephalopods, and some insects.

behavior Any action by an organism, often in response to a stimulus.

behavioral ecology The study of how organisms respond to particular abiotic and biotic stimuli from their environment.

beneficial In genetics, referring to any mutation, allele, or trait that increases an individual's fitness.

benign tumor A mass of abnormal tissue that appears due to unregulated growth but does not spread to other organs. Benign tumors are not cancers. Compare with **malignant tumor**.

benthic Living at the bottom of an aquatic environment.

benthic zone The area along the bottom of an aquatic environment.

β-pleated sheet (beta-pleated sheet) A protein secondary structure in which the polypeptide backbone folds into a sheetlike shape stabilized by hydrogen bonding.

bilateral symmetry An animal body pattern in which one plane of symmetry divides the body into a left side and a right side. Typically, the body is long and narrow, with a distinct head end and tail end. Compare with **radial symmetry**.

bilaterian A member of a major lineage of animals (Bilateria) that are bilaterally symmetrical at some point in their life cycle, have three embryonic germ layers, and have a coelom. All protostomes and deuterostomes are bilaterians.

bile A complex solution produced by the liver, stored in the gallbladder, and secreted into the intestine. Contains steroid derivatives called bile salts that are responsible for emulsification of fats during digestion.

binary fission The process of cell division used for asexual reproduction of many prokaryotic cells. The genetic material is replicated and partitioned to opposite sides of a growing cell, which is then divided in half to create two genetically identical cells.

biodiversity The diversity of life considered at three levels: genetic diversity (variety of alleles and/or genes in a population, species, or group of species); species diversity (variety and relative abundance of species present in a certain area); and ecosystem diversity (variety of communities and abiotic components in a region).

biodiversity hotspot A region that is extraordinarily rich in species.

biofilm A complex community of bacteria enmeshed in a polysaccharide-rich, extracellular matrix that allows them to attach to a surface.

biogeochemical cycle The pattern of circulation of an element or molecule among living organisms and the environment.

biogeography The study of how species and populations are distributed geographically.

bioinformatics The field of study concerned with managing, analyzing, and interpreting biological information, particularly DNA sequences.

biological species concept The definition of a species as a population or group of populations that are reproductively isolated from other groups. Members of a species have the potential to interbreed in nature to produce viable, fertile offspring but cannot interbreed successfully with members of other species. Compare with **morphospecies** and **phylogenetic species concepts**.

bioluminescence The emission of light by a living organism via an enzyme-catalyzed reaction.

biomagnification In animal tissues, an increase in the concentration of particular molecules that may occur as those molecules are passed up a food chain.

biomass The total mass of all organisms in a given population or geographical area; usually expressed as total dry weight.

biome A large terrestrial or marine region characterized by distinct abiotic characteristics and dominant types of vegetation.

biomechanics A field of biology that applies the principles of physics and engineering to analyze the mechanical structure and function of organisms.

bioprospecting The effort to find commercially useful compounds by studying organisms—especially species that are poorly studied to date.

bioremediation The use of living organisms, usually bacteria or archaea, to degrade environmental pollutants.

biosphere The thin zone surrounding the Earth where all life exists; the sum of all terrestrial and aquatic ecosystems.

biotechnology The application of biological techniques and discoveries to medicine, industry, and agriculture.

biotic Living, or produced by a living organism. Compare with **abiotic**.

bipedal Walking primarily on two legs; characteristic of hominins.

bipolar cell A type of cell in the vertebrate retina that receives information from one or more photoreceptors and passes it to other bipolar cells or ganglion cells.

bivalent The structure formed by synapsed homologous chromosomes during prophase of meiosis I. Also known as a *tetrad*.

bivalves A lineage of mollusks that have shells made of two parts, or valves, such as clams and mussels.

bladder A mammalian organ that holds urine until it can be excreted.

blade The wide, flat part of a plant leaf.

blastocoel Fluid-filled cavity in the blastula of many animal species.

blastocyst The mammalian blastula. A roughly spherical structure composed of trophoblast cells on the exterior and a cluster of cells (the inner cell mass) that fills part of the interior space.

blastomere A cell created by cleavage divisions in early animal embryos.

blastopore An opening (pore) in the surface of some early embryos, through which cells move during gastrulation.

blastula In vertebrate development, a ball of cells (blastomere cells) typically surrounding a fluid-filled cavity (the blastocoel). The blastula is formed by cleavage of a zygote and undergoes gastrulation. See **blastocyst**.

blood A type of connective tissue consisting of red blood cells and leukocytes suspended in a fluid portion, an extracellular matrix called plasma. Transports materials throughout the vertebrate body.

body mass index (BMI) A mathematical relationship of weight and height used to assess obesity in humans. Calculated as weight (kg) divided by the square of height (m^2).

body plan The basic architecture of an animal's body, including the number and arrangement of limbs, body segments, and major tissue layers.

bog A freshwater wetland that has no or almost no water flow, resulting in very low oxygen levels and acidic conditions.

Bohr shift The rightward shift of the oxygen–hemoglobin equilibrium curve that occurs with decreasing pH. It results in hemoglobin being more likely to release oxygen in the acidic environment of exercising muscle.

bone A type of vertebrate connective tissue consisting of living cells and blood vessels within a hard extracellular matrix composed of calcium phosphate ($CaPO_4$) and small amounts of calcium carbonate ($CaCO_3$) and protein fibers.

bone marrow The soft tissue filling the inside of large bones; contains stem cells that develop into red blood cells and leukocytes throughout life.

Bowman's capsule The hollow, double-walled, cup-shaped portion of a nephron that surrounds a glomerulus in the vertebrate kidney.

brain A large mass of neurons, located in the head region of an animal, that is involved in information processing; may also be called the cerebral ganglion.

brain stem The most posterior portion of the vertebrate brain, connecting to the spinal cord and responsible for autonomic body functions such as heart rate, respiration, and digestion.

braincase See **cranium**.

branch (1) A part of a phylogenetic tree that represents populations through time. (2) Any extension of a plant's shoot system.

brassinosteroids A family of steroid hormones found in plants; stimulate growth.

bronchiole Any of the small tubes in mammalian lungs that carry air from the bronchi to the alveoli.

bronchus (plural: bronchi) In mammals, one of a pair of large tubes that lead from the trachea to each lung.

bryophyte See **non-vascular plants**.

budding Asexual reproduction in which an outgrowth from the parent breaks free as an independent individual; occurs in yeasts and some invertebrates.

buffer A substance that, in solution, acts to minimize changes in the pH of that solution when acid or base is added.

bulbourethral gland In male mammals, either of a small pair of glands at the base of the urethra that secrete an alkaline mucus (part of semen), which lubricates the tip of the penis and neutralizes acids in the urethra during copulation. In humans, also called *Cowper's glands*.

bulk flow The directional mass movement of a fluid due to pressure differences, such as movement of water through plant xylem and phloem, and movement of blood in animals.

bulk-phase endocytosis Nonspecific uptake of extracellular fluid by pinching off the plasma membrane to form small membrane-bound vesicles; considered to be a means of retrieving membrane

from the surface following exocytosis. Compare with **receptor-mediated endocytosis**.

bundle-sheath cell A type of cell found around the vascular tissue (veins) of plant leaves.

C_3 pathway The most common form of photosynthesis in which atmospheric CO_2 is fixed by rubisco to form 3-phosphoglycerate, a three-carbon molecule. Used in first phase of the Calvin cycle.

C_4 pathway A variant type of photosynthesis in which atmospheric CO_2 is first fixed by PEP carboxylase into four-carbon acids, rather than the three-carbon molecules of the classic C_3 pathway. Used to concentrate CO_2 to reduce photorespiration in the Calvin cycle while stomata are closed.

C_4 photosynthesis A variant type of photosynthesis in which atmospheric CO_2 is first fixed into four-carbon sugars, rather than the three-carbon sugars of classic C_3 photosynthesis. Enhances photosynthetic efficiency in hot, dry environments by reducing loss of oxygen due to photorespiration.

cadherin Any of a class of cell-surface proteins involved in selective cell–cell adhesion. Important for coordinating movements of cells and the establishment of tissues during embryological development.

callus In plants, a mass of undifferentiated cells that can generate roots and other tissues necessary to create a mature plant.

Calvin cycle In photosynthesis, the set of reactions that use NADPH and ATP formed in the light-dependent reactions to drive the fixation of CO_2, reduction of the fixed carbon to produce sugar, and the regeneration of the substrate used to fix CO_2. Also called *light-independent reactions*.

calyx All of the sepals of a flower.

CAM See **crassulacean acid metabolism**.

cambium (plural: cambia) In woody plants, tissue that consists of two types of cylindrical meristems that increase the width of roots and shoots through the process of secondary growth. See **vascular cambium** and **cork cambium**.

Cambrian explosion The rapid diversification of animal body types and lineages that occured between the species present in the Doushantuo faunas (around 570 mya), Ediacaran faunas (565–542 mya), and the Early Cambrian faunas (525–515 mya).

cancer General term for any tumor whose cells grow in an uncontrolled fashion, invade nearby tissues, and spread to other sites in the body.

capillarity The tendency of water to move up a narrow tube due to adhesion, cohesion, and surface tension (also called capillary action).

capillary Any of the many small, thin-walled blood vessels that permeate all tissues and organs, and allow exchange of gases and other molecules between blood and body cells.

capillary bed A thick network of capillaries.

capsid A shell of protein enclosing the genome of a virus particle.

carapace In crustaceans, a large platelike section of the exoskeleton that covers and protects the cephalothorax (e.g., a crab's "shell").

carbohydrate Any of a class of molecules that contain a carbonyl group, several hydroxyl groups, and

several to many carbon-hydrogen bonds. See **monosaccharide** and **polysaccharide**.

carbon cycle, global The worldwide movement of carbon among terrestrial ecosystems, the oceans, and the atmosphere.

carbon fixation The process of converting gaseous carbon dioxide into an organic molecule, often associated with photosynthesis. See also **PEP carboxylase** and **rubisco**.

carbonic anhydrase An enzyme that catalyzes the formation of carbonic acid (H_2CO_3) from carbon dioxide and water.

carboxylic acids Organic acids with the form R-COOH (a carboxyl group).

cardiac cycle One complete heartbeat cycle, including systole and diastole.

cardiac muscle The muscle tissue of the vertebrate heart; responsible for pumping blood. Consists of long, branched fibers that are electrically connected and that initiate their own contractions; not under voluntary control. Compare with **skeletal** and **smooth muscle**.

cardiovascular disease A group of diseases of the heart and blood vessels caused by poor diet, obesity, inactivity, genetics, tobacco use, age, and other factors.

carnivore (adjective: carnivorous) An animal whose diet consists predominantly of meat, or other animals. Most members of the mammalian taxon Carnivora are carnivores. Some plants are carnivorous, trapping and killing small animals and then absorbing nutrients from the prey's body. Compare with **herbivore** and **omnivore**.

carotenoid Any of a class of accessory pigments, found in chloroplasts, that absorb wavelengths of light not absorbed by chlorophyll; typically appear yellow, orange, or red. Includes carotenes and xanthophylls.

carpel The female reproductive organ in a flower. Consists of the stigma, to which pollen grains adhere; the style, through which the pollen tube grows; and the ovary, which houses the ovule. Compare with **stamen**.

carrier protein A membrane protein that facilitates diffusion of a small molecule (e.g., glucose) across a membrane by a process involving a reversible change in the shape of the protein. Also called *carrier* or *transporter*. Compare with **channel protein**.

carrier A heterozygous individual carrying a normal allele and a recessive allele for an inherited trait; does not display the phenotype of the recessive trait but can pass the recessive allele to offspring.

carrying capacity (K) The maximum population size of a certain species that a given habitat can support.

cartilage A type of vertebrate connective tissue that consists of relatively few cells scattered in a stiff matrix of polysaccharides and protein fibers. Provides structural support.

Casparian strip In plant roots, a waxy layer containing suberin, a water-repellent substance that prevents movement of water through the walls of endodermal cells, thus blocking the apoplastic pathway of water and ion movement into the vascular tissue.

cast A type of fossil, formed when the decay of a body part leaves a void that is then filled with minerals that later harden.

catabolic pathway Any set of chemical reactions that breaks down large, complex molecules into smaller ones, releasing energy in the process. Compare with **anabolic pathway**.

catalysis (verb: catalyze) Acceleration of the rate of a chemical reaction due to a decrease in the free energy of the transition state, called the activation energy.

catalyst Any substance that increases the rate of a chemical reaction without itself undergoing any permanent chemical change.

catecholamines A class of small compounds, derived from the amino acid tyrosine, that are used as hormones or neurotransmitters. Include epinephrine, norepinephrine, and dopamine.

cation A positively charged ion.

cation exchange The release (displacement) of cations, such as magnesium and calcium from soil particles, by protons in acidic soil water. The released cations are available for uptake by plants.

CD4 A membrane protein on the surface of some T cells in humans. $CD4^+$ T cells can give rise to helper T cells.

CD8 A membrane protein on the surface of some T cells in humans. $CD8^+$ T cells can give rise to cytotoxic T cells.

Cdk See **cyclin-dependent kinase**.

cDNA See **complementary DNA**.

cDNA library A set of cDNAs from a particular cell type or stage of development. Each cDNA is carried by a plasmid or other cloning vector and can be separated from other cDNAs. Compare with **genomic library**.

cecum A blind sac between the small intestine and the colon. Is enlarged in some species (e.g., rabbits) that use it as a fermentation vat for digestion of cellulose.

cell A highly organized compartment bounded by a thin, flexible structure (plasma membrane) and containing concentrated chemicals in an aqueous (watery) solution. The basic structural and functional unit of all organisms.

cell body The part of a neuron that contains the nucleus; where incoming signals are integrated. Also called the *soma*.

cell crawling A form of cellular movement involving actin filaments in which the cell produces bulges (pseudopodia) that stick to the substrate and pull the cell forward. Also called *amoeboid motion*.

cell cycle Ordered sequence of events in which a eukaryotic cell replicates its chromosomes, evenly partitions the chromosomes to two daughter cells, and then undergoes division of the cytoplasm.

cell-cycle checkpoint Any of several points in the cell cycle at which progression of a cell through the cycle can be regulated.

cell division Creation of new cells by division of preexisting cells.

cell-mediated (immune) response The type of immune response that involves generation of cytotoxic

T cells from $CD8^+$ T cells. Defends against pathogen-infected cells, cancer cells, and transplanted cells. Compare with **humoral (immune) response**.

cell membrane See **plasma membrane**.

cell plate A flattened sac-like structure formed in the middle of a dividing plant cell from Golgi-derived vesicles containing cell wall material; ultimately divides the cytoplasm into two separate cells.

cell sap An aqueous solution found in the vacuoles of plant cells.

cell theory The theory that all organisms are made of cells and that all cells come from preexisting cells.

cell wall A fibrous layer found outside the plasma membrane of most bacteria and archaea and many eukaryotes.

cellular respiration A common pathway for production of ATP, involving transfer of electrons from compounds with high potential energy through an electron transport chain and ultimately to an electron acceptor (often oxygen).

cellulase An enzyme that can break down cellulose by catalyzing hydrolysis of the glycosidic linkages between the glucose residues.

cellulose A structural polysaccharide composed of glucose monomers joined by β-1,4-glycosidic linkages. Found in the cell wall of algae, plants, and some bacteria and fungi.

Cenozoic era The most recent interval of geologic time, beginning 65.5 million years ago, during which mammals became the dominant vertebrates and angiosperms became the dominant plants.

central dogma The scheme for information flow in the cell: DNA → RNA → protein.

central nervous system (CNS) Large numbers of neurons aggregated into clusters called ganglia in bilaterian animals. In vertebrates, the central nervous system consists of the brain and spinal cord. Compare with **nerve net** and **peripheral nervous system (PNS)**.

centriole One of two small cylindrical structures found together within the centrosome near the nucleus of a eukaryotic cell (not found in plants). Consists of microtubule triplets and is structurally identical with a basal body.

centromere Constricted region of a replicated chromosome where the two sister chromatids are joined and the kinetochore is located.

centrosome Structure in animal and fungal cells, containing two centrioles, that serves as a microtubule organizing center for the cell's cytoskeleton and for the spindle apparatus during cell division.

cephalization The formation in animals of a distinct anterior region (the head) where sense organs and a mouth are clustered.

cephalochordates One of the three major chordate lineages (Cephalochordata), comprising small, mobile organisms that live in marine sands and suspension feed; also called *lancelets* or *amphioxus*. Compare with **urochordates** and **vertebrates**.

cephalopods A lineage of mollusks including the squid, octopuses, and nautiluses. Distinguished by large brains, excellent vision, tentacles, and a reduced or absent shell.

cerebellum Posterior section of the vertebrate brain; involved in coordination of complex muscle movements, such as those required for locomotion and maintaining balance.

cerebrum The most anterior section of the vertebrate brain. Divided into left and right hemispheres and four lobes: frontal lobe, involved in complex decision making (in humans); occipital lobe, receives and interprets visual information; parietal lobe, involved in integrating sensory and motor functions; and temporal lobe, functions in memory, speech (in humans), and interpreting auditory information.

cervix The bottom portion of the uterus, containing a canal that leads to the vagina.

chaetae (singular: chaeta) Bristle-like extensions found in some annelids.

channel protein A protein that forms a pore in a cell membrane. The structure of most channels allows them to admit just one or a few types of ions or molecules. Compare with **carrier protein**.

character Any genetic, morphological, physiological, or behavioral characteristic of an organism to be studied.

character displacement The evolutionary tendency for the traits of similar species that occupy overlapping ranges to change in a way that reduces interspecific competition.

chelicerae A pair of clawlike appendages found around the mouth of certain arthropods called chelicerates (spiders, mites, and allies).

chemical bond An attractive force binding two atoms together. Covalent bonds, ionic bonds, and hydrogen bonds are types of chemical bonds.

chemical energy The potential energy stored in covalent bonds between atoms.

chemical equilibrium A dynamic but stable state of a reversible chemical reaction in which the forward reaction and reverse reactions proceed at the same rate, so that the concentrations of reactants and products remain constant.

chemical evolution A The theory that simple chemical compounds in the early atmosphere and ocean combined via chemical reactions to form larger, more complex substances, eventually leading to the origin of life and the start of biological evolution.

chemical reaction Any process in which one compound or element is combined with others or is broken down; involves the making and/or breaking of chemical bonds.

chemiosmosis An energetic coupling mechanism whereby energy stored in an electrochemical proton gradient is used to drive an energy-requiring process such as production of ATP.

chemokine Any of a subset of cytokines that acts as a chemical signal attracting leukocytes to a site of tissue injury or infection.

chemolithotroph An organism (bacteria or archaea) that produces ATP by oxidizing inorganic molecules with high potential energy such as ammonia (NH_3) or methane (CH_4). Also called *lithotroph*. Compare with **chemoorganotroph**.

chemoorganotroph An organism that produces ATP by oxidizing organic molecules with high potential energy such as sugars. Also called *organotroph*. Compare with **chemolithotroph**.

chemoreception A sensory system in which receptors are activated in response to the binding of chemicals.

chemoreceptor A sensory cell or organ specialized for detection of specific molecules or classes of molecules.

chiasma (plural: chiasmata) The X-shaped structure formed during meiosis by crossing over between non-sister chromatids in a pair of homologous chromosomes.

chitin A structural polysaccharide composed of *N*-acetyl-glucosamine (NAG) monomers joined end to end by β-1,4-glycosidic linkages. Found in cell walls of fungi and many algae, and in external skeletons of insects and crustaceans.

chitons A lineage of marine mollusks that have a protective shell formed of eight calcium carbonate plates.

chlorophyll Any of several closely related green pigments, found in chloroplasts, that absorb light during photosynthesis.

chloroplast A chlorophyll-containing organelle, bounded by a double membrane, in which photosynthesis occurs; found in plants and photosynthetic protists. Also the location of starch, amino acid, fatty acid, purine, and pyrimidine synthesis.

choanocyte A specialized, flagellated feeding cell found in choanoflagellates (protists that are the closest living relatives of animals) and sponges (the most ancient animal phylum).

cholecystokinin A peptide hormone secreted by cells in the lining of the small intestine. Stimulates the secretion of digestive enzymes from the pancreas and of bile from the liver and gallbladder.

chordate Any member of the phylum Chordata. Chordates are deuterostomes distinguished by a dorsal hollow nerve cord, pharyngeal gill slits, a notochord, and a post-anal tail. Includes vertebrates, cephalochordata, and urochordata.

chromatid One of the two identical double-stranded DNAs composing a replicated chromosome that is connected at the centromere to the other strand.

chromatin The complex of DNA and proteins, mainly histones, that compose eukaryotic chromosomes. Can be highly compact (heterochromatin) or loosely coiled (euchromatin).

chromatin remodeling The process by which the DNA in chromatin is unwound from its associated proteins to allow transcription or replication. May involve chemical modification of histone proteins or reshaping of the chromatin by large multiprotein complexes in an ATP-requiring process.

chromatin remodeling complexes Sets of enzymes that use energy from ATP hydrolysis shift nucleosomes on DNA to expose regulatory sequences to transcription factors.

chromosome theory of inheritance The principle that genes are located on chromosomes and that patterns of inheritance are determined by the behavior of chromosomes during meiosis.

chromosome Gene-carrying structure consisting of a single long molecule of double-stranded DNA and associated proteins (e.g., histones). Most prokaryotic cells contain a single, circular chromosome; eukaryotic cells contain multiple noncircular (linear) chromosomes located in the nucleus.

cilium (plural: cilia) One of many short, filamentous projections of some eukaryotic cells, containing a core of microtubules. Used to move the cell as well as to circulate fluid or particles around the surface of a stationary cell. See **axoneme**.

circadian clock An internal mechanism found in most organisms that regulates many body processes (sleep–wake cycles, hormonal patterns, etc.) in a roughly 24-hour cycle.

circulatory system The system responsible for moving oxygen, carbon dioxide, and other materials (hormones, nutrients, wastes) within the animal body.

cisternae (singular: cisterna) Flattened, membrane-bound compartments that make up the Golgi apparatus.

cisternal maturation The process of cargo movement through the Golgi apparatus by residing in cisternae that mature from *cis* to *trans* via the import and export of different Golgi enzymes.

citric acid cycle A series of eight chemical reactions that start with citrate (deprotonated citric acid) and ends with oxaloacetate, which reacts with acetyl CoA to form citrate—forming a cycle that is part of the pathway that oxidizes glucose to CO_2. Also known as the *Krebs cycle* or *tricarboxylic acid* (*TCA*) *cycle*.

clade See **monophyletic group**.

cladistic approach A method for constructing a phylogenetic tree that is based on identifying the unique traits (shared, derived characters, called synapomorphies) of each monophyletic group.

Class I MHC protein A type of MHC protein that is present on the plasma membrane of virtually all nucleated cells and functions in presenting antigen to CD8+ T cells.

Class II MHC protein A type of MHC protein that is present only on the plasma membrane of certain cells in the immune response, such as dendritic cells, macrophages, and B cells. It functions in presenting epitopes of antigens to CD4+ T cells.

cleavage In animal development, the series of rapid mitotic cell divisions, with little cell growth, that produces successively smaller cells (blastomeres) and transforms a zygote into a multicellular blastula.

cleavage furrow A pinching in of the plasma membrane that occurs as cytokinesis begins in animal cells and deepens until the cytoplasm is divided into two daughter cells.

climate The prevailing, long-term weather conditions in a particular region.

climax community The stable, final community that develops from ecological succession.

clitoris A rod of erectile tissue in the external genitalia of female mammals. Is formed from the same embryonic tissue as the male penis and has a similar function in sexual arousal.

cloaca In a few mammals and many nonmammalian vertebrates, a body cavity opening to the outside and used by both the excretory and reproductive systems.

clonal selection theory The dominant explanation of the generation of an adaptive immune response. According to the theory, the immune system retains a vast pool of inactive lymphocytes, each with a unique receptor for a unique epitope. Lymphocytes that encounter their complementary epitopes are stimulated to divide (selected and cloned), producing daughter cells that combat infection and confer immunity.

clone (1) An individual that is genetically identical to another individual. (2) A lineage of genetically identical individuals or cells. (3) As a verb, to make one or more genetic replicas of a cell or individual.

cloning vector A plasmid or other agent used to transfer recombinant genes into cultured host cells. Also called simply *vector*.

closed circulatory system A circulatory system in which the circulating fluid (blood) is confined to blood vessels and flows in a continuous circuit. Compare with **open circulatory system**.

cnidocyte A specialized stinging cell found in cnidarians (e.g., jellyfish, corals, and anemones) and used in capturing prey.

co-receptor Any membrane protein that acts with some other membrane protein in a cell interaction or cell response.

cochlea The organ of hearing in the inner ear of mammals, birds, and crocodilians. A coiled, fluid-filled tube containing specialized pressure-sensing neurons (hair cells) that detect sounds of different pitches.

coding strand See **non-template strand**.

codominance An inheritance pattern in which heterozygotes exhibit both of the traits seen in each type of homozygous individual.

codon A sequence of three nucleotides in DNA or RNA that codes for an amino acid or a start or stop signal for protein synthesis.

coefficient of relatedness (*r*) A measure of how closely two individuals are related. Calculated as the probability that an allele in two individuals is inherited from the same ancestor.

coelom An internal, usually fluid-filled body cavity that is completely or partially lined with mesoderm.

coelomate An animal that has a true coelom, completely lined with mesoderm. Compare with **acoelomate** and **pseudocoelomate**.

coenocytic Containing many nuclei and a continuous cytoplasm through a filamentous body, without the body being divided into distinct cells. Some fungi are coenocytic.

coenzyme A small organic molecule that is a required cofactor for an enzyme-catalyzed reaction. Often donates or receives electrons or functional groups during the reaction.

coenzyme A (CoA) A molecule that is required for many cellular reactions and that is often transiently linked to other molecules, such as acetyl groups (see **acetyl CoA**).

coenzyme Q A nonprotein molecule that shuttles electrons between membrane-bound complexes in the mitochondrial electron transport chain. Also called **ubiquinone** or *Q*.

coevolution A pattern of evolution in which two interacting species reciprocally influence each other's adaptations over time.

coevolutionary arms race A series of adaptations and counter-adaptations observed in species that interact closely over time and affect each other's fitness.

cofactor An inorganic ion, such as a metal ion, that is required for an enzyme to function normally. May be bound tightly to an enzyme or associate with it transiently during catalysis.

cohesion The tendency of certain like molecules (e.g., water molecules) to cling together due to attractive forces. Compare with **adhesion**.

cohesion-tension theory The theory that water movement upward through plant vascular tissues is due to loss of water from leaves (transpiration), which pulls a cohesive column of water upward.

cohort A group of individuals that are the same age and can be followed through time.

coleoptile A modified leaf that covers and protects the stems and leaves of grass seedlings.

collagen A fibrous, pliable, cable-like glycoprotein that is a major component of the extracellular matrix of animal cells. Various subtypes differ in their tissue distribution, some of which are assembled into large fibrils in the extracellular space.

collecting duct In the vertebrate kidney, a large straight tube that receives filtrate from the distal tubules of several nephrons. Involved in the regulated reabsorption of water.

collenchyma cell In plants, an elongated cell with cell walls thickened at the corners that provides support to growing plant parts; usually found in strands along leaf veins and stalks. Compare with **parenchyma cell** and **sclerenchyma cell**.

colon The portion of the large intestine where feces are formed by compaction of wastes and reabsorption of water.

colony An assemblage of individuals. May refer to an assemblage of semi-independent cells or to a breeding population of multicellular organisms.

commensalism (adjective: commensal) A symbiotic relationship in which one organism (the commensal) benefits and the other (the host) is not harmed. Compare with **mutualism** and **parasitism**.

communication In ecology, any process in which a signal from one individual modifies the behavior of another individual.

community All of the species that interact with each other in a certain area.

companion cell In plants, a cell in the phloem that is connected via many plasmodesmata to adjacent sieve-tube elements. Companion cells provide materials to maintain sieve-tube elements and function in the loading and unloading of sugars into sieve-tube elements.

compass orientation A type of navigation in which movement occurs in a specific direction.

competition In ecology, the interaction of two species or two individuals trying to use the same limited resource (e.g., water, food, living space). May occur between individuals of the same species

(intraspecific competition) or different species (interspecific competition).

competitive exclusion principle The principle that two species cannot coexist in the same ecological niche in the same area because one species will outcompete the other.

competitive inhibition Inhibition of an enzyme's ability to catalyze a chemical reaction via binding of a nonreactant molecule that competes with the substrate(s) for access to the active site.

complement system A set of proteins that circulate in the bloodstream and can destroy bacteria by forming holes in the bacterial plasma membrane.

complementary base pairing The association between specific nitrogenous bases of nucleic acids stabilized by hydrogen bonding. Adenine pairs only with thymine (in DNA) or uracil (in RNA), and guanine pairs only with cytosine.

complementary DNA (cDNA) DNA produced in the laboratory using an RNA transcript as a template and reverse transcriptase; corresponds to a gene but lacks introns. Also produced naturally by retroviruses.

complementary strand A newly synthesized strand of RNA or DNA that has a base sequence complementary to that of the template strand.

complete digestive tract A digestive tract with two openings, usually called a mouth and an anus.

complete metamorphosis See **holometabolous metamorphosis**.

compound eye An eye formed of many independent light-sensing columns (ommatidia); occurs in arthropods. Compare with **simple eye**.

concentration gradient Difference across space (e.g., across a membrane) in the concentration of a dissolved substance.

condensation reaction A chemical reaction in which two molecules are joined covalently with the removal of an −OH from one and an −H from another to form water. Also called a *dehydration reaction*. Compare with **hydrolysis**.

conduction (1) Direct transfer of heat between two objects that are in physical contact. Compare with **convection**. (2) Transmission of an electrical impulse along the axon of a nerve cell.

cone cell A photoreceptor cell with a cone-shaped outer portion that is particularly sensitive to bright light of a certain color. Also called simply *cone*. Compare with **rod cell**.

connective tissue An animal tissue consisting of scattered cells in a liquid, jellylike, or solid extracellular matrix. Includes bone, cartilage, tendons, ligaments, and blood.

conservation biology The effort to study, preserve, and restore threatened genetic diversity, populations, communities, and ecosystems.

constant (*C*) region The invariant amino acid sequence in polypeptides that are used to make antibodies, B-cell receptors, and T-cell receptors. Apart from antibody class types (IgG, IgM, etc.), this region remains constant within an individual. Compare with **variable (*V*) region**.

constitutive Always occurring; always present. Commonly used to describe enzymes and other proteins

that are synthesized continuously or mutants in which one or more genetic loci are constantly expressed due to defects in gene control.

constitutive defense A defensive trait that is always manifested even in the absence of a predator or pathogen. Also called *standing defense*. Compare with **inducible defenses**.

constitutive mutant An abnormal (mutated) strain that produces a product at all times, instead of under certain conditions only.

consumer See **heterotroph**.

consumption Predation or herbivory.

continental shelf The portion of a geologic plate that extends from a continent under seawater.

continuous strand See **leading strand**.

contraception Any of several methods to prevent pregnancy.

control In a scientific experiment, a group of organisms or samples that do not receive the experimental treatment but are otherwise identical to the group that does.

convection Transfer of heat by movement of large volumes of a gas or liquid. Compare with **conduction**.

convergent evolution The independent evolution of similar traits in distantly related organisms due to adaptation to similar environments and a similar way of life.

cooperative binding The tendency of the protein subunits of hemoglobin to affect each other's oxygen binding such that each bound oxygen molecule increases the likelihood of further oxygen binding.

coprophagy The eating of feces.

coral reef A large assemblage of colonial marine corals that usually serves as shallow-water, sunlit habitat for many other species as well.

co-receptor Any membrane protein that acts with some other membrane protein in a cell interaction or cell response.

core enzyme The enzyme responsible for catalysis in a multipart holoenzyme.

cork cambium One of two types of cylindrical meristem, consisting of a ring of undifferentiated plant cells found just under the cork layer of woody stems and roots; produces new cork cells on its outer side. Compare with **vascular cambium**.

cork cell A cell in the protective outermost layer of a woody stem and root that produces and accumulates waxes that make the cell less permeable to water and gases.

corm A rounded, thick underground stem that can produce new plants via asexual reproduction.

cornea The transparent sheet of connective tissue at the very front of the eye in vertebrates and some other animals. Protects the eye and helps focus light.

corolla All of the petals of a flower.

corona The cluster of cilia at the anterior end of a rotifer; in many species it facilitates suspension feeding.

corpus callosum A thick band of neurons that connects the two hemispheres of the cerebrum in the mammalian brain.

corpus luteum A yellowish structure that secretes progesterone in an ovary. Is formed from a follicle that has recently ovulated.

cortex (1) In animals, the outermost region of an organ, such as the kidney or adrenal gland. (2) In plants, a layer of ground tissue found outside the vascular bundles of roots and outside the pith of a stem.

corticotropin-releasing hormone (CRH) A peptide hormone, produced and secreted by the hypothalamus, that stimulates the anterior pituitary to release ACTH.

cortisol A steroid hormone, produced and secreted by the adrenal cortex, that increases blood glucose and prepares the body for stress. The major glucocorticoid hormone in some mammals. Also called *hydrocortisone*.

cost–benefit analysis Decisions or analyses that weigh the fitness costs and benefits of a particular action.

cotransporter A transmembrane protein that facilitates diffusion of an ion down its previously established electrochemical gradient and uses the energy of that process to transport some other substance, in the same or opposite direction, *against* its concentration gradient. Also called *secondary active transporter*. See **antiporter** and **symporter**.

cotyledon The first leaf, or seed leaf, of a plant embryo. Used for storing and digesting nutrients and/or for early photosynthesis.

countercurrent exchanger In animals, any anatomical arrangement that allows the maximum transfer of heat or a soluble substance from one fluid to another. The two fluids must be flowing in opposite directions and have a heat or concentration gradient between them.

covalent bond A type of chemical bond in which two atoms share one or more pairs of electrons. Compare with **hydrogen bond** and **ionic bond**.

cranium A bony, cartilaginous, or fibrous case that encloses and protects the brain of vertebrates. Forms part of the skull. Also called *braincase*.

crassulacean acid metabolism (CAM) A variant type of photosynthesis in which CO_2 is fixed and stored in organic acids at night when stomata are open and then released to feed the Calvin cycle during the day when stomata are closed. Helps reduce water loss and CO_2 loss by photorespiration.

cristae (singular: crista) Sac-like invaginations of the inner membrane of a mitochondrion. Location of the electron transport chain and ATP synthase.

Cro-Magnon A prehistoric European population of modern humans (*Homo sapiens*) known from fossils, paintings, sculptures, and other artifacts.

crop A storage organ in the digestive system of certain vertebrates.

cross A mating between two individuals that is used for genetic analysis.

cross-pollination Pollination of a flower by pollen from another individual, rather than by self-fertilization. Also called *crossing*.

cross-talk Interactions among signaling pathways, triggered by different signals, that modify a cellular response.

crossing over The exchange of segments of non-sister chromatids between a pair of homologous chromosomes that occurs during meiosis I.

crosstalk Interactions among signaling pathways that modify a cellular response.

crustaceans A lineage of arthropods that includes shrimp, lobster, and crabs. Many have a carapace (a platelike portion of the exoskeleton covering the cephalothorax) and mandibles for biting or chewing.

cryptic species A species that cannot be distinguished from similar species by easily identifiable morphological traits.

culture In cell biology, a collection of cells or a tissue growing under controlled conditions, usually in suspension or on the surface of a dish of solid growth medium.

Cushing's disease A human endocrine disorder caused by loss of feedback inhibition of cortisol on ACTH secretion. Characterized by high ACTH and cortisol levels and wasting of body protein reserves.

cuticle A protective coating secreted by the outermost layer of cells of an animal or a plant; often functioning to reduce evaporative water loss.

cyanobacteria A lineage of photosynthetic bacteria formerly known as blue-green algae. Likely the first life-forms to carry out oxygenic photosynthesis.

cyclic AMP (cAMP) Cyclic adenosine monophosphate; a small molecule, derived from ATP, that is widely used by cells in signal transduction and transcriptional control.

cyclic electron flow Path of electrons in which excited electrons of photosystem I are transferred back to plastoquinone (PQ), the start of the electron transport chain normally associated with photosystem II. Instead of reducing NADP$^+$ to make NADPH, the electron energy is used to make ATP via photophosphorylation. Compare with **noncyclic electron flow**.

cyclin One of several regulatory proteins whose concentrations fluctuate cyclically throughout the cell cycle. Involved in the control of the cell cycle via cyclin-dependent kinases.

cyclin-dependent kinase (Cdk) Any of several related protein kinases that are functional only when bound to a cyclin and are activated by other modifications. Involved in control of the cell cycle.

cytochrome *c* (cyt *c*) A soluble protein that shuttles electrons between membrane-bound complexes in the mitochondrial electron transport chain.

cytokine Any of a diverse group of signaling proteins, secreted largely by cells of the immune system, whose effects include stimulating leukocyte production, recruiting cells to the site of infection, tissue repair, and fever. Generally function to regulate the type, intensity, and duration of an immune response.

cytokinesis Division of the cytoplasm to form two daughter cells. Typically occurs immediately after division of the nucleus by mitosis or meiosis.

cytokinins A class of plant hormones that stimulate cell division and retard aging.

cytoplasm All the contents of a cell, excluding the nucleus, bounded by the plasma membrane.

cytoplasmic determinant A regulatory transcription factor or signaling molecule that is distributed unevenly in the cytoplasm of the egg and that directs early pattern formation in an embryo.

cytoplasmic streaming The directed flow of cytosol and organelles that facilitates distribution of materials within some large plant and fungal cells. Occurs along actin filaments and is powered by myosin.

cytoskeleton In eukaryotic cells, a network of protein fibers in the cytoplasm that are involved in cell shape, support, locomotion, and transport of materials within the cell. Prokaryotic cells have a similar but much less extensive network of fibers.

cytosol The fluid portion of the cytoplasm, excluding the contents of membrane-enclosed organelles.

cytotoxic T cell A type of CD8$^+$ effector T cell that induces apoptosis in infected and cancerous cells. Recognizes target cells via interactions with complementary class I MHC–peptide complexes. Also called *cytotoxic T lymphocyte (CTL)* and *killer T cell*. Compare with **helper T cell**.

dalton (Da) A unit of mass equal to 1/12 the mass of one carbon-12 atom; about the mass of 1 proton or 1 neutron.

daughter strand The strand of DNA that is newly replicated from an existing template strand of DNA.

day-neutral plant A plant whose flowering time is not affected by the relative length of day and night (the photoperiod). Compare with **long-day** and **short-day plant**.

dead space Air passages that are not involved in gas exchange with the blood; examples are the trachea and bronchi.

deciduous Describing a plant that sheds leaves or other structures at regular intervals (e.g., each autumn).

decomposer See **detritivore**.

decomposer food chain An ecological network of detritus, decomposers that eat detritus, and predators and parasites of the decomposers.

deep sequencing A method to learn the types of mRNAs or DNA sequences present in cells, and their relative amounts, involving the preparation and sequencing of cDNA libraries.

definitive host The host species in which a parasite reproduces sexually. Compare with **intermediate host**.

dehydration reaction See **condensation reaction**.

deleterious In genetics, referring to any mutation, allele, or trait that reduces an individual's fitness.

deletion In genetics, refers to the loss of part of a chromosome.

demography The study of factors that determine the size and structure of populations through time.

dendrite A short extension from a neuron's cell body that receives signals from other neurons.

dendritic cell A type of leukocyte that ingests and digests foreign antigens, moves to a lymph node, and presents the antigens' epitopes, in the context of MHC proteins on its membrane, to CD4$^+$ and CD8$^+$ T cells.

dense connective tissue A type of connective tissue, distinguished by having an extracellular matrix dominated by collagen fibers. Found in tendons and ligaments.

density dependent In population ecology, referring to any characteristic that varies depending on population density.

density independent In population ecology, referring to any characteristic that does not vary with population density.

deoxyribonucleic acid (DNA) A nucleic acid composed of deoxyribonucleotides that carries the genetic information of a cell. Generally occurs as two intertwined strands, but these can be separated. See also **double helix**.

deoxyribonucleoside triphosphate (dNTP) A monomer used by DNA polymerase to polymerize DNA. Consists of the sugar deoxyribose, a base (A, T, G, or C), and three phosphate groups.

deoxyribonucleotide See **nucleotide**.

depolarization A change in membrane potential from its resting negative state to a less negative or a positive state; a normal phase in an action potential. Compare with **hyperpolarization**.

depolarization Change in membrane potential from its resting negative state to a less negative or to a positive state; a normal phase in an action potential. Compare with **hyperpolarization**.

deposit feeder An animal that eats its way through a food-containing substrate.

derived trait A trait that is clearly homologous with a trait found in an ancestor of a particular group, but that has a new form.

dermal tissue system The tissue forming the outer layer of a plant; also called *epidermis*.

descent with modification The phrase used by Darwin to describe his hypothesis of evolution by natural selection.

desmosome A type of cell–cell attachment structure, consisting of cadherin proteins, that is anchored to intermediate filaments. Serves to link the cytoskeletons of adjacent animal cells and form strong cell–cell attachments throughout a tissue. Compare with **gap junction** and **tight junction**.

detergent A type of small amphipathic molecule used to solubilize hydrophobic molecules in aqueous solution.

determination In development, the commitment of a cell to a particular differentiated fate. Once a cell is fully determined, it can differentiate only into a particular cell type (e.g., liver cell, brain cell).

detritivore An organism whose diet consists mainly of dead organic matter (detritus). Various bacteria, fungi, protists, and animals are detritivores. Also called *decomposer*.

detritus A layer of dead organic matter that accumulates at ground level or on seafloors and lake bottoms.

deuterostomes A major lineage of bilaterian animals that share a pattern of embryological development, including formation of the anus earlier than the mouth, and formation of the coelom by pinching off of layers of mesoderm from the gut. Includes echinoderms and chordates. Compare with **protostomes**.

developmental homology A similarity in embryonic form, or in the fate of embryonic tissues, that is due to inheritance from a common ancestor.

diabetes mellitus A disease caused by defects in insulin production (type 1) or in the response of cells to insulin (type 2). Characterized by abnormally high blood glucose levels and huge amounts of glucose-containing urine.

diaphragm An elastic, sheetlike structure. In mammals, the muscular sheet of tissue that separates the chest and abdominal cavities. It contracts and moves downward during inhalation, expanding the chest cavity.

diastole The portion of the cardiac cycle during which the atria or ventricles of the heart are relaxed. Compare with **systole**.

diastolic blood pressure The force exerted by blood against artery walls during relaxation of the heart's left ventricle. Compare with **systolic blood pressure**.

dicot Any flowering plant (angiosperm) that has two cotyledons (embryonic leaves) upon germination. The dicots do not form a monophyletic group. Also called *dicotyledonous plant*. Compare with **eudicot** and **monocot**.

dideoxy sequencing A laboratory technique for determining the exact nucleotide sequence of DNA. Relies on the use of dideoxynucleoside triphosphates (ddNTPs), which terminate DNA replication.

diencephalon The part of the mammalian brain that relays sensory information to the cerebellum and functions in maintaining homeostasis.

differential centrifugation Procedure for separating cellular components according to their size and density by spinning a cell homogenate in a series of centrifuge runs. After each run, the supernatant is removed from the deposited material (pellet) and spun again at progressively higher speeds.

differential gene expression Expression of different sets of genes in cells with the same genome. Responsible for creating different cell types.

differentiation The process by which any unspecialized cell becomes a distinct specialized cell type (e.g., liver cell, brain cell), usually by changes in gene expression. Also called *cell differentiation*.

diffusion Spontaneous movement of a substance from one region to another, often with a net movement from a region of high concentration to one of low concentration (i.e., down a concentration gradient).

digestion The physical and chemical breakdown of food into molecules that can be absorbed into the body of an animal.

digestive tract The long tube that begins at the mouth and ends at the anus. Also called *alimentary canal* or *gastrointestinal (GI) tract*.

dihybrid cross A mating between two parents that are heterozygous for two different genes.

dikaryotic Describing a cell or fungal mycelium having two haploid nuclei that are genetically distinct.

dimer An association of two molecules that may be identical (homodimer) or different (heterodimer).

dioecious Describing an angiosperm species that has male and female reproductive structures on separate plants. Compare with **monoecious**.

diploblast (adjective: diploblastic) An animal whose body develops from two basic embryonic cell layers

or tissues—ectoderm and endoderm. Compare with **triploblast**.

diploid (1) Having two sets of chromosomes (2*n*). (2) A cell or an individual organism with two sets of chromosomes, one set inherited from the mother and one set from the father. Compare with **haploid**.

direct sequencing A technique for identifying and studying microorganisms that cannot be grown in culture. Involves detecting and amplifying copies of certain specific genes in the microorganisms' DNA, sequencing these genes, and then comparing the sequences with the known sequences from other organisms.

directional selection A mode of natural selection that favors one extreme phenotype with the result that the average phenotype of a population changes in one direction. Generally reduces overall genetic variation in a population. Compare with **disruptive selection** and **stabilizing selection**.

disaccharide A carbohydrate consisting of two monosaccharides (sugar residues) linked together.

discontinuous strand See **lagging strand**.

discrete trait An inherited trait that exhibits distinct phenotypes rather than the continuous variation characteristic of a quantitative trait such as body height.

dispersal The movement of individuals from their place of origin (birth, hatching) to a new location.

disruptive selection A mode of natural selection that favors extreme phenotypes at both ends of the range of phenotypic variation. Maintains overall genetic variation in a population. Compare with **stabilizing selection** and **directional selection**.

distal tubule In the vertebrate kidney, the convoluted portion of a nephron into which filtrate moves from the loop of Henle. Involved in the regulated reabsorption of sodium and water. Compare with **proximal tubule**.

disturbance In ecology, any strong, short-lived disruption to a community that changes the distribution of living and/or nonliving resources.

disturbance regime The characteristic disturbances that affect a given ecological community.

disulfide bond A covalent bond between two sulfur atoms, typically in the side chains of certain amino acids (e.g., cysteine). Often contributes to tertiary and quaternary levels of protein structure.

DNA See **deoxyribonucleic acid**.

DNA cloning Any of several techniques for producing many identical copies of a particular gene or other DNA sequence.

DNA fingerprinting Any of several methods for identifying individuals by unique features of their genomes. Commonly involves using PCR to produce many copies of certain short tandem repeats (microsatellites) and then analyzing their lengths.

DNA helicase An enzyme that breaks hydrogen bonds between nucleotides of DNA, "unzipping" a double-stranded DNA molecule.

DNA library See **cDNA library** and **genomic library**.

DNA ligase An enzyme that joins pieces of DNA by catalyzing the formation of a phosphodiester bond between the pieces.

DNA methylation The addition of a methyl group ($-CH_3$) to a DNA molecule.

DNA methyltransferase A class of eukaryotic enzymes that add a methyl group to cytosines in DNA. Methylation of DNA leads to chromatin condensation and is an important means of regulating gene expression in eukaryotes.

DNA microarray A set of single-stranded DNA fragments, representing thousands of different genes that are permanently fixed to a small glass slide. Can be used to determine which genes are expressed in different cell types, under different conditions, or at different developmental stages.

DNA polymerase Any enzyme that catalyzes synthesis of DNA from deoxyribonucleotide triphosphates (dNTPs).

domain (1) A taxonomic category, based on similarities in basic cellular biochemistry, above the kingdom level. The three recognized domains are Bacteria, Archaea, and Eukarya. (2) A section of a protein that has a distinctive tertiary structure and function.

dominant Referring to an allele that determines the same phenotype when it is present in homozygous or heterozygous form.. Compare with **recessive**.

dormancy A temporary state of greatly reduced metabolic activity and growth in plants or plant parts (e.g., seeds, spores, bulbs, and buds).

dorsal Toward an animal's back and away from its belly. The opposite of ventral.

dorsal hollow nerve chord See **nerve chord**.

double fertilization An unusual form of reproduction seen in flowering plants, in which one sperm cell fuses with an egg to form a zygote and the other sperm cell fuses with two polar nuclei to form the triploid endosperm.

double helix The secondary structure of DNA, consisting of two antiparallel DNA strands wound around each other.

Down syndrome A human developmental disorder caused by trisomy of chromosome 21.

downstream In genetics, the direction in which RNA polymerase moves along a DNA strand. Compare with **upstream**.

duplication In genetics, refers to an additional copy of part of a chromosome.

dynein A class of motor proteins that uses the chemical energy of ATP to "walk" toward the minus end of a microtubule. Dyneins are responsible for bending of cilia and flagella, play a role in chromosome movement during mitosis, and can transport vesicles and organelles.

early endosome A small transient organelle that is formed by the accumulation of vesicles from receptor-mediated endocytosis and is an early stage in the formation of a lysosome.

ecdysone An insect hormone that triggers either molting (to a larger larval form) or metamorphosis (to the adult form), depending on the level of juvenile hormone.

ecdysozoans A major lineage of protostomes (Ecdysozoa) that grow by shedding their external skeletons (molting) and expanding their bodies. Includes

arthropods, nematodes, and other groups. Compare with **lophotrochozoans**.

echinoderms A major lineage of deuterostomes (Echinodermata) distinguished by adult bodies with five-sided radial symmetry, a water vascular system, and tube feet. Includes sea urchins, sand dollars, and sea stars.

echolocation The use of echoes from vocalizations to obtain information about locations of objects in the environment.

ecological selection Also known as environmental selection. A type of natural selection that favors individuals with heritable traits that enhance their ability to survive and reproduce in a certain physical and/or biological environment, excluding their ability to obtain a mate. Compare with **sexual selection**.

ecology The study of how organisms interact with each other and with their surrounding environment.

ecosystem All the organisms that live in a geographic area, together with the nonliving (abiotic) components that affect or exchange materials with the organisms; a community and its physical environment.

ecosystem diversity The variety of biotic components in a region along with abiotic components, such as soil, water, and nutrients.

ecosystem function The sum of biological and chemical processes that are characteristic of a given ecosystem—such as primary production, nitrogen cycling, and carbon storage.

ecosystem services All of the benefits that humans derive, directly or indirectly, from ecosystem functions.

ecotourism Tourism that is based on observing wildlife or experiencing other aspects of natural areas.

ectoderm The outermost of the three basic cell layers (germ layers) in most animal embryos; gives rise to the outer covering and nervous system. Compare with **endoderm** and **mesoderm**.

ectomycorrhizal fungi (EMF) Fungi whose hyphae form a dense network that covers their host plant's roots but do not enter the root cells.

ectoparasite A parasite that lives on the outer surface of the host's body.

ectotherm An animal that gains most of its body heat from external sources as opposed to metabolic processes. Compare with **endotherm**.

effector Any cell, organ, or structure with which an animal can respond to external or internal stimuli. Usually functions, along with a sensor and integrator, as part of a homeostatic system.

efferent division The part of the nervous system that carries commands from the central nervous system to the body. Consists primarily of motor neurons.

egg A mature female gamete and any associated external layers (such as a shell). Larger and less mobile than the male gamete. In animals, also called *ovum*.

ejaculation The release of semen from the copulatory organ of a male animal.

ejaculatory duct A short duct through which sperm move during ejaculation; connects the vas deferens to the urethra.

electric current A flow of electrical charge past a point. Also called *current*.

electrical potential Potential energy created by a separation of electrical charges between two points. Also called *voltage*.

electrocardiogram (EKG) A recording of the electrical activity of the heart, as measured through electrodes on the skin.

electrochemical gradient The combined effect of an ion's concentration gradient and electrical (charge) gradient across a membrane that affects the diffusion of ions across the membrane.

electrogenic fish Any of various kinds of fishes having specialized electric organs that emit a current into the water to detect objects.

electrolyte Any compound that dissociates into ions when dissolved in water. In nutrition, any of the major ions necessary for normal cell function.

electromagnetic spectrum The entire range of wavelengths of radiation extending from short wavelengths (high energy) to long wavelengths (low energy). Includes gamma rays, X-rays, ultraviolet, visible light, infrared, microwaves, and radio waves (from short to long wavelengths).

electron acceptor A reactant that gains an electron and is reduced in a reduction–oxidation reaction.

electron carrier Any molecule that readily accepts electrons from and donates electrons to other molecules. Protons may be transferred with the electrons in the form of hydrogen atoms.

electron donor A reactant that loses an electron and is oxidized in a reduction–oxidation reaction.

electron shell A group of orbitals of electrons with similar energies. Electron shells are arranged in roughly concentric layers around the nucleus of an atom, and electrons in outer shells have more energy than those in inner shells. Electrons in the outermost shell, the valence shell, often are involved in chemical bonding.

electron transport chain (ETC) Any set of membrane-bound protein complexes and mobile electron carriers involved in a coordinated series of redox reactions in which the potential energy of electrons is successively decreased and used to pump protons from one side of a membrane to the other.

electronegativity A measure of the ability of an atom to attract electrons toward itself from an atom to which it is bonded.

electroreception A sensory system in which receptors are activated by electric fields.

electroreceptor A sensory cell or organ specialized to detect electric fields.

element A substance, consisting of atoms with a specific number of protons. Elements preserve their identity in chemical reactions.

elongation (1) The process by which RNA lengthens during transcription. (2) The process by which a polypeptide chain lengthens during translation.

elongation factors Proteins involved in the elongation phase of translation, assisting ribosomes in the synthesis of the growing peptide chain.

embryo A young, developing organism; the stage after fertilization and zygote formation.

embryo sac The female gametophyte in flowering plants.

embryogenesis The production of an embryo from a zygote. Embryogenesis is an early event in development of animals and plants.

Embryophyta An increasingly popular name for the lineage called land plants; reflects their retention of a fertilized egg.

embryophyte A plant that nourishes its embryos inside its own body. All land plants are embryophytes.

emergent property A property that stems from the interaction of simpler elements and that is impossible to predict from the study of individual elements.

emergent vegetation Any plants in an aquatic habitat that extend above the surface of the water.

emerging disease Any infectious disease, often a viral disease, that suddenly afflicts significant numbers of humans for the first time; often due to changes in the host species for a pathogen or to radical changes in the genetic material of the pathogen.

emigration The migration of individuals away from one population to other populations. Compare with **immigration**.

emulsification (verb: emulsify) The dispersion of fat into an aqueous solution. Usually requires the aid of an amphipathic substance such as a detergent or bile salts, which can break large fat globules into microscopic fat droplets.

endangered species A species whose numbers have decreased so much that it is in danger of extinction throughout all or part of its range.

endemic species A species that lives in one geographic area and nowhere else.

endergonic Referring to a chemical reaction that requires an input of energy to occur and for which the Gibbs free-energy change (ΔG) is greater than zero. Compare with **exergonic**.

endocrine Relating to a chemical signal (hormone) that is released into the bloodstream by a producing cell and acts on a distant target cell.

endocrine disruptor An exogenous chemical that interferes with normal hormonal signaling.

endocrine gland A gland that secretes hormones directly into the bloodstream or interstitial fluid instead of into ducts. Compare with **exocrine gland**.

endocrine system All of the glands and tissues that produce and secrete hormones into the bloodstream.

endocytosis General term for any pinching off of the plasma membrane that results in the uptake of material from outside the cell. Includes phagocytosis, pinocytosis, and receptor-mediated endocytosis. Compare with **exocytosis**.

endoderm The innermost of the three basic cell layers (germ layers) in most animal embryos; gives rise to the digestive tract and organs that connect to it (liver, lungs, etc.). Compare with **ectoderm** and **mesoderm**.

endodermis In plant roots, a cylindrical layer of cells that separates the cortex from the vascular tissue and location of the Casparian strip.

endomembrane system A system of organelles in eukaryotic cells that synthesizes, processes, transports, and recycles proteins and lipids. Includes the endoplasmic reticulum (ER), Golgi apparatus, and lysosomes.

endomycorrhizal fungi See **arbuscular mycorrhizal fungi (AMF)**.

endoparasite A parasite that lives inside the host's body.

endophyte (adjective: endophytic) A fungus that lives inside the aboveground parts of a plant in a symbiotic relationship. Compare with **epiphyte**.

endoplasmic reticulum (ER) A network of interconnected membranous sacs and tubules found inside eukaryotic cells. See **rough** and **smooth endoplasmic reticulum**.

endoskeleton Bony and/or cartilaginous structures within the body that provide support. Examples are the spicules of sponges, the plates in echinoderms, and the bony skeleton of vertebrates. Compare with **exoskeleton**.

endosperm A triploid ($3n$) tissue in the seed of a flowering plant (angiosperm) that serves as food for the plant embryo. Functionally analogous to the yolk in some animal eggs.

endosymbiont An organism that lives in a symbiotic relationship inside the body of its host.

endosymbiosis An association between organisms of two different species in which one lives inside the cell or cells of the other.

endosymbiosis theory The theory that mitochondria and chloroplasts evolved from prokaryotes that were engulfed by host cells and took up a symbiotic existence within those cells, a process termed primary endosymbiosis. In some eukaryotes, chloroplasts may have originated by secondary endosymbiosis; that is, when a cell engulfed a chloroplast-containing protist and retained its chloroplasts.

endotherm An animal whose primary source of body heat is internally generated. Compare with **ectotherm**.

endothermic Referring to a chemical reaction that absorbs heat. Compare with **exothermic**.

energetic coupling In cellular metabolism, the mechanism by which energy released from an exergonic reaction (commonly, hydrolysis of ATP) is used to drive an endergonic reaction.

energy The capacity to do work or to supply heat. May be stored (potential energy) or available in the form of motion (kinetic energy).

enhancer A regulatory sequence in eukaryotic DNA that may be located far from the gene it controls or within introns of the gene. Binding of specific proteins to an enhancer enhances the transcription of certain genes.

enrichment culture A method of detecting and obtaining cells with specific characteristics by placing a sample, containing many types of cells, under a specific set of conditions (e.g., temperature, salt concentration, available nutrients) and isolating those cells that grow rapidly in response.

enthalpy (*H*) A quantitative measure of the amount of potential energy, or heat content, of a system plus the pressure and volume it exerts on its surroundings.

entropy (*S*) A quantitative measure of the amount of disorder of any system, such as a group of molecules.

envelope (viral) A membrane that encloses the capsids of some viruses. Normally includes specialized proteins that attach to host-cell surfaces.

environmental sequencing See **metagenomics**.

enzyme A protein catalyst used by living organisms to speed up and control biological reactions.

epicotyl In some embryonic plants, a portion of the embryonic stem that extends above the cotyledons.

epidemic The spread of an infectious disease throughout a population in a short time period. Compare with **pandemic**.

epidermis The outermost layer of cells of any multicellular organism.

epididymis A coiled tube wrapped around each testis in reptiles, birds, and mammals. The site of the final stages of sperm maturation.

epigenetic inheritance Pattern of inheritance involving differences in phenotype that are not due to differences in the nucleotide sequence of genes.

epinephrine A catecholamine hormone, produced and secreted by the adrenal medulla, that triggers rapid responses related to the fight-or-flight response. Also called *adrenaline*.

epiphyte (adjective: epiphytic) A nonparasitic plant that grows on the trunks or branches of other plants and is not rooted in soil.

epithelial tissues See **epithelium**.

epithelium (plural: epithelia) An animal tissue consisting of sheetlike layers of tightly packed cells that line an organ, a gland, a duct, or a body surface. Also called *epithelial tissue*.

epitope A small region of a particular antigen to which an antibody, B-cell receptor, or T-cell receptor binds.

equilibrium potential The membrane potential at which there is no net movement of a particular ion into or out of a cell.

ER signal sequence A short amino acid sequence that marks a polypeptide for transport to the endoplasmic reticulum, where synthesis of the polypeptide chain is completed and the signal sequence removed. See **signal recognition particle**.

erythropoietin (EPO) A peptide hormone, released by the kidney in response to low blood-oxygen levels, that stimulates the bone marrow to produce more red blood cells.

esophagus The muscular tube that connects the mouth to the stomach.

essential amino acid Any amino acid that an animal cannot synthesize and must obtain from the diet. May refer specifically to one of the eight essential amino acids of adult humans: isoleucine, leucine, lysine, methionine, phenylalanine, threonine, tryptophan, and valine.

essential nutrient Any chemical element, ion, or compound that is required for normal growth, reproduction, and maintenance of a living organism and that cannot be synthesized by the organism.

EST See **expressed sequence tag**.

ester linkage The covalent bond formed by a condensation reaction between a carboxyl group and a hydroxyl group. Ester linkages join fatty acids to glycerol to form a fat or phospholipid.

estradiol The major estrogen produced by the ovaries of female mammals and many other vertebrates. Stimulates development of the female reproductive tract, growth of ovarian follicles, and growth of breast tissue in mammals.

estrogens A class of steroid hormones, including estradiol, estrone, and estriol, that generally promote female-like traits. Secreted by the gonads, fat tissue, and some other organs.

estrous cycle A female reproductive cycle in which the uterine lining is reabsorbed rather than shed in the absence of pregnancy and the female is sexually receptive only briefly during mid-cycle (estrus). It is seen in all mammals except Old World monkeys and apes (including humans). Compare with **menstrual cycle**.

ethylene A gaseous plant hormone associated with senescence that induces fruits to ripen and flowers to fade.

eudicot A member of a monophyletic group (lineage) of angiosperms that includes complex flowering plants and trees (e.g., roses, daisies, maples). All eudicots have two cotyledons, but not all dicots are members of this lineage. Compare with **dicot** and **monocot**.

Eukarya One of the three taxonomic domains of life, consisting of unicellular organisms (most protists, yeasts) and multicellular organisms (fungi, plants, animals) distinguished by a membrane-bound cell nucleus, numerous organelles, and an extensive cytoskeleton. Compare with **Archaea** and **Bacteria**.

eukaryote A member of the domain Eukarya; an organism whose cells contain a nucleus, numerous membrane-bound organelles, and an extensive cytoskeleton. May be unicellular or multicellular. Compare with **prokaryote**.

eusociality A complex social structure in which workers sacrifice most or all of their direct reproduction to help rear the queen's offspring. Common in insects such as ants, bees, wasps, and termites.

eutherians A lineage of mammals (Eutheria) whose young develop in the uterus and are not housed in an abdominal pouch. Also called *placental mammals*.

evaporation The energy-absorbing phase change from a liquid state to a gaseous state. Many organisms evaporate water as a means of heat loss.

evo-devo Popular term for evolutionary developmental biology, a research field focused on how changes in developmentally important genes have led to the evolution of new phenotypes.

evolution (1) The theory that all organisms on Earth are related by common ancestry and that they have changed over time, and continue to change, via natural selection and other processes. (2) Any change in the genetic characteristics of a population over time, especially, a change in allele frequencies.

ex situ conservation Preserving species outside of natural areas (e.g., in zoos, aquaria, or botanical gardens).

excitable membrane A plasma membrane that is capable of generating an action potential. Neurons, muscle cells, and some other cells have excitable membranes.

excitatory postsynaptic potential (EPSP) A change in membrane potential, usually depolarization, at a neuron dendrite that makes an action potential more likely.

exergonic Referring to a chemical reaction that can occur spontaneously, releasing heat and/or increasing entropy, and for which the Gibbs free-energy change (ΔG) is less than zero. Compare with **endergonic**.

exocrine gland A gland that secretes some substance through a duct into a space other than the circulatory system, such as the digestive tract or the skin surface. Compare with **endocrine gland**.

exocytosis Secretion of intracellular molecules (e.g., hormones, collagen), contained within membrane-bound vesicles, to the outside of the cell by fusion of vesicles to the plasma membrane. Compare with **endocytosis**.

exon A transcribed region of a eukaryotic gene or region of a primary transcript that is retained in the mature RNA. Except for 5' and 3' UTRs, mRNA exons code for amino acids. Compare with **intron**.

exoskeleton A hard covering secreted on the outside of the body, used for body support, protection, and muscle attachment. Prominent in arthropods. Compare with **endoskeleton**.

exothermic Referring to a chemical reaction that releases heat. Compare with **endothermic**.

exotic species A nonnative species that is introduced into a new area. Exotic species often are competitors, pathogens, or predators of native species.

expansins A class of plant proteins that break hydrogen bonds between components in the primary cell wall to allow it to expand for cell growth.

exponential population growth The accelerating increase in the size of a population that occurs when the growth rate is constant and density independent. Compare with **logistic population growth**.

expressed sequence tag (EST) A portion of a transcribed gene (synthesized from an mRNA in a cell), used to find the physical location of that gene in the genome.

extant species A species that is living today.

extensor A muscle that pulls two bones farther apart from each other, increasing the angle of the joint, as in the extension of a limb or the spine. Compare with **flexor**.

extinct species A species that has died out.

extracellular digestion Digestion that takes place outside of an organism, as occurs in many fungi that make and secrete digestive enzymes.

extracellular matrix (ECM) A complex meshwork in which animal cells are embedded, consisting of proteins (e.g., collagen, proteoglycan, laminin) and polysaccharides produced by the cells.

extremophile A bacterium or archaean that thrives in an "extreme" environment (e.g., high-salt, high-temperature, low-temperature, or low-pressure).

F_1 generation First filial generation. The first generation of offspring produced from a mating (i.e., the offspring of the parental generation).

facilitated diffusion Passive movement of a substance across a membrane with the assistance of transmembrane carrier proteins or channel proteins.

facilitation In ecological succession, the phenomenon in which early-arriving species make conditions more favorable for later-arriving species. Compare with **inhibition** and **tolerance**.

facultative anaerobe Any organism that can survive and reproduce by performing aerobic respiration when oxygen is available or fermentation when it is not.

FAD/FADH₂ Oxidized and reduced forms, respectively, of flavin adenine dinucleotide. A nonprotein electron carrier that functions in the citric acid cycle and oxidative phosphorylation.

fallopian tube A narrow tube connecting the uterus to the ovary in humans, through which the egg travels after ovulation. Site of fertilization and cleavage. In nonhuman animals, called *oviduct*.

fast muscle fiber Type of skeletal muscle fiber that is white in color, generates ATP by glycolysis, and contracts rapidly but fatigues easily. Also called *fast glycolytic*, or *Type IIb*, *fiber*.

fat A lipid consisting of three fatty acid molecules joined by ester linkages to a glycerol molecule. Also called *triacylglycerol* or *triglyceride*.

fatty acid A lipid consisting of a hydrocarbon chain bonded at one end to a carboxyl group. Used by many organisms to store chemical energy; a major component of animal and plant fats and phospholipids.

fauna All the animal species characteristic of a particular region, period, or environment.

feather A specialized skin outgrowth, composed of β-keratin, present in all birds as well as in some non-avian dinosaurs. Used for flight, insulation, display, and other purposes.

feces The waste products of digestion.

fecundity The average number of female offspring produced by a single female in the course of her lifetime.

feedback inhibition A type of control in which high concentrations of the product of a metabolic pathway inhibit one of the enzymes early in the pathway. A form of negative feedback.

fermentation Any of several metabolic pathways that regenerate oxidizing agents, such as NAD⁺, by transferring electrons to a final electron acceptor in the absence of an electron transport chain. Allows pathways such as glycolysis to continue to make ATP.

ferredoxin In photosynthetic organisms, an iron- and sulfur-containing protein in the electron transport chain of photosystem I. Can transfer electrons to the enzyme NADP⁺ reductase, which catalyzes formation of NADPH.

fertility The average number of surviving children that each woman has during her lifetime.

fertilization Fusion of the nuclei of two haploid gametes to form a zygote with a diploid nucleus.

fertilization envelope A physical barrier that forms around a fertilized egg in many animals. The fertilization envelope prevents fertilization by more than one sperm (polyspermy).

fetal alcohol syndrome (FAS) A condition marked by hyperactivity, severe learning disabilities, and depression. Thought to be caused by exposure of an individual to high blood alcohol concentrations during embryonic development.

fetus In live-bearing animals, the unborn offspring after the embryonic stage. It usually is developed sufficiently to be recognizable as belonging to a certain species.

fiber In plants, a type of elongated sclerenchyma cell that provides support to vascular tissue. Compare with **sclereid**.

Fick's law of diffusion A mathematical relationship that describes the rates of diffusion of gases.

fight-or-flight response Rapid physiological changes that prepare the body for emergencies. Includes increased heart rate, increased blood pressure, and decreased digestion.

filament Any thin, threadlike structure, particularly (1) the threadlike extensions of a fish's gills or (2) part of a stamen: the slender stalk that bears the anthers in a flower.

filter feeder See **suspension feeder**.

filtrate Any fluid produced by filtration, in particular the fluid ("pre-urine") in the Malpighian tubules of insects and the nephrons of vertebrate kidneys.

filtration A process of removing large components from a fluid by forcing it through a filter. Occurs in a renal corpuscle of the vertebrate kidney, allowing water and small solutes to pass from the blood into the nephron.

fimbria (plural: fimbriae) A long, needlelike projection from the cell membrane of prokaryotes that is involved in attachment to nonliving surfaces or other cells.

finite rate of increase (λ) The rate of increase of a population over a given period of time. Calculated as the ending population size divided by the starting population size. Compare with **intrinsic rate of increase**.

first law of thermodynamics The principle of physics that energy is conserved in any process. Energy can be transferred and converted into different forms, but it cannot be created or destroyed.

fission (1) A form of asexual reproduction in which a prokaryotic cell divides to produce two genetically similar daughter cells by a process similar to mitosis of eukaryotic cells. Also called *binary fission*. (2) A form of asexual reproduction in which an animal splits into two or more individuals of approximately equal size; common among invertebrates.

fitness The ability of an individual to produce viable offspring relative to others of the same species.

fitness trade-off See **trade-off**.

fixed action pattern (FAP) Highly stereotyped behavior pattern that occurs in a certain invariant way in a certain species. A form of innate behavior.

flaccid Limp as a result of low internal (turgor) pressure (e.g., a wilted plant leaf). Compare with **turgid**.

flagellum (plural: flagella) A long, cellular projection that undulates (in eukaryotes) or rotates (in prokaryotes) to move the cell through an aqueous environment. See **axoneme**.

flatworms Members of the phylum Platyhelminthes. Distinguished by a broad, flat, unsegmented body

that lacks a coelom. Flatworms belong to the lophotrochozoan branch of the protostomes.

flavin adenine dinucleotide See **FAD/FADH$_2$**.

flexor A muscle that pulls two bones closer together, decreasing the joint angle, as in the flexing of a limb or the spine. Compare with **extensor**.

floral meristem A group of undifferentiated plant stem cells that can give rise to the four organs making up a flower.

florigen In plants, a protein hormone that is synthesized in leaves and transported to the shoot apical meristem, where it stimulates flowering.

flower In angiosperms, the part of a plant that contains reproductive structures. Typically includes a calyx, a corolla, and one or more stamens and/or carpels. See **perfect** and **imperfect flower**.

fluid connective tissue A type of connective tissue, distinguished by having a liquid extracellular matrix; includes blood.

fluid feeder Any animal that feeds by sucking or mopping up liquids such as nectar, plant sap, or blood.

fluid-mosaic model The widely accepted hypothesis that the plasma membrane and organelle membranes consist of proteins embedded in a fluid phospholipid bilayer.

fluorescence The spontaneous emission of light from an excited electron falling back to its normal (ground) state.

follicle In a mammalian ovary, a sac of supportive cells containing an egg cell.

follicle-stimulating hormone (FSH) A peptide hormone, produced and secreted by the anterior pituitary; it stimulates (in females) growth of eggs and follicles in the ovaries or (in males) sperm production in the testes.

follicular phase In a menstrual cycle, the first major phase, during which follicles grow and estradiol levels increase; ends with ovulation.

food Any nutrient-containing material that can be consumed and digested by animals.

food chain A relatively simple pathway of energy flow through a few species, each at a different trophic level, in an ecosystem. Might include, for example, a primary producer, a primary consumer, a secondary consumer, and a decomposer. A subset of a **food web**.

food web The complex network of interactions among species in an ecosystem formed by the transfer of energy and nutrients among trophic levels. Consists of many food chains.

foot One of the three main parts of the mollusk body; a muscular appendage, used for movements such as crawling and/or burrowing into sediment.

foraging Searching for food.

forebrain One of the three main regions of the vertebrate brain; includes the cerebrum, thalamus, and hypothalamus. Compare with **hindbrain** and **midbrain**.

fossil Any physical trace of an organism that existed in the past. Includes tracks, burrows, fossilized bones, casts, and so on.

fossil record All of the fossils that have been found anywhere on Earth and that have been formally described in the scientific literature.

founder effect A change in allele frequencies that often occurs when a new population is established from a small group of individuals (founder event) due to sampling error (i.e., the small group is not a representative sample of the source population).

fovea In the vertebrate eye, a portion of the retina where incoming light is focused; contains a high proportion of cone cells.

frameshift mutation The addition or deletion of a nucleotide in a coding sequence that shifts the reading frame of the mRNA.

free energy The energy of a system that can be converted into work. It may be measured only through the change in free energy in a reaction. See **Gibbs free-energy change**.

free radicals Any substance containing one or more atoms with an unpaired electron. Unstable and highly reactive.

frequency The number of wave crests per second traveling past a stationary point. Determines the pitch of sound and the color of light.

frequency-dependent selection A pattern of selection in which certain alleles are favored only when they are rare; a form of balancing selection.

fronds The large leaves of ferns.

frontal lobe In the vertebrate brain, one of the four major areas in the cerebrum.

fruit In flowering plants (angiosperms), a mature, ripened plant ovary (or group of ovaries), along with the seeds it contains and any adjacent fused parts; often functions in seed dispersal. See **aggregate**, **multiple**, and **simple fruit**.

fruiting body A structure formed in some prokaryotes, fungi, and protists for spore dispersal; usually consists of a base, a stalk, and a mass of spores at the top.

functional genomics The study of how a genome works; that is, when and where specific genes are expressed and how their products interact to produce a functional organism.

functional group A small group of atoms bonded together in a precise configuration and exhibiting particular chemical properties that it imparts to any organic molecule in which it occurs.

fundamental niche The total theoretical range of environmental conditions that a species can tolerate. Compare with **realized niche**.

fungi A lineage of eukaryotes that typically have a filamentous body (mycelium) and obtain nutrients by absorption.

fungicide Any substance that can kill fungi or slow their growth.

G protein Any of various proteins that are activated by binding to guanosine triphosphate (GTP) and inactivated when GTP is hydrolyzed to GDP. In G-protein-coupled receptors, signal binding directly triggers the activation of a G protein, leading to production of a second messenger or initiation of a phosphorylation cascade.

G₁ phase The phase of the cell cycle that constitutes the first part of interphase before DNA synthesis (S phase).

G₂ phase The phase of the cell cycle between synthesis of DNA (S phase) and mitosis (M phase); the last part of interphase.

gallbladder A small pouch that stores bile from the liver and releases it as needed into the small intestine during digestion of fats.

gametangium (plural: gametangia) (1) The gamete-forming structure found in all land plants except angiosperms. Contains a sperm-producing antheridium and an egg-producing archegonium. (2) The gamete-forming structure of some chytrid fungi.

gamete A haploid reproductive cell that can fuse with another haploid cell to form a zygote. Most multicellular eukaryotes have two distinct forms of gametes: egg cells (ova) and sperm cells.

gametogenesis The production of gametes (eggs or sperm).

gametophyte In organisms undergoing alternation of generations, the multicellular haploid form that arises from a single haploid spore and produces gametes. Compare with **sporophyte**.

ganglion (plural: ganglia) A mass of neurons in a centralized nervous system.

ganglion cell In the retina, a type of neuron whose axons form the optic nerves.

gap junction A type of cell–cell attachment structure that directly connects the cytosolic components of adjacent animal cells, allowing passage of water, ions, and small molecules between the cells. Compare with **desmosome** and **tight junction**.

gastrin A hormone produced by cells in the stomach lining in response to the arrival of food or to a neural signal from the brain. Stimulates other stomach cells to release hydrochloric acid.

gastropods A lineage of mollusks distinguished by a large, muscular foot and a unique feeding structure, the radula. Include slugs and snails.

gastrulation The process of coordinated cell movements, including the moving of some cells from the outer surface of the embryo to the interior, that results in the formation of three germ layers (endoderm, mesoderm, and ectoderm) and the axes of the embryo.

gated channel A channel protein that opens and closes in response to a specific stimulus, such as the binding of a particular molecule or a change in voltage across the membrane.

gemma (plural: gemmae) A small reproductive structure that is produced asexually in some plants during the gametophyte phase and can grow into a mature gametophyte; most common in non-vascular plants, particularly liverworts and club mosses, and in ferns

gene A section of DNA (or RNA, for some viruses) that encodes information for building one or more related polypeptides or functional RNA molecules along with the regulatory sequences required for its transcription.

gene duplication The formation of an additional copy of a gene, typically by misalignment of

chromosomes during crossing over. Thought to be an important evolutionary process in creating new genes.

gene expression The set of processes, including transcription and translation, that convert information in DNA into a product of a gene, most commonly a protein.

gene family A set of genetic loci whose DNA sequences are extremely similar. Thought to have arisen by duplication of a single ancestral gene and subsequent mutations in the duplicated sequences.

gene flow The movement of alleles between populations; occurs when individuals leave one population, join another, and breed.

gene pool All the alleles of all the genes in a certain population.

gene therapy The treatment of an inherited disease by introducing a normal form of the gene.

generation The average time between a mother's first offspring and her daughter's first offspring.

genetic bottleneck A reduction in allelic diversity resulting from a sudden reduction in the size of a large population (population bottleneck) due to a random event.

genetic code The set of all codons and their meaning.

genetic correlation A type of evolutionary constraint in which selection on one trait causes a change in another trait as well; may occur when the same gene(s) affect both traits.

genetic diversity The diversity of alleles or genes in a population, species, or group of species.

genetic drift Any change in allele frequencies due to random events. Causes allele frequencies to drift up and down randomly over time, and eventually can lead to the fixation or loss of alleles.

genetic equivalence Having all different cell types of a multicellular individual possess the same genome.

genetic homology Similarity in DNA nucleotide sequences, RNA nucleotide sequences, or amino acid sequences due to inheritance from a common ancestor.

genetic map A list of genes on a chromosome that indicates their position and relative distances from one another. Also called a *linkage map*. Compare with **physical map**.

genetic marker A genetic locus that can be identified and traced in populations by laboratory techniques or by a distinctive visible phenotype.

genetic recombination A change in the combination of alleles on a given chromosome or in a given individual. Also called *recombination*.

genetic screen Any technique that identifies individuals with a particular type of mutation.

genetic variation (1) The number and relative frequency of alleles present in a particular population. (2) The proportion of phenotypic variation in a trait that is due to genetic rather than environmental influences in a certain population in a certain environment.

genetics The study of the inheritance of traits.

genital (plural: genitalia) Any external copulatory organ.

genome All the hereditary information in an organism, including not only genes but also stretches of DNA that do not contain genes.

genome annotation The process of analyzing a genome sequence to identify key features such as genes, regulatory sequences, and splice sites.

genomic library A set of DNA segments representing the entire genome of a particular organism. Each segment is carried by a plasmid or other cloning vector and can be separated from other segments. Compare with **cDNA library**.

genomics The field of study concerned with sequencing, interpreting, and comparing whole genomes from different organisms.

genotype All the alleles of every gene present in a given individual. Often specified only for the alleles of a particular set of genes under study. Compare with **phenotype**.

genus (plural: genera) In Linnaeus' system, a taxonomic category of closely related species. Always italicized and capitalized to indicate that it is a recognized scientific genus.

geologic time scale The sequence of eons, eras, and periods used to describe the geologic history of Earth.

germ cell In animals, any cell that can potentially give rise to gametes. Also called *germ-line cells*.

germ layer In animals, one of the three basic types of tissue formed during gastrulation; gives rise to all other tissues. See **endoderm**, **mesoderm**, and **ectoderm**.

germ line In animals, any of the cells that are capable of giving rise to reproductive cells (sperm or egg). Compare with **germ cell**.

germ theory of disease The theory that infectious diseases are caused by bacteria, viruses, and other microorganisms.

germination The process by which a seed becomes a young plant.

gestation The period of development inside the mother, from implantation to birth, in those species that have live birth.

gibberellins A class of hormones, found in plants and fungi, that stimulate growth. Gibberellic acid (GA) is one of the major gibberellins.

Gibbs free-energy change (ΔG) A measure of the change in enthalpy and entropy that occurs in a given chemical reaction. ΔG is less than 0 for spontaneous reactions and greater than 0 for nonspontaneous reactions.

gill Any organ in aquatic animals that exchanges gases and other dissolved substances between the blood and the surrounding water. Typically, a filamentous outgrowth of a body surface.

gill arch In aquatic vertebrates, a curved region of tissue between the gills. Gills are suspended from the gill arches.

gill filament In fish, any of the many long, thin structures that extend from gill arches into the water and across which gas exchange occurs.

gill lamella (plural: gill lamellae) Any of hundreds to thousands of sheetlike structures, each containing a capillary bed, that make up a gill filament.

gland An organ whose primary function is to secrete some substance, either into the blood (endocrine gland) or into some other space such as the gut or skin (exocrine gland).

glia Collective term for several types of cells in nervous tissue that are not neurons and do not conduct electrical signals but perform other functions, such as providing support, nourishment, or electrical insulation. Also called *glial cells*.

global carbon cycle See **carbon cycle, global**.

global climate change The global sum of all the local changes in temperature and precipitation patterns that accompany global warming (or in some past events, global cooling).

global gene regulation The regulation of multiple bacterial genes that are not part of one operon.

global nitrogen cycle See **nitrogen cycle, global**.

global warming A sustained increase in Earth's average surface temperature.

global water cycle See **water cycle, global**.

glomalin A glycoprotein that is abundant in the hyphae of arbuscular mycorrhizal fungi; when hyphae decay, it is an important component of soil.

glomerulus (plural: glomeruli) (1) In the vertebrate kidney, a ball-like cluster of capillaries, surrounded by Bowman's capsule, at the beginning of a nephron. (2) In the brain, a ball-shaped cluster of neurons in the olfactory bulb.

glucagon A peptide hormone produced by the pancreas in response to low blood glucose. Raises blood glucose by triggering breakdown of glycogen and stimulating gluconeogenesis. Compare with **insulin**.

glucocorticoids A class of steroid hormones, produced and secreted by the adrenal cortex, that increase blood glucose and prepare the body for stress. Include cortisol and corticosterone. Compare with **mineralocorticoids**.

gluconeogenesis Synthesis of glucose, often from non-carbohydrate sources (e.g., proteins and fatty acids). In plants, used to produce glucose from products of the Calvin cycle. In animals, occurs in the liver in response to low insulin levels and high glucagon levels.

glucose Six-carbon monosaccharide whose oxidation in cellular respiration is the major source of ATP in animal cells.

glyceraldehyde-3-phosphate (G3P) The phosphorylated three-carbon compound formed as the result of carbon fixation in the first step of the Calvin cycle.

glycerol A three-carbon molecule that forms the "backbone" of phospholipids and most fats.

glycogen A highly branched storage polysaccharide composed of glucose monomers joined by α-1,4- and α-1,6-glycosidic linkages. The major form of stored carbohydrate in animals.

glycolipid Any lipid molecule that is covalently bonded to a carbohydrate group.

glycolysis A series of 10 chemical reactions that oxidize glucose to produce pyruvate, NADH, and ATP.

Used by organisms as part of fermentation or cellular respiration.

glycoprotein Any protein with one or more covalently bonded carbohydrates, typically oligosaccharides.

glycosidic linkage The covalent linkage formed by a condensation reaction between two sugar monomers; joins the residues of a polysaccharide.

glycosylation Addition of a carbohydrate group to a molecule.

glyoxysome Specialized type of peroxisome found in plant cells and packed with enzymes for processing the products of photosynthesis.

gnathostomes Animals with jaws. Most vertebrates are gnathostomes.

Golgi apparatus A eukaryotic organelle, consisting of stacks of flattened membranous sacs (cisternae), that functions in processing and sorting proteins and lipids destined to be secreted or directed to other organelles. Also called *Golgi complex*.

gonad An organ, such as a testis or an ovary, that produces reproductive cells.

gonadotropin-releasing hormone (GnRH) A peptide hormone, produced and secreted by the hypothalamus, that stimulates release of follicle-stimulating hormone (FSH) and luteinizing hormone (LH) from the anterior pituitary.

grade In taxonomy, a group of species that share some, but not all, of the descendants of a common ancestor. Also called a *paraphyletic group*.

Gram-negative Describing bacteria that look pink when treated with a Gram stain. These bacteria have a cell wall composed of a thin layer of peptidoglycan and an outer phospholipid layer. Compare with **Gram-positive**.

Gram-positive Describing bacteria that look purple when treated with a Gram stain. These bacteria have cell walls composed of a thick layer of peptidoglycan and no outer phospholipid later. Compare with **Gram-negative**.

Gram stain A dye that distinguishes the two general types of cell walls found in bacteria. Used to routinely classify bacteria as Gram-negative or Gram-positive.

granum (plural: grana) In chloroplasts, a stack of flattened, membrane-bound thylakoid discs where the light reactions of photosynthesis occur.

gravitropism The growth or movement of a plant in a particular direction in response to gravity.

grazing food chain The ecological network of herbivores and the predators and parasites that consume them.

great apes See **hominids**.

green algae A paraphyletic group of photosynthetic organisms that contain chloroplasts similar to those in green plants. Often classified as protists, green algae are the closest living relatives of land plants and form a monophyletic group with them.

greenhouse gas An atmospheric gas that absorbs and reflects infrared radiation, so that heat radiated from Earth is retained in the atmosphere instead of being lost to space.

gross primary productivity In an ecosystem, the total amount of carbon fixed by photosynthesis (or more

rarely, chemosynthesis), including that used for cellular respiration, over a given time period. Compare with **net primary productivity**.

ground meristem The middle layer of a young plant embryo. Gives rise to the ground tissue system.

ground tissue An embryonic tissue layer that gives rise to parenchyma, collenchyma, and sclerenchyma—tissues other than the epidermis and vascular tissue. Also called *ground tissue system*.

groundwater Any water below the land surface.

growth factor Any of a large number of signaling molecules that are secreted by certain cells and that stimulate other cells to grow, divide, or differentiate.

growth hormone (GH) A peptide hormone, produced and secreted by the mammalian anterior pituitary, that promotes lengthening of the long bones in children and muscle growth, tissue repair, and lactation in adults. Also called *somatotropin*.

guanosine triphosphate (GTP) A nucleotide consisting of guanine, a ribose sugar, and three phosphate groups. Can be hydrolyzed to release free energy. Commonly used in RNA synthesis and also functions in signal transduction in association with G proteins.

guard cell One of two specialized, crescent-shaped cells forming the border of a plant stoma. Guard cells can change shape to open or close the stoma. See also **stoma**.

gustation The perception of taste.

guttation Excretion of water droplets from plant leaves; visible in the early morning. Caused by root pressure.

gymnosperm A vascular plant that makes seeds but does not produce flowers. The gymnosperms include five lineages of green plants (cycads, ginkgoes, conifers, redwoods, and gnetophytes). Compare with **angiosperm**.

H$^{\boxtimes}$-ATPase See **proton pump**.

habitat degradation The reduction of the quality of a habitat.

habitat destruction Human-caused destruction of a natural habitat, replaced by an urban, suburban, or agricultural landscape.

habitat fragmentation The breakup of a large region of a habitat into many smaller regions, separated from others by a different type of habitat.

Hadley cell An atmospheric cycle of large-scale air movement in which warm equatorial air rises, moves north or south, and then descends at approximately 30° N or 30° S latitude.

hair cell A pressure-detecting sensory cell that has tiny "hairs" (stereocilia) jutting from its surface. Found in the inner ear, lateral line system, and ampullae of Lorenzini.

hairpin A secondary structure in RNA consisting of a stable loop formed by hydrogen bonding between purine and pyrimidine bases on the same strand.

Hamilton's rule The proposition that an allele for altruistic behavior will be favored by natural selection only if *Br C*, where *B* = the fitness benefit to the recipient, *C* = the fitness cost to the actor, and *r* = the coefficient of relatedness between recipient and actor.

haploid (1) Having one set of chromosomes (1*n* or *n* for short). (2) A cell or an individual organism with one set of chromosomes. Compare with **diploid**.

haploid number The number of different types of chromosomes in a cell. Symbolized as *n*.

Hardy–Weinberg principle A principle of population genetics stating that genotype frequencies in a large population do not change from generation to generation in the absence of evolutionary processes (e.g., mutation, gene flow, genetic drift, and selection), and nonrandom mating.

haustorium (plural: haustoria) Highly modified stem or root of a parasitic plant. The haustorium penetrates the tissues of a host and absorbs nutrients and water.

hearing The sensation of the wavelike changes in air pressure called sound.

heart A muscular pump that circulates blood throughout the body.

heart murmur A distinctive sound caused by backflow of blood through a defective heart valve.

heartwood The older xylem in the center of an older stem or root, containing protective compounds and no longer functioning in water transport.

heat Thermal energy that is transferred from an object at higher temperature to one at lower temperature.

heat of vaporization The energy required to vaporize 1 gram of a liquid into a gas.

heat-shock proteins Proteins that facilitate refolding of proteins that have been denatured by heat or other agents.

heavy chain The larger of the two types of polypeptide chains in an antibody or B-cell receptor molecule; composed of a variable (*V*) region, which contributes to the antigen-binding site, and a constant (*C*) region. Differences in heavy-chain constant regions determine the different classes of immunoglobulins (IgA, IgE, etc.). Compare with **light chain**.

helper T cell A CD4+ effector T cell that secretes cytokines and in other ways promotes the activation of other lymphocytes. Activated by interacting with complementary class II MHC–peptide complexes on the surface of antigen-presenting cells such as dendritic cells.

heme A small molecule that binds to each of the four polypeptides that combine to form hemoglobin; contains an iron ion that can bind oxygen.

hemimetabolous metamorphosis A type of metamorphosis in which the animal increases in size from one stage to the next, but does not dramatically change its body form. Also called *incomplete metamorphosis*.

hemocoel A body cavity, present in arthropods and some mollusks, containing a pool of circulatory fluid (hemolymph) bathing the internal organs. Unlike a coelom, a hemocoel is not lined in mesoderm.

hemoglobin An oxygen-binding protein consisting of four polypeptide subunits, each containing an oxygen-binding heme group. The major oxygen carrier in mammalian blood.

hemolymph The circulatory fluid of animals with open circulatory systems (e.g., insects) in which the fluid is not confined to blood vessels.

herbaceous Referring to a plant that is not woody.

herbivore (adjective: herbivorous) An animal that eats primarily plants and rarely or never eats meat. Compare with **carnivore** and **omnivore**.

herbivory The practice of eating plant tissues.

heredity The transmission of traits from parents to offspring via genetic information.

heritable Referring to traits that can be transmitted from one generation to the next.

hermaphrodite An organism that produces both male and female gametes.

heterokaryotic Describing a cell or fungal mycelium containing two or more haploid nuclei that are genetically distinct.

heterospory (adjective: heterosporous) In seed plants, the production of two distinct types of spores: microspores, which become the male gametophyte, and megaspores, which become the female gametophyte. Compare with **homospory**.

heterotherm An animal whose body temperature varies markedly. Compare with **homeotherm**.

heterotroph Any organism that cannot synthesize reduced organic compounds from inorganic sources and that must obtain them from other organisms. Some bacteria, some archaea, and virtually all fungi and animals are heterotrophs. Also called *consumer*. Compare with **autotroph**.

heterozygote advantage A pattern of natural selection that favors heterozygous individuals compared with homozygotes. Tends to maintain genetic variation in a population, thus is a form of balancing selection.

heterozygous Having two different alleles of a gene.

hexose A monosaccharide (simple sugar) containing six carbon atoms.

hibernation An energy-conserving physiological state, marked by a decrease in metabolic rate, body temperature, and activity, that lasts for a prolonged period (weeks to months). Occurs in some animals in response to winter cold and scarcity of food. Compare with **torpor**.

hindbrain One of the three main regions of the vertebrate brain, responsible for balance and sometimes hearing; includes the cerebellum and medulla oblongata. Compare with **forebrain** and **midbrain**.

histamine A molecule released from mast cells during an inflammatory response that, at high concentrations, causes blood vessels to constrict to reduce blood loss from tissue damage.

histone One of several positively charged (basic) proteins associated with DNA in the chromatin of eukaryotic cells.

histone acetyltransferases (HATs) A class of eukaryotic enzymes that loosen chromatin structure by adding acetyl groups to histone proteins.

histone code The hypothesis that specific combinations of chemical modifications of histone proteins contain information that influences chromatin condensation and gene expression.

histone deacetylases (HDACs) A class of eukaryotic enzymes that condense chromatin by removing acetyl groups from histone proteins.

holoenzyme A multipart enzyme consisting of a core enzyme (containing the active site for catalysis) along with other required proteins.

holometabolous metamorphosis A type of metamorphosis in which the animal completely changes its form; includes a distinct larval stage. Also called *complete metamorphosis*.

homeobox A DNA sequence of about 180 base pairs that codes for a DNA binding motif called the homeodomain in the resulting protein. Genes containing a homeobox usually play a role in controlling development of organisms from fruit flies to humans.

homeostasis (adjective: homeostatic) The array of relatively stable chemical and physical conditions in an animal's cells, tissues, and organs. May be achieved by the body's passively matching the conditions of a stable external environment (conformational homeostasis) or by active physiological processes (regulatory homeostasis) triggered by variations in the external or internal environment.

homeotherm An animal that has a constant or relatively constant body temperature. Compare with **heterotherm**.

homeotic mutation A mutation that causes one body part to be substituted for another.

hominids Members of the family Hominidae, which includes humans and extinct related forms, chimpanzees, gorillas, and orangutans. Distinguished by large body size, no tail, and an exceptionally large brain. Also called *great apes*.

hominins Any extinct or living species of bipedal apes, such as *Australopithecus africanus*, *Homo erectus*, and *Homo sapiens*.

homologous See **homology**.

homologous chromosomes In a diploid organism, chromosomes that are similar in size, shape, and gene content. Also called *homologs*.

homology (adjective: homologous) Similarity among organisms of different species due to their inheritance from a common ancestor. Features that exhibit such similarity (e.g., DNA sequences, proteins, body parts) are said to be homologous. Compare with **homoplasy**.

homoplasy (adjective: homoplastic) Similarity among organisms of different species due to reasons other than common ancestry, such as convergent evolution. Features that exhibit such similarity (e.g., the wings of birds and bats) are said to be homoplastic, or convergent. Compare with **homology**.

homospory (adjective: homosporous) In seedless vascular plants, the production of just one type of spore. Compare with **heterospory**.

homozygous Having two identical alleles of a gene.

hormone Any of many different signaling molecules that circulate throughout the plant or animal body and can trigger characteristic responses in distant target cells at very low concentrations.

hormone-response element A specific sequence in DNA to which a steroid hormone–receptor complex can bind and affect gene transcription.

host An individual that has been invaded by an organism such as a parasite or a virus, or that provides habitat or resources to a commensal organism.

host cell A cell that has been invaded by a parasitic organism or a virus and provides an environment that is conducive to the pathogen's growth and reproduction.

***Hox* genes** A class of genes found in several animal phyla, including vertebrates, that are expressed in a distinctive pattern along the anterior–posterior axis in early embryos and control formation of specific structures. *Hox* genes code for transcription factors with a DNA-binding sequence called a homeobox.

human Any member of the genus *Homo*, which includes modern humans (*Homo sapiens*) and several extinct species.

human chorionic gonadotropin (hCG) A glycoprotein hormone produced by a human embryo and placenta from about week 3 to week 14 of pregnancy. Maintains the corpus luteum, which produces hormones that preserve the uterine lining.

Human Genome Project The multinational research project that sequenced the human genome.

human immunodeficiency virus (HIV) A retrovirus that causes acquired immune deficiency syndrome (AIDS) in humans.

humoral (immune) response The type of immune response that is mediated through the production and secretion of antibodies, complement proteins, and other soluble factors that eliminate extracellular pathogens. Compare with **cell-mediated (immune) response**.

humus The decayed organic matter in soils.

hybrid The offspring of parents from two different strains, populations, or species.

hybrid zone A geographic area where interbreeding occurs between two species, sometimes producing fertile hybrid offspring.

hydrocarbon An organic molecule that contains only hydrogen and carbon atoms.

hydrogen bond A weak interaction between two molecules or different parts of the same molecule resulting from the attraction between a hydrogen atom with a partial positive charge and another atom (usually O or N) with a partial negative charge. Compare with **covalent bond** and **ionic bond**.

hydrogen ion (H⁺) A single proton with a charge of 1+; typically, one that is dissolved in solution or that is being transferred from one atom to another in a chemical reaction.

hydrolysis A chemical reaction in which a molecule is split into smaller molecules by reacting with water. In biology, most hydrolysis reactions involve the splitting of polymers into monomers. Compare with **condensation reaction**.

hydrophilic Interacting readily with water. Hydrophilic compounds are typically polar compounds containing partially or fully charged atoms. Compare with **hydrophobic**.

hydrophobic Not readily interacting with water. Hydrophobic compounds are typically nonpolar compounds that lack partially or fully charged atoms. Compare with **hydrophilic**.

hydrophobic interactions Very weak interactions between nonpolar molecules, or nonpolar regions of the same molecule, when exposed to an aqueous solvent. The surrounding water molecules support these interactions by interacting with one another and encapsulating the nonpolar molecules.

hydroponic growth Growth of plants in liquid cultures instead of soil.

hydrostatic skeleton A system of body support involving a body wall in tension surrounding a fluid or soft tissue under compression.

hydroxide ion (OH⁻) An oxygen atom and a hydrogen atom joined by a single covalent bond and carrying a negative charge; formed by dissociation of water.

hygiene hypothesis The claim that immune disorders arise in individuals less likely to have been exposed to pathogens and parasites, especially in early childhood. Provides an explanation for the increased risk of allergies and autoimmune disease in countries with high levels of sanitation.

hyperosmotic Comparative term designating a solution that has a greater solute concentration, and therefore a lower water concentration, than another solution. Compare with **hyposmotic** and **isosmotic**.

hyperpolarization A change in membrane potential from its resting negative state to an even more negative state; a normal phase in an action potential. Compare with **depolarization**.

hypersensitive reaction An intense allergic response by cells that have been sensitized by previous exposure to an allergen.

hypersensitive response In plants, the rapid death of a cell that has been infected by a pathogen, thereby reducing the potential for infection to spread throughout a plant. Compare with **systemic acquired resistance**.

hypertension Abnormally high blood pressure.

hypertonic Comparative term designating a solution that, if inside a cell or vesicle, results in the uptake of water and swelling or even bursting of the membrane-bound structure. This solution has a greater solute concentration than the solution on the other side of the membrane. Used when the solute is unable to pass through the membrane. Compare with **hypotonic** and **isotonic**.

hypha (plural: hyphae) One of the long, branching strands of a fungal mycelium (the mesh-like body of a fungus). Also found in some protists.

hypocotyl The stem of a very young plant; the region between the cotyledon (embryonic leaf) and the radicle (embryonic root).

hyposmotic Comparative term designating a solution that has a lower solute concentration, and therefore a higher water concentration, than another solution. Compare with **hyperosmotic** and **isosmotic**.

hypothalamic–pituitary axis The functional interaction of the hypothalamus and the anterior pituitary gland, which are anatomically distinct but work together to regulate most of the other endocrine glands in the body.

hypothalamus A part of the brain that functions in maintaining the body's internal physiological state by regulating the autonomic nervous system, endocrine system, body temperature, water balance, and appetite.

hypothesis A testable statement that explains a phenomenon or a set of observations.

hypotonic Comparative term designating a solution that, if inside a cell or vesicle, results in the loss of water and shrinkage of the membrane-bound structure. This solution has a lower solute concentration than the solution on the other side of the membrane. Used when the solute is unable to pass through the membrane. Compare with **hypertonic** and **isotonic**.

immigration The migration of individuals into a particular population from other populations. Compare with **emigration**.

immune system The system whose primary function is to defend the host organism against pathogens. Includes several types of cells (e.g., leukocytes). In vertebrates, several organs are also involved where specialized cells develop or reside (e.g., lymph nodes and thymus).

immunity (adjective: immune) State of being protected against infection by disease-causing pathogens.

immunization The conferring of immunity to a particular disease by artificial means.

immunoglobulin (Ig) Any of the class of proteins that are structurally related to antibodies.

immunological memory The ability of the immune system to "remember" an antigen and mount a rapid, effective adaptive immune response to a pathogen encountered years or decades earlier. Based on the formation of memory lymphocytes.

impact hypothesis The hypothesis that a collision between the Earth and an asteroid caused the mass extinction at the K–P boundary, 65 million years ago.

imperfect flower A flower that contains male parts (stamens) *or* female parts (carpels) but not both. Compare with **perfect flower**.

implantation The process by which an embryo buries itself in the uterine or oviductal wall and forms a placenta. Occurs in mammals and some other viviparous vertebrates.

in situ hybridization A technique for detecting specific DNAs and mRNAs in cells and tissues by use of labeled complementary probes. Can be used to determine where and when particular genes are expressed in embryos.

inbreeding Mating between closely related individuals. Increases homozygosity of a population and often leads to a decline in the average fitness via selection (inbreeding depression).

inbreeding depression In inbred offspring, fitness declines due to deleterious recessive alleles that are homozygous, thus exposed to selection.

inclusive fitness The combination of (1) direct production of offspring (direct fitness) and (2) extra production of offspring by relatives in response to help provided by the individual in question (indirect fitness).

incomplete digestive tract A digestive tract that has just one opening.

incomplete dominance An inheritance pattern in which the heterozygote phenotype is in between the homozygote phenotypes.

incomplete metamorphosis See **hemimetabolous metamorphosis**.

independent assortment, principle of The concept that each pair of hereditary elements (alleles of the same gene) segregates (separates) independently of alleles of other genes during meiosis. One of Mendel's two principles of genetics.

indeterminate growth A pattern of growth in which an individual continues to increase its overall body size throughout its life.

induced fit Change in the shape of the active site of an enzyme, as the result of initial weak binding of a substrate, so that it binds substrate more tightly.

inducer A small molecule that triggers transcription of a specific gene, often by binding to and inactivating a repressor protein.

inducible defense A defensive trait that is manifested only in response to the presence of a consumer (predator or herbivore) or pathogen. Compare with **constitutive defense**.

infection thread An invagination of the plasma membrane of a root hair through which beneficial nitrogen-fixing bacteria enter the roots of their host plants (legumes).

inflammatory response An aspect of the innate immune response, seen in most cases of infection or tissue injury, in which the affected tissue becomes swollen, red, warm, and painful.

ingestion The act of bringing food into the digestive tract.

inhibition In ecological succession, the phenomenon in which early-arriving species make conditions less favorable for the establishment of certain later-arriving species. Compare with **facilitation** and **tolerance**.

inhibitory postsynaptic potential (IPSP) A change in membrane potential, usually hyperpolarization, at a neuron dendrite that makes an action potential less likely.

initiation (1) In an enzyme-catalyzed reaction, the stage during which enzymes orient reactants precisely as they bind at specific locations within the enzyme's active site. (2) In DNA transcription, the stage during which RNA polymerase and other proteins assemble at the promoter sequence and open the strands of DNA to start transcription. (3) In translation, the stage during which a complex consisting of initiation factor proteins, a ribosome, an mRNA, and an aminoacyl tRNA corresponding to the start codon is formed.

initiation factors A class of proteins that assist ribosomes in binding to a messenger RNA molecule to begin translation.

innate behavior Behavior that is inherited genetically, does not have to be learned, and is typical of a species.

innate immune response See **innate immunity**.

innate immunity A set of barriers to infection and generic defenses against broad types of pathogens. Produces an immediate response that involves many different leukocytes, which often activate an inflammatory response. Compare with **acquired immunity**.

inner cell mass (ICM) A cluster of cells, in the interior of a mammalian blastocyst, that eventually develop into the embryo. Contrast with **trophoblast**.

inner ear The innermost portion of the mammalian ear, consisting of a fluid-filled system of tubes that includes the cochlea (which receives sound vibrations from the middle ear) and the semicircular canals (which function in balance).

insects A terrestrial lineage of arthropods distinguished by three tagmata (head, thorax, abdomen), a single pair of antennae, and unbranched appendages.

insulin A peptide hormone produced by the pancreas in response to high levels of glucose (or amino acids) in blood. Enables cells to absorb glucose and coordinates synthesis of fats, proteins, and glycogen. Compare with **glucagon**.

integral membrane protein Any membrane protein that spans the entire lipid bilayer. Also called *transmembrane protein*. Compare with **peripheral membrane protein**.

integrated pest management In agriculture or forestry, systems for managing insects or other pests that include carefully controlled applications of toxins, introduction of species that prey on pests, planting schemes that reduce the chance of a severe pest outbreak, and other techniques.

integrator A component of an animal's nervous system that functions as part of a homeostatic system by evaluating sensory information and triggering appropriate responses. See **effector** and **sensor**.

integrin Any of a class of cell-surface proteins that bind to laminins and other proteins in the extracellular matrix, thus holding cells in place.

intercalated disc A type of specialized connection between adjacent heart muscle cells that contains gap junctions, allowing electrical signals to pass between the cells.

intermediate filament A long fiber, about 10 nm in diameter, composed of one of various proteins (e.g., keratins, lamins); one of the three types of cytoskeletal fibers. Used to form networks that help maintain cell shape and hold the nucleus in place. Compare with **actin filament** and **microtubule**.

intermediate host The host species in which a parasite reproduces asexually. Compare with **definitive host**.

intermediate muscle fiber Type of skeletal muscle fiber that is pink in color, generates ATP by both glycolysis and aerobic respiration, and has contractile properties that are intermediate between slow fibers and fast fibers. Also called fast oxidative fiber.

interneuron A neuron that passes signals from one neuron to another. Compare with **motor neuron** and **sensory neuron**.

internode The section of a plant stem between two nodes (sites where leaves attach).

interphase The portion of the cell cycle between one M phase and the next. Includes the G_1 phase, S phase, and G_2 phase.

intersexual selection The sexual selection of an individual of one gender for mating by an individual of the other gender (usually by female choice).

interspecific competition Competition between members of different species for the same limited resource. Compare with **intraspecific competition**.

interstitial fluid The plasma-like fluid found in the region (interstitial space) between cells.

intertidal zone The region between the low-tide and high-tide marks on a seashore.

intrasexual selection Competition among members of one gender for an opportunity to mate (usually male–male competition).

intraspecific competition Competition between members of the same species for the same limited resource. Compare with **interspecific competition**.

intrinsic rate of increase (r_{max}) The rate at which a population will grow under optimal conditions (i.e., when birthrates are as high as possible and death rates are as low as possible). Compare with **finite rate of increase**.

intron A region of a eukaryotic gene that is transcribed into RNA but is later removed. Compare with **exon**.

invasive species An exotic (nonnative) species that, upon introduction to a new area, spreads rapidly and competes successfully with native species.

inversion A mutation in which a segment of a chromosome breaks from the rest of the chromosome, flips, and rejoins in reversed orientation.

invertebrates A paraphyletic group composed of animals without a backbone; includes about 95 percent of all animal species. Compare with **vertebrates**.

involuntary muscle Muscle that contracts in response to stimulation by involuntary (parasympathetic or sympathetic), but not voluntary (somatic), neural stimulation.

ion An atom or a molecule that has lost or gained electrons and thus carries an electric charge, either positive (cation) or negative (anion), respectively.

ion channel A type of channel protein that allows certain ions to diffuse across a plasma membrane down an electrochemical gradient.

ionic bond A chemical bond that is formed when an electron is completely transferred from one atom to another so that the atoms remain associated due to their opposite electric charges. Compare with **covalent bond** and **hydrogen bond**.

iris A ring of pigmented muscle just behind the cornea in the vertebrate eye that contracts or expands to control the amount of light entering the eye through the pupil.

isosmotic Comparative term designating a solution that has the same solute concentration and water concentration as another solution. Compare with **hyperosmotic** and **hyposmotic**.

isotonic Comparative term designating a solution that, if inside a cell or vesicle, results in no net uptake or loss of water and thus no effect on the volume of the membrane-bound structure. This solution has the same solute concentration as the solution on the other side of the membrane. Compare with **hypertonic** and **hypotonic**.

isotope Any of several forms of an element that have the same number of protons but differ in the number of neutrons.

joint A place where two components (bones, cartilages, etc.) of a skeleton meet. May be movable (an articulated joint) or immovable (e.g., skull sutures).

juvenile An individual that has adult-like morphology but is not sexually mature.

juvenile hormone An insect hormone that prevents larvae from metamorphosing into adults.

karyogamy Fusion of two haploid nuclei to form a diploid nucleus. Occurs in many fungi, and in animals and plants during fertilization of gametes.

karyotype The distinctive appearance of all of the chromosomes in an individual, including the number of chromosomes and their length and banding patterns (after staining with dyes).

keystone species A species that has an exceptionally great impact on the other species in its ecosystem relative to its abundance.

kidney In terrestrial vertebrates, one of a paired organ situated at the back of the abdominal cavity that filters the blood, produces urine, and secretes several hormones.

kilocalorie (kcal) A unit of energy often used to measure the energy content of food. A kcal of energy raises 1 kg of water 1°C.

kin selection A form of natural selection that favors traits that increase survival or reproduction of an individual's kin at the expense of the individual.

kinesin A class of motor proteins that uses the chemical energy of ATP to "walk" toward the plus end of a microtubule. Used to transport vesicles, particles, organelles and chromosomes.

kinetic energy The energy of motion. Compare with **potential energy**.

kinetochore A protein complex at the centromere where microtubules attach to the chromosome. Contains motor proteins and microtubule-binding proteins that are involved in chromosome segregation during M phase.

kinetochore microtubules Microtubules in the spindle formed during mitosis and meiosis that are attached to the kinetochore on a chromosome.

kinocilium (plural: kinocilia) A single cilium that juts from the surface of many hair cells and functions in detection of sound or pressure.

knock-out allele A mutant allele that does not produce a functional product. Also called a *null allele* or *loss-of-function allele*.

Koch's postulates Four criteria used to determine whether a suspected infectious agent causes a particular disease.

labium majus (plural: labia majora) One of two outer folds of skin that surround the labia minora, clitoris, and vaginal opening of female mammals.

labium minus (plural: labia minora) One of two folds of skin inside the labia majora and surrounding the opening of the urethra and vagina.

labor The strong muscular contractions of the uterus that expel the fetus during birth.

lac operon A set of three genes in *E. coli* that are transcribed into a single mRNA and required for lactose metabolism. Studies of the *lac* operon revealed many insights about gene regulation.

lactation (verb: lactate) Production of milk to feed offspring, from mammary glands of mammals.

lacteal A small lymphatic vessel extending into the center of a villus in the small intestine. Receives chylomicrons containing fat absorbed from food.

lactic acid fermentation Catabolic pathway in which pyruvate produced by glycolysis is converted to lactic acid in the absence of oxygen.

lagging strand In DNA replication, the strand of new DNA that is synthesized discontinuously in a series of short pieces that are later joined. Also called *discontinuous strand*. Compare with **leading strand**.

laminins An abundant protein in the extracellular matrix that binds to other ECM components and to integrins in plasma membranes; helps anchor cells in place. Predominantly found in the basal lamina; many subtypes function in different tissues.

large intestine The distal portion of the digestive tract, consisting of the cecum, colon, and rectum. Its primary function is to compact the wastes delivered from the small intestine and absorb enough water to form feces.

larva (plural: larvae) An immature stage of an animal species in which the immature and adult stages have different body forms.

late endosome A membrane-bound vesicle that arises from an early endosome, accepts lysosomal enzymes from the Golgi, and matures into a lysosome.

latency In viruses that infect animals, the ability to coexist with the host cell in a dormant state without producing new virions. The viral genetic material is replicated as the host cell replicates. Genetic material may or may not be integrated into the host genome, depending on the virus.

lateral bud A bud that forms at the nodes of a stem and may develop into a lateral (side) branch. Also called *axillary bud*.

lateral gene transfer Transfer of DNA between two different species.

lateral line system A pressure-sensitive sensory organ found in many aquatic vertebrates.

lateral root A plant root that extends horizontally from another root.

leaching Loss of nutrients from soil via percolating water.

leading strand In DNA replication, the strand of new DNA that is synthesized in one continuous piece. Also called *continuous strand*. Compare with **lagging strand**.

leaf The main photosynthetic organ of vascular plants.

leak channel Ion channel that allows ions to leak across the membrane of a neuron in its resting state.

learning An enduring change in an individual's behavior that results from specific experience(s).

leghemoglobin An iron-containing protein similar to hemoglobin. Found in infected cells of legume root nodules where it binds oxygen, preventing it from poisoning a bacterial enzyme needed for nitrogen fixation.

legumes Members of the pea plant family. Many form symbiotic associations with nitrogen-fixing bacteria in their roots.

lens A transparent structure that focuses incoming light onto a retina or other light-sensing apparatus of an eye.

lenticel Spongy segment in bark that allows gas exchange between cells in a woody stem and the atmosphere.

leptin A hormone produced and secreted by fat cells (adipocytes) that acts to stabilize fat-tissue mass partly by inhibiting appetite and increasing energy expenditure.

leukocyte Any of several types of blood cells, including neutrophils, macrophages, and lymphocytes, that reside in tissues and circulate in blood and lymph. Functions in tissue repair and defense against pathogens. Also called *white blood cell*.

lichen A symbiotic association of a fungus, often in the Ascomycota lineage, and a photosynthetic alga or cyanobacterium.

life cycle The sequence of developmental events and phases that occurs during the life span of an organism, from fertilization to offspring production.

life history The sequence of events in an individual's life from birth to reproduction to death, including how an individual allocates resources to growth, reproduction, and activities or structures that are related to survival.

life table A data set that summarizes the probability that an individual in a certain population will survive and reproduce in any given year over the course of its lifetime.

ligament Connective tissue that joins bones of an endoskeleton together.

ligand Any molecule that binds to a specific site on a receptor molecule.

ligand-gated channel An ion channel that opens or closes in response to binding by a certain molecule. Compare with **voltage-gated channel**.

light chain The smaller of the two types of polypeptide chains in an antibody or B-cell receptor molecule; composed of a variable (*V*) region, which contributes to the antigen-binding site, and a constant (*C*) region. Compare with **heavy chain**.

lignin A substance, found in the secondary cell walls of some plants, that is exceptionally stiff and strong; a complex polymer built from six-carbon rings. Most abundant in woody plant parts.

limiting nutrient Any essential nutrient whose scarcity in the environment significantly reduces growth and reproduction of organisms.

limnetic zone Open water (not near shore) that receives enough sunlight to support photosynthesis.

lineage See **monophyletic group**.

LINEs (long interspersed nuclear elements) The most abundant class of transposable elements in human genomes; can create copies of itself and insert them elsewhere in the genome. Compare with **SINEs**.

lingual lipase An enzyme produced by glands in the tongue. It breaks down fat molecules into fatty acids and monoglycerides.

linkage In genetics, a physical association between two genes because they are on the same chromosome; the inheritance patterns resulting from this association.

linkage map See **genetic map**.

lipid Any organic substance that does not dissolve in water, but dissolves well in nonpolar organic solvents. Lipids include fatty acids, fats, oils, waxes, steroids, and phospholipids.

lipid bilayer The basic structural element of all cellular membranes; consists of a two-layer sheet of phospholipid molecules with their hydrophobic tails oriented toward the inside and their hydrophilic heads toward the outside. Also called *phospholipid bilayer*.

littoral zone Shallow water near shore that receives enough sunlight to support photosynthesis. May be marine or freshwater; often flowering plants are present.

liver A large, complex organ of vertebrates that performs many functions, including storage of glycogen, processing and conversion of food and wastes, and production of bile.

lobe-finned fish Fish with fins supported by bony elements that extend down the length of the structure.

locomotion Movement of an organism under its own power.

locus (plural: loci) A gene's physical location on a chromosome.

logistic population growth The density-dependent decrease in growth rate as population size approaches the carrying capacity. Compare with **exponential population growth**.

long interspersed nuclear elements See **LINEs**.

long-day plant A plant that blooms in response to short nights (usually in late spring or early summer in the Northern Hemisphere). Compare with **day-neutral** and **short-day plant**.

loop of Henle In the vertebrate kidney, a long U-shaped loop in a nephron that extends into the medulla. Functions as a countercurrent exchanger to set up an osmotic gradient that allows reabsorption of water from the collecting duct.

loose connective tissue A type of connective tissue consisting of fibrous proteins in a soft matrix. Often functions as padding for organs.

lophophore A specialized feeding structure found in some lophotrochozoans and used in suspension (filter) feeding.

lophotrochozoans A major lineage of protostomes (Lophotrochozoa) that grow by extending the size of their skeletons rather than by molting. Many phyla have a specialized feeding structure (lophophore) and/or ciliated larvae (trochophore). Includes rotifers, flatworms, segmented worms, and mollusks. Compare with **ecdysozoans**.

loss-of-function allele See **knock-out allele**.

LUCA The *l*ast *u*niversal *c*ommon *a*ncestor of cells. This theoretical entity is proposed to be the product of chemical evolution and provided characteristics of life that are shared by all living organisms on Earth today.

lumen The interior space of any hollow structure (e.g., the rough ER) or organ (e.g., the stomach).

lung Any respiratory organ used for gas exchange between blood and air.

luteal phase The second major phase of a menstrual cycle, after ovulation, when the progesterone levels are high and the body is preparing for a possible pregnancy.

luteinizing hormone (LH) A peptide hormone, produced and secreted by the anterior pituitary, that stimulates estrogen production, ovulation, and formation of the corpus luteum in females and testosterone production in males.

lymph The mixture of fluid and white blood cells that circulates through the ducts and lymph nodes of the lymphatic system in vertebrates.

lymph node Any of many small, oval structures that lymph moves through in the lymphatic system. Filters the lymph and screens it for pathogens and other antigens. Major sites of lymphocyte activation.

lymphatic system In vertebrates, a body-wide network of thin-walled ducts (or vessels) and lymph nodes, separate from the circulatory system. Collects excess fluid from body tissues and returns it to the blood; also functions as part of the immune system.

lymphocyte A cell that circulates through the bloodstream and lymphatic system and is responsible for the development of adaptive immunity. In most cases belongs to one type of leukocyte—either B cells or T cells.

lysogeny In viruses that infect bacteria (bacteriophages), the ability to coexist with the host cell in a dormant state without producing new virions. The viral genetic material is integrated in the host chromosome and is replicated as the host cell replicates. Compare with **lytic cycle**.

lysosome A small, acidified organelle in an animal cell containing enzymes that catalyze hydrolysis reactions and can digest large molecules. Compare with **vacuole**.

lysozyme An enzyme that functions in innate immunity by digesting bacterial cell walls. Occurs in lysosomes of phagocytes and is secreted in saliva, tears, mucus, and egg white.

lytic cycle A type of viral replicative growth in which the production and release of virions kills the host cell. Compare with **lysogeny**.

M phase The phase of the cell cycle during which cell division occurs. Includes mitosis or meiosis and often cytokinesis.

M-phase-promoting factor (MPF) A complex of a cyclin and cyclin-dependent kinase that, when activated, phosphorylates a number of specific proteins needed to initiate mitosis in eukaryotic cells.

macromolecular machine A group of proteins that assemble to carry out a particular function.

macromolecule Any very large organic molecule, usually made up of smaller molecules (monomers) joined together into a polymer. The main biological macromolecules are proteins, nucleic acids, and polysaccharides.

macronutrient Any element (e.g., nitrogen) that is required in large quantities for normal growth, reproduction, and maintenance of a living organism. Compare with **micronutrient**.

macrophage A type of leukocyte in the innate immune system that participates in the inflammatory response by secreting cytokines and phagocytizing invading pathogens and apoptotic cells. Also serves as an antigen-presenting cell to activate lymphocytes.

MADS box A DNA sequence that codes for a DNA-binding motif in proteins; present in floral organ identity genes in plants. Functionally similar sequences are found in some fungal and animal genes.

magnetoreception A sensory system in which receptors are activated in response to magnetic fields.

magnetoreceptor A sensory cell or organ specialized for detecting magnetic fields.

major histocompatibility protein See **MHC protein**.

maladaptive Describing a trait that lowers fitness.

malaria A human disease caused by five species of the protist *Plasmodium* and passed to humans by mosquitoes.

malignant tumor A tumor that is actively growing and disrupting local tissues or is spreading to other organs. Cancer consists of one or more malignant tumors. Compare with **benign tumor**.

Malpighian tubules A major excretory organ of insects, consisting of blind-ended tubes that extend from the gut into the hemocoel. Filter hemolymph to form "pre-urine" and then send it to the hindgut for further processing.

mammals One of the two lineages of amniotes (vertebrates that produce amniotic eggs) distinguished by hair (or fur) and mammary glands. Includes the monotremes (platypuses), marsupials, and eutherians (placental mammals).

mammary glands Specialized exocrine glands that produce and secrete milk for nursing offspring. A diagnostic feature of mammals.

mandibles Any mouthpart used in chewing. In vertebrates, the lower jaw. In insects, crustaceans, and myriapods, the first pair of mouthparts.

mantle One of the three main parts of the mollusk body; the thick outer tissue that protects the visceral mass and may secrete a calcium carbonate shell.

marsh A wetland dominated by grasses and other nonwoody plants.

marsupials A lineage of mammals (Marsupiala) that nourish their young in an abdominal pouch after a very short period of development in the uterus.

mass extinction The extinction of a large number of diverse evolutionary groups during a relatively short period of geologic time (about 1 million years). May occur due to sudden and extraordinary environmental changes. Compare with **background extinction**.

mass feeder An animal that ingests chunks of food.

mass number The total number of protons and neutrons in an atom.

mast cell A type of leukocyte that is stationary (embedded in tissue) and helps trigger the inflammatory response, including secretion of histamine, to infection or injury. Particularly important in allergic responses and defense against parasites.

maternal chromosome A chromosome inherited from the mother.

mechanical advantage The ratio of force exerted on a load to the muscle force of the effort. A measure of the force efficiency of a mechanical system.

mechanoreception A sensory system in which receptors are activated in response to changes in pressure.

mechanoreceptor A sensory cell or organ specialized for detecting distortions caused by touch or pressure. One example is hair cells in the cochlea.

mediator Regulatory proteins in eukaryotes that form a physical link between regulatory transcription factors that are bound to DNA, the basal transcription complex, and RNA polymerase.

medium A liquid or solid that supports the growth of cells.

medulla The innermost part of an organ (e.g., kidney or adrenal gland).

medulla oblongata In vertebrates, a region of the brain stem that along with the cerebellum forms the hindbrain.

medusa (plural: medusae) The free-floating stage in the life cycle of some cnidarians (e.g., jellyfish). Compare with **polyp**.

megapascal (MPa) A unit of pressure (force per unit area) equivalent to 1 million pascals (Pa).

megasporangium (plural: megasporangia) In heterosporous species of plants, a spore-producing structure that produces megaspores, which go on to develop into female gametophytes.

megaspore In seed plants, a haploid (n) spore that is produced in a megasporangium by meiosis of a diploid ($2n$) megasporocyte; develops into a female gametophyte. Compare with **microspore**.

meiosis In sexually reproducing organisms, a special two-stage type of cell division in which one diploid ($2n$) parent cell produces haploid (n) cells (gametes); results in halving of the chromosome number. Also called *reduction division*.

meiosis I The first cell division of meiosis, in which synapsis and crossing over occur and homologous chromosomes are separated from each other, producing daughter cells with half as many chromosomes (each composed of two sister chromatids) as the parent cell.

meiosis II The second cell division of meiosis, in which sister chromatids are separated from each other. Similar to mitosis.

melatonin A hormone, produced by the pineal gland, that regulates sleep–wake cycles and seasonal reproduction in vertebrates.

membrane potential A difference in electric charge across a cell membrane; a form of potential energy. Also called *membrane voltage*.

memory Retention of learned information.

memory cells A type of lymphocyte responsible for maintaining immunity for years or decades after an infection. Descended from a B cell or T cell activated during a previous infection or vaccination.

meniscus (plural: menisci) The concave boundary layer formed at most air–water interfaces due to adhesion and surface tension.

menstrual cycle A female reproductive cycle seen in Old World monkeys and apes (including humans) in which the uterine lining is shed (menstruation) if no pregnancy occurs. Compare with **estrous cycle**.

menstruation The periodic shedding of the uterine lining through the vagina that occurs in females of Old World monkeys and apes, including humans.

meristem (adjective: meristematic) In plants, a group of undifferentiated cells, including stem cells, which can divide and develop into various adult tissues throughout the life of a plant. See also **apical meristem** and **ground meristem**.

mesoderm The middle of the three basic cell layers (germ layers) in most animal embryos; gives rise to muscles, bones, blood, and some internal organs (kidney, spleen, etc.). Compare with **ectoderm** and **endoderm**.

mesoglea A gelatinous material, containing scattered ectodermal cells, that is located between the ectoderm and endoderm of cnidarians (e.g., jellyfish, corals, and anemones).

mesophyll cell A type of cell, found near the surfaces of plant leaves, that is specialized for the light-dependent reactions of photosynthesis.

Mesozoic era The interval of geologic time, from 251 million to 65.5 million years ago, during which gymnosperms were the dominant plants and dinosaurs the dominant vertebrates. Ended with extinction of the dinosaurs (except birds).

messenger RNA (mRNA) An RNA molecule transcribed from DNA that carries information (in codons) that specifies the amino acid sequence of a polypeptide.

meta-analysis A comparative analysis of the results of many smaller, previously published studies.

metabolic pathway A linked series of biochemical reactions that build up or break down a particular molecule; the product of one reaction is the substrate of the next reaction.

metabolic rate The total energy use by all the cells of an individual. For aerobic organisms, often measured as the amount of oxygen consumed per hour.

metabolic water The water that is produced as a by-product of cellular respiration.

metagenomics The inventory of all the genes in a community or ecosystem by sequencing, analyzing, and comparing the genomes of the component organisms. Also called *environmental sequencing*.

metagenomics The inventory of all the genes in a community or ecosystem by sequencing, analyzing, and comparing the genomes of the component organisms. Sequencing of all or most of the genes present in an environment directly (also called *environmental sequencing*).

metallothioneins Small plant proteins that bind to and prevent excess metal ions from acting as toxins.

metamorphosis Transition from one developmental stage to another, such as from the larval to the adult form of an animal.

metaphase A stage in mitosis or meiosis during which chromosomes line up in the middle of the cell.

metaphase plate The plane along which chromosomes line up in the middle of the spindle during metaphase of mitosis or meiosis; not an actual structure.

metapopulation A population made up of many small, physically isolated populations connected by migration.

metastasis The spread of cancerous cells from their site of origin to distant sites in the body where they may establish additional tumors.

methanogen A prokaryote that produces methane (CH_4) as a by-product of cellular respiration.

methanotroph An organism (bacteria or archaea) that uses methane (CH_4) as its primary electron donor and source of carbon.

methyl salicylate (MeSA) A molecule that is hypothesized to function as a signal, transported among tissues, that triggers systematic acquired resistance in plants—a response to pathogen attack.

MHC protein Any of a large set of mammalian cell-surface glycoproteins involved in marking cells as self and in antigen presentation to T cells. Also called *MHC molecule*. Compare with **Class I** and **Class II MHC protein**.

microbe Any microscopic organism, including bacteria, archaea, and various tiny eukaryotes.

microbiology The field of study concerned with microscopic organisms.

microfibril Bundled strands of cellulose that serve as the fibrous component in plant cell walls.

microfilament See **actin filament**.

micronutrient Any element (e.g., iron, molybdenum, magnesium) that is required in very small quantities for normal growth, reproduction, and maintenance of a living organism. Compare with **macronutrient**.

micropyle The tiny pore in a plant ovule through which the pollen tube reaches the embryo sac.

microRNA (miRNA) A small, single-stranded RNA associated with proteins in an RNA-induced silencing complex (RISC). Processed from a longer premiRNA gene transcript. Can bind to complementary sequences in mRNA molecules, allowing the associated proteins of RISC to degrade the bound mRNA or inhibit its translation. See **RNA interference**.

microsatellite A noncoding stretch of eukaryotic DNA consisting of a repeating sequence 2 to 6 base pairs long. Also called *short tandem repeat* or *simple sequence repeat*.

microsporangium (plural: microsporangia) In heterosporous species of plants, a spore-producing structure that produces microspores, which go on to develop into male gametophytes.

microspore In seed plants, a haploid (n) spore that is produced in a microsporangium by meiosis of a diploid ($2n$) microsporocyte; develops into a male gametophyte. Compare with **megaspore**.

microtubule A long, tubular fiber, about 25 nm in diameter, formed by polymerization of tubulin protein dimers; one of the three types of cytoskeletal fibers. Involved in cell movement and transport of materials within the cell. Compare with **actin filament** and **intermediate filament**.

microtubule organizing center (MTOC) General term for any structure (e.g., centrosome and basal body) that organizes microtubules in cells.

microvilli (singular: microvillus) Tiny protrusions from the surface of an epithelial cell that increase the surface area for absorption of substances.

midbrain One of the three main regions of the vertebrate brain; includes sensory integrating and relay centers. Compare with **forebrain** and **hindbrain**.

middle ear The air-filled middle portion of the mammalian ear, which contains three small bones (ossicles) that transmit and amplify sound from the tympanic membrane to the inner ear. Is connected to the throat via the eustachian tube.

migration (1) In ecology, a seasonal movement of large numbers of organisms from one geographic location or habitat to another. (2) In population genetics, movement of individuals from one population to another.

millivolt (mV) A unit of voltage equal to 1/1000 of a volt.

mimicry A phenomenon in which one species has evolved (or learns) to look or sound like another species. See **Batesian mimicry** and **Müllerian mimicry**.

mineral One of various inorganic substances that are important components of enzyme cofactors or of structural materials in an organism.

mineralocorticoids A class of steroid hormones, produced and secreted by the adrenal cortex, that regulate electrolyte levels and the overall volume of body fluids. Aldosterone is the principal one in humans. Compare with **glucocorticoids**.

minisatellite A noncoding stretch of eukaryotic DNA consisting of a repeating sequence that is 6 to 100 base pairs long. Also called *variable number tandem repeat (VNTR)*.

mismatch repair The process by which mismatched base pairs in DNA are fixed.

missense mutation A point mutation (change in a single base pair) that changes one amino acid for another within the sequence of a protein.

mitochondrial matrix Central compartment of a mitochondrion, which is lined by the inner membrane; contains mitochondrial DNA, ribosomes, and the enzymes for pyruvate processing and the citric acid cycle.

mitochondrion (plural: mitochondria) A eukaryotic organelle that is bounded by a double membrane and is the site of aerobic respiration and ATP synthesis.

mitogen-activated protein kinases (MAPK) Enzymes that are involved in signal transduction pathways that often lead to the induction of cell replication. Different types are organized in a series, where one kinase activates another via phosphorylation. See also **phosphorylation cascade**.

mitosis In eukaryotic cells, the process of nuclear division that results in two daughter nuclei genetically identical with the parent nucleus. Subsequent cytokinesis (division of the cytoplasm) yields two daughter cells.

mode of transmission The type of inheritance observed as a trait is passed from parent to offspring. Some common types are autosomal recessive, autosomal dominant, and X-linked recessive.

model organism An organism selected for intensive scientific study based on features that make it easy to work with (e.g., body size, life span), in the hope that findings will apply to other species.

molarity A common unit of solute concentration equal to the number of moles of a dissolved solute in 1 liter of solution.

mole The amount of a substance that contains 6.022×10^{23} of its elemental entities (e.g., atoms, ions, or molecules). This number of molecules of a compound will have a mass equal to the molecular weight of that compound expressed in grams.

molecular chaperone A protein that facilitates the folding of newly synthesized proteins into their correct three-dimensional shape. Usually works by an ATP-dependent mechanism.

molecular formula A notation that indicates only the numbers and types of atoms in a molecule, such as H_2O for the water molecule. Compare with **structural formula**.

molecular weight The sum of the atomic weights of all of the atoms in a molecule; roughly, the total number of protons and neutrons in the molecule.

molecule A combination of two or more atoms held together by covalent bonds.

molting A method of body growth, used by ecdysozoans, that involves the shedding of an external protective cuticle or skeleton, expansion of the soft body, and growth of a new external layer.

monocot Any flowering plant (angiosperm) that has a single cotyledon (embryonic leaf) upon germination. Monocots form a monophyletic group. Also called a monocotyledonous plant. Compare with **dicot**.

monoecious Describing an angiosperm species that has both male and female reproductive structures on each plant. Compare with **dioecious**.

monohybrid cross A mating between two parents that are both heterozygous for one given gene.

monomer A small molecule that can covalently bind to other similar molecules to form a larger macromolecule. Compare with **polymer**.

monophyletic group An evolutionary unit that includes an ancestral population and all of its descendants but no others. Also called a *clade* or *lineage*. Compare with **paraphyletic group** and **polyphyletic group**.

monosaccharide A molecule that has the molecular formula $(CH_2O)_n$ and cannot be hydrolyzed to form any smaller carbohydrates. Also called *simple sugar*. Compare with **oligosaccharide** and **polysaccharide**.

monosomy The state of having only one copy of a particular type of chromosome in an otherwise diploid cell.

monotremes A lineage of mammals (Monotremata) that lay eggs and then nourish the young with milk. Includes just five living species: the platypus and four species of echidna, all with leathery beaks or bills.

morphogen A molecule that exists in a concentration gradient and provides spatial information to embryonic cells.

morphology The shape and appearance of an organism's body and its component parts.

morphospecies concept The definition of a species as a population or group of populations that have measurably different anatomical features from other groups. Also called *morphological species concept*. Compare with **biological species concept** and **phylogenetic species concept**.

motor neuron A nerve cell that carries signals from the central nervous system (brain and spinal cord) to an effector, such as a muscle or gland. Compare with **interneuron** and **sensory neuron**.

motor protein A class of proteins whose major function is to convert the chemical energy of ATP into motion. Includes dynein, kinesin, and myosin.

MPF See **M-phase-promoting factor**.

mRNA See **messenger RNA**.

mucosal-associated lymphoid tissue (MALT) Collective term for lymphocytes and other leukocytes associated with skin cells and mucus-secreting epithelial tissues in the gut and respiratory tract. Plays an important role in preventing entry of pathogens into the body.

mucous cell A type of cell found in the epithelial layer of the stomach; responsible for secreting mucus into the stomach.

mucus (adjective: mucous) A slimy mixture of glycoproteins (called mucins) and water that is secreted in many animal organs for lubrication. Serves as a barrier to protect surfaces from infection.

Müllerian inhibitory substance A peptide hormone, secreted by the embryonic testis, that causes regression (withering away) of the female reproductive ducts.

Müllerian mimicry A type of mimicry in which two (or more) harmful species resemble each other. Compare with **Batesian mimicry**.

multicellularity The state of being composed of many cells that adhere to each other and do not all express the same genes, with the result that some cells have specialized functions.

multiple allelism The existence of more than two alleles of the same gene.

multiple fruit A fruit (e.g., pineapple) that develops from many separate flowers and thus many carpels. Compare with **aggregate** and **simple fruit**.

multiple sclerosis (MS) A human autoimmune disease in which the immune system attacks the myelin sheaths that insulate axons of neurons.

muscle fiber A single muscle cell.

muscle tissue An animal tissue consisting of bundles of long, thin, contractile cells (muscle fibers). Functions primarily in movement.

mutagen Any physical or chemical agent that increases the rate of mutation.

mutant An individual that carries a mutation, particularly a new or rare mutation.

mutation Any change in the hereditary material of an organism (DNA in most organisms, RNA in some viruses). The only source of new alleles in populations.

mutualism (adjective: mutualistic) A symbiotic relationship between two organisms (mutualists) that benefits both. Compare with **commensalism** and **parasitism**.

mutualist Organism that is a participant and partner in a mutualistic relationship. See **mutualism**.

mycelium (plural: mycelia) A mass of underground filaments (hyphae) that form the body of a fungus. Also found in some protists and bacteria.

mycorrhiza (plural: mycorrhizae) A mutualistic association between certain fungi and the roots of most vascular plants, sometimes visible as nodules or nets in or around plant roots.

myelin sheath Multiple layers of myelin, derived from the cell membranes of certain glial cells, wrapped around the axon of a neuron and providing electrical insulation.

myocardial infarction Death of cardiac muscle cells when deprived of oxygen.

myoD A transcription factor that is a master regulator of muscle cell differentiation (short for "*myo*blast *determination*").

myofibril Long, slender structure composed of contractile proteins organized into repeating units (sarcomeres) in vertebrate heart muscle and skeletal muscle.

myosin Any one of a class of motor proteins that use the chemical energy of ATP to move along actin filaments in muscle contraction, cytokinesis, and vesicle transport.

myriapods A lineage of arthropods with long segmented trunks, each segment bearing one or two pairs of legs. Includes millipedes and centipedes.

NAD⊕/NADH Oxidized and reduced forms, respectively, of nicotinamide adenine dinucleotide. A nonprotein electron carrier that functions in many of the redox reactions of metabolism.

NADP⊕/NADPH Oxidized and reduced forms, respectively, of nicotinamide adenine dinucleotide phosphate. A nonprotein electron carrier that is reduced during the light-dependent reactions in photosynthesis and extensively used in biosynthetic reactions.

natural experiment A situation in which a natural change in conditions enables comparisons of groups, rather than a manipulation of conditions by researchers.

natural selection The process by which individuals with certain heritable traits tend to produce more surviving offspring than do individuals without those traits, often leading to a change in the genetic makeup of the population. A major mechanism of evolution.

nauplius A distinct planktonic larval stage seen in many crustaceans.

Neanderthal A recently extinct European species of hominin, *Homo neanderthalensis*, closely related to but distinct from modern humans.

nectar The sugary fluid produced by flowers to attract and reward pollinating animals.

nectary A nectar-producing structure in a flower.

negative control Of genes, when a regulatory protein shuts down expression by binding to DNA on or near the gene.

negative feedback A self-limiting, corrective response in which a deviation in some variable (e.g., concentration of some compound) triggers responses aimed at returning the variable to normal. Represents a means of maintaining homeostasis. Compare with **positive feedback**.

negative pressure ventilation Ventilation of the lungs by expanding the rib cage so as to "pull" air into the lungs. Compare with **positive pressure ventilation**.

negative-sense RNA virus An ssRNA virus whose genome contains sequences complementary to those in the mRNA required to produce viral proteins. Compare with **ambisense virus** and **positive-sense virus**.

nematodes See **roundworms**.

nephron One of many tiny tubules inside the kidney that function in the formation of urine.

neritic zone Shallow marine waters beyond the intertidal zone, extending down to about 200 meters, where the continental shelf ends.

nerve A long, tough strand of nervous tissue, typically containing thousands of axons, wrapped in connective tissue; carries impulses between the central nervous system and some other part of the body.

nerve cord In chordate animals, a hollow bundle of nerves extending from the brain along the dorsal (back) side of the animal, with cerebrospinal fluid inside a central channel. One of the defining features of chordates.

nerve net A nervous system in which neurons are diffuse instead of being clustered into large ganglia or tracts; found in cnidarians and ctenophores.

nervous tissue An animal tissue consisting of nerve cells (neurons) and various supporting cells.

net primary productivity (NPP) In an ecosystem, the total amount of carbon fixed by photosynthesis over a given time period minus the amount oxidized during cellular respiration. Compare with **gross primary productivity**.

net reproductive rate (R_0) The growth rate of a population per generation; equivalent to the average number of female offspring that each female produces over her lifetime.

neural tube A folded tube of ectoderm that forms along the dorsal side of a young vertebrate embryo; gives rise to the brain and spinal cord.

neuroendocrine Referring to nerve cells (neurons) that release hormones into the blood or to such hormones themselves.

neurogenesis The birth of new neurons from central nervous system stem cells.

neurohormones Hormones produced by neurons.

neuron A cell that is specialized for the transmission of nerve impulses. Typically has dendrites, a cell body, and a long axon that forms synapses with other neurons. Also called *nerve cell*.

neurosecretory cell A nerve cell (neuron) that produces and secretes hormones into the bloodstream. Principally found in the hypothalamus. Also called *neuroendocrine cell*.

neurotoxin Any substance that specifically destroys or blocks the normal functioning of neurons.

neurotransmitter A molecule that transmits signals from one neuron to another or from a neuron to a muscle or gland. Examples are acetylcholine, dopamine, serotonin, and norepinephrine.

neutral In genetics, referring to any mutation or mutant allele that has no effect on an individual's fitness.

neutrophil A type of leukocyte, capable of moving through body tissues, that engulfs and digests pathogens and other foreign particles; also secretes various compounds that attack bacteria and fungi.

niche The range of resources that a species can use and the range of conditions that it can tolerate. More broadly, the role that species plays in its ecosystem.

niche differentiation The evolutionary change in resource use by competing species that occurs as the result of character displacement.

nicotinamide adenine dinucleotide See **NAD⊕/ NADH**.

nitrogen cycle, global The movement of nitrogen among terrestrial ecosystems, the oceans, and the atmosphere.

nitrogen fixation The incorporation of atmospheric nitrogen (N_2) into ammonia (NH_3), which can be used to make many organic compounds. Occurs in only a few lineages of bacteria and archaea.

nociceptor A sensory cell or organ specialized to detect tissue damage, usually producing the sensation of pain.

Nod factors Molecules produced by nitrogen-fixing bacteria that help them recognize and bind to roots of legumes.

node (1) In animals, any small thickening (e.g., a lymph node). (2) In plants, the part of a stem where leaves or leaf buds are attached. (3) In a phylogenetic tree, the point where two branches diverge, representing the point in time when an ancestral group split into two or more descendant groups. Also called *fork*.

node of Ranvier One of the unmyelinated sections that occurs periodically along a neuron's axon and serves as a site where an action potential can be regenerated.

nodule Globular structure on roots of legume plants that contain symbiotic nitrogen-fixing bacteria.

noncyclic electron flow Path of electron flow in which electrons pass from photosystem II, through an electron transport chain, to photosystem I, and ultimately to $NADP^+$ during the light-dependent reactions of photosynthesis. See also **Z scheme**.

nondisjunction An error that can occur during meiosis or mitosis, in which one daughter cell receives two copies of a particular chromosome and the other daughter cell receives none.

nonpolar covalent bond A covalent bond in which electrons are equally shared between two atoms of the same or similar electronegativity. Compare with **polar covalent bond**.

nonsense mutation A point mutation (change in a single base pair) that converts an amino-acid-specifying codon into a stop codon.

non-sister chromatids The chromatids of a particular type of chromosome (after replication) with respect to the chromatids of its homologous chromosome. Crossing over occurs between non-sister chromatids. Compare with **sister chromatids**.

non-template strand The strand of DNA that is not transcribed during synthesis of RNA. Its sequence corresponds to that of the mRNA produced from the other strand. Also called *coding strand*.

non-vascular plants A paraphyletic group of land plants that lack vascular tissue and reproduce using spores. The non-vascular plants include three lineages of green plants (liverworts, mosses, and hornworts). These lineages are sometimes called *bryophytes*.

norepinephrine A catecholamine used as a neurotransmitter in the sympathetic nervous system. Also is produced by the adrenal medulla and functions as a hormone that triggers rapid responses relating to the fight-or-flight response.

notochord A supportive but flexible rod that occurs in the back of a chordate embryo, ventral to the developing spinal cord. Replaced by vertebrae in most adult vertebrates. A defining feature of chordates.

nuclear envelope The double-layered membrane enclosing the nucleus of a eukaryotic cell.

nuclear lamina A lattice-like sheet of fibrous nuclear lamins, which are one type of intermediate filament. Lines the inner membrane of the nuclear envelope, stiffening the envelope and helping to organize the chromosomes.

nuclear lamins Intermediate filaments that make up the nuclear lamina layer—a lattice-like layer inside the nuclear envelope that stiffens the structure.

nuclear localization signal (NLS) A short amino acid sequence that marks a protein for delivery to the nucleus.

nuclear pore An opening in the nuclear envelope that connects the inside of the nucleus with the cytoplasm and through which molecules such as mRNA and some proteins can pass.

nuclear pore complex A large complex of dozens of proteins lining a nuclear pore, defining its shape and regulating transport through the pore.

nuclease Any enzyme that can break down RNA or DNA molecules.

nucleic acid A macromolecule composed of nucleotide monomers. Generally used by cells to store or transmit hereditary information. Includes ribonucleic acid and deoxyribonucleic acid.

nucleoid In prokaryotic cells, a dense, centrally located region that contains DNA but is not surrounded by a membrane.

nucleolus In eukaryotic cells, a specialized structure in the nucleus where ribosomal RNA processing occurs and ribosomal subunits are assembled.

nucleosome A repeating, bead-like unit of eukaryotic chromatin, consisting of about 200 nucleotides of DNA wrapped twice around eight histone proteins.

nucleotide excision repair The process of removing a damaged region in one strand of DNA and replacing it with the correct sequence using the undamaged strand as a template.

nucleotide A molecule consisting of a five-carbon sugar (ribose or deoxyribose), a phosphate group, and one of several nitrogen-containing bases. DNA and RNA are polymers of nucleotides containing deoxyribose (deoxyribonucleotides) and ribose (ribonucleotides), respectively. Equivalent to a nucleoside plus one phosphate group.

nucleus (1) The center of an atom, containing protons and neutrons. (2) In eukaryotic cells, the large organelle containing the chromosomes and surrounded by a double membrane. (3) A discrete clump of neuron cell bodies in the brain, usually sharing a distinct function.

null allele See **knock-out allele**.

null hypothesis A hypothesis that specifies what the results of an experiment will be if the main hypothesis being tested is wrong. Often states that there will be no difference between experimental groups.

nutrient Any substance that an organism requires for normal growth, maintenance, or reproduction.

occipital lobe In the vertebrate brain, one of the four major areas in the cerebrum.

oceanic zone The waters of the open ocean beyond the continental shelf.

odorant Any volatile molecule that conveys information about food or the environment.

oil An unsaturated fat that is liquid at room temperature.

Okazaki fragment Short segment of DNA produced during replication of the lagging strand template. Many Okazaki fragments make up the lagging strand in newly synthesized DNA.

olfaction The perception of odors.

olfactory bulb A bulb-shaped projection of the brain just above the nose. Receives and interprets odor information from the nose.

oligodendrocyte A type of glial cell that wraps around axons of some neurons in the central nervous system, forming a myelin sheath that provides electrical insulation. Compare with **Schwann cell**.

oligopeptide A chain composed of fewer than 50 amino acids linked together by peptide bonds. Often referred to simply as *peptide*.

oligosaccharide A linear or branched polymer consisting of less than 50 monosaccharides joined by glycosidic linkages. Compare with **monosaccharide** and **polysaccharide**.

ommatidium (plural: ommatidia) A light-sensing column in an arthropod's compound eye.

omnivore (adjective: omnivorous) An animal whose diet regularly includes both meat and plants. Compare with **carnivore** and **herbivore**.

oncogene Any gene whose protein product stimulates cell division at all times and thus promotes cancer development. Often is a mutated form of a gene involved in regulating the cell cycle. See **proto-oncogene**.

one-gene, one-enzyme hypothesis The hypothesis that each gene is responsible for making one enzyme. This hypothesis has expanded to include genes that produce proteins other than enzymes or that produce RNAs as final products.

oogenesis The production of egg cells (ova).

oogonium (plural: oogonia) In an ovary, any of the diploid cells that can divide by mitosis to create primary oocytes (which can undergo meiosis) and more oogonia.

open circulatory system A circulatory system in which the circulating fluid (hemolymph) is not confined to blood vessels. Compare with **closed circulatory system**.

open reading frame (ORF) Any DNA sequence, ranging in length from several hundred to thousands of base pairs long, that is flanked by a start codon and a stop codon. ORFs identified by computer analysis of DNA may be functional genes, especially if they have other features characteristic of genes (e.g., promoter sequence).

operator In prokaryotic DNA, a binding site for a repressor protein; located near the start of an operon.

operculum The stiff flap of tissue that covers the gills of teleost fishes.

operon A region of prokaryotic DNA that codes for a series of functionally related genes and is transcribed from a single promoter into one mRNA.

opsin A transmembrane protein that is covalently linked to retinal, the light-detecting pigment in rod and cone cells.

optic nerve A bundle of neurons that runs from the eye to the brain.

optimal foraging The concept that animals forage in a way that maximizes the amount of usable energy they take in, given the costs of finding and ingesting their food and the risk of being eaten while they're at it.

orbital The region of space around an atomic nucleus in which an electron is present most of the time.

organ A group of tissues organized into a functional and structural unit.

organ system Groups of tissues and organs that work together to perform a function.

organelle Any discrete, membrane-bound structure within a cell (e.g., mitochondrion) that has a characteristic structure and function.

organic For a compound, containing carbon and hydrogen and usually containing carbon–carbon bonds. Organic compounds are widely used by living organisms.

organism Any living entity that contains one or more cells.

organogenesis A stage of embryonic development that follows gastrulation and that creates organs from the three germ layers.

origin of replication The site on a chromosome at which DNA replication begins.

osmoconformer An animal that does not actively regulate the osmolarity of its tissues but conforms to the osmolarity of the surrounding environment.

osmolarity The concentration of dissolved substances in a solution, measured in osmoles per liter.

osmoregulation The process by which a living organism controls the concentration of water and salts in its body.

osmoregulator An animal that actively regulates the osmolarity of its tissues.

osmosis Diffusion of water across a selectively permeable membrane from a region of low solute concentration (high water concentration) to a region of high solute concentration (low water concentration).

ossicles, ear In mammals, three bones found in the middle ear that function in transferring and amplifying sound from the outer ear to the inner ear.

ouabain A plant toxin that poisons the sodium–potassium pumps of animals.

out-of-Africa hypothesis The hypothesis that modern humans (*Homo sapiens*) evolved in Africa and spread to other continents, replacing other *Homo* species without interbreeding with them.

outcrossing Reproduction by fusion of the gametes of different individuals, rather than by self-fertilization.

outer ear The outermost portion of the mammalian ear, consisting of the pinna (ear flap) and the ear canal. Funnels sound to the tympanic membrane.

outgroup A taxon that is closely related to a particular monophyletic group but is not part of it.

oval window A membrane separating the fluid-filled cochlea from the air-filled middle ear; sound vibrations pass through it from the middle ear to the inner ear in mammals.

ovary The egg-producing organ of a female animal, or the fruit- and seed-producing structure in the female part of a flower.

overexploitation Unsustainable removal of wildlife from the natural environment for use by humans.

oviduct See **fallopian tube**.

oviparous In animals, producing eggs that are laid outside the body where they develop and hatch. Compare with **ovoviviparous** and **viviparous**.

ovoviviparous In animals, producing eggs that are retained inside the body until they are ready to hatch. Compare with **oviparous** and **viviparous**.

ovulation The release of an egg from an ovary of a female vertebrate. In humans, an ovarian follicle releases an egg at the end of the follicular phase of the menstrual cycle.

ovule In flowering plants, the structure inside an ovary that contains the female gametophyte and eventually (if fertilized) becomes a seed.

ovum (plural: ova) See **egg**.

oxidation The loss of electrons from an atom or molecule during a redox reaction, either by donation of an electron to another atom or molecule, or by the shared electrons in covalent bonds moving farther from the atomic nucleus.

oxidative phosphorylation Production of ATP molecules by ATP synthase using the proton gradient established via redox reactions of an electron transport chain.

oxygen–hemoglobin equilibrium curve The graphed depiction of the percentage of hemoglobin in the blood that is bound to oxygen at various partial pressures of oxygen.

oxygenic Referring to any process or reaction that produces oxygen. Photosynthesis in plants, algae, and cyanobacteria, which involves photosystem II, is oxygenic. Compare with **anoxygenic**.

oxytocin A peptide hormone, secreted by the posterior pituitary, that triggers labor and milk production in females and that stimulates pair bonding, parental care, and affiliative behavior in both sexes.

p53 A tumor-suppressor protein (molecular weight of 53 kilodaltons) that responds to DNA damage by stopping the cell cycle, turning on DNA repair machinery, and, if necessary, triggering apoptosis. Encoded by the *p53* gene.

pacemaker cell Any of a group of specialized cardiac muscle cells in the sinoatrial (SA) node of the vertebrate heart that have an inherent rhythm and can generate an electrical impulse that spreads to other heart cells.

paleontologists Scientists who study the fossil record and the history of life.

Paleozoic era The interval of geologic time, from 542 million to 251 million years ago, during which fungi, land plants, and animals first appeared and diversified. Began with the Cambrian explosion and ended with the extinction of many invertebrates and vertebrates at the end of the Permian period.

pancreas A large gland in vertebrates that has both exocrine and endocrine functions. Secretes digestive enzymes into a duct connected to the intestine and secretes several hormones (notably, insulin and glucagon) into the bloodstream.

pancreatic amylase An enzyme produced by the pancreas that breaks down glucose chains by catalyzing hydrolysis of the glycosidic linkages between the glucose residues.

pancreatic lipase An enzyme that is produced in the pancreas and acts in the small intestine to break bonds in complex fats, releasing small lipids.

pandemic The spread of an infectious disease in a short time period over a wide geographic area and affecting a very high proportion of the population. Compare with **epidemic**.

parabiosis An experimental technique for determining whether a certain physiological phenomenon is regulated by a hormone; consists of surgically uniting two individuals so that hormones can pass between them.

paracrine Relating to a chemical signal that is released by one cell and affects neighboring cells.

paraphyletic group A group that includes an ancestral population and *some* but not all of its descendants. Compare with **monophyletic group**.

parapodia (singular: parapodium) Appendages found in some annelids from which bristle-like structures (chaetae) extend.

parasite An organism that lives on a host species (ectoparasite) or in a host species (endoparasite) and that damages its host.

parasitism (adjective: parasitic) A symbiotic relationship between two organisms that is beneficial to one organism (the parasite) but detrimental to the other (the host). Compare with **commensalism** and **mutualism**.

parasitoid An organism that has a parasitic larval stage and a free-living adult stage. Most parasitoids are insects that lay eggs in the bodies of other insects.

parasympathetic nervous system The part of the autonomic nervous system that stimulates responses for conserving or restoring energy, such as reduced heart rate and increased digestion. Compare with **sympathetic nervous system**.

parenchyma cell In plants, a general type of cell with a relatively thin primary cell wall. These cells, found in leaves, the centers of stems and roots, and fruits, are involved in photosynthesis, storage, and transport. Compare with **collenchyma cell** and **sclerenchyma cell**.

parental care Any action by which an animal expends energy or assumes risks to benefit its offspring (e.g., nest building, feeding of young, defense).

parental generation The adults used in the first experimental cross of a breeding experiment.

parental strand A strand of DNA that is used as a template during DNA synthesis.

parietal cell A cell in the stomach lining that secretes hydrochloric acid.

parietal lobe In the vertebrate brain, one of the four major areas in the cerebrum.

parsimony The logical principle that the most likely explanation of a phenomenon is the most economical or simplest. When applied to comparison of alternative phylogenetic trees, it suggests that the one requiring the fewest evolutionary changes is most likely to be correct.

parthenogenesis Development of offspring from unfertilized eggs; a type of asexual reproduction.

partial pressure The pressure of one particular gas in a mixture of gases; the contribution of that gas to the overall pressure.

particulate inheritance The observation that genes from two parents do not blend together in offspring, but instead remain separate or particle-like.

pascal (Pa) A unit of pressure (force per unit area).

passive transport Diffusion of a substance across a membrane. When this event occurs with the assistance of membrane proteins, it is called *facilitated diffusion*.

patch clamping A technique for studying the electrical currents that flow through individual ion channels by sucking a tiny patch of membrane to the hollow tip of a microelectrode.

paternal chromosome A chromosome inherited from the father.

pathogen (adjective: pathogenic) Any entity capable of causing disease, such as a microbe, virus, or prion.

pattern formation The series of events that determines the spatial organization of an entire embryo or parts of an embryo, for example, setting the major body axes early in development.

pattern-recognition receptor On leukocytes, a class of membrane proteins that bind to molecules commonly associated with foreign cells and viruses and signal responses against broad types of pathogens. Part of the innate immune response.

peat Semi-decayed organic matter that accumulates in moist, low-oxygen environments such as *Sphagnum* (moss) bogs.

pectin A gelatinous polysaccharide found in the primary cell wall of plant cells. Attracts and holds water, forming a gel that resists compression forces and helps keep the cell wall moist.

pedigree A family tree of parents and offspring, showing inheritance of particular traits of interest.

penis The copulatory organ of male mammals, used to insert sperm into a female.

pentose A monosaccharide (simple sugar) containing five carbon atoms.

PEP carboxylase An enzyme that catalyzes addition of CO_2 to phosphoenolpyruvate, a three-carbon compound, forming a four-carbon organic acid. See also **C₄ pathway** and **crassulacean acid metabolism (CAM)**.

pepsin A protein-digesting enzyme present in the stomach.

peptide See **oligopeptide**.

peptide bond The covalent bond formed by a condensation reaction between two amino acids; links the residues in peptides and proteins.

peptidoglycan A complex structural polysaccharide found in bacterial cell walls.

perennial Describing a plant whose life cycle normally lasts for more than one year. Compare with **annual**.

perfect flower A flower that contains both male parts (stamens) and female parts (carpels). Compare with **imperfect flower**.

perforation In plants, a small hole in the primary and secondary cell walls of vessel elements that allows passage of water.

pericarp The part of a fruit, formed from the ovary wall, that surrounds the seeds and protects them. Corresponds to the flesh of most edible fruits and the hard shells of most nuts.

pericycle In plant roots, a layer of cells just inside the endodermis that give rise to lateral roots.

peripheral membrane protein Any membrane protein that does not span the entire lipid bilayer and associates with only one side of the bilayer. Compare with **integral membrane protein**.

peripheral nervous system (PNS) All the components of the nervous system that are outside the central nervous system (the brain and spinal cord). Includes the somatic nervous system and the autonomic nervous system.

peristalsis Rhythmic waves of muscular contraction. In the digestive tract, pushes food along. In animals with hydrostatic skeletons, enables crawling.

permafrost A permanently frozen layer of icy soil found in most tundra and some taiga.

permeability The tendency of a structure, such as a membrane, to allow a given substance to diffuse across it.

peroxisome An organelle found in most eukaryotic cells that contains enzymes for oxidizing fatty acids and other compounds, including many toxins, rendering them harmless. See **glyoxysome**.

petal Any of the leaflike organs arranged around the reproductive organs of a flower. Often colored and scented to attract pollinators.

petiole The stalk of a leaf.

pH A measure of the concentration of protons in a solution and thus of acidity or alkalinity. Defined as the negative of the base-10 logarithm of the proton concentration: $pH = -\log[H^+]$.

phagocytosis Uptake by a cell of small particles or cells by invagination and pinching off of the plasma membrane to form small, membrane-bound vesicles; one type of **endocytosis**.

pharyngeal gill slits A set of parallel openings from the throat to the outside that function in both feeding and gas exchange. A diagnostic trait of chordates.

pharyngeal jaw A secondary jaw in the back of the throat; found in some fishes, it aids in food processing. Derived from modified gill arches.

phenology The timing of events during the year, in environments where seasonal changes occur.

phenotype The detectable traits of an individual. Compare with **genotype**.

phenotypic plasticity Within-species variation in phenotype that is due to differences in environmental conditions. Occurs more commonly in plants than animals.

pheophytin The molecule in photosystem II that accepts excited electrons from the reaction center chlorophyll and passes them to an electron transport chain.

pheromone A chemical signal, released by an individual into the external environment, that can trigger changes in the behavior or physiology or both of another member of the same species.

phloem A plant vascular tissue that conducts sugars between roots and shoots; contains sieve-tube elements and companion cells. Primary phloem develops from the procambium of apical meristems; secondary phloem, from the vascular cambium. Compare with **xylem**.

phosphatase An enzyme that removes phosphate groups from proteins or other molecules. Phosphatases are often used in the inactivation of signaling pathways that involve the phosphorylation and activation of proteins.

phosphodiester linkage Chemical linkage between adjacent nucleotide residues in DNA and RNA. Forms when the phosphate group of one nucleotide condenses with the hydroxyl group on the sugar of another nucleotide. Also known as *phosphodiester bond*.

phosphofructokinase The enzyme that catalyzes synthesis of fructose-1,6-bisphosphate from fructose-6-phosphate, a key reaction in glycolysis (step 3). Also called *6-phosphofructokinase*.

phospholipid A class of lipid having a hydrophilic head (including a phosphate group) and a hydrophobic tail (consisting of two hydrocarbon chains). Major components of the plasma membrane and organelle membranes.

phosphorylase An enzyme that breaks down glycogen by catalyzing hydrolysis of the α-glycosidic linkages between the glucose residues.

phosphorylation (verb: phosphorylate) The addition of a phosphate group to a molecule.

phosphorylation cascade A series of enzyme-catalyzed phosphorylation reactions commonly used in signal transduction pathways to amplify and convey a signal inward from the plasma membrane.

photic zone In an aquatic habitat, water that is shallow enough to receive some sunlight (whether or not it is enough to support photosynthesis). Compare with **aphotic zone**.

photon A discrete packet of light energy; a particle of light.

photoperiod The amount of time per day (usually in hours) that an organism is exposed to light.

photoperiodism Any response by an organism to the relative lengths of day and night (i.e., photoperiod).

photophosphorylation Production of ATP molecules by ATP synthase using the proton-motive force generated as light-excited electrons flow through an electron transport chain during photosynthesis.

photoreception A sensory system in which receptors are activated by light.

photoreceptor A molecule, a cell, or an organ that is specialized to detect light.

photorespiration A series of light-driven chemical reactions that consumes oxygen and releases carbon dioxide, basically undoing photosynthesis. Usually occurs when there are high O_2 and low CO_2 concentrations inside plant cells; often occurs when stomata must be kept closed to prevent dehydration.

photoreversibility A change in conformation that occurs in certain plant pigments when they are exposed to the particular wavelengths of light that they absorb; triggers responses by the plant.

photosynthesis The complex biological process that converts the energy of light into chemical energy stored in glucose and other organic molecules. Occurs in most plants, algae, and some bacteria.

photosystem One of two types of units, consisting of a central reaction center surrounded by antenna complexes, that is responsible for the light-dependent reactions of photosynthesis.

photosystem I A photosystem that contains a pair of P700 chlorophyll molecules and uses absorbed light energy to reduce $NADP^+$ to NADPH.

photosystem II A photosystem that contains a pair of P680 chlorophyll molecules and uses absorbed light energy to produce a proton-motive force for the synthesis of ATP. Oxygen is produced as a by-product when water is split to obtain electrons.

phototroph An organism (most plants, algae, and some bacteria) that produces ATP through photosynthesis.

phototropins A class of plant photoreceptors that detect blue light and initiate various responses.

phototropism Growth or movement of an organism in a particular direction in response to light.

phylogenetic species concept The definition of a species as the smallest monophyletic group in a phylogenetic tree. Compare with **biological species concept** and **morphospecies concept**.

phylogenetic tree A branching diagram that depicts the evolutionary relationships among species or other taxa.

phylogeny The evolutionary history of a group of organisms.

phylum (plural: phyla) In Linnaeus' system, a taxonomic category above the class level and below the kingdom level. In plants, sometimes called a *division*.

physical map A map of a chromosome that shows the number of base pairs between various genetic markers. Compare with **genetic map**.

physiology The study of how an organism's body functions.

phytochrome A specialized plant photoreceptor that exists in two shapes depending on the ratio of red to far-red light and is involved in the timing of certain physiological processes, such as flowering, stem elongation, and germination.

pigment Any molecule that absorbs certain wavelengths of visible light and reflects or transmits other wavelengths.

piloting A type of navigation in which animals use familiar landmarks to find their way.

pineal gland An endocrine gland, located in the brain, that secretes the hormone melatonin.

pioneering species Those species that appear first in recently disturbed areas.

pit In plants, a small hole in the secondary cell walls of tracheids and vessel elements that allows passage of water.

pitch The sensation produced by a particular frequency of sound. Low frequencies are perceived as low pitches; high frequencies, as high pitches.

pith In the shoot systems of plants, ground tissue located to the inside of the vascular bundles.

pituitary gland A small gland located directly under the brain and physically and functionally connected to the hypothalamus. Produces and secretes an array of hormones that affect many other glands and organs.

placenta A structure that forms in the pregnant uterus from maternal and fetal tissues. Delivers oxygen to the fetus, exchanges nutrients and wastes between mother and fetus, anchors the fetus to the uterine wall, and produces some hormones. Occurs in most mammals and in a few other vertebrates.

placental mammals See **eutherians**.

plankton Drifting organisms (animals, plants, archaea, or bacteria) in aquatic environments.

Plantae The monophyletic group that includes red, green, and glaucophyte algae, and land plants.

plasma The non-cellular portion of blood.

plasma cell A B cell that produces large quantities of antibodies after being activated by interacting with antigen and a CD4$^+$ T cell via peptide presentation. Also called an *effector B cell*.

plasma membrane A membrane that surrounds a cell, separating it from the external environment and selectively regulating passage of molecules and ions into and out of the cell. Also called *cell membrane*.

plasmid A small, usually circular, supercoiled DNA molecule independent of the cell's main chromosome(s) in prokaryotes and some eukaryotes.

plasmodesmata (singular: plasmodesma) Physical connections between two plant cells, consisting of membrane-lined gaps in the cell walls through which the two cells' plasma membranes, cytoplasm, and smooth ER can connect directly. Functionally similar to gap junctions in animal cells.

plasmogamy Fusion of the cytoplasm of two individuals. Occurs in many fungi.

plastocyanin A small protein that shuttles electrons originating from photosystem II to the reaction center of photosystem I during photosynthesis.

plastoquinone (PQ) A nonprotein electron carrier in the chloroplast electron transport chain. Receives excited electrons from photosystem II (noncyclic) or photosystem I (cyclic) and passes them to more

electronegative molecules in the chain. Also transports protons from the stroma to the thylakoid lumen, generating a proton-motive force.

platelet A small membrane-bound cell fragment in vertebrate blood that functions in blood clotting. Derived from large cells in the bone marrow.

pleiotropy (adjective: pleiotropic) The ability of a single gene to affect more than one trait.

ploidy The number of complete chromosome sets present. *Haploid* refers to a ploidy of 1; *diploid*, a ploidy of 2; *triploid*, a ploidy of 3; and *tetraploid*, a ploidy of 4.

point mutation A mutation that results in a change in a single base pair in DNA.

polar (1) Asymmetrical or unidirectional. (2) Carrying a partial positive charge on one side of a molecule and a partial negative charge on the other. Polar molecules are generally hydrophilic.

polar body Any of the tiny, nonfunctional cells that are made as a by-product during meiosis of a primary oocyte, due to most of the cytoplasm going to the ovum.

polar covalent bond A covalent bond in which electrons are shared unequally between atoms differing in electronegativity, resulting in the more electronegative atom having a partial negative charge and the other atom, a partial positive charge. Compare with **nonpolar covalent bond**.

polar microtubules Mitotic and meiotic microtubules that have arisen from the two spindle poles and overlap with each other in the middle of the spindle apparatus.

polar nuclei In flowering plants, the nuclei in the female gametophyte that fuse with one sperm nucleus to produce the endosperm. Most species have two.

pollen grain In seed plants, a male gametophyte enclosed within a protective coat of sporopollenin.

pollen tube In flowering plants, a structure that grows out of a pollen grain after it reaches the stigma, extends down the style, and through which two sperm cells are delivered to the ovule.

pollination The process by which pollen reaches the carpel of a flower (in flowering plants), transferred from anther to stigma, or reaches the ovule directly (in conifers and their relatives).

pollination syndrome Suites of flower characters that are associated with certain types of pollinators and that have evolved through natural selection imposed by the interaction between flowers and pollinators.

poly(A) signal In eukaryotes, a short sequence of nucleotides near the 3′ end of pre-mRNAs that signals cleavage of the RNA and addition of the poly(A) tail.

poly(A) tail In eukaryotes, a sequence of about 100–250 adenine nucleotides added to the 3′ end of newly transcribed messenger RNA molecules.

polygenic inheritance Having many genes influence one trait.

polymer Any long molecule composed of small repeating units (monomers) bonded together. The main biological polymers are proteins, nucleic acids, and polysaccharides.

polymerase chain reaction (PCR) A laboratory technique for rapidly generating millions of identical

copies of a specific stretch of DNA. Works by incubating the original DNA sequence of interest with primers, nucleotides, and DNA polymerase.

polymerization (verb: polymerize) The process by which many identical or similar small molecules (monomers) are covalently bonded to form a large molecule (polymer).

polymorphic species A species that has two or more distinct phenotypes in the same interbreeding population at the same time.

polymorphism (adjective: polymorphic) (1) The occurrence of more than one allele at a genetic locus in a population. (2) The occurrence of more than two distinct phenotypes of a trait in a population.

polyp The immotile (sessile) stage in the life cycle of some cnidarians (e.g., jellyfish). Compare with **medusa**.

polypeptide A chain of 50 or more amino acids linked together by peptide bonds. Compare with **oligopeptide** and **protein**.

polyphyletic group An unnatural group based on convergent (homoplastic) characteristics that are not present in a common ancestor. Compare with **monophyletic group**.

polyploidy (adjective: polyploid) The state of having more than two full sets of chromosomes, either from the same species (autopolyploidy) or from different species (allopolyploidy).

polyribosome A messenger RNA molecule along with more than one attached ribosome and their growing peptide strands.

polysaccharide A linear or branched polymer consisting of many monosaccharides joined by glycosidic linkages. Compare with **monosaccharide** and **oligosaccharide**.

polytomy A node in a phylogenetic tree that depicts an ancestral branch dividing into three or more descendant branches; usually indicates that insufficient data were available to resolve which taxa are more closely related.

population A group of individuals of the same species living in the same geographic area at the same time.

population density The number of individuals of a population per unit area.

population dynamics Changes in the size and other characteristics of populations through time and space.

population ecology The study of how and why the number of individuals in a population changes over time and space.

population thinking The ability to analyze trait frequencies, event probabilities, and other attributes of populations of molecules, cells, or organisms.

pore In land plants, an opening in the epithelium that allows gas exchange. See also **stoma**.

positive control Of genes, when a regulatory protein triggers expression by binding to DNA on or near the gene.

positive feedback A physiological mechanism in which a change in some variable stimulates a response that increases the change. Relatively rare in organisms but is important in generation of the action potential. Compare with **negative feedback**.

positive pressure ventilation Ventilation of the lungs by using positive pressure in the mouth to "push" air into the lungs. Compare with **negative pressure ventilation**.

positive-sense RNA virus An ssRNA virus whose genome contains the same sequences as the mRNA required to produce viral proteins. Compare with **ambisense virus** and **negative-sense virus**.

posterior Toward an animal's tail and away from its head. The opposite of anterior.

posterior pituitary The part of the pituitary gland that contains the ends of hypothalamic neurosecretory cells and from which oxytocin and antidiuretic hormone are secreted. Compare with **anterior pituitary**.

postsynaptic neuron A neuron that receives signals, usually via neurotransmitters, from another neuron at a synapse. Compare with **presynaptic neuron**.

post-translational control Regulation of gene expression by modification of proteins (e.g., addition of a phosphate group or sugar residues) after translation.

postzygotic isolation Reproductive isolation resulting from mechanisms that operate after mating of individuals of two different species occurs. The most common mechanisms are the death of hybrid embryos or reduced fitness of hybrids.

potential energy Energy stored in matter as a result of its position or molecular arrangement. Compare with **kinetic energy**.

prebiotic soup model Hypothetical explanation for chemical evolution whereby small molecules reacted with one another in a mixture of organic molecules condensed into a body of water, typically in reference to the early oceans.

Precambrian The interval between the formation of the Earth, about 4.6 billion years ago, and the appearance of most animal groups about 542 million years ago. Unicellular organisms were dominant for most of this era, and oxygen was virtually absent for the first 2 billion years.

pre-mRNA In eukaryotes, the primary transcript of protein-coding genes. Pre-mRNA is processed to form mRNA.

predation The killing and eating of one organism (the prey) by another (the predator).

predator Any organism that kills other organisms for food.

prediction A measurable or observable result of an experiment based on a particular hypothesis. A correct prediction provides support for the hypothesis being tested.

pressure-flow hypothesis The hypothesis that sugar movement through phloem tissue is due to differences in the turgor pressure of phloem sap.

pressure potential (ψ_P) A component of the potential energy of water caused by physical pressures on a solution. It can be positive or negative. Compare with **solute potential** (ψ_S).

presynaptic neuron A neuron that transmits signals, usually by releasing neurotransmitters, to another neuron or to an effector cell at a synapse.

prezygotic isolation Reproductive isolation resulting from any one of several mechanisms that prevent individuals of two different species from mating.

primary active transport A form of active transport in which a source of energy like ATP is directly used to move ions against their electrochemical gradients.

primary cell wall The outermost layer of a plant cell wall, made of cellulose fibers and gelatinous polysaccharides, that defines the shape of the cell and withstands the turgor pressure of the plasma membrane.

primary consumer An herbivore; an organism that eats plants, algae, or other primary producers. Compare with **secondary consumer**.

primary decomposer A decomposer (detritivore) that consumes detritus from plants.

primary growth In plants, an increase in the length of stems and roots due to the activity of apical meristems. Compare with **secondary growth**.

primary immune response An adaptive immune response to a pathogen that the immune system has not encountered before. Compare with **secondary immune response**.

primary meristem In plants, three types of partially differentiated cells that are produced by apical meristems, including protoderm, ground meristem, and procambium. Compare with **apical meristem** and **cambium**.

primary oocyte Any of the large diploid cells in an ovarian follicle that can initiate meiosis to produce a haploid secondary oocyte and a polar body.

primary producer Any organism that creates its own food by photosynthesis or from reduced inorganic compounds and that is a food source for other species in its ecosystem. Also called *autotroph*.

primary spermatocyte Any of the diploid cells in the testis that can initiate meiosis I to produce two secondary spermatocytes.

primary structure The sequence of amino acid residues in a peptide or protein; also the sequence of nucleotides in a nucleic acid. Compare with **secondary**, **tertiary**, and **quaternary structure**.

primary succession The gradual colonization of a habitat of bare rock or gravel, usually after an environmental disturbance that removes all soil and previous organisms. Compare with **secondary succession**.

primary transcript In eukaryotes, a newly transcribed RNA molecule that has not yet been processed to a mature RNA. Called *pre-mRNA* when the final product is a protein.

primase An enzyme that synthesizes a short stretch of RNA to use as a primer during DNA replication.

primates The lineage of mammals that includes prosimians (lemurs, lorises, etc.), monkeys, and great apes (including humans).

primer A short, single-stranded RNA molecule that base-pairs with a DNA template strand and is elongated by DNA polymerase during DNA replication.

probe A radioactively or chemically labeled single-stranded fragment of a known DNA or RNA sequence that can bind to and detect its complementary sequence in a sample containing many different sequences.

proboscis A tubular, often extensible feeding appendage with which food can be obtained.

procambium A primary meristem tissue that gives rise to the vascular tissue.

product Any of the final materials formed in a chemical reaction.

progesterone A steroid hormone produced and secreted by the corpus luteum in the ovaries after ovulation and by the placenta during gestation; protects the uterine lining.

programmed cell death Regulated cell death that is used in development, tissue maintainance, and destruction of infected cells. Can occur in different ways; apoptosis is the best-known mechanism.

prokaryote A member of the domain Bacteria or Archaea; a unicellular organism lacking a nucleus and containing relatively few organelles or cytoskeletal components. Compare with **eukaryote**.

prolactin A peptide hormone, produced and secreted by the anterior pituitary, that promotes milk production in female mammals and has a variety of effects on parental behavior and seasonal reproduction in other vertebrates.

prometaphase A stage in mitosis or meiosis during which the nuclear envelope breaks down and microtubules attach to kinetochores.

promoter A short nucleotide sequence in DNA that binds a sigma factor (in bacteria) or basal transcription factors (in eukaryotes) to enable RNA polymerase to begin transcription. In bacteria, several contiguous genes are often transcribed from a single promoter. In eukaryotes, each gene generally has its own promoter.

promoter-proximal element In eukaryotes, regulatory sequences in DNA that are close to a promoter and that can bind regulatory transcription factors.

proofreading The process by which a DNA polymerase recognizes and removes a wrong base added during DNA replication and then continues synthesis.

prophase The first stage in mitosis or meiosis during which chromosomes become visible and the spindle apparatus forms. Synapsis and crossing over occur during prophase of meiosis I.

prosimians One of the two major lineages of primates, a paraphyletic group including lemurs, pottos, and lorises. Compare with **anthropoids**.

prostate gland A gland in male mammals that surrounds the base of the urethra and secretes a fluid that is a component of semen.

prosthetic group A non-amino acid atom or molecule that is permanently attached to an enzyme or other protein and is required for its function.

protease An enzyme that can break up proteins by cleaving the peptide bonds between amino acid residues.

proteasome A macromolecular machine that destroys proteins that have been marked by the addition of ubiquitin.

protein A macromolecule consisting of one or more polypeptide chains composed of 50 or more amino acids linked together. Each protein has a unique sequence of amino acids and generally possesses a characteristic three-dimensional shape.

protein kinase An enzyme that catalyzes the addition of a phosphate group to another protein, typically activating or inactivating the substrate protein.

proteinase inhibitors Defense compounds, produced by plants, that induce illness in herbivores by inhibiting digestive enzymes.

proteoglycan A type of highly glycosylated protein found in the extracellular matrix of animal cells that attracts and holds water, forming a gel that resists compression forces.

proteome The complete set of proteins produced by a particular cell type.

proteomics The systematic study of the interactions, localization, functions, regulation, and other features of the full protein set (proteome) in a particular cell type.

protist Any eukaryote that is not a green plant, animal, or fungus. Protists are a diverse paraphyletic group. Most are unicellular, but some are multicellular or form aggregations called colonies.

protocell A hypothetical pre-cell structure consisting of a membrane compartment that encloses replicating macromolecules, such as ribozymes.

protoderm The exterior layer of a young plant embryo that gives rise to the epidermis.

proto-oncogene Any gene that encourages cell division in a regulated manner, typically by triggering specific phases in the cell cycle. Mutation may convert it into an oncogene. See **oncogene**.

proton pump A membrane protein that can hydrolyze ATP to power active transport of protons (H^+ ions) across a membrane against an electrochemical gradient. Also called H^+-ATPase.

proton-motive force The combined effect of a proton gradient and an electric potential gradient across a membrane, which can drive protons across the membrane. Used by mitochondria and chloroplasts to power ATP synthesis via the mechanism of chemiosmosis.

protostomes A major lineage of animals that share a pattern of embryological development, including formation of the mouth earlier than the anus, and formation of the coelom by splitting of a block of mesoderm. Includes arthropods, mollusks, and annelids. Compare with **deuterostomes**.

proximal tubule In the vertebrate kidney, the convoluted section of a nephron into which filtrate moves from Bowman's capsule. Involved in the largely unregulated reabsorption of electrolytes, nutrients, and water. Compare with **distal tubule**.

proximate causation In biology, the immediate, mechanistic cause of a phenomenon (how it happens), as opposed to why it evolved. Also called *proximate explanation*. Compare with **ultimate causation**.

pseudocoelomate An animal that has a coelom that is only partially lined with mesoderm. Compare with **acoelomate** and **coelomate**.

pseudogene A DNA sequence that closely resembles a functional gene but is not transcribed. Thought to have arisen by duplication of the functional gene followed by inactivation due to a mutation.

pseudopodium (plural: pseudopodia) A temporary bulge-like extension of certain protist cells used in cell crawling and ingestion of food.

puberty The various physical and emotional changes that an immature human undergoes in reaching reproductive maturity. Also the period when such changes occur.

pulmonary artery A short, thick-walled artery that carries oxygen-poor blood from the heart to the lungs.

pulmonary circulation The part of the circulatory system that sends oxygen-poor blood to the lungs. It is separate from the rest of the circulatory system (the systemic circulation) in mammals and birds.

pulmonary vein A short, thin-walled vein that carries oxygen-rich blood from the lungs to the heart. Humans have four such veins.

pulse–chase experiment A type of experiment in which a population of cells or molecules at a particular moment in time is marked by means of a labeled molecule (pulse) and then their fate is followed over time (chase).

pump Any membrane protein that can hydrolyze ATP and change shape to power active transport of a specific ion or small molecule across a plasma membrane against its electrochemical gradient. See **proton pump**.

pupa (plural: pupae) A metamorphosing insect that is enclosed in a protective case.

pupil The hole in the center of the iris through which light enters a vertebrate or cephalopod eye.

pure line In animal or plant breeding, a strain that produces offspring identical with themselves when self-fertilized or crossed to another member of the same population. Pure lines are homozygous for most, if not all, genetic loci.

purifying selection Selection that lowers the frequency of or even eliminates deleterious alleles.

purines A class of small, nitrogen-containing, double-ringed bases (guanine, adenine) found in nucleotides. Compare with **pyrimidines**.

pyrimidines A class of small, nitrogen-containing, single-ringed bases (cytosine, uracil, thymine) found in nucleotides. Compare with **purines**.

pyruvate dehydrogenase A large enzyme complex, located in the mitochondrial matix, that is responsible for converting pyruvate to acetyl CoA during cellular respiration.

quantitative trait A trait that exhibits continuous phenotypic variation (e.g., human height), rather than the distinct forms characteristic of discrete traits.

quaternary structure In proteins, the overall three-dimensional shape formed from two or more polypeptide chains (subunits); determined by the number, relative positions, and interactions of the subunits. In single stranded nucleic acids, the hydrogen bonding between two or more distinct strands will form this level of structure through hydrophobic interactions between complementary bases. Compare with **primary**, **secondary**, and **tertiary structures**.

quorum sensing Cell–cell signaling in unicellular organisms, in which cells of the same species communicate via chemical signals. It is often observed that cell activity changes dramatically when the population reaches a threshold size, or quorum.

radial symmetry An animal body pattern that has at least two planes of symmetry. Typically, the body is in the form of a cylinder or disk, and the body parts radiate from a central hub. Compare with **bilateral symmetry**.

radiation Transfer of heat between two bodies that are not in direct physical contact. More generally, the emission of electromagnetic energy of any wavelength.

radicle The root of a plant embryo.

radioactive isotope A version of an element that has an unstable nucleus, which will release radiation energy as it decays to a more stable form. Decay often results in the radioisotope becoming a different element.

radioimmunoassay A competitive binding assay in which the quantity of hormone in a sample can be estimated. Uses radioactively labeled hormones that compete with the unknown hormone to bind with an antibody.

radula A rasping feeding appendage in mollusks such as gastropods (snails, slugs).

rain shadow The dry region on the side of a mountain range away from the prevailing wind.

range The geographic distribution of a species.

Ras protein A type of G protein that is activated by enzyme-linked cell-surface receptors, including receptor tyrosine kinases. Activated Ras then initiates a phosphorylation cascade, culminating in a cell response.

ray-finned fishes Members of the Actinopterygii, a diverse group of fishes with fins supported by bony rods arranged in a ray pattern.

rays In plant shoot systems with secondary growth, a lateral row of parenchyma cells produced by vascular cambium. Transport water and nutrients laterally across the stem.

Rb protein A tumor suppressor protein that helps regulate progression of a cell from the G_1 phase to the S phase of the cell cycle. Defects in Rb protein are found in many types of cancer.

reactant Any of the starting materials in a chemical reaction.

reaction center Centrally located component of a photosystem containing proteins and a pair of specialized chlorophyll molecules. It is surrounded by antenna complexes that transmit resonance energy to excite the reaction center pigments.

reading frame A series of non-overlapping, three-base-long sequences (potential codons) in DNA or RNA. The reading frame for a polypeptide is set by the start codon.

realized niche The portion of the fundamental niche that a species actually occupies given limiting factors such as competition with other species. Compare with **fundamental niche**.

receptor-mediated endocytosis Uptake by a cell of certain extracellular macromolecules, bound to specific receptors in the plasma membrane, by pinching off the membrane to form small membrane-bound vesicles.

receptor tyrosine kinase (RTK) Any of a class of enzyme-linked cell-surface signal receptors that undergo phosphorylation after binding a signaling molecule. The activated, phosphorylated receptor then triggers a signal transduction pathway inside the cell.

recessive Referring to an allele whose phenotypic effect is observed only in homozygous individuals. Compare with **dominant**.

reciprocal altruism Altruistic behavior that is exchanged between a pair of individuals at different times (i.e., sometimes individual A helps individual B, and sometimes B helps A).

reciprocal cross A cross in which the mother's and father's phenotypes are the reverse of that examined in a previous cross.

recombinant Possessing a new combination of alleles. May refer to a single chromosome or DNA molecule, or to an entire organism.

recombinant DNA technology A variety of techniques for isolating specific DNA fragments and introducing them into different regions of DNA or a different host organism.

rectal gland A salt-excreting gland in the digestive system of sharks, skates, and rays.

rectum The last portion of the digestive tract. It is where feces are held until they are expelled.

red blood cell A hemoglobin-containing cell that circulates in the blood and delivers oxygen from the lungs to the tissues.

redox reaction Any chemical reaction that involves either the complete transfer of one or more electrons from one reactant to another, or a reciprocal shift in the position of shared electrons within one or more of the covalent bonds of two reactants. Also called *reduction–oxidation reaction*.

reduction The gain of electrons by an atom or molecule during a redox reaction, either by acceptance of an electron from another atom or molecule, or by the shared electrons in covalent bonds moving closer to the atomic nucleus.

reduction–oxidation reaction See **redox reaction**.

reflex An involuntary response to environmental stimulation. May involve the brain (conditioned reflex) or not (spinal reflex).

refractory No longer responding to stimuli that previously elicited a response. An example is the tendency of voltage-gated sodium channels to remain closed immediately after an action potential.

regulatory sequence Any segment of DNA that is involved in controlling transcription of a specific gene by binding a regulatory transcription factor protein.

regulatory transcription factor General term for proteins that bind to DNA regulatory sequences (eukaryotic enhancers, silencers, and promoter-proximal elements), but not to the promoter itself, leading to an increase or decrease in transcription of specific genes. Compare with **basal transcription factor**.

regulon A large set of genes in bacteria that are controlled by a single type of regulatory molecule. Regulon genes are transcribed in response to environmental cues and allow cells to respond to changing environments.

reinforcement In evolutionary biology, the natural selection for traits that prevent interbreeding between recently diverged species.

release factors Proteins that trigger termination of translation when a ribosome reaches a stop codon.

renal corpuscle In the vertebrate kidney, the ball-like structure at the beginning of a nephron, consisting of a glomerulus and the surrounding Bowman's capsule. Acts as a filtration device.

replacement rate The number of offspring each female must produce over her entire life to "replace" herself and her mate, resulting in zero population growth. The actual number is slightly more than 2 because some offspring die before reproducing.

replica plating A method of identifying bacterial colonies that have certain mutations by transferring cells from each colony on a master plate to a second (replica) plate and observing their growth when exposed to different conditions.

replication fork The Y-shaped site at which a double-stranded molecule of DNA is separated into two single strands for replication.

replicative growth The process by which viruses produce new virions.

replisome The macromolecular machine that copies DNA; includes DNA polymerase, helicase, primase, and other enzymes.

repolarization Return to a resting potential after a membrane potential has changed; a normal phase in an action potential.

repressor (1) In bacteria, a protein that binds to an operator sequence in DNA to prevent transcription when an inducer is not present and that comes off DNA to allow transcription when an inducer binds to the repressor protein. (2) In eukaryotes, a protein that binds to a silencer sequence in DNA to prevent or reduce gene transcription.

reproductive development The phase of plant development that involves development of the flower and reproductive cells. Follows vegetative development and occurs when a shoot apical meristem (SAM) transitions to a flower-producing meristem.

reptiles One of the two lineages of amniotes (vertebrates that produce amniotic eggs) distinguished by adaptations for life and reproduction on land. Living reptiles include turtles, snakes and lizards, crocodiles and alligators, and birds. Except for birds, all are ectotherms.

resilience, community A measure of how quickly a community recovers following a disturbance.

resistance, community A measure of how much a community is affected by a disturbance.

respiratory system The collection of cells, tissues, and organs responsible for gas exchange between an animal and its environment.

resting potential The membrane potential of a cell in its resting, or normal, state.

restriction endonucleases Bacterial enzymes that cut DNA at a specific base-pair sequence (restriction site). Also called *restriction enzymes*.

retina A thin layer of light-sensitive cells (rods and cones) and neurons at the back of a simple eye, such as that of cephalopods and vertebrates.

retinal A light-absorbing pigment that is linked to the protein opsin in rods and cones of the vertebrate eye.

retrovirus A virus with an RNA genome that reverse-transcribes its RNA into a double-stranded DNA sequence, which is then inserted into the host's genome as part of its replicative cycle.

reverse transcriptase An enzyme that can synthesize double-stranded DNA from a single-stranded RNA template.

rhizobia (singular: rhizobium) Members of the bacterial genus *Rhizobium;* nitrogen-fixing bacteria that live in root nodules of members of the pea family (legumes).

rhizoid The hairlike structure that anchors a nonvascular plant to the substrate.

rhizome A modified stem that runs horizontally underground and produces new plants at the nodes (a form of asexual reproduction). Compare with **stolon**.

rhodopsin A transmembrane complex that is instrumental in detection of light by rods of the vertebrate eye. Is composed of the transmembrane protein opsin covalently linked to retinal, a light-absorbing pigment.

ribonucleic acid (RNA) A nucleic acid composed of ribonucleotides that usually is single stranded. Functions include structural components of ribosomes (rRNA), transporters of amino acids (tRNA), and messages of the DNA code required for protein synthesis (mRNA), among others.

ribonucleotide See **nucleotide**.

ribosomal RNA (rRNA) An RNA molecule that forms part of the ribosome.

ribosome A large macromolecular machine that synthesizes proteins by using the genetic information encoded in messenger RNA. Consists of two subunits, each composed of ribosomal RNA and proteins.

ribosome binding site In a bacterial mRNA molecule, the sequence just upstream of the start codon to which a ribosome binds to initiate translation. Also called the *Shine–Dalgarno sequence*.

ribozyme Any RNA molecule that can act as a catalyst, that is, speed up a chemical reaction.

ribulose bisphosphate (RuBP) A five-carbon compound that combines with CO_2 in the first step of the Calvin cycle during photosynthesis.

RNA See **ribonucleic acid**.

RNA interference (RNAi) Degradation of an RNA molecule or inhibition of its translation following its binding by a short RNA (microRNA) whose sequence is complementary to a portion of the mRNA.

RNA polymerase An enzyme that catalyzes the synthesis of RNA from ribonucleotides using a DNA template.

RNA processing In eukaryotes, the changes that a primary RNA transcript undergoes to become a mature RNA molecule. For pre-mRNA it includes the addition of a 5′ cap and poly(A) tail and splicing to remove introns.

RNA replicase A viral enzyme that can synthesize RNA from an RNA template. Also called an *RNA-dependent RNA polymerase*.

RNA world hypothesis Proposal that chemical evolution produced RNAs that could catalyze key reactions involved in their own replication and basic metabolism, which led to the evolution of proteins and the first life-form.

rod cell A photoreceptor cell with a rod-shaped outer portion that is particularly sensitive to dim light but not used to distinguish colors. Also called simply *rod*. Compare with **cone cell**.

root (1) An underground part of a plant that anchors the plant and absorbs water and nutrients. (2) The most ancestral branch in a phylogenetic tree.

root apical meristem (RAM) A group of undifferentiated plant stem cells at the tip of a plant root that can differentiate into mature root tissue.

root cap A small group of cells that covers and protects the root apical meristem. Senses gravity and determines the direction of root growth.

root hair A long, thin outgrowth of the epidermal cells of plant roots, providing increased surface area for absorption of water and nutrients.

root pressure Positive pressure of xylem sap in the vascular tissue of roots. Generated during the night as a result of the accumulation of ions from the soil and subsequent osmotic movement of water into the xylem.

root system The belowground part of a plant.

rotifer Member of the phylum Rotifera. Distinguished by a cluster of cilia, called a corona, used in suspension feeding in marine and freshwater environments. Rotifers belong to the lophotrochozoan branch of the protostomes.

rough endoplasmic reticulum (rough ER) The portion of the endoplasmic reticulum that is dotted with ribosomes. Involved in synthesis of plasma membrane proteins, secreted proteins, and proteins localized to the ER, Golgi apparatus, and lysosomes. Compare with **smooth endoplasmic reticulum**.

roundworms Members of the phylum Nematoda. Distinguished by an unsegmented body with a pseudocoelom and no appendages. Roundworms belong to the ecdysozoan branch of the protostomes. Also called *nematodes*.

rubisco The enzyme that catalyzes the first step of the Calvin cycle during photosynthesis: the addition of a molecule of CO_2 to ribulose bisphosphate. See also **carbon fixation**.

ruminant Member of a group of hoofed mammals (e.g., cattle, sheep, deer) that have a four-chambered stomach specialized for digestion of plant cellulose. Ruminants regurgitate cud, a mixture of partially digested food and cellulose-digesting bacteria, from the largest chamber (the rumen) for further chewing.

salinity The proportion of solutes dissolved in water in natural environments, often designated in grams of solute per kilogram of water (cited as parts per thousand).

salivary amylase An enzyme that is produced by the salivary glands and that can break down starch by catalyzing hydrolysis of the glycosidic linkages between the glucose residues.

salivary gland A type of vertebrate gland that secretes saliva (a mixture of water, mucus-forming glycoproteins, and digestive enzymes) into the mouth.

sampling error The selection of a nonrepresentative sample from some larger population, due to chance.

saprophyte An organism that feeds primarily on dead plant material.

sapwood The younger xylem in the outer layer of wood of a stem or root, functioning primarily in water transport.

sarcomere The repeating contractile unit of a skeletal muscle cell; the portion of a myofibril located between adjacent Z disks.

sarcoplasmic reticulum Sheets of smooth endoplasmic reticulum in a muscle cell. Contains high concentrations of calcium, which can be released into the cytoplasm to trigger contraction.

saturated Referring to lipids in which all the carbon-carbon bonds are single bonds. Such compounds have relatively high melting points. Compare with **unsaturated**.

scanning electron microscope (SEM) A microscope that produces images of the surfaces of objects by reflecting electrons from a specimen coated with a layer of metal atoms. Compare with **transmission electron microscope**.

scarify To scrape, rasp, cut, or otherwise damage the coat of a seed. Necessary in some species to trigger germination.

Schwann cell A type of glial cell that wraps around axons of some neurons outside the brain and spinal cord, forming a myelin sheath that provides electrical insulation. Compare with **oligodendrocyte**.

scientific name The unique, two-part name given to each species, with a genus name followed by a species name—as in *Homo sapiens*. Scientific names are always italicized, and are also known as Latin names.

sclereid In plants, a relatively short type of sclerenchyma cell that usually functions in protection, such as in seed coats and nutshells. Compare with **fiber**.

sclerenchyma cell In plants, a cell that has a thick secondary cell wall and provides support; typically contains the tough structural polymer lignin and usually is dead at maturity. Includes fibers and sclereids. Compare with **collenchyma cell** and **parenchyma cell**.

scrotum A sac of skin containing the testes and suspended just outside the abdominal body cavity of many male mammals.

second law of thermodynamics The principle of physics that the entropy of the universe or any closed system always increases.

second-male advantage The reproductive advantage, in some species, of a male who mates with a female last, after other males have mated with her.

second messenger A nonprotein signaling molecule produced or activated inside a cell in response to stimulation at the cell surface. Commonly used to relay the message of a hormone or other extracellular signaling molecule.

secondary active transport Transport of an ion or molecule in a defined direction that is often against its electrochemical gradient, in company with an ion or molecule being transported along its electrochemical gradient. Also called *cotransport*.

secondary cell wall The thickened inner layer of a plant cell wall formed by certain cells as they mature and have stopped growing; in water-conducting cells, contains lignin. Provides support or protection.

secondary consumer A carnivore; an organism that eats herbivores. Compare with **primary consumer**.

secondary growth In plants, an increase in the width of stems and roots due to the activity of cambium. Compare with **primary growth**.

secondary immune response The adaptive immune response to a pathogen that the immune system has encountered before. Normally much faster and more efficient than the primary response, due to immunological memory. Compare with **primary immune response**.

secondary metabolites Molecules that are closely related to compounds in key synthetic pathways and that often function in defense.

secondary oocyte A cell produced by meiosis I of a primary oocyte in the ovary. If fertilized, will complete meiosis II to produce an ootid (which develops into an ovum) and a polar body.

secondary spermatocyte A cell produced by meiosis I of a primary spermatocyte in the testis. Can undergo meiosis II to produce spermatids.

secondary structure In proteins, localized folding of a polypeptide chain into regular structures (i.e., alpha-helix and beta-pleated sheet) stabilized by hydrogen bonding between atoms of the peptide backbone. In nucleic acids, elements of structure (e.g., helices and hairpins) stabilized by hydrogen bonding and hydrophobic interactions between complementary bases. Compare with **primary**, **tertiary**, and **quaternary structures**.

secondary succession Gradual colonization of a habitat after an environmental disturbance (e.g., fire, windstorm, logging) that removes some or all previous organisms but leaves the soil intact. Compare with **primary succession**.

secretin A peptide hormone produced by cells in the small intestine in response to the arrival of food from the stomach. Stimulates secretion of bicarbonate (HCO_3^-) from the pancreas.

sedimentary rock A type of rock formed by gradual accumulation of sediment, particularly sand and mud, as in riverbeds and on the ocean floor. Most fossils are found in sedimentary rocks.

seed A plant reproductive structure consisting of an embryo, associated nutritive tissue (endosperm), and an outer protective layer (seed coat). In angiosperms, develops from the fertilized ovule of a flower.

seed bank A repository where seeds, representing many different varieties of domestic crops or other species, are preserved.

seed coat A protective layer around a seed that encases both the embryo and the endosperm.

segment A well-defined, repeated region of the body along the anterior–posterior body axis, containing structures similar to other nearby segments.

segmentation Division of the body or a part of it into a series of similar structures; exemplified by the body segments of insects and worms and by the somites of vertebrates.

segmentation genes A group of genes that control the formation and patterning of body segmentation in embryonic development. Includes maternal genes, gap genes, pair-rule genes, and segment polarity genes.

segregation, principle of The concept that each pair of hereditary elements (alleles of the same gene) separate from each other during meiosis. One of Mendel's two principles of genetics.

selective adhesion The tendency of cells of one tissue type to adhere to other cells of the same type.

selective permeability The property of a membrane that allows some substances to diffuse across it much more readily than other substances.

selectively permeable membrane Any membrane across which some solutes can move more readily than others.

self-fertilization The fusion of two gametes from the same individual to form offspring. Also called *selfing*.

self molecule A molecule that is synthesized by an organism and is a normal part of its cells and/or body; as opposed to nonself, or foreign, molecules.

semen The combination of sperm and accessory fluids that is released by male mammals and reptiles during ejaculation.

semiconservative replication The way DNA replicates, in which each strand of an existing DNA molecule serves as a template to create a new complementary DNA strand. It is called semiconservative because each newly replicated DNA molecule conserves one of the parental strands and contains another, newly replicated strand.

seminal vesicle In male mammals, either of a pair of reproductive glands that secrete a sugar-containing fluid into semen, which provides energy for sperm movement.

senescence The genetically programmed, active process of aging.

sensor Any cell, organ, or structure with which an animal can sense some aspect of the external or internal environment. Usually functions, along with an integrator and effector, as part of a homeostatic system.

sensory neuron A nerve cell that carries signals from sensory receptors to the central nervous system. Compare with **interneuron** and **motor neuron**.

sepal One of the protective leaflike organs enclosing a flower bud and later part of the outermost portion of the flower.

septum (plural: septa) Any wall-like structure. In fungi, septa divide the filaments (hyphae) of mycelia into cell-like compartments.

serotonin A neurotransmitter involved in many brain functions, including sleep, pleasure, and mood.

serum The liquid that remains when cells and clot material are removed from clotted blood. Contains water, dissolved gases, growth factors, nutrients, and other soluble substances. Compare with **plasma**.

sessile Permanently attached to a substrate; not capable of moving to another location.

set point A normal or target value for a regulated internal variable, such as body heat or blood pH.

sex chromosome Chromosomes that differ in shape or in number in males and females. For example, the X and Y chromosomes of many animals. Compare with **autosome**.

sex-linked inheritance Inheritance patterns observed in genes carried on sex chromosomes. In this case, females and males have different numbers of alleles of a gene. Often creates situations in which a trait appears more often in one sex. Also called *sex-linkage*.

sexual dimorphism Any trait that differs between males and females.

sexual reproduction Any form of reproduction in which genes from two parents are combined via fusion of gametes, producing offspring that are genetically distinct from both parents. Compare with **asexual reproduction**.

sexual selection A type of natural selection that favors individuals with traits that increase their ability to obtain mates. Acts more strongly on males than females. (Compare with **ecological selection**.)

shell A hard, protective outer structure.

Shine–Dalgarno sequence See **ribosome binding sequence**.

shoot In a plant embryo, the combination of hypocotyl and cotyledons, which will become the aboveground portions of the plant.

shoot apical meristem (SAM) A group of undifferentiated plant stem cells at the tip of a plant stem that can differentiate into mature shoot tissues.

shoot system The aboveground part of a plant comprising stems, leaves, and flowers (in angiosperms).

short-day plant A plant that blooms in response to long nights (usually in late summer or fall in the Northern Hemisphere). Compare with **day-neutral** and **long-day plant**.

short tandem repeats (STRs) Relatively short DNA sequences that are repeated, one after another, down the length of a chromosome. See **microsatellite**.

shotgun sequencing A method of sequencing genomes that is based on breaking the genome into small pieces, sequencing each piece separately, and then figuring out how the pieces are connected.

sieve plate In plants, a pore-containing structure at each end of a sieve-tube element in phloem.

sieve-tube element In plants, an elongated sugar-conducting cell in phloem that lacks nuclei and has sieve plates at both ends, allowing sap to flow to adjacent cells.

sigma A bacterial protein that associates with the core RNA polymerase to allow recognition of promoters.

signal In behavioral ecology, any information-containing behavior or characteristic.

signal receptor Any cellular protein that binds to a particular signaling molecule (e.g., a hormone or neurotransmitter) and triggers a response by the cell. Receptors for lipid-insoluble signals are transmembrane proteins in the plasma membrane; those for many lipid-soluble signals (e.g., steroid hormones) are located inside the cell.

signal recognition particle (SRP) An RNA–protein complex that binds to the ER signal sequence in a polypeptide as it emerges from a ribosome and transports the ribosome–polypeptide complex to the ER membrane, where synthesis of the polypeptide is completed.

signal transduction The process by which a stimulus (e.g., a hormone, a neurotransmitter, or sensory information) outside a cell is converted into an intracellular signal required for a cellular response. Usually involves a specific sequence of molecular events, or signal transduction pathway, that may lead to amplification of the signal.

signal transduction cascade See **phosphorylation cascade**.

silencer A regulatory sequence in eukaryotic DNA to which repressor proteins can bind, inhibiting gene transcription.

silent mutation A point mutation that changes the sequence of a codon without changing the amino acid that is specified.

simple eye An eye with only one light-collecting apparatus (e.g., one lens), as in vertebrates and cephalopods. Compare with **compound eye**.

simple fruit A fruit (e.g., apricot) that develops from a single flower that has a single carpel or several fused carpels. Compare with **aggregate** and **multiple fruit**.

simple sequence repeat See **microsatellite**.

SINEs (short interspersed nuclear elements) The second most abundant class of transposable elements in human genomes; can create copies of itself and insert them elsewhere in the genome. Compare with **LINEs**.

single nucleotide polymorphism (SNP) A site on a chromosome where individuals in a population have different nucleotides. Can be used as a genetic marker to help track the inheritance of nearby genes.

single-strand DNA-binding proteins (SSBP) A protein that attaches to separated strands of DNA during replication or transcription, preventing them from re-forming a double helix.

sink Any tissue, site, or location where an element or a molecule is consumed or taken out of circulation (e.g., in plants, a tissue where sugar exits the phloem). Compare with **source**.

sinoatrial (SA) node In the right atrium of the vertebrate heart, a cluster of cardiac muscle cells that initiates the heartbeat and determines the heart rate. Compare with **atrioventricular (AV) node**.

siphon A tubelike appendage of many mollusks, often used for feeding or propulsion.

sister chromatids The paired strands of a recently replicated chromosome, which are connected at the centromere and eventually separate during anaphase of mitosis and meiosis II. Compare with **non-sister chromatids**.

sister species Closely related species that occupy adjacent branches in a phylogenetic tree.

skeletal muscle The muscle tissue attached to the bones of the vertebrate skeleton. Consists of long, unbranched muscle fibers with a characteristic striped (striated) appearance; controlled voluntarily. Compare with **cardiac** and **smooth muscle**.

sliding-filament model The hypothesis that thin (actin) filaments and thick (myosin) filaments slide past each other, thereby shortening the sarcomere. Shortening of all the sarcomeres in a myofibril results in contraction of the entire myofibril.

slow muscle fiber Type of skeletal muscle fiber that is red in color due to the abundance of myoglobin, generates ATP by oxidative phosphorylation, and contracts slowly but does not fatigue easily. Also called *slow oxidative*, or *Type I, fiber.*

small intestine The portion of the digestive tract between the stomach and the large intestine. The site of the final stages of digestion and of most nutrient absorption.

small nuclear ribonucleoproteins See **snRNPs**.

smooth endoplasmic reticulum (smooth ER) The portion of the endoplasmic reticulum that does not have ribosomes attached to it. Involved in synthesis and secretion of lipids. Compare with **rough endoplasmic reticulum**.

smooth muscle The unstriated muscle tissue that lines the intestine, blood vessels, and some other organs. Consists of tapered, unbranched cells that can sustain long contractions. Not voluntarily controlled. Compare with **cardiac** and **skeletal muscle**.

snRNPs (small nuclear ribonucleoproteins) Complexes of proteins and small RNA molecules that function as components of spliceosomes during splicing (removal of introns from pre-mRNAs).

sodium–potassium pump A transmembrane protein that uses the energy of ATP to move sodium ions out of the cell and potassium ions in. Also called *Na+/K+-ATPase*.

soil organic matter Organic (carbon-containing) compounds found in soil.

solute Any substance that is dissolved in a liquid.

solute potential (ψ_S) A component of the potential energy of water caused by a difference in solute concentrations at two locations. Can be zero (pure water) or negative. Compare with **pressure potential (ψ_P)**.

solution A liquid containing one or more dissolved solids or gases in a homogeneous mixture.

solvent Any liquid in which one or more solids or gases can dissolve.

soma See **cell body**.

somatic cell Any type of cell in a multicellular organism except eggs, sperm, and their precursor cells. Also called *body cells*.

somatic hypermutation Mutation that occurs in the variable regions of immunoglobulin genes when B cells are first activated and in memory cells, resulting in novel variation in the receptors that bind to antigens.

somatic nervous system The part of the peripheral nervous system (outside the brain and spinal cord) that controls skeletal muscles and is under voluntary control. Compare with **autonomic nervous system**.

somatostatin A hormone secreted by the pancreas and hypothalamus that inhibits the release of several other hormones.

somite A block of mesoderm that occurs in pairs along both sides of the developing neural tube in a vertebrate embryo. Gives rise to muscle, vertebrae, ribs, and the dermis of the skin.

sori In ferns, a cluster of spore-producing structures (sporangia) usually found on the underside of fronds.

source Any tissue, site, or location where a substance is produced or enters circulation (e.g., in plants, the tissue where sugar enters the phloem). Compare with **sink**.

space-filling model A representation of a molecule where atoms are shown as balls—color-coded and scaled to indicate the atom's identify—attached to each other in the correct geometry.

speciation The evolution of two or more distinct species from a single ancestral species.

species An evolutionarily independent population or group of populations. Generally distinct from other species in appearance, behavior, habitat, ecology, genetic characteristics, and so on.

species–area relationship The mathematical relationship between the area of a certain habitat and the number of species that it can support.

species diversity The variety and relative abundance of the species present in a given ecological community.

species richness The number of species present in a given ecological community.

specific heat The amount of energy required to raise the temperature of 1 gram of a substance by 1°C; a measure of the capacity of a substance to absorb energy.

sperm A mature male gamete; smaller and more mobile than the female gamete.

sperm competition Competition between the sperm of different males to fertilize eggs inside the same female.

spermatid An immature sperm cell.

spermatogenesis The production of sperm. Occurs continuously in a testis.

spermatogonium (plural: spermatogonia) Any of the diploid cells in a testis that can give rise to primary spermatocytes.

spermatophore A gelatinous package containing sperm cells that is produced by males of species that have internal fertilization without copulation.

sphincter A muscular valve that can close off a tube, as in a blood vessel or a part of the digestive tract.

spicule Stiff spike of silica or calcium carbonate that provides structural support in the body of many sponges.

spindle apparatus The array of microtubules responsible for moving chromosomes during mitosis and meiosis; includes kinetochore microtubules, polar microtubules, and astral microtubules.

spines In plants, modified leaves that are stiff and sharp and that function in defense.

spiracle In insects, a small opening that connects air-filled tracheae to the external environment, allowing for gas exchange.

spleen A dark red organ, found near the stomach of most vertebrates, that filters blood, stores extra red blood cells in case of emergency, and plays a role in immunity.

spliceosome In eukaryotes, a large, complex assembly of snRNPs (small nuclear ribonucleoproteins) that catalyzes removal of introns from primary RNA transcripts.

splicing The process by which introns are removed from primary RNA transcripts and the remaining exons are connected together.

sporangium (plural: sporangia) A spore-producing structure found in seed plants, some protists, and some fungi (e.g., chytrids).

spore (1) In bacteria, a dormant form that generally is resistant to extreme conditions. (2) In eukaryotes, a single haploid cell produced by mitosis or meiosis (not by fusion of gametes) that is capable of developing into an adult organism.

sporophyte In organisms undergoing alternation of generations, the multicellular diploid form that arises from two fused gametes and produces haploid spores. Compare with **gametophyte**.

sporopollenin A watertight material that encases spores and pollen of modern land plants.

stabilizing selection A mode of natural selection that favors phenotypes near the middle of the range of phenotypic variation. Reduces overall genetic variation in a population. Compare with **disruptive selection** and **directional selection**.

stamen The male reproductive structure of a flower. Consists of an anther, in which pollen grains are produced, and a filament, which supports the anther. Compare with **carpel**.

standing defense See **constitutive defense**.

stapes The last of three small bones (ossicles) in the middle ear of vertebrates. Receives vibrations from the tympanic membrane and by vibrating against the oval window passes them to the cochlea.

starch A mixture of two storage polysaccharides, amylose and amylopectin, both formed from α-glucose monomers. Amylopectin is branched, and amylose is unbranched. The major form of stored carbohydrate in plants.

start codon The AUG triplet in mRNA at which protein synthesis begins; codes for the amino acid methionine.

statocyst A sensory organ of many arthropods that detects the animal's orientation in space (e.g., whether the animal is flipped upside down).

statolith A tiny stone or dense particle found in specialized gravity-sensing organs in some animals such as lobsters, and in gravity-sensing tissues of plants.

statolith hypothesis The hypothesis that amyloplasts (dense, starch-storing plant organelles) serve as statoliths in gravity detection by plants.

stem cell Any relatively undifferentiated cell that can divide to produce a daughter cell that remains a stem cell and a daughter cell that can differentiate into specific cell types.

stems Vertical, aboveground structures that make up the shoot system of plants.

stereocilium (plural: stereocilia) One of many stiff outgrowths from the surface of a hair cell that are involved in detection of sound by terrestrial vertebrates or of waterborne vibrations by fishes.

steroid A class of lipid with a characteristic four-ring hydrocarbon structure.

sticky ends The short, single-stranded ends of a DNA molecule cut by a restriction endonuclease. Tend to form hydrogen bonds with other sticky ends that have complementary sequences.

stigma The sticky tip at the end of a flower carpel to which pollen grains adhere.

stolon A modified stem that runs horizontally over the soil surface and produces new plants at the nodes (a form of asexual reproduction). Compare with **rhizome**.

stoma (plural: stomata) Generally, a pore or opening. In plants, a microscopic pore, surrounded by specialized cells that open the pore, on the surface of a leaf or stem through which gas exchange occurs. See also **guard cells**.

stomach A tough, muscular pouch in the vertebrate digestive tract between the esophagus and small intestine. Physically breaks up food and begins digestion of proteins.

stop codon Any of three mRNA triplets (UAG, UGA, or UAA) that cause termination of protein synthesis. Also called a *termination codon*.

strain The lowest, most specific level of taxonomy that refers to a population of individuals that are genetically very similar or identical.

striated muscle Muscle tissue containing protein filaments organized into repeating structures that give the cells and tissues a banded appearance.

stroma The fluid matrix of a chloroplast in which the thylakoids are embedded. Site where the Calvin cycle reactions occur.

structural formula A two-dimensional notation in which the chemical symbols for the constituent atoms are joined by straight lines representing single (−), double (=), or triple (≡) covalent bonds. Compare with **molecular formula**.

structural homology Similarities in adult organismal structures (e.g., limbs, shells, flowers) that are due to inheritance from a common ancestor.

style The slender stalk of a flower carpel connecting the stigma and the ovary.

suberin Waxy substance found in the cell walls of cork tissue and in the Casparian strip of endodermal cells.

subspecies A population that has distinctive traits and some genetic differences relative to other populations of the same species but that is not distinct enough to be classified as a separate species.

substrate (1) A reactant that interacts with a catalyst, such as an enzyme or ribozyme, in a chemical reaction. (2) A surface on which a cell or organism sits.

substrate-level phosphorylation Production of ATP or GTP by the transfer of a phosphate group from an intermediate substrate directly to ADP or GDP. Occurs in glycolysis and in the citric acid cycle.

succession In ecology, the gradual colonization of a habitat after an environmental disturbance (e.g., fire, flood), usually by a series of species. See **primary** and **secondary succession**.

sucrose A disaccharide formed from glucose and fructose. One of the two main products of photosynthesis.

sugar Synonymous with carbohydrate, though usually used in an informal sense to refer to small carbohydrates (monosaccharides and disaccharides).

summation The additive effect of different post-synaptic potentials on a nerve or muscle cell, such that several subthreshold stimulations can cause or inhibit an action potential.

supporting connective tissue A type of connective tissue distinguished by having a firm extracellular matrix. Includes bone and cartilage.

surface metabolism model Hypothetical explanation for chemical evolution whereby small molecules reacted with one another through catalytic activity associated with a surface, such as the mineral deposits found in deep-sea hydrothermal vents.

surface tension The cohesive force that causes molecules at the surface of a liquid to stick together, thereby resisting deformation of the liquid's surface and minimizing its surface area.

survivorship On average, the proportion of offspring that survive to a particular age.

survivorship curve A graph depicting the percentage of a population that survives to different ages.

suspension feeder Any organism that obtains food by filtering small particles or small organisms out of water or air. Also called *filter feeder*.

sustainability The planned use of environmental resources at a rate no faster than the rate at which they are naturally replaced.

sustainable agriculture Agricultural techniques that are designed to maintain long-term soil quality and productivity.

swamp A wetland that has a steady rate of water flow and is dominated by trees and shrubs.

swim bladder A gas-filled organ of many ray-finned fishes that regulates buoyancy.

symbiosis (adjective: symbiotic) Any close and prolonged physical relationship between individuals of two different species. See **commensalism**, **mutualism**, and **parasitism**.

symmetric competition Ecological competition between two species in which both suffer similar declines in fitness. Compare with **asymmetric competition**.

sympathetic nervous system The part of the autonomic nervous system that stimulates fight-or-flight responses, such as increased heart rate, increased blood pressure, and decreased digestion. Compare with **parasympathetic nervous system**.

sympatric speciation The divergence of populations living within the same geographic area into different species as the result of their genetic (not physical) isolation. Compare with **allopatric speciation**.

sympatry Condition in which two or more populations live in the same geographic area, or close enough to permit interbreeding. Compare with **allopatry**.

symplast In plants, the space inside the plasma membranes. The symplast of adjacent cells is often connected through plasmodesmata. Compare with **apoplast**.

symporter A cotransport protein that allows an ion to diffuse down an electrochemical gradient, using the energy of that process to transport a different substance in the same direction *against* its concentration gradient. Compare with **antiporter**.

synapomorphy A shared, derived trait found in two or more taxa that is present in their most recent common ancestor but is missing in more distant ancestors. Useful for inferring evolutionary relationships.

synapse The interface between two neurons or between a neuron and an effector cell.

synapsis The physical pairing of two homologous chromosomes during prophase I of meiosis. Crossing over is observed during synapsis.

synaptic cleft The space between two communicating nerve cells (or between a neuron and effector cell) at a synapse, across which neurotransmitters diffuse.

synaptic plasticity Long-term changes in the responsiveness or physical structure of a synapse that can occur after particular stimulation patterns. Thought to be the basis of learning and memory.

synaptic vesicle A small neurotransmitter-containing vesicle at the end of an axon that releases neurotransmitter into the synaptic cleft by exocytosis.

synaptonemal complex A network of proteins that holds non-sister chromatids together during synapsis in meiosis I.

synthesis (S) phase The phase of the cell cycle during which DNA is synthesized and chromosomes are replicated.

system A defined set of interacting chemical components under observation.

systemic acquired resistance (SAR) A slow, widespread response of plants to a localized infection that protects healthy tissue from invasion by pathogens. Compare with **hypersensitive response**.

systemic circulation The part of the circulatory system that sends oxygen-rich blood from the lungs out to the rest of the body. It is separate from the pulmonary circulation in mammals and birds.

systemin A peptide hormone, produced by plant cells damaged by herbivores, that initiates a protective response in undamaged cells.

systems biology The study of the structure of networks and how interactions between individual network components such as genes or proteins can lead to emergent biological properties.

systole The portion of the cardiac cycle during which the heart muscles are contracting. Compare with **diastole**.

systolic blood pressure The force exerted by blood against artery walls during contraction of the heart's left ventricle. Compare with **diastolic blood pressure**.

T cell A type of lymphocyte that matures in the thymus and, with B cells, is responsible for adaptive immunity. Involved in activation of B cells (CD4$^+$ helper T cells) and destruction of infected cells (CD8$^+$ cytotoxic T cells). Also called *T lymphocytes*.

T-cell receptor (TCR) A type of transmembrane protein found on T cells that can bind to antigens displayed on the surfaces of other cells. Composed of two polypeptides, called the alpha chain and beta chain, that consist of variable and constant regions. See **antigen presentation**.

T tubule Any of the membranous tubes that extend into the interior of muscle cells, propagating action potentials throughout the cell and triggering release of calcium from the sarcoplasmic reticulum.

tagmata (singular: tagma) Prominent body regions in arthropods, such as the head, thorax, and abdomen in insects.

taiga A vast forest biome throughout subarctic regions, consisting primarily of short coniferous trees. Characterized by intensely cold winters, short summers, and high annual variation in temperature.

taproot A large, vertical main root of a plant's root system.

taste bud A sensory structure, found chiefly in the mammalian tongue, containing spindle-shaped cells that respond to chemical stimuli.

TATA-binding protein (TBP) A protein that binds to the TATA box in eukaryotic promoters and is a component of the basal transcription complex.

TATA box A short DNA sequence in many eukaryotic promoters about 30 base pairs upstream from the transcription start site.

taxon (plural: taxa) Any named group of organisms at any level of a classification system.

taxonomy The branch of biology concerned with the classification and naming of organisms.

tectorial membrane A membrane, located in the vertebrate cochlea, that takes part in the transduction of sound by bending the stereocilia of hair cells in response to sonic vibrations.

telomerase An enzyme that adds DNA to the ends of chromosomes (telomeres) by catalyzing DNA synthesis from an RNA template that is part of the enzyme.

telomere The end of a linear chromosome that contains a repeated sequence of DNA.

telophase The final stage in mitosis or meiosis during which daughter chromosomes (homologous chromosomes in meiosis I) have separated and new nuclear envelopes begin to form around each set of chromosomes.

temperate Having a climate with pronounced annual fluctuations in temperature (i.e., warm summers and cold winters) but typically neither as hot as the tropics nor as cold as the poles.

temperature A measurement of thermal energy present in an object or substance, reflecting how much the constituent molecules are moving.

template strand An original nucleic acid strand used to make a new, complementary copy based on hydrogen bonding between nitrogeneous bases.

temporal lobe In the vertebrate brain, one of the four major areas in the cerebrum.

tendon A band of tough, fibrous connective tissue that connects a muscle to a bone.

tentacle A long, thin, muscular appendage typically used for feeling and feeding. Occurs in different forms in diverse animals such as cephalopod mollusks and sea anemones.

termination (1) In enzyme-catalyzed reactions, the final stage in which the enzyme returns to its original conformation and products are released. (2) In transcription, the dissociation of RNA polymerase from DNA. (3) In translation, the dissociation of a ribosome from mRNA when it reaches a stop codon.

territory An area that is actively defended by an animal from others of its species and that provides exclusive or semi-exclusive use of its resources by the owner.

tertiary consumers In a food chain or food web, organisms that feed on secondary consumers. Compare with **primary consumer** and **secondary consumer**.

tertiary structure The overall three-dimensional shape of a single polypeptide chain, resulting from multiple interactions among the amino acid side chains and the peptide backbone. In single-stranded nucleic acids, the three-dimensional shape is formed by hydrogen bonding and hydrophobic interactions between complementary bases. Compare with **primary**, **secondary**, and **quaternary structure**.

testcross The breeding of an individual that expresses a dominant phenotype but has an unknown genotype with an individual having only recessive alleles for the traits of interest. Used to order to infer the unknown genotype from observation of the phenotypes seen in offspring.

testis (plural: testes) The sperm-producing organ of a male animal.

testosterone A steroid hormone, produced and secreted by the testes, that stimulates sperm production and various male traits and reproductive behaviors.

tetrad The structure formed by synapsed homologous chromosomes during prophase of meiosis I. Also known as a *bivalent*.

tetrapod Any member of the lineage that includes all vertebrates with two pairs of limbs (amphibians, mammals, and reptiles, including birds).

texture A quality of soil, resulting from the relative abundance of different-sized particles.

theory An explanation for a broad class of phenomena that is supported by a wide body of evidence. A theory serves as a framework for the development of new hypotheses.

thermal energy The kinetic energy of molecular motion.

thermocline A steep gradient (cline) in environmental temperature, such as occurs in a thermally stratified lake or ocean.

thermophile A bacterium or archaean that thrives in very hot environments.

thermoreception A sensory system in which receptors are activated by changes in heat energy.

thermoreceptor A sensory cell or an organ specialized for detection of changes in temperature.

thermoregulation Regulation of body temperature.

thick filament A filament composed of bundles of the motor protein myosin; anchored to the center of the sarcomere. Compare with **thin filament**.

thigmotropism Growth or movement of an organism in response to contact with a solid object.

thin filament A filament composed of two coiled chains of actin and associated regulatory proteins; anchored at the Z disk of the sarcomere. Compare with **thick filament**.

thorax A region of the body; in insects, one of the three prominent body regions, along with the head and abdomen, called tagmata.

thorn A modified plant stem shaped as a sharp, protective structure. Helps protect a plant against feeding by herbivores.

threshold potential The membrane potential that will trigger an action potential in a neuron or other excitable cell. Also called simply *threshold*.

thylakoid A membrane-bound network of flattened sac-like structures inside a plant chloroplast that functions in converting light energy to chemical energy. A stack of thylakoid discs is a granum.

thymus An organ, located in the anterior chest or neck of vertebrates, in which immature T cells that originated in the bone marrow undergo maturation.

thyroid gland A gland in the neck that releases thyroid hormone (which increases metabolic rate) and calcitonin (which lowers blood calcium).

thyroid hormones Either of two hormones, triiodothyronine (T_3) or thyroxine (T_4), produced by the thyroid gland. See **triiodothyronine** and **thyroxine**.

thyroid-stimulating hormone (TSH) A peptide hormone, produced and secreted by the anterior pituitary, that stimulates release of thyroid hormones from the thyroid gland.

thyroxine (T_4) A lipid-soluble hormone, derived from the amino acid tyrosine, containing four iodine atoms and produced and secreted by the thyroid gland. Acts primarily to increase cellular metabolism. In mammals, T_4 is converted to the more active hormone triiodothyronine (T_3) in the liver.

Ti plasmid A plasmid carried by *Agrobacterium* (a bacterium that infects plants) that can integrate into a plant cell's chromosomes and induce formation of a gall.

tight junction A type of cell–cell attachment structure that links the plasma membranes of adjacent animal cells, forming a barrier that restricts movement of substances in the space between the cells. Most abundant in epithelia (e.g., the intestinal lining). Compare with **desmosome** and **gap junction**.

tip The end of a branch on a phylogenetic tree. Represents a specific species or larger taxon that has not (yet) produced descendants—either a group living today or a group that ended in extinction. Also called *terminal node*.

tissue A group of cells that function as a unit, such as muscle tissue in an animal or xylem tissue in a plant.

tolerance In ecological succession, the phenomenon in which early-arriving species do not affect the probability that subsequent species will become established. Compare with **facilitation** and **inhibition**.

tonoplast The membrane surrounding a plant vacuole.

tool-kit genes A set of key developmental genes that establishes the body plan of animals and plants; present at the origin of the multicellular lineages and elaborated upon over evolutionary time by a process of duplication and divergence. Includes *Hox* genes.

top-down control The hypothesis that population size is limited by predators or herbivores (consumers).

topoisomerase An enzyme that prevents the twisting of DNA ahead of the advancing replication fork by cutting the DNA, allowing it to unwind, and rejoining it.

torpor An energy-conserving physiological state, marked by a decrease in metabolic rate, body temperature, and activity, that lasts for a short period (overnight to a few days or weeks). Occurs in some small mammals when the ambient temperature drops significantly. Compare with **hibernation**.

totipotent Capable of dividing and developing to form a complete, mature organism.

toxin A poison produced by a living organism, such as a plant, animal, or microorganism.

trachea (plural: tracheae) (1) In insects, any of the small air-filled tubes that extend throughout the body and function in gas exchange. (2) In terrestrial vertebrates, the airway connecting the larynx to the bronchi. Also called *windpipe*.

tracheid In vascular plants, a long, thin, water-conducting cell that has pits where its lignin-containing secondary cell wall is absent, allowing water movement between adjacent cells. Compare with **vessel element**.

trade-off In evolutionary biology, an inescapable compromise between two traits that cannot be optimized simultaneously. Also called *fitness trade-off*.

trait Any observable characteristic of an individual.

transcription The process that uses a DNA template to produce a complementary RNA.

transcription factor General term for a protein that binds to a DNA regulatory sequence to influence transcription. It includes both regulatory and basal transcription factors.

transcriptional activator A eukaryotic regulatory transcription factor that binds to regulatory DNA sequences in enhancers or promoter-proximal elements to promote the initiation of transcription.

transcriptional control Regulation of gene expression by various mechanisms that change the rate at which genes are transcribed to form messenger RNA. In negative control, binding of a regulatory protein to DNA represses transcription; in positive control, binding of a regulatory protein to DNA promotes transcription.

transcriptome The complete set of genes transcribed in a particular cell.

transduction The conversion of information from one mode to another. For example, the process by which a stimulus outside a cell is converted into a response by the cell.

transfer RNA (tRNA) An RNA molecule that has an anticodon at one end and an amino acid attachment site at the other. Each tRNA carries a specific amino acid and binds to the corresponding codon in messenger RNA during translation.

transformation (1) Incorporation of external DNA into a cell. Occurs naturally in some bacteria; can be induced in the laboratory. (2) Conversion of a normal mammalian cell to one that divides uncontrollably.

transgenic A plant or animal whose genome contains DNA introduced from another individual, often from a different species.

transition state A high-energy intermediate state of the reactants during a chemical reaction that must be achieved for the reaction to proceed. Compare with **activation energy**.

transitional feature A trait that is intermediate between a condition observed in ancestral (older) species and the condition observed in derived (younger) species.

translation The process by which a polypeptide (a string of amino acids joined by peptide bonds) is synthesized from information in codons of messenger RNA.

translational control Regulation of gene expression by various mechanisms that alter the life span of messenger RNA or the efficiency of translation.

translocation (1) In plants, the movement of sugars and other organic nutrients through the phloem by bulk flow. (2) A type of mutation in which a piece of a chromosome moves to a nonhomologous chromosome. (3) The movement of a ribosome down a messenger RNA during translation.

transmembrane protein See **integral membrane protein**.

transmission The passage or transfer of (1) a disease from one individual to another or (2) electrical impulses from one neuron to another.

transpiration Loss of water vapor from aboveground plant parts. Occurs primarily through stomata.

transporter See **carrier protein**.

transposable elements Any of several kinds of DNA sequences that are capable of moving themselves, or copies of themselves, to other locations in the genome. Include LINEs and SINEs.

tree of life The phylogenetic tree that includes all organisms.

trichome A hairlike appendage that grows from epidermal cells in the shoot system of some plants. Trichomes exhibit a variety of shapes, sizes, and functions depending on species.

triiodothyronine (T_3) A lipid-soluble hormone, derived from the amino acid tyrosine, containing three iodine atoms and produced and secreted by the thyroid gland. Acts primarily to increase cellular metabolism. In mammals, T_3 has a stronger effect than does the related hormone thyroxine (T_4).

triose A monosaccharide (simple sugar) containing three carbon atoms.

triplet code A code in which a "word" of three letters encodes one piece of information. The genetic code is a triplet code because a codon is three nucleotides long and encodes one amino acid.

triploblast (adjective: triploblastic) An animal whose body develops from three basic embryonic cell layers or tissues: ectoderm, mesoderm, and endoderm. Compare with **diploblast**.

trisomy The state of having three copies of one particular type of chromosome in an otherwise diploid cell.

tRNA See **transfer RNA**.

trochophore A larva with a ring of cilia around its middle that is found in some lophotrochozoans.

trophic cascade A series of changes in the abundance of species in a food web, usually caused by the addition or removal of a key predator.

trophic level A feeding level in an ecosystem.

trophoblast The exterior of a blastocyst (the structure that results from cleavage in embryonic development of mammals).

tropomyosin A regulatory protein present in thin (actin) filaments that blocks the myosin-binding sites on these filaments in resting muscles, thereby preventing muscle contraction.

troponin A regulatory protein, present in thin (actin) filaments, that can move tropomyosin off the myosin-binding sites on these filaments, thereby triggering muscle contraction. Activated by high intracellular calcium.

true navigation The type of navigation by which an animal can reach a specific point on Earth's surface. Also called *map orientation*.

trypsin A protein-digesting enzyme present in the small intestine that activates several other protein-digesting enzymes.

tube foot One of the many small, mobile, fluid-filled extensions of the water vascular system of echinoderms; the part extending outside the body is called a podium, while the bulb within the body is the ampulla. Used in locomotion, feeding, and respiration.

tuber A modified plant rhizome that functions in storage of carbohydrates.

tuberculosis A disease of the lungs caused by infection with the bacterium *Mycobacterium tuberculosis*.

tumor A mass of cells formed by uncontrolled cell division. Can be benign or malignant.

tumor suppressor A protein (e.g., p53 or Rb) that prevents cell division, such as when the cell has DNA damage. Mutant genes that code for tumor suppressors are associated with cancer.

tundra The treeless biome in polar and alpine regions, characterized by short, slow-growing vegetation, permafrost, and a climate of long, intensely cold winters and very short summers.

turbidity Cloudiness of water caused by sediments and/or microscopic organisms.

turgid Swollen and firm as a result of high internal pressure (e.g., a plant cell containing enough water for the cytoplasm to press against the cell wall). Compare with **flaccid**.

turgor pressure The outward pressure exerted by the fluid contents of a living plant cell against its cell wall.

turnover In lake ecology, the complete mixing of upper and lower layers of water of different temperatures; occurs each spring and fall in temperate-zone lakes.

tympanic membrane The membrane separating the middle ear from the outer ear in terrestrial vertebrates, or similar structures in insects. Also called the *eardrum*.

ubiquinone See **coenzyme Q**.

ulcer A hole in an epithelial layer, exposing the underlying tissues to damage.

ultimate causation In biology, the reason that a trait or phenomenon is thought to have evolved; the adaptive advantage of that trait. Also called *ultimate explanation*. Compare with **proximate causation**.

umami The taste of glutamate, responsible for the "meaty" taste of most proteins and of monosodium glutamate.

umbilical cord The cord that connects a developing mammalian embryo or fetus to the placenta and through which the embryo or fetus receives oxygen and nutrients.

unequal crossover An error in crossing over during meiosis I in which the two non-sister chromatids match up at different sites. Results in gene duplication in one chromatid and gene loss in the other.

unsaturated Referring to lipids in which at least one carbon-carbon bond is a double bond. Double bonds produce kinks in hydrocarbon chains and decrease the compound's melting point. Compare with **saturated**.

upstream In genetics, opposite to the direction in which RNA polymerase moves along a DNA strand. Compare with **downstream**.

urea The major nitrogenous waste of mammals, adult amphibains, and cartilaginous fishes. Compare with **ammonia** and **uric acid**.

ureter In vertebrates, a tube that transports urine from one kidney to the bladder.

urethra The tube that drains urine from the bladder to the outside environment. In male vertebrates, also used for passage of semen during ejaculation.

uric acid A whitish excretory product of birds, reptiles, and terrestrial arthropods. Used to remove from the body excess nitrogen derived from the breakdown of amino acids. Compare with **ammonia** and **urea**.

urochordates One of the three major chordate lineages (Urochordata), comprising sessile or floating, filter-feeding animals that have a polysaccharide covering (tunic) and two siphons through which water enters and exits; include tunicates and salps. Compare with **cephalochordates** and **vertebrates**.

uterus The organ in which developing embryos are housed in mammals and some other viviparous vertebrates.

vaccination Artificially producing immunological memory against a pathogen by using isolated antigens or altered versions of the pathogen to stimulate an adaptive immune response in the absence of disease.

vaccine A preparation designed to stimulate an immune response against a particular pathogen without causing illness. Vaccines consist of inactivated (killed) pathogens, live but weakened (attenuated) pathogens, or parts of a pathogen (subunit vaccine).

vacuole A large organelle in plant and fungal cells that usually is used for bulk storage of water, pigments, oils, or other substances. Some vacuoles contain enzymes and have a digestive function similar to lysosomes in animal cells.

vagina The birth canal of female mammals; a muscular tube that extends from the uterus through the pelvis to the exterior.

valence The number of unpaired electrons in the outermost electron shell of an atom; often determines how many covalent bonds the atom can form.

valence electron An electron in the outermost electron shell, the valence shell, of an atom. Valence electrons tend to be involved in chemical bonding.

valence shell The outermost electron shell of an atom.

valve In circulatory systems, any of the flaps of tissue that prevent backward flow of blood, particularly in veins and in the heart.

van der Waals interactions A weak electrical attraction between two nonpolar molecules that have been brought together through hydrophobic interactions. Often contributes to tertiary and quaternary structures in proteins.

variable number tandem repeat See **minisatellite**.

variable (V) region The amino acid sequence that changes in polypeptides used to make antibodies, B-cell receptors, and T-cell receptors, This portion of the protein is highly variable within an individual and forms the epitope-binding site. Compare with **constant (C) region**.

vas deferens (plural: vasa deferentia) A muscular tube that stores and transports semen from the epididymis to the ejaculatory duct. Also called the *ductus deferens*.

vasa recta In the vertebrate kidney, a network of blood vessels that runs alongside the loop of Henle of a nephron. Functions in reabsorption of water and solutes from the filtrate.

vascular bundle In a plant stem, a cluster of xylem and phloem strands that run the length of the stem.

vascular cambium One of two types of cylindrical meristem, consisting of a ring of undifferentiated plant cells in the stem and root of woody plants; produces secondary xylem (wood) and secondary phloem. Compare with **cork cambium**.

vascular tissue In plants, tissue that transports water, nutrients, and sugars. Made up of the complex tissues xylem and phloem, each of which contains several cell types. Also called *vascular tissue system*.

vector A biting insect or other organism that transfers pathogens from one species to another. See also **cloning vector**.

vegetative development The phase of plant development that involves growth and the the production of all plant structures except the flower.

vein Any blood vessel that carries blood (oxygenated or not) under relatively low pressure from the tissues toward the heart. Compare with **artery**.

veliger A distinctive type of larva, found in mollusks.

vena cava (plural: venae cavae) Either of two large veins that return oxygen-poor blood to the heart.

ventral Toward an animal's belly and away from its back. The opposite of dorsal.

ventricle (1) A thick-walled chamber of the heart that receives blood from an atrium and pumps it to the body or to the lungs. (2) Any of several small fluid-filled chambers in the vertebrate brain.

venule Any of the body's many small veins (blood vessels that return blood to the heart).

vertebrae (singular: vertebra) The cartilaginous or bony elements that form the backbones of vertebrate animals.

vertebrates One of the three major chordate lineages (Vertebrata), comprising animals with a dorsal column of cartilaginous or bony structures (vertebrae) and a skull enclosing the brain. Includes fishes, amphibians, mammals, and reptiles (including birds). Compare with **cephalochordates** and **urochordates**.

vessel element In vascular plants, a short, wide, water-conducting cell that has gaps through both the primary and secondary cell walls, allowing unimpeded passage of water between adjacent cells. Compare with **tracheid**.

vestigial trait A reduced or incompletely developed structure that has no function or reduced function, but is clearly similar to functioning organs or structures in closely related species.

vicariance The physical splitting of a population into smaller, isolated populations by a geographic barrier.

villi (singular: villus) Small, fingerlike projections (1) of the lining of the small intestine or (2) of the fetal portion of the placenta adjacent to maternal arteries. Function to increase the surface area available for absorption of nutrients and gas exchange.

virion The infectious extracellular particle that is produced from a viral infection; used for transmitting the virus between hosts. It consists of a DNA or RNA genome enclosed within a protein shell (capsid) that may be further enveloped in a phospholipid bilayer. Compare with **virus**.

virulence (adjective: virulent) Referring to the ability of pathogens to cause severe disease in susceptible hosts.

virus An obligate, intracellular parasite that is acellular, but uses host-cell biosynthetic machinery to replicate. Compare with **virion**.

visceral mass One of the three main parts of the mollusk body; contains most of the internal organs and external gill.

visible light The range of wavelengths of electromagnetic radiation that humans can see, from about 400 to 700 nanometers.

vitamin Any of various organic micronutrients that usually function as coenzymes.

vitelline envelope A fibrous sheet of glycoproteins that surrounds mature egg cells in many vertebrates. Surrounded by a thick gelatinous matrix (the jelly layer) in some aquatic species. In mammals, called the *zona pellucida*.

viviparous Producing live young (instead of eggs) that develop within the body of the mother before birth. Compare with **oviparous** and **ovoviviparous**.

volt (V) A unit of electrical potential (voltage).

voltage Potential energy created by a separation of electric charges between two points. Also called *electrical potential*.

voltage clamping A technique for imposing a constant membrane potential on a cell. Widely used to investigate ion channels.

voltage-gated channel An ion channel that opens or closes in response to changes in membrane voltage. Compare with **ligand-gated channel**.

voluntary muscle Muscle that contracts in response to stimulation by voluntary (somatic), but not involuntary (parasympathetic or sympathetic), neural stimulation.

vomeronasal organ A paired sensory organ, located in the nasal region, containing chemoreceptors that bind odorants and pheromones.

wall pressure The inward pressure exerted by a cell wall against the fluid contents of a living plant cell.

Wallace line A line in the Indonesian region that demarcates two areas, each of which is characterized by a distinct set of animal species.

water potential (ψ) The potential energy of water in a certain environment compared with the potential energy of pure water at room temperature and atmospheric pressure. In living organisms, ψ equals the solute potential (ψ_S) plus the pressure potential (ψ_P).

water-potential gradient A difference in water potential in one region compared with that in another region. Determines the direction that water moves, always from regions of higher water potential to regions of lower water potential.

water table The upper limit of the underground layer of soil that is saturated with water.

water vascular system In echinoderms, a system of fluid-filled tubes and chambers that functions as a hydrostatic skeleton.

watershed The area drained by a single stream or river.

Watson–Crick pairing See **complementary base pairing**.

wavelength The distance between two successive crests in any regular wave, such as light waves, sound waves, or waves in water.

wax A class of lipid with extremely long, saturated hydrocarbon tails. Harder and less greasy than fats.

weather The specific short-term atmospheric conditions of temperature, moisture, sunlight, and wind in a certain area.

weathering The gradual wearing down of large rocks by rain, running water, temperature changes, and wind; one of the processes that transform rocks into soil.

weed Any plant that is adapted for growth in disturbed soils.

white blood cell Any of several types of blood cells, including neutrophils, macrophages, and lymphocytes, that circulate in blood and lymph and function in defense against pathogens.

wild type The most common phenotype seen in a wild population.

wildlife corridor Strips of wildlife habitat connecting populations that otherwise would be isolated by human-made development.

wilt To lose turgor pressure in a plant tissue.

wobble hypothesis The hypothesis that some tRNA molecules can pair with more than one mRNA codon by tolerating some non-standard base pairing in the third base, so long as the first and second bases are correctly matched.

wood Xylem resulting from secondary growth; forms strong supporting material. Also called *secondary xylem*.

worm An animal with a long, thin, tubelike body lacking limbs.

Woronin body A dense organelle in certain fungi that plugs pores in damaged septa to prevent leakage of cytoplasm.

X-linked inheritance Inheritance patterns for genes located on the mammalian X chromosome. Also called *X-linkage*.

X-ray crystallography A technique for determining the three-dimensional structure of large molecules, including proteins and nucleic acids, by analysis of the diffraction patterns produced by X-rays beamed at crystals of the molecule.

xenoestrogens Foreign chemicals that bind to estrogen receptors or otherwise induce estrogen-like effects.

xeroderma pigmentosum (XP) A human disease characterized by extreme sensitivity to ultraviolet light. Caused by an autosomal recessive allele that inactivates the nucleotide excision DNA repair system.

xylem A plant vascular tissue that conducts water and ions; contains tracheids and/or vessel elements.

Primary xylem develops from the procambium of apical meristems; secondary xylem, or wood, from the vascular cambium. Compare with **phloem**.

Y-linked inheritance Inheritance patterns for genes located on the mammalian Y chromosome. Also called *Y-linkage*.

yeast Any fungus growing as a single-celled form. Also, a specific lineage of Ascomycota.

yolk The nutrient-rich cytoplasm inside an egg cell; used as food for the growing embryo.

Z disk The structure that forms each end of a sarcomere. Contains a protein that binds tightly to actin, thereby anchoring thin filaments.

Z scheme Model for changes in the potential energy of electrons as they pass from photosystem II to photosystem I and ultimately to $NADP^+$ during the light-dependent reactions of photosynthesis. See also **noncyclic electron flow**.

zero population growth (ZPG) A state of stable population size due to fertility staying at the replacement rate for at least one generation.

zona pellucida The gelatinous layer around a mammalian egg cell. In other vertebrates, called the *vitelline envelope*.

zone of (cellular) division In plant roots, a group of apical meristematic cells just behind the root cap where cells are actively dividing.

zone of (cellular) elongation In plant roots, a group of young cells, derived from primary meristem tissues and located behind the apical meristem, that are increasing in length.

zone of (cellular) maturation In plant roots, a group of plant cells, located several millimeters behind the root cap, that are differentiating into mature tissues.

zygosporangium (plural: zygosporangia) The distinctive spore-producing structure in fungi that are members of the Zygomycota.

zygote The cell formed by the union of two gametes; a fertilized egg.

Credits

Photo Credits

Frontmatter **Title page** Eric Isselée/Fotolia **p. iii** IFE, URI-IAO, UW, Lost City Science Party; NOAA/OAR/OER; The Lost City 2005 Expedition **p. v** R. B. Taylor/Photo Researchers, Inc. **p. vi** Brian Johnston **p. viii** Anthony Bannister/Photo Researchers, Inc. **p. x** Tim Laman/National Geographic Stock **p. xiii** Lee W. Wilcox **p. xiv** Steve Winter/National Geographic/Getty Images **p. xvi** Associated Press/Gerald Herbert **p. xviii (bottom left)** Natalie B. Fobes Photography

Chapter 1 **Opener** Thierry Montford/Biosphoto/Photo Researchers Inc. **1.1a** Biophoto Associates/Photo Researchers, Inc. **1.1b** Brian J. Ford **1.1c** The Print Collector/Alamy **1.6a** Steve Gschmeissner/Photo Researchers, Inc. **1.6b** Kwangshin Kim/Photo Researchers, Inc. **1.7** Corbis Premium RF/Alamy **1.10** Reproduced with permission from H. Wolf. 2011. Odometry and Insect Navigation. *Journal of Experimental Biology* 214: 1629–1641.

Chapter 2 **Opener** IFE, URI-IAO, UW, Lost City Science Party; NOAA/OAR/OER; The Lost City 2005 Expedition **2.1** Dragan Trifunovic/Shutterstock **2.6c** Zedcor Wholly Owned/Photos.com **2.11** LianeM/Alamy **2.15b** Dietmar Nill/Getty Images **2.15c** John Sylvester/First Light/AGE fotostock **2.29** picture-alliance/Judaica-Samml/Newscom

Chapter 3 **3.9ab** Janice Carr, CDC

Chapter 4 **Opener** SSPL/The Image Works **4.5** National Cancer Institute

Chapter 5 **Opener** Peter Arnold/Alamy

Chapter 6 **6.2a** Multiart/iStockphoto **6.2b** lepas2004/iStockphoto **6.2c** ilker canikligil/Shutterstock **6.6L** Dr. rer. nat. Markus Drechsler **6.15** Jack W. Szostak **6.18** Don W. Fawcett/Photo Researchers, Inc.

Chapter 7 **Opener** Dr. Torsten Wittmann/SPL/Photo Researchers, Inc. **7.1** SPL/Photo Researchers, Inc. **7.2a** Gopal Murti/Photo Researchers, Inc. **7.2b** Biology Pics/Photo Researchers, Inc. **7.3** Eye of Science/Photo Researchers, Inc. **7.4** Eye of Science/Photo Researchers, Inc. **7.7** Don W. Fawcett/Photo Researchers, Inc. **7.8** Omikron/Photo Researchers, Inc. **7.9LR** Don W. Fawcett/Photo Researchers, Inc. **7.10** Biophoto Associates/Photo Researchers, Inc. **7.11** Don W. Fawcett/Photo Researchers, Inc. **7.12** E.H. Newcomb & W.P Wergin/Biological Photo Service **7.13** Fawcett/Friend/Photo Researchers, Inc. **7.14** Don W. Fawcett/Photo Researchers, Inc. **7.15** E.H. Newcomb & W.P. Wergin/Biological Photo Service **7.16a** Dr. Don Fawcett/S. Ito & A. Like/Photo Researchers, Inc. **7.16b** Don W. Fawcett/Photo Researchers, Inc. **7.16c** Biophoto Associates/Photo Researchers, Inc. **7.16d** From "*Caveolin-1* expression is essential for proper nonshivering thermogenesis in brown adipose tissue." Cohen, A. W., Schubert, W., Brasaemle, D. L., Scherer, P. E., Lisanti, M. P. *Diabetes.* 2005 Mar; 54(3): 679–86, Fig. 6. **7.17** Don W. Fawcett/Photo Researchers, Inc. **7.26** Micrograph by Dr. Conly L. Rieder, Wadsworth Center, Albany, New York 12201-0509 **7.27ab** Reproduced by permission of the American Society for Cell Biology from *Molecular Biology of the Cell* 9 (12), December 1998, cover. ©1999 by the American Society for Cell Biology. Image courtesy of Bruce J. Schnapp, Oregon Health Sciences University. **7.28** John E. Heuser, M.D., Washington University School of Medicine, St. Louis, Missouri **7.29a** SPL/Photo Researchers, Inc. **7.29b** Biomedical Imaging Unit, Southampton General Hospital/Photo Researchers, Inc. **7.30** Don W. Fawcett/Photo Researchers, Inc.

Chapter 8 **Opener** Richard Megna/Fundamental Photographs **8.3** Thomas Eisner

Chapter 9 **Opener** Raiden32/Used under the Creative Commons license. http://creativecommons.org/licenses/by-sa/3.0/deed.en **9.1a** Oliver Hoffmann/Shutterstock **9.1b** Gergo Orban/Shutterstock **9.8** Terry Frey **9.16** Michael Delannoy

Chapter 10 **Opener** R.B. Taylor/Photo Researchers, Inc. **10.3T** John Durham/Science Photo Library/Photo Researchers, Inc. **10.3MB** Barbara Erienborn/Electron micrograph by Wm. P. Wergin, courtesy of E.H. Newcomb, University of Wisconsin **10.5b** Sinclair Stammers/Photo Researchers, Inc. **10.18LR** James A. Bassham, Lawrence Berkeley Laboratory, UCB (retired) **10.21ab** Dr. Jeremy Burgess/Science Photo Library/Photo Researchers, Inc.

Chapter 11 **Opener** Roger J. Bick & Brian J. Poindexter/UT-Houston Medical School/Photo Researchers, Inc. **11.1** Jochen Tack/imagebroker/Alamy **11.2** Biophoto Associates/Photo Researchers, Inc. **11.3b** ©ROCKWATER, Inc./*Journal of Bone and Joint Surgery*, 1997, 79, Instructional Course Lectures, The American Academy of Orthopaedic Surgeons—Articular Cartilage. Part I: Tissue Design and Chondrocyte-Matrix Interactions, Buckwalter, 600–611 **11.5** Biophoto Associates/Photo Researchers, Inc. **11.7aLR** Don W. Fawcett/Photo Researchers, Inc. **11.8** Don W. Fawcett/Photo Researchers, Inc. **11.10a** Dr. Don Fawcett/Photo Researcher's, Inc. **11.10b** E. H. Newcomb & W.P. Wergin/Biological Photo Service **11.17a** A. Nern and R. A. Arkowitz. 2000. "G proteins mediate changes in cell shape by stabilizing the axis of polarity." *Molecular Cell* 5(5): 853–864, Fig. 2C. **11.17b** R. H. Kessin. 2003. "Cell motility: Making streams." *Nature* 422: 481–482. ©2003 Nature Publishing Group. Used with permission.

Chapter 12 **Opener** G. Gimenz-Martin/SPL/Photo Researchers, Inc. **12.1T** Gopal Murti/Photo Researchers, Inc. **12.1B** Biophoto Associates/Photo Researchers, Inc. **12.5(1–7)** Micrographs by Conly L. Rieder, Department of Biology, Rensselaer Polytechnic Institute, Troy, New York. **12.8a** Ed Reschke/Getty **12.8b** Michael Danilchik

Chapter 13 **Opener** David Phillips/The Population Council/Photo Researchers, Inc. **13.1** Look at Sciences/Photo Researchers, Inc. **13.6** Jupiterimages/Photos.com **13.7(1–9)** Warren Rosenberg/Fundamental Photographs **13.15** Dr. Rebecca Shulte

Chapter 14 **Opener** Brian Johnston **14.9a** Benjamin Prud'homme/Nicolas Gompel **14.9bLR** From "Learning to Fly: Phenotypic Markers in Drosophila." A poster of common phenotypic markers used in Drosophila genetics. Jennifer Childress, Richard Behringer, and Georg Halder. 2005. *Genesis* 43(1). Cover illustration. **14.16** Carla Fernanda Reis

Chapter 15 **Opener** Dr. Gopal Murti/Science Photo Library/Photo Researchers, Inc. **15.1** Eye of Science/Photo Researchers, Inc. **15.5** Reproduced by permission of Matthew S. Meselson, Harvard University, from M. Meselson and F.W. Stahl, "The replication of DNA in Escherichia coli." *PNAS* 44(7): 671–682 (July 1958), p. 675, Fig. 4. **15.7** Dr. Gopal Murti/Science Photo Library/Photo Researchers, Inc.

Chapter 16 **Opener** J. Craig Venter Institute **16.4a** Rod Williams/Nature Picture Library **16.4b** Clint Cook & Janet P. Crossland, The Peromyscu Genetic Stock Center at the U. of South Carolina **16.9** Courtesy of Hesed M. Padilla-Nash and Thomas Ried. Affiliation is Section of Cancer Genomics, Genetics Branch, Center for Research, National Cancer Institute, National Institutes of Health, Bethesda, MD 20892

Chapter 17 **Opener** Oscar Miller/SPL/Photo Researchers, Inc. **17.5** Bert W. O'Malley, M.D., Baylor College of Medicine **17.8** From Hamkalo and Miller, "Electronmicroscopy of Genetic Material," Figure 6a, p. 379. Reproduced with permission, from *Annual Review of Biochemistry*, Volume 42. ©1973 by Annual Reviews, Inc. **17.9** Dr. Elena Kiseleva/Photo Researchers, Inc.

Chapter 18 **Opener** Stephanie Schuller/Photo Researchers, Inc. **18.UN1** EDVOTEK, The Biotechnology Education Company (www.edvotek.com)/Jeff Chirikjian

Chapter 19 **19.2** Ada Olins/Don Fawcett/Photo Researchers, Inc. **19.4TB** ©2002 from *Molecular Biology of the Cell* 4/e Fig. 4-23 by Bruce Alberts et al. Reproduced by Permission of Garland Science Taylor & Francis Books, Inc., and Dr. Barbara Hamkalo.

Chapter 20 **Opener** International Rice Research Institute (IRRI) used under Creative Commons 2.0 license. http://creativecommons.org/licenses/by-nc-sa/2.0/deed.en **20.1** Brady-Handy Photograph Collection, Library of Congress. Reproduction number: LC-DIG-cwpbh-02977. **20.12** Science Source/Photo Researchers, Inc. **20.15BLR** Golden Rice

Chapter 21 **Opener** Martin Krzywinski/Science Photo Libary/Alamy **21.8BLR** Test results provided by GENDIA (www.gendia.net) **21.11** Agilent Technologies, Inc. **21.12** Camilla M. Kao and Patrick O. Brown, Stanford University.

Chapter 25 **Opener** R.B. Taylor/Photo Researchers, Inc. **25.2L** Gary Crabbe/AGE Fotostock **25.2RTMB** Michael Quinn, Grand Canyon NPS **25.3a** Gerd Weitbrecht for Landesbildungsserver Baden-Wurttemberg (www.schule-bw.de)/Gerd Weitbrecht **25.3b** angelhell/iStockphoto **25.5L** Januario Dolores **25.5R** BSIP/Photo Researchers, Inc. **25.6a1** AGE fotostock/SuperStock **25.6a2** George D. Lepp/Photo Researchers, Inc. **25.6a3** David Hosking/FLPA **25.6a4** Stefan Huwiler/AGE fotostock **25.8a** Photo by Michael K. Richardson. Reproduced by permission from *Anatomy and Embryology* 305, Fig. 7. Copyright © Springer-Verlag GmbH & Co KG, Heidelberg, Germany. **25.8b** Photo by Professor R. O'Rahilly. Reproduced by permission from *Anatomy and Embryology* 305, Fig.8. Copyright © Springer-Verlag GmbH & Co KG, Heidelberg, Germany. **25.8c** From: Richardson, M. K., et al. *Science*. Vol. 280, p. 983c, Issue #5366, May 15, 1998. Embryo from Professor R. O'Rahilly,

National Museum of Health and Medicine/Armed Forces Institute of Pathology. **25.10** Walter J. Gehring **25.12LT** PetStockBoys/Alamy **25.12LB** Arco Images GmbH/Alamy **25.12RT** Arco Images GmbH/Alamy **25.12RB** Juniors Bildarchiv/Alamy **25.15** Alison Wright/ National Geographic Stock **25.15inset** D. & S. Tollerton/AGE fotostock **25.16** Kim Quillin **25.18a** American Association for the Advancement of Science **25.18b** The Royal Society of London **25.T2-1** dibrova/Shutterstock **25.T2-2** James R. Robinson/Photo Researchers, Inc. **25.T2-3** Erlend Haarberg/NHPA/Photoshot **25.T2-4** D. & S. Tollerton/AGE fotostock

Appendix A: Answers A7.1ab Don W. Fawcett/Photo Researchers, Inc. **A7.1c** Biophoto Associates/Photo Researchers, Inc. **A7.1d** From "*Caveolin-1* expression is essential for proper nonshivering thermogenesis in brown adipose tissue." Cohen, A. W., Schubert, W., Brasaemle, D. L., Scherer, P. E., Lisanti, M. P. *Diabetes.* 2005 Mar; 54(3): 679–86, Fig. 6.

Appendix B: BioSkills B9.3 Reproduced by permission from J. P. Ferris, et al. "Synthesis of long prebiotic oligomers on mineral surfaces." *Nature* 381: 59–61 (1996), Fig. 2. ©1996 Macmillan Magazines Ltd. Image courtesy of James P. Ferris, Rensselaer Polytechnic Institute. **B11.1a** Biology Media/Photo Researchers, Inc. **B11.1b** Janice Carr/Centers for Disease Control and Prevention (CDC) **B11.2ab** Michael W. Davidson/Molecular Expressions **B11.3** Rosalind Franklin/Photo Researchers, Inc. **B12.1aL** National Cancer Institute **B12.1aR** E.S. Anderson/Photo Researchers, Inc. **B12.1b** Sinclair Stammers/Photo Researchers, Inc. **B13.1a** Kwangshin Kim/Photo Researchers, Inc. **B13.1b** Richard L. (Larry) Blanton, Ph.D. **B13.1c** Holt Studios International/Photo Researchers, Inc. **B13.1d** Custom Medical Stock Photo, Inc. **B13.1e** Graphic Science/Alamy Images **B13.1f** Sinclair Stammers/Photo Researchers, Inc. **B13.1g** dra_schwartz/iStockphoto

Illustration and Text Credits

Chapter 1 1.3 Based on S. P. Moose, J. W. Dudley, and T. R. Rocheford. 2004. Maize selection passes the century mark: A unique resource for 21st century genomics. *Trends in Plant Science* 9 (7): 358–364, Fig. 1a; and the Illinois long-term selection experiment for oil and protein in corn (University of Illinois at Urbana–Champaign). **1.7a** Based on T. P. Young and L. A. Isbell. 1991. Sex differences in giraffe feeding ecology: Energetic and social constraints. *Ethology* 87: 79–80, Figs. 5a, 6a. **1.9** Adapted by permission of AAAS and the author from M. Wittlinger, R. Wehner, and H. Wolf. 2006. The ant odometer: Stepping on stilts and stumps. *Science* 312: 1965–1967, Figs. 1, 2, 3. (http://www.sciencemag.org/content/312/5782/1965.short).

Chapter 2 T2-1 Data: D. R. Lide (editor). 2008. Standard thermodynamic properties of chemical substances. In *CRC Handbook of Physics and Chemistry*. 89th ed. Boca Raton, FL: CRC Press. **2.21** After S. L. Miller. 1953. A production of amino acids under possible primitive Earth conditions. *Science* 117 (3046): 528–529.

Chapter 3 Opener PDB ID: 2DN2. S. Y. Park, T. Yokoyama, N. Shibayama, et al. 2006. 1.25 Å resolution crystal structures of human hemoglobin in the oxy, deoxy and carbonmonoxy forms. *Journal of Molecular Biology* 360: 690–701. **3.8a** PDB ID: 1TGH. Z. S. Juo, T. K. Chiu, P. M. Leiberman, et al. 1996. How proteins recognize the TATA box. *Journal of Molecular Biology* 261: 239–254. **3.8b** PDB ID: 2X9K. F. Korkmaz-Ozkan, S. Koster, W. Kuhlbrandt, et al. 2010. Correlation between the OmpG secondary structure and its pH-dependent alterations monitored by FTIR. *Journal of Molecular Biology* 401: 56–67. **3.8c** PDB ID: 2PTC. M. Marquart, J. Walter, J. Deisenhofer, et al. 1983. The geometry of the reactive site and of the peptide groups in trypsin, trypsinogen and its complexes with inhibitors. *Acta Crystallographica* Section B39: 480–490. **3.8d** PDB ID: 1CLG. J. M. Chen, C. D. E. King, S. H. Feairheller, et al. 1991. An energetic evaluation of a "Smith" collagen microfibril model. *Journal of Protein Chemistry* 10: 535–552. **3.11b, left** PDB ID: 2MHR. S. Sheriff, W. A. Hendrickson, and J. L. Smith. 1987. Structure of myohemerythrin in the azidomet state at 1.7/1.3 resolution. *Journal of Molecular Biology* 197: 273–296. **3.11b, middle** PDB ID: 1FTP. N. H. Haunerland, B. L. Jacobson, G. Wesenberg, et al. 1994. Three-dimensional structure of the muscle fatty-acid-binding protein isolated from the desert locust *Schistocerca gregaria. Biochemistry* 33: 12378–12385. **3.11b, right** PDB ID: 1IXA. M. Baron, D. G. Norman, T. S. Harvey, et al. 1992. The three-dimensional structure of the first EGF-like module of human factor IX: Comparison with EGF and TGF-alpha. *Protein Science* 1: 81–90. **3.12a** PDB ID: 1D1L. P. B. Rupert, A. K. Mollah, M. C. Mossing, et al. 2000. The structural basis for enhanced stability and reduced DNA binding seen in engineered second-generation Cro monomers and dimers. *Journal of Molecular Biology* 296: 1079–1090. **3.12b** PDB ID: 2DN2. S.Y. Park, T. Yokoyama, N. Shibayama, et al. 2006. 1.25 Å resolution crystal structures of human hemoglobin in the oxy, deoxy and carbonmonoxy forms. *Journal of Molecular Biology* 360: 690–701. **3.14a** PDB ID: 1DMO. M. Zhang, T. Tanaka, and M. Ikura. 1995. Calcium-induced conformational transition revealed by the solution structure of apo calmodulin. *Nature Structural Biology* 2: 758–767. **3.14b** PDB ID: 3CLN. Y. S. Babu, C. E. Bugg, and W. J. Cook. 1988. Structure of calmodulin refined at 2.2 A resolution. *Journal of Molecular Biology* 204: 191–204. **3.16** PDB ID: 2PTC. M. Marquart, J. Walter, J. Deisenhofer, et al. 1983.

The geometry of the reactive site and of the peptide groups in trypsin, trypsinogen and its complexes with inhibitors. *Acta Crystallographica* Section B39: 480–490.

Chapter 4 T4-1 PDB ID: 1EHZ. H. Shi and P. B. Moore. 2000. The crystal structure of yeast phenylalanine tRNA at 1.93 Å resolution: A classic structure revisited. *RNA* 6: 1091–1105. **4.11** PDB ID: 1X8W. F. Guo, A. R. Gooding, and T. R. Cech. 2004. Structure of the *Tetrahymena* ribozyme: Base triple sandwich and metal ion at the active site. *Molecular Cell* 16: 351–362.

Chapter 5 5.6 H. M. Florman, K. B. Bechtol, and P. M. Wassarman. 1984. Enzymatic dissection of the functions of the mouse egg's receptor for sperm. *Developmental Biology* 106: 243–255. Also H. M. Florman and P. M. Wassarman. 1985. O-linked oligosaccharides of mouse egg ZP3 account for its sperm receptor activity. *Cell* 41: 313–324; J. D. Bleil and P. M. Wassarman. 1988. Galactose at the nonreducing terminus of O-linked oligosaccharides of mouse egg zona pellucida glycoprotein ZP3 is essential for the glycoprotein's sperm receptor activity. *PNAS* 85: 6778–6782.

Chapter 6 Opener CHARMM-GUI Archive—Library of Pure Lipid Bilayer (www.charmm-gui.org/?doc=archive&lib=lipid_pure), POPE Bilayer Library (pope_n256.pdb). Reference: S. Jo, T. Kim, and W. Im. 2007. Automated builder and database of protein/membrane complexes for molecular dynamics simulations. *PLoS ONE* 2 (9): e880. **6.10** Data: J. de Gier, J. G. Mandersloot, and L. L. van Deenen. 1968. Lipid composition and permeability of liposomes. *Biochimica et Biophysica Acta* 150: 666–675. **6.21** Data: C. E. Bear, F. Duguay, A. L. Naismith, et al. 1992. Purification and functional reconstitution of the cystic fibrosis transmembrane conductance regulator (CFTR). *Cell* 68: 809–818. **6.22** PDB ID: 2ZZ9. K. Tani, T. Mitsuma, Y. Hiroaki, et al. 2009. Mechanism of aquaporin-4's fast and highly selective water conduction and proton exclusion. *Journal of Molecular Biology* 389: 694–706. **6.23** PDB ID: 1K4C. Y. Zhou, J. H. Morais-Cabral, A. Kaufman, et al. 2001. Chemistry of ion coordination and hydration revealed by a K⁺ channel–Fab complex at 2.0 Å resolution. *Nature* 414: 43–48. **6.23** PDB ID: 3FB7. L. G. Cuello, V. Jogini, D. M. Cortes, et al. Open KcsA potassium channel in the presence of Rb⁺ ion. (To be published.) **7.18** A. D. Mills, R. A. Laskey, P. Black, et al. 1980. An acidic protein which assembles nucleosomes in vitro is the most abundant protein in *Xenopus* oocyte nuclei. *Journal of Molecular Biology* 139: 561–568. Also C. Dingwall, S. V. Sharnick, and R. A. Laskey. 1982. A polypeptide domain that specifies migration of nucleoplasmin into the nucleus. *Cell* 30: 449–458.

Chapter 7 7.5 Reprinted with kind permission from Springer Science+Business Media B.V. from David S. Goodsell, *The Machinery of Life*. 2nd ed., 2009.

Chapter 8 8.8 PDB ID: 1Q18. V. V. Lunin, Y. Li, J. D. Schrag, et al. 2004. Crystal structures of *Escherichia coli* ATP-dependent glucokinase and its complex with glucose. *Journal of Bacteriology* 186: 6915–6927. **8.8** PDB ID: 2Q2R. A. T. Cordeiro, A. J. Caceres, D. Vertommen, et al. 2007. The crystal structure of *Trypanosoma cruzi* glucokinase reveals features determining oligomerization and anomer specificity of hexose-phosphorylating enzymes. *Journal of Molecular Biology* 372: 1215–1226. **8.14a&b** Data: N. N. Nawani, B. P. Kapadnis, A. D. Das, et al. 2002. Purification and characterization of a thermophilic and acidophilic chitinase from Microbispora sp. V2. *Journal of Applied Microbiology* 93: 865–975, Figs. 7, 8a. Also N. N. Nawani and B. P. Kapadnis. 2001. One-step purification of chitinase from *Serratia marcescens* NK1, a soil isolate. *Journal of Applied Microbiology* 90: 803–808, Figs. 3, 4. **8.15** PDB ID: 2ERK. B. J. Canagarajah, A. Khokhlatchev, M. H. Cobb, et al. 1997. Activation mechanism of the MAP kinase ERK2 by dual phosphorylation. *Cell* (Cambridge, MA) 90: 859–869. **8.15** PDB ID 3ERK. Z. Wang, B. J. Canagarajah, J. C. Boehm, et al. 1998. Structural basis of inhibitor selectivity in MAP kinases. *Structure* 6: 1117–1128.

Chapter 9 9.7 PDB ID: 4PFK. P. R. Evans and P. J. Hudson. 1981. Phosphofructokinase: Structure and control. *Philosophical Transactions R. Soc. Lond. B: Biol. Sci.* 293: 53–62. **9.13** Data: X. Li, R. K. Dash, R. K. Pradhan, et al. 2010. A database of thermodynamic quantities for the reactions of glycolysis and the tricarboxylic acid cycle. *Journal of Physical Chemistry B* 114: 16068–16082, Table 4. **9.14** Data: D.F . Wilson, M. Erecinska, and P. L. Dutton. 1974. Thermodynamic relationships in mitochondrial oxidative phosphorylation. *Annual Review of Biophysics and Bioengineering* 3: 203–230, Tables 1, 3. Also V. D. Sled, N. I. Rudnitzky, Y. Hatefit, et al. 1994. Thermodynamic analysis of flavin in mitochondrial NADH: Ubiquinone oxidoreductase (complex I). *Biochemistry* 33: 10069–10075. **9.17** E. Racker and W. Stoeckenius. 1974. Reconstitution of purple membrane vesicles catalyzing light-driven proton uptake and adenosine triphosphate formation. *Journal of Biological Chemistry* 249: 662–663.

Chapter 10 10.6 T. W. Engelmann. 1882. Oxygen excretion from plant cells in a microspectrum. *Botanische Zeitung* 40: 419–426. **10.7** Reprinted with kind permission from Springer Science+Business Media B.V. from The Photosynthetic Process. In *Concepts in Photobiology: Photosynthesis and Photomorphogenesis*, edited by G. S. Singhal, G. Renger, S. K. Sopory et al. Dordrecht: Kluwer Academic; co-published with Narosa Publishing House (New Delhi), pp. 11–51, Fig. 5. **10.11** R. Govindjee, Govindjee, and G. Hoch. 1964. Emerson enhancement effect in chloroplast reactions. *Plant Physiology* 39: 10–14. **10.18** A. A. Benson, J. A. Bassham, M. Calvin, et al. 1950. The path of carbon in photosynthesis. V. Paper chromatography and radioautography of the products. *Journal of the American Chemistry Society* 72: 1710–1718. **10.20a** PDB ID: 1RCX. T. C. Taylor and I. Andersson. 1997. The structure of the complex between rubisco and its natural substrate ribulose 1,5-bisphosphate. *Journal of Molecular Biology* 265: 432–444.

Chapter 11 **11.4** Reprinted with kind permission from Springer Science+Business Media B.V. from David S. Goodsell, *The Machinery of Life*. 2nd ed., 2009. **11.7b** B. Alberts, A. Johnson, J. Lewis, et al. 2002. *Molecular Biology of the Cell*. 4th ed., Fig. 19.5, p. 1069. **11.9** K. Hatta and M. Takeichi. 1986. Expression of N-cadherin adhesion molecules associated with early morphogenetic events in chick development. *Nature* 320: 447–449. Also M. Takeichi. 1988. The cadherins: Cell–cell adhesion molecules controlling animal morphogenesis. *Development* 102: 639–655.

Chapter 12 **12.6** G. J. Gorbsky, P. J. Sammack, and G. G. Borisey. 1987. Chromosomes move poleward during anaphase along stationary microtubules that coordinately dissemble from their kinetochore ends. *Journal of Cell Biology* 104: 9–18. **12.9** Based on J. L. Ptacin, S. F. Lee, E. C. Garner, et al. 2010. A spindle-like apparatus guides bacterial chromosome segregation. *Nature Cell Biology* 12: 791–798, Fig. 5. **12.10** Y. Masui and C. L. Markert. 1971. Cytoplasmic control of nuclear behavior during meiotic maturation of frog oocytes. *Journal of Experimental Zoology* 177: 129–145. **12.13** Data: the website of the National Cancer Institute (www.cancer.gov), Common Cancer Types, November 2010.

Chapter 13 **13.13** Data: National Down Syndrome Society, 2012. **13.15** L. T. Morran, O. G. Schmidt, I. A. Gelarden, et al. 2011. Running with the red queen: Host-parasite coevolution selects for biparental sex. *Science* 333: 216–218.

Chapter 14 **14.3** G. Mendel. 1866. Versuche über Pflanzen-hybriden. *Verhandlungen des naturforschenden Vereines in Brünn* 4: 3–47. English translation available from Electronic Scholarly Publishing (www.esp.org). **T14.2** Data: G. Mendel. 1866. Versuche über Pflanzen-hybriden. *Verhandlungen des naturforschenden Vereines in Brünn* 4: 3–47. **14.13** Data: T. H. Morgan. 1911. An attempt to analyze the constitution of the chromosomes on the basis of sex-limited inheritance in *Drosophila*. *Journal of Experimental Zoology* 11: 365–414. **14.20** Data: Pan American Health Organization/WHO. 2004. *Epidemiological Bulletin* 25: 9–13, Graph 1.

Chapter 15 **15.2** A. D. Hershey and M. Chase. 1952. Independent functions of viral protein and nucleic acid in growth of bacteriophage. *Journal of General Physiology* 36: 39–56. **15.5** Adapted by permission of Dr. Matthew Meselson after M. Meselson and F. W. Stahl. 1958. The replication of DNA in *Escherichia coli*. *PNAS* 44: 671–682, Fig. 6. **15.14** Data: R. C. Allsopp, H. Vaziri, C. Patterson, et al. 1992. Telomere length predicts replicative capacity of human fibroblasts. *PNAS* 89: 10114–10118. **15.18a** Data: J. E. Cleaver. 1970. DNA repair and radiation sensitivity in human (xeroderma pigmentosum) cells. *International Journal of Radiation Biology* 18: 557–565, Fig. 3. **15.18b** Data: J .E. Cleaver. 1972. Xeroderma pigmentosum: Variants with normal DNA repair and normal sensitivity to ultraviolet light. *Journal of Investigative Dermatology* 58: 124–128, Fig. 1. **15.UN2** Graph adapted by permission of the Radiation Research Society from P. Howard-Flanders and R. P. Boyce. 1966. DNA repair and genetic recombination: Studies on mutants of *Escherichia coli* defective in these processes. *Radiation Research Supplement* 6: 156–184, Fig. 8.

Chapter 16 **16.2** Data: A. M. Srb and N. H. Horowitz. 1944. The ornithine cycle in *Neurospora* and its genetic control. *Journal of Biological Chemistry* 154: 129–139.

Chapter 17 **17.2a** PDB ID: 3IYD. B. P. Hudson, J. Quispe, S. Lara-Gonzalez, et al. 2009. Three-dimensional EM structure of an intact activator-dependent transcription initiation complex. *PNAS* 106: 19830–19835. **17.11** Based on M. B. Hoagland, M. L. Stephenson, J. F. Scott, et al. 1958. A soluble ribonucleic acid intermediate in protein synthesis. *Journal of Biological Chemistry* 231: 241–257, Fig. 6. **17.13** PDB ID: 1ZJW: I. Gruic-Sovulj, N. Uter, T. Bullock, et al. 2005. tRNA-dependent aminoacyl-adenylate hydrolysis by a nonediting class I aminoacyl-tRNA synthetase. *Journal of Biological Chemistry* 280: 23978–23986. **17.14b** PDB IDs: 3FIK, 3FIH. E. Villa, J. Sengupta, L. G. Trabuco, et al. 2009. Ribosome-induced changes in elongation factor Tu conformation control GTP hydrolysis. *PNAS* 106: 1063–1068.

Chapter 18 **18.2** Data: A. B. Pardee, F. Jacob, and J. Monod. 1959. The genetic control and cytoplasmic expression of "inducibility" in the synthesis of ß-glactosidase by *E. coli*. *Journal of Molecular Biology* 1: 165–178.

Chapter 19 **Opener** PDB ID: 1ZBB. T. Schalch, S. Duda, D. F. Sargent, et al. 2005. X-ray structure of a tetranucleosome and its implications for the chromatin fibre. *Nature* 436: 138–141. **19.5** I. Sandovici, N. H. Smith, and M. D. Nitert. 2011. Maternal diet and aging alter the epigenetic control of a promoter–enhancer interaction at the *Hnf4a* gene in rat pancreatic islets. *PNAS* 108: 5449–5454. **19.7b** PDB ID: 1MDY. P. C. Ma, M. A. Rould, H. Weintraub, et al. 1994. Crystal structure of MyoD bHLH domain–DNA complex: Perspectives on DNA recognition and implications for transcriptional activation. *Cell* (Cambridge, MA) 77: 451–459.

Chapter 21 **21.1** Data: European Nucleotide Archive/EMBL–Bank Release Notes. Release 110, December 2011 (www.ebi.ac.uk/embl/). **21.4a&b** Data: (a) Y. Hou and S. Lin. 2009. *PLoS ONE* 4 (9): e6978, Supplemental Table S1. (b) KEGG: *Kyoto Encyclopedia of Genes and Genomes*, KEGG Organisms: Complete genomes (www.genome.jp/kegg/). **21.8** Reproduced by permission of GENDIA from www.paternity.be/information_EN.html#identitytest, Examples 1 and 2. **21.10** Based on G. T. Ryan. 2005. Synergy between sequence and size in large-scale genomics. *Nature Reviews Genetics* 6, Box 3, p. 702. **21.13** V. Pancaldi, O. S. Sarac, C. Rallis, et al. 2012. Predicting the fission yeast protein interaction network. *G3: Genes, Genomes, Genetics* 2 (4): 453–567, Fig. 5.

Chapter 25 **25.4** Based on E. B. Daeschler et al. 2006. A Devonian tetrapod-like fish and the evolution of the tetrapod body plan. *Nature* 440: 757–763, Fig. 6; P. E. Ahlberg and J. A. Clack. 2006. A firm step from water to land. *Nature* 440: 747–749, Fig. 1; N. H. Shubin et al. 2006. The pectoral fin of *Tiktaalik roseae* and the origin of the tetrapod limb. *Nature* 440: 764–771, Fig. 4; M. Hildebrand and G. Goslow. 2001. *Analysis of Vertebrate Structures*, 5th ed. John Wiley and Sons, Inc. **25.11** *Indohyus* reproduced by permission from Macmillan Publishers Ltd after J. G. M. Thewissen, L. N. Cooper, M. T. Clementz, et al. 2007. Whales originated from aquatic artiodactyls in the Eocene epoch of India. *Nature* 450: 1190–1194, Fig. 5. *Rhodhocetus* reproduced by permission of AAAS after P. D. Gingerich, M. ul Haq, I. S. Zalmout, et al. 2001. Origin of whales from early Artiodactyls: Hands and feet of Eocene Protocetidae from Pakistan. *Science* 293: 2239–2242, Fig. 3. (http://www.sciencemag.org/content/293/5538/2239.abstract). *Dorudon* reproduced by permission after P. D. Gingerich, M. ul Haq, W. Von Koenigswald, et al. 2009. New protocetid whale from the middle Eocene of Pakistan: Birth on land, precocial development, and sexual dimorphism. *PLoS ONE* 4 (2): e4366, Fig. 1B. New data for Dorudon from M. D. Uhen. 2004. Form, function, and anatomy of *Dorudon atrox* (Mammalia, Cetacea): An Archaeocete from the Middle to Late Eocene of Egypt. University of Michigan Papesrs on Paleontology No. 34. *Delphinapterus* reproduced by permission of Skulls Unlimited International, Inc. (www.SkullsUnlimited.com). **25.14** Adapted by permission from D. P. Genereux and C. T. Bergstrom. 2005. Evolution in action: Understanding antibiotic resistance. In *Evolutionary Science and Society: Educating a New Generation*, edited by J. Cracraft and R. W. Bybee. Colorado Springs, CO: BSCS, 145–153, Fig 3. Data: Centers for Disease Control, 2004. **25.16** Data: P. T. Boag and P. R. Grant. 1981. Intense natural selection in a population of Darwin's finches (*Geospizinae*) in the Galápagos. *Science New Series* 214 (4516): 82–85, Table 1. **25.17** Body size and beak shape graph reproduced by permission of AAAS from P. R. Grant and B. R. Grant. 2002. *Science* 296:707–711, Fig. 1. Beak size graph reprinted by permission of AAAS from P. R. Grant and B. R. Grant. 2006. Evolution of character displacement in Darwin's finches. *Science* 313: 224–226, Fig. 2. (http://www.sciencemag.org/content/296/5568/707.abstract; http://www.sciencemag.org/content/313/5784/224.abstract).

Appendix B: BioSkills **TB16.1** A. Crowe, C. Dicks, and M. P. Wenderoth. 2008. Biology in bloom: Implementing Bloom's Taxonomy to enhance student learning in Biology. *CBE–Life Sciences Education* 7: 368–381, Table 3.

Index

Boldface page numbers indicate a glossary entry; page numbers followed by an *f* indicate a figure; those followed by *t* indicate a table.

2′ carbon, 58, 65
3′ carbon, 58, 59–60
3′ end, DNA, 289–92, 318
3-D imaging, B:20–B:21
3-phosphoglycerate (3PGA), 190*f*–91, 194
3′ poly(A) tail, mRNA, 323–24
5′ caps, mRNA, **323**–24
5′ carbon, 59–60
5′ end, DNA, 289–92, 318
−10 box, 319, 325*t*
30-nm fibers, 350–51
−35 box, 319, 325*t*

A

A site, ribosome, 328–29*f*
ABC model, 440–41
Abdomen, 670, **675**
Abiotic factors, **1061**
  in community structure, 1135
  in density-independent population growth, 1108, 1109
  for detritus decomposition rate, 1156–57
  in ecosystem diversity, 1175
  in ecosystem ecology, 1061
  in geographic distribution and abundance of organisms, 1102
  in geographic distribution and abundance of species, 1062–65
  of natural biomes, 1068–69
ABO blood group types, human, 272, 468–69
Abomasum, 891
Abortions, spontaneous, 470
Aboveground biomass, **1069**
Abramsky, Zvika, 1086–87
Abscisic acid (ABA), 214, **808**–13, 836–37
Abscissa, graph, B:4–B:5
Abscission, leaf, **807**, 813
Abscission zone, leaf, **813**
Absolute dating, 446–47, 453, 513
Absorption, animal, 883*f*, **886**, 892–96
Absorption, plant, 733
Absorption spectrum, **180**–81*f*
Absorptive feeding
  fungal, 616–17, 621
  protist, 564
Abstract, primary literature, B:27*t*
Abundance. *See also* Geographic distribution and abundance of organisms
  animal, 658
  fossil record bias for, 513
  prokaryotic, 530
  vertebrate, 691*f*
  viral, 712
Acacia trees, 1133, 1134*f*
Acceptor (A) site, ribosome, 328–329*f*
Accessory fluids, male reproductive, 1022–23*t*
Accessory photosynthetic pigments, 182
Acclimation, **459**
Acclimatization, **459**–60, **845**

Accuracy, precision vs., B:2–B:3
Acetaldehyde, 172–73*f*
Acetic acid, 36
Acetyl CoA, 36, 156–57, **161**–65
Acetyl groups, 351–52
Acetylation, **352**
Acetylcholine, 941*t*, **976**–77
Achilles tendon, 984, 986
Achromatopsia, 481–82
Acid-base reactions, 28–30
Acid-growth hyothesis, **800**
Acid hydrolases, 114
Acidic habitats, 548
Acidic side chains, 43*f*, 44
Acidic soils, 781–82
Acidification, ocean, 1166*t*, 1167–68, 1182
Acids, **28**
  in acid-base reactions, 28–30
  stomach, 890–91
Acoela, 643, 644
Acoelomates, 638*t*, **644**
Acorn worms, 682
Acoustic communication, 1093
Acquired characters, 257, 446, 459
Acquired immune deficiency syndrome (AIDS), 309, **712**–14, **1056**. *See also* HIV (human immunodeficiency virus)
Acrosomes, 420–21, **1017**
Actin, 54, 127, **974**–76
Actin filaments (microfilaments), 106*f*, **127**–29, 228
Actinistia, 699
Actinobacteria, 544, 546
Actinopterygii, 698–99
Action potentials, **806**, **933**. *See also* Electrical signaling, animal
  depolarization and repolarization of, 934
  in initiation of muscle contraction, 976–77
  in photoreception, 962–63
  in plant wind/touch responses, 806
  propagation of, 936–38
  in sensory transduction, 953–54
  three phases of, 933–34
  triggering of neurotransmitter release by, 939*f*
  voltage-gated channels and, 934–35
Action spectrum, 180–81*f*
Activation
  adaptive immune response, 1047–51
  enzyme, 149*f*
  lymphocyte, 1043, 1048
  MPF, 231
  T-cell, 1048–50
  transcriptional (*see* Transcriptional activators)
Activation energy, **145**–47
Active ion exclusion, plant, 785–87
Active site, enzyme, **54**, **145**
Active transport, **99**, **769**, **864**
  in osmoregulation, 864–68
  in proximal tubule, 873–74

  by pumps, 99–101*f*
  in translocation, 769–72
Adaptation(s), **6**, **454**, **659**, **843**. *See also* Evolution
  acclimation (acclimatization) vs., 459–60, 845
  in animal mouthparts, 884–86
  animal surface area, 852–53
  in consumption, 1132
  giraffe necks as, 9–11
  to global climate change, 1166*t*, 1167
  in metamorphosis, 672
  mutations and (*see* Mutation[s])
  natural selection, fitness, and, 6, 454, 465 (*see also* Fitness; Fitness trade-offs; Natural selection)
  plant nutritional, 789–90
  of plants to salty or dry habitats, 757–58, 765–66
  terrestrial, by protostomes, 659–60
  thermoregulation, 855–57
Adaptive immune response, **1041**–55. *See also* Immune systems
  activation and function of cells of, 1054*t*
  activation phase of, 1047–51
  adaptive immunity vs. innate immunity and, 1038
  B-cell activation and antibody secretion in, 1050–51
  B-cell receptors and T-cell receptors in antigen recognition by, 1044–46, 1047*f*
  B cells and T cells as lymphocytes in, 1042–43
  cell-mediated response in, 1051, 1052–53
  characteristics of, 1038, 1041–42
  clonal-selection theory on, 1048
  distinguishing self from nonself in, 1046–47
  extracellular pathogen elimination by, 1052
  humoral response in, 1051–52
  immunological memory in, 1053–55
  intracellular pathogen elimination by, 1052–53
  recognition phase of, 1041–47
  response phase of, 1051–53
  T-cell activation in, 1048–50
Adaptive immunity, **1038**. *See also* Adaptive immune response
Adaptive radiations, **516**, **596**, **884**
  angiosperm, 595–97*f*
  Cambrian explosion as animal, 518–20, 636–37
  of cichlids, 884–86
  ecological opportunity as trigger for, 516–17
  green plant, 582
  of Hawaiian silverswords, 736
  of humans, 707–8
  as major patterns in history of life, 516 (*see also* History of life)
  morphological innovation as trigger for, 517
  of ray-finned fishes, 692
  seed plant, 592

Adaxial-abaxial leaf axis, 436–37*f*
Addition rule, probability, B:8
Adenine, 58–59, 61–63, 65–66, 287, 318, 326
Adenosine diphosphate (ADP). *See* ADP (adenosine diphosphate)
Adenosine monophosphate (AMP), 162
Adenosine triphosphate (ATP). *See* ATP (adenosine triphosphate)
Adenoviruses, 715
Adhesion, 26, **26**, **761**
Adhesion proteins, 206–7
Adipocytes, **1000**–1001
Adipose tissue, 1000–1001
Adjacent cells. *See* Cell–cell attachments; Cell–cell gaps; Intercellular connections
ADP (adenosine diphosphate)
  in ATP synthesis, 81
  in glycolysis, 158*f*–59*f*, 160*f*
  in muscle contraction, 974–76
  phosphorylation of, in cellular respiration, 155–56
  photophosphorylation of, 186
  synthesis of ATP from, 128, 169–70
Adrenal glands, 994*f*, **995**–97, 1000
Adrenaline. *See* Epinephrine (adrenaline)
Adrenocorticotropic hormone (ACTH), **1004**
Adult mortality, endangered species, 1118
Adults, **651**
Adventitious roots, **734**–35, 807
Aerobic respiration, **171**, **542**
  anaerobic respiration vs., 170–71
  Cambrian explosion and, 519
  efficiency of, 171–72
  fermentation vs., 172–73
  in muscle contraction, 979–80
Afferent division, PNS, **942**
Aflatoxin, 298
Africa, human evolution out of, 707–8
African elephants, 392
African wild dogs, 1098
Agar, B:23
Age class, **1104**, 1115–16
Age pyramids, 1115–16
Age-specific fecundity, **1105**
Age structure, **1103**–4, 1115–16
Agglutination, pathogen, **1052**
Aggregate fruits, **834**, 835*f*
Aggregate structure, cellular slime mold, B:23–B:25
Aging, plant, 812–13
Agre, Peter, 98
Agriculture
  biological control agents in, 628
  fungi and, 613
  global water cycle and, 1160
  green plants in, 579
  habitat destruction by, 1179
  protostomes and, 658
  soil erosion and, 779
  sustainable, 781
  transgenic plants in (*see* Transgenic plants)
Agrobacterium tumefaciens, 385–86, 547
Aguinaldo, Anna Marie, 638, 645

AIDS (acquired immune deficiency syndrome), 309, **712**–14, **1056**. *See also* HIV (human immunodeficiency virus)

Air
animal locomotion in, 984
animal olfaction (smell) and, 965–66
behavior of oxygen and carbon dioxide in, 903–4
circulation patterns of, 1065–66
lichens and quality of, 631 (*see also* Atmosphere)
nitrogen fixation from, 787–89
plant essential nutrients from, 780*t*
water potential in, 758–59

Alarm calling, prairie dog, 1095–97
Albino sea turtle, 465*f*
Albumen, **693**
Alcohol fermentation, 172–73*f*
Alcohol use, 1033
Alcohols, 37*t*
Aldehydes, 37*t*, 73
Aldoses, 73
Aldosterone, **877**, **1003**
Alexander, R. McNeill, 984, 986

Algae
blooms of, 555–56, 1148*f*, 1160
brown, 7, 552*f*, 557, 568–69, 574
green (*see* Green algae)
in lichens, 623, 631
photosynthesis in, 180–81*f*, 184, 190–91
protist lineages of, 569, 572, 574
red, 572
rRNA sequences for, 7

Alkaline mucus, 1023*t*
Alkaline soil, 781–82
Alkalinity, pH scale of, 29
Allantois membrane, 694
All-cells-from-cells hypothesis, 3–5
All-taxa surveys, 1175

Alleles, **238**, **261**
in central dogma of molecular biology, 308–9
codominance and incomplete dominance of, 272, 273*f*
female choice for good, 475–76
foraging, 1085
frequencies of, in populations, 465–71*f*
genes and, 238, 239*f*, 247 (*see also* Genes)
genetic bottlenecks and, 481–82
genetic drift and, 479
in human inheritance, 277–79
linkage, crossing over, and recombination of, 270–71, 274*f*
in Mendelian genetics, 258*t*, 277*t*
multiple alleleism and, 271–72
mutations and, 305, 313, 483–84, 486
in particulate inheritance, 261–63
plant pathogen resistance, 815
wild-type, 267–69

Allergens, **1055**–56
Allergies, **1055**–56
Alligators, 703
Allolactose, 341
Allopatric speciation, **494**–95
Allopatry, **494**–95, 500
Allopolyploids, **498**–99
Allosteric regulation, **149**, **343**
Aloe vera, 739*f*
α-amylase, **809**
α-glucose, 74, 75*f*, 76

α-glycosidic linkages, 75*f*–76
α-helix (alpha helix), **48**–49
α-tubulin, 129
Alpine skypilots, 831
ALS (Lou Gehrig's disease), 408
Alternate leaves, 738*f*
Alternation of generations, **567**, **588**, **823**
fungal, 625–26*f*
in land plants, 588–89, 823–25
in protists, 567–69
Alternative splicing, RNA, 357–**58**, 360–61, **400**
Altman, Sidney, 67–68
Altruism, **1095**–98
Alvarez, Luis and Walter, 521
Alveolata, 558*t*, 570, 573
Alveoli, 570, **909**, 910*f*
Amazon rain forest, 1168, 1179, 1180. *See also* Tropical wet forests
Ambisense RNA viruses, **716**
American chestnut trees, 815
American elm trees, 613
Amines, 37*t*
Amino acids, 42. *See also* Proteins
amphipathic proteins and, 94, 95*f*
as animal nutrients, 883
carbohydrates and, 78
in central dogma of molecular biology, 308
functional groups and, 38
genetic code for, 310–12
hormones as derivatives of, 995–96
major, found in organisms, 43*t*
in metabolic pathways, 157
as neurotransmitters, 941*t*
in one-gene, one-enzyme hypothesis on gene expression, 305–7
Oparin–Haldane theory on chemical evolution of, 41–42
in peptidoglycan, 76
in point mutations, 313–14
polymerization of, to form proteins, 44–47
ribosomal polypeptide synthesis from, in translation, 328–31
sequences of, in genetic homologies, 450–51
sequences of, in protein primary structure, 47–48
side chains (R-groups) of, 42–44
specification of, in translation, 325–26
structure of, 42
transfer of, to proteins by tRNAs, 326–28
Aminoacyl tRNAs, 326–**27**, 328–31
Aminoacyl-tRNA synthetases, **327**, 328*f*
Amino functional group, 37*t*–38, 42, 46, 48–49*f*
Amino-terminus, 46, 328
Ammonia, **865**
in archaea metabolism, 539*t*
molecular structure of, B:12*f*
in nitrogen fixation, 542–44, 787
as nitrogenous waste, 865, 866*t*
in origin-of-life experiments, 33–34
simple molecules of, 23*f*, 24*f*
Amnion, **1032**
Amniotes, **689**
Amniotic eggs, **689**–91, 693–94
Amniotic fluid, 1032
Amoeba, as model organism, B:23–B:25
Amoebic dysentery, 555*t*

Amoeboid motion, **565**
Amoebozoa, 558*t*, 569, 570
AMP (adenosine monophosphate), 162
Amphibians, **696**
fungal parasites of, 629
hormones in metamorphosis of, 997–98
impacts of global climate change on, 1167
lineages of, 696, 700
mechanoreception by lateral line system of, 958–59
Amphioxus, 686, 687
Amphipathic compounds, **87**, 87, 94, 95*f*
Amplification
cell-cell signal, 211–12
chemical signal, 1010
sensory signal, 953
Ampullae of Lorenzini, **967**–68
Amylases, **81**, 895*t*
Amylopectin, 76
Amyloplasts, **804**
Amylose, 76
Anabolic pathways, **151**–52, 157–58. *See also* Catabolic pathways
Anadromous organisms, **697**
Anaerobic respiration, 170–**71**, **542**. *See also* Aerobic respiration; Fermentation
Analyze (Bloom's taxonomy skill), B:29*f*–B:30*t*
Anaphase, **225**–27, 245*f*
Anaphase I, 242*f*, 243–44, 245*f*
Anaphase II, 243*f*, 244
Anaphylactic shock, 1056
Anatomy, **843**. *See also* Animal form and function
Anatomy, levels of organization, 849*f*
Ancestral groups, phylogenetic trees and, B:10–B:11
Ancestral traits, 491–92, **506**–10, B:10–B:11. *See also* Common ancestry
Anchor roots, 734–35*f*
Anemones, 653–54, 887*t*
Anfinson, Christian, 52
Angiosperms, **581**. *See also* Plant(s); Seed plants
adaptive radiation of, 517, 595–97*f*
Anthophyta lineage of, 608–9*f*
in Cenozoic era, 515
characteristics of, 581
diversification of, 582
flowers in, 592–93, 595*f*
form and function of, 732 (*see also* Plant form and function)
fruits in, 594–95
life cycle of, 824*f*–25
molecular phylogeny of, 583
parasitic, 789, 790*f*
pollination in, 593–94, 608–9*f*
reproduction in, 823 (*see also* Plant reproduction)
Anguilla, 481
Anhydrite, 522
Animal(s), **637**. *See also* Animal cells; Animal development; Animal form and function; Animal movement; Animal nutrition; Animal reproduction
appearance of, in Paleozoic era, 515
biological methods for studying, 637–38
Cambrian explosion and adaptive radiation of, 518–20, 636–37
carbohydrate hydrolysis by digestive enzymes in, 80–81
cell-cell attachments in, 204–7

chemical signals of, 992–93
chitin as structural polysaccharide in, 76, 78
cloning of, 409
cytokinesis in, 228
electrolytes of, 862
endocrine systems and hormones of, 991–92, 993, 994*f*–95 (*see also* Hormones, animal)
evolutionary innovations of, 637–46
food sources and feeding strategies of, 646–49
gap junctions in tissues of, 207–8
gas exchange and circulation in, 902–3 (*see also* Circulatory systems; Respiratory systems)
glycogen as storage polysaccharide in, 76
as heterotrophs, 176
immune systems of (*see* Immune systems)
impact of global warming on, 1166–68
key lineages of non-bilaterian, 652–54
life cycles of, 651–52
major phyla of, 638*t*
mass extinctions of, 520–23
as models of disease, 382
nervous systems of (*see* Nervous systems)
nitrogenous wastes of, 865–66
osmoregulation by (*see* Osmoregulation)
phylogenetic relationship of fungi to, 8, 618
phylogenies of, 637*f*, 639*f*
pollination by, 593–94, 608–9*f*, 830–32
populations of (*see* Population[s])
prions and diseases of, 53
protostome and deuterostome, 644–45 (*see also* Deuterostomes; Protostomes)
relative diversity of lineages of, 658*f*
seed dispersal by, 835–37
sensory systems of (*see* Sensory systems, animal)
shared traits of, 637

Animal cells. *See also* Eukaryotic cells
anatomy and physiology at level of, 849*f*
blood, 912, 982–83, **1039**–41, 1042*t*
cultures of, B:21, B:22*f* (*see also* Cultures, cell and tissue)
extracellular matrix in, 202–4
lysosomes in, 114
meiosis and mitosis in cell cycle of, 219–20 (*see also* Cell cycle)
plant cells vs., 110*f*, 742–43 (*see also* Plant cells)
sensory, 929
shared development processes of, 406–9
whole-cell dynamism of, 118–19

Animal development, 419–31. *See also* Development
cleavage in, 423–24
developmental principles in, 419–20
early marsupial, 1031
fertilization in, 420–23
gastrulation in, 424–26
germ cells in, 438
germ line in, 433
hormones in, 997–1000
Hox genes in, 414–15
human embryo image, 419*f*
lophotrochozoan vs. ecdysozoan, 670
ordered phases of, 420*f*
organogenesis in, 426–29
plant development vs., 432–33, 438 (*see also* Plant development)

Boldface page numbers indicate a glossary entry; page numbers followed by an *f* indicate a figure; those followed by *t* indicate a table.

Animal form and function, 842–60
  adaptations of, 843–45
  anatomy and physiology in, 843, 849f
  body size effects on physiology in, 850–53
  body temperature regulation in, 854–58
  dry habitats and, 842–43
  fitness trade-offs in, 843–45
  homeostasis in, 853–54
  organs and organ systems in, 849–50
  structure-function relationships in, 845–46
  tissues in, 845–49
Animal models, disease, **382**
Animal movement
  bipedalism, 705–7
  diversification of limbs for, 649–50f
  ecdysozoan, 674–78
  echinoderm, 685–86
  evolution of muscle-generated, 972–73
  hydrostatic skeletons and, 644
  invertebrate, 687–88
  locomotion in, 983–88
  lophotrochozoan, 665–69
  mollusk, 663–64f, 669
  muscle contraction in, 973–77
  muscle tissue and, 847–48, 977–80
  neurons and muscle cells of, 637
  skeletal systems in, 980–83
  types of, 973
  vertebrate, 697–703
Animal nutrition, 882–901
  cellulose as dietary fiber for, 78
  digestion and absorption of nutrients in, 886–97
  fetal, during pregnancy, 1032–33
  food capture and mouthparts in, 884–86
  food types in, 892–93
  four steps of, 883f
  glucose and nutritional homeostasis in, 897–99
  glycogen and starch hydrolysis in, 76, 80–81
  herbivore limitation by poor, 1131–32
  human digestive tract, 887f
  human mineral and electrolyte requirements, 885t
  human vitamin requirements, 884t
  mammalian digestive enzymes in, 895t
  nutritional homeostasis in, 897–99
  nutritional requirements and, 883–84
  waste elimination in, 896–97
Animal reproduction, 1013–36
  asexual vs. sexual, 1014
  deceitful communication in, 1094–95
  diversity in, 650–51
  ecdysozoan, 674–78
  echinoderm, 685–86
  in energy flow, 1149
  fertilization and egg development in, 1018–21
  fitness trade-offs in, 843–45
  gametogenesis in, 1016–18f
  hormones in, 998–99
  invertebrate, 687–88
  life cycles of, 651–52
  life tables and, 1104–5, 1106f
  lophotrochozoan, 665–69
  mammalian pregnancy and birth in, 1030–34
  mammalian reproductive systems in, 1021–25
  mammalian sex hormones in, 1025–30
  mating behaviors and (see Mating)

  migration and, 1091
  net reproductive rate in, 1105
  parthenogenesis, 665
  sexual selection and, 475–78
  switching modes of, between asexual and sexual, 1014–16
  vertebrate, 693–94, 697–703
Anion(s), **22**f, 781–83
Annelids, 638t, 657–58, 667
Aniston, Jennifer, 946, 947f
Annual growth rings, tree, 751, 1139
Annuals, **599**
Anolis lizards, 516, 1087–89, 1125
Anoxic oceans, 521
Anoxygenic photosynthesis, **186**, 539t, **541**, 545
Antagonistic muscle groups, **981**
Antagonistic-pair feedback systems, 857
Antarctic fur seals, 1086
Antbirds, 1124–25
Antenna complex, photosystem, **182**–83
Antennae, insect, **675**
Anterior body axis, **410**
Anterior pituitary gland, **1004**, 1006
Antheridia, **587**
Anthers, **827**
Anthocerophyta, 602
Anthophyta (angiosperms), 608–9f. See also Angiosperms
Anthrax, 532
Anthropocene epoch, 515
Anthropogenic biomes, 1069
Anthropoids, 704f–5
Antibacterial compounds, 815
Antibiotic resistance, 395, 454–56
Antibiotics, **532**, **1039**
  actinobacteria and, 546
  bacterial ribosomes and, 529
  fungi and, 613, 632
  in human semen, 1023t
  lysozyme as, 1039
  pathogenic bacteria and, 532–33
Antibodies, **206**, **717**, **1042**
  adaptive immune response and, 1042 (see also Adaptive immune response)
  B-cell activation and secretion of, 1050–51
  binding of, to epitopes, 1045
  cell adhesion proteins and, 206–7
  five classes of immunoglobulins and, 1045t (see also Immunoglobulins)
  in fluorescent microscopy, B:18
  in HIV research, 717–18
  humoral response and, 1051–52
  as probes, B:16
  proteins as, 54
  specificity and diversity of, 1045–46
Anticodons, **327**, 328–29f
Antidiuretic hormone (ADH), **877**–78, **1003**, 1005–6
Antifungal compounds, 815
Antigen presentation, **1045**, 1048–49
Antigens, **1040**, 1044–50
Antilogs, logarithms and, B:9
Antiparallel DNA strands, **62**, 286–87
Antiporters, **770**, 786–**87**, **865**
Antiviral drugs, 714
Ants, 11–14, 623, 1063–64, 1083–85, 1124–25, 1133–35
Anus, 644–45, 658, 886, 887f
Aorta, **917**
Aphids, 485, 672f, 768–69f
Aphotic zone, lake and pond, **1077**
Aphotic zone, ocean, **1079**
Apical-basal axis, **434**, 435–36

Apical buds, **735**
Apical cells, **434**
Apical dominance, **806**–7
Apical meristems, 436, 437f, **740**–42, 748
Apical mutants, 435
Apical side, epithelium, **849**
Apicomplexans, 573
Apodemes, **983**
Apomixis, **825**
Apoplast, **208**–9f, **760**
Apoplastic pathway, 760–61, 785
Apoptosis, **232**, **407**, **1053**
  in cancer, 362–63
  in cell-mediated response, 1053–54
  in Huntington's disease, 382
  in organogenesis, 426
  as programmed cell death, 406t, 407–8
  tumor suppressors and, 232
Appendix, 887f, **896**
Apple maggot flies, 496–97
Apply (Bloom's taxonomy skill), B:29f–B:30t
Aquaporins, **98**, **865**, **896**
  large intestine water absorption and, 896
  in osmoregulation, 865, 877–78
  in plant water movement, 760
  selectivity and structure of, 98
Aquatic biomes
  animal locomotion in, 984, 985, 988
  animal transition to terrestrial environments from, 659–60
  behavior of oxygen and carbon dioxide in, 904–5
  direct and indirect human impacts on, 1076
  estuaries as freshwater and marine, 1078
  external fertilization in, 1018
  freshwater lakes, ponds, wetlands, and streams, 1077–78
  gas exchange by gills in, 906–7
  global net primary productivity of, 1154–56
  global water cycle and, 1159–60
  nitrogen pollution in, 1160
  nutrient availability in, 1075–76
  oceans as marine, 1079
  osmoregulation in, 862–64, 866–68
  plant transition to terrestrial environments from, 584–95
  protists in, 553, 556
  salinity in, 1074
  water depth and water flow in, 1074–75
Aqueous solutions
  acid-base reactions in, 28–30
  chemical evolution in, 24
  molarity of, 29
  properties of water and, 25–28
Aquifers, 1159–**60**
ara operon, **344**, 345f
Arabian oryx, 842–43, 855, 864
Arabidopsis thaliana. See Mustard plant
Arabinose, 344, 345f
araC gene, **344**
AraC protein, **344**, 345f
Arachnids, 678
Arbuscular mycorrhizal fungi (AMF), **620**–22, 630
Arcese, Peter, 1111–12
Archaea, **529**. See also Archaea domain
  aerobic vs. anaerobic respiration in, 171
  ammonia-oxidizing, 539t
  bacteria vs., as prokaryotes, 528–29 (see also Bacteria; Prokaryotes)

  citric acid cycle in, 162
  human diseases and, 531
  phospholipids in plasma membranes of, 529
  phylogeny of, 536f
  as prokaryotes, 107
Archaea domain. See also Archaea
  characteristics of, 529t
  key lineages of, 544, 548–49
  phospholipids in, 87
  phylogeny of, 7f–8, 536f
  as prokaryotic, 107, 528–29 (see also Prokaryotes)
Archaeopteryx, 512
Archegonia, **587**
Arctic terns, 1091
Arctic tundra, **1072**, 1073f, 1165, 1167
Ardipithecus genus, 705t
Area, metric units and conversions for, B:1t
Area and age hypothesis on species richness, 1145
Argentine ant, 1063–64, 1083–84, 1085. See also Ants
Arginine, 305–6
Aristotle, 445
Armor, defensive, 1129f
Arms races, coevolutionary, 1124, 1132
Arrangement, leaf, 738
Arrhenius, Svante, 1163
Arteries, 871, **917**–18, 921
Arterioles, **917**–18, 924
Arteriosclerosis, **924**
Arthrobacter, 546
Arthropods, **670**
  body plan of, 670–71
  as ecdysozoans, 673
  exoskeletons of, 983
  key lineages of, 638t, 675–78
  metamorphosis in, 672
  origin of wings in evolution of, 671–72
  as protostomes, 657–58
Articulations (joints), **981**–82
Artificial membranes, 88–89
Artificial selection, 5–6, 257, **453**, **579**. See also Crosses
Artiodactyls, 510–11f
Ascaris (roundworms), 238. See also Roundworms
Asci, **617**–18
Ascidians, 688
Ascomycetes, 617–18, 627, 631–32
Ascorbic acid, 884t
Asexual reproduction, **220**, **825**, **1014**. See also Animal reproduction
  animal, 650, 1014
  by fragmentation, 601, 603
  fungal, 617, 625
  mitosis and, 220 (see also Mitosis)
  plant, 825–26
  prokaryotic vs. eukaryotic, 566
  sexual reproduction vs., 247, 566, 1014 (see also Sexual reproduction)
  switching between sexual and, 1014–16
Asteroidea, 685
Asteroid impact hypothesis, 521–23
Asthma, 1056
Astragalus, 510
Astral microtubules, **225**
Astrobiologists, 531
Asymmetric cell division, plant, 433–34
Asymmetric competition, **1125**–26
Athletes
  EPO abuse by, 1003
  human growth hormone and, 374

Atlantic cod, 1153
Atlantic salmon, 483
Atmosphere. *See also* Air
  behavior of oxygen and carbon dioxide in, 903–4
  Cambrian explosion and oxygen in, 519–20
  chemical evolution conditions in, 30, 33–35
  end-Permian mass extinction and carbon dioxide in, 521
  greenhouse effect from carbon dioxide in, 1163
  plant nitrogen fixation of nitrogen from, 787–89
  prokaryotic oxygen revolution and oxygen in, 541–42
  water potential in, 758–59
Atomic level, anatomy and physiology at, 849f
Atomic number, **19**
Atomic weight, **20**, 29
Atoms
  chemical bonding of, in molecules, 21–24
  in chemical structures, B:12–B:13
  energy transformation in, 138f
  linking carbon, into organic molecules, 36
  radioactive decay of, 446–47
  structure of, 19–21
ATP (adenosine triphosphate), **60**, **143**
  actin filaments and, 128–29
  in active transport by pumps, 99–100
  in attachment of amino acids to tRNAs, 327
  in Calvin cycle, 191–92
  cell usage of, 119
  in cytokinesis, 228
  in endergonic reactions, 143–44
  as energy source for nucleic acid polymerization, 60
  energy transfer from glucose to, 81
  in enzyme catalysis, 145
  in glycolysis, 158f–61
  GTP vs., 162, 325
  microtubules, vesicle transport, and, 130–31
  in muscle contraction, 974–76, 979
  in photosynthesis, 178
  in photosystems, 185–89
  prokaryotic metabolic diversity in producing, 538–41
  synthesis of, by ATP synthase and chemiosmosis, 168–70
  synthesis of, from glucose oxidation in cellular respiration, 154–56
  synthesis of, in fermentation, 172–73
  synthesis of, in mitochondria, 115–16
  yield of, in cellular respiration, 170–72
ATP synthase, 168–**69**, 170–71, 185–86, 189
Atria, 919, 921
Atrioventricular (AV) node, **922**
Atrioventricular valves, 919
Attachments, intercellular. *See* Cell–cell attachments
Attenuated virus vaccines, 1055
Australia, 701
Australian redback spiders, 1020
Australopithecus genus, 705t, 706, B:11
Autocrine signals, **992**

Autoimmune diseases, 1056
Autoimmunity, **1056**
Autonomic nervous system, **942**–43, 977–78
Autophagy, **126**
Autopolyploids, **497**–98
Autoradiography, 948–49, B:15–B:16
Autosomal genes, 258t, 268
Autosomal inheritance, **269**, 277–78, 299
Autosomal traits
  Huntington's disease as, 378
  pituitary dwarfism as, 369
  recessive and dominant, 277–78
Autosomes, **238**, 240t
Autotrophs, **176**–77, **538**, **1149**–50
Auxin, **798**
  in apical dominance, 806–7
  as blue-light phototropic hormone, 797–800
  in cell and tissue cultures, B:22
  as gravitropic signal, 804–5
  as morphogen in plant development, 412
  as plant growth regulator, 813t
  in setup of body axes in embryogenesis, 435–36
  structure and function of, 210t
Averages, standard error and, B:6–B:7
Averof, Michalis, 671
Aves, 703. *See also* Birds
Avian malaria, 1062
Axel, Richard, 966
Axes, body, 425, 435–36
Axes, graph, B:4–B:5
Axes, leaf, 436–38
Axillary buds, **735**
Axon hillock, **942**
Axons, **847**, **930**
  action potential propagation down, 936–38
  measuring membrane potentials of, 932–33
  in neuron anatomy, 847, 930
  squid, 130
Azoneme, **132**

B

B-cell receptors (BCRs), **1043**–47, 1048, 1050–51
B-cell tumors, 1045–46
B cells, **1043**
  activation and function of, 1054t
  activation of, 1050–51
  antigen receptors of, 1044–47
  as lymphocytes, 1042–43
  memory cells and, 1053–55
Baboons, 1013f
BAC libraries, **390**–91
Bacillus anthracis, 532
Bacillus thuringiensis, 385, 545
Backbones
  nucleic acid, 59–63, 65
  peptide, 46, 48–50
Background extinctions, 520–21. *See also* Extinctions
Bacteria, **529**. *See also* Bacteria domain; Prokaryotes
  aerobic vs. anaerobic respiration in, 171
  archaea vs., 528–29
  in bioremediation, 151

cell division by binary fission in, 228–29
in cell theory experiment, 3–5
citric acid cycle in, 162
DNA of, 107–8
DNA synthesis in, 291f
evolution of antibiotic resistance in, 454–56
flagella of, 131
gene regulation in (*see* Gene regulation, bacterial)
introducing recombinant plasmids into cells of, for transformation, 372
isolating, with enrichment cultures, 534f
as model organism (*see Escherichia coli* [*E. coli*])
nitrogen-fixing, 542–43, 787–89, 1133, 1158, 1160
optimal temperature and pH for enzyme function in, 148
origin of viruses in symbiotic, 723
pathogenic, 531–33
peptidoglycan as structural polysaccharide in, 76, 78, 529
phospholipids in, 87
photosynthesis in, 177, 184, 186–87, 515
proteins as defense against, 54
RNA polymerase in, 318
transcription and translation in, 318–20f, 324f–25, 329–30
in transgenic plant development, 385–86
Bacteria domain. *See also* Bacteria
  characteristics of, 529t
  key lineages of, 544, 545–47
  phylogeny of, 7f, 8, 536f
  as prokaryotic, 107, 528–29 (*see also* Prokaryotes)
Bacterial artificial chromosomes (BACs), **390**–91
Bacteriophages, 50, 715, **716**
Bacteriorhodopsin, 169, 541
Baculum, **1022**–23
Baker's yeast. *See Saccharomyces cerevisiae*
Balancing selection, **474**–75t
Ball-and-stick models, 24, B:12f–B:13
Baltimore, David, 725
Bands, molecular, B:14–B:16
Banting, Frederick, 897
Baobab trees, 731f
Bar charts, B:5–B:7
Bar coding, species, **1174**
Bark, **750**, 750
Barnacles, 677, 1126, 1127f
Barometric pressure, animal sensing of, 646, 647t
Baroreceptors, **924**
Barriers
  to conception, 1030t
  to dispersal, 1063
  to pathogens, 848–49, 1038–39
  plant cuticle as, 743, 815
  to polyspermy, 421–23
Bartel, David, 68–69
Basal body, **132**
Basal cells, **434**
Basal lamina, epithelium, **849**
Basal metabolic rate (BMR), **851**–52
Basal mutants, 435–36
Basal transcription factors, **320**, 325t, **356**
Basalts, 521
Base, exponential notation, B:9

Base(s), **28**–30, 38. *See also* Nitrogenous bases, nucleotide
Base *e*, exponential notation, B:9
Base 10
  exponential notation and, B:9
  metric system scientific notation and, B:1–B:2
Basic-odor hypothesis, 966
Basic side chains, 43f, 44
Basidia, **617**–18, 626–27
Basidiomycetes, 617–18, 626–27, 630
Basilar membrane, **956**–57
Basilisk lizards, 972f
Basket stars, 684
Basolateral side, epithelium, **849**
Bateman, A. J., 475
Bateman-Trivers theory, 475
Bates, Henry Walter, 1129–30
Batesian mimicry, 1129–**30**
Bateson, William, 273–75
Bats, 694, 952–53, 957–58
Bayliss, William, 893
Bdelloids, 650, 665
Bdellovibrios, 547
Beadle, George, 305
Beagle naval ship, 449–50
Beaks, cepalopod, **669**
Beaks, finch, 494–95, 1128
Beaumont, William, 890
Bedbugs, 1020
Bees, 594, 826–27, 856, 1092–93, 1097–98, 1133
Beeswax, 86f
Beetles, 138, 139f, 268, 1166t, 1167
Behavior, **1082**–85, 1129f. *See also* Behavioral ecology
Behavioral contraception methods, 1030t
Behavioral ecology, **1083**
  altruism in, 1095–98
  behaviors in, 1082–83, 1084–85
  communication in, 1091–95
  five questions of, 1085
  foraging in, 1085–87
  mating in, 1087–89
  migration in, 1089–91
  proximate and ultimate causation in, 1083–84
Behavioral prezygotic isolation, 491t
Bendall, Faye, 184
Beneficial alleles, **484**–85
Beneficial mutations, 313
Benign tumors, **233**
Benthic habitats, 519
Benthic organisms, 651, **652**
Benthic zone, lake and pond, **1077**
Benthic zone, ocean, **1079**
Benzene, 27t
Benzo[α]pyrene, 299
Beriberi, 147
Bermingham, Eldredge, 500–501
Bertness, Mark, 1130, 1131f
Beschta, Robert, 1153
Best, Charles, 897
Beta-blockers, 210
β-carotene, 180–81f, 385
β-galactosidase, 338–43
β-globin genes, 351, 399
β-glucose, 74, 75f, 76
β-glycosidic linkages, 75f–76
β-pleated sheet (beta-pleated sheet), **48**–49
β-tubulin, 129
Beutler, Bruce, 1040
Biewener, Andrew, 987–88
Bikonta, 558

Boldface page numbers indicate a glossary entry; page numbers followed by an *f* indicate a figure; those followed by *t* indicate a table.

Bilateral symmetry, **641**–44, 682–83*f*
Bilaterians, 638*t*, 641–**42**
Bile, **894**–96
Binary fission, **228**–29
Bindin, 421
Biochemical pathways, plant, 766
Bioclimate envelope models, 1183
Biocontrol agents, consumers as, 1133
Biodiversity, **1173**
  biological benefits of, 1184–87
  changes in, through time, 1174–75
  economic and social benefits of
    ecosystem services and, 1187–88
  estimating, using surveys, 1175
  ethical issues on, 1188–89
  genetic, species, and ecosystem levels
    of, 1173–74
  global climate change and, 1073
  loss of, in Borneo, 1172–73
  mapping, 1176–77
  preserving ecosystem function and,
    1189–93 (*see also* Conservation
    biology)
  threats to, 1178–84 (*see also* Threats,
    biodiversity)
  tree of life and, 1173
  ultimate causes of losses in, 1189
Biodiversity hotspots, **1177**, 1190–91
Biofilms, **532**
Biogeochemical cycles, **1156**, 1159–62.
  See also Nutrient cycling
Biogeography, **494**, **1062**. *See also*
  Geographic distribution and
  abundance of organisms
Bioindicators, lichens as, 631
Bioinformatics, 391–**92**. *See also*
  Genomics
Biological benefits, biodiversity, 1184–87
Biological control agents, 628
Biological evolution, chemical evolution
  vs., 19, 57–58. *See also* Chemical
  Evolution; Evolution
Biological imaging techniques, 119
Biological impact, prokaryotic, 530
Biological species concept, **490**, 492*t*
Biology
  astrobiology, 531
  biogeography, 494
  biomechanics, 973, 984–88
  cell theory and cells in, 2–5 (*see also*
    Cell[s])
  characteristics of living organisms in, 2
    (*see also* Life; Organisms)
  chemical evolution and (*see* Chemical
    evolution)
  chemical reactions in (*see* Chemical
    reactions)
  conservation biology and
    bioremediation, 533 (*see also*
    Conservation biology)
  developmental, 405–6 (*see also*
    Development)
  evo-devo (evolutionary-
    developmental), 416
  forensic, 376
  genetic engineering in (*see* Genetic
    engineering)
  microbiology, 530
  nanobiology, 714
  science and methods of, 1, 9–14 (*see
    also* Quantitative Methods boxes;
    Science; Bioskills; Process boxes)
  speciation, phylogenetic tree of
    life, and taxonomy in, 6–9 (*see
    also* Phylogenies; Speciation;
    Taxonomy; Tree of life)

systems biology, 402
  theory of evolution by natural
    selection in, 5–6 (*see also*
    Evolution; Natural selection)
Bioluminescence, **573**
Biomagnification, **1152**–53
Biomass, **1069**, **1149**, **1180**
  loss of, by habitat fragmentation and
    degradation and, 1180
  net primary production and, 1149–50
    (*see also* Net primary productivity
    [NPP])
  plants and, 776
  recovery of, after disturbances,
    1191–92
  in terrestrial biomes, 1069
  trophic structure and (*see* Trophic
    structure)
Biomechanics, **973**, 984–88
Biomes, **1068**. *See also* Aquatic biomes;
  Terrestrial biomes
  effects of global climate change
    on, 1182
  most productive, 1154–56
Biophilia, 1188
Bioprospecting, **1187**
Bioremediation, **151**, **533**, 632. *See also*
  Conservation biology
Bioskills, B:1–B:30
  biological imaging with microscopy
    and x-ray crystallography,
    B18–B:21
  cell and tissue culture methods,
    B:21–B:22
  combining probabilities, B:8
  Latin and Greek word roots, B:3
  making concept maps, B:28
  metric system and significant figures,
    B:1–B:3
  model organisms, B:23–B:26
  primary literature and peer review,
    B:26–B:27
  reading chemical structures, B:12–B:13
  reading graphs, B:4–B:6
  reading phylogenetic trees, B:10–B:11
  separating and visualizing molecules,
    B:13–B:16
  separating cell components by
    centrifugation, B:17–B:18
  using Bloom's taxonomy, B:29–B:30*t*
  using logarithms, B:9
  using statistical tests and interpreting
    standard error bars, B:6–B:7
Biosphere, 1060*t*, **1061**, **1148**–49. *See
  also* Ecosystem ecology; Global
  ecology
Biotechnology, **374**
  agricultural, 385–86 (*see also*
    Transgenic organisms)
  recombinant DNA technology in,
    374 (*see also* Recombinant DNA
    technology)
Biotic factors, **1062**
  in community structure, 1135
  in density-dependent population
    growth, 1108–12
  in geographic distribution and
    abundance of organisms,
    1062–65, 1102
  of natural biomes, 1068–69
Bipedal organisms, **705**, 706–7
Bipolar cells, **960**, 961*f*
Birds
  adaptive radiations of, 517
  allopatric speciation in, 494–95
  biotic factors in distribution of, 1062

crop as modified esophagus in, 889
  disruptive selection of, 473–74
  evolution of wings and flight in,
    694–95
  female choice for good alleles in, 475–76
  female reproductive tract in, 1024
  form-function correlation in, 845–46*f*
  fossils of, 512
  gizzards as modified stomachs in,
    891–92
  impacts of global climate change on,
    1166–67
  loss of species of, from invasive
    species, 1181
  magnetoreception by, 968–69
  mapping species richness and
    endemism of, 1176
  mating behaviors of, 1020, 1082*f*
  maturation of eggs of, 1024*f*
  migration of, 1089–91
  neurogenesis in, 948–49
  nitrogenous wastes of, 865
  parental care in, 694
  as reptiles, 696–97, 703
  seed dispersal by, 835–36
  sexual dimorphism in, 478*f*
  survivorship curves for, 1105
  ventilation of lungs of, 910–11*f*
  in vertebrate phylogeny, 691
Birth, human, 473, 1034
Birth control, human, 1029–30
Birth rates, 1103–7, 1108, 1109
Bisphenol A, 1000
Bis prefix, 158
Bitterness taste receptors, 965
Bivalents, 240*t*, **242**, 244, 246*f*
Bivalves, **662**, 668
Black-bellied seedcrackers, 474
Blackburn, Elizabeth, 296
Black-tailed prairie dogs, 1095–97
Bladders, **872**, 879
Blade, leaf, **737**
BLAST program, 392
Blastocoel, **425**
Blastocysts, **424**
Blastomeres, **423**, 425
Blastopores, **425**
Blastula, **423**
Bleaching, coral, 1167–68
Blending inheritance hypothesis, 257
Blind spot, 960
Blindness, 385, 547
Blobel, Günter, 123–24
Blood, **847**. *See also* Leukocytes (white
  blood cells)
  acclimatization vs. adaptation for
    oxygen content of, 459–60
  alveoli and, in mammal lungs, 909, 916
  in bird lungs, 910
  blood vessels and, 917–18
  bones, bone marrow, and, 982–83
  carbon dioxide transport in, 915–16
  chromatin remodeling in, 351
  circulation of, through hearts, 919–21
  connective tissue of, 846*f*
  glucagon and sugar levels in, 54
  glucose carrier protein for cells of
    human, 99
  hemoglobin and oxygen in, 54 (*see also*
    Hemoglobin)
  hemophilia and human, 278
  homeostasis for oxygen in, 911–12
  human ABO types of, 272, 468–69
  immune systems and transfusions
    of, 1053
  insulin and sugar levels in, 47–48

measuring hormone amounts in, using
    radioimmunoassay, B:16
  microscopic images of cells of
    human, 3*f*
  oxygen transport in hemoglobin of,
    912–15
  patterns in pressure and flow of,
    923–25
  regulation of oxygen levels in, 1003
  serum of, in cell cultures, B:21
  sickle-cell disease and human, 48
Blood cells, 912, 982–83, **1039**–41, 1042*t*
Blood pressure, 923–24
Blood serum, 233
Blood types, human, 272, 468–69
Blood vessels
  cancer and, 233*f*
  in closed circulatory systems, 917–18
  kidney, 871, 873, 876, 877*f*
Blooms, algal, 555–56, 1148*f*, 1160
Bloom's taxonomy, B:29–B:30*t*
Blotting techniques, B:16
Blue light, 179–81*f*
Blue light phototropic responses, plant,
    796–800, 818*t*
Blue mussels, 1130, 1131*f*
Blue opsin, 963–64
Bluegill sunfish, 1094–95
Bluetongue virus, 727
Bmp4 gene, 458–59*f*
Body. *See also* Body plans
  animal locomotion and size of, 986–88
  animal regulation of temperature of
    (*see* Thermoregulation)
  barriers to entry of pathogens into,
    1038–39
  brassinosteroids in size of plant, 812
  Cambrian explosion and new, 519–20
  convergent evolution of streamlined,
    509–10
  definition of axes of, in
    gastrulation, 425
  differential gene expression in
    development of, 410–15 (*see also*
    Differential gene expression)
  directional selection on size of cliff
    swallow, 473
  fungal, 615–18
  gas exchange through diffusion across,
    905–6, 916
  genes and proteins in setup of axes of,
    in plant embryogenesis, 435–36
  organogenesis and, 426–29
  physiological effects of size of animal,
    850–53
  plant (*see* Primary growth, plant;
    Secondary growth, plant)
  plant nutrition and plant, 775
  skeletal systems in maintenance of
    posture of, 980
Body mass index, **899**
Body odor, genotypes and, 470
Body plans, **638**. *See also* Bodies
  arthropod, 670–71
  bilateral symmetry in animal, 641–44
  chelicerate, 678
  chordate, 686–87
  comparative morphology and animal,
    638 (*see also* Evolutionary
    innovations, animal)
  crustacean, 677
  echinoderm, 682–83
  insect, 675
  modular protostome, 660
  mollusk, 662–64
  myriapod, 675

Bogs, **1077**
Bohr shift, **914**, 915
Boluses, 884
Bombadier beetles, 138, 139*f*
Bond saturation, lipid, 85–86, 90
Bonds, B:12–B:13. *See also* Covalent bonds; Hydrogen bonds; Ionic bonds
Bone, 427–29, **689**, 846*f*, **847**, **981**–82
Bone marrow, 982–83, **1043**
Bone marrow transplants, 384
Bony fishes, osmoregulation by, 862–63
Boreal forests, **1072**, 1157
Bormann, Frank, 1149–50
Borneo, 1172–73, 1191
Borthwick, H. A., 800–801
Both-and rule, probability, B:8
Bottom-up limitation hypothesis, herbivore population, 1131–32
Bottom-up research approach, chemical evolution, 32–33
Bouchet Philippe, 1175
Boveri, Theodor, 257, 266–67
Bowerbird, 1082*f*
Bowman's capsule, **873**, 878*t*
Box-and-whisker plots, B:5–B:6
Bracket fungi, 617, 626–27
Brain stem, **944**
Braincase, **707**
Brains, **643**
    anatomy of, 944–46
    central nervous system and, 929
    diffusion spectrum imaging of neurons in, 928*f*
    in hormonal control of urine formation, 877
    Huntington's disease and degeneration of, 278, 378, 382
    in initiation of muscle contraction, 976–77
    neural tubes and, 427
    origin of, in animal evolution, 643
    primate, 705
    prions and diseases of, 53, 369–70
    sensory organ transmission of information to, 954
    in thermoregulation, 856–57
    vertebrate, 688
Brakefield, Paul, 1167
Branches, phylogenetic tree, **506**, B:10–B:11
Branches, plant, **735**
Branching adaptations, animal surface-area, 852–53
Brassinosteroids, 210*t*, **812**, 813*t*
Bread mold, 305, 617. *See also Neurospora crassa*
Bread yeast. *See Saccharomyces cerevisiae*
Breathing. *See* Ventilation
Breeding. *See also* Artificial selection
    captive, 482–83, 1189–90
    selective, 257 (*see also* Crosses)
Brenner, Sydney, 310–11, B:25
Brewer's yeast. *See Saccharomyces cerevisiae*
Bridled goby fish, 1109–11
Briggs, Winslow, 799
Brine shrimp, 671
Bristlecone pine trees, 432*f*, 607, 732
Brittle stars, 684
Britton, Roy, 324

Broca, Paul, 944–45
Bronchi, **909**
Bronchioles, **909**
Bronstein, Judith, 1134
Brown algae, 7, 552*f*, 557, 568–69, 574. *See also* Algae
Brown fat cells, 118
Brown kiwis, 476
Brown tree snake, 1181
Brushtail possums, 1031*f*
Bryophytes (mosses), 580–81, 601–2, 824*f*–25
Bryozoans, 638*t*, 665
Buchner, Hans and Edward, 158
Buck, Linda, 966
Budding, animal, 654, 685, 688, **1014**
Budding, viral, 720, 721*f*
Buds, axillary and apical, 735
Buds, flower, 826
Buffers, pH, **30**, **916**
Buikema, Arthur, 1136–37
Building materials, 579–80
Bulbourethral gland, **1022**–23*f*
Bulbs, 739
Bulk flow, **762**
Bulk-phase endocytosis, **127**
Bundle-sheath cells, **193**–94, **766**
Burials, fossils and, 512
Bursa-dependent lymphocytes, 1043. *See also* B cells
Bursting, viral, 720, 721*f*
Butter, 86*f*
Buttercup root, 72*f*
Butterflies, 1091, 1112–13, 1129–30
Bypass vessels, 920–21

C

C-terminus, 46, 328
C_3 pathway, **193**
C_4 pathway, **193**–94, **766**
Cacti, 194, 736–37
Cactus mice, 835–36
Cadherins, **207**
Caecilians, 700
Caenorhabditis elegans. *See* Roundworms
Caffeine, 815
Calcium. *See also* Calcium ions
    animal bones and, 982–83
    in ecosystem nutrient cycles, 1156
    as human nutrient, 885*t*
    as plant nutrient, 780*t*
Calcium carbonate, 556–57, 572, 600, 981
Calcium ions
    as electrolytes, 862
    in polyspermy prevention, 421–23
    protein folding and, 53
    as second messengers, 213*t*
Calcium phosphate, 981
Calculators, scientific, B:9
Calibration, accuracy and, B:2–B:3
California mussel, 1137–38
Callus, **744**, B:22
Calmodulin, 53, 458
Calvin, Melvin, 178, 190–91
Calvin cycle, **178**, 190–95, 541, 766. *See also* Photosynthesis
Calyx, **826**
CAM (crassulacean acid metabolism), **194**–95, 766, **766**, 1070
Cambium, **748**–50

Cambrian explosion, **518**–20, **636**–37
cAMP (cyclic adenosine monophosphate; cyclic AMP), 213*t* **1009**–10
Cancer, **232**
    anticancer drugs, 607
    cell cultures of, B:21, B:22*f*
    chromosome mutations and, 314–15
    defective Ras proteins and, 214
    as family of diseases, 234
    from gene therapy for severe combined immunodeficiency (SCID), 384–85
    genetic basis of uncontrolled cell growth in, 361–63
    genetic testing for, 382
    homology and, 451
    loss of cell-cycle control and, 233–34
    mutations and, 298–301
    properties of cancer cells, 233
    retroviruses and, 728
    telomerase and, 297
    types and severity of, 232*t*
    types of cell division defects in, 232–33
Cannabis sativa, 828*f*
Cannibalization, mating and, 1020
Capillaries, **852**–53*f*, 873, **917**–18, 923
Capillarity, **761**
Capillary action, plant, 759, 761–62
Capillary beds, **917**–18
Caps, mRNA, 323–24
Capsaicin, 835–36
Capsids, **285**–86, **715**, 720
Captive breeding, 482–83, 1189–90
Carapace, **677**
Carbohydrates, **72**
    animal digestion and transportation of, 883, 888, 893–94
    cell characteristics and, 107
    cell identity functions of, 78–80
    energy storage functions of, 76, 80–81
    fermentation of, 540
    glucose production from, 155
    glycosylation of, to form glycoproteins, 124
    in metabolic pathways, 157–58
    monosaccharides, 73–75
    photosynthetic production of, 176–78 (*see also* Photosynthesis)
    polysaccharide types and structures, 77*t*
    polysaccharides, 75–78
    processing of, in photosynthesis, 195
    reduction of carbon dioxide to produce (*see* Calvin cycle)
    structural functions of, 76, 78, 117
    types of, 72–73
Carbon
    in amino acid structure, 42
    Calvin cycle fixation of, during photosynthesis (*see* Calvin cycle)
    in citric acid cycle, 162
    in ecosystem nutrient cycles, 1156
    electronegativity of, 21
    functional groups and atoms of, 37*t*
    lipids, hydrocarbons, and, 85–86
    in living organisms, 19
    in metabolic pathways, 157
    in net primary productivity, 1069
    in organic molecules, 36–38
    prokaryotic strategies for obtaining and fixing, 538–41
    in protein secondary structure, 48–49
    in redox reactions, 141–42
    simple molecules from, 23
Carbon–carbon bonds, 36

Carbon cycle, **614**
    global, 1161–62
    plants and, 579
    saprophytic fungi and, 614–15
    Sphagnum moss and, 602
Carbon dioxide
    animal gas exchange and, 902–3
    atmospheric, in global carbon cycle, 1161
    behavior of, in air, 903–4
    behavior of, in water, 904–5
    carbonic anhydrase protein and, 54
    covalent bonds of, 23
    end-Permian atmospheric, 521
    global climate change and, 556–57, 579, 1073
    land plants and, 584
    mechanisms for increasing concentration of, 193–95
    in origin-of-life experiments, 34–36
    oxidation of acetyl CoA to, in citric acid cycle, 162–65
    passage of, through stomata of leaves, 192–93
    photosynthetic carbohydrate production from, 177–78 (*see also* Photosynthesis)
    plant pathways to increase, in dry habitats, 766
    plant water loss and requirements for, 754–55
    in prokaryotic metabolism, 539*t*, 541
    in pyruvate processing, 161–62
    reduction of, in Calvin cycle (*see* Calvin cycle)
    transport of, in blood, 915–16
    in volcanic gases, 30
Carbon fixation, **190**, 541. *See also* Calvin cycle
Carbonic acid, 30
Carbonic anhydrase, 54, **890**, **915**–16
Carboniferous period, 582
Carbonyl functional group, 37*t*–38, 45–46, 48–49*f*, 73–74
Carboxy-terminus, 46, 328
Carboxyl functional group, 37*t*–38, 42, 45–46, 85–87, 162
Carboxylic acids, 37*t*, **162**
Carboxypeptidase, 895*t*
Cardiac cycle, **923**. *See also* Hearts
Cardiac muscle, 847*f*–48, 978
Cardiac tissue, 200*f*
Cardiovascular disease, **924**
Carnauba palms, 743
Carnivores, 579, **647**–48, **1128**
Carnivorous plants, **789**–90
Carotenes, 180–82
Carotenoids, **180**. *See also* Pigments, photosynthetic
    in photosynthesis, 180–82
    in sexual selection, 475–76
    synthesis of, by aphids, 485
Carpellate flowers, 827(*footnote*)
Carpels, **439**, **592**, **827**–28
Carrier proteins, **99**, **769**, **864**
    facilitated diffusion via, 99
    in osmoregulation, 864–65
    in translocation, 769–72
Carriers, recessive trait, **277**–78
Carrion flowers, 594
Carroll, Sean, 419, 649–50*f*, 660
Carrying capacity, **1108**–9*f*, 1112, 1130–31, 1189
Carson, Rachel, 999–1000, 1152–53
Cartilage, **689**, 846*f*, **847**, **981**–82
Cascades, regulatory gene, 413–14

Boldface page numbers indicate a glossary entry; page numbers followed by an *f* indicate a figure; those followed by *t* indicate a table.

Casein, 358
Casparian strip, **760**–61, 785
Casts, fossil, **512**
Catabolic pathways, **151**–52, 157. *See also* Anabolic pathways
Catalase, 115
Catalysis. *See also* Enzymes
    DNA as poor catalytic molecule, 64–65
    environmental factors affecting, 148
    enzyme helpers and, 147
    enzyme regulation and, 149–50
    enzymes and, 54
    eukaryotic organelles and, 110
    factors limiting rate of, 147
    of hydrolysis of carbohydrates to release glucose, 80–81
    lowering of activation energy in, 145–47
    nucleic acid polymerization and, 60–61
    polysaccharides and, 78
    RNA as catalytic molecule, 67–68
    smooth ER and, 114
    substrate positioning in, 144–45
Catalysts, 35–**36**, 144. *See also* Catalysis; Enzymes
Catalyze, **54**
Catastrophic events, habitat fragmentation and, 1179
Catecholamines, **1006**
Caterpillars, 818–19
Cation exchange, **781**–82
Cations, **22**f, 781–83
Causation, proximate and ultimate, 1083–84. *See also* Proximate causation; Ultimate causation
Cavali-Sforza, Luigi, 707
Cavities, body, 643–44
CD4 protein, **717**–78, **1048**
CD4⁺ T cells, 1048–50, 1054t
CD8 protein, **1048**
CD8⁺ T cells, 1048–50, 1052–53, 1054t
cDNA libraries, **372**–73, 381t
Cech, Thomas, 67–68
Cecum, **896**
Cedar Creek, 1150, 1185–86
Cell(s), **2**, 106–35. *See also* Animal cells; Plant cells
    animal anatomy and physiology at, 849f
    cancer and uncontrolled growth of, 233, 297, 361–63
    cell cycle of cell division of (*see* Cell cycle)
    cell theory and key concepts about, 2, 3–5, 106–7
    cultures of (*see* Cultures, cell and tissue)
    determination of, 427–29, 436–38
    developmental processes of, 406–8 (*see also* Development)
    eukaryotic vs. prokaryotic, 8, 107, 110t (*see also* Eukaryotic cells)
    functions of carbohydrates in, 78–80
    inserting genes into human, 383
    interactions between (*see* Cell–cell interactions)
    life cycles and diploid vs. haploid, 566–69
    lipid bilayers and first, 93–94
    living organisms and, 2–3
    microscopic images of, 3f
    microscopy in study of (*see* Microscopy)
    nucleus of (*see* Nucleus, cell)
    plasma membranes and intracellular enviroment of, 84, 100–101 (*see also* Plasma membranes)

protein functions in, 54
separating components of (*see* Centrifugation)
in top-down research approach to chemical evolution, 32
using microscopes to study structure of protist, 557–58
viral host (*see* Host cells)
vocabulary for describing chromosomal makeup of, 240t
water in living, 25
Cell adhesion proteins, 206–7
Cell body, **930**
Cell–cell attachments, 204–7, B:25
Cell–cell gaps, 207–9
Cell–cell interactions, 200–218. *See also* Chemical signaling
    connection and communication between adjacent cells, 204–9
    as developmental process, 406t, 407
    extracellular layers and, 201–4
    signaling between distant cells, 209–15
    signaling between unicellar organisms, 215–16
    for unicellular and multicellar organisms, 200–201
Cell–cell signaling
    carbohydrates in, 78–80
    chemical signals in, 992–93 (*see also* Chemical signaling)
    crosstalk and synthesizing input from many signals in, 215
    hormones and, in multicellular organisms, 209 (*see also* Hormones, animal)
    hormone structures and functions for, 210t
    in natural selection, 458–59f
    plant, 794–96
    proteins and, 54
    signal processing in, 210–14
    between unicellular organisms, 215–16
    in vegetative development, 436–38
Cell crawling, **129**
Cell cycle, **221**
    cancer as out-of-control cell division in, 232–34
    cell-cycle checkpoints and regulation of, 231–32
    cell division by meiosis and mitosis and cytokinesis in, 219–20
    cell replication in phases of, 220–23
    cytokinins and, 808
    discovery of cell–cell regulatory molecules, 229–31
    mitosis in M phase of, 223–29
    overview of, 223f
    regulation of, 229–32
Cell-cycle checkpoints, **231**–34
Cell-cycle control
    cancer and, 361–63
    cancer development from faulty, 233–34
    in cell division, 406
    checkpoints in, 231–32
    M phase–promoting factor in, 229–31
Cell death. *See* Apoptosis; Programmed cell death
Cell determination, 427–**29**, 436–38
Cell differentiation, 406t, **407**–10, 428f–29, 434–36, B:23
Cell division, **219**
    animal cytokinesis as, 128f–29 (*see also* Cytokinesis)
    bacterial, by binary fission, 228–29
    cancer and out-of-control, 232–34

cell cycle of, 219–20 (*see also* Cell cycle)
as developmental process, 406–7
plant, 433–34, 808
telomerase and somatic cell, 297
Cell-elongation responses, plant, 799–800
Cell expansion, 406t, 407
Cell extracts, B:17–B:18
Cell-fusion experiments, 229–30f
Cell homogenates, B:17–B:18
Cell identity, carbohydrates in, 78–80
Cell-mediated response, **1051**–53
Cell membranes. *See* Plasma membranes
Cell movement
    actin filaments and, 127–29
    as developmental process, 406t, 407
    flagella, cilia, and, 131–33
    gastrulation and, 424–26
    microtubules and vesicle transport, 129–31
    proteins and, 54
Cell plate, **228**
Cell proliferation, 406–8
Cell sap, **743**
Cell signaling. *See* Cell–cell signaling
Cell-surface hormone receptors, 1008–10
Cell theory, 2, **3**–6, 106
Cell walls, **76**, 109, **742**
    cellulose as structural polysaccharide in, 72f, 76, 78
    as characteristic of domains of life, 529t
    cohesion-tension theory and secondary, 762–63
    in cytokinesis, 228
    eukaryotic, 116, 117t
    ingestive feeding and, 563–64
    plant cell–cell attachments and, 204
    in plants, 76, 201–2, 580, 742, 745–46
    prokaryotic diversity in, 109, 529, 536–38
    protist, 562
Cellular respiration, **156**, 539
    aerobic vs. anaerobic respiration in, 170–72
    ATP, ADP, glucose, and metabolism in, 154–55
    ATP synthesis in, 166–72
    catabolic pathways of, 152
    citric acid cycle in, 162–65
    in energy flow, 1149
    evolution of, in prokaryotes, 538
    fermentation as alternative pathway to, 155, 172–73
    free energy changes in, 165f
    gas exchange and, 903
    in global carbon cycle, 1161–62f
    glucose oxidation in four-step process of, 155–56, 164–65
    glycolysis as processing of glucose to pyruvate in, 158–61
    in metabolism, 156–58
    overview of, 156f, 164f
    photosynthesis and, 177, 195
    processing of pyruvate to acetyl CoA in, 161–62
    prokaryotic, 538–40
    summary of, 164f, 171f
Cellular slime molds, 216, 569, B:23–B:25
Cellulases, 624, **891**
Cellulose, **76**, **745**
    bird digestion of, 889
    in cell walls, 202, 745
    fungal digestion of, 612–15, 623, 624

as plant structural polysaccharide, 72f, 76, 78
ruminant digestion of, 891
structure of, 77t
Cenozoic era, **515**
Census of Marine Life, 1175
Centipedes, 675
Central dogma of molecular biology, 307–9, 317–18
Central mutants, 435
Central nervous system (CNS), **643**, **929**
    brain in, 942, 944–46 (*see also* Brains)
    hormones and, 991–94, 1003–6 (*see also* Hormones, animal)
    neurons in, 929
    origin of, in animal evolution, 643
    spinal cord in, 942, 943–44
    vertebrate, 688
Centrifugation
    in discovery of Okazaki fragments, 293
    in estrogen receptor research, 1007
    in Hershey–Chase experiment, 286
    in Meselson–Stahl experiment, 289
    separating cell components with, 118–19, B:17–B:18
Centrioles, **129**, **224**, 226t
Centromeres, **220**, 221f, 223–26, **241**
Centrosomes, **129**, **224**, 226t
Cephalization, **643**, 929
Cephalochordates, **686**–87
Cephalopods, **662**, 669
Cerebellum, **688**, 944
Cerebral ganglion, 929
Cerebrum, **688**, **944**–46
Cervix, **1024**–25f
Cestodes, 666
Cetaceans, evolution of, 452–53
CFTR (cystic fibrosis transmembrane conductance regulator), 97–98, 867–68
Chaetae, **667**
Chagas disease, 555t
Chambers, heart, 919–21
Channel proteins, **98**, 769–72, **864**–65. *See also* Ion channels
Chaperone proteins, 360
Character displacement, **1127**–28
Characters, **506**. *See also* Phenotypes; Traits
Chargaff, Erwin, 61–62
Charophyceae (stoneworts), 582, 587, 600
Chase, Martha, 285–86
Checkpoints, cell-cycle, 231–34
Chelicerae, **678**
Chelicerae, **678**
Chemical bonds, **21**
    carbon–carbon, 36
    covalent, 21–23
    ionic, 22–23f
Chemical digestion, 888. *See also* Digestion, animal
Chemical energy, **31**
    carbohydrates in storage and release of, 80–81
    cellular respiration and, in fats and storage carbohydrates, 155 (*see also* Cellular respiration)
    in chemical reactions, 137–40f
    conversion of light energy to, in photosynthesis (*see* Photosynthesis)
    in energetic coupling of exergonic and endergonic reactions, 141–44
    as potential energy in chemical bonds, 31
    primary producers and, 1149–50
    secondary active transport and, 100

Chemical equilibrium, **30**
Chemical evolution, **18**–**40**
  atoms, ions, and molecules as building
    blocks of, 19–24
  biological evolution vs., 57–58
  chemical reactions, chemical energy,
    and, 30–32
  deep-sea hydrothermal vents and, 18f
  importance of carbon and organic
    molecules from, 36–38
  monosaccharides in, 73, 74
  nucleic acid formation by, 60–61
  nucleotide production by, 59
  Oparin–Haldane theory of, 41–42
  pattern and process components of
    theory of, 18–19
  polysaccharides and monosaccharides
    in, 78
  properties of water and early oceans as
    environments for, 25–30
  protein polymerization in, 44–45, 55
  proton-motive force in, 170
  research approaches and model
    systems for, 32–36
  RNA as first self-replicating molecule
    in, 57–58, 68–69
  switch from, to biological evolution, 19
Chemical modifications, post-
    translational, 332
Chemical reactions, **28**, 136–53
  acid-base reactions, 28–30
  chemical evolution conditions for, 30
  chemical structures and, B:13
  dynamics of, 30–31
  effects of temperature and concentra-
    tion on reaction rates of, 139–40f
  energetic coupling of exergonic and
    endergonic reactions in, 141–44
  energy transformations in, 31, 137–39
  enzyme catalysis of, 54, 144–47,
    150–52
  eukaryotic organelles and, 110
  factors affecting enzyme function in,
    148–50
  life, energy, enzymes, and, 136–37
  in origin-of-life experiments, 33–36
  plasma membranes and, 84
  rate of, in cells, 119
  spontaneous, 31–32
Chemical signaling
  in animals, 992–93 (see also
    Hormones, animal)
  in cell–cell interactions of
    development, 406t, 407
  in differential gene expression and
    body pattern formation, 410–15
Chemical structures, reading, B:12–B:13
Chemicals
  animal sensing of (see
    Chemoreception)
  biomagnification of, 1152–53
  as constitutive defenses, 1129f
  endocrine disruptors, 999–1000
  transfer of toxic, from human mother
    to fetus, 1033
Chemiosmosis, **169**–70, 186
Chemokines, **1040**–41, 1042t
Chemolithotrophs, **538**
Chemoorganotrophs, **538**–41
Chemoreception, **964**–67
  gustation (taste) as, 964–65
  olfaction (smell) as, 964, 965–67

Chemoreceptors, **953**
Chestnut blight, 613, 632, 815
Chewing, 888
Chiasmata (chiasma), **243**
Chicken-of-the-woods fungus, 612f
Childbirth, 1034
Chimpanzees, 705, 724–25, 1098,
    B:10–B:11
Chitin, **76**, 77t, 78, 618
Chitons, **662**, 669, 983
Chlamydiae, 544, 547
Chlamydia trachomatis, 547
Chlamydomonas reinhardii, B:25
Chloride cells, 866–67, 868
Chloride ions, 97–98, 862
Chlorophyll *a*, 180–81f
Chlorophyll *b*, 180–81f
Chlorophylls, 178, **180**–82, 796. See also
    Pigments, photosynthetic
Chloroplasts, **116**, **178**, **743**
  Calvin cycle in, 191
  in green plants, 580
  in moss cells, 176f
  origin of, in protists, 563–64
  photosynthesis in, 116, 117t, 118, 178–
    79f (see also Photosynthesis)
  phototropins and, 797
Choanocytes, **639**
Choanoflagellates
  animals and, 638–39
  fungi and, 619
Chocolate, fungi and, 614
Choice, behavioral, 1084–85
Cholecystokinin, **893**
Cholesterol, 87, 90, 91f, 995
Cholodny, N. O., 799
Cholodny–Went hypothesis, 799
Chondrichthyes, 698
Chordates, **426**, **686**
  body plans of, 686
  brains and spinal chords in, 427
  as deuterostomes, 682
  key lineages of invertebrate, 687–88
  notochords in, 426
  phylogenetic tree of, 638t, 690f
  subphyla of, 686–87
  vertebrate (see Vertebrates)
Chorion membrane, 694
Chromatids, **220**, 226t
Chromatin, **223**–26, **349**–53
Chromatin remodeling, 349–53
  bacterial vs. eukaryotic gene regulation
    and, 360–61t
  chromatin's basic structure and, 350–51
  in eukaryotic transcription initiation
    model, 356, 357f
  evidence for, in active genes, 351
  inheritance of chromatin
    modifications and, 352–53
  mechanisms of, 351–52
Chromatin-remodeling complexes, **352**,
    356, 357f
Chromatography, 180, 190–91,
    B:14–B:15
Chromosome theory of inheritance,
    266–79. See also Genetics;
    Mendelian genetics
  allele codominance and incomplete
    dominance in, 272, 273f
  exceptions and extensions to
    Mendelian rules in, 269–77t
  human inheritance in, 277–79

  importance of, 256–57
  linkage in, 270–71, 274f
  meiosis as explanation for Mendelian
    principles in, 266–67
  multiple allelism in, 271–72
  phenotypes vs. genotypes in, 273–75
  pleiotropic genes in, 272–73
  quantitative traits and polygenic
    inheritance in, 275–76
  sex linkage in, 268–69
  testing of, 267–69
Chromosomes, **107**, **220**. See
    also Chromosome theory
    of inheritance; DNA
    (deoxyribonucleic acid); Genes
  in characteristics of domains of life, 529t
  in chloroplasts, 116
  discovery of, 220
  eukaryotic, 112
  gene loci on, 266
  genetic maps of (see Genetic maps)
  Hox genes on, 414–15
  linkage and linked genes of,
    270–71, 274f
  in meiosis, 238
  in mitosis, 223–27
  mutations of, 314–15, 483–84
  nuclear lamina and, 119
  number of, found in some
    organisms, 223
  number of human, 238, 239
  prokaryotic, in nucleoids, 107–8
  sex (see Sex chromosomes)
  sister chromatids of, 239–40
  sympatric speciation by polyploidy in,
    497–99
  synthesis of telomeres of, 295–97
  types of, 238
  vocabulary for cell makeup of, 240t
Chrysanthemum, 815
Chymotrypsin, 895t
Chytrids, 617, 618, 625, 626f, 629
Cichlid jaws, 884–86
Cigarette smoke, 298
Cilia, **131**
  cell movement by, 132–33
  flagella vs., 131–32
  protist, 565–66
  rotifer, 665
Ciliates, 573
Circadian clock, **1089**–90
Circular chromosomes, 529t
Circulatory systems, **903**, 912–25
  blood pressure and blood flow in,
    923–25
  closed, 917–19
  hearts in, 919–23
  open, 916–17
  oxygen and carbon dioxide transport
    in blood of, 912–16
  respiratory systems and, in gas
    exchange and circulation, 902–3
    (see also Respiratory systems)
Cis surface, Golgi appartus, 113f–14,
    124–25
Cisternae, **113**–14, 124–25
Cisternal maturation, **125**
Citrate, 162
Citric acid, 632, 1023t
Citric acid cycle, 156, **162**–65
Citrulline, 305
Clades, **491**–93, **507**, 536, B:10–B:11.
    See also Lineages; Monophyletic
    groups
Cladistic approach (analysis), **507**–8
Cladograms, 508

Clams, 662, 668, 916–17
Class I and class II MHC proteins,
    1048–51
Classification, viral, 725–26
Clausen, Jens, 736
Clay, 781–82
Cleaner shrimp, 1133, 1134f
Cleavage, **423**–24, 660–61
Cleavage furrow, **228**
Cleaver, James, 299–300
Clefts, chemical structure, B:13
Clements, Frederick, 1136–37
Clements–Gleason dichotomy, 1136–37
Cliff swallows, 473
Climate, **1065**
  global change of (see Global climate
    change)
  global patterns in, 1065–67
  green plants, water, and moderation
    of, 578
  tree growth rings and research on, 751
  weather and, 1065, 1066
Climax community, **1136**
Clinton, Bill, 399
Clitoris, **1024**–25f
Cloaca, **878**–79, **897**, **1019**
Clonal selection theory, **1048**
Clones, **247**, **409**, **825**, **1014**
  asexual reproduction and, 247,
    825–26, 1014
  in clonal selection theory, 1048
  fungal, 625
  nuclear transfer techniques for
    creating, 409
Cloning vectors, **370**. See also Plasmids
Closed circulatory systems, **917**–19
Clostridium acetium, 539t, 540
Clotting, blood, 278
Club fungi, 617–18, 630. See also
    Basidiomycetes
Club mosses, 603
Clumped distribution, 1102
CNGB3 gene, 481–82
Cnidaria, 638t, 641, 653–54
Cnidocytes, **653**–54
Coal, 579, 582, 603
Coat color, mouse, 308, 309f, 313
Cocaine, 815
Cochlea, **956**–57
Coconut palms, 1106–7
Coding strands, DNA, 318–20f
Codominance, **272**, 277t
Codons, **310**
  in genetic code, 310–12
  in genome annotation, 392–93
  in mRNA specification of amino acids,
    325–26
  in point mutations, 313–14
  in ribosomal translation, 328–31
  in wobble hypothesis on types of
    tRNAs, 327–28
Coefficient of relatedness, **1096**
Coelacanths, 699, 964
Coelom, **644**, **658**
  formation of, in embryonic
    development, 644–45
  lophotrochozoan, 661
  origin of, in animal evolution, 643–44
  protostome vs. deuterostome, 658
Coelomates, **644**
Coenocytic fungi, **616**
Coenzyme A (CoA), 161–62
Coenzyme Q (ubiquinone), **166**–68
Coenzymes, **147**
Coevolution, 815, **830**, 831f, **1124**, 1132
Coevolutionary arms race, **1124**, 1132

Boldface page numbers indicate a glossary entry; page numbers followed by an
f indicate a figure; those followed by *t* indicate a table.

Coexistence, niche differentiation and, 1127–28
Cofactors, **147**, 166
Cognitive skills, Bloom's taxonomy of, B:29–B:30*t*
Cohen, Stephen, 671
Cohesins, 246
Cohesion, **26**, **762**
Cohesion-tension theory, 759, **762**–64
Cohorts, **1104**
Cold virus, 727
Coleochaetes, 600
Coleoptiles, **796**, 798–99
Collagen, 47, **202**–3
Collecting duct, 872–73, **877**–78
Collenchyma cells, **744**–45, 748*t*
Colon, **896**
Colonies, **639**, 665
Colonization. *See* Dispersal; Migration
Color, flower, 593–94, 595*f*, 826–27
Color blindness, 278–79, 481–82, 963–64
Colorimetric signals, B:16
Color variations, mutations and, 485
Coloration, cryptic, 1129*f*
Colorized scanning electron micrographs, 1037*f*
Comb jellies, 653
Commensalism, **1124**–25, 1136*t*
Commensal relationships, 620
Commercial applications, extremophiles and, 531
Common ancestry, 4–5, 8, 446, 449–51. *See also* Ancestral traits
Communication, animal, **1091**–95
Communication, intercellular. *See* Cell–cell gaps; Cell–cell signaling
Communication, plant, 817–18
Communities, **1061**, **1123**
  biodiversity and stability of, 1186–87
  community ecology and, 1060*t*, 1061, 1123 (*see also* Community ecology)
  disturbance regimes in, 1138–39
  effects of global climate change on, 1182
  environmental sequencing (metagenomics) of, 395
  genetic diversity of, 1173–74
  key attributes of, 1135
  keystone species in, 1137–38
  post-disturbance succession in, 1139–42
  predictability of, 1135–37
  structure of, 1135–38
Community ecology, 1123–47
  communities in, 1060*t*, 1061, 1123 (*see also* Communities)
  community dynamics in, 1138–42
  community structure in, 1135–38
  global patterns in species richness in, 1142–45
  species interactions in, 1124–35, 1136*t*
Companion cells, **747**, **767**
Comparative genomics, 638, 640
Comparative morphology, 638–39
Compartmentalization, eukaryotic cell, 110
Compass orientation, migration and, **1089**–90
Competition, **1124**, 1125–28
  in ant behavior, 1083–84
  as biotic factor in geographic distribution and abundance of organisms, 1062
  competitive exclusion principle of, 1125–26

experimental studies of, 1126
fitness and impacts of, 1136*t*
fitness trade-offs in, 1126–27
giraffe necks and food vs. sexual, 9–11
intraspecific vs. interspecific, 1125
male-male, 476–77
niche differentiation and mechanisms of coexistence vs., 1127–28
niches and, 1125
as threat to biodiversity, 1178
Competitive exclusion principle, **1125**–26
Competitive inhibition, **149**
Complement system proteins, 54, **1052**
Complementary base pairing, **63**, **287**. *See also* Nitrogenous bases, nucleotide
  DNA double helix model and, 63
  in mistakes in DNA synthesis, 298–99
  polysaccharides and, 78
  RNA secondary structure and, 65–66
  transcription factors and, 355–56
  in wobble hypothesis on types of tRNAs, 327–28
Complementary DNAs (cDNAs), **370**, 372, 401–2, **720**
Complementary strand, DNA, **64**
Complete digestive tracts, **886**–87
Complete metamorphosis, **672**
Complex tissues, plant, 746
Complexes I–IV (of electron transport chain), 167*f*–68*t*
Complexity, evolution and, 460
Compound eyes, **675**, **960**
Compound leaves, 737–38*f*
Compound light microscopes, B:18
Compression fossils, 512
Compression-resisting elements, 201
Computer programs
  asteroid impact models, 522
  genetic drift simulations, 479
  global climate change models, 1073
  in parsimony analysis, 508
Concentration
  hormone, 995–96
  reactant, 139–40*f*
Concentration gradients, **92**, **862**
  in diffusion and osmosis across lipid bilayers, 91–93
  electrochemical gradients as, 97 (*see also* Electrochemical gradients)
  morphogen, 411–12
Concept maps, B:28
Concurrent exchange, 907*f*
Condensation, chromosome, 246
Condensation reactions, **45**, 59–61, 75–76. *See also* Dehydration reactions
Condensed replicated chromosomes, 220, 221*f*, 223
Condoms, 722, 1030*t*
Conducting cells, plant, 760. *See also* Phloem tissue; Xylem tissue
Conduction, heat exchange and, **855**
Cones, eye, **960**–64
Cones, gymnosperm, 592, 607
Confocal microscopy, B:20
Conformational homeostasis, 853
Connections, intercellular. *See* Intercellular connections
Connective tissue, **847**, 848*f*
Connell, Joseph, 1126, 1127*f*
Conservation, soil, 779–81
Conservation biology, **1061**. *See also* Biodiversity
  addressing ultimate causes of biodiversity losses in, 1189

bioremediation in, 151, 533, 632
conservation of ecosystem function in, 1191–93
conservation of genetic diversity, populations, and species in, 1189–91
ecology and, 1061
estimating biodiversity using surveys in, 1175
genetic drift in, 479
mapping of biodiversity in, 1176–77
phylogenetic species concept and, 492–93
population ecology in preservation of endangered species by, 1118–20
population growth equations in, 1110*f*–11*f*
predator-removal programs in, 1130–31
predicting extinctions in, 1182–84
preservation of phylogenetically distinct species by, 1174
Conservation International, 1177
Conservative, genetic code as, 312
Conservative replication, DNA, 287–89
Constant (C) regions, **1045**–46
Constitutive defenses, **1129**–30
Constitutive mutants, **340**–41
Constitutive transcription, **338**
Constraints, natural selection, 461–62
Consumers, **1150**
  animals as, 637, 647–49
  as biocontrol agents, 1133
  biomagnification in, 1152–53
  top-down control by, and trophic cascades, 1153, 1154*f*
  in trophic structure, 1150–52
Consumption, **1124**, 1128–33
  adaptation and arms races in, 1132
  constitutive defenses against, 1129–30
  consumers as biocontrol agents and, 1133
  efficiency of predators at reducing prey populations by, 1130–31
  fitness and impacts of, 1136*t*
  human, of resources, 1164, 1189
  inducible defenses against, 1130, 1131*f*
  limitations on herbivore, 1131–32
  parasite manipulation of hosts in, 1132–33
  types of, 1128
Continental shelf, **1079**
Continents, in time line of life, 515–16
Continuous data, graphing, B:4–B:6
Continuous population growth, 1110*f*–11*f*
Continuous strands, **292**
Contraception, human, **1029**–30
Contractile proteins, 54
Contraction, muscle. *See* Muscle contraction
Control groups, 13, B:6–B:7
Convection, heat exchange and, **855**
Convention on Biological Diversity (CBD), 1189
Convergent evolution, **508**–10, 642–43, 986
Conversions, metric unit to English unit, B:1*t*
Cooperation, 1098. *See also* Altruism; Mutualism(s)
Cooperative binding, 912, **913**–14
Copepods, 677, 1167
Copper, as plant nutrient, 777–78, 785
Coprophagy, **896**
Copulation, 1019. *See also* Mating

Copulatory plugs, 1022
Copying
  DNA, 64, 287–89 (*see also* DNA synthesis)
  RNA, 67
Coral polyps, 650
Coral-reef fish, 1109–11
Coral reefs, **1079**
  communities of, 1123*f*
  impacts of global climate change on, 1167–68, 1182
  in ocean biomes, 1079
  red algae and, 572
  sea stars and, 685
Corals, 653–54, 1166*t*
Co-receptors, viral, **718**
Core enzymes, **319**
Cork cambium, **748**, 750
Cork cells, **750**
Corms, **825**
Corn, 5–6, 385, 392, 579, 828*f*
Cornea, **960**, 961*f*
Corolla, flower, **827**
Corona, **665**
Corpus callosum, **944**
Corpus luteum, **1027**
Corridors, wildlife, 1120, 1190, 1191*f*
Cortex, kidney, **872**
Cortex, plant root, **759**–61
Cortex, plant shoot, **742**
Cortical granules, 422
Corticosteroids, 1055
Corticotropin-releasing hormone (CRH), **1004**
Cortisol, 995, **1000**–1001
Costanza, Robert, 1187
Costa Rica, ecotourism in, 1192
Cost, of animal locomotion, 986, 987*f*, 988
Cost-benefit analysis, **1084**–87, 1093, 1134–35
Cotransport. *See* Secondary active transport (cotransport)
Cotransporters, **770**, **864**
  in animal glucose transport, 893–94
  in osmoregulation, 864–65, 867–68
  in plant nutrient uptake, 784
  resting potential and, 931
Cotton, 579
Cotyledons, **434**–35, **596**, **833**–34, 837
Countercurrent exchangers, 857–58, 875, 907
Covalent bonds, **21**
  in chemical structures, B:12–B:13
  nonpolar and polar, of molecules, 21–23*f*
  in organic molecules, 36, 38
  protein tertiary structure and, 49–50*f*
  single, double, and triple, 23
Covalent modifications, enzyme regulation via, 149–50
Cowpox, 1054–55
Coyne, Jerry, 500
Crabs, 677, 1130, 1131*f*
Crane, Peter, 1187
Cranium, **688**
Crassulacean acid metabolism (CAM), **194**–95, 766, **766**, 1070
Create (Bloom's taxonomy skill), B:29*f*–B:30*t*
Creemers, Raymond, 1104–5
Crenarchaeota, 544, 548
Creosote bushes, 825
Crescent-tail bigeyes, 1101*f*
Cress. *See* Mustard plant
Cretaceous mass extinction, 521–23

Crews, David, 1087–88
Crick, Francis
   adaptor molecule hypothesis of, for mRNA specification of amino acids, 325–26
   articulation of central dogma of molecular biology by, 308
   discovery of double helix secondary structure of DNA by, 57f, 61–63, 286–87
   genetic code hypothesis of, 307
   triplet code hypothesis experiments of, 310–11
   wobble hypothesis of, on types of tRNAs, 327–28
Crickets, 843–45
Cristae, 115, 161, 166–68
Cro protein, 50–51f
Crocodiles, 703, 882f
Cro-Magnons, 707
Crop, bird, 889
Crops, transgenic. See Transgenic plants
Cross-links, concept map, B:28
Cross-pollination, 830
Crosses (cross fertilization), 257–58, B:25–B:26. See also Dihybrid crosses; Monohybrid crosses; Reciprocal crosses; Testcrosses
Crossing over, 243
   calculating frequencies of, for genetic maps, 274f
   chromosome exchange by, 243
   genetic variation from, 248, 249f
   role of, in chromosome theory of inheritance, 270–71
   unequal, 397–98
Crosstalk, 215, 814–15
Crustaceans, 677, 917, 983
Cryoelectron tomography, of mitochondrion, 161f
Cryptic coloration, 1129f
Cryptic female choice, 1020
Cryptic species, 491
Crystal lattice, ice, 27f
Ctenophora, 638f, 641, 653
Cultural services, ecosystem, 1187t, 1188
Cultures, cell and tissue, 122
   animal and plant, B:21–B:22
   in anthrax research, 532
   in cytokinin research, 807
   discovery of gap phases with, 221–22
   in DNA nucleotide excision repair research, 299–300
   genetic equivalence in differentiated plant cells and, 408
   for model organisms, B:23
   in prokaryotic research, 534, 540
   in pulse-chase experiments, 122
Cupressophyta, 607
Curve-billed thrashers, 835–36
Curved lines, scatterplot, B:5
Cushing's disease, 1004
Cushman, J. Hall, 1134–35
Cuticle, 670, 743, 870
   as defense barrier, 815, 1038
   fossilized, 581–82
   water loss prevention by, 584–85, 765–66, 869–71
Cuticle
   of roundworm as model organism, B:25
Cuttings, plant, 438, 736f, 744
Cuttlefish, 669

Cuvier, Baron George, 447
Cyanobacteria, 542
   as bacterial lineage, 544, 545
   chloroplasts and photosynthesis of, 564–65
   in lichens, 598, 623, 631
   metabolic diversity and, 539t
   photosystems in, 184
   prokaryotic oxygen revolution and, 541–42
Cycads, 606
Cyclic adenosine monophosphate (cyclic AMP; cAMP), 213t, 1009–10
Cyclic electron flow, Z-scheme model, 189
Cyclic guanosine monophosphate (cGMP), 213t, 214, 962
Cyclic photophosphorylation, 189
Cyclin-dependent kinase (Cdk), 230, 234
Cyclins, 230, 234, 360
Cyclostomata hypothesis, 691
Cysteine, 49, 308, 324
Cystic fibrosis (CF), 97–98, 867–68
Cystic fibrosis transmembrane regulator (CFTR), 867–68
Cytochrome c, 167, 168t
Cytochrome complex, 185, 189
Cytochromes, 166–67
Cytokines, 992, 1040–41, 1042t, B:22
Cytokinesis, 129, 220, 243
   as animal cell division, 128f–29
   daughter cells resulting from, 227–29
   mitosis, meiosis, and, 220, 223, 225f, 243–44
Cytokinins, 807–8, 813t
Cytoplasm, 109. See also Cytosol
   cleavage of, 423–24
   cytokinesis as division of, 220, 223, 227–29 (see also Cytokinesis)
   prokaryotic, 109
   protein synthesis in, 119–20
Cytoplasmic determinants, 423
Cytoplasmic streaming, 129
Cytosine, 58–59, 61–63, 65–66, 287
Cytoskeletons, 109
   eukaryotic, 116, 117t, 127–32, 204
   prokaryotic, 109
   prokaryotic vs. eukaryotic, 110t
   protist, 562
Cytosol, 110, 129, 159, 164f. See also Cytoplasm
Cytotoxic T cells, 1050–53, 1054t

D

Daddy longlegs, 678
Dalton, 20
Dalton, John, 963–64
Daltonism, 963(footnote)
Damaged DNA
   in cancer, 362–63
   cell-cycle checkpoints and, 231–32
   repair of, 299–301
Damschen, Ellen, 1190
Dance hypothesis, honeybee language, 1092–93
Danielli, James, 94–96f
Daphnia, 1014–16, 1167
Darwin, Charles
   experiments of, on gravitropic response, 803–4
   experiments of, on phototropic response, 796, 797–98

on pollination, 830
postulates of, on natural selection, 453–54
on sexual selection, 475
on speciation, 489
testing of postulates of, 456
theory of evolution by natural selection by, 5, 444, 446
Darwin, Francis, 796, 797–98, 803–4
Data, graphing, B:4–B:6
Data, scientific, 9–10
Data matrix, phylogenetic, 506–8
Data points, graph, B:4–B:5
Databases, genome, 390, 392
Databases, online scientific literature, B:27
Dating, geological, 572
Dating, radiometric, 446–47, 453, 513
Daughter cells
   in meiosis, 240–45
   in mitosis, 223–26
Daughter strands, DNA, 287–89
Davson, Hugh, 94–96f
Day length, mating and, 1087–88
Day-neutral plants, 802
DDT (dichlorodiphenyltrichloroethane), 1152–53
Deactivation, cell–cell signal, 214
Deactivation, M phase-promoting factor, 231
Dead space, 910
Dead zones, 544, 1160
Death, cell. See Apoptosis; Programmed cell death
Death, plant, 812–13
Death rates, animal, 1103–7, 1108, 1109, 1118, 1119f. See also Survivorship
Death rates, human, 473, 1034
Deceitful communication, animal, 1094–95
Deciduous plants, 606, 1071
Decisions, behavioral, 1084–85
Decomposer food chains, 1150
Decomposers, 564, 1150
   fungal, 612–15, 623–24, 629
   nutrient cycling rates and, 1156–57
   plasmodial slime molds as, 570
   protist, 574
   in trophic structure, 1150–51
Decomposition rates, 1156–57
De-differentiation, cell, 407, 438
Deep-sea hydrothermal vents. See also Chemical evolution; Origin-of-life research
   chemical evolution conditions at, 18f, 30, 74
   nucleic acid polymerization at, 60
   photosynthesis at, 541
   proton-motive force and chemical evolution at, 170
   ribose problem and, 59
   in surface metabolism model of chemical evolution, 33, 35–36
Deep sequencing, 400–402
Deepwater Horizon oil spill, 1059f
Deer, 478f
Defense, protein functions in, 54
Defense responses, plant
   epidermis as barrier, 743
   to herbivore attacks, 817–19
   noxious compounds in vacuoles and, 115
   overview of, 818t
   to pathogens, 815–17
   poor herbivore nutrition as, 1131–32
Defenses, constitutive (or standing), 1129–30

Definition, species, 490–92
Definitive hosts, 666
Deforestation
   erosion from, 779–81
   and global carbon cycle, 1160
   habitat destruction by, 1179
   loss of biodiversity from, 1172–73
   nutrient cycling and, 1158–59
   reducing emissions from, 1192–93
Degeneration hypothesis, 723
Dehydration, human, 843
Dehydration reactions, 45, 75–76, 86–87
De Jong, Peter, 1167
Deleterious alleles, 471–72, 484
Deleterious mutations, 313
Deletions, chromosome, 314
De Meester, Luc, 1167
Demography, 1103–7
Denaturation, DNA, 375–76
Denatured proteins, 52
Dendrites, 847, 930
Dendritic cells, 1048–50
Dense connective tissue, 846t, 847
Density, water, 26–27, 28t
Density-dependent population growth, 1108–12
Density-gradient centrifugation, 289, 1007
Density-independent population growth, 1107–8, 1109
Dental disease, 531
Deoxyribonucleic acid (DNA). See DNA (deoxyribonucleic acid)
Deoxyribonucleoside triphosphates (dNTPs), 290
Deoxyribonucleotides, 58–59, 285–87. See also Nucleotides
Deoxyribonucleotide triphosphates (dNTPs), 377–78
Deoxyribose, 58–60, 78
Dependent assortment, 264f–65
Dependent variables, graphing, B:4–B:6
Dephosphorylation, 150, 332
Depolarization, 933–35
Depolarized membranes, sensory transduction and, 953–54
Deposit feeders, 648, 662f, 884
Derived traits, 506, B:10–B:11. See also Synapomorphies
Dermal tissue systems, plant, 740
   embryogenesis and, 833
   primary plant body and tissues of, 740, 742, 748t
   protection of surfaces by epidermal cells in, 743
   regulation of gas exchange and water loss by stomata in, 743–44
   trichomes in, 744
Descartes, René, 973
Descendent groups, phylogenetic trees and, B:10–B:11
Descending limb, loop of Henle, 876, 878t
Descent from common ancestors. See Common ancestry
Descent with modification, 5, 446
Desert gerbils, 1086–87
Desert locust, 869
Deserts
   rain shadows and, 1066–67
   subtropical, 1070
Design, experimental, 11–14, B:28
Desmosomes, 205f, 206
Detergents, 96
Determination, cell, 427–29, 436–38
Detritivores, 647–48, 1150

Boldface page numbers indicate a glossary entry; page numbers followed by an *f* indicate a figure; those followed by *t* indicate a table.

Detritus, **564**, **1077**, **1150**–51, 1156–57
Deuterostomes, **644**, **681**–710
  chordates, 686–88
  echinoderms, 682–86f
  embryonic development of, 681
  origin of, in animal evolution, 644–45
  phylogenetic tree of, 638t, 682f
  primates and hominins, 704–8
  protostomes vs., 658
  vertebrates, 688–703 (see also Vertebrates)
Devegetation, nutrient cycling and, 1158–59
Development, 405–18. See also Animal development; Plant development
  challenges of embryonic, 405–6
  evolutionary change from changes in gene expression in, 416
  five essential processes of, 406t
  genetic equivalence and differential gene expression in, 408–10
  model organisms in, B:25–B:26
  shared processes of, 406–8
  triggering of differential gene expression by chemical signals in, 410–15
Developmental biology, 405–6, B:25–B:26. See also Development
Developmental homologies, **450**
Devonian explosion, 520
Diabetes mellitus, **897**
  chromatin remodeling and, 352–53
  cytotoxic T cells and type 1, 1056
  insulin and types of, 369, 897–99
Diacylglycerol (DAG), 213t
Diaphragm, vertebrate, **910**
Diaphragms, contraceptive, 1030t
Diarrhea, 555t, 727, 896
Diastole, **923**
Diastolic blood pressure, **923**
Diatomaceous earth, 574
Diatoms, 556, 574
Dicots, **596**
Dictyostelium, 216, 569
Dictyostelium discoideum (cellular slime mold), B:23–B:25
Dideoxyribonucleoside triphosphates (ddNTPs), 377–78
Dideoxy sequencing, **377**
  in genetic engineering, 381t
  Huntington's disease gene search and, 381–82
  value of, 376–78
Diencephalon, **944**
Diet, animal and human, 883–84, 885t. See also Animal nutrition
Dietary fiber, 78
Differential centrifugation, **118**–19, B:17–B:18. See also Centrifugation
Differential gene expression, **349**
  body axes and, 410
  in cell differentiation, 409–10
  eukaryotic gene regulation and, 349
  evolutionary conservation of chemical signals and regulatory genes in, 414–15
  morphogens in setup of body axes in, 410–12
  multiple uses of regulators in, 415
  regulatory genes and body positional information in, 412–14
  regulatory transcription factors in, 354–56
  transcriptional control as, in development, 409–10

Differentiation, 406t, **407**–10, 428f–29, 434–36. See also Cell differentiation
Diffusion, **92**, **862**. See also Facilitated diffusion; Osmosis
  across lipid bilayers, 91–92
  across prokaryotic cell walls, 109
  gas exchange by, 905–6, 916
  in osmoregulation, 862, 863f
  as passive transport, 101f
  skin-breathing and, 852
  surface area adaptions for, 852–53
Diffusion spectrum imaging, 928f
Digestion, animal, **886**–97. See also Animal nutrition
  carbohydrate hydrolysis by digestive enzymes in, 81
  complete human digestive tract in, 887f
  dietary fiber and human, 78
  digestive processes in, 888
  digestive tracts in, 886–87
  large intestine in, 896–97
  of lipids in small intestine, 895f
  lysosomes and, 114
  mammalian digestive enzymes in, 895t
  mouth and esophagus in, 888–89
  pancreatic enzymes and, 118
  plant proteinase inhibitors and, 817
  small intestine in, 892–96
  as step in animal nutrition, 883f
  stomachs in, 889–92
Digestion, fungal, 623–24
Digestive processes, animal, 888
Digestive system, human, 848f
Digestive tracts, **886**–87
Digits, significant figures and metric system, B:2–B:3
Dihybrid crosses, **263**–65
Dikaryotic fungi, **624**–25
Dimers, 50–51f, **129**
Dinoflagellates, 555–56, 573
Dinosaurs
  birds as, 694–95, 703
  flying, 517
  mass extinction of, 515, 521–23
Dioecious species, **827**, 828f
Diploblasts, **640**–41
Diploid cells, life cycles dominated by, 566–69
Diploid number, 240t
Diploid organisms, **239**, 240t
Diplomonads, 571
Dipnoi, 699
Direct sequencing, **535**, **557**
  studying fungi with, 615
  studying prokaryotes with, 535
  studying protists with, 558–59
Directed-pollination hypothesis, 593–94
Directional selection, **472**–73, 475t
Disaccharides, **75**–76
Discontinuous replication hypothesis, 292
Discontinuous strands, DNA. See Lagging strands, DNA
Discrete data, graphing, B:4–B:6
Discrete population growth, 1110f–11f
Discrete traits, **275**, 277t
Discussion, primary literature, B:27t
Diseases, animal
  fungal, 628–29
  in herbivore populations, 1131
  prions and, 53
  viral, 726–28
Diseases, plant
  fungal, 613, 632
  viral, 715–16, 727–28

Diseases and disorders, human
  achromatopsia from genetic bottleneck, 481–82
  allergies, 1055–56
  anthrax, 532
  autoimmune, 1056
  bacterial, 531t, 545–47
  beriberi, 147
  blindness from vitamin A deficiencies, 385
  cancer (see Cancer)
  cardiovascular disease and arteriosclerosis, 924
  caused by protists, 554–56
  color blindness, 278–79
  Cushing's disease, 1004
  cystic fibrosis, 97–98, 867–68
  diabetes mellitus (see Diabetes mellitus)
  diarrhea, 896
  elephantiasis, 919, 1037f
  emerging viruses and emerging, 723–25
  food poisoning, 532
  fungal, 613, 618, 628, 632
  from gas exchange and circulation failures, 903
  gene therapy for, 383–85
  genetic, 277–79
  genetic bottlenecks and, 481–82
  genetic testing for, 382
  germ theory of, 532
  hemophilia, 278
  HIV/AIDS (see AIDS [acquired immune deficiency syndrome]; HIV [human immunodeficiency virus])
  Huntington's disease, 278, 378–82
  hypertension, 923
  hypophosphatemia (vitamin D–resistant rickets), 279
  immunodeficiency, 1056
  malaria, 573, 1132
  Marfan syndrome, 272–73
  multiple sclerosis (MS), 937–38, 1056
  muscular dystrophy, 200f
  myocardial infarctions, 925
  nematodes and, 674
  neurodegenerative, 408
  organs and systems parasitized by viral, 713f
  phenylketonuria, 273
  pituitary dwarfism, 369–70
  polymerase chain reaction and inherited, 376
  prions and spongiform encephalopathies, 53
  prokaryotes and, 531–33
  proteins in defense against, 54
  protostomes and, 658
  red-green color blindness, 963–64
  rheumatoid arthritis, 1056
  severe combined immunodeficiency (SCID), 383–84, 1056
  sickle-cell disease, 48, 278
  smallpox, 715, 726
  systems biology and, 402
  trypanosomiasis, 1062
  ulcers, 891
  vaccination, immunization, and, 1054–55
  viral, 712–13, 726–28
  whole-genome sequencing and, 392
  xeroderma pigmentosum (XP), 299–301

Dispersal, **1063**
  allopatric speciation by, 494–95
  in geographic distribution and abundance of species, 1062–63
  patterns of, for populations, 1102–3
  seed, 834–36
Dispersive replication, DNA, 288f, 289
Disruptive selection, **473**–74, 475t, 496–97
Dissecting microscopes, B:18
Distal tubule, 872, **877**–78
Distortion, experimental, 13
Distribution, biodiversity, 1176–77
Distribution, population, 1102–3
Distribution, reference, B:7
Distribution of organisms. See Geographic distribution and abundance of organisms
Disturbance regimes, **1138**–39, 1145, 1175, 1178, 1191–92
Disturbances, **1138**–39
Disulfide bonds, 38, **49**–50f
Dittmer, Howard, 733
Divergence, genetic. See Genetic divergence
Diversification
  in adaptive radiations, 516
  animal, 646–52
  of animal feeding strategies, 648–49
  in Cambrian explosion, 518–20
  fungal, 619–28
  land plant, 583–97f
  prokaryotic, 536–44
  protist, 559–69
  protostome, 657–58
  viral, 722–25
Diversity. See also Biodiversity; Species diversity
  adaptive immune response, 1042
  of animal large intestines, 896–97
  of animal mouthparts, 884–86
  antibody, 1045–46
  ecological, of prokaryotes, 541–44
  fungal, 615
  of hearts, 919, 920f
  in testes size, 1020
  of vertebrate lungs, 909
  viral, 712
Division, cell. See Cell division
Dixon, Henry, 762
Dll gene, 649–50f
DNA (deoxyribonucleic acid), **58**. See also Nucleic acids; RNA (ribonucleic acid)
  amplification of, with polymerase chain reaction, 374–76
  cancer from damage to, 362–63
  cell-cycle checkpoints and damaged, 231–32
  in central dogma of molecular biology, 307–9
  in characteristics of domains of life, 529t
  chromosomes, genes, and, 220 (see also Chromosomes; Genes)
  cloning of, 370, 374–76
  comparing *Homo sapiens* and *Homo neanderthalensis*, 376
  components of, 58–59
  in condensed chromatin as protected from DNase enzyme, 351
  damage. See Damaged DNA
  dedeoxy sequencing of, 376–78
  directionality of strands of, 59–60
  discovery of, as genetic material in genes, 284–86, 304

DNA (deoxyribonucleic acid)
(*continued*)
discovery of double helix secondary
structure of, 61–63, 286–87
electron micrograph of, 317*f*
eukaryotic, 112
expression of (*see* Gene expression)
as genetic information–containing
molecule, 64
metabolic pathways and, 157
methylation of, 351
mitochondrial, 115–16
model of condensed eukaryotic, 348*f*
mutations in, 483–84
next-generation technologies for
sequencing of, 378
in nucleus, 119–20
physical model of, 57*f*, 62*f*
polymerization of
deoxyribonucleotides to
form, 59–61
as poor catalytic molecule, 64–65
primary structure and secondary
structure of, 286*f*
prokaryotic, 107–8
as probe(s), 372–73, 381*t*, 401–2,
B:15–B:16
prokaryotic vs. eukaryotic, 110*t*
repair of damaged, 297–99
RNA structure vs. structure of, 66*t*
using restriction endonucleases and
DNA ligase to cut and paste,
370–72
visualizing, B:15–B:16
DNA cloning, 370, 374–76
DNA fingerprinting, 397–98*f*
DNA helicase, 290–91, 294*t*
DNA libraries, 372–73, 381*t*
DNA ligases, 293–94*t*, 370, 371–72, 380*t*
DNA methylation, 351
DNA methyl-transferases, 351
DNA microarrays, 400–402
DNA polymerases, 289
in DNA synthesis, 289–94*t*, 295
in genetic engineering, 380*t*
in polymerase chain reaction, 374–76
proofreading by, 297
RNA polymerases vs., 318
in telomere synthesis, 295–96
DNA sequences
cancer and regulatory, 363
in genetic code, 310–12
genetic homology and, 450–51
phylogenies based on, 510, 511*f*,
558–59
regulatory, in transcription initiation,
353–54
silent mutations in, as nonadaptive
traits, 461
transcription factors and specific,
355–56
DNA sequencing, 376–78. *See also*
Whole-genome sequencing
DNA synthesis, 284–303
comprehensive model of, 289–95
correcting mistakes in, 298–99
in dideoxy sequencing, 377–78
discovery of DNA as genetic material
in genes and, 284–86
discovery of secondary structure of
DNA and, 286–87
DNA polymerase in, 289–90

electron micrograph of, 284*f*
opening and stabiliizing of double
helix in, 290–91
process of, 64
proteins required for bacterial, 294*t*
repairing damaged DNA and
correcting mistakes in, 297–301
starting of replication in, 290
synthesis of lagging strand in, 292–95
synthesis of leading strand in, 291–92
telomere replication in, 295–97
testing of early hypotheses about DNA
replication and, 287–89
xeroderma pigmentosum (XP) case
study of damaged DNA, 299–301
DNA viruses, 715–16, 726, 726*f*
DNase enzyme, 351
Dogs, life cycle of, 241–42
Dolly (cloned sheep), 409
Dolphins, 452–53, 509–10, 985, 986
Domains, taxonomic, 7*f*, 8, 107, 528–29
Dominant alleles, 258*t*, 272, 273*f*, 277*t*
Dominant traits, 259. *See also* Recessive
traits
codominance and incomplete
dominance of, 272, 273*f*, 277*t*
human, 277–79
Huntington's disease as, 378
in Mendelian genetics, 259–60
Dopamine, 941*t*
Dormancy, plant, 751
Dormancy, seed, 808, 809–10, 836–37
Dormancy, viral, 721–22
Dorsal body axis, 410
Dorsal hollow nerve cord, 686
Dot-to-dot lines, scatterplot, B:5
Double bonds, 23
Double fertilization, plant, 593, 832–33
Double helix secondary structure, DNA,
62, 286
discovery of, 61–63, 286–87
electron micrograph of, 284*f*
opening and stabiliizing of, in DNA
synthesis, 290–91, 294*t*
transcription factors and, 355–56
Double-stranded DNA (dsDNA)
viruses, 726
Double-stranded RNA (dsRNA)
viruses, 727
Double-stranded viruses, 716, 726–27
Doubly compound leaves, 737–38*f*
Doughnut-shaped proteins, 47*f*
Doushantuo microfossils, 518
Downstream DNA, 319
Drag, animal locomotion and, 985
Drosophila bifurca. See Fruit flies
Drosophila melanogaster. See Fruit flies
Drought, natural selection in Galápagos
finches and, 456–59*f*
Drugs. *See also* Diseases and disorders,
human; Medicine
anti-AIDS, 309
anticancer, 607
anti-HIV, 719, 720
antiviral, 714, 719, 722
beta-blocker, 210
derived from green plants, 580
derived from land plants, 580*t*
ephedrine, 608
evolution of bacterial resistance to,
454–56
fungal infections and fungicides, 618

fungi in production of, 629, 632
homology and, 451
plants and, 580
resistance to, 532–33
Dryer, W. J., 1046
Dry habitats
carbon dioxide concentration
mechanisms for, 193–95
gas exchange in, 905
plant adaptations to, 754–55, 757–58,
765–66
Drying, seed maturation and, 834
Dscam gene, 358
Duero river hydroelectric dam, 154*f*
Duplications, chromosome, 314
Dusky seaside sparrow, 492–93
Dutch elm disease, 632, 1063
Dwarf plants, defective gibberellin in,
808–9
Dwarfism, pituitary. *See* Pituitary
dwarfism
Dyes, microscopy, B:18
Dynamite tree, 834–35
Dynein, 133
Dysentery, 555*t*
Dystrophin, 200*f*

E

E site, ribosome, 328–29*f*
E2F protein, 234
Eardrums, 956
Early endosome, 126
Early prophase I, 242, 244
Ear ossicles, 956
Ears, mammalian, 955–58
Earthworms, 658, 659
Ebola virus, 723, 728
Ecdysone, 670, 998
Ecdysozoans, 638*t*, 645, 658, 659*f*, 670–
78. *See also* Protostomes
Echidnas, 700
Echinoderms, 638*t*, 641, 682–86*f*
Echinoidea, 685–86*f*
Echolocation, 957–58
Ecological selection, 478
Ecology, 1059–81. *See also* Community
ecology; Conservation biology;
Ecosystem ecology; Global
ecology; Population ecology
aquatic biomes in, 1074–79
biodiversity scenarios in, 1182–84
climate patterns in, 1065–67
geographic distribution and
abundance of organisms in,
1061–65
levels of study in, 1060–61
organismal, 1060–61
pyramid of production in, 1152
summary of levels of study of, 1060*t*
terrestrial biomes in, 1068–74
Economic benefits
of biodiversity, 1187–88
of fungi, 613–15
Ecosystem diversity, 1174–75
Ecosystem ecology, 1148–59
in ecology, 1060*t*, 1061
ecosystem energy flow in, 1149–56
ecosystem nutrient cycling in, 1156–59
ecosystems and biosphere in, 1148–49
(*see also* Global ecology)
Ecosystem function, 1174
in biodiversity, 1174–75
conservation of, 1191–93
Ecosystem services, 578, 1187
benefits of, 1187–88

of green plants, 578–79
protostome, 658
quantifying, 1192–93
Ecosystems, 578, 1061, 1148
animal locomotion in, 986
animals in, 647–48
biosphere and, 1148–49 (*see also*
Global ecology)
ecosystem ecology and, 1060*t*, 1061
(*see also* Ecosystem ecology)
energy flow in (*see* Energy flow,
ecosystem)
fungi in, 613–15
human impacts on, 1149
impacts of global climate change on,
1168–69
most productive, 1154–56
nutrient cycling in, 1156–59
prokaryotes in, 541–44
protists in, 556–57
protostomes in, 658
restoration of, 1191–93
services of (*see* Ecosystem services)
Ecotourism, 1192
Ectoderm, 424*f*-25, 640–41
Ectomoss, 665
Ectomycorrhizal fungi (EMF), 620–21,
622*f*, 632
Ectoparasites, 648, 666, 667
Ectotherms, 697, 855–56, 1152
Edge effects, habitat fragmentation
and, 1180
Ediacaran fauna fossils, 518
Education, human population growth
and, 1117
Effector B cells, 1050–51
Effector cells, hormone, 993–94, 1001
Effector genes, 414*f*
Effector T cells, 1050–51
Effectors, 854
Efferent division, PNS, 942
Eggs, 237, 823, 1014
amniotic, 689–91, 693–94
bird, 1024*f*
cell-cycle regulation and frog, 229–30*f*
fertilization of, 5, 420–21, 433,
1018–20
gametogenesis of, 241
glycoproteins in fertilization of, 79–80
human, 237*f*
insect, 659
land plant, 587–88
mammalian, 1023–25
meiosis and, 219, 237–38
of monotreme mammals, 701
plant, 438, 823, 827–28
polyspermy prevention and, 421–23
reptile and bird, 696
in sexual reproduction, 1014–15
sexual selection and, 475
structure and function of, 1017–18*f*
variations in development of, 1020–21
Either-or rule, probability, B:8
Ejaculation, 1022
Ejaculatory duct, 1022–23*t*
Elastase, 895*t*
Electric current, 931
Electrical activation, heart, 921–22
Electrical energy, chemical evolution
and, 31, 33–34
Electrical fields
electroreception of, 646, 647*t*, 967–68
in gel electrophoresis, B:13–B:14
generation of, by electrogenic fishes,
968, 969*f*
Electrical potential, 930

Boldface page numbers indicate a glossary entry; page numbers followed by an
f indicate a figure; those followed by *t* indicate a table.

I:12   INDEX

Electrical signaling, animal, 928–42
  action potentials in, 933–38 (see also
    Action potentials)
  calculating equilibrium potentials with
    Nernst equation, 932f
  electrical activation of hearts, 921–22
  hormones and, 993–94
  membrane potentials in, 930–33
  nervous tissue and, 847
  neurons in, 928–30
  resting potential in, 931–32
  synapses in, 938–42 (see also
    Synapses)
  types of nervous systems and, 929 (see
    also Nervous systems)
Electrical signaling, plant, 806
Electrical stimulation of brain areas,
    945–46
Electrically charged side chains, 43f, 44
Electrocardiogram (EKG), 922
Electrochemical gradients, 97, 931
  active transport and, 99–100
  facilitated diffusion and, 96–99
  neurons and, 931
  in photosystems, 185–86
  in plant nutrient uptake, 783–84
  proton gradients as, 168–70
Electrogenic fishes, 968, 969f
Electrolytes, 862, 884. See also
    Osmoregulation
Electromagnetic spectrum, 179–83. See
    also Light-capturing reactions,
    photosynthetic
Electron acceptors, 142, 170–72
Electron carriers, 142
Electron donors, 142
Electron microscopy
  of bacterial translation, 324f
  in cell research, 119
  of DNA replication, 291f
  of DNA synthesis, 284f
  of fossilized plants, 585
  freeze-fracture, of membrane proteins,
    95–96f
  of introns and exons, 321–22
  of karyotypes, 304f, 314f
  of protist cells, 557–58
  in study of muscle contraction, 974
  of transport vesicles, 130f
  types of, B:18–B:19
Electron shells, 20–21
Electron tomography, B:20
Electron transport chains (ETCs), 166
  aerobic vs. anaerobic respiration and,
    170–72
  in cellular respiration, 156, 166–68
  chemiosis hypothesis on, 169–70
  discovery of ATP synthase complex
    and, 168–69
  organization of, 166–67
  in photosystem II, 185–86
  prokaryotic cellular respiration and,
    539–40
  reactions of, 168t
Electronegativity, 21–23f, 31–32, 141–42,
    166, B:13
Electrons
  in atomic structure, 19–21
  covalent bonds of, 21–23
  in energy transformations, 137–38
  excitation of, in photosynthetic
    pigments, 182–84
  ionic bonds and, 22–23f
  in microscopy (see Electron
    microscopy)
  in photosystems, 185–90

potential energy and, 31
prokaryotic donors and acceptors of,
    538–41
transfer of energy in redox reactions
    via, 141–43
Electrophoresis. See Gel electrophoresis
Electroreception, 967–68
Electroreceptors, 953
Elements, 19, B:12
Elephantiasis, 674, 919, 1037f
Elephant seals, 476–77
Elephants, 392, 491f–92, 851, 957
Elevational gradients
  shoot systems and, 736
  tree ranges and, 1137
Elimination, animal nutrition and, 883f,
    888, 896
ELISA (enzyme-linked immunosorbent
    assay), B:16
Ellis, Erle, 1069
Ellis, Hillary, 408
Elongation, stem, 799–802
Elongation factors, 331
Elongation phase, transcription, 320
Elongation phase, translation, 330–31
EMBL Nucleotide Sequence
    Database, 390f
Embryo sac, 828
Embryogenesis, plant, 433–36, 833–34
Embryonic development. See also
    Development
  animal modes of, 650t, 651
  apoptosis in, 408
  deuterostome, 681
  developmental biology and, 405–6
  embryonic tissue layers in, 640–41
  gastrulation in, 644–45
  lophotrochozoan, 660–61
  mammalian pregnancy, gestation, and
    birth in, 1030–34
Embryonic stem cells, 407
Embryonic tissues, animal, 424f–25,
    640–41, 1031–32
Embryonic tissues, plant, 434–35
Embryophytes, 587–88
Embryos, 219, 405
  cell cycle and, 219
  creation of, in cleavage, 423–24
  creation of plant seeds as, in
    embryogenesis, 433–36
  developmental homology in, 450
  gastrulation of, 424–26
  human, 419f
  inner cell mass and, 424
  land plant retention of, 587–88
  organogenesis in, 426–29
Emergent properties, 402
Emergent vegetation, 1077
Emerging diseases, 723–25
Emerging viruses, 723–25
Emerson, Robert, 184
Emigration, 482, 1103
Emulsification, 894
Endangered species, 1178. See also
    Threats, biodiversity
  biodiversity and, 1178
  conservation of, 492–93, 1189–90
  population ecology and conservation
    of, 1118–20
Endangered Species Act, 492–93
End-Cretaceous mass extinction,
    521–23
End-Permian mass extinction, 515, 521
Endemic species, 1176
Endergonic reactions, 139, 141–44
Endocrine disruptors, 999–1000
Entamoeba histolytica, 555t
Enthalpy, 137–38, 139f

Endocrine glands, 993, 994f–95
Endocrine signals, 992t, 993. See also
    Hormones, animal
Endocrine systems, 991–92, 993, 994f–
    95. See also Hormones, animal
Endocytosis, 126, 718–19
Endoderm, 424f–25, 640–41
Endodermis, plant, 760, 785
Endomembrane system, 114, 117t, 121–27
Endomycorrhizal fungi, 621. See also
    Arbuscular mycorrhizal fungi
    (AMF)
Endoparasites, 648, 666
Endophytic fungi, 619, 620–23
Endoplasmic reticulum (ER), 112–13,
    117t, 121–24, 561–62
Endorphins, 941t
Endoskeletons, 682, 689, 980, 981–83
Endosperm, 593, 833
Endosymbionts, 547
Endosymbiosis, 560
  in green algae, 598
  in protists, 560–61, 564–65
Endosymbiosis theory, 116, 560–61
Endothermic processes, 30
Endothermic reactions, 138
Endotherms, 695–96, 703, 855–58
Endpoints, phylogenetic tree, B:10–B:11
Endurance training, human, 980
Energetic coupling, 141–44
Energy, 31. See also Chemical energy
  active transport and, 99–100
  in animal locomotion, 980, 985–86, 988
  animal metabolic rates of consumption
    of, 851–52
  capacity of water to absorb, 27–28
  carbohydrates in storage of, 72, 76–77t,
    80–81
  flow of (see Energy flow)
  in formation of micelles and lipid
    bilayers, 88
  hormones in homeostasis of animal,
    1000–1003
  life and forms of, 136–37
  living organisms and, 2
  metabolic diversity of prokaryotes and,
    538–41
  nucleic acid polymerization and, 60
  prokaryotic methods (feeding
    strategies) for obtaining, 538t
  renewable sources of, 1189
  RNA world hypothesis and, 69
  specific heats of some liquids, 27t
  transfer of, in energetic coupling,
    141–44
  transfer of, from glucose to ATP, 81
  transformations of, in chemical
    reactions, 137–40f (see also
    Chemical reactions)
  types and transformations of, 31
Energy flow
  ecosystem, 1149–53
  global, 1153–56
Energy hypothesis on species
    richness, 1145
Enforced altruism, 1097–98
Engelmann, T. W., 180–81f
English system, metric system and,
    B:1–B:3
Enhancement effect, photosystem,
    184, 188
Enhancers, 354, 355f, 356, 357f
Enkephalins, 941t
Enrichment cultures, 534, 540

Entropy, 31–32, 52, 138
Envelope, fertilization, 422–23
Envelope, viral, 715
Enveloped viruses, 715, 720–21
Environment(s). See also Biomes;
    Ecosystems
  animal color vision and, 963–64
  animal sensing of changes in, 952–53
  animal sensory organs and, 646, 647t
  animals and extreme, 842–43
  background extinctions vs. mass
    extinctions and, 520–21
  balancing selection and, 474
  changes of, in time line of life, 515–16
  as context for succession, 1141, 1142
  cues from, in mating, 1087–88
  ecology and, 1059–60 (see also
    Ecology)
  effects of, on phenotypes, 273, 277t
  environmental sequencing
    (metagenomics) of, 395
  eukaryotic differential gene expression
    and internal, 349
  factors in, affecting enzyme
    function, 148
  gene expression and, 337
  natural selection and changes in,
    456–59f
  plant adaptations to dry and salty,
    754–55, 757–58, 765–66
  plant development in response to, 433
  plant sensory systems and, 793–94
  plant shoot systems and, 736
  plasma membranes and intracellular,
    100–101
  prokaryotic impacts on, 541–49
  seed germination and conditions in,
    836–37
  in triggering switch between
    reproductive modes in
    Daphnia, 1015
  whole-genome sequencing and study
    of, 392
Environmental selection, 478
Environmental sequencing
    (metagenomics), 395, 534–35,
    1173, 1175
Enzymatic combustion, fungal, 623–24
Enzyme kinetics, 147
Enzyme-linked immunosorbent assay
    (ELISA), B:16
Enzyme-linked receptors, 213–14
Enzymes, 54. See also Catalysis
  active transport and, 99–100
  animal digestive, 114, 118, 889,
    892–93, 895t
  in attachment of amino acids to
    tRNAs, 327, 328f
  catalysis of chemical reactions by, 54,
    144–47
  in cell–cell signal deactivation, 214
  in central dogma of molecular biology,
    308–9
  in chromatin remodeling, 351
  in citric acid cycle, 162–63f, 164t
  in DNA mismatch repair, 298–99
  in DNA synthesis, 289–95
  environmenal factors affecting
    function of, 148
  eukaryotic organelles and, 110
  folding and unfolding of, 52
  fungal, 614, 623–24
  in genetic engineering, 380t
  in glycolysis, 159–61
  helpers for, 147
  homeostasis and, 854

Enzymes (continued)
  hydrolysis of carbohydrates by, to release glucose, 80–81
  nucleic acid polymerization and, 60–61
  in one-gene, one-enzyme hypothesis on gene expression, 305–7
  origin-of-life research on, as first living molecules, 55
  in peroxisomes, 115
  post-translational control by, 360
  prokaryotic, 108
  in pyruvate processing, 161–62
  in regulation and evolution of metabolic pathways, 150–52
  regulation of, 149–50
  in replisomes, 294–95
  ribozymes vs., 330–31
  RNA ribozymes as, 67–69
  in RNA synthesis, 307–8
  smooth ER and, 114
  in telomere synthesis, 296–97
  in visualizing molecules, B:15–B:16
Ephedrine, 608
Epicotyl, **833**
Epidemics, **712**
  diabetes mellitus, 898–99
  fungal, 613
  viral, 712
Epidermal cells, plant, 743, 748t
Epidermal tissue, plant, 435, 437f
Epidermis, plant, **435**, 437f, **740**, **759**, 833
Epididymis, **1022**–23f
Epigenetic inheritance, 352–53
Epinephrine (adrenaline), **977**, **1000**
  adrenal glands and, 995
  beta-blockers and, 210
  binding of, to receptor, 1008–10
  control of, by sympathetic nerves, 1006
  fight-or-flight response and, 922, 1000
  model for action of, 1009f
  smooth muscle and, **977**–78
Epiphyseal plate, 999
Epiphytes, **603**, **789**
Epithelia, **204**, **639**, **848**–49, 854, 873–74
Epitopes, **1045**
Epochs, 515
Equilibrium, 30, 91–93
Equilibrium potentials, **931**, 932f
Equisetophyta (horsetails), 605
Equivalence, genetic, 408–9
ER lumen, 123–24
ER signal sequence, **123**–24
Erosion
  devegetation and, 578
  soil composition and, 778
  soil conservation and, 779–81
Error, standard, B:6–B:7
Errors, DNA synthesis, 297–301, 313–14
Erwin, Terry, 1175
Erythropoietin (EPO), **1003**
Escape behavior, 1129f
Escaped-genes hypothesis, 723
Escherichia coli (*E. coli*)
  BAC libraries and, 390
  cell structures of, 107–9
  discovery of DNA in genes of, in Hershey–Chase experiment, 285–86
  DNA synthesis mistakes and mutations of, 297–99

food poisoning and, 532
gene expression in, 336–37
genetic engineering of recombinant human growth hormone using, 370–74
genome of, 393–94
lactose metabolism of, as model, 338–44
in Meselson–Stahl DNA replication experiment, 288f, 289
metabolic diversity and, 539t
as model organism, B:23, B:24f
mutations and fitness in, 484–85
as proteobacteria, 547
scanning electron micrograph of, 336f
types of lactose metabolism mutants in, 340t
Esophagus, 848f, 887f, **889**
Essay on the Principle of Population, An (book), 453, 1116
Essential amino acids, **883**
Essential nutrients, animal and human, **883**–84, 885t
Essential nutrients, plant, **776**–78, 780t
Ester linkages, 86–87
Estradiol, **999**, **1025**
  binding of, to intracellular receptors, 1006–8f
  in mammalian reproduction, 1025–26
  in mating, 1087–88
  ovaries and, 999
  in puberty, 1026–27
Estrogens, **999**
  binding of, to intracellular receptors, 1006–8f
  structure and function of, 210t
Estrous cycle, **1027**
Estrus, 11
Estuaries, **1078**
Ethanol, 27t, 115, 172–73f, 540
Ethical issues
  on biodiversity, 1188–89
  on gene therapy, 384–85
  on genetic testing, 382
  on recombinant human growth hormone, 374
Ethylene, 210t, **812**–13
Eudicots, **596**, 742f, 834, 837
Euglenids, 571
Eukarya domain, **552**. See also Eukaryotes
  characteristics of, 529t
  phospholipids in, 87
  in phylogenetic tree of life, 7f–8
  protists in, 552–53
Eukaryotes, **8**. See also Eukarya domain
  aerobic respiration in, 170–72
  cell–cell attachments in, 204–7
  cells of (see Eukaryotic cells)
  characteristics of, 552–53
  discovery of split genes and introns in, 321–22
  DNA synthesis in, 291f (see also DNA synthesis)
  embryos of, 219 (see also Embryos)
  genomes of (see Eukaryotic genomes)
  initiating translation in, 330
  major lineages of protists and, 558t
  model of condensed DNA of, 348f
  model organisms for (see Model organisms)
  phylogenetic tree of, 559f

prokaryotes vs., 8, 552–53
regulation of gene expression in (see Gene regulation, eukaryotic)
RNA polymerases for, 318
RNA processing in, 321–24, 325t
transcription and translation in, 320–21f, 325
Eukaryotic cells, 110–33. See also Cell(s)
  animal and plant, 111f (see also Animal cells; Plant cells)
  cytoskeletons of, 127–33
  endomembrane system of, 121–27
  images of, 106f, 111f, 118f
  nuclear transport in, 119–21
  organelles in, 110–17t
  prokaryotic cells vs., 8, 107, 110
  whole-cell dynamism of, 118–19
Eukaryotic genomes
  challenges in sequencing of, 395–96
  gene families in, 398–99
  identifying genes in, 393
  insights from Human Genome Project and human, 399–400
  number of genes in, 394f
  prokaryotic genomes vs., 393–96
  transposable elements and repeated sequences in genomes of, 396–98f
  whole-genome sequencing of, 392
Euler, Leonhard, B:9
Euler's number, B:9
European robins, 968–69
Euryarchaeota, 544, 549
Eusociality, **1097**–98
Eutherians, 696, **701**, 1031–34
Evaluate (Bloom's taxonomy skill), B:29f–B:30t
Evaporation, **855**
  gas exchange and, 907
  in global water cycle, 1159
  heat exchange and, 855
  insects and, 869–70
  plants and (see Transpiration)
Evergreen trees, 1071
Evidence, evolutionary, 446–53
Evo-devo (evolutionary-developmental biology), **415**, 790
Evolution, **5**, **445**. See also Adaptation(s); Natural selection
  of aerobic respiration, 542
  of animal innovations (see Evolutionary innovations, animal)
  of animal locomotion, 986
  Aristotle's great chain of being and, 445
  arms races in, 815, 1124, 1133
  behavior causation in (see Ultimate causation)
  cell theory and theory of, 6
  changes in developmental gene expression and, 416
  common misconceptions about natural selection, adaptation, and, 459–62
  of contemporary populations, 449
  convergent, 508–10
  current examples of, 448
  evidence for, as pattern component of theory of, 446–53
  evolutionary conservation of chemical signals and regulatory genes, 414–15
  of evolutionary theories, 445–46
  experimental, 484–85
  of giraffe necks, 9–11
  global climate change and, 1166t, 1167
  human, 705–8
  of introns, 323

lateral gene transfer and, 394–95
mapping land plants, on phylogenetic trees, 586, 587f
of metabolic pathways, 150–52
of mouthparts, 884–86
of multichambered hearts with multiple circulations, 919–21
of muscle-generated animal movement, 972–73
mutations and, 485
natural selection as process component of theory of, 453–54 (see also Natural selection)
of neurons and muscle cells, 929
niche differentiation in, 1127–28
nitrogenous wastes and, 865
as not goal oriented, 460–61
of oviparous, viviparous, and ovoviviparous species, 1020–21
of oxygenic photosynthesis, 189
phylogenetic trees of (see Phylogenetic trees)
Plato's typological thinking and, 445–46
point mutations and, 313
of pollination, 830–31
of populations, 2
of predation, 519–20
processes of (see Evolutionary processes)
prokaryotic impact on, 541–44
religious faith vs. theory of, 9
RNA world hypothesis and, as characteristic of life, 69
selfish vs. self-sacrificing behavior and, 461
speciation and, 489–90 (see also Speciation)
summary of common misconceptions about, with corrections, 460t
summary of evidence for, 452t
switch from chemical, to biological, 19 (see also Chemical evolution)
theory of, by Charles Darwin and Alfred Russel Wallace, 5–6, 444–45, 446
theory of, by Jean-Baptiste de Lamarck, 445–46
vertebrate, 689–91
of whales, 510–11f
whole-genome sequencing and study of, 392
Evolutionary-developmental (evo-devo) biology, **415**, 790
Evolutionary innovations, animal, 637–46. See also Animal(s)
  data on, 637–38
  origin of bilateral symmetry, 641–44
  origin of coelom, 643–44
  origin of embryonic tissue layers, 640–41
  origin of multicellularity, 638–40
  origin of nervous system and cephalization, 643
  origin of protostomes and deuterostomes, 644–45
  origin of segmentation, 645–46
Evolutionary processes, 465–88. See also Evolution
  effects on evolution of four, 465–66
  gene flow, 466, 482–83
  genetic drift, 465, 478–82
  Hardy–Weinberg principle in analyzing change in allele frequencies, 466–70
  mutation, 466, 483–86

Boldface page numbers indicate a glossary entry; page numbers followed by an *f* indicate a figure; those followed by *t* indicate a table.

I:14   INDEX

natural selection, 465, 472–78 (see also Natural selection)

nonrandom mating, 470–72

speciation and, 489–90 (see also Speciation)

summary of, 486t

Ex situ conservation, **1189**–90

Exam preparation, Bloom's taxonomy and, B:20–B:30t

Excavata, 558t, 569, 571

Exceptions, central dogma, 308–9

Exceptions, Mendelian extensions and. See Extensions, Mendelian exceptions and

Excitable membranes, **934**

Excitatory postsynaptic potentials (EPSPs), **940**–42, 947–48

Excretory systems. See also Kidneys

insect, 870–71

nitrogenous wastes and, 864–65, 866t

shark, 866–68

waste elimination by, 883f, 888, 896

Exergonic reactions, **139**, 141–44. See also Spontaneous chemical reactions

Exhalation, 909–11f

Exit (E) site, ribosome, 328–29f

Exocrine glands, **995**

Exocytosis, **126**

Exons, **322**, 357–58, 381–82

Exoskeletons, 109, **670**–71, **689**, 980, **983**, 1038

Exothermic processes, **30**

Exothermic reactions, **138**

Exotic pets, 1181

Exotic species, **1063**, **1181**

Expansins, **202**, **800**

Expansion, cell, 406t, 407

Experiments

cell-fusion, 229–30f

design of, 11–14, B:28

global climate change, 1073

hypothesis testing with, 3–5, 9–11

natural, 457

pulse–chase (see Pulse–chase experiments)

single-trait, by Gregor Mendel, 259–63

in study of evolution, 484–85

two-trait, by Gregor Mendel, 263–66

Exponential notation, B:9

Exponential population growth, **1107**–8

Export, nutrient, 1157–59

Expressed sequence tags (ESTs), **393**

Extant species, **446**

Extension, polymerase chain reaction, 375–76

Extensions, Mendelian exceptions and, 269–77t

allele codominance and incomplete dominance of, 272

gene-by-environment interactions, 273

gene-by-gene interactions, 273–75

linkage, 270–71

multiple allelism, 271–72

overview of, 277t

pleiotropic genes, 272–73

quantitative traits in polygenic inheritance, 275–76

Extensors, **982**–83

External fertilization, animal, 650–51, 1018–19

Extinct species, **447**

Extinctions

animal, 637

current rates of, as biodiversity threat, 1178

global climate change and, 1166t, 1167

human population size and species, 1117

mass extinctions, 505f, 520–23, 1178

metapopulation migration vs., 1112f–13

predicting effects of biodiversity threats on rates of, 1182–84

species richness and rates of, 1143–44

Extracellular appendages, prokaryotic, 109

Extracellular digestion, fungal, **623**

Extracellular layers, 201–4

Extracellular matrix (ECM), **202**–4, **637**, 639, 847

Extraterrestrial life, 531

Extremophiles, **530**–31

Eye color, fruit fly, 268–69

eyeless gene, 451

Eyes

cancers of human, 234

insect, 675, 960

primate, 705

vertebrate, 960–64, 999, 1000f

F

F₁ generation, **259**

Facilitated diffusion, **99**, **769**, **864**

in osmoregulation, 864–65

as passive transport, 101f

in translocation, 769–72

via carrier proteins, 99

via channel proteins, 96–99

Facilitation, enzyme catalysis transition state, 146f–47

Facilitation, species richness and species, 1186

Facilitation, successional, **1141**

Facultative anaerobes, **173**

FAD (flavin adenine dinucleotide). See Flavin adenine dinucleotide (FAD)

FADH₂, 142, 147, 156, 162–72

Faith vs. science, 9

Fallopian tubes, **1024**–25f

Families, gene, 398–99

Fast (fast glycolytic) muscle fibers, **979**–80

Fat cells, 118

Fate, cell, 425, 427–29, 434–35. See also Cell determination

Fats, **86**–87, 157

Fatty acids, **85**

cortisol and, 1001

fermentation and, 172

membranes and, 94

in metabolic pathways, 157

saturated and unsaturated, 85–86

in transgenic plants, 385

Fauna, **518**

FBN1 gene, 272–73

Feather stars, 684

Feathers, 517, 695, **703**

Features. See Traits

Feces, **888**

formation of, in large intestine, 888, 896

insect, 870–71

Fecundity, **1105**

in density-dependent logistic population growth, 1109–12

in human population growth, 1115–18

in life histories, 1105–7

in life tables, 1105, 1106f

in preservation of endangered species, 1118, 1119f

Feder, Jeffrey, 496–97

Feedback

in action potential depolarization, 935

in global climate change, 1164–66

in homeostasis, 854

in thermoregulation, 857

Feedback inhibition, **150**, **993**

in citric acid cycle, 162–63f

by glucocorticoids, 1004

in glycolysis regulation, 160–61

in hormone signaling pathways, 993–94

of metabolic pathways, 150, 151f

in pyruvate processing, 162

Feeding strategies, animal

diversification of, 648–49

ecdysozoan, 674–78

echinoderm, 683–84, 685–86f

fish, 692

invertebrate, 687–88

lophotrochozoan, 665–69

mouthpart adaptations for, 884

in trophic structure, 1150–51

vertebrate, 697–703

worm, 662

Feeding strategies, prokaryote, 538

Feeding strategies, protist, 563–65

Female choice, 475–76, 1020

Female gametes. See Eggs

Female reproductive systems

in birds, 1024

external and internal anatomy of human, 1024–25

hormonal control of menstrual cycle in, 1027–30

mating strategies and, 1020

oogenesis in mammalian, 1017–18f

ovaries and eggs in, 1023–24

pregnancy and birth in mammalian, 1030–34

Females

in age structure of human population, 1115–16

childbirth and maternal mortality rates in human, 1034

chromosomes of, 238

eggs as reproductive cells of, 237

embryos and animal, 651

gametangia of, 587

human population growth and, 1115–18

male mimicking of, 1094–95

mate choice by, 1088–89

mating cues for, 1087–88

plant flower parts as, 827–28

sex chromosomes of, 268

sex hormones of, 999

sex-linked diseases of, 278–79

sexual selection and, 475–78

Femmes fatales, 1020

Fermentation, **172**, **540**

as alternative to cellular respiration, 155, 172–73

prokaryotic, 538, 539t, 540–41

in vitro study of, 158

Ferns, 522–23, 581, 604, 789

Ferredoxin, **186**–87, 188

Fertility rates, global human population and, **1117**–18

Fertilization, **237**

cell cycle and, 5

fungal, 624–25

genetic variation and types of, 248–49

glycoproteins in cell identity for, 79–80

meiosis and, 237–38, 241–42

Fertilization, animal, **420**, **1014**

contraceptive methods to prevent human, 1030t

development and, 420–23

egg development after, 1020–21

external, 1018–19

human pregnancy and, 1031

image of human, 237f

internal, 1019–20

in reproduction, 650–51, 1014–15

unusual mating strategies and, 1020 (see also Mating)

Fertilization, plant, **823**

angiosperm pollination as, 593–94 (see also Pollination)

in development, 433

double, 593

model organism, B:25–B:26

pollen grains and, 590–91

in reproduction, 823, 832–33

Fertilization, protist, **566**

Fertilization envelope, **422**–23

Fertilizers, soil, 533, 787, 1155, 1158, 1160

Fetal alcohol syndrome (FAS), **1033**

Fetal hemoglobin, 915

Fetus, **1032**

gestation of, 1031–32

nourishment of, 1030–31, 1032–33

Fiber, dietary. See Dietary fiber

Fiber composites, extracellular layer, 201, 202f

Fibers, muscle. See Muscle fibers

Fibers, plant, 579–80, **745**–47

Fick, Adolf, 905–6

Fick's law of diffusion, **905**–6

Fight-or-flight response, 921–22, 977–78, **1000**, 1001f, 1006, 1008–10

Filament, stamen, **827**

Filament proteins, 129

Filamentous algae, 180–81f

Filaments, cytoskeletal, 127–31

Filter feeders, **648**

Filtrate, **870**

insect, 870–71

mammal, 873–78

Filtration, renal corpuscle, **873**

Fimbriae, **109**

Finches, 449–50, 456–59f, 494–95, 845–46f, 1127

Finite rate of increase, **1110**f–11f

Finnerty, John, 642

Fins, fish, 692–93

Fire

disturbance regimes and, 1138–39

seed germination and, 837

tree bark and, 750

Fireflies, 1094

Firmicutes, 544, 545

Firs, 607

First law of thermodynamics, **31**, **137**–38

Fischer, Emil, 54, 144–45

Fishes

cichlid jaws, 884–86

electrogenic, 968, 969f

embryonic development of, 405f

evolution of, 689

female choice for paternal care in, 476

gene flow in, 482–83

gills of, 906–7

lineages of, 696, 698–99

mating and external fertilization in, 1018–19

mechanoreception by lateral line system of, 958–59

mutualisms with, 1133, 1134f

Fishes (*continued*)
nitrogenous wastes of, 865
osmoregulation by, 862–64, 866–69
overfishing and, 1153, 1181
populations of, 1101*f*
in vertebrate phylogeny, 691
Fission, 654, 667, **1014**
Fitness, **6**, **454**, **1124**
altruism and, 1095–98
effects of evolutionary processes on, 465–66, 486*t*
gene flow and, 482–83
genetic drift and, 479
hemoglobins and, 915
heterozygous individuals and, 470
inbreeding depression and, 471–72
maladaptive traits and, 192
mutations and, 484–85
natural selection, adaptation, and biological, 6, 454
point mutations and, 313
sexual selection and, 475
species interactions and, 1124
Fitness trade-offs, **462**, **1105**, **1126**
in animal form and function, 843–45
in competition, 1126–27
as constraint on natural selection, 462
endothermy vs. ectothermy, 856
in life histories, 1105–6
of mutualisms, 1134–35
nitrogenous wastes and, 865
parental care and, 694
between skeletal protection and mobility, 980
Fixation phase, Calvin cycle, 191
Fixed action patterns (FAPs), **1084**
Flaccid cells, **756**
Flagella, **109**, **557**, **1017**
bacterial vs. eukaryotic, 131
cell movement by, 132–33
in characteristics of domains of life, 529*t*
fungal, 617, 618
prokaryotic, 109
protist, 557, 565–66
of sperm, 1017
Flagellin, 131
Flattening adaptations, animal surface-area, 852–53
Flatworms, 638*t*, 666
Flavin adenine dinucleotide (FAD), **142**, 163*f*–65
Flavin-containing protein (FMN), 166
Flavins, 166
Flemming, Walther, 220
Flexibility, behavioral, 1084–85
Flexibility, polypeptide, 46
Flexors, **982**–83
Flies. *See* Fruit flies
Flight
animal locomotion in, 984
bird, 703
evolution of vertebrate, 694–95
insect, 671–72
Flightless birds, 703
Flocking, 1129*f*
Flood basalts, 521
Floods, succession after, 1139
Floral meristems, 438, **439**–41
Floral mimics, 739*f*
Florida panthers, 471–72, 1190
Florigen, **803**
Flour beetle, 869

FLOWERING LOCUS T (FT) gene, 803
Flowers, **592**, **823**
angiosperm radiation and, 596
buds and, 735
fading of, 812
in female gametophyte production, 827–28
floral meristems and formation of, 438–41
light reception and flowering of, 802–3
in male gametophyte production, 828–29
as morphological innovations, 517
in plant reproduction, 592–93, 823
pollination of, 593–94, 608–9*f*
as reproductive structures, 826–29
Flu virus. *See* Influenza viruses
Fluid connective tissue, 846*t*, **847**
Fluid feeders, 648*t*, **649**, **884**
Fluid-mosaic model, **94–95**, 96*f*
Fluidity, plasma membrane, 90, 91*f*
Fluids, human seminal, 1023*t*
Flukes, 666
Fluorescence, **182**–84, 377, B:15–B:16
Fluorescence microscopy, B:18, B:20
Folate, 884*t*
Folding
animal surface-area adaptations in, 852–53
protein, 48–49, 51–53, 331–32, 359–60
small intestine, 892
Follicle-stimulating hormone (FSH), 210*t*, **1006**, **1026**, 1027–30
Follicles, **1026**
Follicular phase, **1027**
Food, **883**
angiosperms as human, 608
animal communication and, 1092–93
animal mouthparts and, 884–86
animal nutrition and, 882–83
animal sources of, 646–48
disruptive selection and, 474
as ecosystem provisioning service, 1187
foraging behaviors and (*see* Foraging)
fungi and human, 613–14, 630
giraffe necks and competition for, 9–11
green plants as human, 579
migration and, 1091
model organism, B:23
plant pathogens and human, 815
plant reproduction and human, 823
in population cycles, 1114–15
protostomes as human, 658
transgenic crops as, 385–86
Food and Drug Administration (FDA), 374
Food and Nutrition Board, U.S. National Academy of Sciences, 883
Food chains, **556**, **1150**–51
Food poisoning, 532
Food webs, **1138**, 1150–51, 1169
Foot, mollusk, **662**–63
Foraging, 11–14, **1085**–87
Foraminiferans, 572
Forces, animal locomotion, 985–86
Forebrain, **688**
Foreign cells, immune system and, 1046–47, 1053
Forensic biology, 376, 397–98*f*
Forestry
green plants in, 579–80
sustainable, 781

Forests
boreal, 1072
decomposition rates in, 1157
fires in, 1165
net primary production of, 1155, 1156
temperate, 1071
tropical wet, 1070
Forks, phylogenetic tree, B:10–B:11
Form-function correlations, 19, 118, 845–46, 884–85, 984–85
Formaldehyde, 34, 73, 74
Formulas, molecular and structural, 24, B:12–B:13
Forrester, Graham, 1109–11
Fossil fuels
in biodiversity loss, 1189
in global carbon cycle, 1161–62
global climate change and, 1163
in global nitrogen cycle, 1160
Fossil record, **446**, **511**
animals in, 636, 637, 638
bryozoans in, 665
of Cambrian explosion, 518–19*f*
cetaceans in, 452–53
DNA in, 64–65
evidence for evolutionary change in, 446–49
feathered dinosaurs in, 694–95
fish in, 692–93
fossil formation and, 511–12
fungi in, 616
hominins and humans in, 705–8
life's time line in, 513–16
limitations of, 512–13
mass extinctions in, 520–23
pollen grains in, and ranges of species, 1137
prokaryotes in, 530
studying green plants using, 581–82
studying history of life using, 511 (*see also* History of life)
vertebrates in, 689–91
Fossilization, 511–12
Fossils, **446**, **511**
amplification of DNA in, with polymerase chain reaction, 375–76
formation of, 511–12
ginkgoes as living, 606
spores, 581–82
trilobytes, 505*f*
vascular tissue in, 585
Founder effect, **481**, 495
Four-o'-clocks, 272, 273*f*
Fovea, 961*f*-**62**
Fox, Arthur, 965
Fraenkel-Conrat, Heinz, 715–16
Fragmentation, 601, 603, 652, 654, 667
Frameshift mutations, **313**–14*t*
Franklin, Rosalind, 61–63
Free energy, **137**–39, 145–47, 165*f*
Free radicals, 34, 182, 298
Free ribosomes, 123–24
Freeze-fracture electron microscopy, 95–96*f*
Frequencies, genetic maps and recombination, 274*f*
Frequency, sound, **955**–58
Frequency-dependent selection, **474**
Frequency distributions, histograms of, 275–76, B:5–B:6
Freshwater biomes
characteristics of, 1076–78
fish osmoregulation in, 863–64, 868
global water cycle and, 1159–60
Frogs, 229–30*f*, 317*f*, 424*f*–25, 700, 909, 997–98

Fronds, **604**
Frontal lobe, **944**, 945
Fructose, 157, 195, 1023*t*
Fructose-1,6-bisphosphate, 158*f*–59, 160*f*
Fructose-6-phosphate, 158*f*–59, 160*f*
Fructose bisphosphate, 158
Fruit flies
bicoid gene of, 411–12
chromosomes of, 238
foraging alleles in, 1085
genetic drift in, 479–81
genetic map of, 274*f*
genome of, 392
giant sperm of, 1020
Hox genes of, 412–16, 508–9
innate immunity in, 1039–40
in linked gene experiments, 270–71
as model organism, 675, B:24*f*, B:25
mRNA sequences from one gene in, 358
number of chromosomes in, 238
as protostome, 658
reinforcement of divergence in, 500
second-male advantage in, 1019–20
in testing of chromosome theory of inheritance, 267–69
Fruiting bodies, **547**, **563**, B:23–B:25
Fruits, **594**, **823**
angiosperm radiation and, 596
animal color vision and, 964
auxin and, 807
development of, for seed dispersal, 833, 834–36
ethylene and ripening of, 812–13*f*
in plant reproduction, 594–95, 823
Fuel, green plants as, 579
Function-form correlations, 19, 118, 845–46, 884–85, 984–85
Functional genomics, **389**–90, 400–402. *See also* Genomics
Functional groups, **37**–38, 44
Functions, exponential, B:9
Fundamental niches, **1125**
Fungi, **612**–35
adaptations of, as decomposers, 612–13, 623–24
appearance of, in Paleozoic era, 515
biological methods for studying, 615–19
biological reasons for studying, 613–15
in cell theory experiment, 3–5
chitin as structural polysaccharide in, 76, 78
diversification themes of, 582, 619–28
economic and ecological impacts of, 613–14
in ecosystems, 612–13
key lineages of, 618–19, 628–32
lichens as green algae and, 598
life cycles of, 625–28
molecular phylogenies of, 618–19
morphological traits of, 615–18
mycorrhizal, 614, 784, 1133
phylogenetic relationship of animals to, 8, 618
reproductive variation in, 624–25
saprophytic, and carbon cycle on land, 614–15
in symbiotic relationships, 613, 619–23
vacuoles in cells of, 114–15
Fungicides, **618**
Fusion
fungal, 624–25
gamete, 241, 246–47, 420–21
interbreeding and, 499, 502*t*

Boldface page numbers indicate a glossary entry; page numbers followed by an *f* indicate a figure; those followed by *t* indicate a table.

G

G-protein-coupled receptors, 211–14, 216
G proteins, **212**
G_0 state, 229, 233–34
G_1 phase, 221–**22**, 223f, 229, 231–34
G_2 phase, 221–**22**, 223f, 232
G3P. *See* Glyceraldehyde-3-phosphate (G3P)
Gage, Phineas, 945
Gaits, 986, 987f
Galactose, 73–74, 354
Galactoside permease, 340
Galápagos finches, 449–50, 456–59f, 494–95, 845–46f, 1127
Galen, 973
Galileo, 987
Gallbladder, 887f, **894**
Galls, 385–86
Galvani, Luigi, 973
Gametangia, **587**
Gametes, **219, 238, 823**. *See also* Eggs; Sperm
  in external fertilization, 1018
  in fertilization, 237–38, 241–42, 420–21
  fungal, 617, 624
  gametogenesis of plant, 433, 438, 588–89
  meiosis and, 219
  in plant reproduction, 823–25
  polyspermy prevention and, 421–23
Gametic barriers and prezygotic isolation, 491t
Gametogenesis, **241, 1016**. *See also* Oogenesis; Spermatogenesis
  animal, 1016–18f
  in external fertilization, 1018
  meiosis and, 241
  plant, 433, 438, 588–89
Gametophytes, **567, 588, 823**
  in alternation of generations, 588–89
  land plant evolution away from life cycles dominated by, 589–90
  in land plant life cycles, 823–25
  production of, 827–29
  protist, 568–69
  in seed evolution, 592
Gamma-aminobutyric acid (GABA), 941t
Gamow, George, 310
Ganglia, **643**
Ganglion cells, **960**, 961f
Gap Analysis Program (GAP), 1191
Gap genes, 412, 413f, 414f
Gap junctions, 205f, **207–8**
Gap phases, 221–22, 223f
Gaps, cell–cell. *See* Cell–cell gaps
Garden peas, Mendelian genetics and, 257–66. *See also* Mendelian genetics
Gas exchange
  amniotic egg, 693
  amphibian, 700
  animal, 902–3 (*see also* Circulatory systems; Respiratory systems)
  diffusion and skin-breathing in, 852
  fish lungs in, 692–93
  gills in (*see* Gills)
  during human pregnancy, 1032–33
  insect, 869
  in osmoregulation, 862–63
  plant stomata in, 743–44
  pneumatophore roots in, 734, 735f
  by protostomes, 659–60
  by salmon, 851–52

terrestrial adaptations for, 659–60
  tree bark and, 750
Gases
  chemical evolution and volcanic, 24, 30, 34–35
  greenhouse, 1163, 1192–93
Gastric juice, 890–91
Gastrin, **893**
Gastropods, **662**, 668
Gastrovascular cavities, 886–87f
Gastrula, 424
Gastrulation, **407, 424**
  in animal embryonic development, 644–45
  cell movement in, 407, 424–25
  definition of body axes in, 425
  formation of germ layers in, 425
  in frog embryo, 424f
  protostome vs. deuterostome, 658
Gated channels, **98–99**. *See also* Membrane proteins
Gause, G. F., 1125–26
GDP (guanosine diphosphate), 211, 214
Gel electrophoresis, 378, 894, B:13–B:14
Gemmae, **601**, 603
Gene-by-environment interactions, 273, 277t
Gene-by-gene interactions, 273–75, 277t
Gene duplication, **398–99**, 483, 485
Gene expression, **305–16, 337**
  bacterial gene regulation and, 336–37 (*see also* Gene regulation, bacterial)
  bacterial vs. eukaryotic, 360–61
  in cell determination, 429
  in cell differentiation, 409–10 (*see also* Differential gene expression)
  central dogma of molecular biology on, 307–9
  eukaryotic gene regulation and (*see* Gene regulation, eukaryotic)
  evolutionary change from changes in, 416
  functional genomics and, 400–402
  genetic code and, 307, 310–12
  linking genotypes and phenotypes in, 308
  molecular biology, DNA, and, 304–5
  mutations of genes and chromosomes and, 313–15
  one-gene, one-enzyme hypothesis on, 305–7
  plant cell–cell signals and, 795–96
  point mutations and, 483
  protein synthesis and, 317–18 (*see also* Protein synthesis)
  RNA as intermediary between genes and proteins in, 307–8
  steroids and, 1007–8f
  transcription and translation in, 308
Gene families, **398–99**, 508
Gene flow, **466, 482**
  in allopatric speciation, 494–95
  effects of, on fitness, 483
  as evolutionary process, 466, 486t
  genetic diversity and, 483
  genetic restoration with artificial, 1190
  Hardy–Weinberg principle and, 468
  measuring, 482–83
  reproductive isolation and, 490
  speciation and, 489
  in sympatric speciation, 495
Gene pools, **466–67**
Gene recombination, immune system, 1046, 1047f. *See also* Recombinant DNA technology

Gene regulation, bacterial, 336–47
  eukaryotic vs., 348–49, 360–61
  of gene expression, 336–37 (*see also* Gene expression)
  global, 344–45
  identifying regulated genes for, 339–41
  information flow and overview of, 337–39f
  negative control of transcription in, 341–44
  positive control of transcription in, 344, 345f
Gene regulation, eukaryotic, 348–65
  bacterial gene regulation vs., 348–49, 360–61
  cancer and defects in, 361–63
  chromatin remodeling in, 349–53
  environment, differential gene expression, and, 348–49
  overview of levels of, 349
  post-transcriptional, 356–60
  in transcription initiation, 353–56
  translational and post-translational, 359–60
Gene therapy, 381, **383–85**
Generations, 1103
Genes, **107, 238, 261**. *See also* Chromosomes; DNA (deoxyribonucleic acid); Genomes
  alleles of, 238, 239f, 247, 261 (*see also* Alleles)
  in animal diversification, 646
  Cambrian explosion and new, 519–20
  cancer and tumor-suppressor, 361–63
  case study of *HLA* genes in humans, 469–70
  chromosomes, DNA, and, 220
  cloned, in DNA libraries, 372
  for color vision, 964
  control of flower structures by, 439–41
  in control of plant body axes, 435–36
  definitions of, 392
  in determination of leaf shape, 436–38
  developing phylogenetic tree of life from rRNA sequences in, 6–8
  discovery of split eukaryotic, 321–22
  dwarf plants and defective, 808–9
  effects on phenotypes of interactions between, 273–75, 277t
  eukaryotic cell nucleus and, 112
  exceptions and extensions to Mendelian rules on, 277t
  expression of (*see* Gene expression)
  finding disease-causing, 378–82
  gene families of, 398–99
  in genetic constraints on natural selection, 461–62
  in genetic homologies, 450–51
  genetic information in, 2 (*see also* Genetics)
  genetic maps of (*see* Genetic maps)
  Hershey–Chase experiment on DNA as genetic material in, 285–86
  hormones and, in leptin and energy homeostasis, 1001–3
  identifying, in genome sequences, 392–93
  identifying regulated, with replica plating, 339–41
  inserting, into human cells, 383
  inserting, into plasmids, 370, 371f
  lactose metabolism, 340–44
  lateral gene transfer of, 394–95, 399
  linkage and linked, 270–71, 274f, 277t

loci of, on chromosomes, 266
  in Mendelian genetics, 258t
  multiple traits and pleiotropic, 272–73
  mutations of (*see* Mutation[s])
  natural selection of, in Galápagos finches, 458–59f
  number of, in genomes, 394–96, 399–400
  in one-gene, one-enzyme hypothesis on gene expression, 305–7
  in particulate inheritance, 261–63
  plant pathogen resistance, 815
  polygenic inheritance and, 275–76
  prokaryotic, 107–8
  redefinition of, 358
  regulation of bacterial (*see* Gene regulation, bacterial)
  regulatory (*see* Regulatory genes)
  RNA as intermediary between proteins and, 307–8
  for taste receptors, 965
  tumor suppressors, 232–33
Genes-in-pieces hypothesis, 321–22
Genetic bottlenecks, **481–82**
Genetic code, **310**
  code words in, 310–11
  cracking of, 311–12
  hypothesis of, by Francis Crick, 307
  in mRNA specification of amino acids, 325–26
  in transfer of amino acids to proteins by tRNAs, 326–28
Genetic constraints, natural selection and, 461–62
Genetic correlation, **461**–62
Genetic counselors, 376
Genetic disorders, human, 97–98, 277–79, 383–85. *See also* Diseases and disorders, human
Genetic divergence
  in allopatric speciation, 494f
  interbreeding and reinforcement of, 499–500
  speciation and, 490
  in sympatric speciation, 496f
Genetic diversity, **1173**. *See also* Genetic variation
  behavior and, 1083–84
  biodiversity and, 1173–74
  conservation of, 1189–90
  directional selection and, 473
  fungal, 615
  genetic drift, gene flow, mutations, and, 483–84
  habitat fragmentation and loss of, 1182
  in preservation of metapopulations, 1120
  switching of reproductive modes for, 1016
Genetic drift, **465, 478–82**
  in allopatric speciation, 495
  causes of, in natural populations, 481–82
  effects of, on laboratory populations, 480f
  as evolutionary process, 465, 486t
  experimental studies of, 479–81
  founder effect and, 481
  genetic bottlenecks and, 481–82
  genetic diversity and, 483
  Hardy–Weinberg principle and, 468
  key points about fitness, genetic variation, and, 479
  loss of biodiversity from, 1180
  simulation studies of, 478–79

Genetic engineering, 368–88
  agricultural biotechnology and
      development of transgenic golden
      rice in, 385–86
  in agriculture, 579
  amplification of DNA with polymerase
      chain reaction in, 374–76
  common techniques used in, 381t
  common tools used in, 380t
  dideoxy DNA sequencing in, 376–78
  gene therapies in, 383–85
  genetic mapping in, 378–82
  of human growth hormone for pituitary
      dwarfism using recombinant DNA
      technology, 369–74
  molecular biology techniques and
      recombinant DNA technology in,
      368–69
  plant cell and tissue cultures in, B:22
  in video microscopy, B:20
Genetic equivalence, **408**, 409
Genetic homologies, **450**–51
Genetic isolation, 490, 494–99
Genetic libraries. *See* DNA libraries
Genetic maps, **271**, **379**
  benefits of finding disease genes
      with, 382
  crossing over and, in chromosome
      theory of inheritance, 271
  development of first, 274f
  ethical concerns over genetic testing
      and, 382
  finding Huntington's disease gene
      with, 378–82
  in genetic engineering, 381t
Genetic markers, **379**, **479**
  finding Huntington's disease gene
      with, 379
  in hybridization research, 502
  in studies of genetic drift, 479–80
Genetic recombination, 247–**48**,
      270–71, 274f
Genetic restoration, 1190
Genetic screens, **305**–6, 339
Genetic testing, 382
Genetic variation, **472**. *See also* Genetic
      diversity
  asexual vs. sexual reproduction
      and, 247
  from crossing over, 248
  drug resistance and, 455–56
  effects of evolutionary processes on,
      466, 486t
  effects of modes of natural selection
      on, 472, 475t
  genetic drift and, 479
  from independent assortment, 247–48
  lack of, as genetic constraint, 462
  mutations and, 485
  natural selection and, 454, 456
  sexual reproduction and, 566
  types of fertilization and, 248–49
Genetically modified food, 385–86
Genetics, **257**. *See also* Genes
  behavior causation in (*see* Proximate
      causation)
  chromosome theory of inheritance
      and, 256–57 (*see also* Chromosome
      theory of inheritance)
  combining probabilities in, B:8
  developing tree of life from rRNA
      sequences in, 6–8

DNA in, 64 (*see also* DNA
      [deoxyribonucleic acid])
genetic disorders (*see* Genetic
      disorders, human)
Mendelian (*see* Mendelian genetics)
model organisms in, B:23
protostome, 660
RNA in, 67 (*see also* RNA [ribonucleic
      acid])
RNA world hypothesis and, 69
Genitalia, **1022**–23
Gennett, J. Claude, 1046
Genome annotation, **392**–93
Genome sequencing, 389f, 391, 725, 1173
Genomes, **289**, **389**
  emerging viruses from reassortment
      of, 723–24
  eukaryotic, 393, 395–400, 628 (*see also*
      Eukaryotic genomes)
  genetic homology and, 451
  genomics and, 389–90 (*see also*
      Genomics)
  identifying genes in, 392–93
  in Meselson–Stahl experiment, 289
  model organism, B:23–B:26
  origin of multicellularity in, 640
  prokaryotic, 392–95
  Saccharomyces cerevisiae, 618
  selecting organisms for sequencing
      of, 392
  technologies for sequencing, 376, 378
  viral, 715–16, 719–22
  whole-genome sequencing of, 390–93
Genomic libraries, 372, 381t
Genomic reassortment, viruses and,
      723–24
Genomics, **389**–404
  bacterial and archaeal genomes in,
      393–95
  comparative, in studying evolutionary
      innovations of animals, 638
  development of, 389–90
  eukaryotic genomes in, 395–400
  functional genomics and, 400–402
  genome sequencers in, 389f, 391
  Human Genome Project in, 389–90,
      399–400
  metagenomics (environmental
      sequencing) in, 395, 534–35
  proteomics and, 402
  systems biology and, 402
  whole-genome sequencing in, 390–93
Genotypes, **261**
  central dogma and linking phenotypes
      and, 308, 309f
  effect of inbreeding on frequencies of,
      470–71f
  exceptions and extensions to
      Mendelian rules on, 277t
  frequencies of, for human MN blood
      group, 468–69
  Hardy–Weinberg principle and
      frequencies of, 466–70
  mating, body odor, and, 470
  in Mendelian genetics, 258t
  mutations as changes in, 313–15 (*see
      also* Mutation[s])
  in particulate inheritance, 261–63
  phenotypes and, 261, 273–75 (*see also*
      Phenotypes)
  predicting, with Punnett square,
      262–63

Genus, taxonomic, **8**
Geographic distribution and abundance
      of organisms
  abiotic factors in, 1062
  allopatric speciation and, 494–95
  biodiversity hotspots and, 1176–77
  biogeography and, 1079
  biotic factors in, 1062
  ecology and, 1059–65 (*see also*
      Ecology)
  estimating effects of global climate
      change on, 1183–84
  evidence for evolutionary change in,
      449–50
  global climate change and, 1073–74,
      1166t, 1167
  historical factors in, 1062–63
  interaction of biotic and abiotic factors
      in, 1063–65
  island biogeography and, 1144
  mapping current and past, 1137
  in population ecology, 1102–3
  protected areas and, 1190–91
  species interactions and, 1124
Geologic time scale, **446**–47
Geothermal radiation, 541
Gerbils, 1086–87
Germ cells, **438**
Germ layers, 424f–25, 639, **640**–41
Germ line, **433**
Germ theory of disease, **532**
Germination, **433**, 800–801, 809–10,
      832, 836–37
Gestation, **694**, **1031**–33
GH1 gene, pituitary dwarfism, 369, 373
Giant axon, squid, 130
Giant sequoias, 1138–39
Giant sperm, 1020
Giardia, 555t, 557, 571
Giardiasis, 555t, 571
Gibberellins, **808**–10, 813t, 836–37
Gibbons, Ian, 132–33
Gibbs free-energy change, 138–39
Gila monsters, 878f, 879
Gilbert, Walter, 322
Gill arches, **692**
Gill filaments, **906**–7f
Gill lamellae, **852**–53f, **906**–7
Gill pouches, 450
Gills, **668**, **687**, **852**, **906**
  developmental changes in gas
      exchange with, 851–52
  mollusk, 662, 668
  in origin of insect wings, 671–72
  in osmoregulation, 862–64, 868
  protostome, 659
  structure and function of, 906–7
  vertebrate, 686–87
Ginkgoes, 606
Giraffe neck hypothesis testing, 9–11
Gizzards, avian, 891–92
Glabe, Charles, 421
Glacier Bay succession case history,
      1141–42
Glands, **848**, **993**, 994f–95
Glanville fritillaries (butterflies), 1112–
      13, 1118–20
Glaucophyte algae, 569
Gleason, Henry, 1136–37
Glia, **937**
Global air circulation patterns, 1065–66
Global biogeochemical cycles, **1156**,
      1159–62. *See also* Nutrient cycling
Global carbon cycle, **556**, **1161**–62
Global climate change, **1163**–69
  causes of, 1163–64

devegetation and, 579
effects of, on aquatic biomes, 1076
effects of, on terrestrial biomes,
      1073–74
estimating effects of, on species
      distributions, 1183–84
global warming and, 1163
impact of, on ecosystem net primary
      productivity, 1168–69
impact of, on organisms, 1166–68
life-history traits of endangered species
      and, 1118
local consequences of, 1169
positive and negative feedback in,
      1164–66
protists and limitation of, 556–57
Sphagnum moss and, 602
summary of impacts on organisms
      of, 1166t
temperature and precipitation changes
      from, 1164, 1166
as threat to biodiversity, 1181t, 1182
Global ecology, 1159–69
  biosphere and ecosystems in, 1060t,
      1061, 1148–49 (*see also* Ecosystem
      ecology)
  global biogeochemical cycles in,
      1159–62
  global climate change in, 1163–69
  global net primary productivity
      patterns in, 1153–56
Global gene regulation, 344–**45**
Global human population, 1101–2,
      1117–18
Global net primary productivity
      patterns, 1153–56
Global nitrogen cycle, **1160**–61
Global warming, global climate change
      and, 1163. *See also* Global climate
      change
Global water cycle, **1159**–60, 1166
Globin genes, 399
Globular proteins, 47
Glomalin, **621**
Glomeromycota, 618, 630
Glomeruli, **873**, 878t, **966**
Glucagon, 54, **897**, **992**
Glucocorticoids, 1000–**1001**, 1004–6
Glucokinase, 145
Gluconeogenesis, **195**, **897**
Glucose, **154**
  animal absorption of, 893–94
  ATP synthesis from, 81
  ATP synthesis from oxidation of, in
      cellular respiration, 154–56, 170–72
  ATP synthesis from oxidation of, in
      fermentation, 155, 172–73
  carrier protein for, in human red blood
      cells of, 99
  configurations of, 73–74
  cortisol and availability of, 1000–1001
  in diabetes mellitus and nutritional
      homeostasis, 897–99
  enzyme catalysis of phosphorylation
      of, 145
  free energy changes in oxidation
      of, 165f
  glycogen and, 76
  glycolysis as processing of, to pyruvate,
      158–61
  hydrolysis of carbohydrates by
      enzymes to release, 80–81
  lac operon regulation by, 343
  lactose metabolism and preference for,
      338–39f
  in metabolic pathways, 157

as organic molecule, 36f
in photosynthesis, 177, 195
in redox reactions, 141–42
secondary active transport of, 100
spontaneous chemical reactions and, 32f
summary of oxidation of, 164f
Glucose-6-phosphate, 158f–59, 160f
GLUT-1 membrane carrier protein, 99
Glutamate, 48, 941t, 965
Glutamine, 328, 381–82
Glyceraldehyde-3-phosphate (G3P), **191**, 195
Glycerol, 27t, **86**, 157
Glycogen, **76**
as animal storage polysaccharide, 76
fungi and, 618
hydrolysis of, to release glucose, 80–81
in metabolic pathways, 157
structure of, 77t
Glycolipids, **109**
Glycolysis, **156**
in cellular respiration, 156
discovery of, 158–59
enzymes and reactions of, 160t
free energy changes in, 165f
in muscle contraction, 979
NADH and $FADH_2$ in, 164–65
overview of, 158f–59f
reactions of, 159
regulation of, 159–61
Glycophosphate, 385
Glycoproteins, 78, **79**–80, **124**, 1053
Glycosidic linkage, **75**
Glycosylation, **124**
Glyoxysomes, **115**
GMP (Guanosine monophosphate), 962
Gnathostomes, 638t, **688**, 691
Gnetophytes, 608
Golden rice, 385–86
Goldman, Steven, 948
Golgi, Camillo, 929–30
Golgi apparatus, **113**
in cytokinesis, 228
ECM components and, 202–3
post-translational protein modifications in, 332
protein modification, sorting, and transport inside, 124–26
structure and function of, 113–14, 117t
Gonadal hormones, 1025–26
Gonadotropin-releasing hormone (GnRH), **1026**, 1027–30
Gonads, **999**, **1016**–18f. See also Ovaries, animal; Testes
Google Scholar (online database), B:27
Gorillas, 705
Gracile austalopithecines, 706
Graded postsynaptic potentials, 940–41
Grades (paraphyletic lineages), **691**
Grafting, plant, 802–3
Gram-negative cells, **536**
Gram-positive cells, **536**
Gram stain technique, **536**
Grana, **116**, **178**–79f, 189
Grant, James, 1178
Grant, Peter and Rosemary, 456–58, 461, 494–95, 1127
Graphic concept maps, B:28
Graphs, B:4–B:6
Grasses, 1071
Grasslands, temperate, 1071
Gravitational forces, animal locomotion and, 985
Gravitropism, plant, **803**–5, 818t

Gravity
animal sensing of, 647t
hearts and, 919
Gray whales, 857–58
Grazing food chains, **1150**–51
Great apes, **705**
Great chain of being, 445
Great tits, 1166
Greek and Latin word roots, B:3
Green algae, **597**. See also Algae
key lineages of, 569, 597–98, 599–600
land plants and, as green plants, 577–78 (see also Green plants)
in lichens, 598, 623, 631
as model organism, B:25
photosystems and, 184
rRNA sequences for, 7
similarities between land plants and, 580
Green fluorescent protein (GFP), B:20
Greenhouse effect, 1163. See also Global climate change
Greenhouse gases, **1163**, 1192–93
Green iguanas, 481
Green light, 178, 180
Green opsin, 963–64
Green plants, 577–611
analysis of morphological traits of, 580–81
biological methods for studying, 580–83
ecosystem services of, 578–79
in fossil record, 581–82
green algae and land plants as, 577–78 (see also Green algae; Land plants)
green algae lineages, 597–98, 599–600
importance of, to humans, 579–80
key lineages of, 597–609f
molecular phylogenies of, 582–83
non-vascular plant lineages, 598, 601–2
seedless vascular plant lineages, 598–99, 603–5
seed plant lineages, 599, 606–9f
Green sea turtles, 1090–91
Greider, Carol, 296–97
Grooves, chemical structure, B:13
Gross primary productivity (GPP), **1149**
Groudine, Mark, 351
Ground finches, 494–95
Ground force, animal locomotion, 986
Ground meristem, **740, 833**
Ground tissue, **435**, 437f
Ground tissue systems, **740**, 742, 744–46, 748t, 833
Groundwater, **1159**–60
Groups, control, 13, B:6–B:7
Growing seasons, plant translocation and, 766
Growth. See also Development
cancer as out-of-control, 232–34
in energy flow, 1149
lophotrochozoan vs. ecdysozoan, 670
mammalian, 999
mitosis and, 220
plant, 436, 437f, 585, 805–6
population (see Population growth)
Growth factors, **233**–34
Growth hormone (GH), **995**–96, 999
Growth hormone therapy, 369–70. See also Human growth hormone (HGH)
Growth regulators, plant, 806–15
Growth rings, tree, 751, 1139
GTP (guanosine triphosphate), **162**
ATP vs., in citric acid cycle, 162
ATP vs., in translation, 326

in cell–cell signal deactivation, 214
in cell–cell signal processing, 211
Guanine, 58–59, 61–63, 65–66, 287, 326
Guanosine diphosphate (GDP), 211, 214
Guanosine monophosphate (GMP), 962
Guanosine triphosphate (GTP). See GTP (guanosine triphosphate)
Guard cells, 193, **584**–85, **744**, 810, **811**–12
Gustation (taste), **964**–65
Guttation, **761**
Gymnosperms, **582**. See also Seed plants
diversification of, 582
lineages of, 599, 606–8
in Mesozoic era, 515
molecular phylogeny of, 583
seed evolution in, 592

H

H^+-ATPases. See Proton pumps
Haberl, Helmut, 1156
Habitat degradation, **1179**–80, 1181t
Habitat destruction, 1117–20, **1178**–79, 1181t
Habitat fragmentation, **1179**–80, 1181t
Habitats
animal communication modes and, 1093
carrying capacity of, 1108–9f, 1112
fossil record bias for, 512
metapopulation, 1112–13, 1118–20
model organism, B:23
nitrogenous wastes and, 865–66
prezygotic isolation and, 491t
prokaryotic diversity in, 530
species richness and area of, 1182–83
sympatric speciation and, 496–97
Hadley, George, 1065
Hadley cell, **1065**–66
Haeckel, Ernst, 1060
Haemophilus influenza, 392
Hagfish, 691, 697
Hair cells, mechanoreception by, **954**–58
Hairpin RNA secondary structure, **66**, 320
Haldane, J. B. S., 41–42
Hamadryas baboons, 1013f
Hamilton, William D., 1096–97
Hamilton's rule, **1096**–97
Hamstring muscles, 982
Hands, primate, 705
Hanski, Ilkka, 1113
Hanson, Jan, 974
Hantaan virus, 725
Haploid cells, life cycles dominated by, 566–69
Haploid number, **239**, 240t
Haploid organisms, **239**, 240t
Harbeespoort Dam, 1148f
Hardiness zones, plant, 1167
Hardy, G. H., 466–67
Hardy–Weinberg principle, **466**–70
Harrison, William, 369f
Hartwell, Leland, 231
Hatch, Hal, 194
Haustoria, **789**, 790f
Havasupai tribe, 469–70
Hawaiian silverswords, 516, 736
Hawksworth, David, 615
Hawkmoths, 908
Hawthorn maggot flies, 496–97
Hay fever, 1056
Head
arthropod, 670
cephalization and, 643

insect, 675
sperm, 422
Head-to-tail axes, 412, 413f
Health, human. See Diseases and disorders, human
Hearing, 646, 647t, **955**–58
Heart attacks, 925
Heart murmurs, **921**
Heart-wood, **751**
Hearts, **916**, 919–23
blood vessels and, 917–18
cardiac cycle of, 923
cardiac muscle in, 847f–48, 978
in closed circulatory systems, 917
electrical activation of, 921–22
evolution of multichambered, with multiple circulations, 919–21
human, 921
in open circulatory systems, 916–17
phylogenetic tree of, 920f
Heat, **31**
animal thermoregulation and (see Thermoregulation)
in chemical reactions, 137–40f
denatured proteins and, 52–53
DNA replication and, 64
in endothermic and exothermic processes, 30
in nucleic acid polymerization, 60
in spontaneous chemical reactions, 31–32
sterilization by, 3–4
as thermal energy, 31
thermoreception of, 967, 968f
water and, 27–28
Heat exchange mechanisms, animal, 855, 857–58
Heat of vaporization, **28**
Heat-shock proteins, 52–53, **857**
Heavy chain polypeptides, **1044**–46
HeLa cells, B:21, B:22f
Helianthus, 501–2
Helicase. See DNA helicase
Helicobacter pylori, 891
Heliobacteria, 186, 539t
Helper T cells, 713–14, 717–18, **1050**–51, 1054t
Hemagglutinin, 1045
Heme, **912**
Hemichordates, 638t, 682
Hemimetabolous metamorphosis, **672**
Hemocoel, **663**, 671
Hemoglobin, **912**
acclimatization vs. adaptation for oxygen content of, 459–60
β-globin in, 351
in blood oxygen transport, 54, 912–15
in carbon dioxide transport and blood pH buffering, 914–16
globin genes and, 399
levels of structure of, 51t
sickle-cell disease and, 48
space-filling model of, 41f
Hemolymph, **870**, 916–17
Hemophilia, 278
Henle, Jacob, 874
Hepaticophyta (liverworts), 601
Hepatitis viruses, 727, 1055
Herbaceous plants, **734**
Herbicides, 182, 385, 1182
Herbivores, **647, 737, 1128**
animals as, 647–48
limitations on consumption by, 1131–32
in nutrient cycling, 1157–58

Herbivores (continued)
  plant defense responses to, 815–19
  plants as food for, 579
  transgenic crops and, 385
Herbivory, **1128**
Heredity, 247, **257**. *See also* Genetics;
  Inheritance; Mendelian genetics
Heritable traits, **5**
Hermaphroditic species, **1020**
Hermit warblers, 500–501, 1062
Hershey, Alfred, 285–86
Hershey–Chase experiment, 285–86
Heterokayrotic fungi, **624**–25
Heterokonts, 570, 574
Heterospory, **590**, 591*f*, 592*f*
Heterotherms, **855**–56
Heterotrophs, **176**–77, **538**, 637
Heterozygote advantage, 471–72, **474**
Heterozygous genes, 258*t*, **262**, 272, 273*f*,
  277–79
Heterozygous genotypes, 469–72
Hexokinase, 145*f*
Hexoses, 59, **73**–74
Hibernation, **855**
High-order cognitive (HOC) skills,
  B:20–B:30*t*
High-productivity hypothesis for species
  richness, 1145
High-throughput robotic genome
  sequencer, 389*f*
Hill, Robin, 184
Hindbrain, **688**
Hindenburg disaster, 32
Hindgut, insect, 870–71
Hippos, 510–11*f*
Histamine, **1040**–41, 1042*t*, 1056
Histidine, 311
Histograms, 275–76, 457, B:5–B:6
Histone acetyltransferases (HATs), **352**
Histone code, **352**
Histone deacetylases (HDACs), **352**
Histone mutants, 351
Histones, **220**, **350**–53, 529*t*
Historical factors
  in geographic distribution and
    abundance of species, 1062–63
  in natural selection, 462
  in study of global climate
    change, 1073
  in succession, 1141, 1142
History of life, 505–27. *See also* Life
  adaptive radiations in, 516–20
  fossil record as tool for studying,
    511–16 (*see also* Fossil record)
  mass extinctions in, 520–23 (*see also*
    Mass extinctions)
  phylogenies and phylogenetic trees
    as tools for studying,
    506–11*f* (*see also* Phylogenetic trees;
    Phylogenies)
  time line of, in fossil record, 513–16
HIV (human immunodeficiency virus),
  712, **1056**
  in AIDS pandemic, 712–14
  CD4 protein as receptor used by, to
    enter cells, 717–18
  as emerging virus, 723
  immunodeficiency and, 1056
  latency of, 722
  phylogenetic tree of, 724*f*
  protease inhibitors for, 719
  as retrovirus, 720, 728

reverse transcriptase in, 309
  as RNA virus, 309
  strains of, 724–25
  Toxoplasma and, 573
  vaccines and, 1055
Hives, 1056
HLA genes, 469–70
H.M.S. *Beagle* naval ship, 449–50
Hodgkin, A. L., 932–36
Hoffmann, Jules, 1039–40
Holocene epoch, 515
Holoenzymes, **319**–20*f*, 373
Holometabolous metamorphosis, **672**
Holway, David, 1064
Homeobox genes, **413**, 441, 508
Homeostasis, animal, **853**–58
  of blood oxygen, 911–12
  of blood pH, 915–16
  of blood pressure, 924
  general principles of, 853–54
  hormones in, 1001–3
  nutritional, 897–99
  osmoregulation and (*see*
    Osmoregulation)
  regulation and feedback in, 854
  thermoregulation in, 854–58
Homeostasis, cellular, **30**, **157**
Homeotherms, **855**–58
Homeotic genes. *See Hox* genes
Homeotic mutations, **413**, 439–41
Hominids, **705**
Hominins, **705**–8, B:10–B:11
Homo genus, 705*t*, 706, B:11
Homo neanderthalensis, 376, B:11
Homo sapiens, 8–9, 376, 705–8, B:11. *See
  also* Human(s)
Homologies, **393**, **450**, **508**
  bilateral symmetry as, 642–43
  as evidence of common ancestry,
    450–51
  in genome annotation, 393
  homoplasies vs., 508–10
  mapping, on phylogenetic trees, 508*t*
  model organisms and, B:25–B:26
Homologous chromosomes (homologs),
  238, 240–48, 249*f*, 304*f*
Homologous genes, **415**
Homoplasies, **508**–10
Homospory, **590**
Homozygous genes, 258*t*, **262**, 277–79
Homozygous genotypes, 469–72
Honduras, 1115–16
Honeybees, 856, 1085, 1092–93. *See
  also* Bees
Hooke, Robert, 2, 3
Horizontal gene transfer. *See* Lateral
  gene transfer
Hormone-based contraception methods,
  1029–30
Hormone-response elements, **1007**
Hormones, **209**. *See also* Cell–cell
  signaling
  in cell–cell signaling, 209, 210*t*
  lipid-soluble vs. lipid-insoluble, 209,
    210–11
Hormones, animal, **877**, **893**, **991**
  binding of, to cell-surface receptors,
    1008–10
  binding of steroid, to intracellular
    receptors, 1006–8*f*
  biological identification of, 996–97
  blood pressure control by, 924

categories of chemical signals and,
    992–93
  central nervous system (CNS),
    endocrine system, and, 991–92, 993
  chemical characteristics and types of,
    995–96
  control of urine formation by, 877–78
  direction of developmental processes
    by, 997–1000
  discovery of first, 893
  diversity of target-cell responses
    to, 1010
  as endocrine and neuroendocrine
    signals, 993
  endocrine system and, 991–92, 993,
    994*f*–95
  in homeostasis, 1001–3
  human endocrine glands and, 994*f*
  insulin and blood sugar levels, 47–48
  isolating estradiol receptor with
    labeled, 1007*f*
  in mating, 1087–88
  measurement of levels of, 997
  measuring amounts of, using
    radioimmunoassay, B:16
  in muscle contraction, 977–78
  regulation of, by hypothalamus and
    pituitary gland, 1004–6
  regulation of epinephrine by
    sympathetic nerves, 1006
  regulation of production of, by
    nervous system, 1003–6
  in responses to stress, 1000–1001
  sex (*see* Sex hormones, mammalian)
  signaling pathways of, 993–94
  testis cells and, 118
Hormones, plant, **795**
  auxin as blue-light phototropic,
    797–800
  auxin as development morphogen, 412
  auxin as gravitropic signal, 804–5
  cell and tissue cultures and, B:22
  in cell–cell signaling, 794–96
  flowering, 802–3
  growth regulators, 806–15
  hypersensitive response, systemic
    acquired resistance, and, 815–16
  in seed dormancy, 836–37
Hornworts, 602
Horowitz, Norman, 150–51, 305–7
Horses, 985, 986, 987*f*, 1098
Horseshoe crabs, 678
Horsetails, 605
Horticulture, 579
Horvitz, Robert, 408
Host cells, **711**
  in viral classification, 725
  viral infection of, 711–12 (*see also*
    Replicative growth, viral)
  viral latency in, 721–22
Hosts, parasite, **1128**, 1132–33
Hot springs, prokaryotic life in, 528*f*,
  530–31
Hotspots, biodiversity, 1177, 1190–91
House mouse (*Mus musculus*), 392,
  B:24*f*, B:26. *See also* Mice
Howard, Alma, 221–22
Hox genes, **412**
  arthropod, 671
  in bilateral symmetry, 642
  Cambrian explosion and, 519–20
  in evolutionary change, 416
  evolutionary conservation of, 414–15
  as homologous, 508–9
  MADS-box genes and, 441
  mollusk, 663–64

as regulatory genes for body pattern
    formation, 412–14
  in segmentation, 645
  as tool-kit genes, 415
Hoyt, Dan, 986, 987*f*
Hubbard Brook Experimental Forest,
  1149–52, 1158–59
Human(s), **707**. *See also* Human
  population; Human reproduction
  benefits of biodiversity and ecosystem
    services for, 1187–88, 1192–93
  Bloom's taxonomy for cognitive skills
    of, B:29–B30*t*
  development of, 419*f*, 420*f*, 423–25 (*see
    also* Animal development)
  digestive system of, 80–81, 848*f*, 887*f*
  diseases and disorders of (*see* Diseases
    and disorders, human)
  ecological impacts of (*see* Human
    impacts)
  endocrine system and hormones
    of, 991–95 (*see also* Hormones,
    animal)
  endoskeletons of, 981–83
  essential nutrients for, 884*t*, 885*t* (*see
    also* Animal nutrition)
  ethical issues of (*see* Ethical issues)
  evolution of, 705–8
  eyes of, 960–64
  gas exchange in (*see* Gas exchange)
  genome size of, 390, 396
  hearts of, 921–23 (*see also* Circulatory
    systems)
  Homo sapiens scientific name for, 8–9
  hormones in stress responses of,
    1000–1001
  Human Genome Project and genome
    of, 378, **389**, 391, 399–400
  immune system of (*see* Immune
    systems)
  importance of green plants to, 579–80
  importance of protostomes to, 658
  inflammatory response in,
    1040–41, 1042*t*
  inheritance in, 277–79
  memory and learning in, 945–49
  nervous system of, 942–49 (*see also*
    Nervous systems)
  number of chromosomes in, 238, 239
  phylogenetic tree of, B:10–B:11
  prokaryotic impacts on, 541–49
  sensory systems of (*see* Sensory
    systems, animal)
  thermoregulation in (*see*
    Thermoregulation)
  urinary system and kidney of, 872*f* (*see
    also* Kidneys)
  ventilation of lungs of, 909–10, 911*f*
    (*see also* Respiratory systems)
Human chorionic gonadotropin (hCG),
  1031
Human Genome Project, 378, **389**, 391,
  399–400
Human growth hormone (HGH), 369–74
Human immunodeficiency virus
  (HIV). *See* HIV (human
  immunodeficiency virus)
Human impacts
  anthropogenic biomes and, on
    terrestrial biomes, 1069
  on aquatic biomes, 1076
  on biodiversity (*see* Threats,
    biodiversity)
  on dispersal of species, 1063–64
  ecology and, 1059–60
  on ecosystems, 1149

on global carbon cycle, 1161–62
global climate change from (see Global climate change)
on global net primary productivity, 1156
on global water cycle, 1160
human population growth and, 1101–2, 1117–18
on nutrient cycling, 1158
protection of metapopulations from, 1118–20
on soil erosion, 779–81
Human population
  age structure of, 1115–16
  analyzing changes in growth rate of, 1116–18
  biodiversity loss and growth of, 1173, 1189
  global climate change and growth of, 1163–64
  impact of global growth of, 1101–2
  impacts of, 1069
  survivorship curves for, 1105
Human reproduction. See also Animal reproduction
  accessory fluids in semen in, 1023t
  childbirth and maternal mortality rates in, 1034
  contraception in, 1029–30
  female reproductive systems in, 1024–25
  gametogenesis in, 1016–18f
  male reproductive system in, 1021–23
  menstrual/ovarian cycle in, 1027–30
  pregnancy and gestation in, 1031–33
  puberty in, 1026–27
Hummingbirds, 594
Humoral response, **1051**–53
Humus, **778**–79f, **1156**–57
Huntington's disease, 278, 378–82
Hutchinson, G. Evelyn, 1125
Hutterites, 470
Huxley, Andrew, 932–36
Huxley, Hugh, 974
Hybridization, 498–502
Hybrid sterility as postzygotic isolation, 491t
Hybrid viability as postzygotic isolation, 491t
Hybrid zones, **500**–501
Hybrids, 258t, **259**
Hydrocarbons, 85–86, 90. See also Lipids
Hydrochloric acid, 28, 890–91
Hydrogen
  electronegativity of, 21
  lipids, hydrocarbons, and, 85–86
  in living organisms, 19
  molecules of, 21–23f, 33–36, 142–43
  in protein secondary structure, 48–49
  simple molecules from, 23
Hydrogen bonds, **25**
  of amino acids, 43f
  DNA complementary base pairing and, 62–63, 287
  in plant water transport, 765
  protein structure and, 48–50f
  RNA complementary base pairing and, 65–66
  specific heat of liquids and, 27t
  of water, 25–28
Hydrogen cyanide, 34–35
Hydrogen ions, **28**–30
Hydroids, 653–54
Hydrolysis, **45**
  of ATP to drive endergonic reactions, 143–44

of carbohydrates by enzymes to release glucose, 80–81
lysosomses, digestive enzymes, and, 114
of polymers to release monomers, 45
Hydronium ions, 28–29
Hydrophilic side chains, **44**
Hydrophilic substances, **25**, 44, 63, 87f
Hydrophobic interactions, **25**–26, 49–50f
Hydrophobic side chains, **44**
Hydrophobic substances, **25**, 63, 85–87f
Hydroponic growth, 777–78
Hydrostatic skeletons, **644**, 661–63, 980–**81**
Hydrostats, 981
Hydrothermal vents. See Deep-sea hydrothermal vents
Hydroxide ions, 28–30
Hydroxyl functional group, 37t–38, 58, 73–74, 85–87, 298, 318
Hyenas, 1024–25f
Hygiene hypothesis, **1056**
Hyperosmotic solutions, **862**–63
Hyperpolarization, **933**–34, 936
Hyperpolarized membranes, sensory transduction and, **953**–54
Hypersensitive reaction, **1055**–56
Hypersensitive response (HR), **815**–17, 818t
Hypertension, **923**
Hypertonic solutions, **93**
Hyphae, **574**, **616**–18, 624, 784
Hypocotyl, **434**, 833
Hypodermic insemination, 1020
Hypophasphatemia (vitamin D-resistant rickets), 279
Hyposmotic solutions, **863**–64
Hypothalamic–pituitary axis, **1005**, 1026–27
Hypothalamus, **856**, **1004**
  hormones of, in mammalian puberty, 1026–27
  photoperiod, sex hormones, and, 999, 1000f
  regulation of hormone production by, 1004–6
  thermoreception and, 967
  in thermoregulation, 856–57
Hypotheses, 3–5, 9–12, B:7
Hypotonic solutions, **92**, **755**

I

Ice, floating of, 26–27
Ichthyosaurs, 509–10, 985, 986
Ichthyostega, 984–85
Identification, species, 490, 492–93
Iguanas, 481
Imaging techniques, 119, B:18–B:21
Immigration, 482, **1103**, 1120, 1143–44
Immune systems, 713, **1037**–58
  adaptive immunity activation in, 1047–51
  adaptive immunity recognition in, 1041–47
  adaptive immunity responses and memory in, 1051–55
  coevolution of, 1133
  failures of, 1055–56
  fitness trade-offs and, 843–45
  HIV and helper T cells of human, 713–14
  HLA genes in human, 469–70
  inbreeding and, 471–72
  innate immunity in, 1038–41, 1042t
  micrograph of human, 1037f

pathogens, immunity, and three processes of, 1037–38
sexual selection, carotenoids, and, 475–76
Immunity, **1037**
Immunization, **1054**–55
Immunodeficiency diseases, 383–85, 724–25, 1056. See also AIDS (acquired immune deficiency syndrome); HIV (human immunodeficiency virus)
Immunoglobulins, **1044**–47. See also Antibodies
Immunological memory, 1053, **1054**–55
Immunostaining, cell, B:18–B:19
Impact hypothesis, **521**–23
Imperfect flowers, **827**
Implantation, **1031**
Import, nutrient, 1157–58
In situ conservation, 1189–91
In situ hybridization, **411**–12, 440, 458–59f
In vitro metabolic pathway research, 158
In vitro protein-synthesis systems, 326–27
In vitro translation systems, 324
In vivo vs. in vitro, 122
Inactivated virus vaccines, 1055
Inbreeding, **470**–72
Inbreeding depression, **471**–72, 1180
Inclusive fitness, **1096**–97
Incomplete digestive tracts, 886–87
Incomplete dominance, **272**, 273f, 276, 277t
Incomplete metamorphosis, **672**
Independent assortment, principle of, 247–48, 249f, 263–64, **265**–67, 270
Independent variables, graphing, B:4–B:6
Indeterminate growth, **732**
Indole acetic acid (IAA). See Auxin
Induced fit, **145**
Inducers, **338**, 343
Inducible defenses, **815**, **1130**, 1131f
Industrial pollutants, 1182
Inertia, population growth, 1116
Infant diarrhea, 727
Infection threads, nitrogen-fixing bacteria, **788**
Infectious diseases. See Diseases, animal; Diseases and disorders, human
Infidelity, bird, 1020
Inflammatory response, **1040**–41, 1042t
Influenza viruses, 712, 713f, 723–24, 728, 1039, 1055
Information
  as characteristic of life, 69
  gene regulation and, 337–39f
  genetic, 2, 64, 67, 256–57 (see also Genes)
  hormones as carriers of, 209–10t
  plant processing of, 794–96
Infrasound detection, elephant, 957
Ingestion, 563–64, 637, 882–83f, 884–**86**
Inhalation, 909–11f
Inheritance. See also Chromosome theory of inheritance; Genetics; Mendelian genetics
  of acquired characters, 257, 446, 459
  autosomal, 269
  epigenetic, 352–53
  human, 277–79
  hypotheses on, 257
  particulate, 261–63
  polygenic, 275–76, 277t
  sex-linked, 268–69, 277t

Inhibition, enzyme, 149, 150
Inhibition, successional, **1141**
Inhibitory postsynaptic potentials (IPSPs), **940**–42
Initiation factors, **330**
Initiation phase
  enzyme catalysis, 146f–47
  eukaryotic transcription, 353–56 (see also Transcriptional control, eukaryotic)
  transcription, **318**–20
  translation, 329–30
Innate behavior, **1084**
Innate immune response, **1039**–41, 1042t. See also Immune systems
Innate immunity, **1038**–41, 1042t. See also Immune systems
Inner cell mass (ICM), **424**
Inner ear, **956**
Inorganic soil elements, 778–79f
Inositol triphosphate (IP$_3$), 213t
Inoue, Shin-ichiro, 797
Insecticides, 555, 1152–53
Insects, **675**. See also Arthropods
  altruism in, 1097–98
  characteristics and orders of, 675–76t
  competition in, 1083–84
  exoskeletons of, 983
  fungal infections of, 628–29
  fungal mutualisms with, 623
  honeybee language in, 1092–93
  metamorphosis in, 651, 672, 991f, 998
  mimicry in, 1129–30
  mutualisms of, 1133–35
  open circulatory systems of, 917
  osmoregulation in, 869–71
  photoreception by eyes of, 960
  plant defense responses to, 815, 817–19
  pollination by, 593–94, 608–9f
  as protostomes, 657–58
  taxon-specific survey of, 1175
  terrestrial adaptations of, 659
  tracheae of, 907–9
Insemination, hypodermic, 1020
Instantaneous rate of increase, **1111**f
Insulin, 47–48, 210t, 369, **897**–99, 992
Integral membrane proteins, 95
Integrated pest management, **1133**
Integrators, **854**, 1001
Integrins, 203f–**4**
Interactions. See Cell-cell interactions; Species interactions
Interbreeding, 499–502
Intercalated discs, **922**
Intercellular attachments. See Cell-cell attachments
Intercellular communication. See Cell-cell gaps
Intercellular connections, 204–9
Intergovernmental Panel on Climate Change (IPCC), 1164–66
Interleukin 2, 992
Intermediate filaments, 128t, **129**
Intermediate hosts, **666**
Intermediate (fast oxidative) muscle fibers, **979**–80
Intermediate phenotypes, 273f
Intermediates, catabolic, 157–58
Internal consistency, evolution and, 451–53
Internal environments, eukaryotic differential gene expression and, 349
Internal fertilization, animal, 650, 1019–20
Internal membranes, 108, 110

International DNA sequence repositories, 390
International System of Units, B:1
International Union for the Conservation of Nature (IUCN), 1178
Internet genome databases, 392
Interneurons, **929**
Internodes, stem, **735**
Interphase, **220**, 223f, 224f, 242f
Intersexual selection, **475**. *See also* Sexual selection
Interspecific competition, 1124–**25**
Interspecific interactions, 1113–15
Interstitial fluid, **918**–19
Intertidal zone, **1079**
Intestines. *See* Large intestines; Small intestines
Intrasexual selection, **475**. *See also* Sexual selection
Intraspecific competition, **1125**
Intraspecific interactions, 1113–15
Intrinsic rate of increase, population, **1107**
Introduction, primary literature, B:27t
Introns, **322**–23, 354, 357–58
Invasive species, **1063**, 1064f, 1083–84, **1181**, 1189
Inversions, chromosome, **314**
Invertebrates, **645**, 682, 686–88, 862
Involuntary muscles, **977**–78
Ion channels, **96**–99, 931
Ionic bonds, **22**–23f, 50
Ions, **22**, 781
  diffusion of, across lipid bilayers, 91–94
  electrolytes as, 862
  as enzyme cofactors, 147
  essential nutrients for animals and humans as, 884, 885t
  ionic bonds and, 22–23f
  lipid bilayer selective permeability and, 89
  plant exclusion mechanism for, 785–87
  plant nutrients in soil as, 781–82
  plant uptake mechanisms for, 783–84
Iridium, 521–22f
Iris, **960**, 961f
Irish elk, 447
Irish potato famine, 554, 574, 815
Iron, 166, 557, 885t
Irrigation, 1160
Island biogeography theory, 1143–45
Islets of Langerhans, 992–93
Isolation. *See* Genetic isolation; Physical isolation; Reproductive isolation
Isopods, 677
Isoprene, 85, 529
Isoprenoids, 85, 87
Isosmotic solutions, **862**
Isotonic solutions, **93**, 755
Isotopes, **20**, 621, B:15–B:16
Isthmus of Panama, 1063

J

Jacob, François, 2, 307–8, 338–39f, 342–43
Jawless vertebrates, 692
Jaws
  cichlid, 884–86
  hominin, 707
  vertebrate, 689, 692

Jeffreys, Alec, 397
Jellyfish, 653–54
Jenkins, David, 1136–37
Jenner, Edward, 1054–55
Jet propulsion, mollusk, 663–64f, 669
Joint angles, 981–82
Jointed appendages, 670–71
Jointed limbs, 649t
Joints (articulations), **981**–82
Joly, John, 762
Jones, Holly, 1191–92
Jürgens, Gerd, 435–36
Juvenile hormone (JH), **998**
Juveniles, **651**

K

K-P mass extinction, 521–23
Kandel, Eric, 946–48
Kangaroo rats, 1084
Karpilov, Y. S., 193
Karyogamy, **625**, 626–27
Karyotypes, **238**–39, 304f, 314f–**15**
Keeling, Charles David, 1163
Kelp forests, 685
Kelvin scale, 138
Kenrick, Paul, 585
Keratins, 129
Kerr, Warwick, 479–81
Keystone species, 1137–**38**
Kidneys, **871**–79
  antidiuretic hormone and, 1003
  filtration by renal corpuscle of, 873
  function of, 872–73
  hormonal control of, 877–78
  osmoregulation by distal tubule and collecting duct of, 877–78
  osmotic gradient creation by loop of Henle of, 874–77f
  reabsorption by proximal tublule of, 873–74
  structure and function of nephron regions and collecting duct, 878t
  structure of, 871–72
  urine formation in nonmammalian, 878–79
Killer T cells, 1050
Kilocalorie (kcal), **143**
Kinesin, **130**–31
Kinetic energy, **31**, 80, **137**–39, 145–47
Kinetochore microtubules, **224**–27, 241, 243
Kinetochores, **224**–27, **241**
Kingdoms, taxonomic, 8
Kinocilium, **955**
Kin selection, 1095–**97**
Knock-out alleles, **305**
Koch, Robert, 532
Koch's postulates, **532**
Komai, Yutaka, 908
Kortschak, Hugo, 193
Krebs, Hans, 162
Krill, 1086
Kudzu, 1063, 1064f
Kuhn, Werner, 875

L

Labia majora, **1024**–25f
Labia minora, **1024**–25f
Labor, childbirth and, **1034**
Laboratory mice, B:26. *See also* Mice

lac operon, **342**–44
Lacerta vivipara lizards, 1102–3, 1104–6
Lacks, Henrietta, B:21, B:22f
Lactate, 157, 172–73f
Lactation, **694**, 696, **1030**–31
Lacteals, **892**
Lactic acid fermentation, **172**–73f
Lactose, 75–76
Lactose fermentation, 540
Lactose metabolism, 338–44
Ladybird beetles, 1166t, 1167
Lagging strands, DNA, **292**–96
Lakes, 1075–76, **1077**
Lamarck, Jean-Baptiste de, 445–46, 459
Laminins, 203f–**4**
Lampreys, 691, 697
Lancelets, 686–87
Land plants, 583–97f. *See also* Plant(s)
  angiosperm radiation of, 595–97f
  appearance of, in Paleozoic era, 515
  creosote bushes as oldest living, 825
  Devonian explosion diversification of, 520
  drugs derived from, 580t
  fungal mutualisms with, 613, 614, 619–23
  green plants as green algae and, 577–78 (*see also* Green plants)
  key lineages of, 598–99, 601–9f
  life cycles of, 823–25
  molecular phylogeny of, 583
  morphological differences among, 580–81
  origin of, 581–82
  phylogenetic tree and evolutionary changes of, 586, 587f
  phylogenetic tree of pollination in, 831f
  Plantae and, 569
  reproductive adaptations of, 586–95 (*see also* Plant reproduction)
  rRNA sequences for, 7
  similarities between green algae and, 580
  terrestrial adaptations of, 584–95
  upright growth of, 585
  UV radiation protection in, 585
  vascular tissue in, 585–86
  water loss prevention by cuticles and stomata in, 584–85
Lander, Eric, 400
Language, honeybee, 1092–93
Large intestines, 848f, 887f, 888, **896**–97
Larvae, **651**, 660–61f, 668, 998
Late endosome, **126**
Late prophase I, 242–43, 244
Latency, viral, 721–**22**
Lateral buds, **735**
Lateral gene transfer, **394**, 561, **712**
  in eukaryotes, 396, 399
  mutations and, 483–84, 485
  in origin of mitochondria, 561
  in prokaryotes, 394–95
  by viruses, 712
Lateral line system, **958**–59
Lateral roots, **733**, 734–35f, 742
Latin and Greek word roots, B:3
Latitudinal gradients
  in net primary production of terrestrial biomes, 1155–56
  in species richness, 1144–45, 1176
Laurance, William, 1180
Law of succession, 447
Leaching, soil, **781**
Lead, 446
Lead, electron microscopy and, B:19

Leading strands, DNA, 291–**92**, 294t, 295
Leak channels, **931**
Learning, 946, **1084**
  behaviors and, 1084–85
  memory and, 945–49
Leaves (leaf), **735**
  abscission of, 807, 813
  cells of, 118
  characteristics of, 737, 738f
  cotyledons as, 833–34
  genetic control of shape of, 436–38
  modified, 739–40, 790
  morphological diversity in, 737–38
  passage of oxygen and carbon dioxide through stomata of, 192–93
  phenotypic plasticity in, 738–39f
  in shoot systems, 735 (*see also* Shoot systems)
  water loss prevention by, 754–55, 765–66
Leeches, 667
Leghemoglobin, **787**–88
Legumes, **787**–88
Leishmaniasis, 555t
Lemmings, 461
Lemurs, 704
Length, metric units and conversions for, B:1t
Lens, **960**, 961f
Lenski, Richard, 484–85
Lenticels, **750**
Lentiviruses, 724
Lepidosaurs, 702
Leptin, **1000**–1003, 1026
Lesion studies, 944–45
Leucine, 122, 326–27
Leukocytes (white blood cells), **912**, **1039**–41, 1042t
Libraries, DNA. *See* DNA libraries
Lichens, **598**, **623**, 631
Life, 1–15
  ATP as energy for, 154 (*see also* ATP (adenosine triphosphate); Cellular respiration; Metabolic pathways)
  biological science in the study of, 1, 9–14 (*see also* Biology; Science)
  cell theory and cells of, 2–5 (*see also* Cell[s])
  characteristics of, in living organisms, 2 (*see also* Organisms)
  characteristics of viruses vs. characteristics of, 711–12
  chemical evolution of (*see* Chemical evolution)
  chemical reactions in, 136–37 (*see also* Chemical reactions)
  domains of, 528–29 (*see also* Archaea domain; Bacteria domain; Eukarya domain)
  experiments on origin of, 33–36
  extremophiles and extraterrestrial, 531
  history of (*see* History of life)
  origin of viruses in origin of, 723
  RNA world hypothesis and characteristics of, 69
  speciation and tree of, 6–8 (*see also* Speciation; Tree of life)
  taxonomy and classification of, 8–9 (*see also* Taxonomy)
  theory of evolution of, by natural selection, 5–6 (*see also* Evolution; Natural selection)
  time line of, in fossil record, 513–16
Life cycles, **241**
  animal, 651–52, 654f
  dog, 241–42

fungus, 625–27
land plant, 589–90, 823–25
plant, 433f
protist, 566–69
Life histories, 1105, **1106–7**, 1118. *See also* Life tables
Life spans, protein, 360
Life tables, **1104–5**, 1106f, 1118, 1119f. *See also* Life histories
Lifelong plant growth, 436
Ligaments, **982**
Ligand-gated channels, **940**
Ligands, **940**
Ligase. *See* DNA ligases
Light-capturing reactions, photosynthetic, 177–90. *See also* Photosynthesis
  absorption of light energy by pigments, 179–82
  in chloroplasts, 178–79f
  discovery of, 177–78
  electromagnetic spectrum and, 179
  electron excitation in, 182–84
  photosystem I in, 186–87
  photosystem II in, 184–86
  Z-scheme model for photosystem interactions in, 187–90
Light chain polypeptides, **1044–46**
Light energy
  animal sight and, 647t (*see also* Photoreception, animal)
  in aquatic biomes, 1074, 1075f
  capture of, in photosynthesis (*see* Light-capturing reactions, photosynthetic)
  carbohydrate storage of, as chemical energy, 80
  chemical evolution and, 31, 34–35
  in chemical reactions, 137
  electromagnetic spectrum of, 179
  land plant adaptations to, 584–85
  in mating, 1087–88
  in plant water transport, 765
  primary producers and, 1149–50
  prokaryotic photosynthesis and, 541
  in terrestrial biomes, 1068–69
  transformation of, into biomass, 1149–50
  in tropical and polar climates, 1066
  vegetative development and, 436
Light microscopy, 119, 241, 557–58, B:18
Lightning, chemical evolution and, 31, 33–34
Lignin, **202**, **585**, **745**
  in decomposition rates, 1157
  fungal digestion of, 612–15, 623–24
  in secondary cell walls, 202, 585, 745, 763
Likens, Gene, 1149–50
Limbs
  animal movement and, 649–50f
  arthropod, 670–71
  evolutionary loss of, 416, 644
  as structural homology, 450
  tetrapod, 448, 689, 692–93
Limiting factors, population size and growth, 1109–12
Limiting nutrients, **777**
Limnetic zone, **1077**
Lincoln, Abraham, 273
Lindeman, Raymond, 1150
Line of best fit, scatterplot, B:5
Lineages, **491–93**, **507**, B:10–B:11. *See also* Clades; Monophyletic groups
Lines, scatterplot, B:5
Lingual lipase, **889**, 895t

Linkage, **270–71**, 274f, 277t
Linkage maps, **379**. *See also* Genetic maps
Linked genes. *See* Linkage
Linnaeus, Carolus, 8–9
Lipid bilayers, **88**. *See also* Plasma membranes
  artificial membranes as experimental, 88–89
  in chemical evolution, 93–94
  membrane proteins and, 94–101
  permeability of, 89–92
  space-filling model of, 84f
Lipid-insoluble hormones, 209, 210–11
Lipid-soluble hormones, 209, 210, 211f, 996, 1006
Lipids, **85**
  animal digestion of, 888, 889, 894–96
  bond saturation and hydrocarbon structure of, 85–86
  in characteristics of domains of life, 529t
  chemical evolution of, 88
  nucleic acid polymerization and, 60–61
  prokaryotic glycolipids and, 109
  smooth ER and, 114
  structure of membrane, 87–88, 90
  types of, 86–87
Lipopolysaccharide (LPS), 845
Liposomes, 88–89, 90, 92–93
Liquids, specific heat of some, 27t
Literature, primary, B:26–B:27
Littoral zone, **1077**
Live virus vaccines, 1055
Liver, 115, 162, 848f, 887f, **894**
Liverworts, 601
Lizards
  adaptive radiations of, 516
  extinction rates of, 1183–84
  impacts of global climate change on, 1167
  life table and life history of, 1104–6
  mating in, 1087–89
  movement of, 972f
  niche concept and interspecific competition of, 1125
  pineal eye of, 999, 1000f
  range of, 1102–3
  as reptiles, 702
  urine formation in, 878f–79
ln notation, logarithms and, B:9
Loams, 778
Lobe-finned fishes, **699**
Lobes, brain, 944
Lobsters, 677
Lock-and-key model, enzyme catalysis, 54, 144–45
Locomotion, animal, **973**, 983–88. *See also* Animal movement
Locomotion, protist, 565–66
Locus (loci), gene, **266**
Loewi, Otto, 938–39
Log notation, logarithms and, B:9
Logarithms, B:9
Logistic population growth, **1108–12**
Lohmann, Kenneth, 1090–91
Long-day plants, **802**
Long interspersed nuclear elements (LINEs), **396**, 397f
Loop of Henle, 872, **874–77f**, 878t
Loose connective tissue, 846t, **847**
Lophophores, **660–61f**
Lophotrochozoans, 638t, **645**, 658, 659f, 660–70. *See also* Protostomes
Lorenz, Konrad, 1084

Lorises, 704
Losos, Jonathan, 516
Loss-of-function alleles, **305**
Loss-of-function mutations, 471, 481–82, 485
Lou Gehrig's disease (ALS), 408
Love darts, 1020
Lovejoy, Thomas, 1180
Low-order cognitive (LOC) skills, B:20–B:30t
LUCA (last universal common ancestor), **8, 32**
Lumen, **112, 178**
Luminescence, 377
Lungfish, 448, 692–93, 699
Lungs, 692–93, **909–12**, 916
LUREs, 832
Luteal phase, **1027**
Luteinizing hormone (LH), **1006, 1026**, 1027–30
Lycophytes (club mosses), 603
Lyme disease, 546
Lymph, **919**, **1043**
Lymph nodes, **1043**
Lymphatic system, 233f, **919**, **1043**
Lymphocytes, **1042–48**. *See also* B cells; T cells
Lynx, 1113–15
Lysine, 311
Lysogeny, **721–22**
Lysosomes, **114**, 117t
Lysozyme, 716, **1039**
Lytic cycle, viral, **716**. *See also* Replicative growth, viral

M

M phase, **220**, 223–29, 232
M phase-promoting factor (MPF), **229–31**
MacArthur, Robert, 1143–44
MacArthur–Wilson model, 1143–45
McClintock, Barbara, 396
McClintock, Martha, 967
McGinnis, William, 415
Macromolecular machines, **50**
Macromolecules, **44**, **54**, 157–58, B:13–B:14, B:20–B:21. *See also* Carbohydrates; Lipids; Molecules; Nucleic acids; Organic molecules; Proteins
Macronutrients, **777**, 780t
Macrophages, **1040–41**, 1042t
Mad cow disease, 53
MADS box, **441**
Maggot flies, 496–97
Magnesium, 777, 780t, 885t
Magnetic fields, 646, 647t, 968–69, 1090–91
Magnetite, 108, 534, 1090
Magnetoreception, **968–69**
Magnetoreceptors, **953**
Magnifications, microscope, B:18
Maidenhair ferns, 498
Maize, 5–6, 579
Major histocompatibility (MHC) proteins, **1048–51**, 1053
Maladaptive traits, **192**
Malaria, 554–55, 573, 1132
Malaria, avian, 1062
Male gametes. *See* Sperm
Male reproductive systems, 1016–17, 1019–23
Males
  in age structure of human population, 1115–16

  chromosomes of, 238
  female mate choice and, 475–76, 1088–89
  female-mimicking behaviors of, 1094–95
  gametangia of, 587
  male-male competition of, 476–77
  plant flower parts, 827
  plant gametophytes, 828–29
  sex chromosomes of, 268
  sex hormones of, 999
  sex-linked diseases of, 278–79
  sexual selection and, 475–78
  sperm as reproductive cells of, 237
  visual cues from, in mating, 1088
Malignant tumors, **233**
Malpighian tubules, **870–71**
Malthus, Thomas Robert, 453, 1116
Mammals, **696**. *See also* Animal(s); Vertebrates
  amniotic eggs in, 693–94
  in Cenozoic era, 515
  citric acid cycle in, 162
  cleavage of, 423–24
  cloning of, 409
  digestive enzymes of, 895t
  diversification of, 522–23
  ecological efficiency of biomass production by, 1152
  fungal mutualisms with, 629
  gametogenesis in, 1016–18f
  hormones in growth of, 999
  house mouse as model organism for, B:26
  lineages of, 696, 700–701
  mouthparts of, 884, 885f
  nitrogenous wastes of, 865
  osmoregulation in, 871–79
  ovarian cycle of, 1027f
  overhunting of, 1181
  parental care in, 694
  pregnancy in, 1029–34
  primates, hominids, and humans, 704–8 (*see also* Human[s])
  reproduction in, 1021–30
  seed dispersal by, 835
Mammary glands, **696**
Mandibles, arthropod, **677**
Manipulation, altruism and, 1097–98
Mantle, **662–63**
Map orientation (true navigation), migration and, 1089, 1090–91
Mapping
  biodiversity hotspots and, 1177
  communities, 1137
  concept, B:28
  genetic (*see* Genetic maps)
  species richness and endemism, 1176
Marfan syndrome, 272–73
Margulis, Lynn, 560
Marine biomes
  carbon cycle in, 556–57
  characteristics of, 1075, 1078–79
  impacts of global climate change on net primary productivity of, 1168–69
  loss of biodiversity from overfishing of, 1181
  net primary production of, 1154–56
  osmoregulation in, 862–63, 866–68
Mark-recapture studies, 1103f, 1113, 1113
Markow, Therese, 469–70
Marshes, **1077**
Marsupials, 696, **701**, 1031
Martindale, Mark, 642, 663–64

Mass, metric units and conversions for, B:1t
Mass extinctions, 505f, **520**–23, 1178. See also Extinctions
Mass feeders, 648t, **649**, 662f, **884**
Mass number, **19**
Mast cells, **1040**–41, 1042t
Mate choice, female, 475–76, 1088–89
Materials and methods, primary literature, B:27t
Maternal chromosome, **239**
Maternal nurture, mammalian, 1030–33
Mathematical models, population ecology, 1061
Mating
  body odor and, 470
  deceitful communication in, 1094–95
  environmental cues in proximate causation of, 1087–88
  fertilization and, 1018–20
  fungal hyphae mating types in, 624
  giraffe necks and, 9–11
  Hardy–Weinberg principle and random vs. nonrandom, 468–70
  inbreeding as nonrandom, 470–72
  in Mendelian genetics, 257–58 (see also Crosses)
  penis size and, 1022–23
  pheromones and, 215–16, 966–67
  sexual selection and, 475–78, 1088–89
  speciation in interbreeding of isolated populations, 499–502
  unusual strategies for, 1020
Matthaei, Heinrich, 311–12
Maturation
  bird egg, 1024f
  lymphocyte, 1043
  seed, 834
Mayr, Ernst, 490, 495, 1083
Measles virus, 728, 1055
Measurements, combining, B:3
Mechanical energy, 137
Mechanical prezygotic isolation, 491t
Mechanistic causation. See Proximate causation
Mechanoreception, **954**–59
Mechanoreceptors, **953**, 954
Mediator, **356**
Medicine. See also Diseases and disorders, human; Drugs
  bacteria in, 531–33, 545–47
  ecosystem provisioning services and, 1187
  preventive, for HIV/AIDS, 722
Mediolateral leaf axis, 436–37f
Medium, growth, **339**
Medulla, kidney, **872**
Medulla oblongata, **688**
Medullary respiratory center, 911–12
Medusa, **653**–54
Megapascal (MPa), **756**
Megasporangia, **590**, 592, 828
Megaspores, **590**, 592, **828**
Meiosis, 219, 238, 823
  asexual vs. sexual reproduction and, 247
  chromosome types and, 238
  discovery of, 237–38
  in eukaryotes, 553
  as explanation for Mendelian principles, 266–67
  genetic variation from, 247–49

heredity and chromosome changes in, 247
  meiosis I and meiosis II in, 240–46
  mistakes in, 249–51
  mitosis and, in cell cycle, 219–20, 244t, 245f (see also Cell cycle; Mitosis)
  overview of, 239–42
  paradox of sexual reproduction and, 251–53
  in plant reproduction, 823
  ploidy concept and, 238–39
  sex-linked inheritance and, 268–69
  synapsis and crossing over in prophase I of, 246
  theories on existence of sexual reproduction and, 251–53
  types of mistakes in, 249–51
  vocabulary for describing cell chromosomal makeup, 240t
Meiosis I, **240**–44, 245f
Meiosis II, **240**–41, 244–46
Melatonin, **999**
Melotto, Maeli, 816
Membrane channels, plasmodesmata and, 208–9
Membrane lipids, 87. See also Lipid bilayers; Lipids; Plasma membranes
Membrane potentials, **783**, **806**, **930**. See also Action potentials
  calculating, with Nernst equation, 932f
  as electrical potentials across plasma membranes, 930–33
  in photoreception, 962–63
  in plant nutrient uptake, 783–84
  in plant wind/touch responses, 806
  in sensory transduction and, 953–54
Membrane proteins, 94–101
  active transport by pumps, 99–100
  amphipathic proteins as, 94
  cell adhesion proteins and, 206–7
  cellular slime molds and, B:25
  development of fluid-mosaic model of plasma membranes and, 94–96f
  in extracellur matrix, 204
  facilitated diffusion via, 96–99
  functions of, 54
  isolating with detergents, 96
  in osmoregulation, 867–88
  plant cell–cell signals and, 795
  plasma membranes, intracellular environment, and, 100–101
  summary of passive and active transport by, 101f
  systems for studying, 96
  in translocation, 769–72
  in water and electrolyte movement, 864–65
Membranes. See also Endomembrane system; Plasma membranes
  artificial, 88–89
  internal, 108, 110t
  mitochondrial, 115, 166–68
  thylakoid, 116
Memory, 945, **946**–49. See also Immunological memory; Learning
Memory cells, **1053**–55
Mendel, Gregor, 257–66. See also Mendelian genetics
Mendelian genetics, 256–79. See also Genetics
  applying rules of, to human inheritance, 277–79

chromosome theory of inheritance and, 256–57, 266–69 (see also Chromosome theory of inheritance)
  dihybrid crosses in, 263–65
  discrete traits in, 275
  exceptions and extensions to rules of, 269–77t (see also Extensions, Mendelian exceptions and)
  experimental system of Gregor Mendel in, 257–61
  importance of, 256–57
  meiosis and principles of, 266–67
  particulate inheritance in, 261–63
  rediscovery of, 266
  single-trait experiments in, 259–63
  testcrosses in, 265–66
  two-trait experiments in, 263–66
  vocabulary of, 258t
Meniscus, 26, **762**
Menke, Sean, 1064
Menstrual cycle, mammalian, **1027**–30
Menstruation, **1027**
Meristems, **407**, **434**, **740**
  cambrium, 748–50
  floral, in reproductive development, 438–41
  in plant development, 407, 412, 434
  production of primary plant bodies by, 740–42
  in vegetative development, 436, 437f
Meselson, Matthew, 288f, 289
Meselson–Stahl experiment, 288f, 289
Mesoderm, 424f–**25**, 426–29, **641**
Mesoglea, **653**
Mesophyll cells, **193**–94
Mesozoic era, **515**
Messenger RNAs (mRNAs), **119**, **307**. See also RNA (ribonucleic acid)
  alternative splicing of, 357–58
  alternative splicing of, and human genome size, 400
  bacterial vs. eukaryotic processing of, 361f
  in cDNA libraries, 372f
  eukaryotic processing of, 321–24, 349, 356–59
  in functional genomics, 400–402
  in gene expression, 307–8
  in genetic code, 310–12
  in morphogen research, 411–12
  RNA interference and, 358–59
  synthesis of, in transcription, 318–21f, 325t
  in transcription and translation, 308
  translation of, into polypeptides, 324–26, 328–31 (see also Translation)
  viral, 719
  visualizing, via in situ hybridization, 411f
Meta-analysis, **1131**
Metabolic diversity
  animal, 646–49
  fungal, 623–24
  prokaryotic, 538–41, 545–49
  protist, 563–69
Metabolic pathways, 150–52, 156–58, 172–73f, 305–7. See also Cellular respiration
Metabolic rate, **851**–52
Metabolic water, **843**, 864
Metabolomics, 390
Metagenomics (environmental sequencing), 395, 534–**35**, 1173, 1175
Metallothioneins, 785–**86**

Metamorphosis, **651**, **997**
  amphibian, 696, 997–98
  in animal life cycles, 651
  arthropod, 672
  echinoderm, 685
  insect, 675, 991f, 998
Metaphase, 224f, **225**, 245f
Metaphase I, 242f, 243, 244, 245f
Metaphase II, 243f, 244
Metaphase plate, **225**, 243
Metapopulations, **1103**
  dynamics of, 1112–13
  habitat fragmentation and, 1179–80
  in population ecology, 1103
  preserving endangered, 1118–20
  theory of island biogeography and, 1143–44
Metastasis, cancer, **233**
Meteorites, 33, 74
Methane, 23, 24f, 33–34, 541, 549, 1163, B:12–B:13
Methanotrophs, 541
Methionine, 311, 324, 329–30
Methly salicylate (MeSA), **816**
Methods, biological. See also Bioskills; Process boxes
  enrichment cultures, 534, 540
  environmental sequencing (see Environmental sequencing [metagenomics])
  genetic engineering (see Genetic engineering)
  Gram stains, 536–37
  histograms, 457
  quantitative (see Quantitative Methods boxes)
  replica plating, 339–41
  for studying animals, 637–38
  for studying fungi, 615–18
  for studying green plants, 580–83
  for studying prokaryotes, 533–36
  for studying protists, 557–59
  for studying viruses, 714–22
Methods and materials, primary literature, B:27t
Metric system, B:1–B:3
Meyerowitz, Elliot, 439–41
MHC proteins. See Major histocompatibility (MHC) proteins
Mice, 308, 309f, 313, 414–15, 851, 1001–3, B:24f, B:25
Micelles, 88, 94
Microarrays, DNA, 400–402
Microbes, **530**. See also Archaea; Bacteria
Microbiology, **530**
Microelectrodes, measuring membrane potentials with, 932–33
Microfibrils, **202**
Microfilaments (actin filaments), 106f, 127–29, 228
Micrographs, B:19
Micronutrients, 777, 780t
Micropyle, **828**
MicroRNAs (miRNAs), 358–**59**
Microsatellites, 396–**98**f
Microscopy
  of muscle fibers, 973–74
  studying cell structure with, 2, 107, 118–19, 557–58
  types of, B:18–B:21
  video, 170, B:20
Microsporangia, **590**, 592, 828–29
Microspores, **590**, 592, **829**
Microsporidia, 618, 628
Microsporocytes, 828–29

Boldface page numbers indicate a glossary entry; page numbers followed by an *f* indicate a figure; those followed by *t* indicate a table.

Microtektites, 521–22f
Microtubule organizing centers (MTOCs), **129**, 224–25, 226t
Microtubules, **129**. *See also* Cytokinesis
  image of, 106f
  in meiosis, 241
  in mitosis, 224–27
  structure and function of, 128t, 129–31
Microvilli, **873**–74, **892**
Midbrain, **688**
Middle ear, **956**
Middle lamella, 204
Migration, **1089**
  allopatric speciation by, 494–95
  hypotheses on ultimate causation of, 1091
  magnetoreception in bird, 968–69
  metapopulation extinction vs., 1112f–13
  navigation strategies in proximate causation of, 1089–91
Miller, Stanley, 33–34, 59
Millipedes, 675
Millivolt (mV), **930**
Milner, Brenda, 945
Mimicry, 1094–95, **1129**–30
Mineralocorticoids, **1003**
Minerals, **884**
  as essential nutrients for animals and humans, 884, 885t
  nucleic acid polymerization and, 60–61
  as nutrients for plants, 776–79f, 780t (*see also* Nutrients, plant)
  synthesis of monosaccharides from, 74
Minisatellites, 396–98f
Miscarriages, 470
Misfolding, protein, 53
Mismatch repair, DNA, **298**–99
Missense mutations, 313–14t
Mistakes, DNA synthesis, 297–301, 313–14
Mistletoe, 789, 790f
Mitchell, Peter, 169
Mitochondria, **115**
  citric acid cycle in, 162–65
  functions of, 115–16
  origin of, in protists, 560–61
  oxidation of NADH and FADH$_2$ in, 166–68
  in parietal cells, 891
  in proximal tubules, 874
  pyruvate processing in, 161–62
  replacement rate for, 119
  structure and function of, 117t
Mitochondrial DNA (mtDNA), 500–501, 560–61
Mitochondrial matrix, **115**, **161**, 162–65
Mitogen-activated protein kinase (MAPK), 150, **213**–14
Mitosis, **219**–29
  asexual reproduction vs. sexual reproduction and, 247
  cell cycle and, 222–23
  daughter cell production by cytokinesis in, 227–29
  discovery of phases of, 220–22
  events in, 223–26
  meiosis and, in cell cycle, 219–20, 244t, 245f (*see also* Cell cycle; Meiosis)
  movement of chromosomes during anaphase of, 226–27
Mitosis-promoting factor (MPF), 406
Mitotic spindle forces, 226
Mockingbirds, 449–50

Model organisms, **257**, B:23–B:26. *See also Escherichia coli* (*E. coli*); Fruit flies; Mustard plant; Roundworms; *Saccharomyces cerevisiae*
  bread mold, 305, 629
  cellular slime mold (*Dictyostelium discoideum*), B:23–B:25
  characteristics of, B:23
  in developmental biology, 408
  genomes of, 392
  liverworts, 601
  peas as, in Mendelian genetics, 257–66
  protostome, 658
Models
  animal, of disease, 382
  condensed eukaryotic DNA, 348f
  DNA synthesis, 289–95
  eukaryotic transcription initiation, 356, 357f
  mathematical, of genetic drift, 480f
  molecular, 24, B:12–B:13
Mode of transmission, **277**
Modified leaves, 739–40, 790
Modified roots, 734–35
Modified stems, 736–37
Moisture
  in decomposition rates, 1157
  terrestrial biomes and, 1068–69 (*see also* Precipitation; Water)
Molaison, Henry Gustav, 945
Molarity, **29**
Mold, bread, 305, 629
Mole, **29**
Molecular biology, 304, 305, 307–9, 368–69, B:13–B:16. *See also* Genetic engineering
Molecular chaperones, **52**–53, **331**–32
Molecular formulas, 24, B:12–B:13
Molecular level, anatomy and physiology at, 849f
Molecular machines, 108
Molecular phylogenies
  of animals, 638, 640f
  eukaryote and protist, 558, 559f
  of fungi, 618–19
  green plant, 582–83
  human, 707–8
  vertebrate, 691
Molecular weight, **29**
Molecules, **21**. *See also* Macromolecules
  atomic structure and, 19–21
  in bottom-up research approach to chemical evolution, 32–33
  carbon and organic, 36–38 (*see also* Organic molecules)
  cell-cycle regulatory, 229–31
  in chemical reactions, 24
  covalent bonding and, 21–23
  development of phylogenetic tree of life from rRNA, 6–8
  DNA (*see* DNA [deoxyribonucleic acid])
  enzyme catalysis and substrate, 54
  ionic bonding and, 22–23f
  measuring amounts of, using radioimmunoassay, B:16
  nuclear transport of, 119–21
  reading chemical structures of, B:13–B:13
  research on proteins as first self-replicating, 42, 55
  RNA (*see* RNA [ribonucleic acid])
  separating and visualizing, B:13–B:16
  shapes and geometry of simple, 23–24
  simple, from carbon, hydrogen, nitrogen, and oxygen, 23

  solutes as (*see* Solutes)
  visualizing, in 3-D, B:20–B:21
Mollusks, 638t, 657–58, 662–64, 668–69, 1175
Molting, **670**, 983
Molybdenum, as plant nutrient, 777, 780t
Momentum, population growth, 1116
Monarch butterflies, 1091
Monkeys, 704–5, 724–25, 1098
Monoamines, 941t
Monocots, **596**, 742f, 834, 837
Monod, Jacques, 307–8, 338–39f, 342–43, B:23
Monoecious species, **827**, 828f
Monogamy, 722
Monohybrid crosses, **259**–61
Monomers, **44**–46, 58–59, 72–75. *See also* Polymerization
Monophyletic groups, **491**–93, **507**–8, **536**, 557, B:10–B:11. *See also* Clades; Lineages
Monosaccharides, **72**–75. *See also* Carbohydrates
Monosodium glutamate (MSG), 965
Monotremes, 696, **700**, 1031
Morgan, Thomas Hunt, 267–71, 274f, B:25
Morphogens, 410–14, 435–36
Morphology, **107**, **450**
  adaptive radiations and, 517
  of eukaryotic lineages, 558t
  evolution of animal (*see* Evolutionary innovations, animal)
  fungal, 615–18
  of green plants, 580–81
  lophotrochozoan, 660–61
  morphospecies concept and, 490–91
  phylogenies based on, 510, 511f
  of prokaryotic and eukaryotic cells, 107
  of protists, 557–58
  structural homology in, 450–51
  viral, 715, 725
Morphospecies concept, **490**–91, 492t
Mortality rates. *See* Death rates, animal
Mosquitos, 555, 672
Mosses, 176f, 581, 601–2, 824f–25
Moths, 952–53, 966–67
Motility. *See* Movement
Motor neurons, **929**, 976–77
Motor proteins, 54, **128**–31, 133, 228, 241
Mountain pine beetles, 1166t, 1167
Mountain ranges, climate and, 1066–67
Mouse, 392, B:24f, B:25. *See also* Mice
Mouths
  digestion in, 888–89
  human, 887f
  lophotrochozoan, 662
  mammalian, 701
  mouthpart adaptations for, 884–86
  protostome vs. deuterostome, 644–45, 658
  taste as chemoreception by, 964–65
Movement
  animal (*see* Animal movement)
  cell (*see* Cell movement)
  prokaryotic, 109, 536, 537f
  protist, 565–66
  wind/touch responses and plant, 806
Mucins, 889
Mucosal-associated lymphoid tissue (MALT), **1043**
Mucous cells, **890**
Mucus, **889**, **1038**, 1042

Mudslides, 779–81
Müller, Fritz, 1130
Müllerian inhibitory substance, **999**
Müllerian mimicry, **1130**
Multicellularity, **204**, **562**, **846**
  cell–cell interactions for, 200–201
  cell–cell signaling and, 209–10t
  in characteristics of domains of life, 529t
  in eukaryotes, 8, 553
  gene regulation and, 348–49
  intercellular connections and, 204–9
  origin of, in animal evolution, 638–40
  in Paleozoic era, 515
  protist, 562–63
Multichambered hearts, 919–21
Multidrug resistance, 456
Multinucleate muscle cells, 977
Multiple allelism, **271**–72, 277t
Multiple fertilization, prevention of, 421–23
Multiple fruits, **834**, 835f
Multiple sclerosis (MS), **937**–38, 1056
Multiplication rule, probability, B:8
Mumps virus, 728
Münch, Ernst, 768
Muscle cells, 162, 200f, 427–29, 637
Muscle contraction, 637, 973–77. *See also* Animal movement
  actin-myosin interactions in, 974–76
  animal locomotion and, 984–88
  endoskeletons and, 982
  in evolution of animal movement, 972–73
  exoskeletons and, 983
  initiation of, by neurons, 976–77
  of skeletal muscles, 979–80
  sliding-filament model of, 973–74
Muscle fibers, **973**–74, 979–80
Muscle tissues, **847**–48, 973–74, 977–80
Muscular dystrophy, 200f
Muscular hydrostats, 981
Musculoskeletal structure, 984–85. *See also* Skeletal systems
Mushrooms, 612f, 614, 617, 626–27, 630. *See also* Fungi
Mus musculus, 392, B:24f, B:26. *See also* Mice
Mussels, 662, 668, 1130, 1131f, 1137–38
Mustard plant
  in blue-light phototropism research, 797
  in cytokinin research, 808
  embryogenesis in, 434f
  in flowering hormone research, 803
  genome of, 392
  in gravitropic response research, 804
  as model organism for plants, 433, B:24f, B:25
  in phloem loading research, 770–71
  in plant active ion exclusion research, 786–87
  in population ecology, 1106–8
  reproductive development of, 438–41
  stages of development of, 433f
  vegetative development of, 436–38
  in wind/touch response research, 805
Mutagens, **339**
Mutants, **268**. *See also* Mutation(s)
  creating experimental, 305, 339
  histone, 351
  homeotic, 413
  in study of flower development, 439–41
  in study of hormones and homeostasis, 1001–3

Mutants (continued)
   in study of plant embryogenesis, 435–36
   in testing of chromosome theory of inheritance, 268–69
   types of, in lactose metabolism, 339–41
Mutation(s), **268**, **313**, **466**, **483**. *See also* Mutants
   animal pollination and plant, 831–32
   antibiotic resistance in bacterial, 454–56
   bicoid gene and, 411
   cancer and, 361–63
   chromosome mutations, 314–15
   DNA and random, 312
   DNA synthesis mistakes and, 297–99
   effects on genetic diversity of types of, 483–84
   as evolutionary process, 460, 466, 484, 485–86*t*
   experimental studies of, 484–85
   gene families and, 398–99
   genetic diversity and, 1174
   genetic drift and silent, 479
   and genetic variation in plants, 438
   Hardy–Weinberg principle and, 468
   homeotic, 413
   of model organisms, B:25–B:26
   in natural populations, 485
   point mutations, 313–14
   in sympatric speciation by polyploidy, 497–99
   types of, 313–15
   in xeroderma pigmentosum (XP), 299–301
Mutualism(s), **830**, **1124**
   cooperation, altruism, and, 1098
   diversity of, 1133
   dynamism of, 1134–35
   endophytes and, 621–23
   fitness and impacts of, 1136*t*
   fungal, 619–23
   impacts of global climate change on, 1167
   mycorrhizae as, 620–21, 784
   natural selection and, 1133–34
   in pollination, 593–94, 830, 831*f*
Mutualistic relationships, **620**, **784**. *See also* Mutualism(s)
Mutualists, **613**. *See also* Mutualism(s)
Muybridge, Eadweard, 984–85
Mycelia, **546**, 615, **616**–18
Mycobacterium, 454–56, 546
Mycorrhizae, **784**
Mycorrhizal fungi, 613, **614**, 619–23, 1133
Myelin sheath, **937**
Myelination, 937–38
Myelomas, B-cell, 1045–46
Myers, Norman, 1177
Myoblasts, 428*f*–29
Myocardial infarctions, **925**
Myofibrils, **973**–74
Myoglobin, 979
Myosin, **974**
   in cytokinesis, 228
   interaction of actin and, 128–29
   movement and, 54
   in muscle contraction, 974–76
Myriapods, 675, **675**
Myxinoidea, 697
Myxogastrida, 570

N

N-terminus, 46, 328
Nabhan, Gary, 835–36
NAD$^+$ (nicotinamide adenine dinucleotide), **142**
   in aerobic respiration, 172
   in cellular respiration, 156
   in citric acid cycle, 163*f*–65
   in fermentation, 172–73*f*
   in glycolysis, 160*f*
   in photosystem I, 186–87
   in pyruvate processing, 161–62
NADH, **142**
   in aerobic respiration, 171–72
   in cellular respiration, 156
   in citric acid cycle, 162–65
   in fermentation, 172–73*f*
   oxidation of, 166–72
   in photosystem I, 186–87
   in pyruvate processing, 161–62
NADP$^+$ (nicotinamide adenine dinucleotide phosphate), **178**, 186–89
NADPH, **178**, 186–87
Na$^+$/K$^+$-ATPase. *See* Sodium-potassium pump
Naked viruses, 715
Names, scientific, 8–9
Nanobiology, 714
National Academy of Sciences, 883
National Center for Biotechnology Information (NCBI), 392
Native Americans, viral epidemics and, 712
Natural catastrophes, genetic bottlenecks and, 481–82
Natural experiments, **457**, **1186**–87
Natural logarithms, B:9
Natural populations, 481–83
Natural selection, 5, **454**, **465**
   in allopatric speciation, 495
   of animal mouthparts, 884
   artificial selection vs., 5–6, 453
   balancing selection, 474
   common misconceptions about evolution, adaptation, and, 459–62
   constraints on, 461–62
   deceitful communication and, 1094–95
   effects of, on individuals and on populations, 444*f*, 459–60
   effects of modes of, on genetic variation, 472
   as evolutionary process, 465, 486*t*
   in evolution of antibiotic resistance, 454–56
   fitness and adaptations in, 6, 454 (*see also* Adaptation(s); Fitness)
   four postulates of Charles Darwin on, 454
   in Galápagos finches, 456–59*f*
   genetic variation and, 482
   Hardy–Weinberg principle and, 468
   modes of, 475*t*
   mutualisms and, 1133–34
   as process component of theory of evolution by, 5–6, 444–45, 453–54 (*see also* Evolution)
   research on, 454–59*f*
   sexual selection and, 475–78
   species interactions and, 1124
   types of, 472–74
   viruses and, 721

Nature, cultural services of, 1188
Nauplius, **677**
Nautilus, 669
Navigation, migration and, 1089–91
Neanderthals, 376, 378, **707**
Nectar, **593**, **827**
Nectary, **827**
Needlelike leaves, 737–38*f*
Negative control, **341**–44, 345*f*, 351
Negative feedback, **231**, **854**, **993**
   in global climate change, 1164–66
   in homeostatic systems, 854, 857
   in hormone signaling pathways, 993–94
Negative pressure ventilation, **909**–10, 911*f*
Negative-sense single-stranded RNA viruses, **716**, 728
Neher, Erwin, 935
Nematodes, 638*t*, **674**. *See also* Roundworms
Nephrons, **872**–78
Neritic zone, **1079**
Nernst equation, 932*f*
Nerve nets, **643**, **929**
Nerves, **929**, 942–43
Nervous systems, **928**–51
   central nervous system, 943–46
   electrical signaling in, 929–42 (*see also* Electrical signaling, animal)
   hormones and, 991–92, 993–94, 1003–6 (*see also* Hormones, animal)
   learning, memory, and, 946–49
   neurons in, 928–30
   origin of, in animal evolution, 643
   peripheral nervous system, 942–43
Nervous tissue, **847**, 848*f*
Net primary productivity (NPP), **1069**, **1149**
   biodiversity and, 1185–86
   in ecosystem energy flow, 1149–53
   as ecosystem supporting service, 1188
   global patterns of, 1153–56
   human appropriation of global, 1156
   impacts of global climate change on, 1168–69
   in oceans, 1079
   species richness and, 1145
   in terrestrial biomes, 1069
Net reproductive rate, **1105**, **1111***f*
Neural signals, 992*t*, 993
Neural tubes, **427**
Neurobiology, 928–29
Neurodegenerative diseases, 408
Neuroendocrine pathways, 993–94, 1005–6
Neuroendocrine signals, 992*t*, **993**–94
Neurogenesis, **948**–49
Neurohormones, 992*f*, **993**–94
Neurons, **847**, **928**
   anatomy of, 929–30
   animal, 637
   diffusion spectrum imaging of, 928*f*
   evolution of muscle cells and, 929
   initiation of muscle contraction by, 976–77
   in learning and memory, 946, 947*f*
   nervous tissue and, 847
   neural and neuroendocrine signals of, 993–94
   neurobiology and study of, 928–29
   neurogenesis of, 948–49
   in olfaction, 965–66
   in photoreception, 960, 961*f*

sodium-potassium pump in membranes of, 933*f*
   types of nervous systems and types of, 929 (*see also* Nervous systems)
Neurosecretory cells, **1005**–6
Neurospora crassa. See Bread mold
Neurotoxins, **935**
Neurotransmitters, **938**
   categories of, 941*t*
   epinephrine and, 1006
   functions of, 938–39, 940
   memory, learning, and, 946–48
   in muscle contraction, 976–78
   as neural signals, 992*f*, 993
   in photoreception, 962–63
   postsynaptic potentials and, 940–42
   synapse structure and release of, 939–40
Neutral mutations, 313
Neutral pH, 29
Neutralization, pathogen, 1052
Neutrons, 19–20
Neutrophils, **1040**–41, 1042*t*
New World monkeys, 705
Next-generation sequencing technologies, 378, 391
Niacin, 884*t*
Niche differentiation, **1127**–28, 1186
Niches, **496**, **1125**
   in animal diversification, 646
   Cambrian explosion and new, 519–20
   in competition, 1125–28
   in sympatric speciation, 496–97
Nicholson, Donald, 170(*footnote*)
Nicolson, Garth, 95–96*f*
Nicotinamide adenine dinucleotide (NAD$^+$). *See* NAD$^+$ (nicotinamide adenine dinucleotide)
Nicotine, 815
Niklas, Karl, 578
Nilsson-Ehle, Herman, 275–76
Nirenberg, Marshall, 311–12
Nitrate, 171, 542–44, 787
Nitrogen
   in bioremediation, 533
   cycads and fixation of, 606
   in ecosystem nutrient cycles, 1156
   electronegativity of, 21
   hornworts and fixation of, 602
   isotopes of, in Meselson–Stahl experiment, 288*f*, 289
   in living organisms, 19
   mycorrhizal fungi and, 784
   in net primary production of terrestrial biomes, 1155
   nitrogen cycle and prokaryotic fixation of, 542–43
   plant fixation of, 787–89
   as plant nutrient, 777, 780*t*
   in protein secondary structure, 48–49
   simple molecules of, 23
   soil fertilization with, 1155
   in volcanic gases, 30
Nitrogen cycle, 542–**43**, 1161
Nitrogen fixation, **542**, **787**
   in global nitrogen cycle, 1160
   prokaryotic, 542–43, 787–89, 1133, 1158, 1160
Nitrogen-fixing bacteria, 542–43, 787–89, 1133, 1158, 1160
Nitrogenous bases, nucleotide complementary pairing of, 287, 298–99 (*see also* Complementary base pairing)
   in dideoxy sequencing, 377–78
   in DNA structure, 286–87

in DNA synthesis mistakes, 298–99
in point mutations, 313–14
purines and pyrimidines, 58–59 (see also Purines; Pyrimidines)
in RNA synthesis, 308
sequences of, in genetic code, 310–12
Nitrogenous wastes, animal, 865–66, 870–71. See also Kidneys
Nitrous oxide, 1163
Nobel Prizes, 67, 997, B:20
Nociceptors, **953**, 967
Nocturnal animals, 964
Nod factors, **788**
Node of Ranvier, **937**
Nodes, phylogenetic tree, **506**, B:10–B:11
Nodes, stem, **735**
Nodules, 787–88
Nonadaptive traits, 461
Non-bilaterian animals, 638t, 652–54
Noncyclic electron flow, Z-scheme model, **188**–89
Nondisjunction, 497f, 498
Nonenveloped viruses, 715, 720–21
Nonpolar covalent bonds, **21**–23f
Nonpolar side chains, 43f, 44
Nonrandom mating, 468–72. See also Sexual selection
Nonself recognition, 1042, 1046–47
Nonsense mutations, 313–14t
Non-sister chromatids, 240t, **242**
Nonspontaneous chemical reactions. See Endergonic reactions
Nonvascular plants, **580**–83, 590, 591f, 598, 601–2
Norepinephrine, 941t, **977**–78, **1006**
Northern blotting, B:16
Notation
  exponential, B:9
  scientific, B:2–B:3
Notochords, **426**–27, **686**
Nottebohm, Fernando, 948
Novak, Joseph, B:28
Nuclear envelope, **112**
  in characteristics of domains of life, 529t
  Eurkarya and, 553
  in meiosis, 242–43, 244
  origin of, in protists, 561–62
  structure and function of, 119–20
Nuclear lamina, **112**, 119, 129
Nuclear lamins, **129**
Nuclear localization signal (NLS), **120**
Nuclear pore complex, **119**–20
Nuclear pores, **119**
Nuclear transfer (cloning), 409
Nucleases, **893**, 895t
Nucleic acids, **58**–71. See also DNA (deoxyribonucleic acid); RNA (ribonucleic acid)
  carbohydrates in, 78
  in cells, 106
  chemical evolution and nucleotide production for, 59
  components of, 58–61
  DNA structure and function, 61–65
  polymerization of nucleotides to form, 59–61
  as probes, B:15–B:16
  in protocells, 94
  RNA structure and function, 65–68
  RNA world hypothesis on RNA as first self-replicating molecule, 57–58, 68–69
  separating and visualizing molecules of, B:13–B:16
Nucleoids, **107**–8

Nucleolus, **112**, 119
Nucleoside triphosphates, 60, 120
Nucleosomes, **350**
Nucleotide excision repair, DNA, **299**–301
Nucleotides, **58**–61, 390
Nucleus, atomic, 19–21
Nucleus, cell, **110**
  chromosomes in, 110, 112
  division of, by meiosis and mitosis in cell cycle, 219–20 (see also Cell cycle; Meiosis; Mitosis)
  eukaryotic cells vs. prokaryotic cells and, 8, 106, 110, 117t
  in fungal fusion, 624–25
  in muscle cells, 977
  transport of molecules into and out of, 119–21
Nudibranchs, 668
Null alleles, **305**
Null hypothesis, **12**, 468–70, B:7
Nüsslein-Volhard, Christiane, 411–12, B:25
Nutrient availability, aquatic biome, 1075–79
Nutrient cycling, 1156–59. See also Biogeochemical cycles
Nutrient deficiency, plant, 777–78
Nutrient pollution, 1148f, 1182
Nutrients, **1148**
  cell-cycle checkpoints and cell, 231
  in ecosystems and biosphere, 1148–49 (see also Biogeochemical cycles; Nutrient cycling)
Nutrients, animal, **883**–84, 885t. See also Animal nutrition
Nutrients, plant, **732**. See also Plant nutrition
  availability of, in soil, 781–82
  deficiencies in, 777–78
  essential, 776–77, 780t
  mycorrhizal fungi and (see Mycorrhizal fungi)
  nitrogen fixation and, 787–89
  uptake of, 782–87

O

Obesity, diabetes mellitus and, 898–99
O'Brien, Stephen, 1190
Observable traits, 258–59. See also Phenotypes; Traits
Observational studies, global climate change, 1073
Occipital lobe, **944**
Oceanic zone, **1079**
Oceans, **1079**
  acidification of, 1166t, 1167–68, 1182
  as aquatic biomes, 1079
  changes of, in time line of life, 515–16
  chemical evolution in early, 25–30, 74 (see also Water)
  effects of, on climate, 1066–67
  in end-Permian extinction, 521
  estuaries and, 1078
  global net primary productivity of, 1154–56
  hydrothermal vents in (see Deep-sea hydrothermal vents)
  impacts of global climate change on, 1166, 1168–69, 1182
  protein polymerization in early, 44–45
  protists in, 552f
  upwelling of, 1075, 1155
Octopuses, 662, 669
Odorants, 496–97, **965**–66

Odum, Howard, 1150
Oil (petroleum), 556, 1059f
Oils, 86
Okazaki, Reiji, 292
Okazaki fragments, 292, **293**–95
Oldfield mice, 308, 309f, 313
Old World monkeys, 705
Olfaction (smell), **964**, 965–67
Olfactory bulbs, 966–67
Oligochaetes, 667
Oligodendrocytes, **937**
Oligopeptides, 46, 55
Oligosaccharides, **72**, 79. See also Carbohydrates
Omasum, 891
Ommatidia, **960**
Omnivores, 579, **647**–48
On the Origin of Species by Means of Natural Selection (book), 445, 446, 453, 489
Oncogenes, **361**
One-gene, one-enzyme hypothesis, **305**–7
One-snip test, phylogenetic tree, B:10
Onychophorans, 672–73
Oogenesis, **1016**, 1017–18f
Oogonia, **1017**
Oparin, Alexander I., 41–42
Oparin–Haldane chemical evolution theory, 41–42
Open circulatory systems, **916**–17
Open reading frames (ORFs), **392**–93
Operators, **343**
Operculum, **906**
Operon model, gene regulation, 342–44
Operons, **342**–44
Opisthokonts, 558t, 569
Opium, 815
Opposite leaves, 738f
Opsins, 961f–**62**, 963–64
Opsonization, pathogen, 1052
Optic nerve, **960**, 961f
Optimal foraging, **1085**–87
Oral rehydration therapy, 896
Orangutans, 705, 1172–73
Orbitals, electron, **20**–21
Ordinate, graph, B:4–B:5
Organ systems, animal, 713f, 848f, **849**–50
Organelles, **108**
  benefits of eukaryotic, 110
  in characteristics of domains of life, 529t
  eukaryotic, 110–17t
  plant cell, 129, 743
  prokaryotic, 108
  prokaryotic vs. eukaryotic, 110t
  separating, from cells (see Centrifugation)
Organic matter, 778–79f, 782t, 1069. See also Biomass
Organic molecules, **36**. See also Carbohydrates; Lipids; Macromolecules; Molecules; Nucleic acids; Proteins
  carbon–carbon bonds in, 36
  functional groups and, 37–38
  Oparin–Haldane theory on chemical evolution of, 41–42
  prokaryote strategies for obtaining, 538–41
  proteins (see Proteins)
  spontaneous formation of, in origin-of-life experiments, 33–36
Organic soils, 781

Organismal ecology, 1060–61
Organisms, **2**
  aerobic vs. anaerobic respiration in, 170–72
  animal anatomy and physiology at level of, 849f
  in aquatic biomes, 1077–79
  atoms of, 19, 20f
  bristlecone pine as oldest living, 432f
  characteristics of living, 2–3 (see also Cell(s); Energy; Evolution; Genes)
  distribution and abundance of (see Geographic distribution and abundance of organisms)
  hybrid, 259
  impact of global warming on, 1166–68
  major amino acids found in, 43f
  microbes as microscopic, 530
  microscopy of living, B:20
  misconceptions about, in evolution, 460–61
  model (see Model organisms)
  multicellular (see Multicellularity)
  number of chromosomes of, 223
  organismal ecology and, 1060–61
  phylogenetic tree of all living, 6–8
  recombinant, 270–71, 274f
  selecting, for whole-genome sequencing, 392
  taxonomy and scientific names for, 8–9
  unicellular (see Unicellular organisms)
  viruses vs. living, 711–12
  water in cells of, 25
Organogenesis, **426**–29, 433, 1032
Organs, animal, **848**
  anatomy and physiology at level of, 849f
  female reproductive, 1023–25
  gas exchange, 905–12, 916
  hydrostats in, 981
  immune system and transplants of, 1053
  male reproductive, 1021–23
  muscle tissue in, 977–78
  organogenesis of, 426–29, 1032
  organ systems and, 849–50
  sensory, 646, 647t
  tissues of, 848
  viruses and human, 713f
Organs, plant, 433, 439
Origin-of-life research
  earliest, 33–36
  extremophiles and, 530–31
  monosaccharides in, 74
  nucleic acid formation, 60–61
  nucleotide formation, 59
  origin of viruses and, 723
  polysaccharides in, 78
  on proteins as first self-replicating molecules, 42, 44–45, 55
  RNA as first self-replicating molecule, 57–58, 68–69
Origin of replication, **290**, 291f
Origin of Species, The (book), 5, 445, 446, 453, 489
Orr, Allen, 500
Oryx, 842–43, 855, 864
Oshima, Yasuji, 354
Osmoconformers, **862**, **866**
Osmolarity, **862**, 875
Osmoregulation, **862**
  diffusion, osmosis, and, 862
  excretion and, 862–66
  in fishes, 866–68
  hormones of, 1003
  overview of, 871

Osmoregulation (*continued*)
in terrestrial insects, 869–71
in terrestrial vertebrates and mammals, 871–79
Osmoregulators, **862**–64, 866
Osmosis, **92**, **756**, **862**
across lipid bilayers, 92–93
across prokaryotic cell walls, 109
in kidneys, 872
in osmoregulation, 862, 863*f*, 871
of water and solutes into roots, 765
Osmotic gradient, loop of Henle and, 874–77*f*
Osmotic stress, 862–66, 869
Ouabain, **867**, 871
Out-of-Africa hypothesis, **707**–8
Outcross fertilization, **830**
Outcrossing, 248–49
Outer ear, **956**
Outgroups, **506**
Outgroup species, phylogenetic tree, B:10–B:11
Oval window, ear, **956**
Ovarian cycle, mammalian, 1027*f*. *See also* Menstrual cycle, mammalian
Ovaries, animal, **999**, **1016**
in cleavage, 423–24
in female reproductive system, 1023–24
hormones of, 994*f*, 999, 1027–29
oogenesis in mammalian, 1016, 1017–18*f*
Ovaries, plant, **592**, **827**
angiosperm, 592–95
female gametophyte production in, 827–28
fruit and, 833
Overexploitation, 1178, **1180**–81
Overfishing, 1153, 1181
Overhunting, 1181
Overwatering, 778
Oviducts, **1024**–25*f*
Oviparous species, 650*t*, **651**, **694**, **1020**–21
Ovoviviparous species, 650*t*, **651**, **694**, **1020**–21
Ovulation, **1024**
Ovules, plant, **827**
in embryogenesis, 433–36
female gametophyte production in, 827–28
fruit and, 833
in plant reproduction, 592–93
Ovum, **1017**
Oxidation, **141**. *See also* Redox (reduction-oxidation) reactions
of acetyl CoA to carbon dioxide, 162–65
of glucose in cellular respiration, 155–56, 164–65, 170–72
of glucose in glycolysis, 158–61
of NADH and FADH$_2$, 166–72
peroxisomes and, 115
of pyruvate, 161–62
of water in photosystem II, 186
Oxidative phosphorylation, **156**, 170–71, 979. *See also* Phosphorylation
Oxygen
aerobic respiration and, 170–72
in animal diversification, 646
animal gas exchange and, 902–3
behavior of, in air, 903–4

behavior of, in water, 904–5
Cambrian explosion and atmospheric, 519–20
consumption of, in animal locomotion, 986, 987*f*
cyanobacteria and, 545
in decomposition rates, 1157
discovery of, 177
electronegativity of, 21, 25
in electron transport chain, 166–67
exchange of, between mother and fetus during pregnancy, 1032–33
in fermentation, 172
hemoglobin and blood levels of, 48, 54, 912–15
homeostasis for blood levels of, 1003
in living organisms, 19
molecular structure of, 24*f*, B:12*f*
passage of, through stomata of leaves, 192–93
photosynthetic production of (*see* Photosynthesis)
Precambrian lack of, 515
prokaryotic oxygen revolution and, 541–42
in protein secondary structure, 48–49
in redox reactions, 141–42
simple molecules of, 23
in soil, 778
in streams, 1078
Oxygen-hemoglobin equilibrium curve, **913**–14, **1033**
Oxygenic photosynthesis, **186**, 189, 539*t*, 541–42, 545, 578
Oxytocin, 1005–**6**, **1034**
Ozone, photons and, 34

P

P site, ribosome, 328–29*f*
p53 protein, **231**–32, 233
p53 tumor-suppressor gene, **361**–63
Pääbo, Svante, 376
Pace, Norman, 530
Pacemaker cells, **921**–22
Packaging, DNA, 360–61*t*
Paine, Robert, 1137–38, 1153
Palade, George, 121–23
Paleontologists, **513**
Paleozoic era, **515**, 909
Palindromes, 371
Palms, coconut, 1106–7
Pancreas, **892**, **992**
digestive enzymes of, 892–93
hormones of, 994*f*, 995, 996–97
human, 848*f*, 887*f*
paracrine signals and, 992–93
pulse–chase experiment on cells of, 121–23
Pancreatic amylase, **893**, 895*t*
Pancreatic lipase, **894**, 895*t*
Pandemics, **712**–13
Panthers, 471–72, 1190
Papermaking, 579–80, 607
Parabasalids, 571
Parabiosis, **1002**–3
Paracrine signals, **992**–93
Paralytic shellfish poisoning, 555–56
Paramecium species, 1108–9*f*, 1125–26
Paranthropus species, B:11
Paraphyletic groups, 508*t*, **553**, 582–83
Parapodia, 649*t*, **667**

Parasites, **564**, **648**, **789**, **1128**
animals as, 648
annelid, 667
coevolution of, 1132
endosymbiont bacterial, 547
flatworms, 666
fungal, 613, 628–29, 632
human intestinal, 571
manipulation of hosts by, 1132–33
nematodes, 674
parasitoid organisms as, 818
plant, 789, 790*f*
plants as, 789, 790*f*
protist, 564, 569
roundworms as, in elephantiasis, 1037*f*
sexual reproduction and, 566
viral, 285–86
Parasitic relationships, **620**. *See also* Parasites
Parasitism, **1128**
Parasitoid organisms, 485, **818**–19
Parasympathetic nervous system, **942**–43
Parathyroid glands, 994*f*
Parenchyma cells, **744**, 745*f*, 747, 748*t*, 749, B:21–B:22
Parental care, **694**
mammalian, 1030–33
reptilian and bird, 703
vertebrate, 694
Parental generation, **259**
Parental strands, DNA, 287–89
Parietal cells, **890**
Parietal lobe, **944**
Parker, Geoff, 1019–20
Parsimony, **508**
Parthenogenesis, **665**, **1014**
Partial pressure, **904**, 905
Particulate inheritance, **261**–63
Pascal (Pa), **756**
Passive transport, **98**, **769**, **864**. *See also* Diffusion; Facilitated diffusion; Membrane proteins
mechanisms of, 101*f*
membrane proteins and, 98–99
in osmoregulation, 864–65
of water and solutes into roots, 759–61
Pasteur, Louis, 3–5, 532
Patch clamping, **935**
Paternal care, 476
Paternal chromosome, **239**
Paternity
bird, 1020
DNA fingerprinting in, 398*f*
Pathogenic bacteria, 531–33
Pathogens, **743**, **815**, **1037**
animal immune system responses to, 1037–38 (*see also* Immune systems)
plant defense responses to, 815–17, 818*t*
Pattern component
of chemical evolution theory, 18–19
of germ theory of disease, 532
of scientific theories, 3, 445
of theory of evolution by natural selection, 5, 446
Pattern formation, body, **410**–15
Pattern-recognition receptors, **1040**
PCR. *See* Polymerase chain reaction (PCR)
Peas, Mendelian genetics and, 257–66. *See also* Mendelian genetics
Peat, **602**
Pectins, **202**
Pedigrees, **277**–79

Pedometer hypothesis, ant navigation, 11–14
Peer-reviewed primary literature, B:26–B:27
Pelc, Stephen, 221–22
Pellets, centrifugation, B:18
Penfield, Wilder, 945–46
Penicillin, 613, 632
Penis, **1019**–23
Pentoses, 59, **73**–74
PEP carboxylase, **193**–94
Pepsin, **890**, 895*t*
Peptide bonds, **45**
formation of, in translation, 328, 330–31
glycosidic linkages vs., 76
in protein polymerization, 45–46
protein structure and, 48–49
Peptides, 45–**46**, 941*t*
Peptidoglycan, **76**, 77*t*, 78, 529, 536–37
Peptidyl (P) site, ribosome, 328–29*f*
Perennial plants, **599**, **734**
Perfect flowers, **827**
Perforations, **746**
Pericarp, **834**, 835*f*
Pericycle, **760**
Periodic table of elements, 19*f*
Periodontitis, 531
Peripheral membrane proteins, **95**
Peripheral nervous system (PNS), **929**, 942–43
Peristalsis, **889**, **981**
Permafrost, **1072**
Permeability, plasma membrane, **88**–94. *See also* Selective permeability, plasma membrane
Permian mass extinction, 521
Permineralized fossils, 512
Peroxisomes, **115**, 117*t*, 580
Persistent organic pollutants (POPs), 1152–53, 1182
Pest control ecosystem services, 1188
Pesticides, 1182
Petals, **439**, **593**, **826**–27
Petiole, leaf, **737**
Petrified wood, 512
Petromyzontoidea, 697
pH, **29**
acid-base reactions and, 29–30
of blood, 912, 914–16
optimal, for enzyme function, 148
of soil, 781–82
of wetlands, 1077
Phagocytosis, **126**, 563–64, 1040–41, 1042*t*, 1052
Phanerozoic eon, 514*f*, 515
Pharmaceutical pollutants, 1182
Pharmaceuticals. *See* Drugs
Pharyngeal gill slits, **686**
Pharyngeal jaws, **692**, 884–86
Pharyngeal pouches, 686–87
Phenology, **1166**–67
Phenotypes, **258**
behavior and, 1083
central dogma and linking genotypes and, 308, 309*f*
codominance and incomplete dominance in, 272, 273*f*
effects of environment on, 273
effects of gene interactions on, 273–74
effects of modes of natural selection on, 475*t*
exceptions and extensions to Mendelian rules on, 277*t*
finding disease genes and, 382

Boldface page numbers indicate a glossary entry; page numbers followed by an *f* indicate a figure; those followed by *t* indicate a table.

I:28   INDEX

genotypes and, 261, 273–75 (*see also* Genotypes)
in human inheritance, 277–79
in Mendelian genetics, 258–59
natural selection and, 472
in particulate inheritance, 261–63
point mutations and, 314
polygenic inheritance and, 275–76
traits and, 258 (*see also* Traits)
wild type, in testing chromosome theory of inheritance, 267–69
Phenotypic plasticity, **734**, 736, 738–39*f*
Phenylalanine, 273, 311
Pheophytin, **185**, 187
Pheromones, 215–**16**, **818**–19, **966**–67, **1018**–19
Phloem tissue, **746**
anatomy of, 767
loading of, in translocation, 769–71
in primary plant body, 748*t*
unloading of, in translocation, 771–72
vascular cambium and, 748–50
vascular tissue system functions of, 746–47
Phosphatases, **214**
Phosphate functional group, 37*t*–38, 58, 60, 87, 99–100, 332. *See also* Phosphorylation
Phosphodiester linkage, **59**–61, 65, 67–68, 76, 286
Phosphofructokinase, **159**–61
Phospholipids, **87**. *See also* Lipid bilayers; Lipids
in archaeal plasma membranes, 529, 536–37
in characteristics of domains of life, 529*t*
effect of temperature on, 90–91
in fluid-mosaic model of plasma membranes, 94–96*f*
as lipids, 87
in metabolic pathways, 157*f*
Phosphorus
in DNA vs. in proteins, 285–86
in ecosystem nutrient cycles, 1156
as human nutrient, 885*t*
as plant nutrient, 777, 780*t*
radioactive, 221
soil fertilization with, 1155
Phosphorylase, **81**, **1008**–9
Phosphorylation, **143**. *See also* Oxidative phosphorylation; Substrate-level phosphorylation
in endergonic reactions, 143–44
in enzyme regulation, 149–50
as post-translational protein modification, 332
translational and post-translational control by, 359–60
Phosphorylation cascades, **213**–14, **794**–95, 797, 1009–10
Photic zone, lake and pond, **1077**
Photic zone, ocean, **1079**
Photomicrographs, 711*f*
Photons, **34**–35, **179**–83. *See also* Light-capturing reactions, photosynthetic
Photoperiod, 999, **999**, 1000*f*
Photoperiodism, **802**
Photophosphorylation, **186**, 189
Photoreception, animal, **959**–64
Photoreceptors, animal, **953**, 960–64, 999, 1000*f*
Photoreceptors, plant, 796–**97**
Photorespiration, 192, **192**
Photoreversibility, **801**

Photosynthesis, **80**, **176**, **541**
anabolic pathways of, 152
in aquatic biomes, 1074, 1075*f*
autotrophs, heterotrophs, and, 176–77
bacterial, 545
blue-light phototropic response and, 796–97
capture of light energy in, by pigments, 179–90 (*see also* Light-capturing reactions, photosynthetic)
carbohydrate storage of energy from, 80
cellular respiration and, 177, 195
chloroplasts in, 116, 178–79*f*, 743
discovery of photosystems I and II of, 184–90
evolution of, in prokaryotes, 538
in global carbon cycle, 1161–62*f*
glucose production by, 155
in green plant diversification, 582
importance of, 731–32
leaves in, 737
oxygenic and anoxygenic, 186, 189
prokaryotic, 108, 110*t*, 541
protist, 556, 564–65, 569
reduction of carbon dioxide to produce sugars in Calvin cycle of, 190–95
regulation of, 195
in terrestrial biomes, 1069, 1155–56
two linked sets of reactions of, 177–78
water conservation and, 754–55, 765–66
Photosystem I, 184–90
Photosystem II, 184–90
Photosystems, **183**–90
Phototrophs, 538, **538**
Phototropins, 796–**97**
Phototropism, 736, **796**–803
Phycoerythrin, 572
Phyla (phylum), **8**, **530**, **637**. *See also* Lineages; Phylogenetic trees; Phylogenies
Phylogenetic species concept, **491**–93
Phylogenetic trees, **450**, **506**. *See also* Phylogenies
anatomy of, 506*t*
branch lengths of, 508*t*
common ancestry on, 450
distinguishing homology from homoplasy in, 508–10
estimation of phylogenies using, 506–8
mapping traits and groups on, 508*t*
reading, B:10–B:11
tree of life as, 6–8, 506
uses and terminology of, 506
Phylogenies, **6**, **107**, **506**. *See also* Phylogenetic trees
animal, 637*f*, 638, 639*f*, 640*f*
of animal locomotion, 986
annelid, 667*f*
cetacean, 452–53, 510–11*f*
chelicerate, 678*f*
chordate, 690*f*
crustacean, 677*f*
deuterostome, 682*f*
developing, of all living organisms from rRNA sequences, 6–8
domains in, 106–7
echinoderm, 684*f*
of emerging viruses, 724–25
endosymbiosis and, 561
estimation of, 506–8
eukaryote, 558, 559*f*
as evolutionary history, 107
of fungi, 618–19

green plant, 582–83, 586, 587*f*
of hearts, 920*f*
history of life and, 505–6 (*see also* History of life)
human, 707–8
of pollination, 831*f*
primate, 704*f*
prokaryotic, 535–36
protist, 558, 559*f*
protostome, 658–59*f*
taxonomy and, 8–9
vertebrate, 691
whale, 510–11*f*
Physical isolation, 494–95, 1144
Physical maps, **379**. *See also* Genetic maps
Physiology, **843**, 849*f*. *See also* Animal form and function
Physiology, levels of organization, 849*f*
Phytochromes, **801**–2
Phytophthora infestans, 554, 555*t*, 574
Phytoplankton, 556
Pigments, **796**
lateral gene transfer and, 485
lipids as, 87
in mice, 308, 309*f*
phototropins as, 796–97
phytochromes as, 801–2
prokaryotic, 541
in vacuoles, 115
Pigments, photosynthetic, **178**–84
Piloting, **1089**
Pineal eye, 999, 1000*f*
Pineal gland, **999**
Pines, 592, 607
Pinophyta (pines, spruces, firs), 607
Pioneering species, **1140**
Pitches, sound, **955**
Pith, **742**
Pits, **746**
Pituitary dwarfism, 369–74
Pituitary gland, **1004**
hormones of, 994*f*, 995–96, 999
hormones of, in menstrual cycle, 1027–30
hormones of, in puberty, 1026–27
pituitary dwarfism and, 369
regulation of hormone production by, 1004–6
Placenta, **424**, **694**, 915, **1017**, 1031–32
Placental mammals, **701**
Plankton, **556**, **1077**, **1136**
community structure of, 1136–37
ctenophores as, 653
green algae, and, 598
impacts of global climate change on, 1167
in lakes and ponds, 1077
protists as, 556, 573
protostomes and, 665
Plant(s). *See also* Plant cells; Plant development; Plant form and function; Plant nutrition; Plant reproduction
as autotrophs, 176
Devonian explosion radiation of, 520
as green plants (*see* Green algae; Green plants)
impact of global warming on, 1166–68
mutualisms with, 1133
photosynthesis by (*see* Photosynthesis)
Plantae and, 558*t*, 569, 572
sensory systems of (*see* Sensory systems, plant)
survivorship curves for, 1105

sympatric speciation by polyploidy in, 497–99
transgenic (*see* Transgenic plants)
types of (*see* Angiosperms; Gymnosperms; Land plants; Seed plants)
water absorption and loss in, 754–55, 765–66
Plantae, 558*t*, **569**, 572
Plant cells. *See also* Eukaryotic cells
animal cells vs., 110*f*, 742–43
cellulose as structural polysaccharide in, 72*f*, 76, 78
cell walls in, 201–2
cultures of, B:21–B:22 (*see also* Cultures, cell and tissue)
cytokinesis in, 228
cytoplasmic streaming in, 129
development processes of, 406–8
differentiation and de-differentiation of, 438
glyoxysomes and peroxisomes in, 115
middle lamella in cell–cell attachments of, 204
plasmodesmata in, 208–9
signal transduction in, 794–95
starch as storage polysaccharide in, 72*f*, 76
stem cells, 407
in tissue systems (*see* Tissue systems, plant)
vacuoles in, 114–15
Plant development, 432–43
animal development vs., 432–33, 438
embryogenesis in, 433–36
reproductive development in, 438–41
stages of, 433*f*
vegetative development in, 436–38
Plant form and function, 731–53
brassinosteroids in body size, 812
flowers, 826–29
indeterminate growth in angiosperm, 731–32
leaves in, 737–40
primary growth in, 740–42
primary plant body cells and tissues, 742–48*t*
root systems in, 733–35
secondary growth in, 748–51
shoot systems in, 735–37
surface area/volume relationships in, 732–33
Plant nutrition, 775–92
adaptations for, 789–90
nitrogen fixation and, 787–89
nutrient requirements for, 774–78, 780*t*
nutrient uptake and, 782–87
soil and, 778–82
starch in, 76
translocation (sugar transport) in, 766–72
water and sugar transport in, 754–55 (*see also* Translocation; Water transport, plant)
water transport in, 759–66
Plant reproduction, 586–95, 822–41
alternation of generations in, 588–89
asexual, 825–26
embryophyte retention of offspring in, 587–88
in energy flow, 1149
evolution from gametophyte-dominant to sporophyte-dominant life cycles in, 589–90
fertilization in, 832–33

Plant reproduction (*continued*)
  flowers as reproductive structures of, 592–93, 826–29
  fruits in, 594–95
  heterospory in, 590, 591*f*, 592*f*
  importance of, 822–23
  plant life cycle and, 823–25
  pollen in, 590–91
  pollination in, 593–94, 608–9*f*, 830–32
  seeds in, 591–92, 833–37
  sexual, 586–87, 823
Plasma, **912**
Plasma cells, **1050**–51, 1054*t*
Plasma membranes, **84**–103
  artificial, 88–89
  carbohydrates in cell identity functions of, 78–80
  cell walls and, 116
  in characteristics of domains of life, 529*t*
  crossing of, by hormones, 996
  in cytokinesis, 228
  diffusion and osmosis across, 91–94
  electron transport chain and ATP synthase in, 171
  eukaryotic, 117*t*
  excitable, 934
  exocytosis and, 126
  extracellular layers and, 201
  fluidity of, 90, 91*f*
  importance of, to cells, 84–85, 100–101
  lipids and, 85–91, 529 (*see also* Lipid bilayers)
  lipid-soluble vs. lipid-insoluble hormones and, 209
  membrane proteins and fluid-mosaic model for, 94–101
  movement of electrolytes and water across, 864–65
  nuclear envelope and, 561–62
  plant passive exclusion at, 785
  in polyspermy prevention, 422–23
  prokaryotic, 109, 536–38
  selective permeability of (*see* Selective permeability, plasma membrane)
  smooth ER and, 114
  transport of solutes across, in plants, 769–71
Plasmids, **108**, **370**
  in DNA cloning, 370
  in genetic engineering, 380*t*
  inserting genes into, 370, 371*f*
  introducing recombinant, into bacterial cells for transformation, 372
  lateral gene transfer and, 395
  origin of viruses in, 723
  prokaryotic, 108
  prokaryotic vs. eukaryotic, 110*f*
  in transgenic plant development, 385–86
Plasmodesmata, **208**–9, **600**, **743**, **806**
Plasmodial slime molds, 570
Plasmodium, 554–55, 573, 1132
Plasmogamy, **624**–26*f*
Plastocyanin, **187**–88
Plastoquinone (PQ), **185**–88
Platelets, **912**, **1040**–41*f*
Platyhelminthes, 638*t*, 666
Platypuses, 392, 700
Pleiotropic genes, **272**–73, 277*t*, 461–62
Ploidy, **238**–**39**, 240*t*, 241–42
Pneumatophore roots, 734–35*f*

Point mutations, 483
  types of, **313**–14
Poisons. *See* Toxins
Polar bears, 1166*t*, 1167
Polar bodies, **1017**
Polar climate, 1066, 1165
Polar covalent bonds, **21**–23*f*
Polar microtubules, **224**
Polar nuclei, **828**
Polar transport, auxin, **807**
Polarity, 21–23*f*, 25, 43*f*, 44, B:13
Polio virus, 727, 1055
Pollen grains, **591**, **829**
  fossilized, 512*f*
  germination of, 832
  in plant reproduction, 433*f*, 590–91
  seed plants and, 599
  stamens and production of, 827, 828–29
Pollen tube, **832**
Pollination, **593**, **830**
  of angiosperms, 593–94, 608–9*f*
  animal speciation and, 831–32
  as ecosystem supporting service, 1188
  evolution of, 830–31
  fertilization after, 832–33
  flower petals and, 826–27
  photoreception of UV light in, 964
  phylogenetic tree of, 831*f*
  in plant development, 433
  self-fertilization vs. cross-fertilization in, 258 (*see also* Crosses; Self-fertilization)
  selfing vs. outcrossing in, 830
  syndromes, 830
Pollination syndromes, **594**, **830**, 831*f*
Pollinators, 593–94, 608–9*f*, 831–32
Pollution
  biomagnification of pollutants in, 1152–53
  bioremediation of, using fungi, 632
  bioremediation of, using prokaryotes, 533
  ecology and, 1059–61
  nitrogen, 1160
  nutrient, 1148*f*
  prokaryotes and nitrate, 543–44
  soil, 785–87
  as threat to biodiversity, 1178, 1181*t*, 1182
Polychaetes, 667
Polygenic inheritance, **275**–**76**, 277*t*, 458–59*f*
Polymerase chain reaction (PCR), **374**
  amplification of fossil DNA with, 376
  in DNA fingerprinting, 397–98*f*
  extremophiles and, 531
  in genetic engineering, 381*t*
  in next-generation sequencing technologies, 378
  requirements of, 374–76
  uses of, in genetic testing, 382
Polymerases. *See* DNA polymerases; RNA polymerase
Polymerization, **44**
  of amino acids to form proteins, 44–47
  chemical evolution and, 78
  of monosaccharides to form polysaccharides, 75–76
  of nucleotides to form nucleic acids, 59–61
  in origin-of-life experiments, 68–69

Polymers, **44**. *See also* Polymerization
  polysaccharides as, 72, 75–78
  proteins as, 44–47
Polymorphic genetic markers, **379**
Polymorphic species, **491**
Polymorphic traits, **272**, 277*t*, 485
Polypeptides, **46**. *See also* Proteins
  as hormones, 995–96, 999
  peptide bonds in formation of proteins and, 45–46
  synthesis of, by ribosomes, 119
  synthesis of, in translation, 324–26, 328–31 (*see also* Translation)
Polyphenylalanine, 311
Polyphyletic groups, 508*t*
Polyplacophorans, 669
Polyploid organisms, **239**, 240*t*
Polyploidy, 314, **497**–99
Polyps, **653**–54
Polyribosomes, 324*f*–**25**
Polysaccharides, **72**–73, 75–81, 117, 202–3
Poly(A) signal, **320**
Poly(A) tail, mRNA, **323**–24
Polyspermy prevention, 421–23
Polytomy, 506*t*, **618**, B:10
Polyunsaturated fats, 85, 86
Ponds, **1077**
Population(s), **5**, **446**, **466**, **1061**, **1102**
  analyzing changes in frequencies of alleles in, 466–70
  conservation of, 1189–91
  contemporary evolution of, 449
  contemporary speciation in, 451
  evolution of, by natural selection, 2, 5–6, 444, 446, 459 (*see also* Evolution; Natural selection)
  genetic diversity of, 1173–74
  genetic drift in, 478, 479, 480*f*, 481–82
  genetic variation in, 472, 475*t*
  growth of (*see* Population growth)
  Hardy–Weinberg principle and, 466
  human (*see* Human population)
  monophyletic, 491–92
  in phylogenetic trees, B:10–B:11
  population ecology and, 1060*t*, 1061, 1102 (*see also* Population ecology)
  population viability analysis for, 1182, 1190
  size and structure of (*see* Demography)
  speciation in, 494–502
Population cycles, 1113–15
Population density, 216, 1015, **1102**–3, 1108–12
Population dynamics, **1112**–15
Population ecology, **1102**. *See also* Population(s)
  in conservation of biodiversity, 1118–20
  demography in, 1103–7
  geographic distribution and abundance of species in, 1102–3
  human population growth in, 1115–18
  population dynamics in, 1112–15
  population growth in, 1107–12
  populations and, 1060*t*, 1061, 1101–2
Population growth, 1106*f*, 1107–12, 1118, 1119*f*
Population pyramids, 1115–16
Population thinking, **446**
Population viability analysis (PVA), 1182, 1190
Pore-like proteins, 98
Pores, **584**–85, **744**
Porifera, 638*t*–41, 652
Positive control, **341**, 344, 345*f*

Positive feedback, **935**, 1164–66
Positive pressure ventilation, **909**
Positive-sense single-stranded RNA viruses, 716, 727
Post-anal tails, 686
Posterior body axis, **410**
Posterior pituitary, **1004**, 1005–6
Postsynaptic neurons, **939**
Postsynaptic potentials, 940–42
Post-transcriptional control, bacterial, 360–61
Post-transcriptional control, eukaryotic, 356–61
Post-translational control, **337**–38*f*
Post-translational modification, 360, 361*t*
Postzygotic isolation, **490**, 491*t*, 499–500
Potassium
  channels for, 98, 931, 934, 935
  electrolytes as, 862
  as human nutrient, 885*t*
  as plant nutrient, 777
  potassium leak channels, 931
Potatoes, 554, 555*t*, 574, 815
Potential energy, **31**, **137**
  aerobic respiration and, 171
  in ATP, 143–44, 154–55
  in chemical reactions, 31–32, 137–39
  phosphate functional group and, 60
  in storage polysaccharides, 80
  water potential and, 755
Prairie dogs, 1095–97
Prairies, 1071, 1191
Prebiotic soup, 57–61, 68–69, 93–94
Prebiotic soup model, chemical evolution, 33–35, 41–42, 44–45, 55
Precambrian, **513**–14
Precipitation
  global climate change and, 1073, 1163, 1166
  in global water cycle, 1159
  rain shadows and, 1066–67
  in terrestrial biomes, 1068–72
  in tropical wet forests, 1065–66
Precision
  accuracy vs., B:2–B:3
  standard error and, B:7
Predation, **1128**. *See also* Predators
  in animal diversification, 646
  by ascomycete fungi, 632
  deceitful communication and, 1094–95
  efficiency of animal, 1130–31
  foraging and, 1086–87
  by keystone species, 1137–38
  lateral line system in fishes and, 958–59
  in population cycles, 1114–15
  as threat to biodiversity, 1178
  top-down control in, and trophic cascades, 1153, 1154*f*
  in triggering of Cambrian explosion, 519–20
Predators, **647**. *See also* Predation
  animals as, 647–48
  deuterostomes as, 681*f*
  echinoderm, 685
  noxious compounds in vacuoles and, 115
  predator-removal programs and, 1130–31
  sharks as, 698
  top-down control by, and trophic cascades, 1153, 1154*f*
Predictability, community structure, 1135–37
Predictions, **3**
  biodiversity, 1182–84
  experimental design and, 13

hypothesis testing and, 3–5, 10–11
inheritance hypotheses and, 257
Punnett squares and, for segregation principle, 262–63
testcrosses and, for independent assortment principle, 265–66
Prefixes, metric system, B:2t
Pregnancy, animal, 1017, 1029–34
Pre-mRNA, 321
Preservation, fossil, 512
Pressure, 138. *See also* Mechanoreception
Pressure-flow hypothesis, 768–69f
Pressure potential, 755f, 756–57
Presynaptic neurons, **939**
Preventive medicine, HIV/AIDS, 722
Prey, 1129–33. *See also* Predation; Predators
Prezygotic isolation, **490**, 491t
Pribnow, David, 319
Priestley, Joseph, 177
Primary active transport, **864**
Primary cell wall, **202**, **585**, **745**
Primary consumers, 556, **1150**
Primary decomposers, **1150**
Primary endosymbiosis, 564–65
Primary growth, plant, **740–43**, 748t
Primary immune response, **1053–54**
Primary literature, B:26–B:27
Primary meristems, **740**–42
Primary oocytes, **1017**
Primary phloem, 748–50
Primary producers, 556, **1149**
ecosystem energy flow and, 1149–50
green algae as, 598
plants as, 578–79
protists as, 556, 573
Primary root systems, 741–42
Primary shoot systems, 742
Primary spermatocytes, **1016**
Primary structure, **48**
DNA, 286–87
DNA vs. RNA, 66t
hemoglobin, 51f
nucleic acid, 59–60
protein, 47–48
RNA, 65
tRNA, 327
Primary succession, **1139**
Primary transcripts, **321**–25
Primary xylem, 748–50
Primase, **292**–94t
Primates, **705**
characteristics of, 704–5
color vision in, 964
hominins and humans as, 705–8 (*see also* Human[s])
Primers, **292**–95, 374–76
Prime symbol ('), 58
Principle of independent assortment. *See* Independent assortment, principle of
Principle of segregation. *See* Segregation, principle of
Prions, **53**, 369–70
Probabilities
combining, B:8
and product rule, B:8
statistical tests and, B:7
Probes, **372**–73, 381t, 401–2, B:15–B:16
Proboscis, **662**
Procambium, **740**–41, 748, **833**
Process boxes. *See also* Bioskills; Quantitative methods
acid-growth hypothesis for cell elongation, 800f

action potential triggering of neurotransmitter release, 939f
activation of α-amylase by gibberellins in seed germination, 809f
allopatric speciation by dispersal and by vicariance, 494f
autophagy and phagocytosis, 127f
auxin as gravitropic signal, 805f
B-cell activation, 1051f
bacterial cell division by binary fission, 228f
cell-mediated response, 1053f
cellular respiration overview, 156f
cellular respiration summary, 171f
chemical energy transformation in atoms, 138f
citric acid cycle, 163f
clonal selection theory, 1048f
cloning sheep, 409f
cohesion-tension theory, 763f
creating cDNA libraries of mRNAs, 372f
dideoxy sequencing of DNA, 377f
diffusion, 863f
diffusion across lipid bilayers, 92f
digestion of lipids in small intestine, 895f
DNA recombination of immunoglobin-gene segments, 1047f
DNA synthesis, 64f
DNA synthesis of lagging strand, 293f
DNA synthesis of leading strand, 291f
electrical activation of hearts, 922f
electron transport between photosystem II and cytochrome complex, 185f
electron transport chain, 167f
elongation of polypetides during translation, 330f–31f
embryo development and seed maturation, 833f
embryogenesis in *Arabidopsis*, 434f
ending transcription in bacteria, 321f
endosymbiosis theory on evolution of mitochondria, 560f
endothermic, 30
energy transformation in waterfalls, 137f
engineering of Ti plasmids, 386f
enzyme action model, 146f
enzyme-linked receptors and phosphorylation cascades, 213f
evolutionary (*see* Evolutionary processes)
evolution of drug resistance, 455f
exothermic, 30
facilitation of glucose diffusion by GLUT-1 membrane carrier protein, 99f
formation of female gametophytes in angiosperms, 828f
formation of male gametophytes in angiosperms, 829f
formation of neural tube and somites, 427f
four-step process of animal nutrition, 883f
G-protein-coupled receptors and second messengers, 212f
gastrulation in frog embryo, 424f
generation of new influenza strains via genomic reassortment, 724f
gene therapy for severe combined immunodeficiency (SCID), 384f
genetically variable offspring from self-fertilization, 249f

gene transfer into host DNA using Ti plasmids, 386f
glucose oxidation summary, 164f
glycolysis, 158f–59f
growth factors and social control of G_1 checkpoint, 234f
human birthing stages, 1034f
human immune defense against *Plasmodium*, 1132f
human pulmonary circulation and systemic circulation, 920f
humoral response, 1052f
infection of roots by nitrogen-fixing bacteria, 788f
inflammatory response of innate immunity, 1041f
initiating translation in bacteria, 329f
injection of viral genes into bacterial cells, 285f
inserting genes into plasmids, 371f
introducing foreign genes into human cells using retroviruses, 383f
isolating estradiol receptor with labeled hormones, 1007f
isolating membrane proteins with detergents, 96f
isolating pigments via thin layer chromatography, 180f
key events in prophase I of meiosis I, 246f
lake turnover, 1076f
leaf senescence and abscission, 813f
lipid-insoluble signal transduction, 211f
lipid-soluble signal processing, 211f
lysogeny, 722f
mammalian ovarian cycle, 1027f
maturation of bird eggs, 1024f
metagenomic analysis, 535f
MHC antigen presentation, 1049f
mitosis and cytokinesis, 224f–25f
model for actin-myosin interaction during muscle contraction, 975f
model for epinephrine action, 1009f
model of salt excretion in shark rectal gland, 867f
nitrate pollution in aquatic ecosystems, 543f
noncyclic electron flow, 188f
nondisjunction, 250f
nucleotide excision repair, 299f
ocean upwelling, 1075f
one-way airflow through avian lung, 911f
origin of nuclear envelope, 561f
osmosis, 93f, 863f
phases of meiosis I and meiosis II, 242f–43f
pollen tube growth and double fertilization, 832f
polymerase chain reaction (PCR), 375f
polyspermy prevention by physical barrier of fertilization envelope, 422f
prebiotic soup model of chemical evolution, 35f
problems with copying ends of linear chromosomes (telomeres), 295f
propagation of action potential, 936f
propagation of action potential down myelinated axons, 937f
protein sorting and vesicle transport in Golgi apparatus, 125f
receptor-mediated endocytosis, 126f
regulon control of gene expression, 341f
replica plating, 340f

retro-evolution hypothesis for metabolic pathway evolution, 151f
RNA interference, 359f
RNA splicing with snRNPs, 322f
RNA synthesis, 67f
screening cDNA libraries, 373f
secondary endosymbiosis, 564f
secretory pathway hypothesis on endomembrane system, 122f
sensory, 953
shotgun sequencing of genomes, 391f
signal hypothesis on endomembrane system, 124f
signal transduction in plants, 795f
signal transduction of sound waves to electrical signals by hair cells, 955f
sodium-potassium pump, 100f–101f
sodium-potassium pump in neuron membranes, 933f
spread of LINE transposable elements within genomes, 397f
steps in information processing in plants, 794f
steroid hormone action, 1008f
stomata closing in response to ABA, 811f
stomata opening in response to blue light, 811f
surface metabolism model of chemical evolution, 35f
sympatric speciation, 496f
systemin as wound-response hormone, 817f
T-cell activation, 1049f
telomerase in telomere replication, 296f
terminating transcription in bacteria, 320f
terminating translation, 331f
testing somite cell determination, 428f
transcription initiation in eukaryotes, 357f
triggering of muscle contractions by action potentials, 976f
unequal crossover, 398f
using DNA microarrays to study changes in gene expression, 401f
using DNA probes, 373f
viral replicative growth cycle (lytic cycle), 716f
viral uncoating at cell surface and in endosome, 718f
visualizing membrane proteins with freeze-fracture preparations, 96f
visualizing mRNAs by in situ hybridization, 411f
Process component
of chemical evolution theory, 18–19
of germ theory of disease, 532
of scientific theories, 3, 445
of theory of evolution by natural selection, 5, 453 (*see also* Natural selection)
Product rule, probability, B:8
Productivity, pyramid of, 1152. *See also* Net primary productivity (NPP)
Products, chemical reaction, 30, 31–32
Progesterone, **1027**–30
Programmed cell death, 406t, **407**–8, 426. *See also* Apoptosis
Prokaryotes, **8**, 528–51
Bacteria and Archaea domains of, 107, 528–29 (*see also* Archaea; Bacteria)
biological importance of studying, 529–33

Prokaryotes (continued)
  biological methods of studying, 533–36
  bioremediation roles of, 532–33
  cells of, 8, 107–10, 131
  characteristics of eukaryotes and, 529t
  diversification themes of, 536–44
  ecological diversity and global impacts of, 541–44
  electron donors and acceptors of, 540t
  eukaryotes vs., 8, 552–53
  fermentation and, 172
  genomes of, 391–96
  importance of extremophile, 530–31
  key lineages of, 544–49
  medical importance of, 531–33
  metabolic diversity of, 538–41
  model organism for (see Escherichia coli [E. coli])
  morphological diversity of, 536–38
  pathogenic bacteria and human illnesses, 531t
Prolactin (PRL), 1006
Proliferation, cell. See Cell proliferation
Prometaphase, 224–25
Promoter-proximal elements, 354, 356, 357f
Promoters, 319, 353
  in bacterial transcription, 319–20f
  chromatin remodeling and, 349
  in eukaryotic transcription, 320
  in eukaryotic transcription initiation, 353–56, 357f
  in transcription, 325t
Proofreading, DNA, 298
Prop roots, 734–35f
Prophase, 224, 224, 245f
Prophase I, 244, 245f
Prophase II, 243f, 244
Propositions, concept map, B:28
Propulsion, seed dispersal by, 834–35
Prosimians, 704
Prostaglandins, 210t, 1023t
Prostate gland, 1022–23f
Prosthetic groups, 147, 166
Protease inhibitors, 719
Proteases, 719, 892
Proteasomes, 231, 360
Protected areas, 1120, 1189–91
Protection, skeletal systems and, 980
Protein channels, gap junctions and, 207–8
Protein filaments, 109, 117
Protein interaction networks, 402
Protein kinases, 212, 230
Protein synthesis, 317–35. See also Gene expression
  central dogma of molecular biology on, 307–9
  gene expression and, 317–18 (see also Gene expression)
  genetic code and, 310–12
  mRNA processing in, 321–24
  mRNA specification of amino acids in, 325–26
  post-translation modifications of proteins in, 331–32
  synthesis of aminoacyl tRNAs in, 326–28
  transcription of genes in DNA templates to mRNAs in, 318–21f, 325t
  translation in, 324–32

Proteinase inhibitors, 817
Proteins, 46. See also Amino acids; Polypeptides
  activator, 341, 344, 345f
  animal digestion of, 883, 888, 890, 892–93
  ATP synthase and, 168–69
  in cancer development, 232–33
  cell adhesion, 206–7
  cell–cell gaps and, 207
  in cell-cycle control, 230–32
  in central dogma of molecular biology, 308–9
  chemical evolution of, 69
  complement, in humoral response, 1052
  cytoskeleton, 117
  in differentiation of muscle cells, 428f–29
  diversity of sizes and shapes of, 47
  in DNA mismatch repair, 298–99
  in DNA synthesis, 294t
  in electron transport chain, 166–68
  endomembrane system and, 121–27
  in extracellular matrix, 203–4
  in fertilization, 421
  folding of, 52–53
  functions of, 54
  G-protein-coupled receptors (see G-protein-coupled receptors)
  genes and, 220, 393
  glycoproteins as carbohydrates and, 79–80
  Hershey–Chase experiment on, as genetic material in genes, 285–86
  human genes for coding, 399
  immunoglobulins, 1044–46, 1047f
  in meiosis, 246
  membrane (see Membrane proteins)
  in metabolic pathways, 157
  motor, 128–31, 133
  in muscle contraction, 975–76
  in nuclear pore complex, 119–20
  in nuclear transport, 119–21
  in one-gene, one-enzyme experiment on gene expression, 306
  Oparin–Haldane theory on chemical evolution of, 41–42
  origin-of-life research on, as first self-replicating molecules, 44–45, 55
  in plant cell–cell signaling, 794–96
  in point mutations, 313–14
  prokaryotic cytoskeletons of, 109
  proteomics in study of, 390, 402
  regulatory (see Regulatory proteins)
  repressor, 341–44, 345f
  separating and visualizing molecules of, B:13–B:16
  structure of, 47–52
  synthesis of (see Protein synthesis)
  systems biology in study of, 402
  in transcription, 319–20f, 325t
  in translocation, 769–72
  as tumor suppressors, 231–34
  viral production of, 719
  visualizing, with fluorescent microscopy, B:18
Proteobacteria, 544, 547
Proteoglycans, 202
Proteomes, 402
Proteomics, 390, 402. See also Genomics

Protists, 553
  biological importance of studying, 554–57
  biological methods of studying, 557–59
  diversification themes in, 559–69
  ecological importance of, 556–57
  Eukarya domain and, 552–53
  feeding and photosynthetic innovations of, 563–65
  impacts of, on human health and welfare, 554–56
  key lineages of, 558t, 559f, 569–74
  life cycles of, 566–69
  morphological innovations of, 559–63
  movement of, 565–66
  reproduction of, 566
Protocells, 94
Protoderm, 740, 833
Proton-motive force, 169–70, 185–86
Proton pumps, 770, 783, 799
  in cell elongation, 799–800
  in closing of stomata guard cells, 811–12
  in plant nutrient uptake, 783–84
  in translocation, 770–72
Protons
  in acid–base reactions, 28–30
  in atomic structure, 19–20
  ATP synthase as channel for, 168–69
  electron transport chain and, 167–68
  gradients of, in chemiosmosis hypothesis, 169–70
  gradients of, in photosystems, 185–86
  in redox reactions, 142–43
Proto-oncogenes, 361
Protostomes, 644, 658
  abundance, diversity, and ecological importance of, 658
  deuterostomes vs., 658
  ecdysozoan lineages of, 659–60f, 670–78 (see also Ecdysozoans)
  lophotrochozoan lineages of, 659–69 (see also Lophotrochozoans)
  major phyla of, 638t, 657–58
  modular body plans of, 660–61
  origin of, in animal evolution, 644–45
  water-to-land transition of, 659–60
Provisioning services, ecosystem, 1187
Proximal-distal leaf axis, 436–37f
Proximal tubule, 872, 873–74, 878t
Proximate causation, 1015, 1083
  of animal communication, 1092–93
  of foraging, 1085
  of mating, 1087–88
  of migration, 1089–91
  ultimate causation vs., 1083–84
Prusiner, Stanley, 53
Pseudocoelomates, 644
Pseudogenes, 399
Pseudopodia, 563, 565
Psilotophyta (whisk ferns), 603
Pteridophyta (ferns), 604
Pterosaurs, 694–95
Puberty, 999, 1026–27
Publications, primary literature, B:26–B:27
PubMed (online database), B:27
Puffballs, 617, 626–27
Pulmonary arteries, 921
Pulmonary circulation, 919–21
Pulmonary veins, 921
Pulse–chase experiments, 122
  on cell cycle gap phases, 222
  on DNA lagging-strand discontinuous replication, 292

on endomembrane system secretory pathway, 121–23
  on ribosomes as protein synthesis site, 324
Pumps, 99, 770
  active transport by, 99–101
  in translocation, 769–72
Punnett, R. C., 262, 273–75
Punnett squares, 262–63, 268–69, 466–67, B:8
Pupa, 672, 998
Pupil, 960, 961f
Pure lines, 258–59, 261–63
Purifying selection, 473
Purines, 58–59, 61–63, 65–66. See also Nitrogenous bases, nucleotide
Purple bacteria, 177, 184
Pyramid of productivity, 1152. See also Net primary productivity (NPP)
Pyramids, age, 1115–16
Pyrimidines, 58–59, 61–63, 65–66. See also Cytosine; Nitrogenous bases, nucleotide; Thymine; Uracil
Pyruvate, 157–61. See also Pyruvate processing
Pyruvate dehydrogenase, 161–62
Pyruvate processing, 156, 161–62, 164–65, 172–73

Q

Q. See Coenzyme Q (ubiquinone)
Quadriceps muscles, 982
Quantitative Methods boxes. See also Bioskills; Process boxes
  calculating coefficient of relatedness, 1096f
  deriving Hardy–Weinberg principle, 467f
  developing and applying population growth equations, 1110f–11f
  genetic mapping of gene locations by frequency of recombination, 274f
  measuring species diversity and species richness, 1143f
  species-area plots of species richness and habitat area, 1183f
  using life tables to calculate population growth rates, 1106f
  using Nernst equation to calculate equilibrium potentials, 932f
Quantitative traits, 275–76, 277t
Quaternary structure, protein, 50–51
Quorum sensing, 216

R

R-groups. See Side chains, amino acid
Racker, Efraim, 168–69
Radial axis, plant, 434
Radial symmetry, 641, 682–83f
Radiation, electromagnetic, 179. See also Light-capturing reactions, photosynthetic
Radiation, heat exchange and, 855
Radiation, ultraviolet (UV), 299–301, 305, 362–63
Radicle, 833
Radioactive decay, 446–47, 513
Radioactive isotopes, 20, B:15–B:16
Radioimmunoassay, 997, B:16
Radiometric dating, 446–47, 453, 513
Radula, 663, 668
Rain shadow, 1066–67
Rainfall. See Precipitation
Ramón y Cajal, Santiago, 930

Boldface page numbers indicate a glossary entry; page numbers followed by an *f* indicate a figure; those followed by *t* indicate a table.

Random distribution, 1102
Random mating, 468–70
Random mutations, 312
Ranges, species, **1062**, **1102**. *See also* Geographic distribution and abundance of organisms
for human population, 1116
impacts of global climate change on, 1166*t*, 1167
mapping, 1137
in population ecology, 1102–3
in preservation of metapopulations, 1120
Ras protein, **213**, 214, 232–33
Ray-finned fishes, 692, **698–99**
Rayment, Ivan, 974–76
Rays, cambium, **749**
Rb protein, **234**
Reabsorption, animal, 870–71, 873–74, 877–78
Reactants, chemical reaction, **30–32**, 139–40*f*, 143–47
Reaction center, photosystem, **183–84**
Reaction rates, chemical reaction, 139–40*f*, 145–47
Reactivity, amino acid side chain, 44
Reading frame, DNA sequence, **310–11**, 313, 392–93
Realized niches, **1126**
Receptacle, plant flower, 826
Receptor-mediated endocytosis, **126**
Receptor tyrosine kinases (RTKs), **213**–14
Receptors. *See also* B-cell receptors (BCRs); Enzyme-linked receptors; G-protein-coupled receptors; Signal receptors; T-cell receptors (TCRs)
animal hormone, 1006–10
animal sensory, 856–57, 953
cell–cell signal, 210
plant sensory system, 794–97, 800–803
Recessive alleles, 258*t*, 471
Recessive traits, **259–60**, 277–79, 299, 369. *See also* Dominant traits
Reciprocal altruism, **1098**
Reciprocal crosses, 258*t*, **260–61**, 268–69
Recognition phase, adaptive immune response, 1041–47
Recolonization, metapopulation, 1112*f*–13
Recombinant DNA technology, **369–74**. *See also* Genetic engineering
agricultural biotechnology, transgenic crops, and, 385–86
creating animal models of disease using, 382
discovery of gene recombination, 1046, 1047*f*
engineering human growth hormone using, 370–74
ethical concerns about, 374
gene therapy and, 383–85
in genetic engineering, 368–69, 381*t*
pituitary dwarfism, human growth hormone, and, 369–70
plant cell and tissue cultures in, B:22
Recombinant organisms, **270–71**, 274*f*
Recommended Dietary Allowances (RDAs), 883
Rectal glands, shark, **866–88**
Rectum, **896**
Red algae, 569, 572. *See also* Algae
Red blood cells, 48, 54, 99, **912**
Red/far-red light responses, plant, 179–81*f*, 800–803, 818*t*, 837

Red-green color blindness, 278–79, 963–64
REDD (Reducing Emissions from Deforestation and Forest Degradation), 1192–93
Re-differentiation, cell, 407
Redox (reduction-oxidation) reactions
in Calvin cycle, 190–92
in electron transport chain, 166–67
peroxisomes and, 115
in photosystems, 183–85
prokaryotic nitrogen fixation and, 542–43
transfer of energy via electrons in, 141–43
Reduction, **141**, 191, 241–42. *See also* Redox (reduction-oxidation) reactions
Re-extension, muscle, 980
Reference distributions, statistical tests and, B:7
Reflex, spinal, **944**
Refractory state, **936**
Regeneration phase, Calvin cycle, 191
Regulating services, ecosystem, 1187*t*, 1188
Regulation
of animal body temperature, 854–58
of animal homeostasis, 853–54
of animal hormone production, 1003–6
of blood pH, 915–16
of blood pressure and blood flow, 924
cancer as loss of cell-cycle, 233–34
of cell cycle, 229–31
of citric acid cycle, 162–63*f*
of enzymes, 149–50
of flower structures, 439–41
of gene expression (*see* Gene regulation, bacterial; Gene regulation, eukaryotic)
of glycolysis, 159–61
homeostatic, of ventilation, 911–12
kidney, 872, 877–78
of mammalian menstrual cycle, 1027–30
of mammalian puberty, 1026–27
of metabolic pathways, 150
of pancreatic enzymes, 893
of photosynthesis, 195
of plant body axes, 435–36
of plant leaf shape, 436–38
of protein folding, 53
of pyruvate processing, 161–62
of telomerase, 297
Regulatory cascades, 413–14, 436–38, 439–41
Regulatory genes
evolutionary change and, 416
evolutionary conservation of, 414–15
Hox genes as, for developmental positional information, 412–14
morphogens, 410–12
tool-kit genes as, 415
transcription factors, 410, 411–15 (*see also* Transcription factors)
Regulatory homeostasis, 853–58
Regulatory hormones, regulation of, 1026–27
Regulatory molecules, cell-cycle, 229–31
Regulatory proteins
in bacterial gene regulation, 337
in control of plant body axes, 435–36
in determination of leaf shape, 436–38
in differentiation of muscle cells, 428*f*–29

in eukaryotic transcription initiation, 353–56, 357*f*
in negative control, 341–44
in positive control, 341, 344, 345*f*
regulatory DNA sequences and, 353–54, 355*f*
as transcription factors in differential gene expression, 354–56
Regulatory sequences, 353–54, 355*f*, 356, 357*f*, 363
Regulatory transcription factors, **410**. *See also* Transcription factors
Regulons, **345**, 360
Reinforcement, **499**–500
Reintroduction programs, species, 1189–90
Relative dating, 446–47, 453
Release factors, **331**, 332*f*
Religious faith vs. science, 9
Remember (Bloom's taxonomy skill), B:29*f*–B:30*t*
Remodeling, chromatin. *See* Chromatin remodeling
Renal blood vessels, 871
Renal corpuscle, 872, **873**, 878*t*
Renewable energy, 1189
Repair, DNA, 297–301
Repetition, scientific experiments and, 13
Replacement rate, **1117**
Replica plating, 339–41
Replicated chromosomes, 239–40
Replication, chromosome, 220–21
Replication, DNA, 287–90. *See also* DNA synthesis
Replication fork, **290–95**
Replicative growth, viral, **716–21**
Replisomes, **294–95**
Repolarization, 933–34
Reports, scientific, B:26–B:27
Repressors, 341–44, 345*f*, **354**
Reproduction
animal (*see* Animal reproduction)
cell cycle and, 219–20 (*see also* Cell cycle)
evolution by natural selection and, 5–6, 454, 456
evolution of giraffe necks and, 9–11
fungal, 616*f*, 617–18, 624–25
as goal of living organisms, 2
mitosis and, 220 (*see also* Mitosis)
in model organisms, B:23
plant (*see* Plant reproduction)
protist, 566
Reproductive development, plant, **433**, 438–41
Reproductive isolation
allopatric speciation and, 494–95
biological species concept and, 490
ecological niches and, 496–97
mechanisms of, 491*t*
sympatric speciation and, 495–99
Reptiles, **696**
birds as, 694–95
lineages of, 696–97, 702–3
nitrogenous wastes of, 865
urine formation in, 878–79
in vertebrate phylogeny, 691
Research papers, B:26–B:27
Reservoirs, biogeochemical, 1159
Residues, amino acids as, 45–46
Resilience, community, **1186–87**, 1191–92
Resistance, community, **1186–87**
Resource partitioning, 1127–28
Resources
as ecosystem provisioning services, 1187

human consumption of, 1164, 1189
species richness and efficient use of, 1186
Respiratory systems, **903–16**
air and water as respiratory media in, 903–5
circulatory systems and, in gas exchange and circulation, 902–3 (*see also* Circulatory systems)
Fick's law of diffusion and, 905–6
fish gills in, 906–7
homeostatic control of ventilation in, 911–12
insect trachaea in, 907–9
organs of, 905–12
pulmonary circulation and, 920*f*
vertebrate lungs in, 909–11*f*
Responder cells, plant, 794–96
Response, cell–cell signal, 214
Resting potentials, **931**–32
Restoration, ecosystem, 1191–92
Restriction endonucleases, **370–72**, 379, 380*t*
Results, primary literature, B:27*t*
Reticulum, 891
Retina, eye, **960**, 961*f*
Retinal, 147, 961*f*–62
Retinoblastoma, 234
Retro-evolution hypothesis, 150–51*f*
Retroviruses, **383–85**, 720, 726*f*, 728
Revelle, Roger, 1163
Reverse transcriptase, **309**, **720**
in gene therapy, 383
in genetic engineering, 380*t*
inhibitors, 720
in long interspersed nuclear elements (LINEs), 396, 397*f*
producing cDNAs with, 370
Rheumatoid arthritis, 1056
Rhinovirus, 727
Rhizaria, 558*t*, 569, 572
Rhizobia, **787–89**
Rhizoids, **598**
Rhizomes, **603**, **737**, **825**
Rhodopsin, 395, 961*f*–62
Rhynie Chert, 585
Ribbon diagrams, 48–49*f*
Ribonuclease, 52
Ribonucleic acid (RNA). *See* RNA (ribonucleic acid)
Ribonucleotides, 6–7, **58**–59, 93–94. *See also* Nucleotides
Ribonucleotide triphosphate (NTP), 318–19
Ribose, 58–60, 65, 68–69, 73, 78
Ribosomal RNAs (rRNAs), **119**, **328**
developing tree of life from sequences of, 6–8
in gene families, 398
phylogenies based on, 535–36
in ribosomes, 328, 330
Ribosome binding sites, **329**–30
Ribosomes, **108**, **324**
in cracking of genetic code, 311
elongation of polypeptides during translation in, 330–31
eukaryotic, 112, 113
initiation of translation in, 329–30
mitochondria and, 115–16
polypeptide synthesis by, 119
post-translational modifications of proteins in, 331–32
prokaryotic, 108
protein synthesis by free, 123–24
ribosomal RNA and structure of, 328–29*f*

Ribosomes (continued)
  as ribozymes, 330–31
  structure and function of, 117t
  termination of translation in, 331, 332f
  in translation, 323–25, 328–32
  in translocation of mRNA, 331
Ribozymes, 67–69, 330–31
Ribulose bisphosphate (RuBP), **191**–92
Rice, 368f, 385, 392. See also Golden rice
Rickets, vitamin D–resistant, 279
Rieseberg, Loren, 501–2
Rifampin, 455–56
Ring structures, 74, 181f
Rings, tree growth, 751
Ripening, fruit, 812–13f
Ripple, William, 1153
Rivers, 1078, 1155
RNA (ribonucleic acid), **58**, 65–69.
    See also DNA (deoxyribonucleic
    acid); Messenger RNAs (mRNAs);
    Nucleic acids; Ribosomal RNAs
    (rRNAs); Transfer RNAs (tRNAs)
  as catalytic molecule, 67–68
  in central dogma of molecular biology,
    308–9
  codons in synthesis of, 311
  components of, 58–59
  directionality of strands of, 59–60
  discovery of variety of types of, 309
  DNA structure vs. structure of, 66t
  in DNA synthesis, 292–94t, 295–97
  electron micrograph of, 317f
  as first self-replicating molecule, 68–69
  gel electrophoresis of, B:13–B:14
  genes and, 220
  in genetic code, 310–12
  genetic homologies and, 450–51
  as genetic information-containing
    molecule, 67
  as intermediary between genes and
    proteins in gene expression, 307–8
  metabolic pathways and, 157
  nucleolus and eukaryotic, 112
  polymerization of ribonucleotides to
    form, 59–61
  ribonuclease enzyme and, 52
  RNA world hypothesis on, as first self-
    replicating molecule, 57–58
  structure of, 65–66
  sugar-phosphate backbone of, 60f
  synthesis of, 67, 119–20
  versatility of, 66–67
  visualizing, B:15–B:16
RNA-induced silencing complex
  (RISC), 359
RNA interference, **358**–59, 361t
RNA polymerase, **292**, **307**, **318**
  chromatin remodeling and, 349
  in DNA synthesis, 292
  in eukaryotic transcription initiation,
    356, 357f
  in recombinant DNA technology,
    373–74
  in RNA interference, 359
  in RNA processing, 325f
  in RNA synthesis, 307–8, 318–20
RNA processing, **324**, **349**
  bacterial vs. eukaryotic, 361t
  eukaryotic, 321–24, 325t, 356–59
RNA replicases, **719**–20
RNA reverse-transcribing viruses. *See*
  Retroviruses

RNA splicing, 322–23
RNA transcripts, 390
RNA viruses, 715–16, 719–20, 726f,
  727–28
RNA world hypothesis, 57–58, 68–69,
  330–31
Roberts, Richard, 322
Robotic genome sequencers, 389f
Robust australopithecines, 706–7,
  778–79f
Rock weathering, 778–79f, 1158
Rods, eye, **960**–64
Rohwer, Steve, 500–501
Root apical meristem (RAM), **434**
Root cap, **741**, **803**–4
Root cortex, water transport through,
  760–61
Root hairs, **742**, **759**–60, **782**–87
Root pressure, 759, **761**
Roots, phylogenetic tree, B:10–B:11
Root systems, **732**
  characteristics of, 733
  formation of, 434
  functions of, 732
  modified roots in, 734–35
  morphological diversity of, 733–34
  organization of primary, 741–42
  phenotypic plasticity in, 734
  soil retention by, 578
  water transport in (*see* Water
    transport, plant)
Roots, **434**, **603**. *See also* Root systems
  auxin and adventitious, 807
  formation of, 434
  infection of, by nitrogen-fixing
    bacteria, 787–89
  as land plant adaptations, 603
  modified, 734–35
  movement of water and solutes into,
    759–61 (*see also* Water transport,
    plant)
  nutrient uptake by, 782–87
  plant nutrition and, 775f
  soil composition and, 778–79f
Rosenzweig, Michael, 1086–87
Rotifers, 638t, 665
Rough ER (rough endoplasmic
    reticulum), **112**
  ECM components and, 202–3
  endoplasmic reticulum and, 112–13
  post-translational protein
    modifications in, 332
  proteins synthesis and transport by,
    121–24
  structure and function of, 117t
Round dance, honeybee, 1092–93
Roundworms, **674**
  apoptosis in, 408
  chromosomes of, 238
  diversity of, 672
  foraging in, 1085
  genome of, 392
  manipulation of hosts by, 1133
  as model organisms, 658, B:24f,
    B:25–B:26
  parasitic, and elephantiasis, 1037f
  phylogeny of, 638t, 674
  as protostome, 658
  terrestrial adaptations of, 659
Rubisco, **192**, 193–95, **766**
RuBP (ribulose bisphosphate), **191**–92
Rumen, 172, 891

Ruminants, 172, **891**
Running, Steve, 1168
Rusts, 630

S

S-shaped curves, scatterplot, B:5
S (synthesis) phase, 220–**21**, 223f
Saccharomyces cerevisiae
  alcohol fermentation with, 172–73f
  complete genome sequence of, 618
  economic value of, 614, 632
  gene regulation in, 348–49
  genome of, 392
  glycolysis discovery from extracts of,
    158–59
  meaning of scientific name of, 9
  as model organism, B:24f, B:25
  sex pheromones of, 215–16
Sac fungi, 617
Saddle-shaped proteins, 47f
Saharan desert ant, 11–14
St. Martin, Alexis, 890
Sakmann, Bert, 935
Salamanders, 700, 1019
Salinity, aquatic biome, **1074**
Saliva, 888, 889
Salivary amylase, 54, **889**, 895t
Salivary glands, 848f, 887f, **889**
Salmon, 483, 851–52, 868, 1060–61,
  1074, 1091
Salmonella, 1042–43
Salps, 688
Salt. *See also* Sodium chloride (table salt)
  in aquatic salinity, 1074
  freshwater fish import of, 868
  shark excretion of, 866–68
Saltiness taste reception, 965
Salty habitats, 492–93, 549, 757–58,
  786–87
Sampling effects, 1186
Sampling error, **478**
Sand dollars, 684–86f
Sandbox model, 834–35
Sandwich model, plasma membrane,
  94–95
Sanger, Frederick, 47–48, 377–78
Saprophytes, **614**–15, 623–24, 629
Sapwood, **751**
Sarcomeres, **973**–74, 980
Sarcoplasmic reticulum, **977**
Sargasso Sea environmental
    sequencing, 395
Satiation hormone, 1001–3
Satin bowerbird, 1082f
Saturated fatty acids, 85f, 385
Saturated lipids, **85**–86
Saxitoxins, 555–56
Scaffold proteins, 350
Scallops, 668
Scanning electron microscope, **95**–96f
Scanning electron microscopy (SEM)
  in biological imaging, B:19
  of DNA and RNA, 317f
  of DNA synthesis, 284f
  of *Escherichia coli*, 336f
  of human fertilization, 237f
  of human immune system cells, 1037f
Scarified seed coats, **836**
Scatterplots, B:4–B:5
Scents
  flower, 593–94
  in sympatric speciation, 496–97
Scheepers, Lue, 10–11
Schmidt-Nielsen, Kurt, 988
Schmitz, Oswald, 1191–92

Schooling, fish, 1129f
Schwann cells, **937**
SCID (severe combined
    immunodeficiency), 383–84, 1056
Science. *See also* Bioskills
Science. *See also* Process boxes;
    Quantitative Methods boxes
  in biological study of life, 1, 9–14 (*see
    also* Biology)
  experimental design in, 11–14
  experiments as hypothesis testing in,
    3–5, 9–11
  pattern and process components of
    theories of, 445
  religious faith vs., 9
  taxonomy and, 8–9
  theories in, 2, 3, 9
Science-Direct (online database), B:27
Scientific journals, B:26–B:27
Scientific names, 8–9
Scientific notation, B:2–B:3
Sclera, 960, 961f
Sclereids, **746**, 747
Sclerenchyma cells, **745**–47, 748t, 749
Scott, J. C., 1175
Screening, DNA library, 372–73, 381t
Scrotum, **1021**, 1023f
Sea anemone, 642
Sea bass, 868
Sea cucumbers, 684
Sea lilies, 684
Sea slugs, 946–48
Sea spiders, 678
Sea squirts, 686–87f, 688
Sea stars, 444f, 684–85, 1018, 1137–38,
  1153
Sea turtles, 465f, 1118, 1119f
Sea urchins, 237–38, 420–23, 684–86f,
  1018f
Seals, 1086
Seaside sparrows, 492–93
Seasons
  global climate change, phenology, and,
    1166–67
  mating and, 1087–88
  migration and, 1091
  plant translocation and, 766
  weather and, 1066, 1067f
Seawater. *See* Marine biomes
Second law of thermodynamics, **31**,
  44, **138**
Second-male advantage, **1019**–20
Second messengers, **212**, **795**, **940**, **1009**
  examples of, 213t
  in hormonal signal transduction,
    1008–10
  neurotransmitters and, 940
  in plant cell–cell signaling, 795
  in signal transduction via G-protein-
    coupled receptors, 211–13
Secondary active transport
    (cotransport), **100**, **770**, **864**–65
Secondary cell wall, **202**, **585**, **745**,
  762–63
Secondary consumers, 556, **1150**
Secondary endosymbiosis, 564–65
Secondary growth, plant, **748**–51
Secondary immune response, **1054**–55
Secondary metabolites, **815**
Secondary oocytes, **1017**
Secondary phloem, 748–50
Secondary spermatocytes, **1016**
Secondary structure, **48**
  DNA, 57f, 61–63 (*see also* Double helix
    secondary structure, DNA)
  DNA vs. RNA, 66t

hemoglobin, 51*t*
   protein, 48–49
   RNA, 65–66
   tRNA, 327
Secondary succession, **1139**–40
Secondary xylem, 748–50
Secretin, **893**, 995, **996**–97
Secretions, barrier, 1038–39
Secretory pathway, endomembrane
   system, 121–26
Secretory vesicles, 123
Sedimentary rocks, **446**, 447*f*
Sediments, fossils and, 512
Seed banks, **1189**
Seed coat, **833**
Seed plants. *See also* Angiosperms;
   Gymnosperms
   characteristics of, 581
   evolution of, 831
   heterospory in, 590, 591*f*, 592*f*
   lineages of, 599, 606–9*f*
   molecular phylogeny of, 583
   pollen grains in, 590–91
   seeds in, 591–92
Seeding, bioremediation with, 533
Seedless vascular plants
   characteristics of, 581
   homospory in, 590, 591*f*
   lineages of, 598–99, 603–5
   molecular phylogeny of, 583
Seeds, **433**, **581**, **823**, 833–37
   creation of, in embryogenesis, 433–36
   dormancy of, 836–37
   embryogenesis and, 833–34
   fruit development and dispersal of,
     834–36
   germination of, 832, 836–37
   gibberellins and abscisic acid in
     dormancy and germination of,
     809–10
   ground tissue, sclereids, and, 746
   in plant reproduction, 591–92, 823
   red/far-red light reception and
     germination of, 800–801
   role of drying in maturation of, 834
   seed coat and, 833
   seed plants and, 581, 599
   vacuoles in, 114
Segment identity genes. *See Hox* genes
Segment polarity genes, 412, 413*f*, 414*f*
Segmentation, **645**–46
Segmentation genes, **412**, 413*f*
Segmented bodies, arthropod, 670–71
Segmented worms, 638*t*, 662, 667
Segments, embryo, **412**
Segregation, principle of, **262**
   meiosis as explanation for, 266–67
   particulate inheritance and, 261–63
   Punnett squares and, 262–63
Selective adhesion, **206**–7
Selective breeding, 257. *See also* Crosses
Selective permeability, plasma
   membrane, **89**, **862**. *See also*
   Permeability, plasma membrane
   importance of, to cells, 84, 107
   intracellular environments and,
     100–101
   ion channel proteins and, 98
   lipid bilayers and, 89
   osmoregulation and, 862
   osmosis and, 92–93
Self-fertilization, **248**–49, **258**, 470–71*f*,
   497–98, **830**, B:25–B:26
Self molecule, **1046**–47
Self recognition, adaptive immune
   response and, 1042, 1046–47

Self-replicating molecules
   DNA as, 64–65
   lipid bilayers and, 93–94
   research on proteins as first, 42,
     44–45, 55
   RNA world hypothesis on RNA as
     first, 57–58, 68–69
Self-sacrificing behavior, 461. *See also*
   Altruism
Selfish DNA sequences, 396, 397*f*
Selfish genes, 461
Semen, **1022**–23*t*
Semiconservative replication, DNA,
   287–89
Seminal vesicles, **1022**–23*f*
Senescence, plant, 812–13
Sensors, **854**
Sensory neurons, **929**
Sensory organs, animal, 646, 647*t*
Sensory receptors, homeostatic, 1001
Sensory systems, animal, 952–71
   chemoreception of chemicals in,
     964–67
   electroreception of electric fields in,
     967–68
   information transmission to brains
     in, 954
   magnetoreception of magnetic fields
     in, 968–69
   mechanoreception of pressure changes
     in, 954–59
   photoreception of light in, 959–64
   processes and receptors in, 953
   senses and sensory organs in, 646, 647*t*
   in sensing of environmental changes,
     952–53
   sensory transduction in, 953–54
   thermoreception of temperature
     in, 967
Sensory systems, plant, 793–821
   defense responses to pathogens and
     herbivores, 815–19
   environments and, 793–94
   germination, stem elongation, and
     flowering responses to red and far-
     red light, 800–803
   gravitropic responses to gravity, 803–5
   growth regulators, 814*t*
   information processing and, 794–96
   phototropic responses to blue light,
     796–800
   responses to wind and touch, 805–6
   selected, 818*t*
   youth, maturity, and aging as growth
     responses, 806–15
Sepals, **439**, **593**, **826**
Separation
   of cell components, B:17–B:18
   of molecules, B:13–B:15
Septa, **616**
Sequences, amino acid, 46, 47–48
Sequences, DNA. *See* DNA sequences
Sequences, rRNA, 6–8
Sequencing technology, 389*f*, 391,
   1173. *See also* Direct sequencing;
   DNA sequencing; Metagenomics
   (environmental sequencing);
   Whole-genome sequencing
Serotonin, 941*t*, **947**
Serum, blood, **233**, B:21
Services, ecosystem. *See* Ecosystem
   services
Sessile organisms, **574**, **638**
Set point, **854**
Severe combined immunodeficiency
   (SCID), 383–84, 1056

Sex chromosomes, **238**, 240*t*, 268–69, 277*t*
Sex hormones
   binding of, to intracellular receptors,
     1006–8*f*
   contraception and, 1029–30
   control of menstrual cycle by,
     1027–30
   control of puberty by, 1026–27
   mammalian, 1025–30
   in mating, 1087–88
   testosterone and estradiol as steroids
     and, 1025–26
   in vertebrate sexual development and
     activity, 998–99
Sex-linked inheritance (sex-linkage), **268**
   in chromosome theory of inheritance,
     268–69
   exceptions and extensions to
     Mendelian rules on, 277*t*
   human, 278–79
   linkage vs., 270
Sex pheromones, 215–16
Sexual abstinence, 722
Sexual activity. *See* Mating
Sexual competition, 9–11
Sexual dimorphism, **477**–78
Sexual reproduction, **247**, **823**, **1014**
   animal, 650–51, 998–99, 1016–18*f* (*see
     also* Animal reproduction)
   asexual reproduction vs., 247, 251–52,
     566, 1014
   changing-environment hypothesis
     on, 253
   in eukaryotes, 553
   fertilization in (*see* Fertilization)
   fungal, 617–18, 624–27
   genetic variation from, 247–49
   hormones in, 998–99
   meiosis and, 219, 237–38 (*see also*
     Meiosis)
   paradox of, 251–52
   plant, 586–87, 823–25 (*see also* Plant
     reproduction)
   protist, 566
   purifying selection hypothesis on,
     252–53
   switching between asexual and, by
     Daphnia, 1014–16
Sexual selection, **472**, 475–78, **1088**–89
Sexually transmitted diseases, 546, 547,
   571. *See also* AIDS (acquired
   immune deficiency syndrome);
   HIV (human immunodeficiency
   virus)
Shade, far-red light as, 800–801
Shade leaves, 738
Shape
   active transport pump, 99–100
   animal locomotion and body, 985, 986
   enzyme, 54, 149–50
   flowers, 593–94
   genetic control of leaf, 436–38
   membrane carrier protein, 99
   organic molecule, 36*f*, 38
   plant receptor cell, 794–95
   prokaryotic diversity in, 536, 537*f*
   protein, 47–53, 331–32
   retinal change in, 962
   shoot system, 735–36
   signal receptor, 210
   simple molecule, 23–24, B:12–B:13
   transcription factors, 355–56
   viral, 715
Shared ancestry. *See* Common ancestry
Sharks, 512, 698, 866–68, 967–68
Sharp, Phillip, 321–22

Sheep, cloned, 409
Shells, **562**
   eggs, 693–94
   mollusk, 663, 668
   turtle, 702
Shine-Dagarno sequences, **329**–30
Shocked quartz, 521–22*f*
Shoot apical meristem (SAM), **434**
   in reproductive development, 438–39
   in vegetative development, 436, 437*f*
Shoot systems, **732**
   adventitious roots and, 734–35
   characteristics of, 735
   collenchyma cells and shoot support
     in, 744–45
   formation of, 434
   functions of, 732
   modified stems in, 736–37
   morphological diversity of, 735–36
   organization of primary, 742
   phenotypic plasticity in, 736
   water transport in (*see* Water
     transport, plant)
Shoots, **434**
Short-day plants, **802**
Short tandem repeats (STRs), **396**–98*f*
Shotgun sequencing, **390**–91
Shrimp, 495, 671, 677, 1133, 1134*f*
SI system, B:1
Sickle-cell disease, 48, 278
Side chains, amino acid
   amphipathic proteins and, 94
   in enzyme catalysis, 144–47
   function of, 42–44
   in major amino acids, 43*f*
   peptide bonds and, 45–46
   polarity of, and water solubility, 44
   protein structure and, 48–50
   of steroids, 87
Sieve plates, **747**, **767**
Sieve-tube elements, **747**, **767**, 770–71
Sig figs, metric system and, B:2–B:3
Sight, 481–82, 646, 647*t*
Sigma proteins, **319**–20*f*, 325*t*
Sigmoid curves, scatterplot, B:5
Signal hypothesis, endomembrane
   system, 123–24
Signal processing, cell–cell, 210–14
Signal receptors, **210**. *See also* Enzyme-
   linked receptors; G-protein-
   coupled receptors
Signal recognition particle (SRP), **124**
Signal response, cell–cell, 214
Signal transduction, **210**, **794**, **1008**
   cross-talk in, 813–14
   via G-protein-coupled receptors,
     211–13
   in hormone binding to cell-surface
     receptors, 1008–10
   of lipid-insoluble signals, 210–11
   in mechanoreception, 955
   in photoreception, 962–63
   in plant cells, 794–96
   via enzyme-linked receptors, 211,
     213–14
Signal transduction cascades, **1009**–10
Signaling, cell–cell. *See* Cell–cell
   signaling
Signaling, chemical. *See* Chemical
   signaling
Signaling pathways, animal hormone,
   993–94
Signals, communication, **1092**
Significant figures, metric system and,
   B:2–B:3
Silencers, **354**

Silent mutations, **313**–14*t*, 479
Silent Spring (book), 999–1000, 1152–53
Silk moths, 966–67
Silurian-Devonian explosion, 582
Simian immunodeficiency viruses (SIVs), 724
Simmons, Robert, 10–11
Simple eyes, **675**, **960**–64
Simple fruits, **834**, 835*f*
Simple leaves, 737–38*f*
Simple molecules, 23–24
Simple sequence repeats, **396**–98*f*
Simulation studies, genetic drift, 478–79
Simulation studies, global climate change, 1073
Sinervo, Barry, 1167, 1183–84
SINEs (short interspersed nuclear elements), **510**, 511*f*
Singer, S. Jon, 95–96*f*
Single bonds, 23
Single nucleotide polymorphisms (SNPs), 379, 380*t*
Single-strand DNA-binding proteins (SSBPs), **290**–91, 294*t*
Single-stranded RNA viruses, 716
Single-trait experiments, Gregor Mendel's, 259–63
Sinks, plant sugar, **766**
   connections between sources and, 766–67
   low pressure near, 768
   phloem unloading into, 771–72
Sinoatrial (SA) node, **921**–22
Siphon, **663**, 688
Sister chromatids, **220**, **239**
   in meiosis, 239–46
   in mitosis, 220, 221*f*, 223–26
Sister species, **495**
Sister taxa, B:10–B:11
Sit-and-wait predators, amphibian, 700
Sixth mass extinction possibility, 523
Size
   animal locomotion and body, 986–88
   cell-cycle checkpoints and cell, 231
   directional selection on cliff swallow body, 473
   disruptive selection on black-bellied seedcracker beak, 474
   genome, 390
   human population, 1117
   island biogeography and island, 1144
   largest fungal mycelium, 616
   male penis, 1021–22
   microsporidia as smallest eurkaryotic genome, 628
   model organism, B:23
   organic molecule, 38
   physiological effects of animal body, 850–53
   population, 1108–12, 1120
   of prokaryotic and eukaryotic cells, 110
   prokaryotic diversity in, 536, 537*f*
   prokaryotic vs. eukaryotic genomes, 393–94, 395–96
   scrotum, 1021
   sperm and egg, 420
   testes, 1020
   virus, 714
Size standards (or "ladders"), gel electrophoresis, B:13
Skeletal muscle, **847**, **978**–80

Skeletal systems, 980–83. *See also* Animal movement
   animal locomotion and size of, 987–88
   endoskeletons, 981–83
   exoskeletons, 983
   functions and types of, 980–81
   hydrostatic skeletons, 981
   skeletal muscle and, 978–80
Skeletons, animal
   cartilaginous, 698
   hydrostatic (*see* Hydrostatic skeletons)
   notochords in organogenesis of, 426
   somites as precursors to bone cells of, in organogenesis, 427–29
   vertebrate bony, 689
Skills, Bloom's taxonomy of, B:29–B:30*t*
Skin
   amphibian, 700
   as barrier to pathogens, 1038–39
   cancer of human, 300–301
   gas exchange via, 852
   lymphocytes and, 1042
   somites as precursors to cells of, in organogenesis, 427–29
   in thermoregulation, 857–58
Skoog, Folke, B:22
Skulls
   reptile, 696
   vertebrate, 688
Slack, Roger, 194
Sleeping sickness, 555*t*
Sliding clamp, 292, 294*t*
Sliding-filament model, 973–**74**
Slime molds, 216, B:23–B:25
Slow (slow oxidative) muscle fibers, **979**–80
Slugs, 662, 668, 1020
Slugs, cellular slime mold, B:23–B:25
Small intestines, **892**–96
   carbohydrate digestion and transportation in, 893–94
   chemical digestion in, 888
   digestion of lipids in, 895*f*
   fermentation in, 172
   folding and projections that increase surface area of, 892
   hormones and, 996–97
   human, 848*f*, 887*f*
   lipid digestion and bile transport in, 894–96
   pancreatic enzyme regulation in, 893
   protein processing by pancreatic enzymes in, 892–93
   water absorption in, 896
Small nuclear rebonucleoproteins (snRNPs), **322**–23
Smallpox virus, 715, 726, 1054–55
Smell, 646, 647*t*, 965–67
Smith, James, 1111–12
Smits, Willie, 1172–73, 1191
Smoke, seed germination and, 837
Smooth ER (smooth endoplasmic reticulum), 112–**13**, 117*t*, 208
Smooth lines, scatterplot, B:5
Smooth muscle, 847*f*–**48**, **977**
Smut, 630
Snails, 662, 668, 1020
Snakes, 416, 702, 884, 885*f*, 967, 968*f*, 1181
Snapping shrimp, 495
Snowshoe hare, 1113–15
Social controls, cell-cycle, 231, 233–34

Social stimulation, mating and, 1087–88
Sockeye salmon, 1060–61, 1074, 1091
Sodium channels, 934, 935
Sodium chloride (table salt), 22–23*f*, 1074
Sodium-glucose cotransporter, 893–94
Sodium hydroxide, 28–29
Sodium ions, electrolytes as, 862
Sodium poisoning, plant, 785
Sodium-potassium pump, **99**, **864**
   active transport and, 99–101*f*
   in animal glucose absorption, 894
   in fish osmoregulation, 867–68
   hormonal control of, 877
   in insect osmoregulation, 871
   in mammalian osmoregulation, 874
   in neuron membranes, 933*f*
   in osmoregulation, 864–65
   resting potentials and, 931–32
Soil, 778–82
   arbuscular mycorrhizal fungi (AMF) and, 621
   effects of composition of, on properties of, 782*t*
   fertilization of, 1155
   formation of, and textures of, 778–79*f*
   green plant building and holding of, 578
   importance of conservation of, 779–81
   lichens and, 631
   nutrient availability in, 781–82
   organic matter and humus in, 1156–57
   plant adaptations to dry and salty, 757–58
   plant nutrients from, 776–78, 780*t*
   plant nutrition and, 775
   Sphagnum moss and, 602
   succession and, 1140
   water potential in, 757–59
Soil conservation, 779–81
Soil organic matter, **1156**–57
Solar energy. *See* Light energy
Solubility
   amino acid, 44
   of gas in water, 904
   of lipids, 85, 86–87
   lipid-soluble vs. lipid-insoluble hormones, 209, 210–11
Solute potential, **756**
   in plant adaptations to dry habitations, 757–58
   water potential and, 755–57
Solutes, **25**, **92**, **755**, **862**
   in aquatic salinity, 1074
   concentration of, and solubility of gases in water, 904
   diffusion and, 91
   diffusion and osmosis of, across lipid bilayers, 91–94
   movement of water and, in plants (*see* Translocation; Water transport, plant)
   transport of, across plasma membranes by membrane proteins (*see* Membrane proteins)
Solutions, **25**, **755**
   acid-base reactions in, 28–30
   aqueous, and properties of water, 25–28
   chemical evolution in aqueous, 24
   molarity of, 29
   oxygen and carbon dioxide amounts in, 904
   pH buffers in, 30
   pH scale of acidity and alkalinity of, 29
Solvent, **25**–26, 28*t*
Soma, **930**

Somatic cells, **219**–20, 297
Somatic hypermutation, **1051**, 1054
Somatic motor neurons, 979
Somatic nervous system, **942**
Somatostatin, **992**
Somites, **426**–29
Songbirds, 948–49, 1109*f*, 1111–12
Sooty mangabeys, 724–25
Sori, **604**
Sound energy, 137. *See also* Mechanoreception
Sources, plant sugar, **766**
   connections between sinks and, 766–67
   high pressure near, 768
   sugar concentration in sieve-tube members at, 770–71
Sourness taste reception, 965
Southern, Edwin, B:16
Southern blotting, B:16
Soybeans, transgenic, 385
Space-filling models, 24, B:12*f*–B:13
Spanish flu, 712, 713*f*. *See also* Influenza viruses
Spanish moss, 789
Spark-discharge experiment, 33–34
Sparrows, 492–93, 1109*f*, 1111–12
Spatial avoidance mechanisms, plant self-fertilization, 830
Spawning, 1018
Special creation, theory of, 445, 446, 447, 453
Speciation, **6**, **490**
   adaptive radiations and (*see* Adaptive radiations)
   allopatric, 494–95
   contemporary, 451
   disruptive selection and, 474
   evolutionary processes and, 489–90
   outcomes of contact between isolated populations and, 499–502
   pollination by animals and, 831–32
   species concepts and, 490–93
   species diversity and, 1175
   species richness and rates of, 1145
   summary of outcomes of contact between isolated populations and, 502*t*
   sympatric, 495–99
   tree of life and, 6
Species, **490**. *See also* Population(s)
   adaptive radiations of, 516–20
   in Aristotle's theory, 445
   biological species concept of, 490, 491*t*
   Cambrian explosion diversification of, 518–20
   with closed circulatory systems, 917
   concepts of, 490–93
   conservation of, 1189–91
   deceitful communication among and between, 1094–95
   disruptive selection and formation of new, 472
   diversity of (*see* Biodiversity; Species diversity; Species richness)
   dusky seaside sparrow as species definition case, 492–93
   endangered (*see* Endangered species)
   endemic, 1176
   estimating probablilites of extinction of individual, 1182
   evolution and common ancestry of, 446, 449–51
   evolution and extinct, 447
   evolution of, by natural selection, 5–6 (*see also* Evolution; Natural selection)

Boldface page numbers indicate a glossary entry; page numbers followed by an *f* indicate a figure; those followed by *t* indicate a table.

evolution of oviparous, viviparous, and
ovoviviparous, 1020–21
exotic and invasive, 1063, 1064*f*
gamete recognition of same, in
fertilization, 421
geographic distribution and
abundance of (*see* Geographic
distribution and abundance of
organisms)
global warming and loss of, 1163
Hox genes of multiple, 414–15
impacts of global climate change on,
1166–68
interactions of (*see* Species
interactions)
keystone, 1137–38
lateral gene transfer between, 394–95
life-history patterns across, 1106–7
mass extinctions of, 520–23
mechanisms of reproductive isolation
of, 491*t*
morphospecies concept of, 490–91
number of animal, 636–37
number of fungal, 615
origination of, 6 (*see also* Speciation)
outgroup, B:10–B11
phylogenetic species concept of,
491–92
population cycles and interactions
within and between, 1113–15
protostome, 657–58
reintroduction of, 1153, 1154*f*
relationships of fungal, 618–19
relative abundance of vertebrate, 691*f*
selecting, for whole-genome
sequencing, 392
successional, 1140–42
summary of concepts of, 492*t*
taxonomy and scientific names for, 8–9
variations in nitrogenous wastes of,
865–66
without circulatory systems, 916
Species-area plots, 1183*f*
Species-area relationships, 1182–**83**
Species diversity, **1142**, **1174**
biodiversity, species richness,
and, 1174
in biodiversity hotspots, 1177
global climate change and, 1073
latitudinal gradient in global, 1144–45
measuring, 1143*f*
of protists, 555
speciation, extinction, and, 1175
species richness and, 1142–43 (*see also*
Species richness)
Species interactions, 1123–35, 1136*t*
commensalism in, 1124–25
competition in, 1125–28
consumption in, 1128–33
four types of, 1123, 1136*t*
mutualisms in, 1133–35
species richness and, 1186
in succession, 1140–41, 1142
three themes of, 1124
Species richness, **1142–45**, **1174**
biodiversity, species diversity,
and, 1174
estimates of, using surveys, 1175
estimating, 1182–83
hypotheses for latitudinal gradient in
global, 1144–45
mapping, 1176
measuring species diversity and, 1143*f*
net primary productivity and, 1185–86
of protostomes, 657–58
species diversity and, 1142–43

theory of island biogeography and
predicting, 1143–44
vertebrate, 691*f*
Specific heat, **27**, 28*t*, **1067**
Specificity
adaptive immune response, 1042
antibody, 1045–46
Spectrophotometer, 845
Sperm, **237**, **823**, **1014**
competition by, 1019–20, 1022
fertilization by, 420–21
gametogenesis of, 241
glycoproteins in fertilization by, 79–80
human, 237*f*
meiosis and, 219, 237–38
microscopic images of cells of
human, 3*f*
plant, 827, 829
plant development of, 438
in plant fertilization, 433
in plant reproduction, 823
polyspermy prevention and, 421–23
in sexual reproduction, 1014–15
sexual selection and, 475
spermatogenesis of, 1016–17, 1022
structure and function of, 1017
testes size and, 1020
transport and delivery of, by male
reproductive systems, 1022
Spermatids, **1016**
Spermatogenesis, **1016–17**, 1022
Spermatogonia, **1016**
Spermatophores, **669**, **843–45**, **1019**
Sperm competition, **1019–20**, 1022
Sphagnum moss, 601–2
Sphenophyta (horsetails), 605
Sphincters, stomach, **889**
Spicules, **639**
Spiders, 678, 1020
Spinal cords, 427, 686, 688, 943–44
Spindle apparatus, **224**, **241**
in meiosis, 241
in mitosis, 224–27
Spine, human, 843
Spines, cactus, **740**
Spiracles, **869**, **907**
Spiral cleavage, 660–61
Spirochetes, 544, 546
Spleen, **1043**
Spliceosomes, **323**, **357**
Splicing, RNA, **322–23**. *See also*
Alternative splicing, RNA
Sponges, 206, 638–41, 652, 981
Spongiform encephalopathies, 53
Spontaneous abortions, 470
Spontaneous chemical reactions. *See also*
Exergonic reactions
characteristics of, 31–32
energetic coupling of endergonic
reactions and, 141–44
in formation of micelles and lipid
bilayers, 88
Gibbs free-energy change and,
138–39
Spontaneous generation hypothesis, 3–4,
18–19, 445–46
Sporangia, **582**, **823–25**
Spores, **567**, **617**, **823**
cellular slime mold, B:23–B:25
fossilized, 581–82
fungal, 617, 624
land plant production of, 588–89
in plant reproduction, 823–25
protist sporophytes and, 568
Sporophytes, **567**, **588**, **823**
in alternation of generations, 588–89

land plant evolution toward life cycles
dominated by, 589–90
in land plant life cycles, 823–25
protist, 568–69
seeds and, 833
Sporopollenin, **582**, 587, 829, **829**
Spotted owls, 1118
Spruces, 607
Squid, 130, 662, 669, 932–33
Srb, Adrian, 305–7
Stability, community, 1186–87
Stability, DNA, 64, 65
Stabilizing selection, **473**, 475*t*
Stahl, Franklin, 288*f*, 289
Staining, cell, B:18–B:19
Stalked bacteria, 547
Stamens, **439**, **592**, **827**, 828–29
Staminate flowers, 827(*footnote*)
Standard error bars, B:6–B:7
Standing defenses, **1129**–30
Stapes, **956**
Staphylococcus aureus, 456
Starch, **76**, **195**
digestion of, 889
hydrolysis of, to release glucose,
80–81
in metabolic pathways, 157
as plant storage polysaccharide, 72*f*,
76, 78
processing of, in photosynthesis, 195
structure of, 77*t*
Starling, Ernest, 893, 918–19
Start codon, **311**, 329–30
Statistical tests, B:5, B:7
Statocyst, **954**
Statolith hypothesis, **804**
Statoliths, **804**
Steelhead trout, 482–83
Stem-and-loop structure, RNA, 66
Stem cells, **407**
in cell proliferation, 407
in gene therapy for severe combined
immunodeficiency (SCID), 384
in plant embryogenesis, 434–35
Stems, **735**
elongation of, 799–802
eudicot vs. monocot, 742*f*
modified, 736–37
in shoot systems, 735 (*see also* Shoot
systems)
Stereocilia, **955**
Stereomicroscopes, B:18
Sterilization, heat, 3–4
Steroids, **87**, **812**. *See also* Sex
hormones
brassinosteroids as plant, 812
fungi in production of, 629
as hormones, 995–96, 999
as lipids, 87
receptors for, 1006–8*f*
testis cells and, 118
Steudle, Ernst, 764
Stevens, Nettie Maria, 238–39, 268
Sticky ends, **371**–72
Stigma, **827**
Stochastic events, biodiversity loss
and, 1179
Stolons, **737**
Stomach acid, 28
Stomachs, **889**–92
avian gizzard as modified, 891–92
chemical digestion in, 888
discovery of digestion in, 890
echinoderm, 683
human, 848*f*, 887*f*
protein digestion in, 890

in ruminants, 891
stomach acid production by parietal
cells of, 890–91
ulcers as infectious disease of, 891
Stomata, **584**, **743**, **810**
abscisic acid in closing of guard cells
of, 810–12
passage of oxygen and carbon dioxide
through, 192–93
phototropins and, 797
regulation of gas exchange and water
loss by, 743–44
water loss prevention by, 584–85, 754,
765–66
Stoneworts, 600
Stop codons, **311**, 313, 331, 332*f*
Storage polysaccharides, 72*f*, 76, 77*t*,
80–81, 155
Strains, viral, **723**–26
Stramenopila, 557, 558*t*, 570, 574
Strands
DNA, 61–63
nucleic acid, 59–60
Stratton, Charles, 369*f*
Streamlined bodies, convergent
evolution of, 509–10
Streams, **1078**
Stress, hormones in, 1000–1001
Striated muscle, **977**, 978
Strijbosch, Henk, 1104–5
Stroma, **116**, **178**–79*f*, 189, 191
Structural formulas, **24**, B:12–B:13
Structural homologies, **450**–51*f*
Structural polysaccharides, 72*f*, 76, 77*t*,
78–80
Structural proteins, 54
Structure-function correlations. *See*
Form-function correlations
Struggle for existence hypothesis, 453
Study guide, Bloom's taxonomy,
B:29–B:30*t*
Sturtevant, A. H., 274*f*
Style, carpel, **827**
Subach, Aziz, 1086–87
Suberin, **760**
Subspecies, **492–93**
Substrate-level phosphorylation,
159, 162–63*f*, 167. *See also*
Phosphorylation
Substrates, **54**, **143**
concentration of, and catalysis
rate, 147
in endergonic reactions, 143–44
enzyme catalysis and, 54, 144–45
eukaryotic organelles and, 110
in evolution of metabolic pathways,
150–51
globular shape of, 47*f*
in nucleic acid polymerization, 60
Subtropical deserts, **1070**
Subunit virus vaccines, 1055
Subunits, polypeptide, 50
Suburbanization, 1161
Succession, **1139**–42
Succession, law of, 447
Succulent leaves, 739
Sucrose, **195**, **767**
in glycolysis experiments, 158–59
plant transport of (*see* Translocation)
processing of, in photosynthesis, 195
Sucrose density-gradient centrifugation,
B:17*f*–B:18
Suess, Hans, 1163
Sugar beets, 771–72
Sugar-phosphate backbone, nucleic acid,
59–63, 65

Sugars, 72
  as carbohydrates, 72–73 (*see also* Carbohydrates)
  chemical evolution and nucleotide production from, 59
  dry seeds and, 834
  glucagon and blood levels of, 54
  insulin and blood levels of, 47–48
  in metabolic pathways, 157
  in nucleotides, 58–60
  photosynthetic production of, 176–78 (*see also* Photosynthesis)
  plant transport of (*see* Translocation)
  in RNA (*see* Ribose)
Sulfate, 171
Sulfhydryl functional group, 37*t*–38
Sulfur, 38, 49, 177, 324
  as human nutrient, 885*t*
  as plant nutrient, 780*t*
  in proteins vs. in DNA, 285–86
Sum rule, probability, B:8
Summation, 941–**42**
Sun, compass orientation by, 1089–90
Sun leaves, 738
Sundews, 790
Sunfish, 1094–95
Sunflowers, 489*f*, 501–2, 1082
Sunlight. *See* Light energy
Supercoiled bacterial DNA, 107–8
Supernatants, centrifugation, B:18
Support structures, protist, 562
Supporting connective tissue, 846*t*, **847**
Supporting services, ecosystem, 1187*t*, 1188
Surface area
  animal adaptations that increase, 852–53
  animal gas exchange and, 905, 916
  fungal mycelia, 616–17
Surface/area relationships, plant, 732–33
Surface area/volume, animal body, 850–53
Surface metabolism model, chemical evolution, **33**, 35–36, 45, 60
Surface tension, 26, **762**
Surgery, cancer, 233
Survival, evolution and, 5–6, 9–11
Survivorship, **1104**
  in density-dependent logistic population growth, 1109–12
  in human population growth, 1115–18
  in life histories, 1105–7
  in life tables, 1104–5, 1106*f*
  in preservation of endangered species, 1118, 1119*f*
Survivorship curves, 1104–**5**
Suspension feeders, 648, 662*f*, **884**
Suspensor, plant, 434
Sussman, Michael, 770
Sustainability, **1189**
Sustainable agriculture, **781**
Sustainable forestry, 781
Sutton, Walter, 257, 266–67
Swallowing, 889
Swammerdam, Jan, 973
Swamps, **1077**
Sweating, 864
Sweden
  age structure of human population in, 1115–16
  maternal mortality rates in, 1034
Sweet potato hawkmoth, 908

Sweetness taste receptors, 965
Swetnam, Thomas, 1139
Swim bladder, **698**
Swimming, 109, 132–33, 617, 984, 985, 988
Symbiosis, **560**, 619–23, 723, **891**. *See also* Mutualism(s)
Symbiotic relationships, **619**, **784**, 787–89. *See also* Mutualism(s)
Symbols, chemical structure, B:12–B:13
Symmetric competition, **1125**
Symmetry, body
  animal bilateral, 641–44
  echinoderm, 682–83*f*
Sympathetic nervous system, 924, **943**, 1006
Sympathetic neurons, 977
Sympatric speciation, **495**–99
Sympatry, **495**, 500
Symplast, **208**–9*f*, **760**
Symplastic route, 760–61
Symporters, **770**, 865
Synapomorphies, 491–**92**, 507–8, 553
Synapses, **939**. *See also* Electrical signaling, animal; Nervous systems
  memory, learning, and changes in, 946–48
  neurotransmitter functions and, 938–39, 940
  neurotransmitter release and structure of, 939–40
  postsynaptic potentials and, 940–42
Synapsis, **242**
Synaptic cleft, **939**
Synaptic plasticity, 946, **947**–48
Synaptic vesicles, **939**
Synaptonemal complex, **246**
Synergids, 832
Synthesis (S) phase. *See* S (synthesis) phase
Syphilis, 546
Systemic acquired resistance (SAR), **816**
Systemic circulation, **919**–21
Systemin, 210*t*, **817**
Systems, **30**–32
Systems biology, 390, **402**. *See also* Genomics
Systole, **923**
Systolic blood pressure, **923**
Szilard, Leo, 342
Szostak, Jack, 94, 296

T

T-cell receptors (TCRs), 1044*f*, **1045**–47, 1048
T cells, **1043**
  activation and function of, 1054*t*
  activation of, 1048–50
  antigen receptors of, 1045–47
  discovery of, 1042–43
  in gene therapy for severe combined immunodeficiency (SCID), 384
  HIV and helper, 713–14, 717–18
  as lymphocytes, 1042–43
  memory cells and, 1053–55
T-DNA, 385–86
T (transverse) tubules, **977**
Tabin, Clifford, 458–59
Table salt. *See* Sodium chloride (table salt)
Tagging, 324, B:15–B:16, B:20

Tagmata, **670**
Taiga, **1072**
Tails, mRNA, 323–24
Tails, post-anal, 686
Tails, vestigial, 448
Talking trees hypothesis, 817–18
Tannins, 115, 815
Tapeworms, 666
Taproots, **733**, 734–35
Taq polymerase, 374–76, 380*t*, 531
Tardigrades, 638*t*, 672–73
Target crops, agricultural biotechnology and, 385
Tarsiers, 704
Taste (gustation), 646, 647*t*, 964–65
Taste buds, **964**–65
TATA box, **320**, 354
TATA box-binding protein (TBP), 47, **354**
Tatum, Edward, 305
Taxol drug, 607
Taxon (taxa), **8**, B:10–B:11
Taxon-specific surveys, 1175
Taxonomic bias, fossil record, 512
Taxonomic diversity, 1174–75
Taxonomy, **8**
  fossil record and taxonomic bias, 511
  scientific names for organisms in, 8–9
Taxonomy, Bloom's, B:29–B:30*t*
Taylor, Richard, 986, 987*f*
Tectorial membrane, **956**–57
Teeth
  adaptations of, 884, 885*f*
  in fossil record, 512
  mammalian, 701
  reptilian, 703
Teleosts, 699
Telomerase, **296**–97
Telomeres, **295**–97
Telophase, 225*f*, **226**, 245*f*
Telophase I, 243–44, 245*f*
Telophase II, 243*f*, 244–45
Temperate forests, **1071**, 1158–59
Temperate grasslands, **1071**, 1184–87
Temperate zone, **1071**
Temperature, **31**
  as abiotic factor in geographic distribution and abundance of organisms, 1062
  animal regulation of body (*see* Thermoregulation)
  animal sensing of, 646, 647*t*
  in aquatic biomes, 1076
  blood flow and body, 924
  in climates, 1066–67
  in decomposition rates, 1157
  effect of, on hemoglobin, 914
  effects of, on reaction rates of chemical reactions, 139–40*f*
  global climate change and, 1073, 1163, 1164–66, 1182
  in mating, 1087–88
  as measure of thermal energy, 31
  membrane permeability and, 90–91
  metric units and conversions for, B:1*t*
  in net primary production of terrestrial biomes, 1155
  optimal, for enzyme function, 148
  spontaneous chemical reactions and, 138–39
  stratification of, in oceans, 1168
  in terrestrial biomes, 1068–72
  thermoreception of, 967, 968*f*
  tropical species richness and, 1145
  of water for gas solubility, 904
Template strands, DNA, **64**, 318, 319–20*f*

Temporal avoidance mechanisms, plant self-fertilization, 830
Temporal bias, fossil record, 512–13
Temporal lobe, **944**, 945–46
Temporal prezygotic isolation, 491*t*
Tendon tissue, 846*t*
Tendons, **981**–82, 984, 986
Tendrils, 739
Tension-resisting elements, 201
Tentacles, 649*t*, 654, **669**
Terminal node, phylogenetic tree, 506*t*, B:10–B:11
Termination phase
  enzyme catalysis, 146*f*–47
  transcription, **320**, 321*f*
  translation, 331, 332*f*
Termites, 571
Terrestrial biomes, 1068–74
  animal locomotion in, 984, 985
  animal transition from aquatic environments to, 659–60
  arctic tundra, 1072
  boreal forests, 1072
  characteristics of natural, 1068–69
  effects of global climate change on, 1073–74
  gas exchange in, 907
  human impacts on, and anthropogenic, 1069
  impacts of global climate change on net primary productivity of, 1168
  insect osmoregulation in, 869–71
  internal fertilization in, 1019
  net primary production of, 1154–56
  nutrient cycling in, 1156–59
  osmoregulation in, 864
  plant adaptations to dry and salty, 754–55, 757–58, 765–66
  plant transition from aquatic environments to, 584–95 (*see also* Land plants)
  protostomes in, 659–60
  species richness of, 1176
  subtropical deserts, 1070
  temperate forests, 1071
  temperate grasslands, 1071
  tropical wet forests, 1070
  vertebrate osmoregulation in, 871–79 (*see also* Kidneys)
Territories, **477**, **1083**–84
Tertiary consumers, 556, **1150**
Tertiary structure, **49**
  DNA vs. RNA, 66*t*
  hemoglobin, 51*t*
  protein, 49–50
  RNA, 66
  tRNA, 327
Test preparation, Bloom's taxonomy and, B:29–B:30*t*
Testcrosses, 258*t*, 265–66
Testes, **999**, **1016**
  cells of, 118
  hormones of, 994*f*, 999
  male reproductive systems and, 1021–23
  spermatogenesis in mammalian, 1016–17
  variable size of, among species, 1020
Testosterone, **999**, **1025**
  in mammalian reproduction, 1025–26
  in mating, 1087–88
  puberty and, 1026–27
  testes and, 118
Tests, statistical, B:5, B:7
Testudinians, 702
Tetrads, 240*t*, **242**

Tetrahydrocannabinol (THC), 815
Tetrahymena, 67–68, 132–33
Tetramers, 50
Tetrapods, 448, **689**, 692–93
Tewksbury, Joshua, 835–36
Texture, soil, **778**–79*f*
Thale cress. *See* Mustard plant
Thalidomide, 1033
Thaumarchaeota, 544
Theories, **2**
  cell theory and theory of evolution
    as, 2
  importance of scientific, 444
  pattern and process components of, 3,
    5, 18–19, 445
Theory of island biogeography, 1143–45
Therapies
  cancer, 234
  gene therapy, 383–85
  genetic maps and development of, 382
  growth hormone therapy for pituitary
    dwarfism, 369–70 (*see also* Human
    growth hormone [HGH])
Thermal energy, **31**, 137. *See also* Heat
Thermoclines, **1076**
Thermodynamics, laws of, 31, 44,
  137–39
Thermophiles, 528*f*, 531, **534**
Thermoreception, **967**, 968*f*
Thermoreceptors, **953**
Thermoregulation, **855**–58
  countercurrent heat exchangers in,
    857–58
  endotherm homeostasis in, 856–57
  endothermy and ectothermy in, 856
  heat exchange mechanisms and, 855
  thermoreception of temperature
    in, 967
  variations in, 855–56
Thermus aquaticus, 375, 531, 1062
Thiamine (Vitamin B_1), 147, 884*t*
Thick ascending limb, loop of Henle,
  876, 878*t*
Thick filaments, **974**
Thigmotropism, **806**
Thin ascending limb, loop of Henle,
  876, 878*t*
Thin filaments, **974**
Thin layer chromatography, 180,
  B:14–B:15
Thinking skills, Bloom's taxonomy of,
  B:20–B:30*t*
Thiols, 37*t*
Thorax, 670, **675**
Thorns, **737**
Threatened species, 1178
Threats, biodiversity, 1178–84. *See also*
  Biodiversity
  extinctions, endangered species,
    and, 1178
  global climate change, 1181*t*, 1182
  habitat destruction, fragmentation,
    and degradation, 1178–80, 1181*t*
  invasive species, 1181
  multiple interacting, 1178
  overexploitation, 1180–81
  pollution, 1181*t*, 1182
  predicting effects of, on extinction
    rates, 1182–84
  summary of, 1181*t*
Three-dimensional imaging, B:20–B:21
Threshold, postsynaptic potential, 942
Threshold potential, **934**
Throwbacks, evolutionary, 603
Thumb, Tom, 369*f*
Thylakoids, **116**, **178**–79*f*, 580

Thymidine, 222, 948–49
Thymine, 58–59, 61–63, 287, 318
Thymine dimers, 299
Thymus, **1043**, 1043
Thymus-dependent lymphocytes, 1043.
  See also T cells
Thyroid gland, 994*f*, **996**, 997–98
Thyroid hormones, **996**
Thyroid-stimulating hormone
  (TSH) **1006**
Thyroxine, 210*t*, **996**
Ti (tumor-inducing) plasmids, **385**–86
Ticks, 678
Tight junctions, **205**
Tilman, David, 1185–87
Time, geologic, 446–47
Tinbergen, Niko, 1084
Tips, phylogenetic tree branch, **506**,
  B:10–B:11
Tissue systems, plant, 742–48*t*
Tissues, **203**, 204
Tissues, animal, **425**, **640**, 846–50
  anatomy and physiology at level of, 849*f*
  blood, 912
  cells and, 846
  connective, 846*t*, 847
  cultures of (*see* Cultures, cell and
    tissue)
  embryonic tissues and, 847
  epithelial, 848–49
  germ layers and, 425
  immune system rejection of foreign,
    1053
  muscle, 847–48
  muscle tissues, 977–80
  nervous, 847
  organogenesis and, 427–29
  organs, organ systems, and, 848*f*,
    849–50
  origin of embryonic tissue layers and,
    640–41
  structure-function relationships in,
    845–46
Tissues, plant, **740**–41, 759–60. *See also*
  Tissue systems, plant
  cultures of (*see* Cultures, cell and
    tissue)
  embryogenesis of, 434–35, 833
  poor herbivore nutrition and, 1131–32
Title, primary literature, B:27*t*
Tobacco cells, B:22
Tobacco mosaic virus (TMV), 715–16
Tolerance, successional, **1141**
Tomatoes, 437–38, 777–78
Tonegawa, Susumu, 354
Tongues, gray whale thermoregulation
  and, 857–58
Tonoplast, **772**, 786–87
Tool-kit genes, **415**, **640**, 660, 661, 671
Top-down control, **1153**, 1154*f*
Top-down control hypothesis, herbivore
  population, 1131
Top-down research approach, chemical
  evolution, 32
Top predators, 1153, 1154*f*
Topoisomerase, **291**, 294*t*
Torpedo-shaped bodies, 985, 986
Torpor, **855**
Totipotent cells, 652, **744**, B:21
Touch
  plant responses to, 805–6, 818*t*
  sensory organs and, 646
Townsend's warblers, 500–501, 1062
Toxins, **532**
  in action potential research, 935
  bacterial, 532

  biomagnification of, 1152–53
  as constitutive defenses, 1129*f*
  plant, 744, 815
  as plant defense responses, 815
  plant exclusion of, 785–87
  sponges and, 652
  transfer of, from mammalian mother
    to fetus, 1033
Toxoplasmosis, 555*t*, 573
Tracers, 621, B:15–B:16
Trachea, vertebrate, **909**
Tracheae, **869**
Tracheae, insect, **907**–9
Tracheids, **585**–86, **746**–47
Trade-offs, fitness, **843**–45
Tragopogon, 498–99
Traits, **257**
  alleles, genes, and, 247
  analyzing morphological, in green
    plants, 580–81
  artificial selection of, 453
  codominance and incomplete
    dominance of, 272, 273*f*
  constraints on natural selection of,
    461–62
  discrete, 275
  dominant vs. recessive, 259–60
  effects of modes of natural selection
    on, 472, 475*t*
  evolution and transitional, 447–48
  evolution and vestigial, 448–49, 461
  evolution of complex, 460
  exceptions and extensions to
    Mendelian rules on, 277*t*
  fitness and adaptations as, 6 (*see also*
    Adaptation(s); Fitness)
  genes and, 247
  heredity and, in Mendelian genetics,
    257–59 (*see also* Mendelian
    genetics)
  heritable, 5
  homology vs. homoplasy in, 508–10
  human, 277–79
  incomplete dominance and
    codominance in, 273*f*
  levels of causation of, 1015
  life-history, 1106–7
  maladaptive, 192
  mapping, on phylogenetic trees, 508*t*
  Mendelian experiments with single,
    259–63
  Mendelian experiments with two,
    263–66
  in Mendelian genetics, 257
  morphological innovations in, 517
  morpological (*see* Morphology)
  natural selection and heritable,
    454, 456
  nonadaptive, 461
  pedigrees and mode of transmission
    of, 277
  phenotypes and, 258 (*see also*
    Phenotypes)
  phylogenetic trees and, B:10–B11
  phylogenies based on morphological,
    510, 511*f*
  pleiotropic genes and multiple,
    272–73
  polymorphic, 272
  quantitative, in polygenic inheritance,
    275–76
  sexually dimorphic, 477–78
  shared animal, 637
  shared derived (*see* Synapomorphies)
  in succession, 1140, 1142
  synapomorphic, 492

Transcription, **308**, 318–21*f*
  bacterial and eukaryotic, 325*t*
  bacterial vs. eukaryotic gene regulation
    of, 360–61
  of DNA to mRNA, 308
  electron micrograph of, 317*f*
  elongation and termination phases of
    bacterial, 320, 321*f*
  eukaryotic, 320
  eukaryotic regulation after, 356–61
  initiation phase of bacterial, 318–20*f*
  model of initiation of eukaryotic,
    356, 357*f*
  regulation of (*see* Transcriptional
    control)
  regulatory sequences and proteins in
    initiation of eukaryotic,
    353–56, 357*f*
  RNA polymerases in synthesis of
    mRNA in, 318
Transcription factors, **355**
  bacterial vs. eukaryotic, 360–61*t*
  bicoid gene as, 411–12
  in cell–cell interactions of
    development, 407
  in cell determination, 428–29
  in differential gene expression, 354–56,
    409–12
  Hox genes and, 413
  p53 tumor-suppressor gene as, 362–63
Transcriptional activators, **341**, **354**,
  356, 357*f*
  bacterial, 341, 344, 345*f*
  eukaryotic, 354, 356, 357*f*
Transcriptional control, **337**
  in bacterial gene regulation, 337–38*f*
  negative bacterial, 341–44, 345*f*
  positive bacterial, 341, 344, 345*f*
Transcriptional control, bacterial,
  360–61
Transcriptional control, eukaryotic,
  353–56
  bacterial vs., 360–61
  in differential gene expression, 409–10
  differential gene expression and
    transcription factors in, 354–56
  enhancers as regulatory sequences in,
    354, 355*f*
  model of, 356, 357*f*
  morphogens in, 411–12
  promoter-proximal elements as
    regulatory sequences in, 354, 355*f*
  promoters and TATA boxes in, 353–54
Transcriptomes, **402**
Transcriptomics, 390
Transects, 1103
Transfer, muscle force, 980
Transfer RNAs (tRNAs), **326**
  anticodons and structure of, 327
  attachment of amino acids to, 327, 328*f*
  function of, 326–27
  in ribosomal translation, 328–31
  wobble hypothesis on types of, 327–28
Transformation, **372**, 395
Transformations, energy, 31
Transfusions, immune systems and
  blood, 1053
Transgenic organisms, **382**
Transgenic plants, 385–86, 437–38
Transitional features, **447**–48
Transition state, enzyme catalysis,
  145–47
Translation, **308**, 324–32
  amino-acid specification by mRNA
    triplets in, 325–26
  bacterial and eukaryotic, 324*f*–25

Translation (continued)
    elongation phase of, 330–31
    initiation phase of, 329–30
    of mRNA to proteins, 308
    post-translational modifications,
        331–32
    ribosomes in, 324, 328–32 (see also
        Ribosomes)
    termination phase of, 331, 332f
    tRNA synthesis in, 326–28
Translation, eukaryotic
    bacterial vs. eukaryotic control of, 361t
    control after, 360
    control of, 359–60
Translational control, 337–38f
Translational control, bacterial, 361t
Translational control, eukaryotic,
    359–60, 361t
Translocation, 331, 766–72
    connections between sugar sources
        and sinks in, 766–67
    phloem anatomy and, 767
    phloem in, 749
    phloem loading in, 769–71
    phloem unloading in, 771–72
    pressure-flow hypothesis on, 768–69f
    sugar sources and sinks in, 766
Translocations, chromosome, 314
Transmembrane proteins, 95
Transmembrane route, 760
Transmission, pedigrees of human trait,
    277. See also Pedigrees
Transmission, sensory signal, 953, 954
Transmission, viral, 720–21, 722, 725
Transmission electron microscopy (TEM)
    biological imaging using, B:18–B:20
    of cells, 118f
    of parietal cells, 891
    studying synapses with, 715
    of synapses, 939
Transpiration, 737, 754–55, 765–66
Transplantation studies, 428–29
Transport, lymphocyte, 1043
Transport, sperm, 1022
Transport functions, plant vascular
    tissue, 749
Transport proteins
    functions of, 54
    nuclear, 119–21
    in osmoregulation, 867–68
    plant active exclusion by, 786–87
    plant cell–cell signals and, 795
Transport vesicles, 130–31
Transposable elements, 396, 397f, 510,
    511f, 723
Trans surface, Golgi appartus, 113f–14,
    124–25
Traps, leaves as, 739f
Treatment groups, B:6–B:7
Tree ferns, 598
Tree of life, 6, 506, 535
    biodiversity and, 1173
    developing phylogenetic, from rRNA
        sequences, 6–8
    lateral gene transfer and, 395f
    molecular phylogenies and, 535
    as molecular phylogeny (see also
        Phylogenies)
    as phylogenetic tree, 7f
    speciation and, 6 (see also Speciation)
    taxonomy and scientific names for, 8–9
        (see also Taxonomy)

Tree-ring research, 1139
Treehoppers, 1134–35
Trees. See also Forests
    baobab, 731f
    bristlecone pine, 432f
    fire history of giant sequoias, 1138–39
    growth rings of, 1139
    impacts of global climate change
        on, 1167
    ranges of, along elevational
        gradients, 1137
    trunk structure of, 751
Trematodes, 666
Trends, graphing, B:5
Triacylglycerols/triaglycerides,
    86–87, 90
Tricarboxylic acid (TCA), 162. See also
    Citric acid cycle
Trichinosis, 674
Trichomes, 744, 765
Trichomoniasis, 555t, 571
Triiodothyronine, 996, 997–98, 1026
Trilobytes, 505f
Trimesters, human pregnancy, 1031–32
Trioses, 73
Triple bonds, 23
Triplet code, 310, 325–28. See also
    Genetic code
Triploblasts, 640–41
Trivers, Robert, 475
Trochophores, 660–61f
Trophic cascades, 1153, 1154f, 1179
Trophic levels, 1150
Trophic structure
    energy flow to grazers vs. decomposers
        in, 1151
    energy transfer between trophic levels
        in, 1151–52
    food chains and food webs in,
        1150–51
    trophic levels in, 1150
Trophoblast, 424
Tropic cascades, 1153
Tropical climate, 1065–66
Tropical rain forests, 1070
Tropical species richness, 1144–45, 1176
Tropical wet forests, 1070
    climate and, 1065–66
    decomposition rates in, 1157
    deforestation in, 1179
    habitat fragmentation and degradation
        in, 1180
    impacts of global climate change
        on, 1168
    net primary production of, 1155, 1156
    restoration of, 1191
    species richness of, 1176
Tropomyosin, 358, 975–76
Troponin, 975–76
Trout, 482–83
True navigation (map orientation),
    migration and, 1089, 1090–91
Trunks, tree, 751
Trypanosomiasis, 555t, 1062
Trypsin, 47, 54, 893, 895t
Tsetse flies, 1062
Tube feet, 649t, 683–84
Tube-within-a-tube body plan, 643–44,
    661–62
Tubellarians, 666
Tuberculosis (TB), 454–56
Tubers, 737

Tubulin dimers, 129, 131
Tumor suppressors, 232, 361
    cancer and, 232–33, 361–63
    p53 protein, 231–32
    Rb protein, 234
Tumors, 231
    cancer, 233 (see also Cancer)
    from faulty checkpoints, 231
    regulatory proteins as suppressors of,
        231–34
Tundra, Arctic, 1072, 1165, 1167
Tunicates, 686–87f, 688
Turbidity, aquatic biome, 1074
Turgid cells, 756
Turgor pressure, 202, 756, 758
Turnovers, lake, 1075–76
Turtles, 702, 1090–91, 1118, 1119f
Two-trait experiments, Gregor Mendel's,
    263–66
Tympanic membrane, 956
Type 1 and type 2 diabetes mellitus,
    898–99, 1056
Typological thinking, 445–46
Tyree, Melvin, 764
Tyrosine, 273

U

Ubiquinone. See Coenzyme Q
    (ubiquinone)
Ubiquitins, 231, 360
Ulcers, 891
Ultimate causation, 1015, 1083
    of animal communication, 1093
    of foraging, 1085–87
    of mating, 1088–89
    of migration, 1091
    proximate causation vs., 1083–84
Ultrasound hearing, bat, 957–58
Ultraviolet (UV) radiation
    cancer and, 362–63
    DNA damage and xeroderma
        pigmentosum (XP) from,
        299–301
    flower color and, 826–27
    land plant protection from, 585
    photoreception of, 964
Ulvophytes, 599
Umami, 965
Umbilical cord, 1032, 1032
Unambiguous, genetic code as, 312
Uncoating, viral, 716–19
Undersea volcanoes, 74
Understand (Bloom's taxonomy skill),
    B:29f–B:30t
Undifferentiated cells, 407
Unequal crossover, 397–98
Unfolding, protein, 52
Unicellular organisms
    cell–cell interactions for, 200–201
    in characteristics of domains of
        life, 529t
    gene regulation in, 348–49
    in Precambrian, 515
    prokaryotes as, 8, 109
    quorum sensing in population-density
        signaling pathways of, 216
    sex pheromones in signaling between,
        215–16
Uniform distribution, 1102
Unikonta, 558
Uninucleate muscle cells, 977
United Nations Food and Agriculture
    Organization, 1179
United Nations Population Division,
    1117–18

United States
    diabetes mellitus epidemic in, 898–99
    FDA ruling on human growth
        hormone in, 374
    human resource use in, 1164
    soil erosion in, 779
Units, metric system, B:1t
Universal, genetic code as, 312
Unreplicated chromosomes, 239–40
Unsaturated fatty acids, 85f, 385
Unsaturated lipids, 85–86
Unstriated muscle, 977
Untranslated regions (UTRs), 323–24
Upright growth, land plant, 585
Upstream DNA, 319
Upwelling, ocean, 1075, 1155
Uracil, 58–59, 65–66, 68–69, 318
Uranium, 446
Urbanization, 1161
Urea, 865
    in collecting duct and distal tubule,
        876–78
    as nitrogenous waste, 865, 866t
Ureter, 872
Urethra, 872, 1022–23t, 1024
Uric acid, 865, 865, 866t, 878–79
Urinary systems
    diabetes mellitus and urine formation
        in, 898
    human, 872f
    osmoregulation by kidneys of, 871–79
        (see also Kidneys)
Urine
    dehydration and, 209
    diabetes mellitus and formation
        of, 898
    formation of, in renal corpuscle, 873
    insect, 870–71
    loss of water in, 864
Urochordates, 686–87f, 688, 691
U.S. Food and Drug Administration
    (FDA), 374
U.S. National Academy of Sciences, 883
U.S. National Center for Biotechnology
    Information, 392
Uterus, 423–24, 1024–25f, 1031–34
UV radiation. See Ultraviolet (UV)
    radiation

V

Vaccination, 1054–55
Vaccines, 714, 1054–55
Vacquier, Victor, 421
Vacuoles, 114, 743
    eukaryotic, 114–15, 117t
    plant active exclusion via, 786–87
    plant cell, 743
Vagina, 1024–25f
Vagus nerve, 938–39
Vale, Ronald, 130–31
Valence, 21
Valence electrons, 20–21
Valence shells, 20–21
Valine, 48
Valves, heart, 921
Valves, vein, 918
Vampire bats, 1098
van der Waals interactions, 49
    in lipid bilayer fluidity and
        permeability, 90
    protein tertiary structure and, 49–50f
Van Helmont, Jean-Baptiste, 776
van Leeuwenhoek, Anton, 2, 3f, 557
Van Niel, Cornelius, 177
Vapor, water, 758

Variable number tandem repeats (VNTRs), **396**–98*f*
Variable (V) regions, **1045**–46
Variables, experimental, 13
Vas deferens, **1022**–23*t*
Vasa recta, **876**, 877*f*
Vascular bundles, **742**
Vascular cambium, **748**
    auxin and, 807
    secondary growth functions of, 748–50
Vascular plants. *See* Seedless vascular plants; Seed plants
Vascular tissue, plant, **435**, **580**, **759**. *See also* Phloem tissue; Xylem tissue
    elaboration of, into tracheids and vessel elements, 585–86
    formation of, 435, 437*f*
    in land plants, 580–81, 585
    root and shoot systems and, 732
    translocation (sugar transport) and, 766–72
    water transport and, 759–65
Vascular tissue systems, plant, **740**. *See also* Phloem tissue; Xylem tissue
    embryogenesis and, 833
    phloem structure in, 747
    primary plant body and tissues of, 740–41, 742, 748*t*
    secondary growth of, 748–51
    xylem structure in, 746–47
Vectors, cloning, **370**. *See also* Plasmids
Vegetation, emergent, 1077
Vegetative development, **433**, 436–38
    flexibility of cell determination in, 438
    genetic control of leaf shape in, 436–38
    meristems in lifelong growth and, 436, 437*f*
    reproductive development vs., 433 (*see also* Reproductive development, plant)
Veins, 871, **917**–18, 921, 924
Veliger, **668**
Velvet worms, 672–73
Venae cavae, **921**
Venter, Oscar, 1178
Ventilation. *See also* Respiratory systems
    of fish gills, 906
    in gas exchange, 903
    homeostatic control of, 911–12
    of insect tracheae, 907
    of vertebrate lungs, 909–11*f*
Ventral body axis, **410**
Ventricles, **919**, 921
Venules, **917**–18
Venus flytraps, 790, 806
Vertebrae, **688**
Vertebral column, 688
Vertebrates, **645**, **682**, 688–703. *See also* Animal(s)
    adaptive immunity in, 1042 (*see also* Adaptive immune response; Immune systems)
    amphibians, 696
    body plan of, 686–87
    closed circulatory systems of, 917 (*see also* Circulatory systems)
    as deuterostome chordates, 682
    endoskeletons of, 981–83
    evolution of, 688–91
    fishes, 696
    in fossil record, 689–91
    hormones in sexual development and activity of, 998–99
    key lineages of, 696–703
    lungs of, 909–12 (*see also* Respiratory systems)

mammals, 696
    molecular phylogenies of, 691
    morphological innovations of, 692–93
    nervous systems of, 942–49 (*see also* Nervous systems)
    osmoregulation in terrestrial, 871–79 (*see also* Kidneys)
    phylogenetic tree of, 690*f*
    primates, hominins, and humans, 704–8 (*see also* Human[s])
    relative abundance of species of, 691*f*
    reproductive innovations of, 693–94
    reptiles, 696–97
    segmentation in, 645
    sensory systems of (*see* Sensory systems, animal)
    vertebrae, cranium, and brain structure of, 688
    wings and flight in, 694–95
Vervet monkeys, 1098
Vesicles
    artificial membrane-bound, 88–89
    in chemical evolution, 94
    in cytokinesis, 228
    in electron transport chain, 168–69
    in endomembrane protein transport, 123–27
    microtubules and transport by, 130–31
    osmosis across membrane-bound, 92–93
    prokaryotic, 108
    rough ER in, 114
    secretory, 123
    synaptic, 939
Vessel elements, **586**, **746**–47
Vessels, angiosperm, 596
Vestigial traits, **448**
    of cetaceans, 453
    as evidence for evolutionary change, 448–49
    as nonadaptive, 461
Vicariance, **494**, 495
Video microscopy
    of ATP synthase, 170
    in biological imaging, B:20
    of transport vesicles, 130*f*
Villi, **852**–53*f*, **892**
Virchow, Rudolf, 3, 219
Virions, **714**–15. *See also* Replicative growth, viral
Virulent infections, 532, **712**
Virus vaccines, 1055
Viruses, **711**–30
    abundance and diversity of, 712
    analyzing coexistence of, with host cells, 721–22
    analyzing genetic material of, 715–16
    analyzing morphological traits of, 715
    analyzing phases of replicative growth of lytic cycle of, 716–21
    bacteriophage λ, 50
    Baltimore classification system for, 725–26
    biological methods of studying, 714–22
    biological reasons for studying, 712–14
    characteristics of living organisms vs. characteristics of, 712*t*
    diversification themes of, 722–25
    emerging diseases and emerging, 723–25
    eukaryotic translation and, 359–60
    in gene therapy, 383–85
    Hershey–Chase experiment on DNA in genes of, 285–86

human epidemics and pandemics from, 712–14
    identification of emerging, 725
    infection of host cells by, 711–12
    key lineages of, 725–28
    living organisms vs., 711–12
    nanobiology in isolation of, 714
    origins of, 723
    photomicrograph of, 711*f*
    proteins as defense against, 54
    RNA in, 309
    in splitting eukaryotic genes, 321–22
    vaccines against, 1055
Visceral mass, **662**–63
Viscosity, animal locomotion and fluid, 988
Visible light, **179**
Vision, animal. *See* Photoreception, animal; Sight
Visual communication, 1093
Visual cues, mating and, 1088
Visualization, molecular, B:15–B:16
Vitamin A deficiency, 385
Vitamin B$_1$, 884*t*
Vitamin B$_6$, 305
Vitamin B$_{12}$, 884*t*
Vitamin C, 884*t*
Vitamin D, 884*t*
Vitamin D-resistant rickets (hypophasphatemia), 279
Vitamins, **883**
    coenzymes and, 147
    as essential nutrients for animals and humans, 883, 884*t*
    lipids as, 87
    transgenic crops and deficiencies of, 385
Vitelline envelope, **1017**–18*f*
Viviparous species, **651**, **694**, **1020**–21
Vivipary, 836
Volcanic gases, 24, 30, 34–35, 45
Volt, **930**
Voltage, **783**, **930**
Voltage clamping, **935**
Voltage-gated channels, 98–99, **934**
Volume, in chemical reactions, 138
Volume, metric units and conversions for, B:1*t*
Volume/surface area, animal body, 850–53
Volume/surface area relationships, plant, 732–33
Voluntary muscles, **977**, 979
Vomeronasal organ, **967**
Von Békésy, Georg, 956–57
Von Frisch, Karl, 1084, 1092–93
von Linné, Karl, 9

W

Waggle dance, honeybee, 1092–93
Waldeyer, Wilhelm, 220
Walking, 986
Wall cress. *See* Mustard plant
Wall pressure, **756**
Wallace, Alfred Russel, 5, 444, 446, 453, 1063
Wallace line, **1063**
Warblers, 1062
Wasps, 485, 818–19
Wasserman, Paul, 79–80
Wastes, 883*f*, 888, 896. *See also* Nitrogenous wastes, animal
Water
    absorption of, in large intestines, 896
    absorption of, in small intestines, 896

in acid-base reactions, 28–30
    angiosperm vessels for conducting, 596
    animal heat exchange by evaporation of, 855
    animal locomotion in, 984, 985, 988
    animal requirements for, 842–43
    aquaporins and transport of, across plasma membranes, 98
    behavior of oxygen and carbon dioxide in, 904–5
    cohesion, adhesion, and surface tension of, 26
    covalent bonds of, 21–23
    in decomposition rates, 1157
    density of, as liquid and as solid, 26–27
    depth and flow of in aquatic biomes, 1074–75, 1077–79
    efficiency of, as solvent, 25–26
    energy absorbing capacity of, 27–28
    green plant holding of, and moderation of climate, 578
    insolubility of lipids in, 85, 86–87
    land plant adaptations to prevent loss of, 584–85
    large intestine absorption of, 888
    lipid bilayers and, 89
    molecular structure of, 24*f*, B:12*f*
    in net primary production of terrestrial biomes, 1155
    nitrate pollution of, 543–44
    noncyclic electron flow between, and NADP$^+$ in Z-scheme model, 188–89
    in nutrient cycling, 1158
    osmosis as diffusion of, across lipid bilayers, 92–93
    oxidation of, in photosystem II, 186
    photosynthetic oxygen production from, 177–78
    plant nutrients from, 780*t*
    plant transport of (*see* Water transport, plant)
    polarity of amino acid side chains and solubility in, 44
    production of, by cellular respiration, 165
    production of, by electron transport chain, 166*f*–67
    properties of, 26–28
    purification of, as ecosystem regulating service, 1188
    in seed germination, 837
    specific heat of, 27*t*
Water balance, animal. *See* Osmoregulation
Water bears, 672–73
Water cycle, global, 1159–60, 1166
Water depth, 1074, 1075*f*, 1077–79
Water flea, 1167
Water flow, 1074–75, 1077–79
Water loss, animal
    terrestrial adaptations to prevent, 662–63
    insect minimization of, 869–70
Water loss, plant
    biochemical pathway adaptations to, 766
    regulation of, 754–55, 765–66
    seed maturation and, 834
    stomata and regulation of, 743–44
    turgor pressure, wilting, and plant, 758
Water molds, 574

Water potential, **755**
  calculating, 756–57
  evaporation, transpiration, and, 754–55
  in plant water transport, 759–66 (see also Water transport, plant)
  as potential energy, 755
  pressure potential in, 756–57
  soil composition and, 778
  in soils, plants, and atmosphere, 757–59
  solute potential in, 755–57
Water-potential gradients, **759**
Water-storage structures, stems as, 736–37
Water table, **1160**
Water transport, plant, 754–66
  cohesion-tension theory on, 762–64
  root pressure in, 761
  into roots, 759–61
  from roots to shoots, 759–65
  via capillary action, 761–62
  water absorption, water loss, and, 754–55, 765–66
  water potential and, 755–59 (see also Water potential)
  xylem in, 749
Water vapor
  in origin-of-life experiments, 33–34
  in volcanic gases, 30
Water vascular system, **682–83**
Waterfalls, energy transformation in, 137f
Watersheds, **1158–59**
Watson, James, 57f, 61–63, 286–87
Watson–Crick base pairing, DNA, **63**, 327–28
Wavelengths, electromagnetic, **179–83**. See also Light-capturing reactions, photosynthetic
Waxes, **86**, 743
Weapons, defensive, 1129f
Weather, **1065**
  climate and, 1065
  global climate change and, 1166
  seasonality of, 1066, 1067f
Weathering, rock, **778–79f**, 1158
Web of life, lateral gene transfer and, 395f
Weeds, 385, **802**, **1140**, B:25
Wei, Chunfang, 764
Weight, animal locomotion and, 987–88
Weinberg, Wilhelm, 466–67
Weinert, Ted, 231
Weintraub, Harold, 351, 428f–29
Weismann, August, 238, 247
Weissbach, Arthur, 192

Went, Fritz, 798–99
West Nile virus, 727
Western blotting, B:16
Wet habitats, pollination in, 831
Wetlands, **1077**
Wexler, Nancy, 379–82
Whales, 452–53, 510–11f
Wheat kernels, 276
Whisk ferns, 603
White blood cells (leukocytes), **912**, **1039**–41, 1042t
Whitham, Thomas, 1134–35
Whole-genome sequencing, 390–93
  bioinformatics and, 391–92
  in cataloging genetic diversity, 1173
  genome annotation in, 392–93
  growth in sequenced data of, 389–90
  impact of next-generation sequencing on, 391
  reasons for selecting organisms for, 392
  shotgun sequencing in, 390–91
Whooping cranes, 1110f, 1118, 1190
Whorled leaves, 738f
Wieschaus, Eric, 411–12, B:25
Wild dogs, 1098
Wild populations. See Natural populations
Wild type phenotypes, **267**
Wildfires, seed germination and, 837
Wildlife corridors, 1120, **1190**, 1191f
Wilkins, Maurice, 61–63
Willow trees, 776
Wilson, Edward O., 1143–44, 1188
Wilson, H. V., 206
Wilting (wilt), **758**
Wind
  erosion from, 779–81
  in nutrient cycling, 1158
  nutrient loss and gain by, 1158
  pollination by, 608–9f, 831
  in terrestrial biomes, 1068–69
Wind/touch responses, plant, 805–6, 818t
Wing development genes, 415
Wings
  evolution of vertebrate, 694–95
  as morphological innovations, 517
  origin of, in arthropod evolution, 671–72
Wittlinger, Matthias, 11–14
Wobble hypothesis, 327–**28**
Woese, Carl, 6–8, 535–36
Wolves, 1153, 1154f
Women. See Females

Wood, 579–80, **586**, 607, 612–14, **748**, 749–50
Word roots, Latin and Greek, B:3
World population. See Global human population
World Wide Web genome databases, 392
Worms, **661**–62, 667
Wound repair, mitosis and, 220
Wounds, plant
  animal pheromone production from, 818–19
  parenchyma cells and, 744
  systemin as hormone response to, 817
Wright, Sewall, 479–81

X

X-axis, graph, B:4–B:5
X chromosomes, 238, 268, 274f, 383–85. See also Sex chromosomes
X-linked inheritance (X-linkage), **268**
  in chromosome theory of inheritance, 268–69
  genetic maps of, 274f
  human, 278–79
  in Mendelian genetics, 258t
  severe combined immunodeficiency (SCID) and, 383–85
X-linked traits, human, 278–79
X-ray crystallography (x-ray diffraction analysis), **62**, 130, B:20–B:21
  of eukaryotic DNA, 350
  in HIV research, 719
  of p53 tumor-suppressor gene, 363
  in study of muscle contraction, 974
  tRNA structure, 327
X-ray film, 190–91, 221, B:15–B:16
Xanthophylls, 180–82
Xenoestrogens, 999–**1000**
Xenopus laevis, 229–30f
Xenoturbella, 682
Xeroderma pigmentosum (XP), **299**–301
Xylem pressure probe, 764
Xylem tissue, **746**
  primary plant body, 748t
  vascular cambium and, 748–50
  vascular tissue system functions of, 746–47
  water transport in (see Water transport, plant)
Xylene, 27t

Y

Y chromosomes, 238, 268. See also Sex chromosomes

Y-linked inheritance (Y-linkage), **268**
  in chromosome theory of inheritance, 268–69
  in Mendelian genetics, 258t
Yalow, Rosalind, 997
Yeast. See Saccharomyces cerevisiae
Yeasts, fungal, **615**
Yellowstone National Park, 376, 1141, 1153, 1154f
Yews, 607
Y-axis, graph, B:4–B:5
Yogurt, 545f
Yoked hyphae, 617, 629
Yolk, egg, **1017**, 1023
Yucatán meteorite crater, 521–22f
Yucca moths, 1062

Z

Z disc, **974**
Z-scheme model, **187**–90
Zamecnik, Paul, 326–27
Zeatin, 807
Zeaxanthin, 180
Zebra finches, 475–76
Zero population growth, **1117**
Zeroes, significant figures and metric system, B:2–B:3
Zhao, Maosheng, 1168
Zinc finger, 1007
Zona pellucida, **1017**–18f
Zone of cellular division, **741**
Zone of cellular elongation, **742**
Zone of cellular maturation, **742**
Zone of maturation, **782**
Zone of nutrient depletion, 782
Zones, lake and pond, 1077
Zones, ocean, 1079
Zoos, 1189–90
Zygomycetes, 617–18, 625–26f, 629
Zygosporangia, **617**–18, 625–26f
Zygotes, **241**, **420**, **823**, **1018**
  cleavage of, 423–24
  creation of, by fertilization, 420–21
  embryogenesis of plant, 433–36
  fertilization and, 1018
  in meiosis, 241–42
  plant embryogenesis from, 833–34
  plant fertilization and, 830, 832–33
  in plant reproduction, 823–25
  reproductive isolation and, 490, 491t

Boldface page numbers indicate a glossary entry; page numbers followed by an *f* indicate a figure; those followed by *t* indicate a table.